CALCULUS

AND

ANALYTIC

GEOMETRY

SECOND EDITION

ABRAHAM SCHWARTZ

The City College of New York

HOLT, RINEHART AND WINSTON

New York   Chicago   San Francisco

Toronto   London

TO MY PARENTS

PREFACE TO THE SECOND EDITION

This edition was written with the same objectives and in the same spirit as the first edition. The organization of the course has been changed only to add a chapter on ordinary differential equations at the end. That chapter discusses topics usually studied in a first course and attempts to make the student aware of questions of existence and uniqueness.

The illustrative examples and the exercises of the first edition seem to have been quite successful, and they have been changed in relatively few places, usually for the purpose of adding some easier exercises. Many three-dimensional figures have been improved in detail, but they are still as simple as possible so that the student can hope to copy from them and thus to improve his own sketches. There have been hundreds of minor changes in exposition in places where experience has shown that particular passages were not quite as clear to the student as had been expected. It is believed that the definition of function in Chapter 1 has been made more rigorous, with subsequent improvements throughout the book, and that the first treatment of integration in Chapter 2 has also been improved.

More instructors and students than I can mention have made encouraging, useful, and significant comments, and I am grateful to all of them. I would especially like to acknowledge here the help I received from Joseph d' Atri, Sidney Neuman, and Bennington Gill, and the comments of J. L. Baker, H. J. Cohen, Gerald Freilich, Edwin Goldfarb, Alvin Hausner, Solomon Hurwitz, Frank Kocher, Henry Malin, T. O. Moore, John Shaw, Fritz Steinhardt, and Fred Supnick.

A.S.

Englewood, New Jersey
February 1967

Three principles guided the writing of this book. First, the student must be able to read his textbook and learn from it. The exposition therefore is detailed and carefully motivated, and there are many illustrative examples. Second, the student should be led to reason carefully and to write precisely. Definitions and theorems are carefully stated, and the theorems are proved with as much rigor as was deemed feasible for a first-year college course. Where no proof is given this is indicated and, if possible, the difficulty pointed out. Third, not only are the ideas of the course important, but also the ability to apply them to specific situations. The author tried to maintain a reasonable balance between theory on the one hand and technique, drill, and application on the other.

The book assumes training on the secondary school level in trigonometry and advanced algebra; there are, however, articles on inequalities and absolute values in the appendix and review articles on the trigonometric functions and the logarithmic function in the text itself.

The book starts with chapters on the differential and integral calculus which rest on an intuitive basis rather than an abstract basis. These chapters are also intended to give the student enough technique and experience with applications to start him in a good physics course. Next, a long chapter on plane analytic geometry introduces vector analysis early and uses the calculus tool previously prepared in a significant role. There follow chapters on the trigonometric, logarithmic, and exponential functions, and a chapter on formal integration.

By this time the student has perhaps gained a certain mathematical maturity and it is wise to examine more closely the underlying assumptions made earlier in the book. No two instructors will place the same relative emphasis on the various ideas of Chapter 7; indeed, only Part 1 of Section 7.5 is indispensable for the reading of the later chapters. Even though most students will find this more abstract theory difficult, the author firmly believes that it should be attempted.

Chapter 8 returns to more applications of the calculus tool, and polar coordinates are studied in Chapter 9. Chapter 10 is devoted to solid analytic geometry, the vector analysis again playing a prominent role. Here, for the first time in this text, the student has to deal with three-dimensional configurations, and an attempt is made to help him with his sketches *before* he is called upon to use them in various theories and applications.

There then follow chapters on the calculus of functions of two or more variables and on applications which use three-dimensional geometry. The last chapter is devoted to infinite series.

The ideas and techniques considered are not of equal difficulty and significance and the sections are not all of equal length. It is not intended that a class consider every part of every section at a uniform rate of one section per lesson. Different instructors will wish to emphasize different points and many of the longer sections are subdivided to allow the instructor more flexibility in making his assignments.

A special effort has been made to supply original exercises and many more are included than any one class can use. These have been carefully graded so that the instructor can select assignments according to the emphasis he wishes to place on the ideas covered. More difficult exercises are included in most sections to motivate the better student and to teach him something significant and new. The answers for many exercises are given in the exercises themselves. For those more formal exercises, which are subdivided into many parts, answers are usually given in the answer section at the back of the book for the alternate parts — (a), (c), (e), etc. The other answers given in the back of the book are for the odd-numbered exercises.

It is difficult to trace the development of one's own ideas about a course of study, but I am keenly aware of how much I have been influenced by my colleagues and students, both at the Pennsylvania State University and at the City College of New York.

It is a pleasure to thank Professors Burton W. Jones, Melvin Henriksen, and Andrew J. Terzuoli, who read the manuscript and made valuable suggestions, and Mrs. Olga Skelley, who typed the manuscript.

Englewood, New Jersey
March 1960

A. S.

CONTENTS

CALCULUS AND ANALYTIC GEOMETRY

The Derivative

1.1 The Definition of a Function

Science studies correspondences between sets of numbers. Thus there may be a relationship between the viscosity η of a certain oil and the temperature T; perhaps with each T number selected from a certain suitable temperature interval we can associate a corresponding viscosity number η. The number N of bacteria in a culture changes as the time t changes; perhaps one can explain how to compute an N number for each t number selected from a certain suitable time interval. The current i flowing in a circuit might depend on the resistance R of the circuit. The volume V of a sphere is related to its radius r.

In describing such correspondences the mathematician uses the word "function."

■ DEFINITION 1

Function; domain; range. We are given a set of numbers, which we shall call the domain D, and instructions for associating a number y with each number x of D. The set of all numbers y associated with numbers x of D shall be called the range R. The correspondence thus created between the sets D and R shall be called a function.

Example 1. The formula for the volume of a sphere, $V = \frac{4}{3} \pi r^3$, associates one number V with each number $r \geq 0$.* For instance, corresponding to $r = 3$ we have $V = \frac{4}{3} \pi 3^3 = 36\pi$. The domain D for this function is the set $D : r \geq 0$; the instructions for associating a V number with each r number of D are furnished by the formula; the range is the set $R : V \geq 0$, because any V number of this range can be achieved by choosing a suitable r number of D.

---

* To review inequalities, see Appendix 1.

1

Example 2. Consider the algebraic instructions furnished by $y = \sqrt{25 - x^2}$.* Here one real number y is associated with each number x of the interval $-5 \leq x \leq 5$. For instance, with $x = 4$ we associate $y = 3$. The domain D for this function is the interval $-5 \leq x \leq 5$, the instructions for associating a y number with each x number of D are furnished by the formula, and the range R is the set $0 \leq y \leq 5$.

Example 3. Consider $y = \sqrt{x^2}$ for all real x. The instructions for finding the number y associated with a particular x call for squaring the x number and then taking the positive square root. For instance, when $x = -2$ we compute $y = \sqrt{(-2)^2} = \sqrt{4} = 2$. These instructions could also have been written

$$y = \begin{cases} x \text{ if } x \geq 0 \\ -x \text{ if } x < 0, \end{cases}$$

or as $y = |x|$.† The domain D for this function is the set of all real numbers; the range R is the set of all nonnegative numbers.

Example 4. Consider

$$C = \begin{cases} 35 \text{ for } 0 \leq d < \frac{1}{5} \\ 40 \text{ for } \frac{1}{5} \leq d < \frac{2}{5} \\ 45 \text{ for } \frac{2}{5} \leq d < \frac{3}{5} \\ 50 \text{ for } \frac{3}{5} \leq d < \frac{4}{5} \\ 55 \text{ for } \frac{4}{5} \leq d < 1. \end{cases}$$

This set of instructions associates a specific number C with each number d of the set $0 \leq d < 1$. Thus, for $d = .24$ we are instructed to take $C = 40$ and for $d = .60$ we are instructed to take $C = 50$. The domain D for this function is the set $0 \leq d < 1$; the range R is the set of five numbers $\{35, 40, 45, 50, 55\}$. The number C might represent the cost of a taxi ride in cents and d the distance traveled in miles.

Example 5. Consider

$$y = \begin{cases} \dfrac{1}{1 + 2^{1/x}} & \text{for } x \neq 0 \\ 0 & \text{for } x = 0. \end{cases}$$

Here the domain D is the set of all real numbers and we have instructions for associating a number y with any real x. For $x = \frac{1}{3}$, for instance, the first line of the instructions tells us to take

$$y = \frac{1}{1 + 2^3} = \frac{1}{9};$$

---

* Recall that the radical notation conventions require that the positive square root be taken here. If both positive and negative square roots are intended, as in the familiar quadratic formula, then both signs must be written. The roots of $ax^2 + bx + c = 0$ are $x = (-b \pm \sqrt{b^2 - 4ac})/2a$.

† The absolute value symbol, $|\ |$, is considered in Appendix 2.

for $x = -\frac{1}{3}$, the first line tells us to take

$$y = \frac{1}{1 + 2^{-3}} = \frac{1}{1 + (1/2^3)} = \frac{8}{8 + 1} = \frac{8}{9};$$

for $x = 0$, the second line of the instructions tells us to take $y = 0$. The range for this function is the set $0 \leq y < 1$. In Exercise 1.1-4 at the end of this section, the reader can draw a graph to illustrate this functional correspondence.

Example 6.   After many experimental determinations of the viscosity η of a certain liquid at various temperatures T taken from the interval $20 < T < 100$, a laboratory worker might sketch a reasonably careful graph to represent his data, and he may be willing to assume that the readings he can make from his graph are accurate enough for the purpose at hand. The instructions for associating an η number with each T number of the interval $20 < T < 100$ this time would call for taking a graph reading.

Example 7.   To each positive number x we can assign a real number called $\log_{10} x$ by taking the exponent one must use when writing x as a power of 10. Thus, to the positive numbers 100, 1, and $1/\sqrt{10}$ this logarithm function assigns the numbers 2, 0, and $-\frac{1}{2}$ because $100 = 10^2$, $1 = 10^0$, and $1/\sqrt{10} = 1/10^{1/2} = 10^{-1/2}$. The domain set for this function is the set of all positive numbers; the range set is the set of all real numbers. A logarithm table like Table 1.1 merely lists

TABLE 1.1

N	0	1	2	3	4	5	6	7	8	9
1.0	.0000	.0043	.0086	.0128	.0170	.0212	.0253	.0294	.0334	.0374
1.1	.0414	.0453	.0492	.0531	.0569	.0607	.0645	.0682	.0719	.0755
...										
9.9	.9956	.9961	.9965	.9969	.9974	.9978	.9983	.9987	.9991	.9996

systematically the four-decimal-place approximations for the range numbers assigned by this logarithm function to the two-decimal-place domain numbers which lie between 1.00 and 9.99.

To summarize, there are many ways of describing functions and some of the most important ways will first become available to us later. But, in every case, as soon as a number is selected from the domain set of the function, instructions must be furnished for finding the corresponding number in the range set.

● **Remark 1**

Three or more number sets may be related. For instance, the pressure of the gas in a container depends on the volume of the container and on the temperature of the gas; with each ordered pair of numbers, the first a volume number and the second a temperature number, we may have instructions for computing a pressure number. The volume of a right circular cylinder depends on the radius of the base and on the height; the formula $V = \pi r^2 h$ tells us how to associate a V number with each ordered number pair consisting of an r number followed by an h number. Thus if we take the r number 2 and the h number 3, the corresponding V number is 12π; we can say that 12π is assigned to the number pair 2, 3. Observe, however, that if we take the r number 3 and the h number 2 the corresponding V number is 18π; 18π is assigned to the number pair 3, 2. The *order* in which the numbers of the number pair are written is significant, and that is why we use the term *ordered* number pair. Definition 1 can be generalized as follows.

■ DEFINITION 2

We are given a set of ordered number pairs, which we shall call the domain D, and instructions for associating a number z with each number pair x, y of D. The set of all numbers z associated with number pairs x, y of D shall be called the range R. Such a correspondence between D and R shall be called a function.*

We shall be concerned primarily with functional correspondences between sets of numbers, as described in Definition 1, in the first nine chapters of this book.

● Remark 2

The concept of function can be significantly broadened to discuss correspondences between sets of ordered n-tuples of numbers and sets of ordered m-tuples of numbers, and, indeed, even to discuss correspondences between sets of objects other than numbers.

● Remark 3

A somewhat looser terminology using the word function is also common in mathematical and scientific literature, and when no ambiguity results we shall occasionally use this other terminology. It is common to think of a *variable* as a symbol that may represent any of the numbers of a specified set. Definition 1 can then be rephrased somewhat more vaguely in variable language. One considers the independent variable x selected from the domain set D and says that the dependent variable y has been defined as a function of x over D if there is a set of instructions for associating a number y with each number x of D. The range R would be, as before, the set of all numbers associated with numbers x of D and the variable y is selected from the range set R.

EXERCISES 1.1

1. Draw a graph for the function of Example 2.
2. Draw a graph for the function of Example 3.
3. Draw a graph for the function of Example 4.

---

* If we dealt with a relationship between four number sets we could talk about a domain D of ordered number triples and a number w associated with each ordered triple x, y, z of D. In still greater generality we might have a set of instructions that associated a number with each ordered n-tuple of numbers selected from a domain D of ordered n-tuples of numbers.

4. Draw a graph for the function of Example 5.

5. Draw a graph for the function

$$y = \begin{cases} 0 & \text{for } t \leq 0, \\ t & \text{for } 0 \leq t < 1, \\ t - 1 & \text{for } 1 \leq t < 2, \\ t - 2 & \text{for } 2 \leq t < 3. \end{cases}$$

6. Each of the following is to be read as a set of instructions for associating a real number y with a specified real number x. What is the largest possible x domain of definition in each case? What is the range for y?

(a) $y = x + 2$.

(b) $y = \sqrt{x + 2}$.

(c) $y = \dfrac{1}{x + 2}$.

(d) $y = \dfrac{1}{\sqrt{x + 2}}$.

(e) $y = \dfrac{1}{\sqrt[3]{x + 2}}$.

(f) $y = \dfrac{1}{\sqrt{x^2 - 4}}$.

(g) $y = \log_2 x$.

(h) $y = \sin x$.

(i) $y = 2^x$.

7. For the sake of amusement, consider a European proverb which suggests that a man ought to choose for his wife a woman whose age is 10 years more than half his age. Describe this functional relationship in mathematical terms and state the domain of age numbers for the man for which you think the relationship has some validity.

1.2 Some Function Notation

Often several functions must be dealt with in the same discussion. For instance, as a particle moves in a plane, its x and y coordinates would usually both depend on the time t for a certain time interval. For the sake of brevity we could refer to the correspondence between the t numbers and the x numbers as the f function and to the correspondence between the t numbers and the y numbers as the g function. Of course the letters F, φ, Φ, h or many others could serve just as well.

Since the ability to specify the number of the range set corresponding to a specific number of the domain set is at the heart of the function concept, it is important to be able to refer to such a number quickly.

■ NOTATION CONVENTION 1

Let a be a number in the domain of function f. Then $f(a)$ is the number f associates with a.

There is some ambiguity here because parentheses are also used to indicate multiplication, but the reader soon learns to tell from the context which usage is intended.

Example 1. The statement "$f(x) = x^2 + 1$ for all real x" says, in words, that the domain for function f is the set of all real numbers and that f associates with any real number x of its domain the range number $f(x)$ arrived at by squaring x and adding 1. The range number 5 is associated with the domain number 2, for we can write $f(2) = 2^2 + 1 = 5$. Similarly, $f(-1) = (-1)^2 + 1 = 2$, $f(a) = a^2 + 1$, $f(b + 1) = (b + 1)^2 + 1 = b^2 + 2b + 2$.

Example 2.   The statement "$\varphi(x) = 2^x$ for all real x" says, in words, that the domain of the φ function is the set of all real numbers and that the φ function associates with each real number x the range number arrived at by taking the xth power of 2. To illustrate, the range number 8 is associated with the domain number 3, for we can write $\varphi(3) = 2^3 = 8$. Similarly, $\varphi(\frac{1}{2}) = 2^{1/2} = \sqrt{2}$, $\varphi(0) = 2^0 = 1$, $\varphi(-2) = 2^{-2} = \frac{1}{2^2} = \frac{1}{4}$, and one of the laws of exponents says that $\varphi(x + y) = 2^{x+y} = 2^x 2^y = [\varphi(x)][\varphi(y)]$.

Example 3.   For a projectile fired with an initial velocity of 1000 ft per sec at a 60° angle of elevation and considered thereafter as a particle moving under the influence of gravity alone, it is found that the horizontal distance traveled x and the height gained y are these functions of the time t measured from the instant of firing:

$$x = f(t) = 500t, \qquad y = g(t) = -16t^2 + 500\sqrt{3}\,t, \qquad 0 \le t \le \frac{125\sqrt{3}}{4}.*$$

At the time $t = 0$ the projectile is at the origin; $x = f(0) = 0$, $y = g(0) = 0$. The projectile will strike the ground (assumed level) after 54.1 sec, since

$$y = g(t) = -16t^2 + 500\sqrt{3}\,t = t(-16t + 500\sqrt{3}),$$

and

$$y = 0 \quad \text{when } t = 0 \quad \text{and} \quad \text{when } t = 500\,\frac{\sqrt{3}}{16} \approx 54.1.\dagger$$

The projectile will strike the ground 27063.3 ft from the origin, since, when $t = 125\sqrt{3}/4$, we have

$$x = f\left(\frac{125\sqrt{3}}{4}\right) = 500\,\frac{125\sqrt{3}}{4} \approx 27063.3.$$

Example 4.   Let us write $f(x) = \sin x$ and $\varphi(x) = \cos x$ for all real x to describe the association instructions furnished for the f and φ functions, it being understood that radian measure is to be used. Then it follows that $f(0) = 0$, $f(\pi/3) = \sqrt{3}/2$, $\varphi(\pi/3) = \frac{1}{2}$, and that the identity

$$\sin (A + B) = \sin A \cos B + \cos A \sin B$$

can be written

$$f(A + B) = f(A)\,\varphi(B) + \varphi(A)\,f(B).$$

As a direct generalization to the case where a function associates a number with an ordered pair of numbers, we adopt the following convention.

---

* These equations are derived in Example 8.4-3.
† The sign $\approx$ means "equals approximately."

■ **NOTATION CONVENTION 2**

Let a, b be an ordered number pair in the domain of function f. Then $f(a, b)$ is the number associated with a, b by f.

Example 5. The statement "$F(x, y) = x^2 - y^2$ for all ordered pairs of real numbers x, y" says, in words, that the domain of F is the set of all ordered pairs of real numbers and that F associates with any ordered pair of real numbers the range number computed by subtracting the square of the second number of the ordered pair from the square of the first. To illustrate, $F(2, 1) = 2^2 - 1^2 = 3$, $F(0, 4) = 0^2 - 4^2 = -16$, $F(h, h) = h^2 - h^2 = 0$.

● **Remark 1**

A statement like "$f(x) = x^2 + 1$ for all real x", discussed in Example 1, explains what the domain of function f is and how f associates a range number with each number of its domain, and hence this statement serves as a complete description of the function. Where no ambiguity will occur, we often write, perhaps loosely, a phrase like "the function $f(x)$" or "the function $x^2 + 1$," meaning by this the functional correspondence whose assignment instructions are given by $f(x)$ or by $x^2 + 1$. Indeed, we have already essentially done this in Example 3, where we wrote that x and y were certain functions of t.

EXERCISES 1.2

1. Let $F(r) = \frac{4}{3}\pi r^3$. Find $F(0), F(\frac{1}{2})$, $F(3)$, $F(a)$, $F(r + h)$, $F(2r)$, and show that $F(2r) = 8F(r)$.

2. Let $\phi(x) = \sqrt{25 - x^2}$. Find $\phi(3)$, $\phi(-4)$, $\phi(x + h)$, $(\phi(a))^2$, $2\phi(a^2)$, and show that $\phi(-x) = \phi(x)$.

3. Let

$$f(x) = \begin{cases} x \text{ if } x \geq 0, \\ -x \text{ if } x < 0; \end{cases}$$

that is, let $f(x) = |x|$. Find $f(-2), f(\frac{1}{6}), \sqrt{f(\frac{1}{4})}, 3f(2)$, and show that $f(-x) = f(x)$.

4. Let $g(d)$ be the function of Example 1.1-4. Find $g(0)$, $g(.1)$, $g(.35), g(.80)$. If the relationship $g(d + a) = g(d) + 5$ is to hold for $0 \leq d < \frac{4}{5}$, how must the number a be chosen?

5. Consider a tank with a faucet through which water can enter at the rate of 3 gal per min and a drain through which water can leave at the rate of 5 gal per min. The tank is empty when the experiment starts. The faucet is then opened. Seven minutes later the drain is also opened. Let t be the time elapsed from the start of the experiment, measured in minutes, and let x be the number of gallons of water in the tank at time t. Write x as a function of t, say $x = f(t)$ for $t \geq 0$. Evaluate $f(3), f(7), f(10)$, and $f(20)$. Draw a graph to show the relationship.

6. Let $f(x) = 3x + 7$ for all real x and let $F(y) = \frac{1}{3}(y - 7)$ for all real y. Find $f(2)$ and $F(13), f(-3)$ and $F(-2)$. Show that $f(F(y)) = y$ for all real y. Does $F(f(x)) = x$ for all real x?

7. Let $\varphi(x) = x^2 + 5$ for all real x and let $\Phi(y) = -\sqrt{y - 5}$ for $y \geq 5$. Find $\varphi(2)$ and $\Phi(9)$, $\Phi(30)$ and $\varphi(-5)$. Is it true that $\varphi(\Phi(y)) = y$ for $y \geq 5$? For which x is it true that $\Phi(\varphi(x)) = x$?

8. Let $f(y) = 5 - 2y$ for all real y. Find a function F such that $f(F(x)) = x$ for all real x.

9. Let $f(x) = \sqrt{x}$, $x \geq 0$. Find $f(1)$, $f(\frac{1}{9})$, $f(a^2)$, $f(a^2 + b^2)$. Is it true that $f(ab) = f(a)f(b)$ for $a, b > 0$? Is it true that $f(a + b) = f(a) + f(b)$ for $a, b > 0$?

10. Let $\varphi(x) = a^x$, $a > 0$. Find $\varphi(2)$, $\varphi(\frac{2}{3})$, $\varphi(-2)$, $\varphi(-\frac{2}{3})$, $\varphi(0)$. Show that $\varphi(b + c) = \varphi(b)\,\varphi(c)$, $\varphi(b - c) = \varphi(b)/\varphi(c)$, $(\varphi(b))^c = \varphi(bc) = (\varphi(c))^b$.

11. Let $\psi(x) = \log_{10} x$, $x > 0$. Find $\psi(1)$, $\psi(10)$, $\psi(100)$, $\psi(\frac{1}{10})$, $\psi(\sqrt{10})$. Show that $\psi(xy) = \psi(x) + \psi(y)$, $\psi(x/y) = \psi(x) - \psi(y)$, $\psi(x^c) = c\psi(x)$ for any real constant c.

12. Let $\psi(x) = \log_{10} x$ for $x > 0$. Let $\varphi(y) = 10^y$ for all real y. Show that $\psi(\varphi(y)) = y$ for all real y and that $\varphi(\psi(x)) = x$ for $x > 0$.

13. Can you write down functions f and F, taken from trigonometry, such that $f(F(x)) = x$ and $F(f(y)) = y$? State for which x and y these statements hold.

14. Let $f(x, y) = \sqrt{16 - x^2 - 2y^2}$ for all real number pairs x, y such that $x^2 + 2y^2 \leq 16$. Find $f(0, 0)$, $f(1, 2)$, $f(0, -\sqrt{8})$.

15. Let $F(x, y) = \cos(x - y)$ for all ordered pairs of real numbers x, y. Find $F(0, 0)$, $F(\pi/2, \pi/4)$, $F(\pi/4, \pi/2)$ and show that $F(a, b) = F(b, a)$.

1.3   The Tangent to a Curve

In this section the reader will be introduced to what has been historically one of the most fruitful problems of mathematics, that of determining the tangent line to a curve at a specific point. We shall appeal to the reader's intuition in this first discussion. Later this problem will be considered with greater precision and rigor.

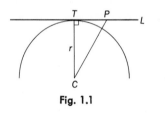

Fig. 1.1

To a given point T on a circle with center C draw the radius line CT and the line L perpendicular to CT; see Fig. 1.1. It can be shown that the distance from any other point P on line L to C must be greater than the radius, and that therefore L meets the circle at no point other than T.* Following our intuition, we call L the tangent line.†

It is possible to find analogous constructions for the tangent lines to the parabola, ellipse, and hyperbola, curves that will be studied in some detail in Chapter 3, but how can it be decided for a curve in general which line through a given point of the curve ought to be called the tangent line?

One suggestion is this: "Take as the tangent line at P a line that intersects the curve at P and at no other point." Figure 1.2 shows that this definition would on occasion accept lines that were not wanted as tangents, Case (a), and on other occasions exclude lines that were wanted, Case (b). Nevertheless, this suggestion has merit, and it can be modified. There are many cases where we want a line through P which does not meet the curve again "near" P‡ and which is such that at least some of the "nearby" lines through P do meet the curve again near P.§

Intuition can suggest another way of attacking the problem: look for a line through P which has the same "direction" as the curve at P. With both the

---

* See Exercise 1.3-11.
† Latin *tangere*, "to touch."
‡ This clause would allow us to accept the line of Case (b).
§ This clause would allow us to reject the line of Case (a).

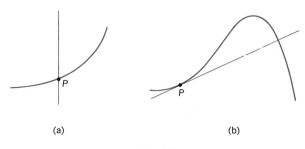

(a)   (b)

Fig. 1.2

"intersection" and "direction" ideas in mind, the tangent line may be selected according to the following definition.

■ DEFINITION 1

The tangent line to a curve at a point P. (a) Select a second point Q on the curve; (b) draw the secant line PQ; (c) let Q approach P, taking into account the possibility of approaching from both sides. If the secant lines approach one line, that line is called the tangent line at P.

Figure 1.3 illustrates the definition. For a tangent line defined this way, at least some "nearby" lines will intersect the curve twice, at P and Q, while the tangent line intersects at P alone. On the other hand, also intuitively, the directions of the secant lines PQ do give better and better approximations to the direction of the curve itself at P.

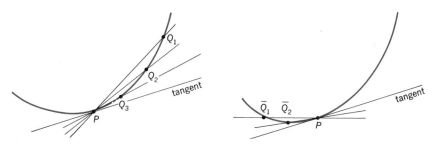

Fig. 1.3

To describe the direction of any line, and the tangent line in particular, we shall define the "slope of a line."

■ NOTATION CONVENTION 1

For "change in q" we shall write Δq.

There is some ambiguity here because Δq does not mean the multiplication of q by Δ; the symbol Δ taken by itself would be meaningless.

Example 1. If y changes from 2 to 5, we have $\Delta y = 3$. If y changes from 6 to 5.94, then $\Delta y = -.06$. In general, if y changes from y_1 to y_2, then $\Delta y = y_2 - y_1$

or $y_2 = y_1 + \Delta y$. Expressed in words, these equations say "the change is the new value minus the old."

■ DEFINITION 2

The slope of a line. Take any two distinct points on a nonvertical line. Let Δx and Δy be the changes in x and y in going from one of these points to the other. Then the slope of the line is $m = \Delta y/\Delta x$.

Different observers might select different pairs of points on a line in measuring its slope, but since the corresponding Δx's and Δy's would be corresponding parts of similar triangles, all observers would compute the same ratio $\Delta y/\Delta x$ and hence the same slope for the same line; see Fig. 1.4. If a line rises as it is traced from left to right, the Δx and Δy measured between any two points will both be positive or will both be negative. The slope of such a line will then be positive. On the other hand, if a line falls as it is traced from left to right, the Δx and Δy measured will have to be of opposite signs and the slope of such a line is negative; see Fig. 1.5. For a horizontal line, $\Delta y = 0$, no matter what the Δx. Hence the slope of such a line is 0; see Fig. 1.6. For a vertical line, $\Delta x = 0$, no matter what the Δy; see Fig. 1.7. In this case Definition 2 does not apply; we do not define a slope for a vertical line.

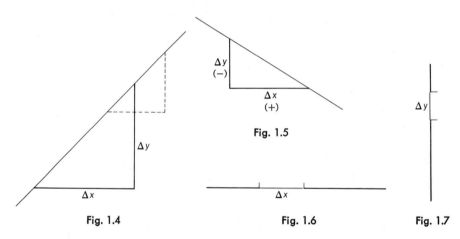

Fig. 1.4   Fig. 1.5   Fig. 1.6   Fig. 1.7

The definition of the tangent line to a curve given earlier may now be illustrated algebraically with a relatively simple case.

Example 2.   Consider the graph of $y = x^2$. The definition of the tangent line will be used to derive instructions for drawing the tangent line at the point $P(1, 1)$.*

---

* In describing points on a graph it is customary to use the following convention: If a point P has coordinates x and y, we shall say that it is the point $P(x, y)$.

Note that the x coordinate is always written first. For "point J with x coordinate -2 and y coordinate 7" we write $J(-2, 7)$. If a point has x coordinate 0 and y coordinate 12, we describe it as the point $(0, 12)$.

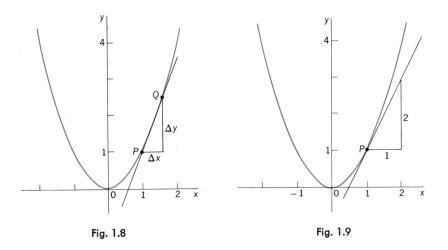

Fig. 1.8   Fig. 1.9

Let Q be a distinct nearby point for which $x = 1 + \Delta x$, $\Delta x \neq 0$; see Fig. 1.8. Point Q lies to the right or left of P according as Δx is greater, or less, than 0. At Q we have $y = 1 + \Delta y$, because for P we had $y = 1$. Since Q lies on the curve, its coordinates satisfy the equation $y = x^2$, giving

$$1 + \Delta y = (1 + \Delta x)^2 \quad \text{or} \quad \Delta y = 2\,\Delta x + (\Delta x)^2.$$

From this, dividing by Δx, which is not 0, we find that the slope of the secant line PQ is

$$\frac{\Delta y}{\Delta x} = 2 + \Delta x. \tag{1}$$

If we let Q approach P from either side, Δx will approach 0, either through positive or negative values, and it is intuitively clear from Eq. (1) that the slope of the tangent line, the line being approached by the secant lines, is 2.

To draw this tangent line, Fig. 1.9, start at point P and locate a second point any convenient number of units to the right of P and twice as many units above P.

Example 3. Consider the same curve, but this time we shall find the slopes of the tangent lines at $(2, 4)$, $(-1, 1)$, $(\frac{1}{2}, \frac{1}{4})$, and indeed the slope of the tangent line at any point $P_1(x_1, y_1)$ on the curve.

The coordinates of P_1 satisfy the equation $y = x^2$; therefore

$$y_1 = x_1^2.$$

Let $Q(x_1 + \Delta x, y_1 + \Delta y)$, $\Delta x \neq 0$, be a second distinct point on the curve; see Fig. 1.10. The coordinates of Q must also satisfy the equation of the curve, so that

$$y_1 + \Delta y = (x_1 + \Delta x)^2 = x_1^2 + 2x_1\,\Delta x + \Delta x^2.$$

Subtracting the preceding equation from this one, we obtain

$$\Delta y = 2x_1\,\Delta x + \Delta x^2,$$

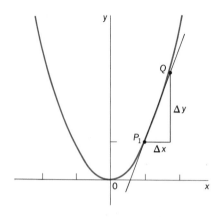

Fig. 1.10

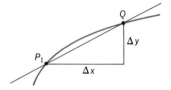

Fig. 1.11

and if we divide by Δx, which is not 0, we get the slope of the secant line P_1Q,

$$\frac{\Delta y}{\Delta x} = 2x_1 + \Delta x.$$

If now Q approaches P_1 from either side, Δx approaches 0, and the slope of the secant line approaches $2x_1$, which must be the slope of the tangent line at $P_1(x_1, y_1)$. The slopes of the tangent lines at $(2, 4)$, $(-1, 1)$, $(\frac{1}{2}, \frac{1}{4})$ are respectively 4, -2, 1.*

The algebraic statement of the definition for the tangent line to a curve is, in general, this: Let $P_1(x_1, y_1)$ be a point on the curve whose equation is

$$y = f(x).$$

Let $Q(x_1 + \Delta x, \ y_1 + \Delta y)$, $\Delta x \neq 0$, be a second distinct point on the curve; see Fig. 1.11. This means that when $x_1 + \Delta x$ is substituted for x in the equation for the curve, the corresponding y value should be $y_1 + \Delta y$; in function notation,

$$y_1 + \Delta y = f(x_1 + \Delta x).$$

Subtract the above equations to get

$$\Delta y = f(x_1 + \Delta x) - f(x_1).$$

If we divide by Δx, which is not 0, we get the slope of the secant line P_1Q:

$$\frac{\Delta y}{\Delta x} = \frac{f(x_1 + \Delta x) - f(x_1)}{\Delta x}.$$

Now let Q approach P_1; that is, let $\Delta x \to 0$, writing "$\to$" for "approach." If the limit exists, we have the slope of the tangent line at P_1. To summarize, Definition 1 can be rewritten in algebraic form.

■ DEFINITION 1A

The slope of the tangent line to a curve at $P_1(x_1, y_1)$. Let $P_1(x_1, y_1)$ be a point on the curve whose equation is $y = f(x)$. Then the slope of the tangent line to the curve at P_1 shall be

$$\lim_{\Delta x \to 0} \frac{\Delta y}{\Delta x} = \lim_{\Delta x \to 0} \frac{f(x_1 + \Delta x) - f(x_1)}{\Delta x},$$

if it exists.

---

* Note that by retaining the letter x_1 in this example instead of specializing to the number 1 as in Example 2, we were able to solve a whole set of specific problems at once.

The following statement explains the convention we used in the preceding definition.

■ NOTATION CONVENTION 2

For $\lim_{b \to c} A$ read "the limit approached by A as b approaches c."

● Remark 1

Note that when we inquire about $\lim_{\Delta x \to 0} (\Delta y / \Delta x)$, we are *not* concerned with the value of $\Delta y / \Delta x$ when $\Delta x = 0$. Algebraically, $\Delta y / \Delta x$ is not defined when $\Delta x = 0$ because the expression $0/0$ is not defined in arithmetic; geometrically, it makes no sense to ask about the slope of the line drawn through P_1 and Q if Q coincides with P_1. We *are* concerned with the values $\Delta y / \Delta x$ has when Δx is near 0; when we say that $\lim_{\Delta x \to 0} (\Delta y / \Delta x) = 2$, we mean that the closer Δx is to 0, the closer $\Delta y / \Delta x$ is to 2. A precise definition for statements like $\lim_{\Delta x \to 0} (\Delta y / \Delta x) = 2$ will be given in Chapter 7, after more experience has been gained. For the present, the definitions of words like "approach," "near," and "limit" are left to the reader's intuition.

Example 4. Not every curve has a tangent at every point. Consider the point for which $x = 0$ on the graph of $y = \sqrt{x^2}$; see Example 1.1-3 and Fig. 1.12. The secant line taken through any point Q which lies to the right of O, no matter how close, will be the fixed line OA. This is, therefore, an especially simple case. As Q approaches O, the secant line does not vary. The line approached by the secant lines is OA itself. However, if $\overline{Q}$ approaches O from the left, the secant line $O\overline{Q}$ will always be $O\overline{A}$, and the line approached by the secant lines this time is $O\overline{A}$. Thus the secant lines do not approach one limiting position as Q approaches O from both sides, and we do not have a tangent line.

● Remark 2

This section began by considering the line the reader had accepted earlier as the tangent line to the circle. The more general definition of tangent line now being discussed should be consistent with the older definition, and when the general definition is applied to the circle, it should lead us to the same tangent line as before. This work will be carried out in Exercise 3.9-23.

● Remark 3

Sometimes one wishes to define the tangent line to a curve at an end point of a region for which it is defined. For instance, he might ask for the line tangent to $y = \sqrt{x^3}$ at O $(0, 0)$; see Fig. 1.13. Here y is not defined for $x < 0$, and therefore when a second point Q is to be selected with which to draw a secant line through O, it must be taken to the right of O. In such a case, one defines a "one-

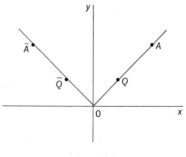

Fig. 1.12

sided" tangent. It might be said that there were two one-sided tangents at the origin in Example 4, but, since these one-sided tangents did not coincide, one could not speak of a tangent at the origin.

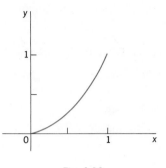

Fig. 1.13

Example 5.   To study the slope of the one-sided tangent to $y = \sqrt{x^3}$ at O $(0, 0)$, consider the nearby, distinct point Q on the curve with coordinates $(0 + \Delta x, 0 + \Delta y)$, $\Delta x > 0$. Since the coordinates of Q satisfy the equation of the curve, we can write

$$\Delta y = \sqrt{(\Delta x)^3},$$

and the slope of OQ is

$$\frac{\Delta y}{\Delta x} = \frac{\sqrt{(\Delta x)^3}}{\Delta x} = (\Delta x)^{1/2}.$$

Now if Δx approaches 0,

$$\frac{\Delta y}{\Delta x} \to 0.$$

The slope of the one-sided tangent line at $(0, 0)$ is 0; we had to restrict the Δx used in our discussion to be greater than 0.

To study the slope of the tangent line to $y = \sqrt{x^3}$ at any other point $P_1(x_1, y_1)$ on the curve, we can select a nearby distinct point $Q(x_1 + \Delta x, y_1 + \Delta y)$, with $\Delta x \neq 0$ and $x_1 + \Delta x \geq 0$, for which

$$y_1 + \Delta y = \sqrt{(x_1 + \Delta x)^3},$$

so that

$$\Delta y = \sqrt{(x_1 + \Delta x)^3} - \sqrt{x_1^3},$$

and the slope of the secant line P_1Q is

$$\frac{\Delta y}{\Delta x} = \frac{\sqrt{(x_1 + \Delta x)^3} - \sqrt{x_1^3}}{\Delta x}.$$

The number approached by $\Delta y / \Delta x$ as Δx approaches 0 is not immediately apparent, and so we rewrite our expression for $\Delta y / \Delta x$, rationalizing the numerator.

$$\frac{\Delta y}{\Delta x} = \frac{\sqrt{(x_1 + \Delta x)^3} - \sqrt{x_1^3}}{\Delta x} \frac{\sqrt{(x_1 + \Delta x)^3} + \sqrt{x_1^3}}{\sqrt{(x_1 + \Delta x)^3} + \sqrt{x_1^3}} = \frac{(x_1 + \Delta x)^3 - x_1^3}{\Delta x[\sqrt{(x_1 + \Delta x)^3} + \sqrt{x_1^3}]}$$

$$= \frac{3x_1^2 \Delta x + 3x_1 \Delta x^2 + \Delta x^3}{\Delta x[\sqrt{(x_1 + \Delta x)^3} + \sqrt{x_1^3}]} = \frac{3x_1^2 + 3x_1 \Delta x + \Delta x^2}{\sqrt{(x_1 + \Delta x)^3} + \sqrt{x_1^3}}.$$

Now if Δx approaches 0,

$$\frac{\Delta y}{\Delta x} \to \frac{3x_1^2}{\sqrt{x_1^3} + \sqrt{x_1^3}} = \frac{3x_1^2}{2\sqrt{x_1^3}} = \frac{3}{2}x_1^{1/2}.$$

The slope of the tangent line at (x_1, y_1), $x_1 > 0$, is $\frac{3}{2} x_1^{1/2}$.

EXERCISES 1.3

1. The points $R(2, 6)$, $S(8, 6)$, $T(1, 1)$, and $U(8, 0)$ are given. Find the slopes of lines RS, RT, RU, and SU if possible.

2. The points $V(0, 3)$, $W(-3, 2)$, $K(0, -2)$, and $L(7, 3)$ are given. Find the slopes of lines KW, KV, KL, and VL if possible.

3. Through the point $V(0, 3)$ draw lines of slope $\frac{3}{2}$, $-\frac{2}{3}$, $\frac{2}{3}$.

4. Through the point $W(-3, 2)$ draw lines of slope $\frac{3}{4}$, $-\frac{4}{3}$, $-\frac{3}{4}$.

5. Consider the distinct points P_1 $(2, 0)$ and $Q(2 + \Delta x, 0 + \Delta y)$, $\Delta x \neq 0$, on the graph of $y = x^2 - 2x$. Find the slope of the secant line P_1Q. What is this slope if $\Delta x = .1$? .01? .001? .0001? What is the slope of the tangent line at P_1? Draw the graph from $x = 1$ to $x = 4$ and construct the tangent at P_1.

6. Consider the distinct points P_1 $(-2, 5)$ and $Q(-2 + \Delta x, 5 + \Delta y)$, $\Delta x \neq 0$, on the graph of $y = 9 - x^2$. Find the slope of the secant line P_1Q. What is this slope if $\Delta x = -.1$? $-.01$? $-.001$? What is the slope of the tangent line at P_1? Draw the graph from $x = -3$ to $x = 0$ and construct the tangent at P_1.

7. Draw the graph of $y = x - x^2$ from $x = -2$ to $x = 3$. Compute the slope of the tangent line at any point. What are the slopes of the tangent lines at $O(0, 0)$ and $S(\frac{3}{2}, -\frac{3}{4})$? With these slopes in mind, construct tangents at O and S. At what point on the graph will the tangent be horizontal?

8. Draw the graph of $y = x^3$ from $x = -2$ to $x = 2$. Compute the slope of the tangent line at any point $P_1(x_1, y_1)$ and in particular at the points $U(-1, -1)$ and $V(\frac{3}{2}, \frac{27}{8})$. Construct tangents at U and V. At what point on the graph, if any, will the tangent be horizontal?

9. Follow the instructions of Exercise 8 for $y = 1/x$. Use the points $U(-1, -1)$ and $V(\frac{1}{2}, 2)$.

10. Draw the graph of $y = \sqrt{x}$ from $x = 0$ to $x = 4$. Compute the slope of the tangent line at any point P_1 and in particular at the points $K(1, 1)$ and $L(3, \sqrt{3})$. Construct tangents at K and L.

11. (a) Why must PC be longer than CT in Fig. 1.1?* (b). Prove this theorem:

Hypothesis: (1) Line L is drawn through point T of a circle with center C. (2) For any other point P of L we have $CP > CT$.
Conclusion: $L \perp CT$.

12. In Example 4 it was shown that $2x_1$ is the slope of the tangent line at a point $P_1(x_1, y_1)$ on the curve whose equation is $y = x^2$. If for each point of the following table we draw a short segment of the corresponding tangent line, we get Fig. 1.14.

x	0	$\frac{1}{2}$	1	$\frac{3}{2}$	$\frac{7}{4}$	2
y	0	$\frac{1}{4}$	1	$\frac{9}{4}$	$\frac{49}{16}$	4
slope	0	1	2	3	$\frac{7}{2}$	4

---

* Some reasoning of Euclidean geometry is expected here.

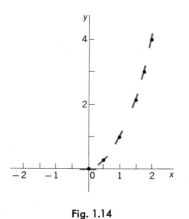

Fig. 1.14

(a) Do the same thing for $y = x - x^2$ from $x = 0$ to $x = 2$.

(b) Do the same thing for the curve for which the following table is valid:

x	0	0.5	1.0	1.5	−0.5	−1.0	−1.5
y	1	1.6	2.7	4.5	0.6	0.4	0.2
slope	1	1.6	2.7	4.5	0.6	0.4	0.2

These drawings suggest how the tangents to a curve determine the curve. In more advanced work, we say that the curve is the "envelope" of its tangent lines.

1.4   Velocity in Rectilinear Motion. Acceleration

To describe a particle moving in a straight-line path, a scale may be laid off on this straight line, and then, if y represents the scale coordinate, an equation of the form $y = f(t)$ tells where the particle is at any particular time t for which the function f is defined.

Example 1.   The height of a ball dropped from a building 320 ft high is given by the equation

$$y = 320 - 16t^2, \qquad 0 \leq t \leq \sqrt{20},$$

where t is measured in seconds from the instant the ball is dropped and the height y is measured in feet, with $y = 0$ assigned to ground level and positive y's assigned to points above ground.* Observe that at $t = 0$ the equation says that $y = 320$, which agrees with the given information. The ball will reach the ground when $y = 0$; thus, when $320 - 16t^2 = 0$, $t = \sqrt{20} \approx 4.5$ sec.

A natural question to ask about a moving body is what its velocity is. For instance, if it is going to strike something, we may want to know its velocity at the instant the collision takes place. Just what is meant by velocity, and how shall we compute it?

To compute an *average velocity for an interval of time* is relatively easy. If a distance of 90 miles is traveled in 3 hr, the average speed for the 3-hr interval is

$$\frac{90 \text{ miles}}{3 \text{ hours}} = 30 \frac{\text{miles}}{\text{hour}}.$$

In general, if a distance D is traveled in time T, the average speed for the interval is D/T. But this definition cannot be applied directly to the problem of the instan-

---

* Several simplifying assumptions have been made. For instance, we assume that the only force acting on the ball is the force of gravity; air resistance, among other things, is neglected. In Chapter 2 the reader will learn how to derive this equation.

taneous velocity, for if the interval is only an instant, $T = 0$ and $D = 0$; D/T is meaningless.

A knowledge of the average velocity for an interval does not tell us the velocity at a particular instant of the interval, for in general the velocity changes during the interval. But if an interval is short enough, so that the velocity cannot change much during the interval, then the velocity at one particular instant of the interval cannot differ much from the average velocity for the whole interval. Moreover, the shorter the interval, the smaller will be the difference between the velocity at one instant and the average velocity for the whole interval. This is the idea used to define instantaneous velocity.

■ DEFINITION 1

The velocity at an instant. Let a particle move on a straight line, its position described by a distance function with time domain D. For any time number t_1 of D: (a) form a time interval that includes t_1, the entire interval to lie in D; (b) compute the average velocity for this interval; and (c) repeat the computation with intervals whose lengths approach 0. If it exists, the limit approached by the average velocities for these intervals is the velocity at t_1.

Example 2. Consider again the ball of Example 1 whose height at time t is given by

$$y = f(t) = 320 - 16t^2, \qquad 0 \le t \le \sqrt{20}.$$

Let us try to compute the velocity of the ball at time $t = 2$.

Consider the interval $t = 2$ to $t = 2 + \Delta t$, $\Delta t \ne 0$; see Fig.1.15. At $t = 2$, the height is

$$y = f(2) = 320 - 64 = 256.$$

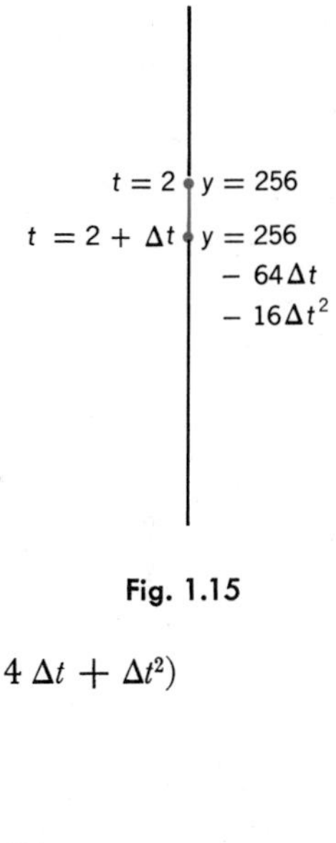

At $t = 2 + \Delta t$, the height is

$$f(2 + \Delta t) = 320 - 16(2 + \Delta t)^2 = 320 - 16(4 + 4\,\Delta t + \Delta t^2)$$
$$= 256 - 64\,\Delta t - 16\,\Delta t^2.$$

Therefore the change in height during the interval is

$$\Delta y = f(2 + \Delta t) - f(2) = -64\,\Delta t - 16\,\Delta t^2.*$$

The average velocity for the interval is obtained by dividing the distance traveled during the interval, Δy, by the time required, Δt;

$$\frac{\Delta y}{\Delta t} = -64 - 16\,\Delta t. \tag{1}$$

In particular, for the intervals listed in Table 1.2 we have the indicated average velocities. We conclude from Eq. (1) that as the intervals approach 0 in length, the

$t = 2 \quad y = 256$

$t = 2 + \Delta t \quad y = 256$
$\qquad\qquad\quad - 64\,\Delta t$
$\qquad\qquad\quad - 16\,\Delta t^2$

Fig. 1.15

---

* Observe that Δy is negative if Δt is positive, which is to be expected for a falling ball.

TABLE 1.2

Interval	Δt	Average velocity	Interval	Δt	Average velocity
$t = 2$ to 2.01	.01	-64.16	$t = 2$ to 1.99	$-.01$	-63.84
$t = 2$ to 2.001	.001	-64.016	$t = 2$ to 1.999	$-.001$	-63.984
$t = 2$ to 2.0001	.0001	-64.0016	$t = 2$ to 1.9999	$-.0001$	-63.9984

average velocities approach -64. *By definition*, the velocity at $t = 2$ is -64. The minus sign indicates that there is a decrease in height with an increase in time; the ball is falling rather than rising.

Example 3. Consider again the same falling ball, but this time compute the velocity at any particular instant t. Form the interval from that time t to time $t + \Delta t$, $\Delta t \neq 0$. At that time t, the height is

$$y = f(t) = 320 - 16t^2;$$

at time $t + \Delta t$ the height is

$$y + \Delta y = f(t + \Delta t) = 320 - 16(t + \Delta t)^2$$
$$= 320 - 16t^2 - 32t\,\Delta t - 16\,\Delta t^2.$$

The distance traveled during the interval is the change in height,

$$\Delta y = -32t\,\Delta t - 16\,\Delta t^2.$$

The average velocity for the interval is

$$\frac{\Delta y}{\Delta t} = -32t - 16\,\Delta t.$$

If now we let the length of the interval approach 0, that is, let $\Delta t \to 0$, we see that the average velocity approaches $-32t$. *By definition*, the velocity at the particular time t is $-32t$. To illustrate, the velocity at $t = \sqrt{20}$, the instant the ball struck the ground, is $-32\sqrt{20} \approx -143.1$ ft per sec.

To summarize, we started with the height function which assigns to any t of the domain interval $0 \leq t \leq \sqrt{20}$ a height number $y = f(t)$ and we derived from it a new velocity function which assigns to any t of the interval $0 \leq t \leq \sqrt{20}$ a velocity number. To distinguish between the two functions while still indicating that one comes from the other, we shall write f' for the second function:

$$y = f(t) = 320 - 16t^2, \qquad 0 \leq t \leq \sqrt{20}.$$
$$v = f'(t) = -32t, \qquad 0 \leq t \leq \sqrt{20}. \tag{2}$$

By writing down the same ideas in the general case, an algebraic statement for Definition 1 can be derived. Let the equation

$$y = f(t)$$

describe a rectilinear motion for certain values of t. Form the time interval which starts at time t and ends at time $t + \Delta t$, $\Delta t \neq 0$, f being defined throughout this interval. In this interval the particle traveled from the position $y = f(t)$ to the position

$$y + \Delta y = f(t + \Delta t).$$

The distance traveled was

$$\Delta y = f(t + \Delta t) - f(t),$$

and the average speed for the interval was

$$\frac{\Delta y}{\Delta t} = \frac{f(t + \Delta t) - f(t)}{\Delta t}.$$

Let $\Delta t \to 0$. If

$$\lim_{\Delta t \to 0} \frac{\Delta y}{\Delta t} = \lim_{\Delta t \to 0} \frac{f(t + \Delta t) - f(t)}{\Delta t}$$

exists, it is the velocity at time t.

◾ DEFINITION 1A

The velocity at an instant. Let a particle move on a straight line and let $y = f(t)$, with domain D, describe the particle's position at time t. Then, if the limit indicated exists, at any t_1 of D the velocity is

$$v = \lim_{\Delta t \to 0} \frac{\Delta y}{\Delta t} = \lim_{\Delta t \to 0} \frac{f(t_1 + \Delta t) - f(t_1)}{\Delta t} = f'(t_1).$$

● Remark 1

Note that, when we inquire about $\lim_{\Delta t \to 0} (\Delta y / \Delta t)$ we are not concerned with the value of $\Delta y / \Delta t$ when $\Delta t = 0$. Indeed, $\Delta y / \Delta t$ is not defined when $\Delta t = 0$, for the arithmetic instructions $0/0$ make no sense. We are concerned with the values of $\Delta y / \Delta t$ for Δt near 0.

We have just defined the velocity of a particle moving in a straight line. This velocity is itself a function of time. At what rate does it change?

◾ DEFINITION 2

The acceleration at an instant. Let a particle move on a straight line, its velocity described by a function with time domain D. For any time number t_1 of D: (a) form a time interval which includes t_1, the entire interval to lie in D; (b) compute the average rate of change of the velocity for the interval; and (c) repeat the computation with intervals whose lengths approach 0. If it exists, the limit approached by the average rates of change of the velocity for these intervals is the acceleration at t_1.

This definition of acceleration as the instantaneous rate of change of velocity is the one we have in mind when we use the word in other contexts also. If one "steps on the accelerator" of an automobile, he will change its velocity. In physics, if a force acts on an object, the velocity of the object changes, and, moreover, the rate at which the velocity changes is proportional to the force. It is this relationship between forces and accelerations that makes the concept of acceleration so important.

Example 4.   Consider again the falling ball of Example 3. From Eq. (2),

$$y = f(t) = 320 - 16t^2, \qquad v = f'(t) = -32t, \qquad 0 \le t \le \sqrt{20}.$$

To find the acceleration at time t, form the interval from time t to time $t + \Delta t$, $\Delta t \ne 0$. At time t, $v = f'(t) = -32t$; at time $t + \Delta t$, the new velocity is

$$v + \Delta v = f'(t + \Delta t) = -32(t + \Delta t)$$
$$= -32t - 32\,\Delta t.$$

The change in velocity for the interval is

$$\Delta v = -32\,\Delta t.$$

The average rate of change of v for the interval is

$$\frac{\Delta v}{\Delta t} = -32.$$

As the interval's length approaches zero, that is, as $\Delta t \to 0$, the average rate of change of v remains -32; the acceleration at time t, the limit being approached by the average rates of change of v for the intervals, is -32.

To summarize, this time we started with the velocity function that assigns to any t of the domain interval $0 \le t \le \sqrt{20}$ a velocity number $v = f'(t) = -32t$ and we derived from it a new acceleration function that assigns the acceleration number $a = -32$ to each t of the domain interval $0 \le t \le \sqrt{20}$.

The physical explanation for the fact that this acceleration is constant is the fact that the force of gravity that caused the motion was assumed to be constant.

In general, reasoning as in Example 4, we may rewrite Definition 2.

■ DEFINITION 2A

The acceleration at an instant. Let a particle move on a straight line and let $v = f'(t)$, with domain D, describe the particle's velocity at time t. Then, if the limit indicated exists, at any t_1 of D the acceleration is

$$a = \lim_{\Delta t \to 0} \frac{\Delta v}{\Delta t} = \lim_{\Delta t \to 0} \frac{f'(t_1 + \Delta t) - f'(t_1)}{\Delta t}.$$

We often write f'' as a name for the acceleration function and indicate the acceleration at t_1 by $f''(t_1)$.

EXERCISES 1.4

1. The height of a ball thrown up from the ground with an initial velocity of 144 ft per sec is given by the formula $y = 144t - 16t^2$. Find the distance traveled in the interval from $t = 1$ to $t = 1 + \Delta t$, $\Delta t \neq 0$. Find the average velocity for this interval. What is the average velocity if $\Delta t = .1? .01? .001?$ What is the velocity at $t = 1$?

2. Consider again the ball of Exercise 1. Find the distance traveled in the interval from $t = 6$ to $t = 6 + \Delta t$, $\Delta t \neq 0$. Find the average velocity for this interval. What is the average velocity if $\Delta t = -.1? -.01? -.001?$ What is the velocity at $t = 6$?

3. Consider again the ball of Exercise 1. Find the velocity at time t. (a) When will the ball strike the ground? (b) With what velocity will it strike the ground? (c) What is the velocity at $t = 1? t = 3? t = 5?$ (d) When is the velocity 0? (e) When is the ball highest? How high?

4. The height of a ball thrown up from a roof 176 ft high with an initial velocity of 56 ft per sec is given by the formula $y = 176 + 56t - 16t^2$. Find a formula for the velocity at time t and answer the questions asked in Exercise 3.

5. A ball is thrown down from a roof 160 ft high with an initial velocity of 48 ft per sec. Its height t seconds later is given by the formula $y = 160 - 48t - 16t^2$. Derive a formula for its velocity at time t from the definition of velocity, and, in particular, compute the velocity with which it struck the ground.

6. A ball is thrown down from a roof 144 ft high with an initial velocity of 32 ft per sec. Its height t sec later is given by the formula $y = 144 - 32t - 16t^2$. Answer the questions asked in Exercise 5.

7. When a ball rolls down a certain inclined plane, its distance from the starting point after t sec is given by the formula $x = 12t^2$. Find its velocity at time t and the time required for the velocity to increase to 36 ft per sec. Find the velocity attained after the ball has rolled 12 ft, 48 ft, x ft.

8. If the same ball is given an initial push of 18 ft per sec, its distance from the starting point after t sec is given by $x = 18t + 12t^2$. Find its velocity at time t and the time required for the velocity to increase to 36 ft per sec. Where would the ball then be?

9. A brick is sliding across the ice with a velocity of 50 ft per sec when first observed. If the distance, in feet, that it travels from this point in t sec is given by $x = 50t - 5t^2$, find its velocity and acceleration at time t. When did the brick stop? How far from the initial point of observation had it then moved? If the force of friction is the only force acting on the brick, what can be said about the force of friction assumed in deriving the formula for x?

10. (a) Find the acceleration of the ball of Exercise 5 at time t. (b) The same for the ball of Exercise 8.

11. The distance moved by a particle in rectilinear motion was given by the formula $x = t^3$. (a) What would be its velocity and acceleration at time t? (b) What would be its average velocity for the interval $t = 0.9$ to $t = 1.1$? (c) What would be its velocity at $t = 0.9? t = 1? t = 1.1?$

12. If the formula $v = t/(1 + t)$ describes the velocity of an object at time t for $0 \leq t \leq 2$, find its acceleration at time t for $0 \leq t \leq 2$.

1.5 Rates of Change. The Derivative

An observant student notices quickly that, although the problem of the slope of the tangent line and the problem of the velocity of a moving particle are taken from entirely different contexts, they are, mathematically, the same problem, as will be seen by reference to Definitions 1.3-1A and 1.4-1A. The same mathematical analysis will apply whenever a rate of change is to be determined. Let $y = f(x)$. What do we mean by "the rate of change of y with respect to x for a particular x"?

It is relatively easy to explain what we mean by the *average rate of change* of y with respect to x for a particular change in x.

Example 1.   Consider the length L of a metal bar as a function of the temperature T. If a change in temperature from $T = 0°C$ to $T = 0.1°C$ is accompanied by a change in length from $L = 1$ meter to $L = 1.0000012$ meter, then $\Delta L = .0000012$ meter, $\Delta T = .1°C$, and the average rate of change of L with respect to T for this particular change in T is $\Delta L/\Delta T = .000012$ meter per deg C.

■ **DEFINITION 1**

The average rate of change for an interval. Let $y = f(x)$ with domain D. Let all the points of the interval with end points x and $x + \Delta x$, $\Delta x \neq 0$, lie in D. The average rate of change of y with respect to x for this interval is

$$\frac{\Delta y}{\Delta x} = \frac{f(x + \Delta x) - f(x)}{\Delta x}.$$

We use the average rate of change to define the instantaneous rate of change.

■ **DEFINITION 2**

Let the function f have domain D. The *instantaneous rate of change* of $y = f(x)$ with respect to x for a particular x of D is the number obtained if we can

(a) take an interval with end points x and $x + \Delta x$, $\Delta x \neq 0$, all of whose points lie in D;

(b) compute the average rate of change of y with respect to x for the interval;

(c) let $\Delta x \to 0$ and take the limit approached by this average rate of change.

Since the average rate of change of y is $\Delta y/\Delta x$, Definition 2 can be restated in another form.

■ **DEFINITION 2A**

Let function f have domain D. The *instantaneous rate of change* of $y = f(x)$ with respect to x for a particular x of D is

$$\lim_{\Delta x \to 0} \frac{\Delta y}{\Delta x} = \lim_{\Delta x \to 0} \frac{f(x + \Delta x) - f(x)}{\Delta x},$$

provided this limit exists.

Example 2.   Coulomb's law says that the force of attraction between two unlike charges is given by $F = k/r^2$, $r > 0$, where r is the distance between the charges and k is a constant. If r changes, at what rate will F change with respect to r at the moment r has a certain value?

Change from r to $r + \Delta r$ with $\Delta r \neq 0$ and $r + \Delta r > 0$. Then

$$F + \Delta F = \frac{k}{(r + \Delta r)^2},$$

$$\Delta F = \frac{k}{(r + \Delta r)^2} - \frac{k}{r^2} = \frac{kr^2}{r^2(r + \Delta r)^2} - \frac{k(r + \Delta r)^2}{r^2(r + \Delta r)^2}$$

$$= \frac{k(-2r\,\Delta r - \Delta r^2)}{r^2(r + \Delta r)^2}.*$$

The average rate of change of F with respect to r for the interval with end points r and $r + \Delta r$ will be

$$\frac{\Delta F}{\Delta r} = \frac{k(-2r - \Delta r)}{r^2(r + \Delta r)^2}.\dagger$$

If we let $\Delta r \to 0$, we find that the rate of change of F with respect to r for this particular r is

$$\lim_{\Delta r \to 0} \frac{\Delta F}{\Delta r} = \frac{-2kr}{r^2 r^2} = -\frac{2k}{r^3}.$$

In particular, at $r = 3$, the rate of change of F with respect to r is $-\frac{2}{27} k$.

In Example 2 we started with the F function which assigns the force number k/r^2 to each distance number $r > 0$ and from it we computed a new function which assigns the number $-2k/r^3$ to each $r > 0$, this new number being the rate of change of the force with respect to the distance at that particular distance r. In general, for those numbers x for which the instructions of Definition 2A can be carried out, we are led from the original function $y = f(x)$ to a new function, the number assigned by the new function to any number x being the rate of change of y with respect to x for that number x. This new function is called the derivative function for f or the derivative of f. To indicate in our notation that it was derived from f, we write f' for that function.

▪ DEFINITION 3

f', *the derivative function for* f. Let function f have domain D. For those x of D for which the limit indicated exists,

$$f'(x) = \lim_{\Delta x \to 0} \frac{f(x + \Delta x) - f(x)}{\Delta x} = \lim_{\Delta x \to 0} \frac{\Delta f}{\Delta x}. \tag{1}$$

---

* Here, in order to subtract fractions, we multiplied the numerator and denominator of each of the original fractions by such quantities as would give them a common denominator. Then we subtracted fractions directly be subtracting numerators.

† In order to divide ΔF, which was shown above to be equal to $[k(-2r\,\Delta r - \Delta r^2)]/[r^2(r + \Delta r)^2]$, by Δr, we divided the numerator of this fraction by Δr. We could also have multiplied the denominator of this fraction by Δr and then simplified the result.

If we start with the statement $y = f(x)$, the derivative of y with respect to x is also often indicated by dy/dx or df/dx. The definition of the rate of change may be stated in the derivative notation.

■ DEFINITION 2B

Let function f have domain D. The rate of change of $y = f(x)$ with respect to x for a particular x_1 of D is $f'(x_1)$, or dy/dx evaluated at $x = x_1$.

As special cases we have two more definitions.

■ DEFINITION 4

The slope of the tangent line to the curve $y = f(x)$ at the point (x_1, y_1) is $f'(x_1)$, or dy/dx evaluated at (x_1, y_1).

■ DEFINITION 5

Let a particle move on a straight line and let $y = f(t)$, with domain D, describe the particle's position at time t. At any t_1 of D the velocity is $f'(t_1)$ or dy/dt evaluated at t_1.

● Remark 1

The notation dy/dx is misleading if it suggests to the reader that we deal here with a fraction whose numerator is dy and whose denominator is dx. *We have not defined quantities dx or dy.* $\Delta y/\Delta x$ is a fraction with numerator Δy and denominator Δx. dy/dx is the limit approached by $\Delta y/\Delta x$ as Δx approaches zero.

Example 3. To find dy/dx if $y = cx$, we have

$$y = f(x) = cx,$$
$$y + \Delta y = f(x + \Delta x) = c(x + \Delta x), \qquad \Delta x \neq 0,$$
$$\Delta y = f(x + \Delta x) - f(x) = c\,\Delta x;$$

the average rate of change of y with respect to x for the interval with end points x and $x + \Delta x$ is

$$\frac{\Delta y}{\Delta x} = c;$$

then
$$f'(x) = \frac{dy}{dx} = \lim_{\Delta x \to 0} \frac{\Delta y}{\Delta x} = c.$$

Example 4. To find dy/dx if

$$y = \frac{x}{x - 2}, \qquad x \neq 2,$$

we write

$$y + \Delta y = f(x + \Delta x) = \frac{x + \Delta x}{x + \Delta x - 2}, \qquad \Delta x \neq 0 \qquad \text{and} \qquad x + \Delta x - 2 \neq 0,$$

$$\Delta y = f(x + \Delta x) - f(x) = \frac{x + \Delta x}{x + \Delta x - 2} - \frac{x}{x - 2}$$

$$= \frac{(x - 2)(x + \Delta x) - (x + \Delta x - 2)x}{(x + \Delta x - 2)(x - 2)} = \frac{-2\,\Delta x}{(x + \Delta x - 2)(x - 2)}.*$$

Now, the average rate of change for the interval x to $x + \Delta x$ is

$$\frac{\Delta y}{\Delta x} = \frac{-2}{(x + \Delta x - 2)(x - 2)},\dagger \tag{2}$$

and the rate of change at x is

$$f'(x) = \frac{dy}{dx} = \frac{-2}{(x - 2)(x - 2)} = \frac{-2}{(x - 2)^2}.$$

To be specific, from Eq. (2), the average rate of change of y with respect to x for the interval from $x = 3$ to $x = 3.1$, $(x = 3, \Delta x = .1)$, is

$$\frac{\Delta y}{\Delta x} = \frac{-2}{(1.1)(1)} \approx -1.818;$$

the rate of change at $x = 3$ is

$$f'(3) = \frac{-2}{(3 - 2)^2} = -2.$$

● **Remark 2**

Definition 3 can also be written

$$f'(x) = \lim_{z \to x} \frac{f(z) - f(x)}{z - x}. \tag{3}$$

Here $z - x$ can be interpreted as a change from x to z, $f(z) - f(x)$ as the corresponding change in f, and

$$\frac{f(z) - f(x)}{z - x} = \frac{\Delta f}{\Delta x}$$

as the average rate of change of f with respect to x for the interval from x to z. If we let $z \to x$, that is, if the change in x approaches 0, the average rate approaches the instantaneous rate, or $f'(x)$. Formally, the substitution of $x + \Delta x$ for z converts Eq. (3) into Eq. (1).

● **Remark 3**

The definition of derivative rests on the concept of limit. In this chapter we shall accept the concept of limit on an intuitive basis and admit the following computations with limits as plausible: If $\lim_{x \to a} f(x) = L$ and $\lim_{x \to a} g(x) = M$, then

---

* See the first footnote in Example 2.
† We were called upon to divide Δy by Δx. We divided the numerator of Δy by Δx.

$$\lim_{x \to a} [f(x) + g(x)] = L + M,$$

$$\lim_{x \to a} [f(x) - g(x)] = L - M,$$

$$\lim_{x \to a} f(x)g(x) = LM;$$

if, further, $M \neq 0$,

$$\lim_{x \to a} \frac{f(x)}{g(x)} = \frac{L}{M};$$

and if $\lim_{x \to a} \sqrt[q]{f(x)}$ exists, then

$$\lim_{x \to a} \sqrt[q]{f(x)} = \sqrt[q]{L}.$$

In words, a sum of two functions will approach the sum of the limits approached by the functions separately, and corresponding statements may be made for differences, products, quotients, and roots. The statement on the limit of a product of two functions includes as a special case the statement that the limit approached by a function multiplied by a constant is the limit approached by the function itself, multiplied by the same constant.

Thus, in Example 4, in going from $\Delta y/\Delta x$ to $f'(x)$ we assumed tacitly that if $x - 2$ approaches $x - 2$ and Δx approaches 0, then $x + \Delta x - 2 = x - 2 + \Delta x$ approaches $x - 2 + 0 = x - 2$; we used the first of the limit statements listed.

These limit statements are all valid; in this work our intuition has not misled us. But a theory cannot be built on definitions whose meanings are left to the reader's intuition. Neither can theorems be accepted because they seem intuitively obvious. In Chapter 7, after the reader has had more experience, these questions will be considered in a more rigorous fashion.

● **Remark 4**

By the very definition of the derivative, f' cannot be determined for a number for which f itself is not defined; the domain of f' cannot be larger than the domain of f. But there may be numbers in the domain of f that are not in the domain of f' because the limit process called for in the definition of f' cannot be carried out at these points. One illustration is furnished by the function $f(x) = \sqrt[3]{x} = x^{1/3}$ whose domain consists of all real x. The student can show in Exercise 1(e) that $f'(x) = \frac{1}{3} x^{-2/3}$ for $x \neq 0$; $x = 0$ is a number of the domain of f but is not a number of the domain of f'. Also, if the domain of f is an interval that includes an end point, it will be possible, at most, to determine a "one-sided" derivative at that end point; Δx will have to approach 0 only through positive values or only through negative values. This situation was met in Remark 1.3-3, where a "one-sided" tangent was discussed.

EXERCISES 1.5

1. In preceding examples and exercises we have already computed the derivative of $f(x) = x^N$ for $N = 1, 2, 3, -1, -2, \frac{3}{2}$. Compute $f'(x)$ or dy/dx by the Δ-process also for the following functions. If there are points in the domain of f not in the domain of f', say so.

(a) $y = f(x) = x^4$.

(d) $y = f(x) = x^{1/2} = \sqrt{x}$.

(b) $y = f(x) = 1 \qquad (= x^0)$.

(e) $y = f(x) = x^{1/3} = \sqrt[3]{x}$.

(c) $y = f(x) = x^{-3} = \dfrac{1}{x^3}$.

2. Compute $f'(x)$ or dy/dx by the Δ-process for the following functions. If there are points in the domain of f not in the domain of f', say so.

(a) $y = f(x) = ax^2 + bx + c$.

(e) $y = f(x) = \dfrac{a}{x+b}$.

(b) $y = f(x) = 5x - x^3$.

(f) $y = f(x) = \dfrac{2x+5}{x+1}$.

(c) $y = f(x) = 4 - \dfrac{2}{x}$.

(g) $y = f(x) = \sqrt{1-x}$.

(d) $y = f(x) = 3x + \dfrac{1}{2x}$.

3. Find $f'(x)$ if $y = f(x) = 9 - x^2$. For the graph of $y = 9 - x^2$: (a) What is the slope of the secant line joining the point at $x = -1.9$ to the point at $x = -2$? (b) What is the slope of the tangent line at $x = -2$? (c) Draw the graph from $x = -4$ to $x = 0$ and draw a tangent at $x = -2$ with the proper slope.

4. Find dx/dt if $x = f(t) = t^3 - 6t^2 + 9t$, $0 \le t \le 4$. Let x describe the position of a particle on a line at time t. (a) Where was the particle at $t = 2$? (b) How far did the particle travel from $t = 2$ to $t = 2.01$? (c) What was the average velocity for this interval? (d) What was the velocity at $t = 2$? (e) For which values of t did the particle travel in the direction of increasing x? decreasing x?

5. According to Stefan's law, a body emits radiant energy according to the formula $R = kT^4$, where R is the rate of emission of radiant energy per unit area, T is the Kelvin temperature of the surface, and k is a physical constant. Find dR/dT. At what rate does R increase with respect to T if $T = 300$?

6. Explain each of the following statements in terms of limits.

   (a) A piston was pushed back by the gas in a chamber; at the instant $t = .02$ the volume of the gas was increasing at the rate of 3 cu cm per sec.

   (b) Some sugar was thrown into a container of water; b sec later the sugar was dissolving at the rate of c oz per sec.

   (c) A metal rod was heated; when its temperature was 26 deg, its length was increasing with respect to the temperature at the rate of .000003 units of length per unit of temperature.

7. In each of the following find a function whose derivative is the limit stated.

   (a) $f'(x) = \lim\limits_{\Delta x \to 0} \dfrac{(x + \Delta x)^3 - x^3}{\Delta x}$.

   (b) $\phi'(x) = \lim\limits_{\Delta x \to 0} \dfrac{\cos(x + \Delta x) - \cos x}{\Delta x}$.

   (c) $F'(y) = \lim\limits_{\Delta y \to 0} \dfrac{2^{y+\Delta y} - 2^y}{\Delta y}$.

(d) $g'(x) = \lim\limits_{h \to 0} \dfrac{[1/(x+h)] - 1/x}{h}.$

(e) $f'(x) = \lim\limits_{w \to x} \dfrac{\sqrt[3]{w} - \sqrt[3]{x}}{w - x}.$

8. We shall compute the derivatives of the following functions in Chapters 4 and 5. The complete derivation would require considerable ingenuity for a beginning student. Nevertheless, carry the computation for dy/dx as far as you can. You will, at the least, see what some of the difficulties are.

(a) $y = f(x) = \sin x$,   all real x.

(b) $y = f(x) = \log x$, $x > 0$.

1.6   Derivatives of Polynomials

The computation of a derivative from its definition, "by the Δ-process," can be a repetitious task. Wherever it is feasible, we work out in general form the derivatives for functions that occur frequently, and then no longer return to the Δ-process for those particular functions.

TABLE 1.3

$f(x)$	$f'(x)$
x^1	1
x^2	$2x^1$
x^3	$3x^2$
x^4	$4x^3$
x^{-1}	$-1x^{-2}$
x^{-2}	$-2x^{-3}$
x^{-3}	$-3x^{-4}$
x^0	0
$x^{1/2}$	$\frac{1}{2} x^{-1/2}$
$x^{3/2}$	$\frac{3}{2} x^{1/2}$

If we state in Table 1.3 the results already obtained for functions of the form x^N,* we are led immediately to the suggestion that, if $y = f(x) = x^N$, then $dy/dx = f'(x) = Nx^{N-1}$; in words, *if y is a power of x with constant exponent, then its derivative is the product of this exponent and a new power of x whose exponent is one less than the original exponent.* This suggestion is indeed a correct one, although the statement cannot be proved in full generality at once.

---

* See Exercise 1.5-1.

■ THEOREM 1

HYPOTHESIS: $y = f(x) = x^N$, for all x, N a positive integer.

CONCLUSION: $dy/dx = f'(x) = Nx^{N-1}$ for all x.

PROOF: Let us work through the definition of the derivative step by step. First,

$$y + \Delta y = f(x + \Delta x) = (x + \Delta x)^N, \qquad \Delta x \neq 0.$$

By the Binomial Theorem, which can be used here because N is a positive integer,

$$y + \Delta y = f(x + \Delta x) = x^N + Nx^{N-1}\,\Delta x^1 + \frac{N(N-1)}{2}x^{N-2}\,\Delta x^2$$

$$+ \text{ terms of higher degree in } \Delta x.*$$

Then,

$$\Delta y = f(x + \Delta x) - f(x) = Nx^{N-1}\,\Delta x + \frac{N(N-1)}{2}x^{N-2}\,\Delta x^2 + \cdots,$$

$$\frac{\Delta y}{\Delta x} = \frac{f(x + \Delta x) - f(x)}{\Delta x} = Nx^{N-1} + \frac{N(N-1)}{2}x^{N-2}\,\Delta x + \cdots,$$

and finally

$$\frac{dy}{dx} = \lim_{\Delta x \to 0} \frac{\Delta y}{\Delta x} = \lim_{\Delta x \to 0} \frac{f(x + \Delta x) - f(x)}{\Delta x} = Nx^{N-1}.$$

We can extend Theorem 1.

---

* The reader who has not yet studied the Binomial Theorem can still work out the essential part of this step.

(a) $(x + \Delta x)^2 = (x + \Delta x)(x + \Delta x) = x^2 + 2x\,\Delta x + \Delta x^2$.

Systematically, we took all the products that could be formed by taking one term from each factor, and then added. It is possible to take the x in each factor in only one way, getting $1x^2$; it is possible to take x in one factor, Δx in the other in two ways, getting $2x\,\Delta x$, and so forth.

(b) $(x + \Delta x)^3 = (x + \Delta x)(x + \Delta x)(x + \Delta x) = 1x^3 + 3x^2\,\Delta x + 3x\,\Delta x^2 + 1\,\Delta x^3$.

Here again we took all the products that could be formed by taking one term from each factor, and then added. First, we can form an x^3 product in only one way: by choosing the x term rather than the Δx term in each factor. But we can form products that contain two x's and one Δx in three ways, for the Δx can be chosen from any one of the three factors. Thus we get the term $3x^2\,\Delta x$, and so on.

(c) $(x + \Delta x)^N = (x + \Delta x)(x + \Delta x) \cdots (x + \Delta x) = x^N + Nx^{N-1}\,\Delta x + \cdots$.

There is only one way to form a product of N x's; hence the term $1x^N$. But one can form a product of $N - 1$ x's and one Δx in N ways; for, the one Δx can be chosen from any one of the N factors. Thus we have the term $Nx^{N-1}\,\Delta x$. There will be terms of higher degree in Δx, although their coefficients will not be computed here because they are not needed in this proof.

THEOREM 2

HYPOTHESIS: $y = f(x) = x^N$, N a negative integer, $x \neq 0$.

CONCLUSION: $dy/dx = f'(x) = Nx^{N-1}$, $x \neq 0$.

PROOF: If N is a negative integer, then $M = -N$ is a positive integer, and we have

$$y = f(x) = x^N = x^{-M} = \frac{1}{x^M}, \qquad x \neq 0.$$

Now

$$y + \Delta y = f(x + \Delta x) = \frac{1}{(x + \Delta x)^M}, \qquad \Delta x \neq 0 \quad \text{and} \quad x + \Delta x \neq 0,$$

$$\Delta y = f(x + \Delta x) - f(x) = \frac{1}{(x + \Delta x)^M} - \frac{1}{x^M} = \frac{x^M - (x + \Delta x)^M}{x^M(x + \Delta x)^M}$$

$$= \frac{x^M - \left[x^M + Mx^{M-1}\,\Delta x + \dfrac{M(M-1)}{2}x^{M-2}\,\Delta x^2 \right. + \text{ terms of higher degree in } \Delta x \left. \right]}{x^M(x + \Delta x)^M}$$

$$= -\frac{Mx^{M-1}\,\Delta x + \dfrac{M(M-1)}{2}x^{M-2}\,\Delta x^2 + \cdots}{x^M(x + \Delta x)^M},$$

$$\frac{\Delta y}{\Delta x} = -\frac{Mx^{M-1} + \dfrac{M(M-1)}{2}x^{M-2}\,\Delta x + \cdots}{x^M(x + \Delta x)^M},$$

and finally

$$\frac{dy}{dx} = -\frac{Mx^{M-1}}{x^M x^M} = -Mx^{-M-1} = Nx^{N-1}.$$

THEOREM 3

HYPOTHESIS: $y = f(x) = x^N$, $N = 0$, $x \neq 0$.

CONCLUSION: $dy/dx = f'(x) = Nx^{N-1}$, $x \neq 0$.

PROOF: See Exercise 1.5-1(b).

● Remark 1

The last two entries of Table 1.3 suggest that perhaps the hypotheses of these theorems can be extended to the case where N is a rational number. This we shall do in Sec. 1.9. In the meantime we shall assume the truth of the extended theorem from time to time in specific exercises.

Our intuition suggests that, if a function f changes at a certain rate, then the function $\phi = 2f$ should change at twice that rate. If the length of a one-meter rod at 0°C increases at the rate of .000012 meter per deg C when the temperature changes, one would expect the length of a two-meter rod to increase at the rate of .000024 meter per deg C under the same physical conditions because the two-meter rod can be thought of as consisting of 2 one-meter rods joined end to end and, if the length of each one-meter rod were to increase by a certain amount, the length of the two-meter rod would have to increase by twice as much.

■ THEOREM 4

The constant multiplier in differentiation.

HYPOTHESIS: (a) $f(x)$ and $f'(x)$ have domain D,
(b) $y = cf(x)$, c a constant.

CONCLUSION: $dy/dx = cf'(x) = c(df/dx)$, with domain D.

PROOF: Let us compute dy/dx from the definition of the derivative. We have for x of D

$$y + \Delta y = cf(x + \Delta x), \qquad \Delta x \neq 0 \text{ and } x + \Delta x \text{ in } D,$$

$$\Delta y = cf(x + \Delta x) - cf(x) = c[f(x + \Delta x) - f(x)],$$

$$\frac{\Delta y}{\Delta x} = c\frac{f(x + \Delta x) - f(x)}{\Delta x},$$

$$\frac{dy}{dx} = \lim_{\Delta x \to 0} \frac{\Delta y}{\Delta x} = \lim_{\Delta x \to 0} c\frac{f(x + \Delta x) - f(x)}{\Delta x}$$

$$= c \lim_{\Delta x \to 0} \frac{f(x + \Delta x) - f(x)}{\Delta x} \quad *$$

$$= cf'(x).$$

Another theorem is needed to help us write down the derivatives of polynomials at sight.

■ THEOREM 5

The derivative of a sum.

HYPOTHESIS: (a) $f(x)$ and $f'(x)$ have domain D.
(b) $g(x)$ and $g'(x)$ have domain D.

CONCLUSION: $y = f(x) + g(x)$ has the derivative $dy/dx = f'(x) + g'(x)$, with domain D.

In words, the derivative of a sum can be obtained by taking the sum of the derivatives of the functions that were summed.

PROOF: Let us return again to the definition of dy/dx. We have for x of D

---

* See Remark 1.5-3. We use here the theorem on the limit of a product of two functions in the special case where one of the functions is a constant function.

$$y + \Delta y = f(x + \Delta x) + g(x + \Delta x), \qquad \Delta x \neq 0 \text{ and } x + \Delta x \text{ in } D,$$

$$\Delta y = [f(x + \Delta x) + g(x + \Delta x)] - [f(x) + g(x)]$$

$$= [f(x + \Delta x) - f(x)] + [g(x + \Delta x) - g(x)],$$

$$\frac{\Delta y}{\Delta x} = \frac{f(x + \Delta x) - f(x)}{\Delta x} + \frac{g(x + \Delta x) - g(x)}{\Delta x},$$

$$\frac{dy}{dx} = \lim_{\Delta x \to 0} \frac{\Delta y}{\Delta x} = \lim_{\Delta x \to 0} \frac{f(x + \Delta x) - f(x)}{\Delta x} + \lim_{\Delta x \to 0} \frac{g(x + \Delta x) - g(x)}{\Delta x} \ *$$

$$= f'(x) + g'(x).$$

Example 1. $y = x - x^2$. We know that

$$\frac{d(x)}{dx} = 1 \quad \text{and} \quad \frac{d(x^2)}{dx} = 2x, \qquad \text{(Theorem 1)}.$$

Then

$$\frac{d(-x^2)}{dx} = -2x, \qquad \text{(Theorem 4)}.$$

Finally,

$$\frac{dy}{dx} = 1 - 2x, \qquad \text{(Theorem 5)}.$$

If x and y refer to graph coordinates, the slope of the tangent line at the point $(2, -2)$ is -3.

Example 2. $y = f(t) = 320 - 16t^2$. We know that

$$\frac{d(1)}{dt} = 0, \quad \frac{d[320(1)]}{dt} = 320(0) = 0,$$

and that

$$\frac{d(t^2)}{dt} = 2t, \quad \frac{d(-16t^2)}{dt} = -32t.$$

Then

$$f'(t) = \frac{dy}{dt} = 0 - 32t = -32t.$$

If y is the height of a falling ball at time t, its velocity at time $t = 3$ is $f'(3) = -96$. We have

$$v = \frac{dy}{dt} = f'(t) = -32t, \quad \text{and} \quad a = \frac{dv}{dt} = f''(t) = -32.$$

Example 3

$$F = \frac{k}{r^2} = k\frac{1}{r^2} = kr^{-2}, \qquad r \neq 0.$$

$$\frac{dF}{dr} = k(-2)r^{-3} = \frac{-2k}{r^3}, \qquad r \neq 0.$$

Example 4

$$y = f(x) = x^3 - 6x + 17 - \frac{6}{x} + \frac{7}{x^3}, \qquad x \neq 0.$$

---

* See Remark 1.5-3.

First we write

$$y = f(x) = x^3 - 6x + 17 - 6x^{-1} + 7x^{-3},$$

and then
$$\frac{dy}{dx} = f'(x) = 3x^2 - 6(1) + 0 + 6x^{-2} - 21x^{-4}$$

$$= 3x^2 - 6 + \frac{6}{x^2} - \frac{21}{x^4}, \qquad x \neq 0.$$

Example 5

$$T = f(s) = (s + 7)(3s^2 - 5s + 5).$$

We can perform the indicated multiplication and write T in polynomial form:

$$T = f(s) = 3s^3 + 16s^2 - 30s + 35.$$

Then we have
$$\frac{dT}{ds} = f'(s) = 9s^2 + 32s - 30.$$

Example 6

$$L = \phi(t) = \frac{t + 7}{\sqrt{t}}, \qquad t \neq 0.$$

Since the denominator has only one term, we can divide:

$$L = \phi(t) = \frac{t}{\sqrt{t}} + \frac{7}{\sqrt{t}} = t^{1/2} + 7t^{-1/2}.$$

Assuming for the moment that we can deal with rational exponents as we did with integral exponents, we get

$$\frac{dL}{dt} = \phi'(t) = \frac{1}{2} t^{-1/2} - \frac{7}{2} t^{-3/2}, \qquad t \neq 0.$$

EXERCISES 1.6

1. (a) $y = 5x^3 + 7x^2 - 6x + 11, \dfrac{dy}{dx} = ?$

(b) $y = 20x^5 + 6x^3 + 7x - \sqrt{11}, \dfrac{dy}{dx} = ?$

(c) $u = ax^2 + bx + c, \dfrac{du}{dx} = ?$

(d) $v = 4 + 5x^2 + 12x^4, \dfrac{dv}{dx} = ?$

(e) $S = 4\pi r^2, \dfrac{dS}{dr} = ?$

(f) $V = \frac{4}{3}\pi r^3, \dfrac{dV}{dr} = ?$

(g) $x = \dfrac{2}{t} + \dfrac{3}{t^2}, \dfrac{dx}{dt} = ?$

(h) $T = 2u^2 + u - 4 + \dfrac{3}{u} - \dfrac{7}{u^2}, \dfrac{dT}{du} = ?$

(i) $y = \dfrac{2r^2 + 4}{r}, \dfrac{dy}{dr} = ?$

(j) $L = (az^2 + b)(z - c), \dfrac{dL}{dz} = ?$

(k) $Q = \dfrac{(x^2 + 2)(x - 5)}{\sqrt{x}}, \dfrac{dQ}{dx} = ?$

(l) $f(x) = 2x^3 - 17x^2 - 5, f'(2) = ?$

(m) $\phi(t) = 3t^2 + \sqrt{t}; \phi'(t) = ?, \phi'(4) = ?$

(n) $y = 6\sqrt{x} + 3\sqrt[3]{x}, \dfrac{dy}{dx} = ?$

(o) $H = 2\sqrt{x^3} - 5\sqrt[3]{x^2}, \dfrac{dH}{dx} = ?$

(p) $f(t) = \dfrac{16}{\sqrt[4]{t^3}}, f'(t) = ?$

(q) $P = \dfrac{k}{V^{1.4}}, \dfrac{dP}{dV} = ?$

2. Consider the graph of $y = x^4 - 2x^2 + 1$. Find the slope of the tangent line at any point. At which points will the tangent lines be horizontal? For which values of x will the graph rise as one moves from left to right?

3. Let the height of a particle at time t be given by the formula $h = 40 + 120t - 16t^2$, $0 \le t \le 7$. Find its velocity and acceleration at any $t, 0 \le t \le 7$. Find its velocity each time its height is 144.

4. Let the position of a rolling ball on an inclined plane be given by the formula $x = 6t + 4t^2, 0 \le t \le 5$, x measured in cm, t in sec. (a) How fast was it rolling when it passed the $x = 108$-cm position? (b) What was its position when it had attained a velocity of 26 cm per sec?

5. If the distance (D ft) required for a certain driver to stop a certain automobile is the function of the velocity (v ft per sec) given by the formula $D = .5v + .02v^2, 0 \le v \le 100$, find the rate at which D increased with v when v was 30 ft per sec; when v was 90 ft per sec.

6. If the velocity of propagation u of a transverse pulse in a string is the function of the tension T given by the formula $u = \sqrt{T/\rho}$, ρ a constant, $0 \le T \le 25$, find the rate at which u increases with T when $T = 16$.

7. Explain precisely where we used the theorems of this section in Example 4.

8. Write out an alternate proof for Theorem 2, using the following suggestion. Write $M = -N$ as in the text proof and compute

$$\dfrac{\Delta y}{\Delta x} = -\dfrac{1}{x^M(x + \Delta x)^M} \cdot \dfrac{(x + \Delta x)^M - x^M}{\Delta x}.$$

Now, what is
$$\lim_{\Delta x \to 0} \frac{1}{x^M(x + \Delta x)^M}?$$

Of what function is
$$\lim_{\Delta x \to 0} \frac{(x + \Delta x)^M - x^M}{\Delta x}$$

the derivative? What does Theorem 1 say about this latter limit?

1.7 The Chain Rule. Derivatives of Powers

In Sec. 1.6 we learned how to predict derivatives for powers of x; if $\varphi(x) = x^3$, then $\varphi'(x) = 3x^2$. But what about powers of $(x + 1)$? If $\varphi(x) = (x + 1)^3$, what is $\varphi'(x)$? If $\varphi(x) = (5 - x^2)^{3/2}$, $-\sqrt{5} \le x \le \sqrt{5}$, what is $\varphi'(x)$? In general, if $\varphi(x) = (u)^N$, where u is itself a function of x, what is $\varphi'(x)$?

In these questions we meet illustrations of a certain chain procedure in which more complex functions are formed by taking composites of simpler functions. Thus we can write

$$y = \varphi(x) = (5 - x^2)^{3/2}, \qquad -\sqrt{5} \le x \le \sqrt{5}$$

or we can write

$$u = g(x) = 5 - x^2, \qquad -\sqrt{5} \le x \le \sqrt{5}$$

and
$$y = f(u) = u^{3/2}, \qquad 0 \le u \le 5.$$

To each x of the domain $-\sqrt{5} \le x \le \sqrt{5}$ the g function assigns the u number $u = 5 - x^2$, this u number falling in the range $0 \le u \le 5$. Then in a chain process, the f function assigns the y number $y = u^{3/2} = (5 - x^2)^{3/2}$ to the u number, this being the same y number that the φ function assigns to the original x number. In function notation

$$y = \varphi(x) = f(g(x)), \qquad -\sqrt{5} \le x \le \sqrt{5}.$$

See Fig. 1.16.

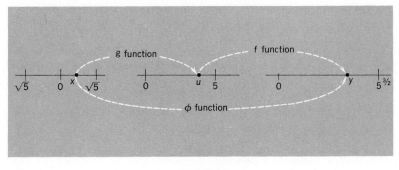

Fig. 1.16

To find the derivative of a function which is a composite of simpler functions in the manner indicated, we use the "chain rule." This rule employs a "divide and conquer" strategy. It tells us first to find the derivatives of the simpler functions of which the composite function is composed and then just to multiply these derivatives to find the derivative of the composite function.

■ THEOREM 1

The chain rule.

HYPOTHESIS: (a) $u = g(x)$ and $du/dx = g'(x)$ have domain D, u has range R.
(b) $y = f(u)$ and $dy/du = f'(u)$ have for their domains precisely the range R of $u = g(x)$.

CONCLUSION: We can form
(a) the composite function $y = \varphi(x) = f(g(x))$ with domain D, and
(b) the derivative function

$$\frac{dy}{dx} = \varphi'(x) = \frac{dy}{du}\frac{du}{dx},$$

with domain D.*

We shall illustrate the statement of this theorem with an example before proceeding to the proof.

Example 1.   Consider again the function

$$y = \varphi(x) = (5 - x^2)^{3/2}, \qquad -\sqrt{5} \le x \le \sqrt{5},$$

which we can write in the alternate composite form

$$\begin{cases} u = g(x) = 5 - x^2, & -\sqrt{5} \le x \le \sqrt{5} \\ y = f(u) = u^{3/2}, & 0 \le u \le 5. \end{cases}$$

We shall compute $\varphi'(1)$ or $\left(\dfrac{dy}{dx}\right)_{x=1}$.

First we compute $\dfrac{du}{dx} = g'(x) = -2x$

$$\left(\frac{du}{dx}\right)_{x=1} = g'(1) = -2,$$

and observe that $u = 4$ when $x = 1$. Then we compute

$$\frac{dy}{du} = f'(u) = \frac{3}{2}u^{1/2}$$

$$\left(\frac{dy}{du}\right)_{u=4} = f'(4) = \frac{3}{2}(4)^{1/2} = 3.$$

The conclusion of Theorem 1 says that in general

$$\frac{dy}{dx} = \varphi'(x) = \frac{dy}{du}\frac{du}{dx} = \left(\frac{3}{2}u^{1/2}\right)(-2x)$$

---

* Using the function notation for greater precision, we can restate Conclusion (b) this way:
For any x_1 of D form $u_1 = g(x_1)$, and take $\varphi'(x_1) = f'(u_1) \cdot g'(x_1)$.

and that, in particular,

$$\left(\frac{dy}{dx}\right)_{x=1} = \varphi'(1) = \left(\frac{dy}{du}\right)_{u=4} \left(\frac{du}{dx}\right)_{x=1} = 3(-2) = -6.$$

PROOF OF THEOREM 1: By Hypothesis (a), to each x of Domain D the function $u = g(x)$ assigns a u of the Range R and then, by Hypothesis (b), to this u the function $y = f(u)$ assigns a y number. By a chain process we have associated a y number with each x of Domain D, and we can say that we have defined the composite function $y = \varphi(x) = f(g(x))$ with domain D.

Next, consider x and $x + \Delta x$, $\Delta x \neq 0$, such that x and $x + \Delta x$ are both numbers of domain D. The g function assigns numbers $u = g(x)$ and $u + \Delta u = g(x + \Delta x)$ to x and $x + \Delta x$, both in the set R, and we can form $\Delta u = g(x + \Delta x) - g(x)$. Then the f function assigns numbers $y = f(u)$ and $y + \Delta y = f(u + \Delta u)$ to u and $u + \Delta u$, and we can form $\Delta y = f(u + \Delta u) - f(u)$. For the most part it will happen that a positive number s can be found such that $\Delta u \neq 0$ whenever $0 < |\Delta x| < s.$* In this case,

$$\frac{\Delta y}{\Delta x} = \frac{\Delta y}{\Delta u}\frac{\Delta u}{\Delta x}, \qquad 0 < |\Delta x| < s. \tag{1}$$

Further, as $\Delta x \to 0$, we must have $\Delta u \to 0$ also, for we can write

$$\Delta u = \frac{\Delta u}{\Delta x}\Delta x \qquad \text{when } 0 < |\Delta x| < s,$$

and since

$$\lim_{\Delta x \to 0} \frac{\Delta u}{\Delta x} = \frac{du}{dx}$$

exists by Hypothesis (a), we have

$$\lim_{\Delta x \to 0} \Delta u = \left(\lim_{\Delta x \to 0} \frac{\Delta u}{\Delta x}\right)\left(\lim_{\Delta x \to 0} \Delta x\right) = \frac{du}{dx}(0) = 0.$$

Now from Eq. (1) we learn that

$$\frac{dy}{dx} = \lim_{\Delta x \to 0} \frac{\Delta y}{\Delta x} = \left(\lim_{\Delta x \to 0} \frac{\Delta y}{\Delta u}\right)\left(\lim_{\Delta x \to 0} \frac{\Delta u}{\Delta x}\right) = \left(\lim_{\Delta u \to 0} \frac{\Delta y}{\Delta u}\right)\left(\lim_{\Delta x \to 0} \frac{\Delta u}{\Delta x}\right),$$

or

$$\frac{dy}{dx} = \frac{dy}{du}\frac{du}{dx}. \tag{2}$$

The proof is not yet complete because there are functions, not often met in elementary work, such that for any positive number s that may be specified, no matter how small, a Δx, $0 < |\Delta x| < s$ can be found such that $\Delta u = 0$. For such functions, Eq. (1) is not valid. Such a function will be presented in Exercise 1.7-6. In Exercise 1.7-7 the reader will be guided through the demonstration of Eq. (2) for this harder case also. The proof of Theorem 1 will then be complete.

A corollary of Theorem 1 tells us how to differentiate powers directly.

---

* For instance, if $u = x^2$ and $x = 3$, we find that $\Delta u = 0$ for $\Delta x \neq 0$ only if $\Delta x = -6$. For, $\Delta u = (u + \Delta u) - (u) = (x + \Delta x)^2 - x^2 = 2x\,\Delta x + \Delta x^2 = 6\Delta x + \Delta x^2 = \Delta x(6 + \Delta x)$. Here $\Delta u \neq 0$ for $0 < |\Delta x| < 6$.

■ THEOREM 2

The power rule.

HYPOTHESIS: (a) $u = g(x)$ and $du/dx = g'(x)$ have domain D.

(b) $y = (u)^N$, N a positive or negative integer or 0, for x of D such that $u \neq 0$ in the cases where $N < 1$.

CONCLUSION:

$$\frac{dy}{dx} = N(u)^{N-1}\frac{du}{dx}$$

for x of D such that $u \neq 0$ in the cases where $N < 1$.

PROOF: $dy/du = N(u)^{N-1}$ by Theorems 1, 2, and 3 of Sec. 1.6. The conclusion then follows directly from Theorem 1:

$$\frac{dy}{dx} = \frac{dy}{du}\frac{du}{dx} = N(u)^{N-1}\frac{du}{dx}.$$

● Remark 1

Most readers would be well advised to remember the working instructions furnished by this theorem in words, perhaps these: The derivative with respect to x of a power of a function of x is the product of (a) the exponent, (b) the very same function raised to an exponent one less than before, and (c) the derivative of that function.

● Remark 2

This theorem will be extended to the case when N is rational in Sec. 1.9; in the meantime, the extended result will occasionally be assumed.

Example 1.   The equation of a circle with center at the origin and radius r is $x^2 + y^2 = r^2$. For the portion of this circle above the x axis, $y = \sqrt{r^2 - x^2} = (r^2 - x^2)^{1/2}$. Following the verbal instructions of Remark 1, the slope of the tangent line at (x, y), $y > 0$, is given by

$$\frac{dy}{dx} = \frac{1}{2}(r^2 - x^2)^{-1/2}(-2x) = -\frac{x}{(r^2 - x^2)^{1/2}}.$$

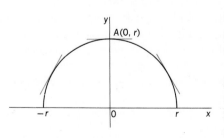

Fig. 1.17

Thus, at $A(0, r)$, the slope is 0; for x positive, the slope is negative; and for x negative, the slope is positive. See Fig. 1.17.

Example 2.   Lay out a coordinate scale on a straight line. Place a fixed positive charge at $x = 2$. The force of repulsion on a second positive charge at point x, $x \neq 2$, is given by $F = k/(x - 2)^2$, where k is constant. The rate at which F

changes with respect to x is given by dF/dx. Then

$$F = k(x - 2)^{-2},$$

$$\frac{dF}{dx} = k(-2)(x - 2)^{-3}(1) = -\frac{2k}{(x - 2)^3},$$

following the verbal instructions of Remark 1.

EXERCISES 1.7

1. Find dy/dx if $y = (2x - 1)^3$ (a) by using the power rule, (b) by expanding $(2x - 1)^3$ before differentiating.

2. (a) $s = 6(4 - t)^4$, $\dfrac{ds}{dt} = ?$

   (b) $y = 3(x^3 - 6)^8$, $\dfrac{dy}{dx} = ?$

   (c) $V = 5(x^2 + x + 7)^4$, $\dfrac{dV}{dx} = ?$

   (d) $y = 16(t^2 + 3t)^3$, $\dfrac{dy}{dt} = ?$

   (e) $x = -4(1 - 2s^2)^5$, $\dfrac{dx}{ds} = ?$

   (f) $L = \dfrac{2(x - 6)^5}{3}$, $\dfrac{dL}{dx} = ?$

   (g) $y = \dfrac{3(1 - x^2)^{10}}{5}$, $\dfrac{dy}{dx} = ?$

   (h) $y = \sqrt{x^2 + 7}$, $\dfrac{dy}{dx} = ?$

   (i) $u = \sqrt[3]{(4 - t^2)^4}$, $\dfrac{du}{dt} = ?$

   (j) $Q = \dfrac{1}{(x^2 + 1)^7}$, $\dfrac{dQ}{dx} = ?$

   (k) $y = \dfrac{16}{5(2 - 5x)^4}$, $\dfrac{dy}{dx} = ?$

   (l) $T = \dfrac{3}{\sqrt{7 - y}}$, $\dfrac{dT}{dy} = ?$

   (m) $S = \dfrac{3}{4\sqrt[3]{y^2 - 1}}$, $\dfrac{dS}{dy} = ?$

   (n) $R = 4\left(\sqrt{t} + \dfrac{1}{\sqrt{t}}\right)^5$, $\dfrac{dR}{dt} = ?$

3. (a) Find the slope of the line tangent to $y = \frac{1}{4}(2x - 3)^4$ at the point $(2, \frac{1}{4})$.
   (b) At which point is the slope of the tangent line 16?

4. A particle moved on a straight line in such a way that its position at time t was given by $x = \sqrt{1 + t^2} - 1$, $t \geq 0$.
   (a) What was its velocity at $t = 2$, $t = 10$?
   (b) Can you predict the limit approached by the velocity as t grows larger and larger, beyond all bounds? In symbols, can you find $\lim_{t \to \infty} v$?

5. If a force has constant vertical component 5 and variable horizontal component h, then the magnitude of the force is given by $F = \sqrt{h^2 + 25}$. Find the rate at which F changes with respect to h when $h = 6$.

6. Here we give an example of a function for which one cannot use Eq. (1) in demonstrating the chain rule, Theorem 1. Consider

$$u = \begin{cases} x^2 \sin \dfrac{1}{x}, & x \neq 0, \\ 0, & x = 0. \end{cases}$$

What values does u take on at $x = 1/n\pi$, n an integer? At $x = 0$, which Δx's have corresponding Δu's which are equal to 0? Can a positive number s be found such that $\Delta u \neq 0$ for all Δx, $0 < |\Delta x| < s$? Why isn't Eq. (1) valid for this u?

7. Here we show that the formula $dy/dx = (dy/du)(du/dx)$ is valid also in the case where for any positive s, no matter how small, there will be a Δx, $0 < |\Delta x| < s$, for which $\Delta u = 0$. Read carefully and fill in details where necessary.

(a) First, we show that $du/dx = 0$. If $s = .1$ we have a Δx, $0 < |\Delta x| < .1$, for which $\Delta u = 0$, and thus $\Delta u/\Delta x = 0$ for this particular Δx. If $s = .01$, we again have a Δx, $0 < |\Delta x| < .01$ for which $\Delta u = 0$ and thus $\Delta u/\Delta x = 0$ for this new particular Δx. If $s = .001$, $.0001$, and so on, we can repeat our statement. Thus there is a sequence of special Δx's that are not 0 but which approach 0 and for all of which $\Delta u/\Delta x = 0$. But Hypothesis (a) of Theorem 1 says that $du/dx = \lim_{\Delta x \to 0} \Delta u/\Delta x$ exists. When a limit exists as $\Delta x \to 0$, we get the same result no matter how Δx approaches 0. For the special sequence of Δx's we have selected, $\Delta u/\Delta x$ approaches 0, and hence

$$\frac{du}{dx} = \lim_{\Delta x \to 0} \frac{\Delta u}{\Delta x} = 0.$$

(b) Next, we show that $dy/dx = 0$ also. [Since dy/du exists by Hypothesis (b), this will mean that $dy/dx = (dy/du)(du/dx)$ is valid, for it will read $0 = 0$]. We must show that $\lim_{\Delta x \to 0} (\Delta y/\Delta x) = 0$, or that for all Δx close enough to 0, $\Delta y/\Delta x$ will be as close to 0 as desired. Consider then a small positive number s, and $0 < |\Delta x| < s$. For those Δx of this set which correspond to Δu's that equal 0 we can say

$$\Delta y = f(u + \Delta u) - f(u) = f(u) - f(u) = 0 \quad \text{and} \quad \frac{\Delta y}{\Delta x} = 0.$$

For these Δx, $\Delta y/\Delta x$ will surely be as close to 0 as desired; indeed, for these Δx, $\Delta y/\Delta x = 0!$ For those Δx of the set $0 < |\Delta x| < s$ which correspond to Δu's $\neq 0$, we can say that $\Delta y/\Delta x = (\Delta y/\Delta u)(\Delta u/\Delta x)$. Here $\Delta y/\Delta u$ is close to dy/du, a finite number by Hypothesis (b). If we want $\Delta y/\Delta x$ to be as close to 0 as desired, all we need do is arrange to have $|\Delta u/\Delta x|$ small enough. But this can be arranged, because we know that $du/dx = 0$ or that $\lim_{\Delta x \to 0} (\Delta u/\Delta x) = 0$.

1.8 Derivatives of Products and Quotients

To find the derivative of a product or a quotient, a "divide and conquer" strategy may be employed again.

■ THEOREM 1

The product rule.

HYPOTHESIS: (a) $u = f(x)$ and $du/dx = f'(x)$ have domain D.
(b) $v = g(x)$ and $dv/dx = g'(x)$ have domain D.

CONCLUSION: $y = uv$ has the derivative

$$\frac{dy}{dx} = u\frac{dv}{dx} + v\frac{du}{dx}, \text{ with domain } D.$$

PROOF: We shall find dy/dx from its definition. If we change from x to $x + \Delta x$, $\Delta x \neq 0$ and $x + \Delta x$ in D,

u will change from $u = f(x)$ to $u + \Delta u = f(x + \Delta x)$,

v will change from $v = g(x)$ to $v + \Delta v = g(x + \Delta x)$,

y will change from $y = uv = f(x)g(x)$ to

$$y + \Delta y = (u + \Delta u)(v + \Delta v) = f(x + \Delta x)g(x + \Delta x).$$

Then

$$\Delta y = (u + \Delta u)(v + \Delta v) - uv = u\,\Delta v + v\,\Delta u + \Delta u\,\Delta v,$$

$$\frac{\Delta y}{\Delta x} = u\frac{\Delta v}{\Delta x} + v\frac{\Delta u}{\Delta x} + \Delta u\frac{\Delta v}{\Delta x},$$

$$\frac{dy}{dx} = \lim_{\Delta x \to 0} \frac{\Delta y}{\Delta x} = u\frac{dv}{dx} + v\frac{du}{dx}.$$

In taking the last step, we used Hypotheses (a) and (b) when we said that

$$\lim_{\Delta x \to 0} \frac{\Delta v}{\Delta x} = \frac{dv}{dx}, \qquad \lim_{\Delta x \to 0} \frac{\Delta u}{\Delta x} = \frac{du}{dx},$$

and that

$$\lim_{\Delta x \to 0} \Delta u = \lim_{\Delta x \to 0}\left(\frac{\Delta u}{\Delta x}\Delta x\right) = \left(\lim_{\Delta x \to 0}\frac{\Delta u}{\Delta x}\right)\left(\lim_{\Delta x \to 0}\Delta x\right) = \frac{du}{dx}(0) = 0.$$

● **Remark 1**

Again, it is perhaps wiser to remember the working instructions given by Theorem 1 in words rather than in symbols. To differentiate a product, take the product of the first factor by the derivative of the second and add the product of the second factor by the derivative of the first.

● **Remark 2**

Theorem 1 explains how to form the derivative of a product once the derivatives of the separate factors are known. But notice that the instructions furnished are not those that some readers would have guessed. If "the derivative of a sum is the sum of the derivatives," Theorem 1.6-5, then perhaps one would expect that "the derivative of a product is the product of the derivatives." Here is a fairly simple case where one's intuition might lead him astray.

Example 1. Consider $y = (x - 5)(x^2 + 7)$. We could multiply and write $y = x^3 - 5x^2 + 7x - 35$, then get dy/dx by means of term-by-term differentiation, but we prefer to use the product rule for the sake of drill. Using the verbal instructions of Remark 1, we have

$$\frac{dy}{dx} = (x - 5)(2x) + (x^2 + 7)(1) = 2x^2 - 10x + x^2 + 7 = 3x^2 - 10x + 7.$$

Example 2. $v = (t^2 + 5)^3(3t - 2)^4$. Following the same verbal instructions, we have

$$\frac{dv}{dt} = (t^2 + 5)^3 4(3t - 2)^3(3) + (3t - 2)^4 3(t^2 + 5)^2(2t).$$

Now we look for common factors, and we get

$$\frac{dv}{dt} = 6(t^2 + 5)^2(3t - 2)^3[2(t^2 + 5) + t(3t - 2)]$$

$$= 6(t^2 + 5)^2(3t - 2)^3[5t^2 - 2t + 10].$$

Example 3. $y = x\sqrt{a^2 - x^2} = x(a^2 - x^2)^{1/2}$, $-a \le x \le a$. By the product rule,

$$\frac{dy}{dx} = x\frac{1}{2}(a^2 - x^2)^{-1/2}(-2x) + (a^2 - x^2)^{1/2}(1)$$

$$= \frac{-x^2}{(a^2 - x^2)^{1/2}} + (a^2 - x^2)^{1/2} = \frac{-x^2 + (a^2 - x^2)^1}{(a^2 - x^2)^{1/2}} = \frac{a^2 - 2x^2}{(a^2 - x^2)^{1/2}}$$

for $-a < x < a$.

Example 4. $L = r^3 \sqrt[3]{(r + a)^4} = r^3(r + a)^{4/3}$. Here we get

$$\frac{dL}{dr} = r^3 \frac{4}{3}(r + a)^{1/3}(1) + (r + a)^{4/3}(3r^2).$$

Take out common factors to simplify:

$$\frac{dL}{dr} = r^2(r + a)^{1/3}\left[\frac{4}{3}r + 3(r + a)\right]$$

$$= \frac{1}{3}r^2(r + a)^{1/3}[4r + 9(r + a)]$$

$$= \frac{1}{3}r^2(r + a)^{1/3}[13r + 9a].$$

Example 5

■ THEOREM 1A

HYPOTHESIS: u, v, and w are differentiable functions of x, with domain D.

CONCLUSION: $y = uvw$ has the derivative,

$$\frac{dy}{dx} = uv\frac{dw}{dx} + uw\frac{dv}{dx} + vw\frac{du}{dx}, \text{ with domain } D.$$

PROOF: Write $y = uvw = (uv)w$. Then, by Theorem 1,

$$\frac{dy}{dx} = (uv)\frac{dw}{dx} + w\frac{d(uv)}{dx}.$$

Using Theorem 1 again to expand the second term, we get

$$\frac{dy}{dx} = uv\frac{dw}{dx} + w\left(u\frac{dv}{dx} + v\frac{du}{dx}\right) = uv\frac{dw}{dx} + wu\frac{dv}{dx} + wv\frac{du}{dx}.$$

■ THEOREM 2

The quotient rule.

HYPOTHESIS: (a) $u = f(x)$ and $du/dx = f'(x)$ have domain D.
(b) $v = g(x)$ and $dv/dx = g'(x)$ have domain D.

CONCLUSION: For those x of D for which $v \neq 0$ we can write $y = u/v$ and

$$\frac{dy}{dx} = \frac{v(du/dx) - u(dv/dx)}{v^2}.$$

In words, the derivative of a fraction is a fraction whose denominator is the square of the original denominator and whose numerator is the product of the denominator and the derivative of the numerator minus the product of the numerator and the derivative of the denominator.

PROOF: Return again to the definition of dy/dx. Let x change by $\Delta x \neq 0$ such that $x + \Delta x$ is in D and $v + \Delta v = g(x + \Delta x) \neq 0$. Then from $y = u/v$ we go to

$$y + \Delta y = \frac{u + \Delta u}{v + \Delta v}.$$

But then

$$\Delta y = \frac{u + \Delta u}{v + \Delta v} - \frac{u}{v} = \frac{uv + v\,\Delta u - uv - u\,\Delta v}{v(v + \Delta v)} = \frac{v\,\Delta u - u\,\Delta v}{v(v + \Delta v)},$$

$$\frac{\Delta y}{\Delta x} = \frac{v\,\dfrac{\Delta u}{\Delta x} - u\,\dfrac{\Delta v}{\Delta x}}{v(v + \Delta v)},$$

and finally, because by hypothesis

$$\lim_{\Delta x \to 0} \frac{\Delta u}{\Delta x} = \frac{du}{dx}, \qquad \lim_{\Delta x \to 0} \frac{\Delta v}{\Delta x} = \frac{dv}{dx},$$

and

$$\lim_{\Delta x \to 0} \Delta v = \lim_{\Delta x \to 0} \left(\frac{\Delta v}{\Delta x} \Delta x \right) = \frac{dv}{dx}(0) = 0,$$

we get

$$\frac{dy}{dx} = \lim_{\Delta x \to 0} \frac{\Delta y}{\Delta x} = \frac{v(du/dx) - u(dv/dx)}{v^2}.$$

Example 6

$$y = \frac{3x + 2}{x - 1}, \qquad x \neq 1.$$

The verbal instructions following the statement of Theorem 2 lead to

$$\frac{dy}{dx} = \frac{(x - 1)(3) - (3x + 2)(1)}{(x - 1)^2} = \frac{-5}{(x - 1)^2}, \qquad x \neq 1.$$

Example 7

$$v = \frac{(3t + 5)^4}{(t^2 + 1)^2}.$$

Using the same verbal instructions, we get

$$\frac{dv}{dt} = \frac{(t^2 + 1)^2 4(3t + 5)^3 (3) - (3t + 5)^4 \, 2(t^2 + 1)^1 (2t)}{(t^2 + 1)^4}.$$

To simplify, we divide numerator and denominator by $t^2 + 1$ and then take out common factors in the numerator.

$$\frac{dv}{dt} = \frac{(t^2 + 1)4(3t + 5)^3(3) - (3t + 5)^4(4t)}{(t^2 + 1)^3}$$

$$= \frac{4(3t+5)^3[3t^2 + 3 - t(3t+5)]}{(t^2+1)^3}$$

$$= \frac{4(3t+5)^3(3-5t)}{(t^2+1)^3}.$$

Example 8

$$S = \frac{r}{\sqrt{r^2-1}} = \frac{r}{(r^2-1)^{1/2}}, \qquad |r| > 1.$$

By the quotient rule,

$$\frac{dS}{dr} = \frac{(r^2-1)^{1/2}(1) - r(\frac{1}{2})(r^2-1)^{-1/2}(2r)}{r^2-1}.$$

One method of simplifying this derivative recognizes that

$$(r^2-1)^{-1/2} = \frac{1}{(r^2-1)^{1/2}}$$

and that we really have a complex fraction to deal with. As always with complex fractions, we can simplify by multiplying both numerator and denominator by the same suitably chosen nonzero number. Here we rewrite dS/dr and then multiply numerator and denominator by $(r^2-1)^{1/2}$.

$$\frac{dS}{dr} = \frac{(r^2-1)^{1/2} - r^2/(r^2-1)^{1/2}}{r^2-1} = \frac{(r^2-1) - r^2}{(r^2-1)^{3/2}} = \frac{-1}{(r^2-1)^{3/2}}$$

$$= -(r^2-1)^{-3/2}, \qquad |r| > 1.$$

Example 9

$$y = \sqrt[3]{\frac{x^2+4}{x^2-4}} = \left(\frac{x^2+4}{x^2-4}\right)^{1/3}, \qquad |x| \neq 2.$$

Using first the power rule and then the quotient rule, we get

$$\frac{dy}{dx} = \frac{1}{3}\left(\frac{x^2+4}{x^2-4}\right)^{-2/3} \frac{d}{dx}\left(\frac{x^2+4}{x^2-4}\right),$$

$$\frac{dy}{dx} = \frac{1}{3}\left(\frac{x^2-4}{x^2+4}\right)^{2/3} \frac{(x^2-4)(2x) - (x^2+4)(2x)}{(x^2-4)^2}.$$

Dividing numerator and denominator by $(x^2-4)^{2/3}$ and taking out the common factor $2x$, we have

$$\frac{dy}{dx} = \frac{1}{3}\frac{2x[x^2-4-(x^2+4)]}{(x^2+4)^{2/3}(x^2-4)^{4/3}} = -\frac{16}{3}\frac{x}{(x^2+4)^{2/3}(x^2-4)^{4/3}}, \qquad |x| \neq 2.$$

One may also write

$$y = \frac{(x^2+4)^{1/3}}{(x^2-4)^{1/3}}$$

and start with the quotient rule.

Example 10

$$L = \frac{12}{7(1 - 2t)^5}, \qquad t \neq \frac{1}{2}.$$

The quotient rule may be used to find dL/dt, but it is easier to write

$$L = \frac{12}{7} \frac{1}{(1 - 2t)^5} = \frac{12}{7} (1 - 2t)^{-5},$$

and then to use the power rule:

$$\frac{dL}{dt} = -\frac{60}{7} (1 - 2t)^{-6}(-2) = \frac{120}{7} (1 - 2t)^{-6} = \frac{120}{7(1 - 2t)^6}, \qquad t \neq \frac{1}{2}.$$

Example 11

$$y = \frac{x^3 + 5x + 7}{x^2}, \qquad x \neq 0.$$

Again the quotient rule might be used, but since the denominator is a monomial, it is easier to rewrite the problem first by dividing;

$$y = x + 5x^{-1} + 7x^{-2},$$

$$\frac{dy}{dx} = 1 - 5x^{-2} - 14x^{-3} = 1 - \frac{5}{x^2} - \frac{14}{x^3}, \qquad x \neq 0.$$

EXERCISES 1.8

1. $y = x^2(2x - 5)^3, \dfrac{dy}{dx} = ?$

2. $Q = t^3(2 - 3t)^4, \dfrac{dQ}{dt} = ?$

3. $f(r) = (r + 2)^3(2r - 3)^7, f'(r) = ?$

4. $y = (3u^2 + 5)^5(3u^2 - 5)^4, \dfrac{dy}{du} = ?$

5. $x = s^2\sqrt{5 - s^2}, \dfrac{dx}{ds} = ?$

6. $F(x) = x^3\sqrt{(x^2 + 7)^3}, F'(x) = ?$

7. $T = x\sqrt[3]{5 - x}, \dfrac{dT}{dx} = ?$

8. $Q = t^2\sqrt[3]{(2t + 1)^2}, \dfrac{dQ}{dt} = ?$

9. $f(x) = \dfrac{2x - 3}{3x - 4}, f'(x) = ?$

10. $y = \dfrac{ax + b}{cx + d}, \dfrac{dy}{dx} = ?$

11. $v = \dfrac{au^2 + b}{u}, \dfrac{dv}{du} = ?$

12. $\phi(u) = \dfrac{u}{au^2 + b}, \phi'(u) = ?$

13. $y = \dfrac{(2x + 1)}{(4x - 5)^3}, \dfrac{dy}{dx} = ?$

14. $x = \dfrac{(2s^2 - 7)^3}{5s + 2}, \dfrac{dx}{ds} = ?$

15. $g(x) = \dfrac{(x + 5)^3}{3(4 - 3x^2)^2}, g'(x) = ?$

16. $S = \dfrac{7(1 + 3t^2)^4}{2(1 - 3t^2)^3}, \dfrac{dS}{dt} = ?$

17. $r = \dfrac{\sqrt{5 - s^2}}{s}$, $\dfrac{dr}{ds} = ?$

18. $r = \dfrac{s}{\sqrt{5 - s^2}}$, $\dfrac{dr}{ds} = ?$

19. $y = \dfrac{(t^2 + 7)^{3/2}}{t^2}$, $\dfrac{dy}{dt} = ?$

20. $y = \dfrac{t^{5/2}}{(t - 5)^2}$, $\dfrac{dy}{dt} = ?$

21. $L = \dfrac{x^2 + 10}{3\sqrt{4 + x}}$, $\dfrac{dL}{dx} = ?$

22. $y = \dfrac{3x^2}{\sqrt[3]{x^2 + 1}}$, $\dfrac{dy}{dx} = ?$

23. $y = \dfrac{5x}{\sqrt[3]{(1 - x)^2}}$, $\dfrac{dy}{dx} = ?$

24. $v = \dfrac{16}{(t^2 - 5)^{3/2}}$, $\dfrac{dv}{dt} = ?$

25. $v = \dfrac{16t^2}{(t^2 - 5)^{3/2}}$, $\dfrac{dv}{dt} = ?$

26. $f(x) = \sqrt{\dfrac{x^2 + 7}{x^2 - 7}}$, $f'(x) = ?$

27. For a thin lens of focal length a, the object distance s and the image distance s' are related: $1/s + 1/s' = 1/a$. Consider s' as a function of s and solve for s'. Find the rate of change of s' with respect to s when s is twice the focal length.

28. Find the slope of the line tangent to

$$y = \frac{\sqrt{x^2 - 5}}{x}, \qquad x \geq \sqrt{5}, \text{ at } \left(3, \frac{2}{3}\right).$$

Is the tangent line to this curve ever horizontal? vertical?

29. (a) Write $y = u^2 = u \cdot u$ and use the product rule to find dy/dx. (b) Find the derivative of $y = u^N$, N a positive integer, by using the product rule and mathematical induction.

30. Write $y = u/v = uv^{-1}$ and derive the formula for the derivative of a quotient from that for a product.

1.9   Implicit Functions and Their Derivatives

If y is given as a function of x by a statement of the form

$$y = f(x) \qquad \text{for } x \text{ of } D$$

we say that the function has been described *explicitly*. However, we must often deal with relationships described by statements of the form

$$F(x, y) = 0.$$

Thus we might read that $(4, 3)$ is a point on the circle with equation

$$F(x, y) = x^2 + y^2 - 25 = 0, \tag{1}$$

or that the image distance s' and the object distance s for a thin lens of focal length a are related according to

$$\phi(s, s') = \frac{1}{s} + \frac{1}{s'} - \frac{1}{a} = 0. \tag{2}$$

For the thin lens, s' can be described explicitly as a function of s rather easily. If we solve Eq. (2) for s' we get

$$s' = \frac{as}{s - a}, \qquad s \neq a. \tag{2a}$$

In the case of the circle, we can also solve for one variable in terms of the other, obtaining

$$y = \pm \sqrt{25 - x^2}.$$

For the upper half of the circle, on which half the point $(4, 3)$ lies, y can be described explicitly as a function of x:

$$y = +\sqrt{25 - x^2}, \qquad |x| < 5. \tag{1a}$$

But there are statements of the form $F(x, y) = 0$ that allow no explicit statement for one variable as a function of the other. Thus, if

$$x^2 + y^2 + 1 = 0,$$

for no real x can a real y be found that will satisfy the equation.

If we start with a statement of the form $F(x, y) = 0$ and a pair of numbers x_0 and y_0 such that $F(x_0, y_0) = 0$, there is a theorem, called the Implicit Function Theorem, which tells us when we can be sure that there is one and only one function $y = f(x)$ whose domain is an interval I which includes $x = x_0$ and which function is

(a) such that $f(x_0) = y_0$,

(b) such that the y's given by $y = f(x)$ for each x of interval I satisfy $F(x, y) = 0$; in function notation $F(x, f(x)) = 0$ for all x of I,

(c) differentiable for x of interval I.

In the case of the circle with Eq. (1) and the specific point $(4, 3)$, the explicit function given in Eq. (1a) has the desired properties. For instance, to check on Statement (b), we compute

$$F(x, f(x)) = x^2 + [f(x)]^2 - 25 = x^2 + 25 - x^2 - 25 = 0$$

for all x of the interval $-5 \leq x \leq 5$.

The proof of the Implicit Function Theorem is a fundamental part of an advanced calculus course.* In this text we can only state its hypothesis and conclusion and illustrate it, and this we shall do in detail in Chapter 11. We shall have to assume until then that the hypothesis of the Implicit Function Theorem is satisfied whenever we wish to say that a statement $F(x, y) = 0$ defines a function $y = f(x)$ over an interval and that f has the properties (a), (b), and (c) just listed.

In a specific case the Implicit Function Theorem may assure us that y can be considered as a function of x, but finding that function in detail in explicit form may be a very difficult matter. We propose to find $dy/dx = f'(x)$ without finding $f(x)$ itself! Let us consider, then, a statement $F(x, y) = 0$ for which there is an explicit

---

* See, for instance, A. E. Taylor, *Advanced Calculus*. Boston: Ginn and Company, 1955, Chapter VIII.

statement $y = f(x)$, defined for an interval, such that $f'(x)$ exists for this interval and such that if we imagine $f(x)$ substituted for y in $F(x, y) = 0$, we get an *identity*, an equation true for all x of the interval.

Now, when two functions of x are equal for all x of an interval, their derivatives are equal for all x of that interval also. This is true because the derivatives are found by studying certain increments, and two identically equal functions would have equal increments. Therefore, when we replace y in $F(x, y) = 0$ in such a way that the left and right members of $F(x, y) = 0$ become identically equal, we can be sure that *the derivatives, with respect to x, of these left and right members are equal*. To get dy/dx, we differentiate both members of $F(x, y) = 0$ with respect to x, considering y as if it were an explicit function of x wherever it occurs, and then we equate the derivatives.

Example 1. The points $Q(4, 3)$ and $R(3, -4)$ lie on the circle $x^2 + y^2 = 25$ because their coordinates satisfy the equation. Let us find the slopes of the tangent lines at Q and R.

If we consider y to be a function of x in the circle equation and differentiate both members with respect to x, we get

$$2x + 2(y)^1 \frac{dy}{dx} = 0.$$

Here we used the power rule, Theorem 1.7-2, to get $d(y)^2/dx$. Since dy/dx evaluated at (x_1, y_1) gives the slope of the tangent line at (x_1, y_1) we solve for dy/dx:

$$\frac{dy}{dx} = -\frac{x}{y}, \qquad y \neq 0.$$

At Q,
$$\frac{dy}{dx} = -\frac{4}{3}.$$

At R,
$$\frac{dy}{dx} = -\frac{3}{-4} = \frac{3}{4}.$$

In this particular problem one could easily differentiate explicitly also. For point $Q(4, 3)$,

$$y = +\sqrt{25 - x^2} = (25 - x^2)^{1/2},$$

$$\frac{dy}{dx} = \frac{1}{2}(25 - x^2)^{-1/2}(-2x) = -\frac{x}{\sqrt{25 - x^2}} = -\frac{4}{3}.$$

For point $R(3, -4)$, however, whose y coordinate is negative,

$$y = -\sqrt{25 - x^2} = -(25 - x^2)^{1/2},$$

$$\frac{dy}{dx} = -\frac{1}{2}(25 - x^2)^{-1/2}(-2x) = \frac{x}{\sqrt{25 - x^2}} = \frac{3}{4}.$$

Example 2. $x^3 + 3xy^2 + y^3 = 5$. Here it would not be at all convenient to solve for y as a function of x, but imagine that this has been done and that y stands for a certain function of x whenever it occurs. Differentiating both sides of the resulting identity with respect to x, we obtain

$$3x^2 + 3\left[x\,2(y)^1\frac{dy}{dx} + y^2(1)\right] + 3(y)^2\frac{dy}{dx} = 0.$$

To differentiate the third term of the left member the power rule was used; to differentiate the second term the product rule and the power rule were used. We now solve for dy/dx by dividing both sides by 3 and collecting like terms:

$$2xy\frac{dy}{dx} + y^2\frac{dy}{dx} = -x^2 - y^2,$$

$$(2xy + y^2)\frac{dy}{dx} = -(x^2 + y^2),$$

$$\frac{dy}{dx} = -\frac{x^2 + y^2}{2xy + y^2},$$

provided that $y \neq 0$ and $y \neq -2x$. If x and y refer to rectangular coordinates, then $(1, 1)$ is a point on the graph and the slope of the tangent line at that point is $-\frac{2}{3}$.

Example 3.   Find dy/dx if

$$y = f_1(x) = \sqrt{\frac{x^2 + 7}{x - 2}}, \qquad x > 2. \tag{3}$$

Let us square both sides and multiply by $x - 2$:

$$(x - 2)y^2 = x^2 + 7. \tag{4}$$

Now differentiate implicitly. For the left side we use the product and power rules, obtaining

$$(x - 2)2(y)^1\frac{dy}{dx} + y^2 = 2x,$$

$$\frac{dy}{dx} = \frac{2x - y^2}{2y(x - 2)}, \qquad x > 2. \tag{5}$$

Observe that we can divide by y, because there is no number pair x, y that satisfies Eq. (3) for which $y = 0$. Observe also that not only does each number pair x, y that satisfies Eq. (3) also satisfy Eq. (4), but so does each number pair x, y that satisfies

$$y = f_2(x) = -\sqrt{\frac{x^2 + 7}{x - 2}}, \qquad x > 2. \tag{3a}$$

If in Eq. (5) we substitute a number pair that satisfies Eq. (3), we get $f_1'(x)$; if we substitute a number pair that satisfies Eq. (3a) we get $f_2'(x)$. For the sake of comparison, the reader should find $f_1'(x)$ explicitly also and compare his answer with Eq. (5).

Example 4.   The statement $x^2 - 49 = (x - 7)(x + 7)$ is an identity, true for all values of x. The derivative of the left side is $2x$. The derivative of the right side, using the product rule, is $(x - 7)\,1 + 1(x + 7) = 2x$.

Example 5. The statement $x^2 = 3x + 28$ is not an identity; it is true only for $x = 7$ and $x = -4$. The derivatives of the left and right members are respectively $2x$ and 3. These derivatives are not even equal when $x = 7$ and $x = -4$! One cannot say that "if two functions are equal, their derivatives are equal"; the functions must be *identically* equal! $f_1(x) = x^2$ and $f_2(x) = 3x + 28$ are equal for $x = 7$; $f_1(7) = f_2(7)$. But $f_1(7 + \Delta x) \neq f_2(7 + \Delta x)$ if $\Delta x \neq 0$, $\Delta f_1 \neq \Delta f_2$, and one cannot expect that $f_1'(7)$ will equal $f_2'(7)$.

We are now in a position to extend Theorems 1, 2, and 3 of Sec. 1.6 to the case where N is rational.

■ THEOREM 1

HYPOTHESIS: $y = f(x) = x^N$, N a rational number, $x \neq 0$ if $N \leq 1$.

CONCLUSION:

$$\frac{dy}{dx} = f'(x) = Nx^{N-1}, \qquad x \neq 0 \text{ if } N \leq 1.$$

PROOF: Let us write the rational number N in the form p/q, where p and q are integers. Then if x and y satisfy

$$y = x^N = x^{p/q}, \tag{6}$$

they also satisfy

$$y^q = x^p. \tag{7}$$

Here we differentiate implicitly with respect to x, obtaining

$$q(y)^{q-1}\frac{dy}{dx} = px^{p-1},$$

$$\frac{dy}{dx} = \frac{p}{q}\frac{x^{p-1}}{y^{q-1}},$$

provided that $y \neq 0$ and hence that $x \neq 0$. Substituting for y from Eq. (6), and then using the laws of exponents, we find that

$$\frac{dy}{dx} = \frac{p}{q}\frac{x^{p-1}}{(x^{p/q})^{q-1}} = \frac{p}{q}\frac{x^{p-1}}{x^{p-(p/q)}} = \frac{p}{q}x^{(p/q)-1},$$

which is our conclusion:

$$\frac{dy}{dx} = Nx^{N-1}.*$$

The derivation of dy/dx for $x = 0$ is called for in Exercise 1.9-15.

---

* If q is an odd number, Eqs. (6) and (7) are equivalent. If q is an even number, x's and y's for which $y = -x^{p/q}$ will also satisfy Eq. (7). In the latter case, it is understood that we are trying to find by implicit differentiation the slope of the tangent line to the curve with Eq. (7) at a point that also lies on the curve with Eq. (6).

Theorem 1.7-2 can now be extended in a similar way, the proof quoting Theorem 1 of this section rather than theorems of Sec. 1.6.

■ THEOREM 2

The power rule.

HYPOTHESIS: (a) $u = g(x)$ and $du/dx = g'(x)$ have domain D.
(b) $y = (u)^N$, N a rational number, for x of D such that $u \neq 0$ in the cases where $N \leq 1$.

CONCLUSION:

$$\frac{dy}{dx} = N(u)^{N-1}\frac{du}{dx}$$

for x of D such that $u \neq 0$ in the cases where $N \leq 1$.

● Remark 1

The alert reader should ask at this point whether a further extension is possible. Is $d(x^N)/dx = Nx^{N-1}$ for all real N, rational or irrational? For instance, if $f(x) = x^{\sqrt{2}}$, is $f'(x) = \sqrt{2}\, x^{\sqrt{2}-1}$? If $\phi(x) = x^{\pi}$, is $\phi'(x) = \pi x^{\pi-1}$? The answer is "yes." We are not in a position to prove the broader theorems because we have not studied the concept of number systematically. We have not yet stated clearly what an irrational number is. An advanced calculus course can start with a systematic exposition of the real number system and then be in a position to prove many fundamental theorems that we have to accept on an intuitive basis (or on faith altogether) in this course. On the rare occasions when we shall need the power rule for irrational exponents, we shall assume the truth of the extended theorem.

Example 6. If

$$y = f(x), \tag{8}$$

we have

$$\frac{dy}{dx} = f'(x).$$

If now Eq. (8) be construed as an implicit statement for x as a function of y, we find upon differentiating both members with respect to y and using the chain rule that

$$1 = \frac{df(x)}{dy} = \frac{df(x)}{dx}\frac{dx}{dy} = f'(x)\frac{dx}{dy},$$

$$\frac{dx}{dy} = \frac{1}{f'(x)} = \frac{1}{dy/dx}, \tag{9}$$

provided $f'(x) \neq 0$.

EXERCISES 1.9

1. $(1 - x)^2 + y^3 = 5$, $\dfrac{dy}{dx} = ?$ **2.** $x^2 + y^2 = 4xy + 6$, $\dfrac{dy}{dx} = ?$

3. $x^3 + y^2x^2 + 2y^3 = 40, \dfrac{dy}{dx} = ?$

6. $x^n + y^n = a^n, \dfrac{dy}{dx} = ?$

4. $L^2 = a(L + t)^3, \dfrac{dL}{dt} = ?$

7. $(x + y)^{1/2} + (x - y)^{1/2} = 6, \dfrac{dy}{dx} = ?$

5. $x^{2/3} + y^{2/3} = a^{2/3}, \dfrac{dy}{dx} = ?$

8. $3x^2 + x^2y^2 = y^4 + 15, \dfrac{dy}{dx} = ?$

9. (a) Find the slope of the tangent line to the curve $x^2/16 + y^2/7 = 1$ at the point $(3, -\frac{7}{4})$ by implicit methods. (b) Solve for y first and find the same slope by explicit methods.

10. Repeat Exercise 9, using the curve $x^2/30 - y^2/20 = 1$ and the point $(6, 2)$.

11. For the adiabatic expansion of a gas we have $PV^\gamma = C$, where P and V are the pressure and volume and γ and C are constants. Find dP/dV by implicit and explicit methods.

12. For the volume of a cone we have $V = \frac{1}{3}\pi r^2 h$, where r is the radius of the base and h is the height. If r is changed while V is kept constant, h will change accordingly. Find dh/dr by implicit and explicit methods.

13. The curved surface of a cone is given by $S = \pi r\sqrt{r^2 + h^2}$. If S is kept constant and r is varied, h will change. Find dh/dr.

14. The volume of a spherical segment is $V = \frac{1}{3}\pi h^2 (3r - h)$, where r is the radius of the sphere and h is the height of the segment. If V is held fixed and r is varied, h will vary. Find dh/dr.

15. In Theorem 1 we showed that $dy/dx = f'(x) = Nx^{N-1}$ when $y = f(x) = x^N$, N a rational number, provided that $x = 0$ be excluded in order to permit a division by a power of y. Show, by direct resort to the Δ process, that $f'(0) = 0$ if $N > 1$ but that $f'(0)$ is not defined if $0 < N < 1$. Of course $f(0)$ itself is not defined for $N < 0$. Thus we still have $f'(x) = Nx^{N-1}$ when $x = 0$, provided $N > 1$.

1.10 Higher Derivatives

In differentiation, the process of finding a derivative, we have an operation that assigns to each differentiable function $f(x)$, a new function $f'(x)$. If $f'(x)$ is differentiable and this operation is applied to it, still another function, $f''(x)$, is obtained. The operation can often be repeated many times, each time leading to a new function.

■ NOTATION CONVENTION 1

The derivative of dy/dx or $f'(x)$ with respect to x is called the second derivative of y with respect to x and is written d^2y/dx^2 or $f''(x)$. The derivative of d^2y/dx^2 or $f''(x)$ with respect to x is called the third derivative of y with respect to x and is written $f'''(x)$ or d^3y/dx^3; and so on.

Example 1. We saw in Sec. 1.4 that, when y and t refer to distance traveled and time, $v = dy/dt$ refers to velocity and $a = dv/dt$ refers to acceleration. In the language of the present section, the acceleration is the second derivative of the distance traveled with respect to the time, or

$$a = \frac{dv}{dt} = \frac{d^2y}{dt^2}.$$

Example 2. If $y = \frac{1}{6} x^5 + 3x^3 + 7x$, then

$$\frac{dy}{dx} = \frac{5}{6} x^4 + 9x^2 + 7, \qquad \frac{d^5y}{dx^5} = 20,$$

$$\frac{d^2y}{dx^2} = \frac{10}{3} x^3 + 18x, \qquad \frac{d^6y}{dx^6} = 0,$$

$$\frac{d^3y}{dx^3} = 10x^2 + 18, \qquad \frac{d^ky}{dx^k} = 0 \qquad \text{for } k \geq 6.$$

$$\frac{d^4y}{dx^4} = 20x,$$

Example 3. If $y = x\sqrt{a^2 - x^2}$, $-a \leq x \leq a$, then, as in Example 1.8-3,

$$\frac{dy}{dx} = \frac{a^2 - 2x^2}{(a^2 - x^2)^{1/2}}, \qquad -a < x < a,$$

and

$$\frac{d^2y}{dx^2} = \frac{(a^2 - x^2)^{1/2}(-4x) - (a^2 - 2x^2)\frac{1}{2}(a^2 - x^2)^{-1/2}(-2x)}{(a^2 - x^2)^1},$$

according to the quotient rule. To simplify, multiply both numerator and denominator by $(a^2 - x^2)^{1/2}$, which gives

$$\frac{d^2y}{dx^2} = \frac{(a^2 - x^2)^1(-4x) + (a^2 - 2x^2)(x)}{(a^2 - x^2)^{3/2}}$$

$$= \frac{x[-4(a^2 - x^2) + (a^2 - 2x^2)]}{(a^2 - x^2)^{3/2}} = \frac{x(2x^2 - 3a^2)}{(a^2 - x^2)^{3/2}}, \qquad -a < x < a.$$

Example 4. If

$$x^2 + y^2 = 25, \tag{1}$$

then, as in Example 1.9-1,

$$\frac{dy}{dx} = -\frac{x}{y}, \qquad y \neq 0. \tag{2}$$

To get d^2y/dx^2, we differentiate dy/dx with respect to x and remember that y is thought of as representing an explicit function of x. Using the quotient rule, we have

$$\frac{d^2y}{dx^2} = -\frac{y(1) - x(dy/dx)}{y^2}.$$

If we substitute for dy/dx its value as given by Eq. (2), we obtain

$$\frac{d^2y}{dx^2} = -\frac{y - x[-(x/y)]}{y^2} = -\frac{y^2 + x^2}{y^3}.$$

Here we simplified by multiplying numerator and denominator by y. Then, since y represents a function of x that satisfies Eq. (1) identically,

$$\frac{d^2y}{dx^2} = -\frac{25}{y^3} = -25(y)^{-3}, \qquad y \neq 0.$$

We also have

$$\frac{d^3y}{dx^3} = +75(y)^{-4}\frac{dy}{dx} = 75\frac{1}{y^4}\left(-\frac{x}{y}\right) = -\frac{75x}{y^5}, \qquad y \neq 0.$$

Example 5. Consider

$$4xy^3 + 3y^4 = 6. \tag{3}$$

By implicit differentiation we have

$$4\left[x3(y)^2\frac{dy}{dx} + y^3\right] + 12(y)^3\frac{dy}{dx} = 0,$$

$$\frac{dy}{dx} = -\frac{y^3}{3xy^2 + 3y^3} = -\frac{1}{3}\frac{y}{x+y}. \tag{4}$$

Observe that we divided by $3y^2(x+y)$ in the last step but that there is no point (x, y) that satisfies Eq. (3) and which is such that $y = 0$ or $y = -x$. To differentiate again with respect to x, we use the quotient rule:

$$\frac{d^2y}{dx^2} = -\frac{1}{3}\frac{(x+y)(dy/dx) - y[1 + (dy/dx)]}{(x+y)^2} = -\frac{1}{3}\frac{x(dy/dx) - y}{(x+y)^2}.$$

Now we substitute for dy/dx its value as given by Eq. (4),

$$\frac{d^2y}{dx^2} = -\frac{1}{3}\frac{x[-y/3(x+y)] - y}{(x+y)^2},$$

and simplify this complex fraction by multiplying numerator and denominator by $3(x+y)$. This gives

$$\frac{d^2y}{dx^2} = -\frac{1}{3}\frac{-xy - 3y(x+y)}{3(x+y)^3} = \frac{3y^2 + 4xy}{9(x+y)^3} = \frac{2}{3y^2(x+y)^3}.$$

In the last step of this simplification we took advantage of the fact that y represents a function of x which satisfies Eq. (3).

Example 6. In Example 1.9-6 it was pointed out that if $y = f(x)$ is construed as an implicit statement for x as a function of y, then

$$\frac{dx}{dy} = \frac{1}{f'(x)} = \frac{1}{dy/dx},$$

provided $f'(x) \neq 0$. To continue, using the chain rule,

$$\frac{d^2x}{dy^2} = \frac{d}{dy}\left[\frac{1}{f'(x)}\right] = \left\{\frac{d}{dx}\left[\frac{1}{f'(x)}\right]\right\}\frac{dx}{dy} = \left\{-\frac{1}{[f'(x)]^2}f''(x)\right\}\frac{1}{f'(x)}$$

$$= -\frac{f''(x)}{[f'(x)]^3} = -\frac{d^2y/dx^2}{(dy/dx)^3},$$

provided that $f'(x) \neq 0$.

We have mentioned the fact that the acceleration in rectilinear motion is a second derivative, but in this section we have considered higher derivatives primarily from a formal, computational point of view. In Chapter 3 we shall see what significance d^2y/dx^2 has in a rectangular coordinate graph context. The higher derivatives will be used in other ways as well.

EXERCISES 1.10

1. $y = x^4 + 5x^3 - 6x$, $\dfrac{d^6y}{dx^6} = ?$

2. $y = x^3 - 2x^2 + 7x - 5$, $\dfrac{d^3y}{dx^3} = ?$

3. $y = x^n$, n a positive integer, $\dfrac{d^ny}{dx^n} = ?$

4. $y = x^n$, n and k positive integers with $k > n$, $\dfrac{d^ky}{dx^k} = ?$

5. $f(t) = 6 - \dfrac{1}{t}$, $f'''(t) = ?$

6. $v = 2y^2 + 7 - \dfrac{1}{2y^2}$, $\dfrac{d^3v}{dy^3} = ?$

7. $f(x) = (1 + 2x)^4$, $f'''(x) = ?$

8. $x = (1 - t)^7$, $\dfrac{d^2x}{dt^2} = ?$

9. $y = \dfrac{2}{5(x + 1)^{3/2}}$, $\dfrac{d^3y}{dx^3} = ?$

10. $\phi(r) = \dfrac{r}{\sqrt{r^2 - 1}}$, $\phi''(r) = ?$

11.* $Q = t^3(2 - 3t)^4$, $\dfrac{d^2Q}{dt^2} = ?$

12.† $T = x\sqrt[3]{5 - x}$, $\dfrac{d^2T}{dx^2} = ?$

13.‡ $v = \dfrac{au^2 + b}{u}$, $\dfrac{d^2v}{du^2} = ?$

14.§ $v = \dfrac{16}{(t^2 - 5)^{3/2}}$, $\dfrac{d^2v}{dt^2} = ?$

15. $6x^2 - 7y^2 = 42$, $\dfrac{d^2y}{dx^2} = ?$, $\dfrac{d^3y}{dx^3} = ?$

16. $x^3 + 3y^3 = 23$, $\dfrac{d^2y}{dx^2} = ?$

17. $x^{1/2} + 4y^{1/2} = 4$, $\dfrac{d^2y}{dx^2} = ?$

18. $ax^n + by^n = c$, $\dfrac{d^2y}{dx^2} = ?$

19. $5y^6 + 6xy^5 = 60$, $\dfrac{d^2y}{dx^2} = ?$

20. $\dfrac{3}{y^2} = \dfrac{2}{x^3} - 12$, $\dfrac{d^2y}{dx^2} = ?$

21. $y^4 = \dfrac{6}{x^2} + 10$, $\dfrac{d^2y}{dx^2} = ?$

22. Suppose that the distance x a particle has traveled in time t, $0 \le t \le 1$, is given by the formula $x = 1 - \sqrt{1 - t}$. Where is the particle at $t = .75$? What is its velocity then? What is its acceleration then? At what rate is its acceleration changing then?

23. The same as Exercise 22 for the motion $x = 16t^2 + 18t - .1t^3$, $0 \le t \le 10$, at the instant $t = 2$.

---

* This exercise continues an exercise of Sec. 1.8.
† Ibid.
‡ Ibid.
§ Ibid.

24. At what rate with respect to horizontal displacements is the slope of the tangent line changing?

(a) $y = 4 - x^2$.

(b) $y = \dfrac{1}{x}$ at $(2, \frac{1}{2})$.

25. *Leibniz' rule.* Let u and v be functions of x which can be differentiated as many times as required. Let $D^n q$ stand for $d^n q/dx^n$, n a positive integer. Let $D^0 q$ stand for q.

(a) Show that

$$D^2(uv) = 1(D^2u)(D^0v) + 2(D^1u)(D^1v) + 1(D^0u)(D^2v).$$

(b) Show that

$$D^3(uv) = 1(D^3u)(D^0v) + 3(D^2u)(D^1v) + 3(D^1u)(D^2v) + 1(D^0u)(D^3v).$$

(c) Show by induction that

$$D^n(uv) = 1(D^nu)(D^0v) + n(D^{n-1}u)(D^1v) + \frac{n(n-1)}{2}(D^{n-2}u)(D^2v)$$
$$+ \cdots + n(D^1u)(D^{n-1}v) + 1(D^0u)(D^nv),$$

where the coefficients are those of the binomial expansion.

Integration

2.1 The Antiderivative of a Function

In Chapter 1 the derivative of a function was defined, and we learned to compute certain derivatives fairly efficiently. Here an invere question is asked. Given a first function, can we construct a second function whose derivative is the first function? A function $\varphi(x)$ whose derivative is $f(x)$ is called an antiderivative of $f(x)$; if $\varphi'(x) = f(x)$, then $f(x)$ is the derivative of $\varphi(x)$ and $\varphi(x)$ is an antiderivative of $f(x)$.

Example 1.   Consider a particle with known mass moving in a straight line. If the force acting on the particle is known as a function of time, its acceleration is known through Newton's law, $F = ma$. Knowing the acceleration a as a function of time means that we know the derivative of the velocity, for $a = dv/dt$. Can the velocity v be reconstructed? If it can, we know the derivative of the distance traveled, for $v = dx/dt$. Knowing dx/dt, can we then reconstruct x, and thus know the position of the particle at any time?

Example 2.   Suppose that we know how much salt is dissolved in a tank of water to start with and know the rate at which additional salt is being dissolved as a function of the time. Can the amount of salt dissolved at any time be determined? Restated, can we find N, the number of grams of salt dissolved at time t, if we know N at time $t = 0$ and know dN/dt as a function of time?

To be more specific, consider Example 3.

Example 3.   Given that $y = f(t) = 6$ when $t = 0$, or

$$f(0) = 6, \tag{1}$$

and that

$$\frac{dy}{dt} = f'(t) = t \text{ for all } t. \tag{2}$$

What can be said about y? We know that the differentiation of a power of t lowers the exponent by 1, and we expect therefore that y was a multiple of t^2 if

dy/dt is a multiple of t. Since the derivative of t^2 is $2t$, not t as required in Eq. (2), we soon guess that if $dy/dt = f'(t) = t$, then $y = f(t)$ might have been $\frac{1}{2} t^2$, or $\frac{1}{2} t^2 + 1$, or $\frac{1}{2} t^2 + C$, where C is a constant. Of these possibilities, however, only $y = f(t) = \frac{1}{2} t^2 + 6$ will suffice, for $f(0) = 6$ means $\frac{1}{2}(0)^2 + C = 6$, or $C = 6$. Thus y might be $f(t) = \frac{1}{2} t^2 + 6$. *But must it be this particular function?* Could there be another function, perhaps one not yet studied, with the properties expressed by Eqs. (1) and (2)?

If the questions asked in these examples did not have *unique* answers, if a knowledge of the derivative left us with essentially different alternate choices for the original function, then the usefulness of the antiderivative process we propose to study would be severely limited. Fortunately, we have the following theorem.

■ THEOREM 1

The uniqueness of the antiderivative.

HYPOTHESIS: $f'(x) = \phi'(x)$ for x of domain D.

CONCLUSION: There is a constant C such that

$$f(x) = \phi(x) + C \qquad \text{for } x \text{ of } D.$$

Two functions with the same derivative can differ only by a constant.

PLAUSIBILITY ARGUMENT.* Let $F(x) = f(x) - \phi(x)$. Then, by hypothesis,
$$F'(x) = f'(x) - \phi'(x) = 0 \qquad \text{for } x \text{ of } D.$$
In words, the rate of change of $F(x)$ is 0 for the domain. It seems plausible to conclude that functions that have a zero rate of change are constant, and therefore that
$$F(x) = C \qquad \text{for } x \text{ of } D,$$
$$f(x) - \phi(x) = C \qquad \text{or} \qquad f(x) = \phi(x) + C.$$

Example 4. Theorem 1 assures us that $y = f(t) = \frac{1}{2} t^2 + 6$ is the *only* function that can satisfy Eqs. (1) and (2) of Example 3. For if $y = \phi(t) = \frac{1}{2} t^2$ is one function that satisfies Eq. (2), then, according to Theorem 1, any other function that satisfies this equation *must* be of the form $y = f(t) = \phi(t) + C = \frac{1}{2} t^2 + C$, where C is a constant. As already pointed out in Example 3, C should be 6 if Eq. (1) is also to be satisfied.

Example 3 used a specific antiderivative fact that is part of the following frequently used theorem.

■ THEOREM 2

The antiderivative for x^N.

HYPOTHESIS: (a) N is a rational number $\neq -1$, D is such that x^N is defined for each x of D.
(b) $dy/dx = f'(x) = x^N$.

---

* We shall return to the proof of this theorem in Chapter 7.

CONCLUSION:

$$y = f(x) = \frac{x^{N+1}}{N+1} + C \qquad \text{for each } x \text{ of } D.$$

In words, if the derivative of a function is a rational power of x other than x^{-1}, the function itself can be reconstructed by (a) taking a power of x with exponent one greater, (b) dividing by this higher exponent, and (c) adding a constant.

PROOF: If x^N is defined, then so is $x^{N+1} = x \cdot x^N$. Hence

$$\phi(x) = \frac{1}{N+1} x^{N+1} \qquad \text{for } x \text{ of } D$$

is such that $\qquad \phi'(x) = \dfrac{1}{N+1} (N+1)x^N = x^N,$

and then, by Theorem 1, the conclusion follows.

Example 5.   If $f'(x) = 1 = x^0$, Theorem 2 says that

$$f(x) = \frac{x^1}{1} + C = x + C.$$

For $\varphi'(x) = \sqrt{x} = x^{1/2}$, $x \geq 0$, Theorem 2 says that

$$\phi(x) = \frac{x^{3/2}}{3/2} + C = \tfrac{2}{3} x^{3/2} + C.$$

For $dy/dx = 1/x^2 = x^{-2}$, $x \neq 0$, Theorem 2 says that

$$y = \frac{x^{-1}}{-1} + C = -\frac{1}{x} + C.$$

But for $dy/dx = 1/x = x^{-1}$, Theorem 2 says nothing because its hypothesis is not satisfied. We shall close this important gap in Chapter 5.

We know that $y = \tfrac{1}{3} x^3 + C$ if $dy/dx = x^2$, but what can we say if dv/dx is five times as large as dy/dx? Will v be five times as large as y? Is it true that $v = \tfrac{5}{3} x^3 + C$ if $dv/dx = 5x^2$? If $du/dx = x^3$, we know that $u = \tfrac{1}{4} x^4 + C$. If dw/dx is the sum of dy/dx and du/dx, however, will w be the sum of y and u? If $dw/dx = x^2 + x^3$, is it true that $w = \tfrac{1}{3} x^3 + \tfrac{1}{4} x^4 + C$? The answers to these questions are given by Theorems 3 and 4.

■ THEOREM 3

The constant multiplier in antidifferentiation.

HYPOTHESIS:

$$\frac{dv}{dx} = k\frac{dy}{dx}, \qquad k \text{ a constant}, \qquad x \text{ in domain } D.$$

CONCLUSION: $v = ky + C, \qquad x \text{ in } D.$

■ THEOREM 4

Antiderivatives of sums.

HYPOTHESIS:

$$\frac{dw}{dx} = \frac{dy}{dx} + \frac{du}{dx} \qquad \text{for } x \text{ in domain } D.$$

CONCLUSION: $w = y + u + C$ for x in D.

The proofs of these theorems are left to the reader.

Example 6. If

$$\frac{dy}{dx} = 2x^2 - 5x + 4,$$

then $\qquad\qquad y = \tfrac{2}{3} x^3 - \tfrac{5}{2} x^2 + 4x + C.$

This can be checked by making sure that the proposed solution has as its derivative the given expression for dy/dx.

Example 7. If

$$\frac{dL}{dt} = \frac{3}{\sqrt{t}} - \frac{4}{3t^3} = 3t^{-1/2} - \tfrac{4}{3} t^{-3}, \qquad t > 0,$$

then $\qquad L = 3\dfrac{t^{1/2}}{1/2} - \dfrac{4}{3}\dfrac{t^{-2}}{-2} + C = 6\sqrt{t} + \dfrac{2}{3}\dfrac{1}{t^2} + C, \qquad t > 0.$

Example 8. If

$$\frac{dQ}{dt} = \sqrt{2t^3}, \qquad t \geq 0, \tag{3}$$

and $\qquad\qquad Q = 6 \qquad \text{when } t = 2, \tag{4}$

we can find Q for any $t \geq 0$. Rewrite Eq. (3) as $dQ/dt = \sqrt{2}\, t^{3/2}$. Then

$$Q = \sqrt{2}\,\frac{t^{5/2}}{5/2} + C = \frac{2\sqrt{2}}{5} t^{5/2} + C.$$

Now to satisfy Eq. (4) we write

$$6 = \frac{2\sqrt{2}}{5} (2)^{5/2} + C = \frac{16}{5} + C, \qquad \text{or} \qquad C = 6 - \frac{16}{5} = \frac{14}{5}.$$

Thus $\qquad\qquad Q = \dfrac{2\sqrt{2}}{5} t^{5/2} + \dfrac{14}{5}.$

Theorem 2 is part of the following theorem.

■ THEOREM 5

Antiderivatives of powers.

HYPOTHESIS: (a) u and du/dx have domain D.

(b) $dy/dx = f'(x) = (u)^N du/dx$, N a rational number $\neq -1$ and x in D such that $(u)^N$ is defined.

CONCLUSION:

$$y = f(x) = \frac{(u)^{N+1}}{N+1} + C$$

for x in D such that $(u)^N$ is defined.

In words, if $f'(x)$ is the product of a rational power of a function* and the derivative of that function, then $f(x)$ can be reconstructed by (a) taking the power of the very same function with exponent one greater, (b) dividing by this higher exponent, and (c) adding a constant.

PROOF:

$$\phi(x) = \frac{1}{N+1}(u)^{N+1}$$

is certainly one function whose derivative is $(u)^N du/dx$ for those x in D such that $(u)^N$ is defined because $(u)^{N+1} = u(u)^N$ is defined when $(u)^N$ is and because

$$\phi'(x) = \frac{1}{N+1}(N+1)(u)^N \frac{du}{dx} = (u)^N \frac{du}{dx},$$

by Theorem 1.9-2. It then follows from Theorem 1 that $f(x)$ must be of the form $[(u)^{N+1}/(N+1)] + C$.

Example 9. If

$$\frac{dy}{dx} = (x^2 + 5)^6(2x),$$

the hypotheses of Theorem 5 are satisfied. In words, we have (a) the function $(x^2 + 5)$ raised to the sixth power and (b) the derivative of that function, $2x$. Our conclusion is that

$$y = \frac{(x^2 + 5)^7}{7} + C.$$

Example 10. When $f'(x) = x\sqrt{5 + x^2}$, the hypotheses of the antiderivative rule are not quite satisfied, for we have (a) the function $(5 + x^2)$ raised to a power, but we do not quite have (b) $2x$, the derivative of this function. However, we can rewrite the problem as

$$f'(x) = (5 + x^2)^{1/2}(x) = \tfrac{1}{2}[(5 + x^2)^{1/2}(2x)],$$

and then we can conclude that

$$f(x) = \frac{1}{2}\frac{(5 + x^2)^{3/2}}{3/2} + C = \frac{1}{3}(5 + x^2)^{3/2} + C.$$

---

* Only the -1 exponent case is excluded.

Note that for the problem $F'(x) = \sqrt{5 + x^2}$ we cannot find $F(x)$ by this method. We have (a) the function $5 + x^2$ taken to a rational power, but we do not have (b) x, the essential part of the derivative of the function $5 + x^2$. A similar difficulty would arise in finding $g(x)$ when $g'(x) = x^2 \sqrt{5 + x^2}$, for x^2 is not the essential part of the derivative of $5 + x^2$ either.

Example 11. If

$$\frac{dQ}{dt} = \frac{2t^2}{5(a^3 - t^3)^5}, \qquad t \neq a,$$

we can write

$$\frac{dQ}{dt} = \frac{2}{5}(a^3 - t^3)^{-5}(t^2) = \frac{2}{5}\left(-\frac{1}{3}\right)(a^3 - t^3)^{-5}(-3t^2).$$

Now we have the function $a^3 - t^3$ raised to a power, and the derivative of $a^3 - t^3$, namely, $-3t^2$. We conclude that

$$Q = -\frac{2}{15}\frac{(a^3 - t^3)^{-4}}{-4} + C = \frac{1}{30}\frac{1}{(a^3 - t^3)^4} + C, \qquad t \neq a.$$

● **Remark 1**

We shall occasionally assume the validity of the antiderivative rule for irrational N; see Remark 1.9-1.

EXERCISES 2.1

Not every exercise of the following list can be carried out with the help of the theorems of this article. If such is the case, say so.

1. If $dy/dx = 3x^2 + 5x + 6$ and $y = 3$ when $x = 0$, find y.

2. If $f'(x) = 3x^4 + \dfrac{6x^2}{5} - 7$ and $f(1) = 2$, find $f(x)$.

3. If $\phi'(z) = a_2 z^2 + a_1 z + a_0$, find $\phi(z)$.

4. If $d^2y/dt^2 = -32$ for all $t \geq 0$ and $dy/dt = 100$, $y = 0$ when $t = 0$, find dy/dt and y for $t \geq 0$.

5. If $f'(x) = \sqrt{x}$ and $f(4) = 4$, find $f(x)$.

6. If $\dfrac{dx}{dt} = \dfrac{3}{2}t^2 + \dfrac{3}{2t^2}$ find x.

7. If $g'(x) = 2\sqrt[3]{3x}$ and $g(0) = 4$, find $g(x)$.

8. If $\dfrac{du}{dx} = \dfrac{16}{\sqrt{x^3}} + 5$ and $u = 2$ when $x = 1$, find u.

9. If $\dfrac{dv}{dt} = \dfrac{4}{3t^3} - \dfrac{3}{t^4} + \dfrac{12}{t^5}$, find v.

10. If $f''(x) = \sqrt{x} + \dfrac{2}{\sqrt{x}}$ and $f'(1) = 6$, $f(1) = -2$, find $f'(x)$ and $f(x)$.

11. If $dy/dx = 2(3 + x)^{10}$, find y.

12. If $dv/du = 2u(u^2 - 15)^4$, find v.

13. If $f'(x) = \dfrac{3x^2}{(x^3 + 7)^2}$ and $f(0) = 0$, find $f(x)$.

14. If $\phi'(t) = t(t^2 + 7)^{3/2}$, find $\phi(t)$.

15. If $g'(x) = 7x(9 - 2x^2)^3$ and $g(2) = 1$, find $g(x)$.

16. If $\dfrac{dy}{dx} = \dfrac{3x}{\sqrt{x^2 + 1}}$, find y.

17. If $\dfrac{dy}{dx} = \dfrac{2}{3\sqrt[3]{x + 1}}$ and $y = 2$ when $x = 0$, find y.

18. If $\dfrac{dL}{dt} = \dfrac{3}{2(6 - t)^5}$, find L.

19. If $\dfrac{dv}{dr} = \dfrac{r}{r^2 + 1}$ and $v = 1$ when $r = 0$, find v.

20. If $f''(x) = x(x^2 + 4)^{1/2}$ and $f'(0) = 0, f(0) = 1$, find $f'(x), f(x)$.

21. Prove Theorem 3.

22. Prove Theorem 4.

23. Is this proposed theorem valid?

Hypothesis: $\dfrac{dw}{dx} = \dfrac{du}{dx}\dfrac{dv}{dx}$.

Conclusion: $w = uv + C$.

2.2   Rectilinear Motion

Newton's law of gravitation says that the attraction between two bodies is directly proportional to the product of their masses and inversely proportional to the square of the distance between them. If we deal with the case where one of the two bodies is the earth and the other is an object of mass m on the surface of the earth, we have

$$|F| = \frac{k\, m_E m}{r^2}, \tag{1}$$

where m_E is the mass of the earth, r is the distance from the center of gravity of the earth to the center of gravity of our object, and k is a constant of proportionality. The mass of the earth, the radius of the earth, and the constant k are such that Eq. (1) becomes

$$|F| = 32m. \tag{2}$$

Here distances and times have been assumed measured in feet and seconds, and the number 32 represents an approximation.*

On the other hand, according to another of Newton's laws, the force causing an object to move and the acceleration of the ensuing motion are related by

$$F = ma. \tag{3}$$

Thus, from Eqs. (2) and (3), for a body moving freely in a vertical line under the influence of gravity, we have

$$a = -32. \tag{4}$$

---

* A better value would be 32.1. Note that the earth is not a perfect sphere, so that the value of r differs from place to place on the earth's surface, and also that we neglect the slight changes in r as a body moves up or down.

The minus sign was chosen because it seemed convenient to consider the upward vertical direction as positive; the force of gravity pulls objects down.

Because $a = dv/dt$ by definition, Eq. (4) gives us dv/dt as a function of time. Using the techniques of antidifferentiation, we can find v itself:

$$\frac{dv}{dt} = -32,$$

$$v = -32t + C_1, \tag{5}$$

where C_1 is a constant to be determined by the conditions of the particular problem at hand. If y represents the height of the object, Eq. (5) gives us $v = dy/dt$ as a function of time. Hence for y itself we have

$$\frac{dy}{dt} = -32t + C_1,$$

$$y = -16t^2 + C_1 t + C_2, \tag{6}$$

where C_2 is a second constant to be determined by the conditions of the particular problem at hand.

Example 1. Example 1.4-1 stated that the height of a ball dropped from a building 320 ft high is given by the equation $y = 320 - 16t^2$. Let us derive this statement.

As above, we start with the fact that

$$a = \frac{dv}{dt} = -32, \qquad 0 \le t \le \sqrt{20}. \tag{7}$$

We must have for v itself

$$v = -32t + C_1, \qquad 0 \le t \le \sqrt{20}. \tag{8}$$

Since the ball was dropped rather than thrown down or up, we know that $v = 0$ when $t = 0$. Substituting this information in Eq. (8), we learn that $C_1 = 0$ and that

$$v = \frac{dy}{dt} = -32t, \qquad 0 \le t \le \sqrt{20}. \tag{9}$$

Next, $$y = -16t^2 + C_2, \qquad 0 \le t \le \sqrt{20}. \tag{10}$$

But when $t = 0$, we were told that $y = 320$. Hence, upon substitution, we find that $C_2 = 320$ and that

$$y = 320 - 16t^2, \qquad 0 \le t \le \sqrt{20}. \tag{11}$$

From Eq. (11) it follows that $y = 0$ when $16t^2 = 320$ or $t = \sqrt{20}$. The physical conditions of the problem change abruptly when the ball reaches the ground and that is why the interval $0 \le t \le \sqrt{20}$ was taken to be the domain of definition for the acceleration, velocity, and height functions.

Example 2. This time let the ball be thrown down from a height of 320 ft with an initial velocity of 8 ft per sec. We shall derive a formula for its height at any time and shall find the velocity with which it struck the ground.

Again, we start with the pertinent fact from physics:

$$a = \frac{dv}{dt} = -32, \qquad 0 \le t \le 4.23, \tag{12}$$

and find
$$v = -32t + C_1, \qquad 0 \le t \le 4.23. \tag{13}$$

But this time we have $v = -8$ when $t = 0$. Hence, $-8 = 0 + C_1$, $C_1 = -8$, and

$$v = \frac{dy}{dt} = -32t - 8, \qquad 0 \le t \le 4.23. \tag{14}$$

But then
$$y = -16t^2 - 8t + C_2, \qquad 0 \le t \le 4.23, \tag{15}$$

and since $y = 320$ when $t = 0$, we get

$$y = -16t^2 - 8t + 320, \qquad 0 \le t \le 4.23. \tag{16}$$

To find the time at which the ball strikes the ground we set $y = 0$ in Eq. (16) and observe that

$$16t^2 + 8t - 320 = 0.$$

Solving, and selecting the value of t which is valid for this problem, we have

$$2t^2 + t - 40 = 0,$$

$$t = \frac{-1 \pm \sqrt{1 + 320}}{4},$$

$$t \approx 4.23$$

The ball strikes the ground after approximately 4.23 sec. We learn from Eq. (14) that $v \approx -143.4$ at this time.

Example 3. Assume that the forces of friction are such that a certain puck sliding across ice decelerates at a constant rate. When it stops after 8 sec, it has moved 120 ft from the position where we first observed it. What was its velocity when we first observed it, and how far had the puck traveled after 4 sec?

Here the key physical fact is the fact that the deceleration is constant:

$$a = \frac{dv}{dt} = -C_1, \qquad 0 \le t \le 8. \tag{17}$$

Thus
$$v = \frac{dx}{dt} = -C_1 t + C_2, \qquad 0 \le t \le 8, \tag{18}$$

where x is the distance traveled from the position where the puck was first observed and where the time is measured from the time of the first observation. We were told that the puck stopped after 8 sec. Thus $v = 0$ when $t = 8$. Substituting in Eq. (18), we find that

$$0 = -C_1 8 + C_2. \tag{19}$$

Now from Eq. (18) we deduce that

$$x = \frac{-C_1 t^2}{2} + C_2 t + C_3, \qquad 0 \le t \le 8. \tag{20}$$

We have $x = 0$ when $t = 0$ from the very definition of x. Thus

$$0 = 0 + 0 + C_3, \quad \text{or} \quad C_3 = 0.$$

Lastly, we were told that $x = 120$ when $t = 8$. Hence

$$120 = -\frac{C_1}{2}(64) + C_2(8). \tag{21}$$

Solving Eqs. (19) and (21) as two equations in the two unknowns C_1 and C_2, we learn that $C_1 = 15/4$, $C_2 = 30$, so that Eqs. (18) and (20) become

$$v = -\tfrac{15}{4}t + 30, \qquad 0 \le t \le 8, \tag{18a}$$

$$x = -\tfrac{15}{8}t^2 + 30t, \qquad 0 \le t \le 8. \tag{20a}$$

The puck's velocity at $t = 0$ was 30 ft per sec, according to Eq. (18a), and after 4 sec it had traveled 90 ft, according to Eq. (20a).

EXERCISES 2.2

1. A ball is thrown up from the ground with an initial velocity of 54 ft per sec. Find formulas for its velocity and height at any later time. How high does it go? When will it strike the ground?

2. An object is dropped from a height of 484 ft. Find formulas for its velocity and height at any later time. When will it strike the ground and with what velocity?

3. An object is thrown upward from a height of 200 ft with an initial velocity of 40 ft per sec. Find formulas for its velocity and height at any later time. When will it pass a ledge at a height of 144 ft on its way down?

4. From what height must an object be dropped if it is to reach the ground in 1.75 sec?

5. With what initial speed must an object be thrown upward from the ground if it is to reach a maximum height of 72 ft?

6. With what initial speed must an object be thrown downward from a height of 168 ft if it is to strike the ground with a velocity of 136 ft per sec?

7. A ball rolls down an inclined plane with a constant acceleration of 14 ft per sec², the motion starting from rest. Find formulas for its velocity and for the distance rolled at any later time. Find a formula for the velocity as a function of the distance rolled.

8. We know from the inclination of a certain inclined plane that a ball will roll down the plane with a constant acceleration of 10 ft per sec², but we do not know the initial velocity with which the ball was pushed to start the motion. We observe that in 2 sec the ball has rolled a distance of 36 ft. What was the initial velocity?

9. If the angle of inclination of a plane is α, the acceleration of a ball rolling down that plane can be taken to be $32 \sin \alpha$. What should be the angle of inclination of a plane 20 ft long if a ball is to start from rest at the top of the plane and reach the bottom in 5 sec?

10. The motor driving a rotating wheel is shut off at a time when a point on the rim of the wheel is traveling with a speed of 4π ft per sec. Let us assume a constant deceleration of 0.1 ft per sec² for the motion of this point. How long will it take the wheel to stop, and how far will the point have traveled in that time?

11. Let us agree that a sprinter runs with constant acceleration for the first 25 yd of a 100-yd dash and then runs the rest of the race at constant velocity. What would his constant acceleration have to be if he is to run the race in 10 sec?

12. Assume that the speed of a certain car decreases at the same constant rate whenever the brakes are applied. On a test run the car is brought to a stop from a speed of

45 miles per hr in 9 sec. How long will it take to bring the car to a stop from a speed of 60 miles per hr? In this case, if we agree that 1 sec elapses from the instant the driver sees an obstruction to the instant he applies the brakes, how many feet will he travel from the point where he first observed the obstruction?

13. If the acceleration of a moving body at time t is given by the formula $a = 6 - .1t$ ft per sec², and if it starts from rest at time $t = 0$, how long will it travel in the direction of increasing x? How far will it travel in that direction before reversing its direction?

14. If the acceleration of a moving body at time t is given by the formula $a = 1/\sqrt{2 + t}$ ft per sec², $t \geq 0$, and if it is observed that the velocity is 7 ft per sec at the instant $t = 2$, derive formulas for the velocity at any time t, $t \geq 0$, and for the distance traveled from the $t = 0$ position.

15. A train's steady running speed is 60 miles per hr, which it gains or loses by constant acceleration in 6 min. As compared with a nonstop run at 60 miles per hr, how much time is given up for a 1-min stop at a station?

2.3 Areas by Antidifferentiation

We seek a method for associating a nonnegative area number with a specific region presented to us. In this section we shall apply to this problem the same strategy we used in Sec. 2.2, namely that of studying a function by inquiring about its derivative rather than by inquiring directly about the function itself.

Because of our experience, we agree that any definition of area must be consistent with the following assumptions:

(a) The area number assigned to a region shall be nonnegative.

(b) The area numbers assigned to congruent regions shall be equal.

(c) The area number assigned to a region formed by uniting two nonoverlapping regions shall be the sum of the area numbers assigned to those regions.

■ DEFINITION 1

The area of a rectangle shall be (base) × (height).

The motivation for this definition also arises from experience. A rectangle of dimensions 5 units by 3 units will contain 3 rows of 5 square units each or $(3)(5)$ square units; see Fig. 2.1(a). Observe that this definition for the area of a rectangle meets the three requirements just listed for any acceptable area definition.

Definition 1 and the basic area definition requirements force us to take (base) × (height) for the area of a parallelogram also. For, given a parallelogram $ABCD$, we can form from it a rectangle $ABC'D'$ of the same base and height by taking off triangle $AD'D$ and adding congruent triangle $BC'C$; see Fig. 2.1(b). The area of a

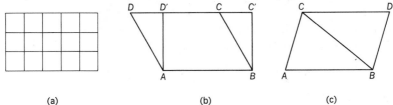

(a) (b) (c)

Fig. 2.1

triangle must then be ½(base) × (height). For, given triangle *ABC*, we can form a parallelogram *ABDC* of the same base and height as the triangle by uniting congruent triangle *BCD* with triangle *ABC*; see Fig. 2.1(c). Finally, we take for the area of a polygon the sum of the areas of a set of triangles into which the polygon can be divided.

To learn how to associate an area number with a region whose boundaries are not all straight lines is a much more difficult task. We shall restrict our attention at first to certain special regions with one curved boundary. Let $f(x)$ be ≥ 0 for the interval $a \leq x \leq b$, and let us inquire about the area of the region under the graph $y = f(x)$, above the x axis, to the right of $x = a$, and to the left of $x = b$; see Fig. 2.2. We shall assume that $f(x)$ is a continuous function for $a \leq x \leq b$; that is, $f(x)$ is defined for all x of that interval and changes gradually, without gaps, in that interval. If for any x of the interval we compute $f(x)$, and then at nearby $x + \Delta x$, also of the interval, we compute $f(x + \Delta x)$, we require that $\Delta f = f(x + \Delta x) - f(x)$ approach 0 as Δx approaches 0. The graph $y = f(x)$ drawn in Fig. 2.2 represents a continuous function, but

$$y = f(x) = \begin{cases} 5 - x & \text{for } x \leq 2, \\ 2 + x & \text{for } x > 2, \end{cases}$$

whose graph appears in Fig. 2.3, is not a continuous function, and neither is

$$w = \phi(x) = \frac{1}{(x - 2)^2}, \qquad x \neq 2,$$

whose graph appears in Fig. 2.4. The latter is discontinuous at $x = 2$, because $\phi(2)$ is not defined; the former is discontinuous at $x = 2$ even though $f(2)$ is defined to be 3, because for $\Delta x > 0$ we have $f(2 + \Delta x) = 4 + \Delta x$, and $\Delta f = f(2 + \Delta x) - f(2) = 4 + \Delta x - 3 = 1 + \Delta x$ does not approach 0 as Δx does. The fact that Δf does not approach 0 corresponds to the gap we observe in the graph.*

Imagine now that one has chosen a definition of area for the special regions with one curved boundary described above and that this definition is consistent with Assumptions (a), (b), and (c) listed at the beginning of this section and with Definition 1 for rectangles. Refer again to Fig. 2.2, and consider the function $A(x)$ defined for $a \leq x \leq b$ as the area of the region bounded by the curve $y = f(x)$, $x = a$, the x axis, and the ordinate line at x. The area we seek is the number $A(b)$.

We shall study $A'(x)$ rather than $A(x)$ itself. By definition,

$$A'(x) = \lim_{\Delta x \to 0} \frac{A(x + \Delta x) - A(x)}{\Delta x}, \tag{1}$$

if this limit exists. Our program is therefore clear. We shall consider first $A(x + \Delta x)$ for $\Delta x \neq 0$ and $x + \Delta x$ between a and b, then $\Delta A = A(x + \Delta x) - A(x)$, then

$$\frac{\Delta A}{\Delta x} = \frac{A(x + \Delta x) - A(x)}{\Delta x},$$

and finally $A'(x)$.

---

* A more complete discussion of continuity will be given in Chapter 7.

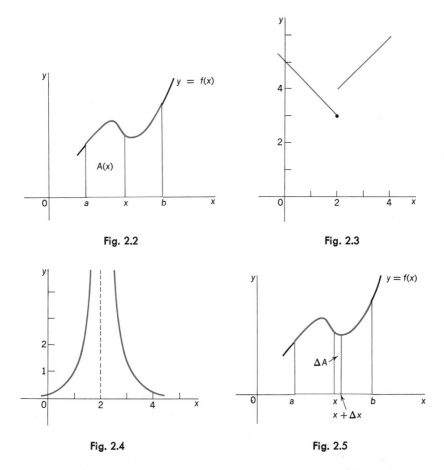

Fig. 2.2

Fig. 2.3

Fig. 2.4

Fig. 2.5

Step (a): $A(x + \Delta x)$ is the area bounded by the curve $y = f(x)$, the line $x = a$, the x axis, and the ordinate at $x + \Delta x$; see Fig. 2.5.

Step (b): $\Delta A = A(x + \Delta x) - A(x)$ is the area below the curve and above the axis bounded by the ordinates at x and at $x + \Delta x$. Although ΔA cannot be computed directly because the top boundary is not a straight line, still some useful comparisons can be made. Let M and m be the maximum and minimum values assumed by $f(x)$ in the interval bounded by x and $x + \Delta x$. In Fig. 2.6, M happens to be $JL = f(x)$ and m is $NK = f(x + \Delta x)$. If we compare ΔA with the areas of the rectangles $JLPN$ and $JQKN$, and use Assumptions (a) and (c) made at the beginning of this section, we have

$$m\,\Delta x \le \Delta A \le M\,\Delta x \tag{2a}$$

if Δx is positive. If Δx is negative, so that the ordinate at $x + \Delta x$ lies to the left of the ordinate at x, as in Fig. 2.7, then $\Delta A = A(x + \Delta x) - A(x)$ will be negative because $A(x)$ will be larger than $A(x + \Delta x)$. In this case we have

$$M\,\Delta x \le \Delta A \le m\,\Delta x. \tag{2b}$$

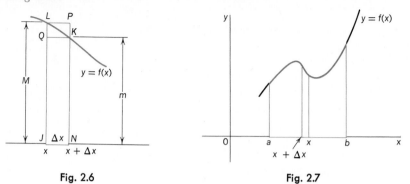

Fig. 2.6   Fig. 2.7

Step (*c*)*:* Now, if Δx is positive, it follows from Eq. (2a) that

$$m \leq \frac{\Delta A}{\Delta x} \leq M. \tag{3}$$

If Δx is negative, the same conclusion will follow from Eq. (2b).*

Step (*d*)*:* If we let $\Delta x \rightarrow 0$, so that $x + \Delta x \rightarrow x$, then both M and m approach $f(x)$.† It will then follow from Eq. (3) that

$$f(x) \leq \lim_{\Delta x \to 0} \frac{\Delta A}{\Delta x} \leq f(x)$$

or that

$$\frac{dA}{dx} = \lim_{\Delta x \to 0} \frac{\Delta A}{\Delta x} = f(x). \tag{4}$$

We have now proved:

■ THEOREM 1

Areas by antidifferentiation.

HYPOTHESIS: (a) Let $f(x)$ be continuous and ≥ 0 for $a \leq x \leq b$.

(b) For any number x, $a \leq x \leq b$, consider the region bounded by $y = f(x)$, the x axis, and the ordinates at a and x. Let there be a definition of area for this region that is consistent with the Assumptions (a), (b), (c) and Definition 1 made at the beginning of this section.

(c) Let the function $A(x)$ assign to each x of $a \leq x \leq b$ the area of the region described in (b).

CONCLUSION:

$$\frac{dA}{dx} = f(x), \qquad a \leq x \leq b.$$

Example 1.   Consider the region bounded by $y = 2x - 1$, the x axis, $x = 1$, and $x = 4$; see Fig. 2.8. For $1 \leq x \leq 4$, we define $A(x)$ as the area of the region bounded by the x axis, $y = 2x - 1$, and the ordinates at 1 and x. The function

---

* Remember that the sense of an inequality is reversed if one divides by a negative number.

† Because we have assumed that $f(x)$ is a continuous function and thus that Δf approaches 0 as Δx does.

$f(x) = 2x - 1$ satisfies Hypothesis (a) of Theorem 1, and we take the conclusion of that theorem:

$$\frac{dA}{dx} = f(x) = 2x - 1, \qquad 1 \leq x \leq 4. \tag{5}$$

This statement for the derivative of $A(x)$ requires that

$$A(x) = x^2 - x + C, \qquad 1 \leq x \leq 4. \tag{6}$$

$A(1)$ is, by definition of $A(x)$, the area bounded by $y = 2x - 1$, the x axis and the lines $x = 1$ and $x = 1$. It is natural to expect $A(1)$ to be 0, and indeed this fact is a consequence of the Assumption (c) we agreed to make for all definitions of area, as the reader can show in Exercise 2.3-18. Hence

$$A(1) = 1 - 1 + C = 0 \qquad \text{or} \qquad C = 0,$$

and Eq. (6) can be rewritten as

$$A(x) = x^2 - x, \qquad 1 \leq x \leq 4. \tag{7}$$

Finally, the area we seek is $A(4) = 4^2 - 4 = 12$.

We can check our answer in this particular problem by elementary geometric computations; for instance, by splitting the desired area into a triangle and a rectangle.

Example 2. Find the area of the region bounded by the x axis and $y = f(x) = \frac{1}{2}(6 - x - 2x^2)$.

To draw the graph quickly, we start by noting that

$$y = \frac{1}{2}(6 - x - 2x^2) = \frac{1}{2}(3 - 2x)(2 + x),$$

so that the curve crosses the x axis at $(\frac{3}{2}, 0)$ and $(-2, 0)$; see Fig. 2.9.

Theorem 1 tells us that

$$\frac{dA}{dx} = y = \frac{1}{2}(6 - x - 2x^2), \qquad -2 \leq x \leq \frac{3}{2},$$

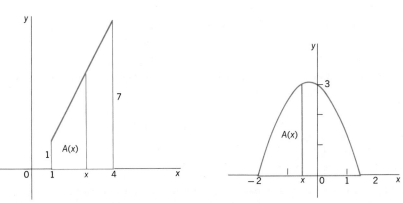

Fig. 2.8   Fig. 2.9

from which we conclude that

$$A(x) = \tfrac{1}{2}(6x - \tfrac{1}{2}x^2 - \tfrac{2}{3}x^3) + C, \qquad -2 \le x \le \tfrac{3}{2}.$$

Now $A(-2) = 0$, so that

$$A(-2) = \tfrac{1}{2}(-12 - 2 + 16\tfrac{2}{3}) + C = 0 \qquad \text{or} \qquad C = 13\tfrac{2}{3}.$$

Thus $\qquad\qquad A(x) = 3x - \tfrac{1}{4}x^2 - \tfrac{1}{3}x^3 + 13\tfrac{2}{3}, \qquad -2 \le x \le \tfrac{3}{2}.$

Finally, the area we seek is

$$A(\tfrac{3}{2}) = \tfrac{9}{2} - \tfrac{9}{16} - \tfrac{9}{8} + 13\tfrac{2}{3} \approx 7.15.$$

As a common-sense check, note that this is a reasonable answer for a figure whose base is 3.5 units and whose maximum height is slightly greater than 3 units.*

● **Remark 1**

Theorem 1 says that, *if* a suitable area definition can be found for the special regions with one curved boundary considered, then the area function $A(x)$ based on that definition must be such that $dA/dx = f(x)$. We have tacitly assumed in each example that such a definition of area could be found.

EXERCISES 2.3

Find the area of the region above the x axis, below the given curve, and between the given vertical boundaries. Check each answer by estimating the area from the graph.

1. $y = x + 1$ from $x = 0$ to $x = 7$.

2. $y = x^2 + x + 1$ from $x = -1$ to $x = +1$.

3. $y = 2 - \tfrac{1}{2}x^3$ from $x = -2$ to $x = 0$.

4. $y = (x^2 + 1)^3$ from $x = 0$ to $x = 1$.

5. $y = \sqrt{x+1}$ from $x = 3$ to $x = 8$.

6. $y = \dfrac{x}{(x^2+1)^2}$ from $x = 0$ to $x = 4$.

7. $y = \dfrac{3}{(2x+1)^3}$ from $x = 1$ to $x = 2$.

8. $y = \sqrt[3]{4-x}$ from $x = -4$ to $x = 3$.

9. $y = x\sqrt{6-x^2}$ from $x = 0$ to $x = \sqrt{6}$.

10. $y = \dfrac{x}{\sqrt{x^2-9}}$ from $x = 5$ to $x = 7$.

Find the area of the region bounded by the x axis and each of the following curves. Check each answer by estimating the area from the graph.

11. $y = 9 - x^2$.

12. $y = 2x^2 - x^3$.

13. $y = 10 + x - 2x^2$.

14. $y = -x^3 - 6x^2 - 9x$.

15. $y = x^4 - 8x^2 + 16$.

---

* Looked at from another point of view, our computation tells us that the region in question has the same area as a rectangle with the same base, 3.5, and a height of $7.15/3.5 \approx 2.04$. If one had to choose one height to represent the graph for this interval, 2.04 would be a reasonable choice. It is called the "average height" for the interval $-2 \le x \le \tfrac{3}{2}$.

16. A region of area 10 is to be bounded above by $y = \sqrt{x + 1}$, below by the x axis, on the left by $x = 3$. If the right boundary is to be a vertical line, where should this vertical line be placed?

17. Repeat Exercise 16 for $y = 1/(2x + 1)^2$, using $x = -2$ as a left boundary.

18. In Example 1 we said that the definition of $A(x)$ and Assumption (c) to be made when accepting any area definition would require $A(1)$ to be 0. Consider region R_1 bounded by $y = 2x - 1$, the x axis, and the lines $x = 1$ and $x = 1$, consider region R_2 bounded by $y = 2x - 1$, the x axis and the lines $x = 1$ and $x = 4$, and let region R_3 be the region formed by uniting R_1 and R_2. Explain why R_3 and R_2 are identical. $A(1)$ is the area of R_1, $A(4)$ is the area of R_2. What does Assumption (c) require the area of R_3 to be? Why is $A(1) = 0$?

2.4   Areas as Limits of Sums

In the last section we considered a certain kind of region with one curved boundary and we showed that, if there existed a definition of area for these regions that was consistent with the customary rectangle area definition and with the three basic requirements listed at the beginning of Sec. 2.3, then Theorem 2.3-1 applied and those areas could be computed by the antidifferentiation technique when anti-derivative functions were known. For regions of the kind considered, it would appear that either no acceptable area definition can be made or only one can be made, for Theorem 2.3-1 and the antidifferentiation technique force us to unique area numbers, at least in those cases where antiderivative functions exist.

Archimedes and others studied the problem of area more than 2000 years ago; in this section we shall rewrite and enlarge upon the method Archimedes used. We shall try to show that there does exist a definition of area that is consistent with the rectangle area definition and with the three basic area definition requirements by actually constructing such a definition.

Let us consider the area of a circle, following the ancient "method of ex-haustion." First, inscribe a square in the circle as in Fig. 2.10 (a). If we let the area of the square serve as a first approximation to the area of the circle, we make an error indicated by the shaded portion of the figure. How can one improve on this approximation? Take next a regular octagon inscribed in the circle, as in Fig. 2.10 (b), and compute its area as a second approximation to the area of the circle. Con-sider the area of a regular polygon of 16 sides as a third approximation, and so on. By using an inscribed regular polygon of 96 sides and a circumscribed regular

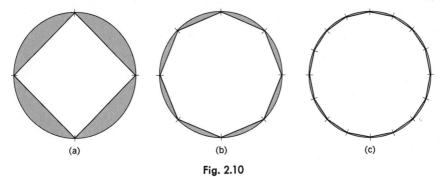

(a)   (b)   (c)

Fig. 2.10

polygon of 96 sides, Archimedes found upper and lower bounds for the area of the circle which enabled him to state a value for π that is accurate to seven decimal places in our notation. This was a method of "exhausting the error." To summarize, this work suggests:

■ DEFINITION 1

The area of a circle. Let A_n be the area of a regular polygon of n sides inscribed in the circle. The area of the circle shall be $\lim_{n \to \infty} A_n$.

Let us return now to a region bounded by $y = f(x)$, the x axis, $x = a$ and $x = b$, it being understood that $f(x)$ is nonnegative and continuous for $a \le x \le b$. Divide the interval $a \le x \le b$ into n parts by using partition points $a = x_0 < x_1 < x_2 < \cdots < x_{n-1} < x_n = b$, and erect ordinates at these partition points. The region is thus divided into n parts; the first subregion is bounded on the right by x_1, the second by x_2, and so on. See Fig. 2.11(a), where an $n = 8$ case is pictured.

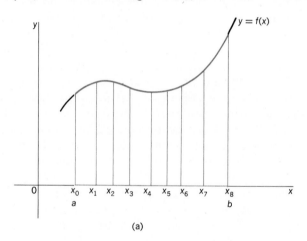

(a)

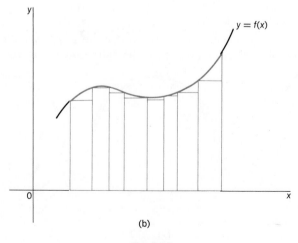

(b)

Fig. 2.11

In each subregion there is a minimum value for $y = f(x)$ and a maximum value. It will often happen that the minimum ordinate for a subregion occurs at one of the end points, but this need not always be the case. Now approximate to the area of each subregion by taking the area of the rectangle which has the same base as the subregion and height equal to the minimum height for that subregion; see Fig. 2.11(b). If we add up the areas of the approximating rectangles, we have an approximation for the area of the region.

This approximation is too small, to be sure, but it can be improved upon by taking more partition points and forming new approximating rectangles. Fig. 2.12 shows in detail a typical subregion of Fig. 2.11(b) and points out graphically how a new partition, which divides this subregion into two new subregions, will improve on the first partition. The shaded region was not taken into account in the first approximation process, but it was

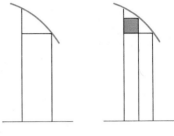

Fig. 2.12

in the second. It seems intuitively clear that we can compute the area as the limit approached by the sum of the areas of the "minimum height rectangles" as the number of rectangles increases, the maximum rectangle width approaching 0.

If the maximum ordinate in each subregion were used instead of the minimum, the approximating rectangles would be too large; however, as more and more rectangles were taken, the error in the area estimate would be reduced. The area might also be computed as the limit approached by the sum of the areas of the maximum height rectangles as the number of rectangles increases, the maximum rectangle width approaching 0.

Next, we shall rewrite these ideas in more concise language. Let the minimum ordinate in the kth subregion be called m_k, and let it occur at x'_k; thus $m_k = f(x'_k)$.*
Let the maximum ordinate be M_k, and let it occur at x''_k; thus $M_k = f(x''_k)$.
Let the width of the kth subregion be $(\Delta x)_k$. Then the area of the kth approximating rectangle is

$$m_k(\Delta x)_k = f(x'_k)(\Delta x)_k \qquad \text{or} \qquad M_k(\Delta x)_k = f(x''_k)(\Delta x)_k,$$

according as we take the minimum or maximum case. The sums of the areas of these rectangles are

$$f(x'_1)(\Delta x)_1 + f(x'_2)(\Delta x)_2 + \cdots + f(x'_n)(\Delta x)_n = \sum_{k=1}^{n} f(x'_k)(\Delta x)_k$$

or $\qquad f(x''_1)(\Delta x)_1 + f(x''_2)(\Delta x)_2 + \cdots + f(x''_n)(\Delta x)_n = \sum_{k=1}^{n} f(x''_k)(\Delta x)_k.$†

---

* In the first subregion of Fig. 2.11(a), for instance, we have $m_1 = f(x_0) = y_0$; in the last subregion we have $m_8 = f(x_7) = y_7$; in the third subregion we have $m_3 = f(x_3) = y_3$.

† The summation notation used here is perhaps new to the reader. The symbol $\sum_{k=q}^{n}$ is used to instruct the reader to take a sum of terms, each one of the form indicated after the $\sum$ symbol, with k replaced in turn by $q, q+1, q+2, \cdots, n-1, n$. To illustrate, $\sum_{k=1}^{5} k = 1 + 2 + 3 + 4 + 5$; $\sum_{k=1}^{6} k/(k+1) = \frac{1}{2} + \frac{2}{3} + \frac{3}{4} + \frac{4}{5} + \frac{5}{6} + \frac{6}{7}$; $\sum_{j=2}^{4} 7j^2 = 7(2)^2 + 7(3)^2 + 7(4)^2$; and $\sum_{k=1}^{n} A_k = A_1 + A_2 + A_3 + \cdots + A_n$.

The suggested definitions for the area of the whole region are, then,

$$\lim_{n\to\infty} \sum_{k=1}^{n} f(x_k')(\Delta x)_k \quad \text{and} \quad \lim_{n\to\infty} \sum_{k=1}^{n} f(x_k'')(\Delta x)_k,$$

it being understood that the length of the largest of the $(\Delta x)_k$'s approaches 0 as n grows beyond all bounds.

To go the least bit further, if we are led to the same area number when we use minimum ordinates and when we use maximum ordinates, then surely we would arrive at the same area number if in each subregion we used an ordinate of intermediate height. Let x_k^* be any point of the kth subinterval. Then $m_k \le f(x_k^*) \le M_k$ and we could also take for our computation of area

$$\lim_{n\to\infty} \sum_{k=1}^{n} f(x_k^*)(\Delta x)_k,$$

it being understood that the largest of the $(\Delta x)_k$'s approaches 0 as n grows beyond all bounds.

■ NOTATION CONVENTION 1

The definite integral. The symbol $\int_{x=a}^{b} f(x)\, dx$, $b > a$, stands for the number arrived at in the following way:

(a) Divide the interval $a \le x \le b$ into n subintervals, the kth subinterval of length $(\Delta x)_k$.

(b) Let x_k^* be any point in the kth subinterval.

(c) Form the sum

$$f(x_1^*)(\Delta x)_1 + f(x_2^*)(\Delta x)_2 + \cdots + f(x_n^*)(\Delta x)_n = \sum_{k=1}^{n} f(x_k^*)(\Delta x)_k.$$

(d) Take the limit of this sum as n grows beyond all bounds and the largest of the $(\Delta x)_k$'s approaches 0.

$$\int_{x=a}^{b} f(x)\, dx = \lim_{n\to\infty} \sum_{k=1}^{n} f(x_k^*)(\Delta x)_k.$$

● Remark 1

This notation is meaningful only if the limit required exists and has the same value no matter which set of subintervals is chosen and no matter how the points x_k^* are chosen in the various subintervals.

● Remark 2

For the expression $\int_{x=a}^{b} f(x)\, dx$ we read "the integral of $f(x)\, dx$ from $x = a$ to $x = b$." The integral symbol, $\int$, is a modified capital letter S, printed in a style common several centuries ago, the letter S being chosen because it is the first letter of the word "sum." The word "integration" itself carries with it the connotation of summing up, of putting together parts. When no ambiguity can result we shall often write

$$\int_{a}^{b} f(x)dx \quad \text{for} \quad \int_{x=a}^{b} f(x)\, dx.$$

With this new notation, we can state concisely the area definition we have been seeking.

■ DEFINITION 2

Let $f(x)$ be nonnegative and continuous for $a \leq x \leq b$. The area of the region bounded by $y = f(x)$, $x = a$, $x = b$ and the x axis shall be $\int_{x=a}^{b} f(x)\, dx$.

● Remark 3

Observe that our agreement on definite integral notation is more general than would be needed for our present area definition alone because Notation Convention 1 does not restrict $f(x)$ to be nonnegative or even continuous. The definite integral does exist when $f(x)$ is continuous for $a \leq x \leq b$, whether $f(x)$ is nonnegative for $a \leq x \leq b$ or not. This is a point we shall discuss in some detail in Chapter 7. The definite integral exists also even when certain kinds of discontinuities are allowed, but that is a matter beyond the scope of this textbook.

● Remark 4

Observe also that Definition 2 summarizes a discussion that was consistent with the basic requirements agreed on for all area definitions at the beginning of Sec. 2.3 and with the rectangle area definition. To illustrate in some detail, when we say that the area of the first subregion is at least as large as $m_1(\Delta x)_1$ we really quote Assumption (a) when we say that the area of the part of the first subregion not in the first rectangle of Fig. 2.11(b) is a nonnegative number, then we quote Assumption (c) when we say that the difference between the areas of the first subregion and the first rectangle is this nonnegative number just discussed, and finally we quote Definition 2.3-1 when we say that the area of the first rectangle is $m_1(\Delta x)_1$.

It is not surprising then to find that the definition of area furnished by Definition 2 is itself consistent with the basic requirements for area definitions. This will be discussed in Sec. 2.6.

● Remark 5

Notice that the value of $\int_{x=a}^{b} f(x)\, dx$ does not depend on the fact that we used the letter x to describe our independent variable. Had we used $\int_{t=a}^{b} f(t)\, dt$ the value would have been the same, for the steps taken in forming one integral are numerically identical with those taken in forming the other. In other words, our area definition has the following intuitively necessary property: The same area number is assigned to the region of the ty plane bounded by $y = f(t)$, $t = a$, $t = b$, and the t axis as to the region of the xy plane bounded by $y = f(x)$, $x = a$, $x = b$, and the x axis.

Example 1A. Consider again the area bounded by the x axis, $y = f(x) = 2x - 1$, $x = 1$, and $x = 4$ (Example 2.3-1). We know that the area is 12, but let us illustrate the ideas of this section.

(a) Break the interval $1 \leq x \leq 4$ into 15 equal parts by using partition points $x_0 = 1$, $x_1 = 1.2$, $x_2 = 1.4$, $x_3 = 1.6, \cdots, x_{14} = 3.8$, $x_{15} = 4$. It is not necessary for us to use equal subintervals but the computation will be easier if we do.

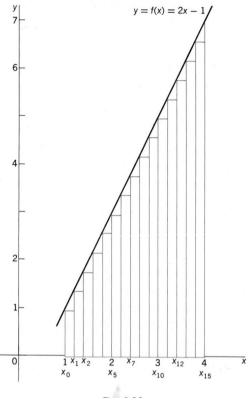

Fig. 2.13

(b) Break the region studied into 15 parts as in Fig. 2.13 by erecting ordinates at the partition points. For this particular graph, the minimum ordinate for each subregion will be the left ordinate. Draw the rectangles whose heights are these minimum ordinates.

(c) In Table 2.1 we compute a "lower approximation" to the area we seek by adding up the areas of the 15 rectangles. We get 11.40.

Example 1B. To repeat the same approximation process with 30 subdivisions, 60 subdivisions, and so on, would be quite tedious. Let us repeat the work using n subdivisions.

(a) Break the interval $1 \le x \le 4$ into n equal subintervals by using partition points $x_0 = 1$, $x_1 = 1 + \Delta x$, $x_2 = 1 + 2 \Delta x$, $x_3 = 1 + 3 \Delta x, \cdots$, $x_n = 1 + n \Delta x = 4$, where $\Delta x = 3/n$.

(b) Erect ordinates at the partition points. Again, the minimum ordinate for each subregion occurs at the left end. Thus $m_1 = f(x_0) = f(1) = 1$; $m_2 = f(x_1) = f(1 + \Delta x) = 2(1 + \Delta x) - 1 = 1 + 2 \Delta x$; $m_3 = f(x_2) = f(1 + 2 \Delta x) = 2(1 + 2 \Delta x) - 1 = 1 + 4 \Delta x$; and so forth. Imagine drawn the rectangles of base Δx whose heights are the minimum ordinates.

TABLE 2.1

Rectangle	Base	Height	Area
1	.2	$f(1) = 1$	.20
2	.2	$f(1.2) = 1.4$	.28
3	.2	1.8	.36
4	.2	2.2	.44
5	.2	2.6	.52
6	.2	$f(2) = 3$	.60
7	.2	3.4	.68
8	.2	3.8	.76
9	.2	4.2	.84
10	.2	4.6	.92
11	.2	$f(3) = 5$	1.00
12	.2	5.4	1.08
13	.2	5.8	1.16
14	.2	6.2	1.24
15	.2	6.6	1.32
Total			11.40

(c) The areas of the various rectangles are given in Table 2.2. Summing up the areas of the n rectangles, we find that

$$\text{lower approximation} = \left[\begin{array}{l} 1 + (1 + 2\,\Delta x) + (1 + 4\,\Delta x) \\ \quad + (1 + 6\,\Delta x) + \cdots \\ \quad\quad + (1 + \{2n - 2\}\,\Delta x) \end{array} \right] \Delta x. \qquad (1)$$

TABLE 2.2

Rectangle	Base	Height	Area
1	Δx	$f(x_0) = f(1) = 1$	$1\Delta x$
2	Δx	$f(x_1) = f(1 + \Delta x) = 1 + 2\,\Delta x$	$(1 + 2\Delta x)\,\Delta x$
3	Δx	$f(x_2) = f(1 + 2\,\Delta x) = 1 + 4\,\Delta x$	$(1 + 4\Delta x)\,\Delta x$
4	Δx	$f(x_3) = f(1 + 3\,\Delta x) = 1 + 6\,\Delta x$	$(1 + 6\Delta x)\,\Delta x$
.	.	.	.
k	Δx	$f(x_{k-1}) = 1 + (2k - 2)\,\Delta x$	$[1 + (2k - 2)\,\Delta x]\,\Delta x$
.	.	.	.
n	Δx	$f(x_{n-1}) = 1 + (2n - 2)\,\Delta x$	$[1 + (2n - 2)\,\Delta x]\,\Delta x$

Here we have taken out the common factor Δx as we added. In the sum notation Eq. (1) would read

$$\text{lower approximation} = \sum_{k=1}^{n} f(x'_k)\,\Delta x = \sum_{k=1}^{n} [1 + (2k - 2)\,\Delta x]\,\Delta x. \qquad (2)$$

It happens that the expression appearing in the square brackets of Eq. (1) is an arithmetic progression.* We can rewrite it as follows:

$$[1 + (1 + 2\,\Delta x) + (1 + 4\,\Delta x) + (1 + 6\,\Delta x) + \cdots + (1 + \{2n - 2\}\,\Delta x)]$$
$$= n(1) + 2\,\Delta x + 4\,\Delta x + 6\,\Delta x + \cdots + (2n - 2)\,\Delta x$$
$$= n + 2\,\Delta x[1 + 2 + \cdots + (n - 1)]$$
$$= n + 2\,\Delta x\,\frac{(n - 1)n}{2}$$
$$= n + n(n - 1)\,\Delta x.$$

Return now to Eq. (1). We see that

$$\text{lower approximation} = [n + n(n - 1)\,\Delta x]\,\Delta x. \tag{3}$$

Since $\Delta x = 3/n$, Eq. (3) becomes

$$\text{lower approximation} = \left[n + n(n - 1)\,\frac{3}{n}\right]\frac{3}{n} = [n + 3n - 3]\,\frac{3}{n} = 12 - \frac{9}{n}. \tag{4}$$

As a check on Eq. (4), refer to Example 1A. There we considered the specific case $n = 15$ and found that the lower approximation was 11.40 $(= 12 - \tfrac{9}{15})$. What would happen now if we increased the number of partition points? It is intuitively clear that

$$\text{area} = \int_1^4 f(x)\,dx = \lim_{n \to \infty} \sum_{k=1}^{n} f(x_k')\,\Delta x = \lim_{n \to \infty}\left[12 - \frac{9}{n}\right] = 12. \tag{5}$$

---

* The reader is probably familiar with the formulas for arithmetic progressions. If not, the formula

$$1 + 2 + 3 + \cdots + (t - 1) + t = \frac{t(t + 1)}{2}$$

can be demonstrated by induction. [In the text we shall use the case $t = (n - 1)$.]

(a) It is clear that the formula holds for the special cases $t = 1$, $t = 2$, $t = 3$. We need merely verifty that

$$1 = \frac{1(1 + 1)}{2}, \qquad 1 + 2 = \frac{2(2 + 1)}{2}, \qquad 1 + 2 + 3 = \frac{3(3 + 1)}{2}.$$

(b) Suppose the formula has already been demonstrated for the case $t = q$; thus we are supposing that

$$1 + 2 + 3 + \cdots + q = \frac{q(q + 1)}{2}.$$

Will the formula hold for $t = q + 1$ as well? Direct computation shows that it will. For we have

$$1 + 2 + 3 + \cdots + q + (q + 1) = [1 + 2 + 3 + \cdots + q] + (q + 1)$$
$$= \left[\frac{q(q + 1)}{2}\right] + (q + 1) = (q + 1)\left(\frac{q}{2} + 1\right)$$
$$= \frac{(q + 1)(q + 2)}{2}.$$

Substitution of $(q + 1)$ for t in the formula shows that this result is precisely the one the formula states. Thus we know that if the formula can be demonstrated for any one case, $t = q$, it holds for the next case, $t = q + 1$, also.

(c) We know that the formula holds for cases $t = 1, 2, 3$ by direct computation in (a). Because it holds for the case $t = 3$, it holds for the case $t = 4$ by (b). Because it now holds for the case $t = 4$, it holds for the case $t = 5$. Because it holds for the case $t = 5$, it holds for the case $t = 6$, and so on to any positive integer t desired.

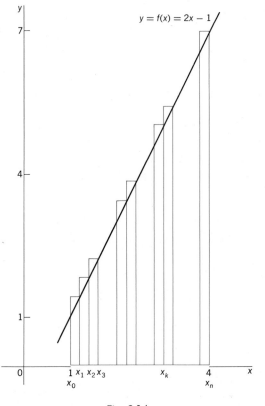

Fig. 2.14

Example 1C. The same approximation process will be repeated here, but this time the maximum ordinates in the various subdivisions, rather than the minimum ordinates, will be used and "upper approximations" will be determined.

(a) As before, break the interval $1 \leq x \leq 4$ into n equal subintervals by using partition points $x_0 = 1$, $x_1 = 1 + \Delta x$, $x_2 = 1 + 2 \Delta x, \cdots$, $x_k = 1 + k \Delta x$, $\cdots, x_n = 1 + n \Delta x$, where $\Delta x = 3/n$.

(b) Erect ordinates at the partition points. This time, the maximum ordinate for each subregion occurs at the right end of that subregion. Thus $M_1 = f(x_1)$ $= f(1 + \Delta x) = 2(1 + \Delta x) - 1 = 1 + 2 \Delta x$; $M_2 = f(x_2) = f(1 + 2 \Delta x) = 2(1 + 2 \Delta x) - 1 = 1 + 4 \Delta x, \cdots$; $M_k = f(x_k) = f(1 + k \Delta x) = 1 + 2k \Delta x$. Draw the rectangles of base Δx whose heights are these maximum ordinates. See Fig. 2.14.

(c) The areas of the various rectangles are given in Table 2.3. Summing up the areas of the n rectangles, we find that

$$\text{upper approximation} = \left[\begin{array}{c} (1 + 2 \Delta x) + (1 + 4 \Delta x) \\ + (1 + 6 \Delta x) + \cdots \\ + (1 + 2n \Delta x) \end{array} \right] \Delta x. \qquad (6)$$

TABLE 2.3

Rectangle	Base	Height	Area
1	Δx	$f(x_1) = f(1 + 1\,\Delta x) = 1 + 2\,\Delta x$	$(1 + 2\,\Delta x)\,\Delta x$
2	Δx	$f(x_2) = f(1 + 2\,\Delta x) = 1 + 4\,\Delta x$	$(1 + 4\,\Delta x)\,\Delta x$
3	Δx	$f(x_3) = f(1 + 3\,\Delta x) = 1 + 6\,\Delta x$	$(1 + 6\,\Delta x)\,\Delta x$
.		.	.
k	Δx	$f(x_k) = f(1 + k\,\Delta x) = 1 + 2k\,\Delta x$	$(1 + 2k\,\Delta x)\,\Delta x$
.		.	.
n	Δx	$f(x_n) = f(1 + n\,\Delta x) = 1 + 2n\,\Delta x$	$(1 + 2n\,\Delta x)\,\Delta x$

In sum notation, Eq. (6) could be written

$$\text{upper approximation} = \sum_{k=1}^{n} f(x_k'')\,\Delta x = \sum_{k=1}^{n} (1 + 2k\,\Delta x)\,\Delta x. \qquad (7)$$

Aagin, we deal in Eq. (6) with an arithmetic progression. We have

$$(1 + 2\,\Delta x) + (1 + 4\,\Delta x) + (1 + 6\,\Delta x) + \cdots + (1 + 2n\,\Delta x)$$
$$= n(1) + 2\,\Delta x + 4\,\Delta x + 6\,\Delta x + \cdots + 2n\,\Delta x$$
$$= n + 2\,\Delta x(1 + 2 + 3 + \cdots + n)$$
$$= n + 2\,\Delta x\,\frac{n(n + 1)}{2},*$$

and thus

$$\text{upper approximation} = [n + n(n + 1)\,\Delta x]\,\Delta x. \qquad (8)$$

Since $\Delta x = 3/n$, Eq. (8) becomes

$$\text{upper approximation} = \left[n + n(n + 1)\,\frac{3}{n}\right]\frac{3}{n} = [4n + 3]\,\frac{3}{n} = 12 + \frac{9}{n}. \qquad (9)$$

Now it is intuitively clear that, if the number of subdivision points is increased,

$$\text{area} = \int_{1}^{4} f(x)\,dx = \lim_{n \to \infty} \sum_{k=1}^{n} f(x_k'')\,\Delta x = \lim_{n \to \infty}\left(12 + \frac{9}{n}\right) = 12. \qquad (10)$$

In Example 1B a minimum ordinate was used in each subregion. The use of a maximum ordinate in Example 1C resulted in the same number, 12, for the limit computation. For this region, we are now sure that, if we use subintervals of equal length, the same number for the limit is obtained no matter which set of ordinates is chosen for the various subregions, whether of maximum, minimum, or intermediate height.

Example 2. Find the area of the region bounded by $y = f(x) = x^2$, the x axis, and $x = 1$. See Fig. 2.15.

(a) Break the interval $0 \le x \le 1$ into n equal subintervals by choosing partition points $x_0 = 0$, $x_1 = 1\,\Delta x$, $x_2 = 2\Delta x, \cdots, x_{n-1} = (n - 1)\,\Delta x$, $x_n = n\,\Delta x = 1$, where $\Delta x = 1/n$.

(b) For each subinterval the minimum ordinate will occur at the left end. Consider the rectangles with base Δx and heights equal to these minimum ordinates.

---

* Substitute n for t in the formula of the preceding footnote.

(c) The sum of the areas of these rectangles will be

$$\text{lower approximation} = \sum_{k=1}^{n} f(x'_k)\, \Delta x = \sum_{k=1}^{n} f(x_{k-1})\, \Delta x$$
$$= f(x_0)\, \Delta x + f(x_1)\, \Delta x + f(x_2)\, \Delta x + f(x_3)\, \Delta x + \cdots + f(x_{n-1})\, \Delta x$$
$$= 0^2\, \Delta x + (1\, \Delta x)^2\, \Delta x + (2\, \Delta x)^2\, \Delta x + (3\, \Delta x)^2\, \Delta x + \cdots + ([n-1]\, \Delta x)^2\, \Delta x$$
$$= [1^2 + 2^2 + 3^2 + \cdots + (n-1)^2]\, \Delta x^3. \tag{11a}$$

Since the formula

$$1^2 + 2^2 + 3^2 + 4^2 + \cdots + t^2 = \frac{t(t+1)(2t+1)}{6} \tag{12}$$

can be demonstrated by mathematical induction,* we can continue the computa-

---

* To prove this formula by induction: (a) Observe that it holds for the cases $t = 1, 2, 3$ by direct observation. For instance, for $t = 3$ we have

$$1^2 + 2^2 + 3^2 = \frac{3(4)(7)}{6} \qquad \text{or} \qquad 1 + 4 + 9 = 14.$$

(b) Observe that, if the formula has been demonstrated somehow for $t = q$, so that

$$1^2 + 2^2 + 3^2 + \cdots + q^2 = \frac{q(q+1)(2q+1)}{6},$$

then it is valid for $t = q + 1$ also. For we have

$$1^2 + 2^2 + 3^2 + \cdots + (q+1)^2 = [1^2 + 2^2 + 3^2 + \cdots + q^2] + (q+1)^2$$
$$= \frac{q(q+1)(2q+1)}{6} + (q+1)^2 = \frac{q+1}{6}[q(2q+1) + 6(q+1)]$$
$$= \frac{q+1}{6}[2q^2 + 7q + 6] = \frac{(q+1)(q+2)(2q+3)}{6},$$

and this is what the formula states for $t = q + 1$.

(c) Step (b) tells us that the formula holds for $t = 4$ because it held for $t = 3$. The repetition of the application of Step (b) shows that the formula holds for $t = 5$ because it held for $t = 4$. Continuing in this way, we can show eventually that the formula holds for any integer t one might name.

The formula can be proved in a second way, which will only be sketched here. First,

$$\sum_{k=1}^{t} [(k+1)^3 - k^3] = [2^3 - 1^3] + [3^3 - 2^3] + [4^3 - 3^3]$$
$$+ \cdots + [(t+1)^3 - t^3] = (t+1)^3 - 1^3.$$

On the other hand, we also have

$$\sum_{k=1}^{t} [(k+1)^3 - k^3] = \sum_{k=1}^{t} (3k^2 + 3k + 1) = 3\sum_{k=1}^{t} k^2 + 3\sum_{k=1}^{t} k + t.$$

Combining these results, and using the fact that

$$\sum_{k=1}^{t} k = \frac{t(t+1)}{2},$$

which we derived in an earlier footnote, we have

$$3\sum_{k=1}^{t} k^2 + 3\sum_{k=1}^{t} k + t = (t+1)^3 - 1,$$

$$3\sum_{k=1}^{t} k^2 = (t+1)^3 - 1 - \frac{3t(t+1)}{2} - t,$$

$$\sum_{k=1}^{t} k^2 = \frac{t(t+1)(2t+1)}{6}.$$

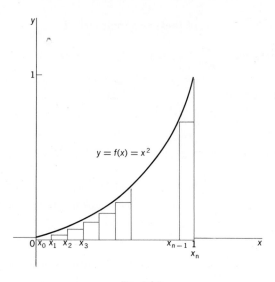

Fig. 2.15

tion of Eq. (11a), substituting $(n - 1)$ for t and obtaining

$$\text{lower approximation} = \frac{(n - 1)n(2n - 1)}{6} \Delta x^3. \qquad (11b)$$

Finally, since $\Delta x = 1/n$, we have

$$\text{lower approximation} = \frac{(n - 1)n(2n - 1)}{6} \frac{1}{n^3}$$

$$= \frac{2n^3 - 3n^2 + n}{6n^3} = \frac{1}{3} - \frac{1}{2}\frac{1}{n} + \frac{1}{6}\frac{1}{n^2}. \qquad (11c)$$

Now, if we increase the number of partition points, we conclude that the

$$\text{area} = \int_0^1 f(x)\, dx = \lim_{n \to \infty} \sum_{k=1}^n f(x'_k)\, \Delta x = \lim_{n \to \infty} \left(\frac{1}{3} - \frac{1}{2}\frac{1}{n} + \frac{1}{6}\frac{1}{n^2}\right) = \frac{1}{3}. \qquad (13)$$

The reader can check this result by using the method of Sec. 2.3 to find the same area.

Example 3. Using 10 subintervals, find lower and upper approximations for the area of the region bounded by $y = f(x) = 1/x$, the x axis, and the ordinates $x = 1$ and $x = 2$. See Fig. 2.16. Note first that we cannot yet find this area by using the antidifferentiation technique, because we do not yet know a function whose derivative is $1/x$.

Let us write this computation out systematically in Table 2.4. In

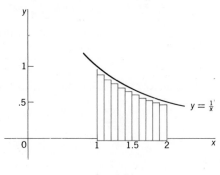

Fig. 2.16

TABLE 2.4

Base of Rectangle	Length of Base	Minimum Ordinate	Area	Maximum Ordinate	Area
$1 \to 1.1$	.1	$1/1.1 = .909$	.0909	$1/1 = 1.000$	.1000
$1.1 \to 1.2$	.1	$1/1.2 = .833$	.0833	$1/1.1 = .909$	.0909
$1.2 \to 1.3$	.1	.769	.0769	$1/1.2 = .833$	.0833
$1.3 \to 1.4$	.1	.714	.0714	.769	.0769
$1.4 \to 1.5$	.1	.667	.0667	.714	.0714
$1.5 \to 1.6$	.1	.625	.0625	.667	.0667
$1.6 \to 1.7$	.1	.588	.0588	.625	.0625
$1.7 \to 1.8$	.1	.556	.0556	.588	.0588
$1.8 \to 1.9$	.1	.526	.0526	.556	.0556
$1.9 \to 2.0$	.1	$\tfrac{1}{2} = .500$	.0500	.526	.0526
Total			.6687		.7187

the third column we notice that the minimum ordinates occur at the right ends of the intervals, and we round off the $f(x_k')$ computations at three decimal places. From the fourth column we see that

$$\text{lower approximation} = \sum_{k=1}^{10} f(x_k')\, \Delta x = .6687. \tag{14a}$$

In the fifth column we notice that the maximum ordinates occur at the left ends of the intervals. From the sixth column,

$$\text{upper approximation} = \sum_{k=1}^{10} f(x_k'')\, \Delta x = .7187. \tag{14b}$$

Hence, we can conclude that

$$.6687 < \text{area} < .7187. \tag{15}$$

Actually, after studying Chapter 5 the reader will be able to show that the area, correct to four decimal places, is .6931.

● **Remark 6**

In the illustrative examples of this section we subdivided intervals into subintervals of equal length for the sake of simplicity and assumed that other subdivision methods would not have led to different results. We shall continue to do this in this chapter. In Chapter 7 there is an exercise in which subintervals of unequal lengths are considered.

EXERCISES 2.4

1. Return to Example 2 of this section and find the area bounded by $y = x^2$, the x axis, and $x = 1$ by using upper approximations to the area.

2. Read the footnotes of this section and prove that

$$\sum_{k=1}^{t} k^3 = 1^3 + 2^3 + 3^3 + \cdots + t^3 = \frac{t^2(t+1)^2}{4}.$$

3. Assume the truth of the formula stated in Exercise 2. Work directly from the definition of the definite integral to find the area bounded by $y = x^3$, the x axis, and $x = 2$, or $\int_0^2 x^3 \, dx$.

4. Use the idea of approximation to an area by rectangles to find the area bounded by $y = 3x - 2$ from $x = 2$ to $x = 4$.

5. Evaluate $\int_0^1 (1 - x^2) \, dx$ directly from the definition stated in this section. Describe a region with base on the x axis whose area this integral can be said to represent.

6. Use a table for $y = \sin x$ where x is given in radians. Using 5 equal subintervals, find lower and upper approximations for the area of the smaller region bounded by $y = f(x) = \sin x$, the x axis, and $x = .20$.

7. Use a table for $y = \cos x$ where x is given in radians. Using 5 equal subintervals, find lower and upper approximations for the area of the region bounded by $y = f(x) = \cos x$, the x axis, $x = .10$ and $x = .30$.

8. Using 8 equal subintervals, find upper and lower approximations for the area of the region bounded by the normal probability curve, the x axis, $x = 0$, and $x = .40$. Some information about the normal probability curve, a continuous curve which decreases steadily for $x \geq 0$, is given in the following table:

x	.00	.05	.10	.15	.20	.25	.30	.35	.40
$F(x)$	.399	.398	.397	.394	.391	.387	.381	.375	.368

9. (a) Write down the limit of a sum equivalent to $\int_1^2 \log x \, dx$. (b) Describe a region with base on the x axis whose area this integral can be said to represent.

10. Repeat Exercise 9 for $\displaystyle\int_{-2}^{3} \frac{1}{1 + x^2} \, dx$.

2.5 Distance in Rectilinear Motion as a Limit of a Sum

It has just been pointed out that an area problem of fairly general scope can be studied either as an antidifferentiation problem or as an integration problem. Sec. 2.2 showed that the distance traveled by a particle in rectilinear motion could be computed by the antidifferentiation technique. Here it will be shown that this distance problem can also be studied from the integration point of view. For a second time, the same problem can be treated either from the antidifferentiation point of view or from the integration point of view.

Example 1.   If the velocity of a freely falling particle is given by the formula $v = f(t) = 32t$, find the distance traveled by the particle from the time $t = 1$ to the time $t = 3$.

Step (a): Let us start by dividing the given time interval into n equal subintervals, using partition points $t_0 = 1$, $t_1 = 1 + 1 \, \Delta t$, $t_2 = 1 + 2 \, \Delta t$, $t_3 = 1 + 3\Delta t$, $\cdots$, $t_n = 1 + n \, \Delta t = 3$, where

$$\Delta t = \frac{3 - 1}{n} = \frac{2}{n}.$$

See Fig. 2.17.

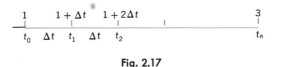

Fig. 2.17

Step (b): Inspection of the velocity formula shows that the velocity increases steadily with time, and that therefore the minimum velocity for a subinterval will be achieved at the beginning of that interval, the maximum velocity at the end of that interval. For the first subinterval, for instance, the minimum velocity is $f(t_1') = f(1) = 32$; the maximum velocity is $f(t_1'') = f(1 + 1\,\Delta t) = 32(1 + \Delta t)$. For the second subinterval, the minimum and maximum velocities are $f(t_2') = 32(1 + 1\,\Delta t)$ and $f(t_2'') = 32(1 + 2\,\Delta t)$. For the kth subinterval, the minimum and maximum velocities will be respectively $f(t_k') = f(1 + [k-1]\,\Delta t) = 32(1 + [k-1]\Delta t)$ and $f(t_k'') = f(1 + k\,\Delta t) = 32(1 + k\,\Delta t)$.

Step (c): The distance actually traveled by the particle during a subinterval will be the product of its average velocity for that subinterval and the time required for that subinterval; $\Delta s = (\Delta s/\Delta t)\Delta t$. We can say that

$$f(t_k') = \text{min velocity} \leq \text{average velocity} \leq \text{max velocity} = f(t_k'') \qquad (1)$$

and hence

$$f(t_k')\,\Delta t \leq \text{distance traveled during subinterval} = (\Delta s)_k \leq f(t_k'')\,\Delta t. \qquad (2)$$

If we add up for the various subintervals, we will find that

$$\text{lower approximation} = \sum_{k=1}^{n} f(t_k')\,\Delta t$$

$$\leq \text{total distance traveled} \leq \sum_{k=1}^{n} f(t_k'')\,\Delta t$$

$$= \text{upper approximation.} \qquad (3)$$

Step (d): For the lower approximation computation we have

$$\text{lower approximation} = \sum_{k=1}^{n} f(t_k')\,\Delta t = 32\,\Delta t + 32(1 + \Delta t)\,\Delta t$$
$$+ 32(1 + 2\,\Delta t)\,\Delta t + \cdots + 32(1 + [n-1]\,\Delta t)\,\Delta t$$
$$= 32\,\Delta t[1 + (1 + \Delta t) + (1 + 2\,\Delta t) + \cdots + (1 + [n-1]\,\Delta t)]$$
$$= 32\,\Delta t[n(1) + 1\,\Delta t + 2\,\Delta t + \cdots + (n-1)\,\Delta t]$$
$$= 32\,\Delta t[n + \Delta t(1 + 2 + \cdots + [n-1])]$$
$$= 32\,\Delta t\left[n + \Delta t\,\frac{(n-1)n}{2}\right]. \qquad (4a)$$

Here we have used a formula for an arithmetic progression already discussed in the last section. If we note further that $\Delta t = 2/n$, we get

$$\text{lower approximation} = 32\left(\frac{2}{n}\right)\left[n + \frac{2}{n}\,\frac{(n-1)(n)}{2}\right]$$
$$= 32\left(\frac{2}{n}\right)(2n - 1) = 32\left(4 - \frac{2}{n}\right). \qquad (4b)$$

Step (e): Similarly, for the upper approximation computation we have

$$\text{upper approximation} = \sum_{k=1}^{n} f(t_k'') \, \Delta t = 32(1 + \Delta t) \, \Delta t + 32(1 + 2 \, \Delta t) \, \Delta t$$
$$+ 32(1 + 3 \, \Delta t) \, \Delta t + \cdots + 32(1 + n \, \Delta t) \, \Delta t$$
$$= 32 \, \Delta t [(1 + \Delta t) + (1 + 2 \, \Delta t) + (1 + 3 \, \Delta t) + \cdots + (1 + n \, \Delta t)]$$
$$= 32 \, \Delta t [n(1) + \Delta t (1 + 2 + 3 + \cdots + n)] = 32 \, \Delta t \left[n + \Delta t \, \frac{n(n + 1)}{2} \right]$$
$$= 32 \left(\frac{2}{n} \right) \left[n + \frac{2}{n} \frac{n(n + 1)}{2} \right] = 32 \left(\frac{2}{n} \right) (2n + 1) = 32 \left(4 + \frac{2}{n} \right). \tag{4c}$$

Step (f): Finally, the shorter the subinterval, the smaller the difference between the maximum and minimum velocities and the better each one of them approximates the average velocity for the subinterval. Hence we would expect to get better and better lower and upper approximations to the distance traveled if we repeat these computations with larger and larger values for n. In fact,

$$\lim_{n \to \infty} \sum_{k=1}^{n} f(t_k') \, \Delta t = \lim_{n \to \infty} 32 \left(4 - \frac{2}{n} \right) = 128, \tag{5a}$$

and

$$\lim_{n \to \infty} \sum_{k=1}^{n} f(t_k'') \, \Delta t = \lim_{n \to \infty} 32 \left(4 + \frac{2}{n} \right) = 128. \tag{5b}$$

From this we conclude that

$$\text{distance traveled} = \int_{t=1}^{3} f(t) \, dt = 128. \tag{6}$$

The student should check this result by computing from the antidifferentiation point of view also.

We repeat our procedure in a case more general than the case $v = f(t) = 32t$ just discussed. Let us find the distance traveled from time $t = a$ to time $t = b$ by a particle whose velocity is given by $v = f(t)$. First, divide the time interval $t = a$ to $t = b$ into n subintervals, $(\Delta t)_k$ being the length of the kth subinterval. Second, in each subinterval select the minimum and maximum velocities. In the kth interval we shall say that the minimum velocity is achieved at $t = t_k'$, the maximum at $t = t_k''$; thus these velocities are $f(t_k')$ and $f(t_k'')$. Third, the distance traveled in each subinterval, $(\Delta s)_k$, will satisfy the inequalities

$$f(t_k')(\Delta t)_k \leq (\Delta s)_k \leq f(t_k'')(\Delta t)_k. \tag{7}$$

Fourth, the total distance traveled, which we seek, will then satisfy the inequalities

$$\sum_{k=1}^{n} f(t_k')(\Delta t)_k \leq \text{distance traveled} \leq \sum_{k=1}^{n} f(t_k'')(\Delta t)_k. \tag{8}$$

Fifth, in Eq. (8) we already have upper and lower approximations for the distance traveled. For shorter time subintervals, the difference between the maximum and minimum velocities will be smaller. If it should happen that the upper and lower approximations approach the same limit as the number of time subintervals grows beyond all bounds, the longest subinterval approaching 0, then we could take this common limit as the distance traveled. In Chapter 7 we shall show that there will be a common limit for these upper and lower approximations if the $f(t)$ with which we start is continuous for the interval $t = a$ to $t = b$.

Lastly, if it turns out that the sums appearing in Eq. (8) have a common limit, then it will follow that any computation that replaced these minimum or maximum velocities by velocities which were intermediate between them would also approach the same limit. If $t = t_k^*$ is any t of the kth subinterval, we shall surely have $f(t_k')$ $\leq f(t_k^*) \leq f(t_k'')$, and hence also:

■ **THEOREM 1**

HYPOTHESIS: The velocity of a particle, $v = f(t)$, is continuous for $a \leq t \leq b$.

CONCLUSION: The distance traveled from $t = a$ to $t = b$ is given by $\int_{t=a}^{b} f(t)dt$.

● **Remark 1**

Observe that the hypothesis of this theorem does not require that $f(t)$ be non-negative. If $f(t_k^*)$ is negative, then the velocity for the kth subinterval is taken as negative and the numerical contribution to the distance sum for the kth subinterval, namely $f(t_k^*) (\Delta t)_k$, will be negative and will represent a displacement in the negative direction rather than the positive direction. The integral $\int_{t=a}^{b} f(t) \, dt$ really gives us the net displacement from $t = a$ to $t = b$.

Example 2. A particle that moves on a straight line with velocity v $= 3 \sin 2t$ performs a periodic motion. For $0 \leq t \leq \pi/2 \approx 1.5708$, we have $v \geq 0$, and the particle moves in the positive direction, to the right. We have $v \leq 0$ for $\pi/2 \leq t \leq \pi$, and the particle then moves to the left. It will continue this motion in alternating directions indefinitely. Later we shall study such motions in some detail. At the moment we shall use 6 equal subintervals to compute upper and lower approximations for the distance traveled from the time $t = .2$ to the time $t = .5$.

We shall use a table that gives sine function values for arguments expressed in radians and round off the entries to three decimal places. Table 2.5 describes

TABLE 2.5

Subinterval	Length of subinterval	$f(t_k')$ Minimum velocity	Lower estimate for $(\Delta s)_k$	$f(t_k'')$ Maximum velocity	Upper estimate for $(\Delta s)_k$
$.20 \rightarrow .25$	.05	1.167	.05835	1.437	.07185
$.25 \rightarrow .30$	.05	1.437	.07185	1.695	.08475
$.30 \rightarrow .35$	.05	1.695	.08475	1.932	.09660
$.35 \rightarrow .40$	.05	1.932	.09660	2.151	.10755
$.40 \rightarrow .45$	.05	2.151	.10755	2.349	.11745
$.45 \rightarrow .50$	.05	2.349	.11745	2.523	.12615
			.53655		.60435

the subintervals chosen and the upper and lower estimates for the distances traveled in those subintervals. Hence we conclude that

$$.53655 \leq \text{distance traveled} \leq .60435.$$

If we had 10 equal subintervals, we would have found that

$$.55062 \leq \text{distance traveled} \leq .59130.$$

The correct answer is

$$\text{distance traveled} \approx .57114,$$

as the reader will be able to verify after he has studied Chapter 4.

EXERCISES 2.5

1. A ball rolls down an inclined plane with velocity $v = 6t$. Compute the distance it rolled from the time $t = 0$ to the time $t = 2$, using the summation-of-parts point of view. Check by computing the same distance from the point of view of antidifferentiation.

2. Consider again the ball described in Exercise 1. Compute the distance it rolled from the time $t = 0$ to the time $t = a$, using first the point of view of summation of parts and then computing again from the point of view of antidifferentiation.

3. A particle that moves on a straight line with velocity $v = \cos t$ performs a periodic motion. (a) Use 5 equal subintervals, and then (b) 10 equal subintervals to compute upper and lower approximations for the distance traveled from the time $t = 0$ to the time $t = .20$.

4. A particle moves on a straight line with velocity $v = \cos t$. Explain why $\int_{t=0}^{\pi} \cos t \, dt = 0$; that is, explain why the net displacement for the interval $t = 0$ to $t = \pi$ is 0. (It is not necessary to perform a detailed computation.)

5. A particle moves on a straight line with velocity $v = (t - 1)^3$. Using the summation-of-parts point of view, explain why $\int_{t=0}^{2} (t - 1)^3 \, dt = 0$; that is, explain why the net displacement for the interval $t = 0$ to $t = 2$ is 0.

2.6 Some Fundamental Theorems of Integral Calculus

I

First we develop some of the properties of the definite integral written down in Notation Convention 2.4-1.

■ THEOREM 1

HYPOTHESIS: $f(x) = 1$ for $a \leq x \leq b$.

CONCLUSION: $\int_a^b f(x) \, dx = \int_a^b 1 \, dx = b - a$.

PROOF: We subdivide the interval $a \leq x \leq b$ into n parts by choosing subdivision points $a = x_0 < x_1 < x_2 \cdots < x_n = b$, write $(\Delta x)_k = x_k - x_{k-1}$ for the length of the kth subinterval, and choose a representative number x_k^* in the kth subinterval, $k = 1, 2, \cdots, n$. Then we write

$$\sum_{k=1}^{n} f(x_k^*)(\Delta x)_k = f(x_1^*)(\Delta x)_1 + f(x_2^*)(\Delta x)_2 + \cdots + f(x_n^*)(\Delta x)_n$$

$$= 1(\Delta x)_1 + 1(\Delta x)_2 + \cdots + 1(\Delta x)_n = b - a,$$

observing that the sum of the lengths of the subintervals is the length of the interval. Now if we repeat the computation with n growing beyond all bounds and the length of the largest subinterval approaching 0, we have

$$\int_a^b 1 \, dx = \lim_{n \to \infty} \sum_{k=1}^{n} f(x_k^*)(\Delta x)_k = b - a.$$

■ THEOREM 2

HYPOTHESIS: $\int_a^b f(x) \, dx$ exists.

CONCLUSION: $\int_a^b cf(x) \, dx = c \int_a^b f(x) \, dx$ for any constant c.

PROOF: Write $g(x) = cf(x)$, subdivide the interval $a \leq x \leq b$ into n parts as usual, and choose representative numbers x_k^* for the various subintervals. Then

$$\sum_{k=1}^{n} g(x_k^*)(\Delta x)_k = g(x_1^*)(\Delta x)_1 + g(x_2^*)(\Delta x)_2 + \cdots + g(x_n^*)(\Delta x)_n$$
$$= cf(x_1^*)(\Delta x)_1 + cf(x_2^*)(\Delta x)_2 + \cdots + cf(x_n^*)(\Delta x)_n$$
$$= c[f(x_1^*)(\Delta x)_1 + f(x_2^*)(\Delta x)_2 + \cdots + f(x_n^*)(\Delta x)_n]$$
$$= c \sum_{k=1}^{n} f(x_k^*)(\Delta x)_k.$$

Now, if we repeat the computation with n growing beyond all bounds and the length of the largest subinterval approaching 0, we have

$$\int_a^b g(x) \, dx = c \int_a^b f(x) \, dx$$

$$\int_a^b cf(x) \, dx = c \int_a^b f(x) \, dx.$$

■ THEOREM 3

HYPOTHESIS: $\int_a^b f(x) \, dx$ and $\int_a^b g(x) \, dx$ exist.

CONCLUSION: $\int_a^b [f(x) + g(x)] \, dx = \int_a^b f(x) \, dx + \int_a^b g(x) \, dx.$

PROOF: Write $h(x) = f(x) + g(x)$, subdivide the interval $a \leq x \leq b$ into n parts as usual, and choose representative numbers x_k^* in the various subintervals. Then

$$\sum_{k=1}^{n} h(x_k^*)(\Delta x)_k = h(x_1^*)(\Delta x)_1 + h(x_2^*)(\Delta x)_2 + \cdots + h(x_n^*)(\Delta x)_n$$
$$= [f(x_1^*) + g(x_1^*)](\Delta x)_1 + [f(x_2^*) + g(x_2^*)](\Delta x)_2$$
$$+ \cdots + [f(x_n^*) + g(x_n^*)](\Delta x)_n$$
$$= [f(x_1^*)(\Delta x)_1 + f(x_2^*)(\Delta x)_2 + \cdots + f(x_n^*)(\Delta x)_n]$$
$$+ [g(x_1^*)(\Delta x)_1 + g(x_2^*)(\Delta x)_2 + \cdots + g(x_n^*)(\Delta x)_n]$$
$$= \sum_{k=1}^{n} f(x_k^*)(\Delta x)_k + \sum_{k=1}^{n} g(x_k^*)(\Delta x)_k,$$

and our conclusion will follow upon taking limits properly.

■ THEOREM 4

HYPOTHESIS: (a) $f(x)$ is continuous for $a \leq x \leq b$.

(b) $a < c < b$.

CONCLUSION: $\int_a^c f(x)\, dx + \int_c^b f(x)\, dx = \int_a^b f(x)\, dx.$

PROOF: (a) Subdivide the interval $a \leq x \leq c$ into n parts, select a representative point for each subinterval, and form the sum

$$\sum_1 = \sum_{k=1}^{n} f(x_k^*)(\Delta x)_k.$$

(b) Subdivide the interval $c \leq x \leq b$ into p parts, but label the consecutive subintervals $(n+1)$, $(n+2)$, and so forth, the last being the $(n+p)$th. Select a representative point for each subinterval and form the sum

$$\sum_2 = \sum_{k=n+1}^{n+p} f(x_k^*)(\Delta x)_k.$$

(c) But the subdivision processes of Steps (a) and (b) automatically constitute a subdivision of the interval $a \leq x \leq b$ into $(n+p)$ parts for which we have the sum

$$\sum_3 = \sum_{k=1}^{n+p} f(x_k^*)(\Delta x)_k = \sum_1 + \sum_2.$$

(d) Now if we allow n and p to grow beyond all bounds, all $(\Delta k)_k$'s approaching 0 in length, the conclusion of our theorem follows from the last equation because

$$\lim_{n \to \infty} \sum_1 = \int_a^c f(x)\, dx,$$

$$\lim_{p \to \infty} \sum_2 = \int_c^b f(x)\, dx,$$

$$\lim_{n+p \to \infty} \sum_3 = \int_a^b f(x)\, dx.$$

■

Definition 2.4-2 says that, if $f(x)$ is nonnegative and continuous for $a \leq x \leq b$, then the area of the region bounded by $y = f(x)$, $x = a$, $x = b$ and the x axis is $\int_a^b f(x)\, dx$. We can now point out that this definition is consistent with the three requirements laid down for any definition of area at the beginning of Sec. 2.3 and in Definition 2.3-1, our definition for the area of a rectangle.

First, the fact that the area number assigned by $\int_a^b f(x)\, dx$ is nonnegative follows from the fact that $f(x)$ itself is nonnegative for the interval $a \leq x \leq b$. For, we have $f(x_k^*) \geq 0$, $f(x_k^*)(\Delta x)_k \geq 0$ for each k, and then $\sum_{k=1}^{n} f(x_k^*)(\Delta x)_k \geq 0$. Since the sums of which $\int_a^b f(x)\, dx$ is a limit are nonnegative, $\int_a^b f(x)\, dx$ is nonnegative also.

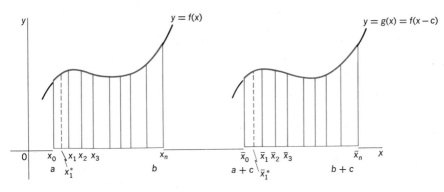

Fig. 2.18

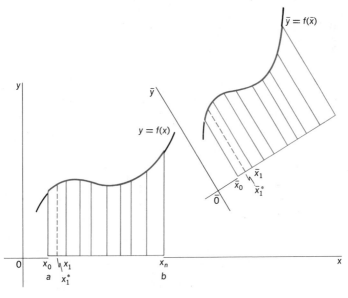

Fig. 2.19

Second, if we consider two congruent regions, as in Fig. 2.18, the area numbers furnished by the definite integral definition of area will be the same, because the subdivisions of the base intervals and the representative numbers for the subintervals can be so chosen that there will be identical terms in the sums of which the definite integrals are the limits. Thus in Fig. 2.18 we have $(\Delta x)_1 = (\overline{\Delta x})_1$, $f(x_1^*)$ $= g(\bar{x}_1^*)$ and $f(x_1^*)(\Delta x)_1 = g(\bar{x}_1^*)(\overline{\Delta x})_1$, and so forth. Even if one of the congruent regions must be rotated to be brought into coincidence with the other, as in Fig. 2.19, it will still be possible to choose subdivisions of the base intervals and representative numbers for the subintervals, so that the definite integrals are the same.

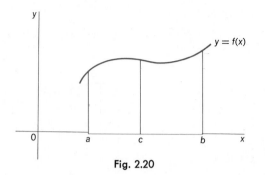

Fig. 2.20

Third, Theorem 4 above says that the area number assigned to a region formed by uniting two nonoverlapping regions shall be the sum of the area numbers assigned to these regions. See Fig. 2.20.

Finally, Theorems 1 and 2 above say that if $c > 0$, then the rectangle bounded by $y = c$, $x = a$, $x = b$, and the x axis is $\int_a^b c\, dx = c \int_a^b 1\, dx = c(b - a)$, which is the product of the base and height of the rectangle. See Fig. 2.21.

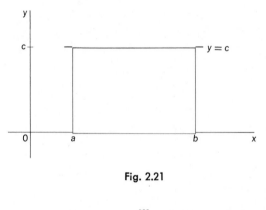

Fig. 2.21

III

On two occasions, in a special problem of the area of a region with one curved boundary and in a rectilinear distance problem, we have considered an anti-differentiation point of view and a summation-of-parts point of view. We can try now to describe the relationship between the two points of view.

■ THEOREM 5

The Fundamental Theorem of Integral Calculus.

HYPOTHESIS: (a) $f(x)$ is continuous for $a \leq x \leq b$.
(b) $\phi(x)$ is such that $\phi'(x) = f(x)$ for $a \leq x \leq b$.

CONCLUSION: $\int_a^b f(x)\, dx = \phi(b) - \phi(a)$.

DISCUSSION: (a) The definite integral $\int_a^b f(x)\, dx$ represents a limit of a sum:

$$\int_a^b f(x)\, dx = \lim_{n \to \infty} \sum_{k=1}^n f(x_k^*)(\Delta x)_k,$$

where x_k^* is a number of the kth of n subintervals of $a \le x \le b$, $(\Delta x)_k$ is the length of the kth subinterval, and it is understood that the largest $(\Delta x)_k$ approaches 0 as n grows beyond all bounds. Such a limit of a sum might arise in an area problem, or in a distance problem, or in any other situation where one (1) breaks an interval up into small parts, (2) computes an approximation to the quantity desired for each of the small parts, (3) adds up, and then (4) strives to improve the net approximation by repeating the process with more and smaller subdivisions. This strategy is very powerful and is of wide application. A significant portion of this course is devoted to illustrating its application in different situations.

(b) Hypothesis (a) does not require that $f(x)$ be nonnegative for $a \le x \le b$, but let us assume for the present that this is the case. Then, no matter what the context from which the number $\int_a^b f(x)\, dx$ was taken, there will be a region of the xy plane whose area is $\int_a^b f(x)\, dx$, namely, the region bounded by $y = f(x)$, the x axis, $x = a$ and $x = b$.

(c) We have pointed out that the definite integral definition for the area of such a region is consistent with the basic requirements laid down for any area definition and with the customary definition for the area of a rectangle. Theorem 2.3-1 then says that, if $A(x)$ is the area of the region bounded by $y = f(x)$, the x axis, and the ordinates at a and x, we must have $dA/dx = f(x)$ for $a \le x \le b$.

(d) Both $A(x)$ and the $\phi(x)$ of the hypothesis have the same derivative for $a \le x \le b$; $A'(x) = f(x)$ and $\phi'(x) = f(x)$. Therefore, by Theorem 2.1-1 we have

$$A(x) = \phi(x) + C, \qquad a \le x \le b.$$

(e) Since we begin to measure area at $x = a$, $A(a) = 0$; thus

$$0 = \phi(a) + C \qquad \text{or} \qquad C = -\phi(a).$$

Hence the area function is

$$A(x) = \phi(x) - \phi(a), \qquad a \le x \le b.$$

(f) The area of the region bounded by the ordinates at a and b is the number

$$A(b) = \phi(b) - \phi(a).$$

We have thus shown that

$$\int_a^b f(x)\, dx = \phi(b) - \phi(a)$$

if $f(x)$ is not only continuous but also nonnegative for $a \le x \le b$.

(g) To complete our discussion, we take the case where $f(x)$ is negative for some or all of the numbers of the interval $a \le x \le b$. It seems plausible to agree that a continuous function cannot be unbounded on an interval like $a \le x \le b$. We shall discuss this property of continuous functions later in Sec. 7.4, but let us accept it here. This means that there is a lower bound number, which is negative, for $f(x)$ of the interval; there is a number $-B$, $B > 0$, such that $f(x) \geq -B$ for all x of $a \leq x \leq b$. If we then write $g(x) = f(x) + B$, we can conclude that $g(x) \geq 0$ for all x of $a \leq x \leq b$ and that $g(x)$ is continuous, along with $f(x)$, for that interval.

(h) But now the result of Step (f) applies to $g(x)$. By Hypothesis (b) we know that $\phi'(x) = f(x)$; if $\psi(x) = \phi(x) + Bx$ we shall have $\psi'(x) = \phi'(x) + B = f(x) + B = g(x)$. Hence Step (f) enables us to write

$$\int_a^b g(x) \, dx = \psi(b) - \psi(a).$$

(i) We can now write the last equation in the form

$$\int_a^b [f(x) + B] dx = [\phi(b) + Bb] - [\phi(a) + Ba]$$

$$\int_a^b f(x) \, dx + B \int_a^b 1 dx = \phi(b) - \phi(a) + B(b - a)$$

$$\int_a^b f(x) \, dx + B(b - a) = \phi(b) - \phi(a) + B(b - a)$$

$$\int_a^b f(x) \, dx = \phi(b) - \phi(a),$$

using Theorems 1, 2, and 3. This concludes our first discussion of the Fundamental Theorem of the Integral Calculus.

● **Remark 1**

The conclusion of Theorem 5, $\int_a^b f(x) \, dx = \phi(b) - \phi(a)$, has for its left member a number derived from $f(x)$ by following out the summation-of-parts technique. To get the right member, one starts by looking for a function $\phi(x)$ whose derivative is $f(x)$; the right member is therefore a number derived from $f(x)$ by following the antidifferentiation technique. This theorem furnishes the bridge between the two points of view.

Example 1A.   Evaluate $\int_1^4 (2x - 1) \, dx.$* We look for a function whose derivative with respect to x is $2x - 1$, evaluate at $x = 4$ and at $x = 1$, and subtract. In symbols,

$$\int_1^4 (2x - 1) \, dx = (x^2 - x) \Big|_{x=1}^4 = (16 - 4) - (1 - 1) = 12.$$

Example 2.   Evaluate

$$\int_0^3 \frac{1}{(t + 1)^2} \, dt.$$

---

* See Examples 2.3-1 and 2.4-1.

We look for a function whose derivative with respect to t is $1/(t+1)^2$, evaluate at $t = 3$ and at $t = 0$, and subtract. In symbols,

$$\int_0^3 \frac{1}{(t+1)^2} \, dt = \int_0^3 (t+1)^{-2}(1) \, dt$$

$$= \frac{(t+1)^{-1}}{-1} \Big|_{t=0}^{3} = -\frac{1}{t+1} \Big|_{t=0}^{3} = \left(-\frac{1}{4}\right) - \left(-\frac{1}{1}\right) = \frac{3}{4}.$$

● **Remark 2**

It was pointed out in Remark 2.4-3 that the value of $\int_a^b f(x) \, dx$ depends on the boundary numbers a and b and on the numbers assigned by f for $a \le x \le b$ but does not depend on the name of the letter used to "carry" the integration; $\int_a^b f(x) \, dx = \int_a^b f(t) \, dt$. Now consider the same fact from another point of view. Theorem 5 says that $\int_a^b f(x) \, dx$ is a number arrived at by taking a function $\phi(x)$ such that $\phi'(x) = f(x)$, replacing x by b and then by a, and subtracting. You get the same number if you take $\phi(t)$ such that $\phi'(t) = f(t)$, replace t by b and then by a, and subtract. Thus

$$\int_a^b f(t) \, dt = \int_a^b f(x) \, dx = \phi(b) - \phi(a).$$

Example 1B

$$\int_{t=1}^4 (2t - 1) \, dt = (t^2 - t) \Big|_{t=1}^{4} = (16 - 4) - (1 - 1) = 12.$$

Compare this with Example 1A.

IV

The Fundamental Theorem, Theorem 5, tells how to use antiderivatives to evaluate certain limits of sums called definite integrals. Next, we look at the relationship between antidifferentiation and summation from the other direction. We consider a theorem that tells how to use a definite integral to find an antiderivative function. The question, then, is this: if given a function $f(x)$ that is continuous for $a \le x \le b$, how can we form an antiderivative function ϕ?

What is required is that (a) for every number x of the interval $a \le x \le b$ we shall furnish instructions for determining the number $\phi(x)$; (b) the function ϕ thus determined shall be an antiderivative of f; that is, $\phi' = f$ for $a \le x \le b$.

In the case in which $f(x)$ is not only continuous but nonnegative for $a \le x \le b$, Theorem 2.3-1 supplies the function ϕ we seek. That theorem says that for $\phi(x)$ we should take the area of the region bounded by $y = f(x)$, the x axis, and the ordinates at a and x; this area is described by $\int_a^x f(t) \, dt$.

■ **THEOREM 6**

Antiderivatives furnished by definite integrals.

HYPOTHESIS: (a) $f(t)$ is continuous for $a \le t \le b$.
(b) $\phi(x) = \int_a^x f(t) \, dt$, $a \le x \le b$.

CONCLUSION: $\phi'(x) = f(x)$, $a \leq x \leq b$.

REMAINDER OF PROOF: The reader can show in Exercise 2.6-14 that the case in which f is continuous but not necessarily nonnegative for $a \leq x \leq b$ depends on the case in which f is nonnegative. A device very much like that used in the discussion of the Fundamental Theorem can be used again.

● **Remark 3**

Theorem 6 says that, if $f(x)$ is continuous for $a \leq x \leq b$, there exists a $\varphi(x)$ such that $\varphi'(x) = f(x)$ for $a \leq x \leq b$, but it may not be possible to describe $\varphi(x)$ in a finite number of elementary steps. To get $\varphi(x)$ each time an x is specified, it may be necessary to go through a computation using limits of sums.

Example 3A. Consider $f(x) = 2x - 1$, which is continuous for all x. There is a $\phi(x)$ such that $\phi'(x) = f(x)$ for all x, and in this case $\phi(x)$ can be described by the algebraic formula: $\phi(x) = x^2 - x$.

Example 3B. Consider $f(x) = 2^{-x^2}$, which is also continuous for all x. Here it will be found that there is a $\phi(x)$ such that $\phi'(x) = f(x)$ for all x, but we cannot describe $\varphi(x)$ in a finite number of elementary steps. We can describe $\varphi(x)$ by the definite integral

$$\phi(x) = \int_{t=0}^{x} 2^{-t^2}\, dt,$$

and we can also describe it by an infinite series.*

● **Remark 4**

The Fundamental Theorem is very powerful because it enables us to use two tools interchangeably. Some problems are easier to analyze by a summation-of-parts technique; these are usually problems in which one can visualize separate parts into which the problem can be divided. Other problems are easier to analyze by an antidifferentiation technique; for instance, problems that use definitions and laws of science stated in terms of rates of change. Having set up a problem we can compute the answer according to the point of view used in the analysis; or we can use the Fundamental Theorem and then compute the answer according to the other point of view. If when confronted with $\int_a^b f(x)\, dx$, the mathematician has an antiderivative function whose values are known to him, then the antiderivative technique is likely to be the easier for computation purposes. If an antiderivative function with known values is not available, then the summation-of-parts technique would have to be used for computation purposes. It is obvious that fast adding machines have a role to play in helping with the summations.

● **Remark 5**

The discussions of Theorems 5 and 6 given here are inelegant in that they emphasize the area application and that no one application ought to be emphasized. In Secs. 7.6 and 7.7 we shall return to these theorems.

---

* Infinite series descriptions of functions will be studied in Chapter 13.

V

Thus far we have always spoken of integrals with definite boundaries. Because the conclusion of the Fundamental Theorem starts by telling us that $\int_a^b f(x)\,dx$ can be evaluated by looking for a function whose derivative is $f(x)$, we find it convenient to adopt the following definition for integral notation:

■ **DEFINITION 1**

The indefinite integral. By $\int f(x)\,dx$ we shall mean the set of functions of x whose derivatives with respect to x are $f(x)$.

Example 4. $\int x^n\,dx = ?$ In words, "Which functions must we differentiate with respect to x to get x^n?" Theorem 2.1-2 tells us that

$$\int x^n\,dx = \frac{x^{n+1}}{n+1} + C$$

if $n \neq -1$. If $n = -1$, we do not yet know the answer to the question.

Example 5. We can rewrite Theorem 2.1-5 in the integral notation:

$$\int (u)^n \frac{du}{dx}\,dx = \frac{(u)^{n+1}}{n+1} + C, \qquad n \neq -1.$$

In words, $(u)^{n+1}/(n+1) + C$ is a function whose derivative with respect to x is $(u)^n\,(du/dx)$.

We conclude this section with two frequently used theorems about integrals, which are really direct restatements in integral language of earlier theorems about derivatives. We also extend one definition slightly.

■ **THEOREM 7**

The constant multiplier in integration.

HYPOTHESIS: (a) $f(x)$ is continuous.
(b) k is a constant.

CONCLUSION: $\int k f(x)\,dx = k \int f(x)\,dx$.

PROOF: This is a restatement of Theorem 2.1-3.

● Remark 6

This theorem says that we can "take a constant through the integral sign." Note that this can be done only for constants! Consider the following.

Example 6. Does $\int x\,x^2\,dx = x \int x^2\,dx$? The answer is "No" for the reason that

$$\int x\,x^2\,dx = \int x^3\,dx = \tfrac{1}{4}\,x^4 + C,$$

whereas
$$x \int x^2\,dx = x[\tfrac{1}{3}\,x^3 + C].$$

Example 7A

$$I = \int x\sqrt{5 + x^2}\,dx = \int (5 + x^2)^{1/2}x\,dx$$
$$= \int \tfrac{1}{2}(5 + x^2)^{1/2}(2x)\,dx = \tfrac{1}{2}\int (5 + x^2)^{1/2}(2x)\,dx.$$

So far we have taken the constant, $\frac{1}{2}$, through the sign of integration. But we must still inquire about the set of functions whose derivative is the product of the power of $5 + x^2$ with exponent $\frac{1}{2}$ and the derivative of $5 + x^2$. According to Example 5,

$$I = \frac{1}{2} \frac{(5 + x^2)^{3/2}}{3/2} + C = \frac{1}{3}(5 + x^2)^{3/2} + C.$$

Example 7B.   Evaluate $\int_2^4 x\sqrt{5 + x^2}\, dx$. We take a function whose derivative is $x\sqrt{5 + x^2}$, evaluate at $x = 4$ and at $x = 2$, and subtract. In symbols,

$$\int_2^4 x\sqrt{5 + x^2}\, dx = \tfrac{1}{3}(5 + x^2)^{3/2}\big|_2^4 = \tfrac{1}{3}(21)^{3/2} - \tfrac{1}{3}(9)^{3/2}$$

$$= \tfrac{1}{3}[(21)^{3/2} - 27] \approx 23.$$

■ THEOREM 8

Integrals of sums.

HYPOTHESIS: $\psi(x)$ and $\phi(x)$ are continuous.

CONCLUSION: $\int[\psi(x) + \phi(x)]\, dx = \int\psi(x)\, dx + \int\phi(x)\, dx$.

PROOF: This is a restatement of Theorem 2.1-4.

The definite integrals we have considered to this point were all of the form $\int_a^b f(x)\, dx$ with $a \le b$.* What definition should we choose for $\int_a^b f(x)\, dx$ with $a > b$? Since we would like to have Theorem 5 hold for these definite integrals also, the following definition is suggested:

■ DEFINITION 2

$$\int_a^b f(x)\, dx, \ a > b, \ \text{shall be} - \int_b^a f(x)\, dx.$$

Now we have

$$\int_a^b f(x)\, dx = -\int_b^a f(x)\, dx = -[\phi(a) - \phi(b)] = \phi(b) - \phi(a),$$

and this is the conclusion of Theorem 5, which we wanted to be valid in the case $a > b$ as well as in the case $a \le b$.

EXERCISES 2.6

Evaluate each of the following definite integrals by using Theorem 5, if this can be done. If the hypotheses of Theorem 5 are not satisfied, say so.

1. $\displaystyle\int_0^1 (1 - x^2)\, dx.$

3. $\displaystyle\int_3^8 \sqrt{1 + x}\, dx.$

2. $\displaystyle\int_0^1 (1 - t^2)\, dt.$

4. $\displaystyle\int_0^4 \frac{2}{(1 + t)^2}\, dt.$

---

* See Notation Convention 2.4-1.

5. $\displaystyle\int_{-3}^{-2} \frac{2}{(1+t)^2}\, dt.$

9. $\displaystyle\int_{2}^{4} \frac{5y}{(y^2-1)^3}\, dy.$

6. $\displaystyle\int_{-3}^{0} \frac{2}{(1+t)^2}\, dt.$

10. $\displaystyle\int_{1}^{2} \frac{x^2+1}{x^2}\, dx.$

7. $\displaystyle\int_{2}^{3} \sqrt{x^2+4}\; x\, dx.$

11. $\displaystyle\int_{2}^{1} \frac{x^2+1}{x^2}\, dx.$

8. $\displaystyle\int_{0}^{2} \frac{3x}{\sqrt{x^2-1}}\, dx.$

12. Exercises 3, 6, 9, 11, 12, 14, 16, 18 of Sec. 2.1 can all be rewritten in the indefinite integral notation. For instance, Exercise 3 would read

$$\phi(z) = \int (a_2 z^2 + a_1 z + a_0)\, dz = a_2 \frac{z^3}{3} + a_1 \frac{z^2}{2} + a_0 z + C_1.$$

(a) Rewrite Exercise 2.1-6 in the indefinite integral notation.
(b) Do the same for Exercise 2.1-9.   (e) Exercise 2.1-14.
(c) Exercise 2.1-11.   (f) Exercise 2.1-16.
(d) Exercise 2.1-12.   (g) Exercise 2.1-18.

13. Consider Hypothesis (b) of Theorem 5. There will be not one but many antiderivative functions for a given $f(x)$. Suppose student A says "$\phi'(x) = f(x)$, and therefore $\int_a^b f(x)\, dx = \phi(b) - \phi(a)$." Student B may say "$\psi'(x) = f(x)$, and therefore $\int_a^b f(x)\, dx = \psi(b) - \psi(a)$." Will they both obtain the same numerical value for $\int_a^b f(x)\, dx$?

14. The conclusion of Theorem 6 was made plausible in the text only for the special case where $f(x)$ was nonnegative as well as continuous for $a \le x \le b$. If $f(x)$ is continuous but not nonnegative for this interval, there will be a lower bound number, $-B$ with $B > 0$, such that $f(x) \ge -B$ for $a \le x \le b$. But then $g(x) = f(x) + B$ would be ≥ 0 and also continuous for $a \le x \le b$. Show that $\psi(x) = \phi(x) + B(x - a)$ is such that $\psi(x) = \int_{t=a}^{x} g(t)\, dt$, draw what conclusion you can for $\psi'(x)$, and show that $\phi'(x) = f(x)$ for $a \le x \le b$.

15. Let the interval $1 \le x \le 2$ be divided into n subintervals by using partition points $x_0 = 1 < x_1 < x_2 < \cdots < x_n = 2$, with $(\Delta x)_k = x_k - x_{k-1}$. Use Theorem 5 to evaluate

(a) $\displaystyle\lim_{n\to\infty} \sum_{k=1}^{n} (x_k)^5\, (\Delta x)_k,$

(c) $\displaystyle\lim_{n\to\infty} \sum_{k=1}^{n} \frac{1}{x_k^2}\, (\Delta x)_k,$

(b) $\displaystyle\lim_{n\to\infty} \sum_{k=1}^{n} \sqrt{x_{k-1}}\, (\Delta x)_k,$

(d) $\displaystyle\lim_{n\to\infty} \sum_{k=1}^{n} \frac{1}{\sqrt{x_k}}\, (\Delta x)_k,$

it being understood that the largest $(\Delta x)_k$ approaches 0 as n grows beyond all bounds.

2.7 Areas of More General Regions

In Secs. 2.3 and 2.4 we dealt only with areas of regions of a certain restricted nature; the x axis had to be one of the boundaries, and two of the other boundaries were usually vertical lines. Here our regions will be of a more general nature. Important as the concept of area is for its own sake, however, our goal at the moment is

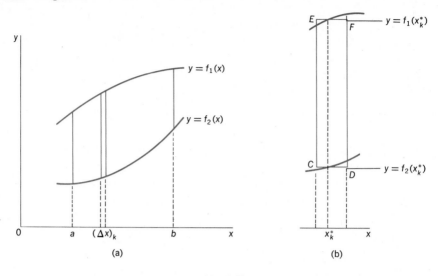

(a)   (b)

Fig. 2.22

primarily to illustrate a powerful technique. We shall analyze from the limit-of-a-sum point of view, but evaluate the definite integral that is then presented from the antiderivative point of view.

Consider the region bounded by $y = f_1(x)$, $y = f_2(x)$, $x = a$, and $x = b$; see Fig. 2.22(a). Divide the region into n subregions of widths $(\Delta x)_1$, $(\Delta x)_2, \cdots, (\Delta x)_n$ by drawing vertical lines. In the kth subregion select an x, call it x_k^*, and draw horizontal lines CD at $y = f_2(x_k^*)$ and EF at $y = f_1(x_k^*)$; see Fig. 2.22 (b). We thus get a rectangle with which to approximate the area of the subregion;

$$\text{area of } k\text{th subregion} \approx [f_1(x_k^*) - f_2(x_k^*)](\Delta x)_k,\dagger$$

$$\text{area of region} \approx \sum_{k=1}^{n} [f_1(x_k^*) - f_2(x_k^*)](\Delta x)_k.$$

There is a choice of x_k^*, say x_k', for which the height of the rectangle is a minimum, and another choice of x_k^*, say x_k'', for which the height of the rectangle is a maximum. If we use the x_k''s, the approximation to the area of the region is too small; if we use the x_k'''s, the approximation is too large. Our intuition tells us that, if we let the number of subregions increase, the difference between these approximations approaches 0; the limit approached by either sum or by any intermediate sum can serve as our area.

■ **DEFINITION 1**

The area of the region bounded by $y = f_1(x)$, $y = f_2(x)$, $x = a$, and $x = b$, $f_1(x) \geq f_2(x)$ for $a \leq x \leq b$, shall be

$$\int_{x=a}^{b} [f_1(x) - f_2(x)] \, dx.$$

---

† A vertical distance between two points is always computed by subtracting the y coordinate of the lower point from the y coordinate of the higher point. The distance from (x, y_L) to (x, y_H), $y_H > y_L$, is $y_H - y_L$. See Theorem 3.2-1.

Similarly, we draw horizontal subdivision lines for a region bounded by $x = f_1(y)$, $x = f_2(y)$, $y = a$, and $y = b$; see Fig. 2.23 (a). In the kth subregion select a y, call it y_k^*, and draw vertical lines CD at $x = f_2(y_k^*)$ and EF at $x = f_1(y_k^*)$; see Fig. 2.23 (b). Then

$$\text{area of } k\text{th subregion} \approx [f_1(y_k^*) - f_2(y_k^*)](\Delta y)_k,\dagger$$

$$\text{area of region} \approx \sum_{k=1}^{n} [f_1(y_k^*) - f_2(y_k^*)](\Delta y)_k.$$

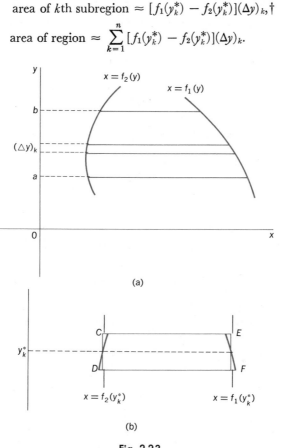

(a)

(b)

Fig. 2.23

Our intuition tells us that, if we let the number of subdivisions increase, these approximations will approach the area number we seek, and so we choose Definition 2.

■ DEFINITION 2

The area of the region bounded by $x = f_1(y)$, $x = f_2(y)$, $y = a$, and $y = b$, with $f_1(y) \geq f_2(y)$ for $a \leq y \leq b$, shall be

$$\int_{y=a}^{b} [f_1(y) - f_2(y)]\, dy.$$

---

† A horizontal distance between two points is always computed by subtracting the x coordinate of the left end point from that of the right end point. The distance from (x_L, y) to (x_R, y), $x_R > x_L$, is $x_R - x_L$. See Theorem 3.2-1.

Example 1A.   Find the area of the region bounded by $y = f_1(x) = 5 - x^2$ and $y = f_2(x) = 5 - 2x$.

We solve the equations simultaneously and find that the curves intersect at $A(0, 5)$ and $B(2, 1)$. In detail, we have $5 - x^2 = 5 - 2x$; $x^2 - 2x = 0$; $x(x - 2) = 0$; $x = 0$ or $x = 2$. See Fig. 2.24 (a).

Now imagine the region subdivided by vertical lines and take x_k^* to be an x coordinate of the kth subregion. We have

$$\text{area of } k\text{th subregion} \approx [f_1(x_k^*) - f_2(x_k^*)]\,(\Delta x)_k$$

$$\text{area of region} \approx \sum_{k=1}^{n} [f_1(x_k^*) - f_2(x_k^*)]\,(\Delta x)_k$$

$$\text{area of region} = \lim_{n \to \infty} \sum_{k=1}^{n} [f_1(x_k^*) - f_2(x_k^*)]\,(\Delta x)_k,$$

it being understood that the largest $(\Delta x)_k$ approaches 0 as n grows beyond all bounds. Then

$$\text{area of region} = \int_{x=0}^{2} [f_1(x) - f_2(x)]\,dx$$

$$= \int_{x=0}^{2} [(5 - x^2) - (5 - 2x)]\,dx = \int_{x=0}^{2} [2x - x^2]\,dx.$$

To evaluate the definite integral we turn to the antidifferentiation point of view:

$$\text{area of region} = (x^2 - \tfrac{1}{3} x^3)\,\Big|_{x=0}^{2} = (4 - \tfrac{8}{3}) - (0 - 0) = \tfrac{4}{3}.$$

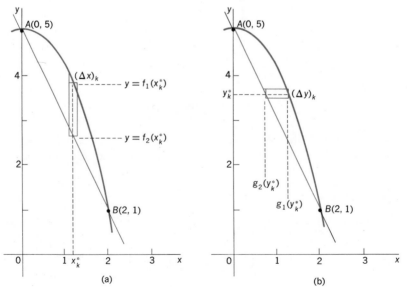

(a)   (b)

Fig. 2.24

Example 1B.   Consider the same region, but this time subdivide by horizontal lines; see Fig. 2.24(b). The description of the boundary curves can be rewritten as

$$x = g_1(y) = \sqrt{5 - y} \quad \text{and} \quad x = g_2(y) = \tfrac{1}{2}(5 - y),$$

and if y_k^* is a y coordinate of the kth subregion, the problem can be analyzed as follows:

$$\text{area of } k\text{th subregion} \approx [g_1(y_k^*) - g_2(y_k^*)] \, (\Delta y)_k,$$

$$\text{area of region} \approx \sum_{k=1}^{n} [g_1(y_k^*) - g_2(y_k^*)] \, (\Delta y)_k,$$

$$\text{area of region} = \int_{y=1}^{5} [g_1(y) - g_2(y)] \, dy = \int_{y=1}^{5} [\sqrt{5-y} - \tfrac{1}{2}(5 - y)] \, dy.$$

To evaluate this definite integral we turn to the antidifferentiation point of view:

$$\text{area of region} = \int_{y=1}^{5} (5 - y)^{1/2} \, dy - \tfrac{1}{2} \int_{1}^{5} (5 - y) \, dy$$

$$= -\int_{y=1}^{5} (5 - y)^{1/2}(-1) \, dy + \tfrac{1}{2} \int_{1}^{5} (5 - y)(-1) \, dy$$

$$= [-\tfrac{2}{3}(5 - y)^{3/2} + \tfrac{1}{4}(5 - y)^2] \Big|_{y=1}^{5}$$

$$= [0 + 0] - [-\tfrac{2}{3}(4)^{3/2} + \tfrac{1}{4}(4)^2]$$

$$= 0 + {}^{16}\!/_3 - 4 = \tfrac{4}{3}.$$

Example 2.   Find the area of the region bounded by $3x = 8 + 2y - y^2$ and $y = -\tfrac{3}{5} x$.

To plot the first of these curves, we notice first that the equation can be written $3x = (4 - y)(2 + y)$ so that two intercept points on the curve are $(0, 4)$ and $(0, -2)$. If we solve the two equations simultaneously, we have

$$x = g_1(y) = \tfrac{1}{3}(8 + 2y - y^2) \quad \text{and} \quad x = g_2(y) = -\tfrac{5}{3}y;$$

therefore

$$\tfrac{1}{3}(8 + 2y - y^2) = -\tfrac{5}{3}y \quad \text{or} \quad 8 + 7y - y^2 = 0;$$

$$(8 - y)(1 + y) = 0; \quad \text{and} \quad y = 8 \quad \text{or} \quad y = -1.$$

Hence the points of intersection are $A(-\tfrac{40}{3}, 8)$ and $B(\tfrac{5}{3}, -1)$; see Fig. 2.25(a).

In Example 1, the analyses by vertical and by horizontal subdivision were of about equal difficulty. Here analysis by horizontal subdivision is easier because there are two different types of vertical subregions. Subregions to the left of $x = \tfrac{5}{3}$ run from the straight line to the curve; those to the right of $x = \tfrac{5}{3}$ run from one portion of the curve to another. When we use horizontal subregions, however,

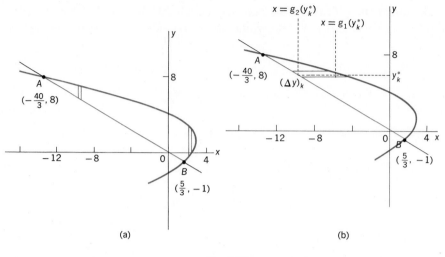

Fig. 2.25

all subregions are of the same type; they all run from the straight line to the curve; see Fig. 2.25(b).

Let y_k^* be a y coordinate of the kth subregion. Then

$$\text{area of } k\text{th subregion} \approx [g_1(y_k^*) - g_2(y_k^*)](\Delta y)_k,$$

$$\text{area of region} \approx \sum_{k=1}^{n} [g_1(y_k^*) - g_2(y_k^*)](\Delta y)_k,$$

$$\text{area of region} = \int_{y=-1}^{8} [g_1(y) - g_2(y)] \, dy$$

$$= \int_{y=-1}^{8} [\tfrac{1}{3}(8 + 2y - y^2) - (-\tfrac{5}{3}y)] \, dy$$

$$= \tfrac{1}{3} \int_{y=-1}^{8} [8 + 7y - y^2] \, dy.$$

To evaluate this integral, we turn to the antidifferentiation point of view:

$$\text{area of region} = \tfrac{1}{3}[8y + \tfrac{7}{2}y^2 - \tfrac{1}{3}y^3]_{y=-1}^{8}$$

$$= \tfrac{1}{3}[(64 + 224 - \tfrac{512}{3}) - (-8 + \tfrac{7}{2} + \tfrac{1}{3})] = 40.5.$$

Example 3. Find the area of the region bounded by (a) that portion of $y = f_1(x) = x^2$ which lies between $(0, 0)$ and $(2, 4)$;

(b) that portion of $y = f_2(x) = 12 - x^3$ which lies between $(2, 4)$ and $(3, -15)$;

(c) that portion of $y = f_3(x) = -2x - x^2$ which lies between $(0, 0)$ and $(3, -15)$. See Fig. 2.26.

If we use vertical subregions, it will be necessary to find the areas of the regions that lie to the left and right of $x = 2$ separately. If, as usual, x_k^* is an x coordinate of the kth subregion, then for the left region we have

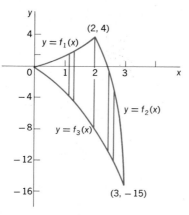

Fig. 2.26

$$\text{area of } k\text{th subregion} \approx [f_1(x_k^*) - f_3(x_k^*)](\Delta x)_k,$$

$$\text{area of left region} \approx \sum_{k=1}^{n} [f_1(x_k^*) - f_3(x_k^*)](\Delta x)_k,$$

$$\text{area of left region} = \int_{x=0}^{2} [f_1(x) - f_3(x)] \, dx$$

$$= \int_{x=0}^{2} [(x^2) - (-2x - x^2)] \, dx = \int_{x=0}^{2} (2x^2 + 2x) \, dx$$

$$= (\tfrac{2}{3} x^3 + x^2) \Big|_0^2 = (\tfrac{16}{3} + 4) - (0 + 0) = \tfrac{28}{3}.$$

For the right region we have

$$\text{area of } k\text{th subregion} \approx [f_2(x_k^*) - f_3(x_k^*)](\Delta x)_k,$$

$$\text{area of right region} \approx \sum_{k=1}^{n} [f_2(x_k^*) - f_3(x_k^*)](\Delta x)_k,$$

$$\text{area of right region} = \int_{x=2}^{3} [f_2(x) - f_3(x)] \, dx$$

$$= \int_{x=2}^{3} [(12 - x^3) - (-2x - x^2)] \, dx$$

$$= \int_{x=2}^{3} (12 + 2x + x^2 - x^3) \, dx$$

$$= (12x + x^2 + \tfrac{1}{3} x^3 - \tfrac{1}{4} x^4) \Big|_2^3$$

$$= (36 + 9 + 9 - 8\tfrac{1}{4}) - (24 + 4 + \tfrac{8}{3} - 4) = \tfrac{85}{12}.$$

Thus the area of the entire region is

$$\tfrac{28}{3} + \tfrac{85}{12} = \tfrac{197}{12} \approx 16.42.$$

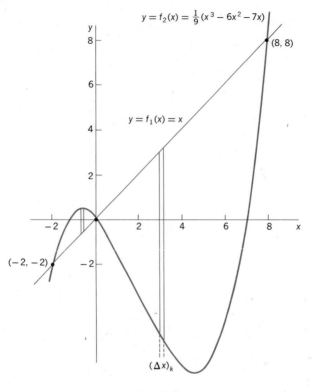

$$y = f_2(x) = \tfrac{1}{9}(x^3 - 6x^2 - 7x)$$

$y = f_1(x) = x$

(8, 8)

(-2, -2)

$(\Delta x)_k$

Fig. 2.27

This area might have been analyzed by using horizontal subdivisions. We would have had to set up separate integrals for the regions above and below the x axis, and in solving the various equations for x in terms of y we would have had to deal with somewhat inconvenient radicals.

Example 4. Find the areas of the regions bounded by $y = f_1(x) = x$ and $y = f_2(x) = \tfrac{1}{9}(x^3 - 6x^2 - 7x)$.

To plot the second of these curves, we notice first that the equation can be written in factored form as $y = \tfrac{1}{9}x(x^2 - 6x - 7) = \tfrac{1}{9}x(x - 7)(x + 1)$ so that three intercepts on the curve are $(0, 0)$, $(7, 0)$ and $(-1, 0)$. If we solve the equations simultaneously, we have

$$\tfrac{1}{9}(x^3 - 6x^2 - 7x) = x$$

$$x^3 - 6x^2 - 16x = 0$$

$$x(x - 8)(x + 2) = 0$$

so that the points of intersection are $(0, 0)$, $(8, 8)$, $(-2, -2)$. See Fig. 2.27.

Consider first the region that lies to the right of the origin. We can take vertical subregions and, if x_k^* is an x coordinate of the kth subregion, we can write

$$\text{area of } k\text{th subregion} \approx [f_1(x_k^*) - f_2(x_k^*)]\,(\Delta x)_k$$

area of region $\approx \sum_{k=1}^{n} [f_1(x_k^*) - f_2(x_k^*)] \, (\Delta x)_k$

$$\text{area of region} = \int_{x=0}^{8} [f_1(x) - f_2(x)] \, dx = \int_{x=0}^{8} [x - \tfrac{1}{9}(x^3 - 6x^2 - 7x)] \, dx$$

$$= \frac{1}{9} \int_{x=0}^{8} [-x^3 + 6x^2 + 16x] \, dx = \frac{1}{9} \left[-\frac{x^4}{4} + 2x^3 + 8x^2 \right]_0^8$$

$$= \frac{1}{9} \left\{ \left[-\frac{8^4}{4} + 2(8)^3 + 8(8)^2 \right] - [0] \right\} = \frac{1}{9} 8^3 = \frac{512}{9}$$

$$\approx 56.89.$$

For the region that lies to the left of the origin we can again take vertical subregions, but this time the cubic curve lies above the straight line and we must write

area of the kth subregion $\approx [f_2(x_k^*) - f_1(x_k^*)] \, (\Delta x)_k$,

area of region $\approx \sum_{k=1}^{n} [f_2(x_k^*) - f_1(x_k^*)] \, (\Delta x)_k$,

$$\text{area of region} = \int_{x=-2}^{0} [f_2(x) - f_1(x)] \, dx = \int_{x=-2}^{0} [\tfrac{1}{9}(x^3 - 6x^2 - 7x) - x] \, dx$$

$$= \frac{1}{9} \int_{-2}^{0} (x^3 - 6x^2 - 16x) \, dx = \frac{1}{9} \left[\frac{x^4}{4} - 2x^3 - 8x^2 \right]_{-2}^{0}$$

$$= \frac{1}{9} \left\{ [0] - \left[\frac{(-2)^4}{4} - 2(-2)^3 - 8(-2)^2 \right] \right\}$$

$$= -\tfrac{1}{9}\{4 + 16 - 32\} = \tfrac{12}{9} = \tfrac{4}{3} \approx 1.33.$$

EXERCISES 2.7

In each problem check your answer for gross errors by estimating an answer from the diagram.

Find the area of the region bounded by

1. $y = 11 - x^2$ and $y = 2$.

2. $y = \dfrac{1}{x^2}$, $y = 1$, and $x = 4$.

3. $y = x^3 - 1$, $x = 2$, $y = -3$, and the y axis.

4. $x = -(y^2 - 6y + 5)$ and the y axis.

5. $y^2 = x^3$ and $x = 4$.

6. $y = x^2 - 2x - 3$ and $y = 2x + 2$.

7. $y = 8 + 2x - x^2$ and $y = 5x - 10$.

8. $y^2 = 9 - x$ and $y = x - 7$.

9. $y = \dfrac{1}{(2x - 1)^2}$, $y = 1$, and $x = -1$.

10. $y = \dfrac{2}{\sqrt{x + 2}}$ and $x + 3y - 5 = 0$.

11. $y = x, y = 2x$, and $y + 2x - 12 = 0$.

12. $y = x + 1, y + x + 3 = 0$, and $11x - y - 39 = 0$.

13. All three of the curves whose equations are $y = \frac{1}{2} x, y^2 = x$, and $y = 2x$.

14. The arc of $y = (2x + 1)^2$ from $(-\frac{1}{2}, 0)$ to $(0, 1)$, the arc of $y = \frac{1}{9}(2x - 3)^2$ from $(0, 1)$ to $(\frac{3}{2}, 0)$, and the arc of $y = 4x^2 - 4x - 3$ from $(\frac{3}{2}, 0)$ to $(-\frac{1}{2}, 0)$.

Find the areas of the regions bounded by

15. $y = \frac{1}{3} x \sqrt{x^2 + 16}$, the x axis, $x = -3$ and $x = 3$.

16. $y = x^3 - 2x^2 - 8x$ and the x axis.

17. $y = x - x^3$ and $y = x^3 - x^2 - 2x$.

18. Draw the following regions. Consider the subregions into which they might be divided and explain why these regions have the same areas.

Region 1: bounded by $y = x^2$, the x axis, $x = 1$, and $x = 3$;
Region 2: bounded by $y = x^2 - x + 5, y = 5 - x, x = 1$, and $x = 3$.

2.8 Work

Work must be done in order to move an object against an opposing force.

■ DEFINITION 1

If an object is moved a distance D directly against a force of constant magnitude F, then the work done against the force shall be FD.

This definition is a plausible one, because it says that more work must be done in moving against a stronger force and that more work must be done if an object is to be moved through a greater distance.

Example 1.   The "weight" of an object is, by definition, the force with which that object is attracted to the earth (force of gravitation). For an object moving on the surface of the earth, this force of attraction is often assumed to remain constant in magnitude and is always directed toward the center of the earth.*
If, then, an object that weighs 10 lb is lifted vertically a distance of 2 ft, we say that the work done is $W = FD = (10 \text{ lb})(2 \text{ ft}) = 20$ ft-lb.

But many forces do not remain constant as work is performed, and sometimes different parts of a body move different distances against the same force. In these cases Definition 1 does not apply; a new definition is formed by analyzing the work done according to the summation-of-elements technique.

Suppose, then, that an object is moved on a straight line from $x = a$ to $x = b$ against a varying, but continuous, force $F = F(x)$. Divide the interval $a \le x \le b$ into n subintervals of lengths $(\Delta x)_1, (\Delta x)_2, \cdots, (\Delta x)_n$, and take x_k^* to be a point of the kth subinterval. At x_k^* the force has magnitude $F(x_k^*)$. If it had this magnitude throughout the kth subinterval, the work done against the force in moving the object through the kth subinterval would be $F(x_k^*)(\Delta x)_k$, and thus

$$\text{work done for } k\text{th subinterval} \approx F(x_k^*)(\Delta x)_k, \tag{1}$$

$$\text{work done} \approx \sum_{k=1}^{n} F(x_k^*)(\Delta x)_k. \tag{2}$$

---

* This point was discussed in Sec. 2.2.

In the kth subinterval $F(x)$ has a minimum value, say $F(x_k')$ and a maximum value, say $F(x_k'')$. If x_k^* is taken to be x_k' for each k, Eq. (2) will give too small an approximate value for the work done. If x_k^* is taken to be x_k'' for each k, Eq. (2) will give too large an approximate value. If more subintervals are taken, the difference between the overestimate and the underestimate for the work done decreases,* and it seems intuitively reasonable to choose Definition 2.

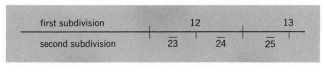

Fig. 2.28

■ DEFINITION 2

If an object is moved in a straight line from $x = a$ to $x = b$ against a continuous force $F(x)$, the work done shall be $\int_{x=a}^{b} F(x)\, dx$.

Example 2. Let an iron ball be attracted to a magnet by the force $F = 12/r^2$, where r is the distance from the magnet to the ball. How much work is done in moving the ball in a straight line, directly away from the magnet, from a point where $r = 3$ to a point where $r = 5$? See Fig. 2.29.

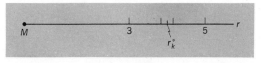

Fig. 2.29

Notice that F is continuous for $3 \leq r \leq 5$, and start by breaking the interval

---

* In greater detail, suppose that in a subdivision into 20 equal subintervals, the minimum value for F for the 12th subinterval is $F(x_{12}')$, so that an underestimate for the work done in this subinterval is

$$F(x_{12}')(\Delta x)_{12} = F(x_{12}')\frac{b - a}{20}.$$

Now suppose that we have 40 equal subintervals instead; see Fig. 2.28. The new underestimate for work done in the 23d and 24th subintervals (the old 12th subinterval) is

$$F(\bar{x}_{23}')\frac{b - a}{40} + F(\bar{x}_{24}')\frac{b - a}{40}.$$

But from the very definition of minimum for an interval, we must have the new $F(\bar{x}_{23}')$ and $F(\bar{x}_{24}')$ at least as great as the old $F(x_{12}')$. Hence for the new underestimate we can write

$$F(\bar{x}_{23}')\frac{b - a}{40} + F(\bar{x}_{24}')\frac{b - a}{40} \geq F(x_{12}')\frac{b - a}{40} + F(x_{12}')\frac{b - a}{40} = F(x_{12}')\frac{b - a}{20},$$

thus making the new underestimate larger than the old, in general, and a better underestimate.

into n subintervals of lengths $(\Delta r)_1, (\Delta r)_2, \cdots, (\Delta r)_n$. If r_k^* is a point of the kth subinterval, then

$$\text{work done during } k\text{th subinterval} \approx \frac{12}{(r_k^*)^2}\,(\Delta r)_k,$$

$$\text{work done} \approx \sum_{k=1}^{n} \frac{12}{(r_k^*)^2}\,(\Delta r)_k,$$

$$\text{work done} = \int_{r=3}^{5} \frac{12}{r^2}\,dr.$$

Turning to the antiderivative point of view to evaluate, we have

$$\text{work done} = 12 \int_{r=3}^{5} r^{-2}\,dr = 12\,\frac{r^{-1}}{-1}\Big|_3^5 = -12\,\frac{1}{r}\Big|_3^5 = -12\Big(\frac{1}{5} - \frac{1}{3}\Big) = \frac{8}{5}.$$

Example 3. Given a cylindrical tank of radius a ft and height b ft, filled with water to a depth c ft; see Fig. 2.30. How much work is done in pumping the water out over the edge of the tank? (Assume that 1 cu ft of water weighs 62.5 lb.)

Start by breaking the h-interval, $0 \le h \le c$, into n subintervals of lengths $(\Delta h)_1, (\Delta h)_2, \cdots, (\Delta h)_n$; see Fig. 2.31. Physically, this means considering the water in the tank to be subdivided into n layers. Each layer has its own weight, and the different layers must be lifted through different distances. We can analyze the problem as follows:

$$\text{volume of } k\text{th layer} = \pi a^2\,(\Delta h)_k.$$
$$\text{weight of } k\text{th layer} = 62.5\pi a^2\,(\Delta h)_k.$$

Let h_k^* be a height of the kth subinterval. Then

$$\text{distance } k\text{th layer must be lifted} \approx b - h_k^*,$$
$$\text{work done on } k\text{th layer} \approx 62.5\pi a^2\,(\Delta h)_k(b - h_k^*),$$
$$\text{work done} \approx \sum_{k=1}^{n} 62.5\pi a^2\,(b - h_k^*)(\Delta h)_k.$$

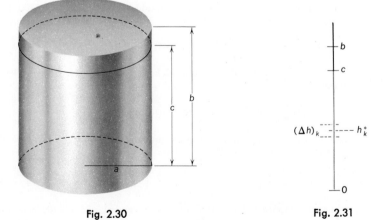

Fig. 2.30   Fig. 2.31

It now seems natural to take this statement for the work done:

$$\text{work done} = \lim_{n \to \infty} \sum_{k=1}^{n} 62.5\pi a^2 (b - h_k^*)(\Delta h)_k = \int_{h=0}^{c} 62.5\pi a^2 (b - h) \, dh.$$

Here it is understood that the largest $(\Delta h)_k$ approaches 0 as n grows beyond all bounds.

To evaluate this definite integral, we turn to the antidifferentiation technique. We have

$$\text{work done} = 62.5\pi a^2 \int_{h=0}^{c} (b - h) \, dh = 62.5\pi a^2 \left(bh - \frac{h^2}{2} \right) \Big|_{h=0}^{c}$$

$$= 62.5\pi a^2 \left[\left(bc - \frac{c^2}{2} \right) - (0 - 0) \right] = 62.5\pi a^2 c \left(b - \frac{c}{2} \right).$$

● **Remark 1**

This particular problem can be solved by considering Definition 1 directly, because the symmetry of the cylinder makes it possible to say that the water is lifted through an *average* distance of $b - (c/2)$ ft. The water weighs $62.5\pi a^2 c$ lb and hence the work done is $62.5\pi a^2 \, c[b - (c/2)]$. For other containers, for instance for a conical container, the average distance is not obvious and the analysis by subdivision and summation has a vital role to play. Such problems will be considered again in Chapter 8. The primary goal here is to illustrate the summation technique.

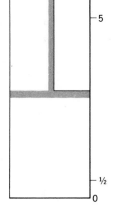

Example 4. Consider some gas at pressure 14 psi in a cylinder of radius 1 in., height 5 in.; see Fig. 2.32. Suppose a piston compresses the gas adiabatically from height 5 to height $\frac{1}{2}$. How much work did the piston do? (Assume that in an adiabatic compression the pressure and volume are related by $PV^{1.4} = \text{const.}$)

Fig. 2.32

We know that $PV^{1.4} = C$ and that $P = 14$ when $V = \pi(1)^2 5$. Hence

$$14(5\pi)^{1.4} = C, \tag{3}$$

and we can say that

$$P = \frac{C}{V^{1.4}},$$

where the value of C is given by Eq. (3). Also, the face area of the piston is π sq in., so that the force pressing against the piston at any height h is

$$F = \left(P \frac{\text{lb}}{\text{sq in.}} \right) (\pi \text{ sq in.}) = \pi P \text{ lb.}$$

Finally, V and h are related:

$$V = \pi(1)^2 h \quad \text{or} \quad h = \frac{1}{\pi} V.$$

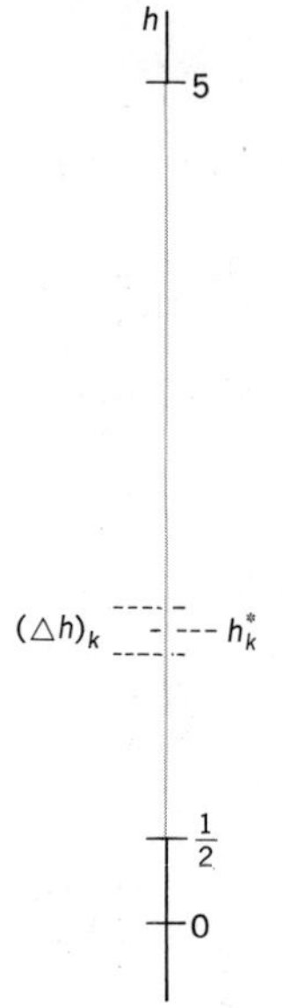

Now let us break the interval $\frac{1}{2} \leq h \leq 5$ into n subintervals; see Fig. 2.33. Physically, this means that we consider the piston's trip from $h = 5$ to $h = \frac{1}{2}$ to consist of n smaller trips of lengths $(\Delta h)_1, (\Delta h)_2, \cdots, (\Delta h)_n$. Let h_k^* be a height of the kth subinterval and let P_k^* be the corresponding pressure. We have

$$\text{distance moved during } k\text{th subinterval} = (\Delta h)_k = \frac{1}{\pi} (\Delta V)_k,$$

$$\text{force against which piston works during } k\text{th subinterval} \approx \pi P_k^*,$$

$$\text{work done for } k\text{th subinterval} \approx \pi P_k^* (\Delta h)_k = P_k^* (\Delta V)_k.$$

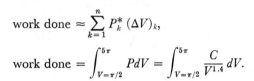

$$\text{work done} \approx \sum_{k=1}^{n} P_k^* (\Delta V)_k,$$

$$\text{work done} = \int_{V=\pi/2}^{5\pi} P \, dV = \int_{V=\pi/2}^{5\pi} \frac{C}{V^{1.4}} \, dV.$$

We can evaluate this integral by using the antiderivative point of view:

Fig. 2.33

$$\text{work done} = C \int_{V=\pi/2}^{5\pi} V^{-1.4} \, dV$$

$$= C \left. \frac{V^{-0.4}}{-0.4} \right|_{\pi/2}^{5\pi} = -\frac{C}{0.4} \left. \frac{1}{V^{0.4}} \right|_{\pi/2}^{5\pi}$$

$$= -\frac{14(5\pi)^{1.4}}{0.4} \left[\frac{1}{(5\pi)^{0.4}} - \frac{1}{(0.5\pi)^{0.4}} \right]$$

$$= -\frac{14(5\pi)}{0.4} [1 - (10)^{0.4}],$$

$$\text{work done} \approx 831.2 \text{ in.-lb} \approx 69.3 \text{ ft-lb}.$$

● **Remark 2**

If a compression takes place slowly so that the heat generated is allowed to escape and the temperature remains constant, the compression is isothermal. In that case the relationship between the pressure and volume is $PV = C$. If we had dealt with an isothermal compression instead of an adiabatic compression, we would have been led to an integral of the form $\int (1/V) \, dV$. We could not have evaluated such an integral from the antiderivative point of view at this time.*

EXERCISES 2.8

The goal here is to practice the limit-of-a-sum method of analyzing problems and the evaluation of the resulting definite integrals. The following of illustrative problems too closely, instead of analyzing each problem according to its own details, would defeat the purpose of these exercises.

1. How much work is done in moving directly against a force F from $x = 1$ to $x = 5$ if $F = -.1x$?

---

* This problem will be considered in Example 5.3-8.

2. Assume that in stretching a spring one works against a force F which is proportional to x, the displacement from equilibrium, and oppositely directed.
(a) Write down a statement for F.
(b) How much work is done in stretching the spring from equilibrium to $x = 1$?

3. Coulomb's law says that two like electrostatic charges repel each other with a force inversely proportional to the square of the distance between them. Suppose charge A repels charge B with a force $F = 16/r^2$, where r is the distance between them. What work must be done to bring charge B from a point 8 units from charge A to a point 4 units from charge A, moving directly toward A?

4. In Exercise 3, suppose 4 units of work were available for moving B toward A. How far directly toward A could B be moved from a point 8 units from A?

5. Let the force of attraction between a body and the earth be given by Newton's law of gravitation, $F = kmm_E/r^2$. If the body weighs 100 lb at the surface of the earth, $r = 4000$ miles, with what force would it be attracted to the earth if placed 1000 miles from the earth's surface? How much work would have to be done against the force of gravitation to get it to a point 1000 miles from the surface of the earth?

6. We are given a pail that weighs 2 lb and contains 20 lb of sand at the start. The pail is lifted slowly a distance of 4 ft, but, as it is lifted, sand leaks out of a hole at the uniform rate of 2 lb of sand per foot lifted. Use integration to find the work done in lifting the pail. Check by using Definition 1 directly.

7. We are given a circular cylinder of radius 2 ft and height 6 ft, filled with water to within 1 ft of the top. Use integration to find the work done in pumping out half the water. (Water weighs 62.5 lb per cu ft.) Check by using Definition 1 directly.

8. In Exercise 7, how much of the water could be lifted out if 1000π ft-lb of energy are available for lifting the water?

9. Let the circular cylinder of radius 2 ft and height 6 ft be filled to a depth of 2 ft with water and then, above the water, to the 5-ft mark with an oil that weighs 40 lb per cu ft. Use integration to find the work done in lifting the oil and water out of the cylinder. Check by using Definition 1 directly.

10. Let a gas be compressed in a cylinder of cross-section area A sq in. in such a way that the pressure and volume are related by $PV^\gamma = C$, γ a constant, $\gamma > 1$. If the piston starts from a height of a in., at which place the pressure is 14 psi, how much work is done in pushing the piston down to a height of b in.?

11. Consider a cylinder of cross-section area 6 sq ft floating in water (which weighs 62.5 lb per cu ft). Archimedes' law says that a floating body is buoyed up by a force equal to the weight of the displaced water.
(a) Show that there will be an upward force of $(62.5)6x$ lb acting on the cylinder if it is displaced a distance x feet down from its equilibrium position.
(b) How much work must be done to force the cylinder down $\frac{1}{2}$ ft from its equilibrium position?

Plane Analytic Geometry

3.1 The Point of View of Analytic Geometry

Analytic geometry attempts to set up a correspondence between geometry and algebra. The basic concepts and theorems of geometry can be described and proved algebraically; the basic concepts and processes of algebra can be illustrated geometrically. When a geometric problem seems to be difficult, the corresponding algebraic problem can be considered instead. If the algebraic tools at our disposal are more powerful in this particular situation, we can solve the problem algebraically, and then translate the result into geometric language. Often it is the other way around. The geometric counterpart of an algebraic problem may indicate what results can be expected and point to an efficient method for attacking the problem. As we study analytic geometry many important facts about certain curves and the corresponding equations will appear, and the reader will surely be expected to add some of these facts to his general working mathematical background. But the reader's primary goal should be to understand how the correspondence between algebra and geometry is set up, so that he can use this correspondence whenever he needs it, not just in the particular situations that time permits us to touch on in a first course.

A correspondence between algebra and geometry can start with a coordinate system. Such a system sets up a correspondence between the points of a plane and pairs of numbers. There are many such correspondences. Here we shall work with rectangular or Cartesian coordinates; later we shall study polar coordinates, but these are only the two most frequently used coordinate systems.

We have already assumed a certain familiarity with the rectangular coordinate system. Now we want to emphasize the fact that with its help we can associate with each point in the plane one ordered pair of numbers, called the point's

coordinates, and that with each ordered pair
of numbers we can associate one point in the
plane.

Example 1. Given the point A in Fig.
3.1. By dropping perpendiculars to the coordinate axes we see that the coordinates
associated with A are $x = 2$ and $y = 1.5$. We
write $A(2, 1.5)$.

Example 2. Given the coordinates x
$= -3, y = 1$ or $(-3, 1)$. By moving 3 units
in the negative x direction from the origin
and then 1 unit in the positive y direction we

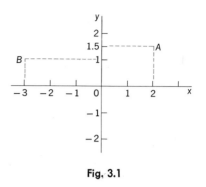

Fig. 3.1

locate the point B. One could also have located B by moving first 1 unit in the
positive y direction and then 3 units in the negative x direction.

3.2 The Distance between Two Points

It is reasonable to start with the concepts of distance and direction when studying
geometry by algebraic methods.

▉ DEFINITION 1

Directions on lines parallel to axes. On the x axis or a line parallel to it, a directed
distance is to be considered positive if its direction is that of increasing x, negative
if its direction is that of decreasing x. On the y axis or a line parallel to it, a directed
distance is to be considered positive if its direction is that of increasing y, negative
if its direction is that of decreasing y.

▉ THEOREM 1A

HYPOTHESIS: $P_1(x_1, y)$ and $P_2(x_2, y)$ lie on a line parallel to the x axis.

CONCLUSION: The directed distance $\overline{P_1 P_2}$ is $x_2 - x_1$.

▉ THEOREM 1B

HYPOTHESIS: $P_1(x, y_1)$ and $P_2(x, y_2)$ lie on a line parallel to the y axis.

CONCLUSION: The directed distance $\overline{P_1 P_2}$ is $y_2 - y_1$.

In words: To get a directed distance parallel to one of the axes, take the x
(or y) coordinate of the terminal point and subtract the x (or y) coordinate of the
initial point.

PROOF: We shall prove Theorem 1B. Let S be the point of intersection of the
x axis and the line joining P_1 and P_2, extended if necessary.

In Fig. 3.2(a), $\overline{SP_1} = y_1$ and $\overline{SP_2} = y_2$ by the definition of y coordinate and

$$\overline{P_1 P_2} = y_2 - y_1.$$

In the special case where P_1 and S coincide we have $y_1 = 0$, but the argument is
the same.

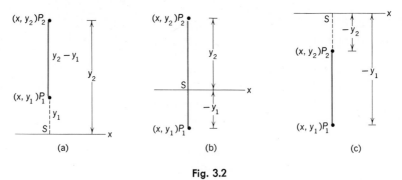

Fig. 3.2

In Fig. 3.2(b), we must remember that y_1 is a negative number because P_1 lies below the x axis. Since the directed distance $\overline{P_1S}$ must be positive, we must assume $\overline{P_1S} = -y_1$. But $\overline{SP_2} = y_2$, and then

$$\overline{P_1P_2} = \overline{P_1S} + \overline{SP_2} = (-y_1) + (y_2) = y_2 - y_1.$$

In Fig. 3.2(c), both y_2 and y_1 are negative numbers. Hence the directed distances $\overline{P_1S}$ and $\overline{P_2S}$ are $-y_1$ and $-y_2$, respectively. Then

$$\overline{P_1P_2} = \overline{P_1S} - \overline{P_2S} = (-y_1) - (-y_2) = y_2 - y_1$$

also. In the special case where P_2 and S coincide we have $y_2 = 0$, but the same argument holds.

We have considered the various possibilities for a positively directed $\overline{P_1P_2}$. If $\overline{P_1P_2}$ were negatively directed, then $\overline{P_2P_1}$ would be positively directed, and what we have already proved could be applied to $\overline{P_2P_1}$. Hence $\overline{P_2P_1} = y_1 - y_2$, and then

$$\overline{P_1P_2} = -\overline{P_2P_1} = -(y_1 - y_2) = y_2 - y_1.$$

In all cases the conclusion of the theorem holds and we have completed the proof.

Example 1.   In rectangle $ABCD$ of Fig. 3.3,

$$\overline{AB} = y_B - y_A = (2) - (\tfrac{1}{2}) = +\tfrac{3}{2},$$

$$\overline{BC} = x_C - x_B = (-3) - (-1) = -2,$$

$$\overline{CD} = y_D - y_C = (\tfrac{1}{2}) - (2) = -\tfrac{3}{2},$$

$$\overline{DA} = x_A - x_D = (-1) - (-3) = +2.$$

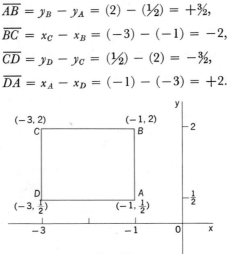

Fig. 3.3

We made specific agreements about the positive and negative directions on lines parallel to the axes. For other lines no general agreements are made at this time. If later we wish to use directed distances on such lines, we shall define the positive directions in specific cases as needed. For many purposes the ability to compute undirected distances will suffice.

■ THEOREM 2

The distance between two points.

HYPOTHESIS: The coordinates of P_1 and P_2 are (x_1, y_1) and (x_2, y_2).

CONCLUSION: $P_1P_2 = \sqrt{(x_2 - x_1)^2 + (y_2 - y_1)^2}$.

In words: The distance between two points is found by
(a) taking the difference between the x coordinates and squaring,
(b) taking the difference between the y coordinates and squaring,
(c) adding these two numbers, and
(d) taking the square root of the sum.

PROOF: Our proof amounts essentially to an algebraic restatement of the Pythagorean Theorem.

(a) Through P_2 draw P_2S parallel to the y axis, and through P_1 draw P_1S parallel to the x axis. The coordinates of S are (x_2, y_1); see Fig. 3.4.

(b) The lines P_1S and SP_2 are parallel to the axes. By Theorem 1, no matter what the location of the points P_1, P_2, S, we have $\overline{P_1S} = x_2 - x_1$ and $\overline{SP_2} = y_2 - y_1$. Then, by the Pythagorean Theorem,

$$(P_1P_2)^2 = (x_2 - x_1)^2 + (y_2 - y_1)^2.$$

● Remark 1

Observe how these theorems on the distance between two points are part of the geometry-algebra correspondence. The distance between two points is a geometric concept. Theorems 1 and 2 give us algebraic computations for that distance.

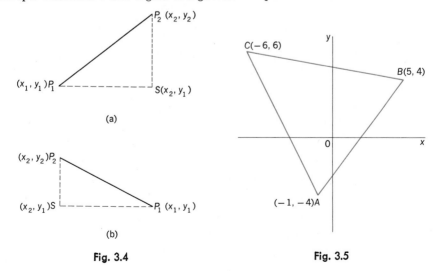

(a)

(b)

Fig. 3.4   **Fig. 3.5**

Example 2. Show that $A(-1, -4)$, $B(5, 4)$, $C(-6, 6)$ is an isosceles triangle and find its perimeter. See Fig. 3.5. Using the distance formula, we have

$$AB = \sqrt{[5 - (-1)]^2 + [4 - (-4)]^2} = \sqrt{36 + 64} = 10,$$
$$BC = \sqrt{[(-6) - 5]^2 + [6 - 4]^2} = \sqrt{125},$$
$$CA = \sqrt{[(-1) - (-6)]^2 + [(-4) - 6]^2} = \sqrt{125}.$$

Thus the triangle is isosceles because $BC = CA$, and the perimeter is $10 + 2\sqrt{125}$ or $10(1 + \sqrt{5}) \approx 32.36$.

3.3 On the Direction of a Line

To continue our study of the correspondence between geometry and algebra, we consider next the concept of direction.* To compare the directions of different lines, we first select one direction as a standard with which other directions can be compared. This standard direction is the positive x axis direction.

■ DEFINITION 1

Inclination of a line. Through any point of a line L draw a line parallel to the x axis. The inclination angle of L is the smallest angle from the positive x axis direction to L, measured in the counterclockwise direction.

● Remark 1

From the definition these facts follow:
(a) Lines parallel to the x axis have inclination $\alpha = 0°$;
(b) Lines parallel to the y axis have inclination $\alpha = 90°$;
(c) For the inclination angle α, we always have $0° \leq \alpha < 180°$. See Fig. 3.6.

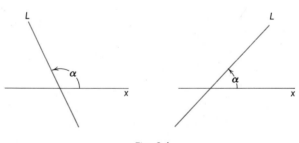

Fig. 3.6

Because we have the definition of derivative in mind, we find it convenient to use $\tan \alpha$ rather than $\sin \alpha$ or $\cos \alpha$ in defining the slope of a line.

■ DEFINITION 2

The slope of a line. For any line other than one parallel to the y axis, the slope is the tangent of the inclination angle:

$$m = \tan \alpha. \tag{1}$$

---

* We repeat some of the work of Sec. 1.3 and then go on.

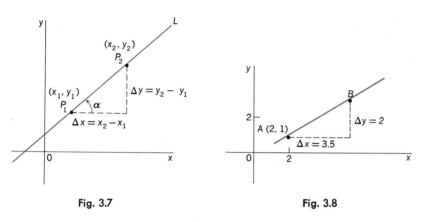

Fig. 3.7   Fig. 3.8

● **Remark 2**

Observe from Eq. (1) that, if a line has any finite slope m, positive or negative, it has a uniquely defined inclination angle not equal to 90°. The lines parallel to the y axis do not have finite slope; since the prefix "in" means "not," we sometimes say that the slope of a line parallel to the y axis is not finite or is infinite.

● **Remark 3**

It is often convenient to remember the slope in the following ways. Let $P_1(x_1, y_1)$ and $P_2(x_2, y_2)$ be any two points on line L. Then if L is not parallel to the y axis,

$$m = \frac{\Delta y}{\Delta x} = \frac{y_2 - y_1}{x_2 - x_1} = \frac{\text{"rise"}}{\text{"run"}}. \tag{2}$$

See Fig. 3.7.

● **Remark 4**

If line L rises as one moves along it in the direction of increasing x, it has positive slope and an acute inclination angle, for Δy and Δx are both positive. But if L falls, it has negative slope and an obtuse inclination angle, for Δy is then negative.

Example 1. Draw a line through $A(2, 1)$ with slope $\frac{4}{7}$. See Fig. 3.8. We locate point A first. Next we know that $\Delta y/\Delta x$ is to be $\frac{4}{7}$. It is convenient to choose $\Delta x = 3.5$ and $\Delta y = 2$. Accordingly, we locate point B by moving 3.5 units in the x direction from A, then 2 units in the y direction. The line joining A to B is the desired line.

Example 2. Draw a line through $C(-1, 3)$ with slope $-\frac{2}{3}$. See Fig. 3.9. Locate point C first. Then, with $\Delta y/\Delta x = -\frac{2}{3}$, it is convenient to choose $\Delta x = 3$, $\Delta y = -2$. Locate point D by moving 3 units in the x direction from C, and 2 units in the negative y direction. The line joining C to D is the desired line. The choice $\Delta x = -3$, $\Delta y = +2$, leading to D', would have been just as convenient.

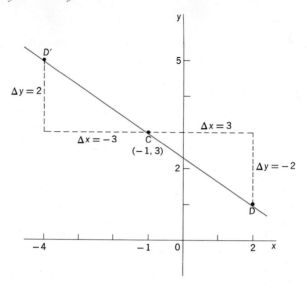

Fig. 3.9

Example 3. Show that $Q(-1, 1)$, $V(4, 2)$, $S(3, -2)$, $U(-2, -3)$ is a parallelogram and find the slopes of its sides. See Fig. 3.10. First we compute

$$QV = \sqrt{(4 + 1)^2 + (2 - 1)^2} = \sqrt{26},$$
$$US = \sqrt{(3 + 2)^2 + (-2 + 3)^2} = \sqrt{26},$$
$$UQ = \sqrt{(-1 + 2)^2 + (1 + 3)^2} = \sqrt{17},$$
$$SV = \sqrt{(4 - 3)^2 + (2 + 2)^2} = \sqrt{17}.$$

Thus we see that $QVSU$ is a parallelogram because opposite sides are equal. But, in a parallelogram, opposite sides are parallel. When we use Eq. (2) to find the slopes of these opposite sides, we have

$$m_{UQ} = \frac{(1) - (-3)}{(-1) - (-2)} = 4, \qquad m_{SV} = \frac{(2) - (-2)}{(4) - (3)} = 4,$$

$$m_{QV} = \frac{(2) - (1)}{(4) - (-1)} = \frac{1}{5}, \qquad m_{US} = \frac{(-2) - (-3)}{(3) - (-2)} = \frac{1}{5}.$$

In Example 3 we found that parallel lines had equal slopes. These computations in Example 3 illustrate a fact of more general occurrence.

■ THEOREM 1A

Slopes of parallel lines.

HYPOTHESIS: $L_1 \parallel L_2$.

CONCLUSION: Either $m_1 = m_2$ or both m_1 and m_2 are infinite.

PROOF: Since $L_1 \parallel L_2$, the inclination angles α_1 and α_2 are equal, according to a theorem of Euclid on parallel lines cut by a transversal; see Fig. 3.11. If

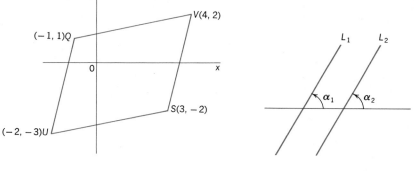

Fig. 3.10

Fig. 3.11

$\alpha_1 = \alpha_2 = 90°$, then L_1 and L_2 are vertical and both have infinite slopes. Otherwise $\tan \alpha_1 = \tan \alpha_2$ and thus $m_1 = m_2$.

■ THEOREM 1B (CONVERSE OF THEOREM 1A)

HYPOTHESIS: $m_1 = m_2$ or m_1 and m_2 are both infinite.

CONCLUSION: $L_1 \parallel L_2$.

PROOF: If m_1 and m_2 are both infinite, then L_1 and L_2 are both parallel to the y axis and parallel to each other. If $m_1 = m_2$, then $\tan \alpha_1 = \tan \alpha_2$. Since $0° \leq \alpha_1, \alpha_2 < 180°$, it follows that $\alpha_1 = \alpha_2$. But then $L_1 \parallel L_2$.

● Remark 5

Again it has been shown how a geometric statement corresponds to an algebraic statement. The geometric statement, "Two lines are parallel," is equivalent to a simple algebraic statement about their slopes: "Either their slopes are equal or both are infinite."

Another fundamental theorem on describing directions concludes this section.

■ THEOREM 2A

Slopes of perpendicular lines.

HYPOTHESIS: $L_1 \perp L_2$, but these lines are not parallel to the axes.

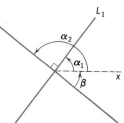

Fig. 3.12

CONCLUSION: $m_1 = -1/m_2$.

PROOF: See Fig. 3.12. By hypothesis, $\alpha_1 + \beta = 90°$. Therefore

$$\tan \alpha_1 = \cot \beta = \frac{1}{\tan \beta} = \frac{1}{\tan (180° - \alpha_2)} = -\frac{1}{\tan \alpha_2},$$

or

$$m_1 = -\frac{1}{m_2}.$$

Observe also that $m_1 m_2 = -1$ and that

$$m_2 = -\frac{1}{m_1}.$$

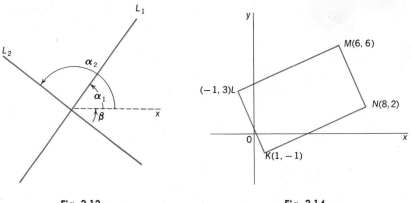

Fig. 3.13   Fig. 3.14

■ THEOREM 2B (CONVERSE OF THEOREM 2A)

HYPOTHESIS: $m_1 = -1/m_2$.

CONCLUSION: $L_1 \perp L_2$.

PROOF: By hypothesis, m_1 and m_2 are of opposite signs, and therefore one of α_1, α_2 must be acute, the other not. Without loss of generality we can assume that α_1 is acute, α_2 not; see Fig. 3.13. Then since $m_1 = -1/m_2$, we write

$$\tan \alpha_1 = -\frac{1}{\tan \alpha_2}.$$

The angle $\beta = 180° - \alpha_2$ is acute, and $\tan \beta = -\tan \alpha_2$, so that

$$\tan \alpha_1 = \frac{1}{\tan \beta} = \cot \beta.$$

If the tangent of one acute angle equals the cotangent of another, they must be complementary. Hence

$$\alpha_1 + \beta = 90°,$$
$$\alpha_1 + (180° - \alpha_2) = 90°,$$
$$\alpha_2 - \alpha_1 = 90°,$$

and thus $L_1 \perp L_2$.

● Remark 6

The geometric statement, "Two lines are perpendicular," is equivalent to the algebraic statement, "Their slopes are negative reciprocals," unless the lines are parallel to the coordinate axes, in which case perpendicularity is easy enough to detect without algebraic aid.

Example 4. Show that $L(-1, 3)$, $M(6, 6)$, $N(8, 2)$, $K(1, -1)$ is a parallelogram, but not a rectangle. See Fig. 3.14.

$$\text{(a)} \ m_{LM} = \frac{(6) - (3)}{(6) - (-1)} = \frac{3}{7}; \quad m_{KN} = \frac{(2) - (-1)}{(8) - (1)} = \frac{3}{7}.$$

Therefore $LM \parallel KN$.

(b) $m_{KL} = \dfrac{(3) - (-1)}{(-1) - (1)} = -2; \; m_{MN} = \dfrac{(6) - (2)}{(6) - (8)} = -2.$

Therefore $KL \parallel MN$ and $LMNK$ is a parallelogram.

(c) But LM is not perpendicular to LK, because their slopes are not negative reciprocals. Therefore $LMNK$ is not a rectangle.

EXERCISES 3.3

1. Is the triangle with the following vertices isosceles? right? neither?

   (a) $(-4, -5)$, $(8, 11)$, $(-2, 6)$.
   (b) $(-1, 0)$, $(1, 3)$, $(7, -1)$.
   (c) $(0, 0)$, $(5, 12)$, $(-1\%_2, 11)$.
   (d) $(3, -4)$, $(9, 4)$, $(2, 3)$.

   (e) $(1, 4)$, $(4, 2)$, $(1, -2)$.
   (f) $(-7, -7)$, $(9, 5)$, $(4, -5)$.
   (g) $(0, -5)$, $(24, 5)$, $(17, -12)$.
   (h) $(-3, -2)$, $(-1, 5)$, $(6, 3)$.

2. Is the quadrilateral with the following vertices a trapezoid, a parallelogram, a rectangle, a rhombus, a square, or none of these?

   (a) $(-6, -1)$, $(-2, 5)$, $(1, 3)$, $(-3, -3)$.
   (b) $(2, 2)$, $(5, 6)$, $(1, 9)$, $(-2, 5)$.
   (c) $(3, -1)$, $(6, 6)$, $(2, 8)$, $(-3, 2)$.
   (d) $(1, 2)$, $(5, 6)$, $(10, 1)$, $(6, -3)$.
   (e) $(0, 0)$, $(3, 4)$, $(\%_5, 4\%_5)$, $(-\%_5, 2\%_5)$.
   (f) $(5, -2)$, $(3, 1)$, $(-4, -4)$, $(-2, -7)$.
   (g) $(9, 3)$, $(11, -1)$, $(4, -5)$, $(2, 0)$.
   (h) $(1, -5)$, $(6, 0)$, $(5, 7)$, $(0, 2)$.
   (i) $(1, -4)$, $(6, 8)$, $(-6, 13)$, $(-11, 1)$.
   (j) $(2, 7)$, $(-2, 3)$, $(3, -3)$, $(7, 1)$.

3. (a) Draw a line through $(0, 2)$ with slope $\%_4$.
   (b) Draw a line through $(-1, -2)$ with slope $-\%_2$.
   (c) Draw a line through $(5, 0)$ with slope $\%_5$.
   (d) Draw a line through $(4, -3)$ with slope $-\%_{11}$.

4. Decide whether these points are collinear (lie on a line):

   (a) $(-1, 4)$, $(2, 6)$, $(8, 10)$;
   (b) $(-1, 4)$, $(4, -12)$, $(1, -2)$;
   (c) $(-1, 4)$, $(6, -1)$, $(\%_3, \%_3)$.

5. We are given $x^2 + y^2 = a^2$ as the equation of a circle of radius a with center at the origin. Let $Q(b, c)$ be any point on the circle.

   (a) Find the slope of the radius OQ.

   (b) Find $\dfrac{dy}{dx}$ and the slope of the tangent line at Q.

   (c) Show that the tangent and radius are perpendicular.

6. In finding the inclination angle of a line by following Definition 1 of this section, two different observers might start with two different parallels to the x axis. Would they compute the same inclination angle?

7. (a) Our theorem for measuring distances, Theorem 3.2-2, should give us the same value for the distance between two points when the order in which the points are taken is reversed. Prove that it does.

   (b) Since we get the same line joining P_1 and P_2 when we draw from P_2 to P_1 that we get when we draw from P_1 to P_2, the slope should be the same if we reverse the order in which the points are taken. Prove that when the slope is computed according to Eq. (2) of this section, the order in which the two points are taken can be interchanged.

3.4 The Definition of Vector. Addition of Vectors

A velocity requires for its description a statement of direction and a statement of numerical magnitude. Thus one might say that the wind blew in the north direction with a magnitude of 15 miles per hr. The following definition is helpful in studying such quantities.

■ DEFINITION 1

A *vector* is a directed line segment.

In Fig. 3.15(a) we have indicated a directed line segment or vector with initial point A and terminal point B. Vectors can be used to represent velocities or forces or other quantities that require for their description statements of direction and magnitude, because a vector can be given the same direction as that of the velocity to be represented and a length equal to the magnitude of the velocity (on a suitably chosen scale). Indeed, the physicist gives the name *vector quantity* to a quantity that can be represented by a vector.

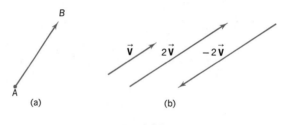

Fig. 3.15

There are also in physics quantities like the temperature of a body, the height of a falling body, or the viscosity of an oil that are called *scalar quantities*. As the word "scalar" suggests, these quantities can be "scaled," or described by comparison with a real-number scale. For such a quantity, only a numerical statement of magnitude need be made. Thus, one might say that the temperature was 60°C.

■ DEFINITION 2

A *scalar* is a real number. (And a *scalar quantity* is one that can be represented by a scalar.)

To distinguish between scalars and vectors in writing by hand as well as in printing, we agree to use the following convention.

■ NOTATION CONVENTION 1

Vectors will be indicated by bold-faced print and by placing the symbol $\rightarrow$ above the letter representing the vector. *Scalars* will be indicated by italic print.

■ NOTATION CONVENTION 2

The length or magnitude of vector $\vec{\mathbf{v}}$ will be denoted by $\|\vec{\mathbf{v}}\|$.

■ NOTATION CONVENTION 3

A zero vector is one whose initial and terminal points coincide. For a zero vector we shall write $\vec{0}$. A zero vector has length 0 but arbitrary direction.

● Remark 1

Sometimes in describing a force it is necessary to state the point of application of the force or the line along which it acts. Two parallel forces can have the same sense and equal magnitudes and yet cause different rotations about a given axis, for instance. Occasionally, then, it may be necessary to modify the following statement, but unless otherwise stated, the vector equation $\vec{a} = \vec{b}$ shall mean either that the vectors $\vec{a}$ and $\vec{b}$ are parallel and have the same sense and the same nonzero length, or else that they are both zero vectors.

■ DEFINITION 3

Multiplying a vector by a scalar. The vector $c\vec{v}$ is a vector parallel to $\vec{v}$ with length $|c|$ times that of $\vec{v}$. If $c > 0$, $c\vec{v}$ has the same sense as $\vec{v}$; if $c < 0$, $c\vec{v}$ has the opposite sense; if $c = 0$, $c\vec{v}$ is a zero vector. See Fig. 3.15(b).

Multiplying by a scalar adjusts the length of a vector. If given a vector $\vec{v}$, not a zero vector, one can always get a unit vector in the same direction by dividing $\vec{v}$ by its own length;

$$\frac{1}{\|\vec{v}\|}\,\vec{v}$$

has unit length.

Our definition for the sum of two vectors is motivated by observed results in important physical applications. In adding forces or velocities we find that the "parallelogram" law applies.

■ DEFINITION 3A

The addition of vectors. $\vec{a} + \vec{b}$ is the vector obtained by

(a) moving, if necessary, one vector parallel to itself until both vectors have the same initial point;

(b) drawing the parallelogram determined by these vectors;

(c) taking the diagonal that has the same initial point as $\vec{a}$ and $\vec{b}$.

Example 1. Given $\vec{a}$ and $\vec{b}$ as in Fig. 3.16(a). We move $\vec{a}$ parallel to itself until $\vec{a}$ and $\vec{b}$ have the same initial point, Fig. 3.16(b). Then we complete the parallelogram and take for $\vec{a} + \vec{b}$ the diagonal from the common initial point, Fig. 3.16(c).

Since opposite sides of a parallelogram are equal and parallel, we have congruent triangles in Fig. 3.16(c). Either triangle would suffice for constructing $\vec{a} + \vec{b}$, as in Figs. 3.16(d) and 3.16(e). We can therefore state a more efficient, alternate definition.

■ DEFINITION 3B

The addition of vectors. $\vec{a} + \vec{b}$ is the vector obtained by

(a) moving vector $\vec{b}$ parallel to itself until its initial point coincides with the terminal point of $\vec{a}$;

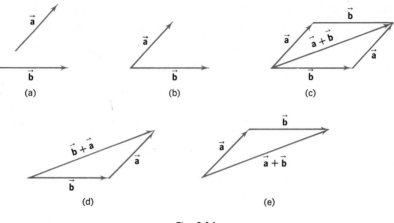

Fig. 3.16

(b) taking the vector whose initial point is the initial point of $\vec{a}$ and whose terminal point is the terminal point of $\vec{b}$.

Figures 3.16(d) and 3.16(e) give us our next theorem.

■ THEOREM 1

The commutative law for the addition of vectors.

HYPOTHESIS: $\vec{a}$ and $\vec{b}$ are vectors.

CONCLUSION: $\vec{a} + \vec{b} = \vec{b} + \vec{a}$.

A sum of three vectors, $\vec{a} + \vec{b} + \vec{c}$, could mean the sum of $(\vec{a} + \vec{b})$ and $\vec{c}$, in symbols $(\vec{a} + \vec{b}) + \vec{c}$; or it could mean the sum of $\vec{a}$ and $(\vec{b} + \vec{c})$, in symbols $\vec{a} + (\vec{b} + \vec{c})$. Unless these sums are equal, $\vec{a} + \vec{b} + \vec{c}$ is not clearly defined.

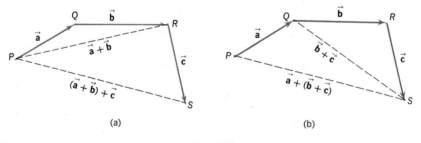

Fig. 3.17

In Fig. 3.17(a), $\vec{a} + \vec{b}$ is vector $\overrightarrow{PQ} + \overrightarrow{QR} = \overrightarrow{PR}$, because P is the initial point of $\overrightarrow{PQ}$ and R is the terminal point of $\overrightarrow{QR}$. Next, $(\vec{a} + \vec{b}) + \vec{c}$ is the vector $\overrightarrow{PR} + \overrightarrow{RS} = \overrightarrow{PS}$. From Fig. 3.17(b) we see that $\vec{b} + \vec{c}$ is vector $\overrightarrow{QR} + \overrightarrow{RS} = \overrightarrow{QS}$, and that $\vec{a} + (\vec{b} + \vec{c}) = \overrightarrow{PQ} + \overrightarrow{QS} = \overrightarrow{PS}$. Thus $(\vec{a} + \vec{b}) + \vec{c} = \vec{a} + (\vec{b} + \vec{c}) = \overrightarrow{PS}$. We have proved another theorem:

■ THEOREM 2

The associative law for the addition of vectors.

    HYPOTHESIS: $\vec{a}$, $\vec{b}$, and $\vec{c}$ are vectors.

    CONCLUSION: $(\vec{a} + \vec{b}) + \vec{c} = \vec{a} + (\vec{b} + \vec{c})$.

The fact that corresponding sides of similar triangles are proportional makes possible the following statement.

■ THEOREM 3

A distributive law.

    HYPOTHESIS: $\vec{A}$ and $\vec{B}$ are vectors, c is a scalar.

    CONCLUSION: $c(\vec{A} + \vec{B}) = c\vec{A} + c\vec{B}$.

    PROOF: We take c positive at first. In triangle PQR of Fig. 3.18 the addition of $\vec{A}$ and $\vec{B}$ to form $\vec{A} + \vec{B}$ is described. Triangle $P'Q'R'$ is similar to triangle PQR, each side c times as long as the corresponding side of triangle PQR and parallel to it, with the same sense. Thus $\overrightarrow{P'Q'} = c\vec{A}$, $\overrightarrow{Q'R'} = c\vec{B}$, and $\overrightarrow{P'R'} = c(\vec{A} + \vec{B})$.

But we also read from triangle $P'Q'R'$ that

$$\overrightarrow{P'R'} = \overrightarrow{P'Q'} + \overrightarrow{Q'R'}.$$

Thus
$$c(\vec{A} + \vec{B}) = c\vec{A} + c\vec{B},$$

and the theorem is demonstrated for c positive.

If c were negative, we would consider triangle $P''Q''R''$. This triangle is similar to triangle PQR, each side $-c$ times as long as the corresponding side of triangle PQR and parallel to it, but with the opposite sense.

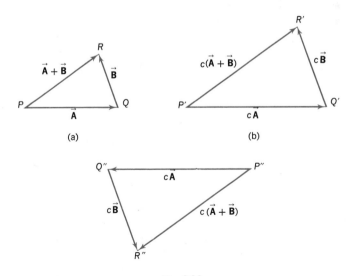

(a)   (b)

Fig. 3.18

If $c = 0$, then $c(\vec{A} + \vec{B})$, $c\vec{A}$, and $c\vec{B}$ are all zero vectors and $c(\vec{A} + \vec{B}) = c\vec{A} + c\vec{B}$ because, by Definition 3B, the sum of two zero vectors is again a zero vector.

■ THEOREM 4

A distributive law.

HYPOTHESIS: $\vec{A}$ is a vector; b and c are scalars.

CONCLUSION: $b\vec{A} + c\vec{A} = (b + c)\vec{A}$.

PROOF: We leave the proof for the reader to work out in Exercise 3.4-14.

Example 2. Show that the line joining the midpoints of two sides of a triangle is parallel to the third side and half its length.

(a) Let M and N be the midpoints of sides AB and BC; see Fig. 3.19. Since $\overrightarrow{AM}$ and $\overrightarrow{MB}$ are equal in length and in the same direction, they represent equal vectors, and we shall say that $\overrightarrow{AM} = \overrightarrow{MB} = \vec{a}$.

(b) Similarly, $\overrightarrow{BN} = \overrightarrow{NC} = \vec{b}$.

(c) $\overrightarrow{MN} = \overrightarrow{MB} + \overrightarrow{BN} = \vec{a} + \vec{b}$.

(d) But $\overrightarrow{AB} = 2\vec{a}$ and $\overrightarrow{BC} = 2\vec{b}$, so that

$$\overrightarrow{AC} = \overrightarrow{AB} + \overrightarrow{BC} = 2\vec{a} + 2\vec{b} = 2(\vec{a} + \vec{b}).$$

(e) Thus $\overrightarrow{AC} = 2\overrightarrow{MN}$, or $\overrightarrow{MN} = \frac{1}{2}\overrightarrow{AC}$, and the demonstration is completed, for this vector equation says that $\overrightarrow{MN}$ and $\overrightarrow{AC}$ are parallel and that $\|\overrightarrow{MN}\| = \frac{1}{2}\|\overrightarrow{AC}\|$.

Example 3. Show that a line drawn from a vertex of a parallelogram to a midpoint of an opposite side trisects a diagonal and is itself trisected by that diagonal. Consider parallelogram $PQRS$, Fig. 3.20.

(a) Let U be the midpoint of QR. Since QU and UR are parallel and equal in length, we can write $\overrightarrow{QU} = \overrightarrow{UR} = \vec{a}$. Further, $\overrightarrow{PS} = 2\vec{a}$ because opposite sides of a parallelogram are parallel and equal.

(b) Let T be the intersection of PU and diagonal QS. We write $\overrightarrow{PT} = \alpha\overrightarrow{PU}$, $\overrightarrow{QT} = \beta\overrightarrow{QS}$ and we expect to show that $\alpha = \frac{2}{3}$, $\beta = \frac{1}{3}$.

(c) $\overrightarrow{PT} = \alpha\overrightarrow{PU} = \alpha(\vec{b} + \vec{a})$.

(d) $\overrightarrow{PT} = \overrightarrow{PQ} + \overrightarrow{QT} = \overrightarrow{PQ} + \beta\overrightarrow{QS} = \vec{b} + \beta(2\vec{a} - \vec{b})$.

(e) From (c) and (d),

$$\alpha(\vec{b} + \vec{a}) = \vec{b} + \beta(2\vec{a} - \vec{b}),$$
$$(\alpha - 2\beta)\vec{a} = (1 - \alpha - \beta)\vec{b}.$$

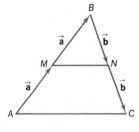

Fig. 3.19

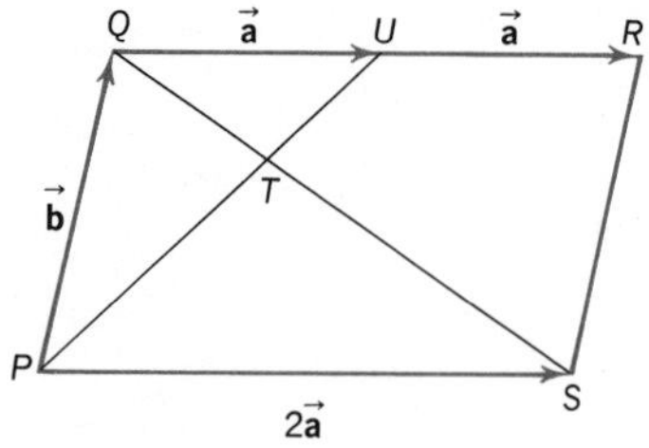

Fig. 3.20

(f) Unless the coefficients vanish, the last equation says that certain multiples of $\vec{a}$ and $\vec{b}$ are equal and that therefore $\vec{a} \parallel \vec{b}$. But $\vec{a}$ and $\vec{b}$ cannot be parallel. Hence $\alpha - 2\beta = 0$ and $1 - \alpha - \beta = 0$, from which it follows that $\alpha = \frac{2}{3}$, $\beta = \frac{1}{3}$.

EXERCISES 3.4

1. We are given that $\vec{a}$ is in the positive x axis direction and has magnitude 2 while $\vec{b}$ has magnitude 3 and a direction reached by a 60° counterclockwise rotation from the positive x direction.
   (a) Draw vectors $\vec{a}$, $\vec{b}$, $\vec{a} + \vec{b}$.   (c) Draw vectors $\frac{1}{2}\vec{a}$, $-\vec{b}$, $\frac{1}{2}\vec{a} - \vec{b}$.
   (b) Draw vectors $2\vec{a}$, $\frac{1}{2}\vec{b}$, $2\vec{a} + \frac{1}{2}\vec{b}$.   (d) Draw vectors $-\vec{a}$, $-2\vec{b}$, $-\vec{a} - 2\vec{b}$.

2. Repeat Exercise 1 if $\vec{a}$ is in the positive y axis direction and has magnitude 4 while $\vec{b}$ is a unit vector in a direction reached by a 45° clockwise rotation from the positive x direction.

3. Vectors drawn from the origin to points S, T, U are respectively $\vec{a}$, $\vec{b}$, and $4\vec{a} - 3\vec{b}$. Find $\overrightarrow{ST}$ and $\overrightarrow{TU}$, and show that S, T, and U are collinear; that is, that S, T, and U lie on a line. In what proportion does the interior point divide the two exterior points?

4. Repeat Exercise 3 with $\overrightarrow{OU} = 5\vec{b} - 4\vec{a}$.

5. Use vector analysis to prove that the line joining the midpoints of the nonparallel sides of a trapezoid is parallel to the parallel sides and $\frac{1}{2}$ the sum of their lengths.

6. We are given that the initial points of $\vec{b}$ and $\vec{c}$ coincide with the terminal points of $\vec{a}$ and $\vec{b}$, respectively, and that $\vec{a} + \vec{b} + \vec{c} = \vec{0}$. What can be said about $\vec{a}$, $\vec{b}$, and $\vec{c}$?

7. Use vector analysis to prove that a parallelogram is formed when the midpoints of the sides of a quadrilateral are joined in order.

8. Use vector analysis to show that the medians of a triangle are such that a new triangle may be constructed with sides equal and parallel to these medians. In Exercise 10.5-18 the reader can show that the area of this new triangle is $\frac{3}{4}$ of the area of the original triangle.

9. Complete the following outline of a proof that the medians of a triangle meet at a point which lies $\frac{2}{3}$ of the way from each vertex to the opposite side.
   Step (a). Let P_1 be the point on median QM which is $\frac{2}{3}$ of the way from Q to M; see Fig. 3.21(a). Thus $\overrightarrow{QP_1} = \frac{2}{3}(\overrightarrow{QM}) = \frac{2}{3}(2\vec{a} + \vec{b})$.
   Step (b). Let P_2 be the point on median SL which is $\frac{2}{3}$ of the way from S to L; see Fig. 3.21(b). Then $\overrightarrow{QP_2} = \overrightarrow{QR} + \overrightarrow{RS} + \overrightarrow{SP_2} = \overrightarrow{QR} + \overrightarrow{RS} + \frac{2}{3}\overrightarrow{SL} = \cdots$. Therefore $\overrightarrow{QP_2} = \overrightarrow{QP_1}$; P_2 and P_1 must coincide.
   Step (c). Let P_3 be the point on median RN which is $\frac{2}{3}$ of the way from R to N. Then $\overrightarrow{QP_3} = \cdots$. Therefore $\overrightarrow{QP_3} = \overrightarrow{QP_1}$; P_3 and P_1 must also coincide.

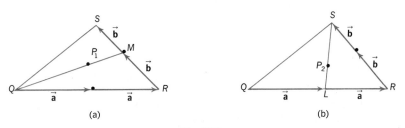

(a)   (b)

Fig. 3.21

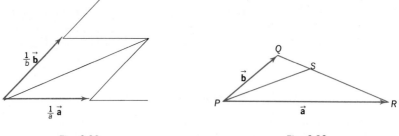

Fig. 3.22   **Fig. 3.23**

10. Given $a = \|\vec{a}\| \neq 0$ and $b = \|\vec{b}\| \neq 0$. Then $(1/a)\,\vec{a}$ and $(1/b)\,\vec{b}$ are unit vectors in the directions of $\vec{a}$ and $\vec{b}$. Show that $(1/a)\vec{a} + (1/b)\vec{b}$ lies in the direction of the bisector of the angle between $\vec{a}$ and $\vec{b}$. See Fig. 3.22.

11. Complete the following outline of a proof that the bisector of an angle of a triangle divides the opposite side in two segments that have the same ratio as the adjacent sides.

Step (a). If $\overrightarrow{PR} = \vec{a}$ and $\overrightarrow{PQ} = \vec{b}$, then according to Exercise 10, the angle bisector PS has the direction of the vector $(1/a)\vec{a} + (1/b)\vec{b}$, where $a = \|\vec{a}\|$, $b = \|\vec{b}\|$. Let us write $\overrightarrow{PS} = k[(1/a)\vec{a} + (1/b)\vec{b}]$; see Fig. 3.23.

Step (b). $\overrightarrow{QR} = -\vec{b} + \vec{a}$. Let us write $\overrightarrow{QS} = n\overrightarrow{QR} = n(\vec{a} - \vec{b})$ and with it $\overrightarrow{SR} = (1-n)\overrightarrow{QR}$. We must show that $n/(1-n) = b/a$.

Step (c). For $\overrightarrow{PS}$ we not only have (a) but also $\overrightarrow{PS} = \overrightarrow{PQ} + \overrightarrow{QS} = \vec{b} + n(\vec{a} - \vec{b})$.

Step (d). Thus

$$k\left(\frac{1}{a}\vec{a} + \frac{1}{b}\vec{b}\right) = \vec{b} + n(\vec{a} - \vec{b}) \quad \text{and} \quad \cdots.$$

12. In Exercise 11 we showed that $\|\overrightarrow{SQ}\| : \|\overrightarrow{SR}\| = b : a$. Let T be the point at which the external angle bisector at P intersects side RQ extended. Use vector analysis to show that $\|\overrightarrow{TQ}\| : \|\overrightarrow{TR}\| = b : a$ also.

13. In triangle ABC, let point D divide side AB in the ratio $AD : DB = 1 : 3$ and let point E divide side BC in the ratio $BE : EC = 1 : 2$. Let AE and CD intersect at F. In what ratio does F divide AE?

14. Prove Theorem 4. Remember that b and c need not both be positive numbers.

3.5   The Unit Vectors $\vec{i}$ and $\vec{j}$

We introduce the unit vectors $\vec{i}$ and $\vec{j}$ in order to tie vector analysis and rectangular coordinate geometry together.

■ DEFINITION 1

$\vec{i}$ *and* $\vec{j}$. The unit vectors in the positive x and y directions shall be given the names $\vec{i}$ and $\vec{j}$, respectively. (See Fig. 3.24.)

These vectors will form a basis for our vector analysis. Other vectors will be written as sums of multiples of these vectors.

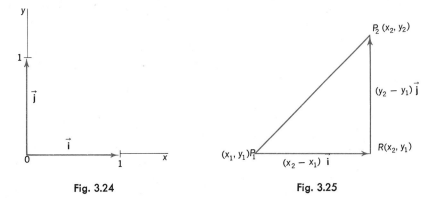

Fig. 3.24   Fig. 3.25

■ THEOREM 1

The vector joining two given points.

HYPOTHESIS: $P_1(x_1, y_1)$ and $P_2(x_2, y_2)$ have the coordinates indicated.

CONCLUSION: $\overrightarrow{P_1P_2} = (x_2 - x_1)\vec{i} + (y_2 - y_1)\vec{j}.$

PROOF: (a) Draw a line through P_1 parallel to the x axis and a line through P_2 parallel to the y axis, intersecting at $R(x_2, y_1)$; see Fig. 3.25.

(b) $\overrightarrow{P_1R}$ is parallel to the x axis and has directed length $x_2 - x_1$; $\overrightarrow{P_1R}$ $= (x_2 - x_1)\vec{i}$. Note that if $x_2 > x_1$, then R lies to the right of P_1 and that $\overrightarrow{P_1R}$ and $(x_2 - x_1)\vec{i}$ both have the direction of $+\vec{i}$. Similarly, if $x_2 < x_1$, then $\overrightarrow{P_1R}$ and $(x_2 - x_1)\vec{i}$ both have the direction of $-\vec{i}$.

(c) $\overrightarrow{RP_2} = (y_2 - y_1)\vec{j}.$

(d) Adding vectors gives

$$\overrightarrow{P_1P_2} = \overrightarrow{P_1R} + \overrightarrow{RP_2} = (x_2 - x_1)\vec{i} + (y_2 - y_1)\vec{j}.$$

● Remark 1

This theorem explains how any vector can be written as a sum of $\vec{i}$ and $\vec{j}$ components when its initial and terminal points are known. Simply subtract the coordinates of the initial point from those of the terminal point to get the $\vec{i}$ and $\vec{j}$ components.

● Remark 2

The theorem can be looked at in a second way. If O is the origin of the coordinates, the vectors $\overrightarrow{OP_1}$ and $\overrightarrow{OP_2}$ are called the *position vectors* for Points P_1 and P_2 for this coordinate system. As Fig. 3.26 points out, the vector $\overrightarrow{OP_1}$ has the $\vec{i}$, $\vec{j}$

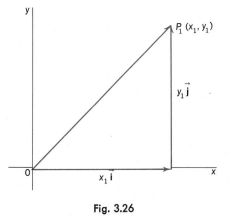

Fig. 3.26

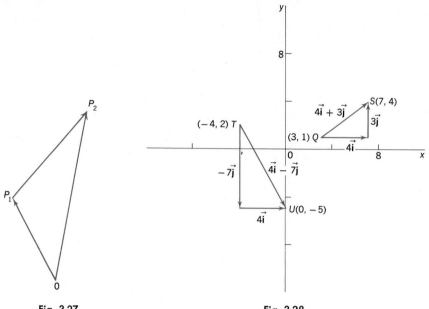

Fig. 3.27   Fig. 3.28

description $\overrightarrow{\mathbf{OP}}_1 = x_1\vec{\mathbf{i}} + y_1\vec{\mathbf{j}}$; similarly, $\overrightarrow{\mathbf{OP}}_2 = x_2\vec{\mathbf{i}} + y_2\vec{\mathbf{j}}$. From Fig. 3.27 we see that

$$\overrightarrow{\mathbf{P}_1\mathbf{P}_2} = \overrightarrow{\mathbf{P}_1\mathbf{O}} + \overrightarrow{\mathbf{OP}}_2 = -\overrightarrow{\mathbf{OP}}_1 + \overrightarrow{\mathbf{OP}}_2 = \overrightarrow{\mathbf{OP}}_2 - \overrightarrow{\mathbf{OP}}_1$$
$$= (x_2\vec{\mathbf{i}} + y_2\vec{\mathbf{j}}) - (x_1\vec{\mathbf{i}} + y_1\vec{\mathbf{j}}) = (x_2 - x_1)\vec{\mathbf{i}} + (y_2 - y_1)\vec{\mathbf{j}}.$$

In words, from this point of view, a vector may be written as the difference of the position vectors for its terminal and initial points.

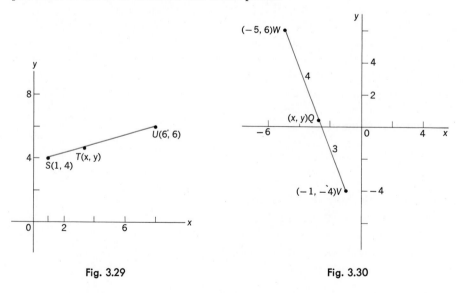

Fig. 3.29   Fig. 3.30

Example 1A. The vector with initial point $Q(3, 1)$ and terminal point $S(7, 4)$ is $\overrightarrow{QS} = 4\vec{i} + 3\vec{j}$; see Fig. 3.28.

Example 1B. The vector with initial point $T(-4, 2)$ and terminal point $U(0, -5)$ is $\overrightarrow{TU} = 4\vec{i} - 7\vec{j}$; see Fig. 3.28.

Example 2. Find the point $\frac{1}{3}$ of the way from $S(1, 4)$ to $U(6, 6)$. See Fig. 3.29.

(a) Let the point we seek be $T(x, y)$. We know that $\overrightarrow{ST} = \frac{1}{3}\overrightarrow{SU}$.

(b) Writing $\overrightarrow{ST}$ and $\overrightarrow{SU}$ in terms of their $\vec{i}$ and $\vec{j}$ components, we have

$$(x - 1)\vec{i} + (y - 4)\vec{j} = \frac{1}{3}(5\vec{i} + 2\vec{j}).$$

(c) Since equal vectors must have equal components, we can say $x - 1 = \frac{5}{3}$, $y - 4 = \frac{2}{3}$; $x = \frac{8}{3}$, $y = \frac{14}{3}$. The point we seek is $T(\frac{8}{3}, \frac{14}{3})$.

(d) Alternatively, we might have reasoned from (b) that

$$(x - \tfrac{8}{3})\vec{i} = (\tfrac{14}{3} - y)\vec{j},$$

and then concluded that $x - \frac{8}{3} = 0$ and $\frac{14}{3} - y = 0$, because $\vec{i}$ and $\vec{j}$ are not parallel.

Example 3. Find the point that divides the segment VW, $V(-1, -4)$ and $W(-5, 6)$, in the ratio $3 : 4$. See Fig. 3.30.

(a) Let $Q(x, y)$ be the point we seek. We know that $\overrightarrow{VQ} = \frac{3}{7}\overrightarrow{VW}$.

(b) Writing $\overrightarrow{VQ}$ and $\overrightarrow{VW}$ in terms of their $\vec{i}$ and $\vec{j}$ components, we have

$$(x + 1)\vec{i} + (y + 4)\vec{j} = \frac{3}{7}(-4\vec{i} + 10\vec{j}).$$

(c) Since equal vectors have equal components, $x + 1 = -\frac{12}{7}$, $x = -\frac{19}{7}$ and $y + 4 = \frac{30}{7}$, $y = \frac{2}{7}$. The point we seek is $Q(-\frac{19}{7}, \frac{2}{7})$.

By following the method presented in Examples 2 and 3 we can divide a segment into any desired parts. We have to find the midpoint of a segment so frequently, however, that the formula for the midpoint coordinates is worth memorizing.

■ **THEOREM 2**

The midpoint formulas.

HYPOTHESIS: A segment has end points $P_1(x_1, y_1)$ and $P_2(x_2, y_2)$.

CONCLUSION: The midpoint of the segment is

$$P\left(\frac{x_1 + x_2}{2}, \frac{y_1 + y_2}{2}\right).$$

In words, to get the coordinates of the midpoint, average the coordinates of the end points.

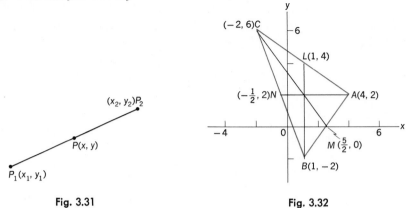

Fig. 3.31   Fig. 3.32

PROOF: (a) See Fig. 3.31. Let $P(x, y)$ be the midpoint. We know that
$\overrightarrow{P_1P} = \frac{1}{2} \overrightarrow{P_1P_2}$.

(b) In $\vec{i}$ and $\vec{j}$ form,

$$(x - x_1)\vec{i} + (y - y_1)\vec{j} = \frac{1}{2}[(x_2 - x_1)\vec{i} + (y_2 - y_1)\vec{j}].$$

(c) Since equal vectors have equal components

$$x - x_1 = \frac{1}{2}(x_2 - x_1) \quad \text{or} \quad x = \frac{x_1 + x_2}{2},$$

$$y - y_1 = \frac{1}{2}(y_2 - y_1) \quad \text{or} \quad y = \frac{y_1 + y_2}{2}.$$

Example 4.   Find the lengths of the medians of triangle $A(4, 2)$, $B(1, -2)$, $C(-2, 6)$. See Fig. 3.32.

(a) Using the midpoint formulas, the midpoints are $L(1, 4)$, $M(\frac{5}{2}, 0)$, and $N(-\frac{1}{2}, 2)$.

(b) If we use the formula for the distance between two points, we have for the lengths of the medians:

$$AN = \sqrt{(\tfrac{9}{2})^2 + 0^2} = \tfrac{9}{2}.$$

$$BL = \sqrt{0^2 + 6^2} = 6.$$

$$CM = \sqrt{(\tfrac{9}{2})^2 + (-6)^2} = \tfrac{15}{2}.$$

We conclude this section with four theorems that we shall use frequently. In fact, Theorem 3 below has already been used in Step (d) of Example 2.

■ **THEOREM 3**

On the addition of vectors.

HYPOTHESIS: $\vec{v}_1 = a_1\vec{i} + b_1\vec{j}; \ \vec{v}_2 = a_2\vec{i} + b_2\vec{j}.$

CONCLUSION: $\vec{v}_1 + \vec{v}_2 = (a_1 + a_2)\vec{i} + (b_1 + b_2)\vec{j}.$

In words, to add vectors, we add their components.

PROOF:
$$\vec{v}_1 + \vec{v}_2 = (a_1\vec{\mathbf{i}} + b_1\vec{\mathbf{j}}) + (a_2\vec{\mathbf{i}} + b_2\vec{\mathbf{j}})$$
$$= a_1\vec{\mathbf{i}} + a_2\vec{\mathbf{i}} + b_1\vec{\mathbf{j}} + b_2\vec{\mathbf{j}}$$
$$= (a_1 + a_2)\vec{\mathbf{i}} + (b_1 + b_2)\vec{\mathbf{j}}.$$

In this proof we used commutative, associative, and distributive laws for the addition of vectors, Theorems 3.4-1, 3.4-2, and 3.4-4.

■ THEOREM 4

A vector in the direction of a line with given slope.

HYPOTHESIS: Line L has slope m.

CONCLUSION: $c(1\vec{\mathbf{i}} + m\vec{\mathbf{j}})$, c any constant not equal to 0, may be chosen as a vector with the same direction as L.

PROOF: The proof is left to the reader; see Exercise 3.5-11.

● Remark 3

If line L is parallel to the y axis so that its slope is not finite, then $c\vec{\mathbf{j}}$, c any constant not equal to 0, may be chosen as a vector with the same direction.

■ THEOREM 5

The length of a vector.

HYPOTHESIS: $\vec{\mathbf{v}} = a\vec{\mathbf{i}} + b\vec{\mathbf{j}}$.

CONCLUSION: $\|\vec{\mathbf{v}}\| = \sqrt{a^2 + b^2}$.

PROOF: According to Theorem 1, the vector $\vec{\mathbf{v}}$ can be described as the vector with initial point $(0, 0)$ and terminal point (a, b). But the distance from $(0, 0)$ to (a, b) is $\sqrt{a^2 + b^2}$.

■ THEOREM 6

On unit vectors.

HYPOTHESIS: $\vec{\mathbf{v}}$ is a unit vector obtained by rotating $\vec{\mathbf{i}}$ about its initial point through an angle α.

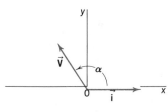

Fig. 3.33

CONCLUSION: $\vec{\mathbf{v}} = (\cos \alpha)\vec{\mathbf{i}} + (\sin \alpha)\vec{\mathbf{j}}$.

The proof is left to the reader; see Exercise 12 and Fig. 3.33.

EXERCISES 3.5

1. Find the vector $\overrightarrow{UV}$:
   (a) $U(0, 0)$, $V(3, 5)$.
   (b) $U(-2, -3)$, $V(3, 4)$.
   (c) $U(4, 2)$, $V(-2, -1)$.
   (d) $U(6, 3)$, $V(6, 1)$.
2. Given the quadrilateral $A(-2, -3)$, $B(3, -1)$, $C(6, 3)$, $D(-1, 5)$. Find the midpoints of the sides. Prove that the lines joining midpoints of opposite sides bisect each other by showing that these lines have a common midpoint.

3. Show that the lines joining the midpoints of opposite sides of any quadrilateral will bisect each other. [One way to start would be to select the quadrilateral with vertices $P_1(x_1, y_1)$, $P_2(x_2, y_2)$, $P_3(x_3, y_3)$, and $P_4(x_4, y_4)$.]

4. Find the lengths of the medians of the triangle:
   (a) $U(2, 8)$, $V(6, 0)$, $W(10, 2)$.   (b) $U(-4, 5)$, $V(0, 3)$, $W(-3, -1)$.

5. Find the point that lies $\frac{2}{5}$ of the way from $(-1, 0)$ to $(9, 5)$.

6. Find the point that lies $\frac{1}{7}$ of the way from $(3, 4)$ to $(6, -3)$.

7. Find the point that divides the line joining $(4, 3)$ to $(0, -3)$ in the ratio $3 : 2$.

8. Find the point that divides the line joining $(-1, 6)$ to $(6, 1)$ in the ratio $1 : 7$.

9. (a) In the triangle of Exercise 4(a), find the point $\frac{2}{3}$ of the way from vertex U to the midpoint of the opposite side.
   (b) Do the same for the triangle of Exercise 4(b).

10. We are given a triangle with vertices $P_1(x_1, y_1)$, $P_2(x_2, y_2)$, $P_3(x_3, y_3)$. Prove that the medians intersect at

$$\left(\frac{x_1 + x_2 + x_3}{3}, \frac{y_1 + y_2 + y_3}{3}\right)$$

by showing that this is the point that lies $\frac{2}{3}$ of the way from each vertex to the midpoint of the opposite side.

11. Prove Theorem 4.

12. Prove Theorem 6.

3.6   The Scalar Product

Let us consider next the important question of finding the angle between two given vectors. Suppose that we are given vectors $\vec{v}_1 = a_1\vec{i} + b_1\vec{j}$ and $\vec{v}_2 = a_2\vec{i} + b_2\vec{j}$, and that we have moved one of these vectors parallel to itself until the initial points of $\vec{v}_1$ and $\vec{v}_2$ coincide at P; see Fig. 3.34. Then for the third side of the triangle pictured we have

$$\overrightarrow{RQ} = \overrightarrow{RP} + \overrightarrow{PQ} = (-\vec{v}_1) + \vec{v}_2 = (a_2 - a_1)\vec{i} + (b_2 - b_1)\vec{j}.$$

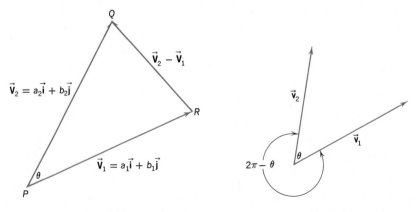

Fig. 3.34   Fig. 3.35

We can determine the angle θ by using the cosine law of trigonometry. We have

$$\|\overrightarrow{\mathbf{RQ}}\|^2 = \|\overrightarrow{\mathbf{PR}}\|^2 + \|\overrightarrow{\mathbf{PQ}}\|^2 - 2\|\overrightarrow{\mathbf{PR}}\|\,\|\overrightarrow{\mathbf{PQ}}\|\cos\theta, \tag{1}$$

or

$$\cos\theta = \frac{\|\overrightarrow{\mathbf{PR}}\|^2 + \|\overrightarrow{\mathbf{PQ}}\|^2 - \|\overrightarrow{\mathbf{RQ}}\|^2}{2\|\overrightarrow{\mathbf{PR}}\|\,\|\overrightarrow{\mathbf{PQ}}\|}, \tag{2}$$

assuming that $\|\overrightarrow{\mathbf{PR}}\| \neq 0$, $\|\overrightarrow{\mathbf{PQ}}\| \neq 0$.

If we apply the theorem on the length of a vector,* we get

$$\cos\theta = \frac{(a_1{}^2 + b_1{}^2) + (a_2{}^2 + b_2{}^2) - [(a_2 - a_1)^2 + (b_2 - b_1)^2]}{2\|\overrightarrow{\mathbf{PR}}\|\,\|\overrightarrow{\mathbf{PQ}}\|}, \tag{3}$$

or, upon simplifying,

$$\cos\theta = \frac{a_1 a_2 + b_1 b_2}{\|\overrightarrow{\mathbf{PR}}\|\,\|\overrightarrow{\mathbf{PQ}}\|}. \tag{4}$$

From this formula we could find angle θ.

If we rewrite Eq. (4) as

$$\|\vec{\mathbf{v}}_1\|\,\|\vec{\mathbf{v}}_2\|\cos\theta = a_1 a_2 + b_1 b_2, \tag{5}$$

we place in evidence a product that arises in other important applications also. We give this product a special name.

■ DEFINITION 1

The scalar product of two vectors. The scalar product of $\vec{\mathbf{v}}_1$ and $\vec{\mathbf{v}}_2$, written $\vec{\mathbf{v}}_1 \cdot \vec{\mathbf{v}}_2$, is the product of their lengths and the cosine of the angle between them. In symbols,

$$\vec{\mathbf{v}}_1 \cdot \vec{\mathbf{v}}_2 = \|\vec{\mathbf{v}}_1\|\,\|\vec{\mathbf{v}}_2\|\cos\theta.$$

The adjective "scalar" is used because this product is a product of three scalars and is therefore itself a scalar.

● Remark 1

In greater detail, by the phrase "angle between two vectors" we mean an angle determined by the vectors when their initial points coincide. There are really two angles between $\vec{\mathbf{v}}_1$ and $\vec{\mathbf{v}}_2$, as in Fig. 3.35, namely θ and $2\pi - \theta$, but their cosines are equal. We can take either angle in computing $\vec{\mathbf{v}}_1 \cdot \vec{\mathbf{v}}_2$.

We use the scalar product primarily in three applications.

■ THEOREM 1

The length of a vector.

HYPOTHESIS: $\vec{\mathbf{v}}$ is a vector.

CONCLUSION: $\|\vec{\mathbf{v}}\|^2 = \vec{\mathbf{v}} \cdot \vec{\mathbf{v}}$.

In words, the length of a vector is the square root of the scalar product of the vector with itself.

---

* Theorem 3.5-5.

PROOF: By the definition of scalar product,

$$\vec{v} \cdot \vec{v} = \|\vec{v}\| \, \|\vec{v}\| \cos 0° = \|\vec{v}\|^2.$$

■ THEOREM 2

The angle between two vectors.

HYPOTHESIS: θ is an angle between vectors $\vec{v}_1$ and $\vec{v}_2$.

CONCLUSION:
$$\cos \theta = \frac{\vec{v}_1 \cdot \vec{v}_2}{\|\vec{v}_1\| \, \|\vec{v}_2\|}.$$

PROOF: The proof follows immediately from the definition of the scalar product.

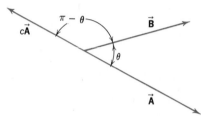

Fig. 3.36

The following corollary is useful.

■ COROLLARY 1

The criterion for perpendicularity.

HYPOTHESIS: $\vec{v}_1 \perp \vec{v}_2$.

CONCLUSION: $\vec{v}_1 \cdot \vec{v}_2 = 0$,

and, conversely,

HYPOTHESIS: $\vec{v}_1 \cdot \vec{v}_2 = 0$ and $\vec{v}_1 \neq \vec{0}$, $\vec{v}_2 \neq \vec{0}$.

CONCLUSION: $\vec{v}_1 \perp \vec{v}_2$.

In order to justify the final step in the proof of our third application of the scalar product (in Theorem 4) we need the following preliminary theorem.

■ THEOREM 3

HYPOTHESIS: $\vec{A}$ and $\vec{B}$ are vectors, c is a scalar.

CONCLUSION: $(c\vec{A}) \cdot \vec{B} = c(\vec{A} \cdot \vec{B})$.

PROOF: (a) If $c > 0$, then $\|c\vec{A}\| = c\|\vec{A}\|$ and the vectors $c\vec{A}$ and $\vec{A}$ are parallel with the same sense. In this case, if θ is an angle between $\vec{A}$ and $\vec{B}$, we have

$$(c\vec{A}) \cdot \vec{B} = \|c\vec{A}\| \, \|\vec{B}\| \cos \theta = c\|\vec{A}\| \, \|\vec{B}\| \cos \theta = c\vec{A} \cdot \vec{B}.$$

(b) If $c < 0$, then $\|c\vec{A}\| = -c\|\vec{A}\|$ and vectors $c\vec{A}$ and $\vec{A}$ are parallel but have opposed senses, as in Fig. 3.36. For this case,

$$(c\vec{A}) \cdot \vec{B} = \|c\vec{A}\| \, \|\vec{B}\| \cos(\pi - \theta) = -c\|\vec{A}\| \, \|\vec{B}\|(-\cos \theta)$$
$$= c\|\vec{A}\| \, \|\vec{B}\| \cos \theta = c\vec{A} \cdot \vec{B}.$$

(c) If $c = 0$, then $\|c\vec{A}\| = 0$, so that $(c\vec{A}) \cdot \vec{B} = 0$. But $c(\vec{A} \cdot \vec{B}) = 0$ also, so that $(c\vec{A}) \cdot \vec{B} = c(\vec{A} \cdot \vec{B})$ again.

Now we write Theorem 4 as our third application of the scalar product.

■ THEOREM 4

The projection of $\vec{A}$ *on* $\vec{B}$*'s direction.*

HYPOTHESIS: $\|\vec{B}\| \neq 0$.

CONCLUSION: The (directed length of the) projection of $\vec{A}$ on $\vec{B}$'s direction is

$$\vec{A} \cdot \frac{\vec{B}}{\|\vec{B}\|}.$$

In words, the (directed length of the) projection of $\vec{A}$ on $\vec{B}$'s direction is to be obtained by taking the scalar product of $\vec{A}$ with a unit vector in $\vec{B}$'s direction.

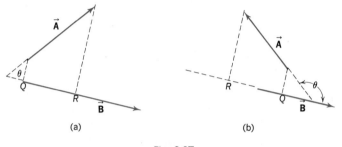

(a)   (b)

Fig. 3.37

PROOF: To get the projection in question, drop perpendiculars on $\vec{B}$'s direction from the end points of $\vec{A}$; see Fig. 3.37(a). By elementary trigonometry,

$$\text{projection} = QR = \|\vec{A}\| \cos \theta.$$

Then, from the definition of scalar product, and applying Theorem 3, we obtain

$$\text{projection} = \frac{\vec{A} \cdot \vec{B}}{\|\vec{B}\|} = \vec{A} \cdot \frac{\vec{B}}{\|\vec{B}\|}.$$

● Remark 2

Note that if the angle between $\vec{A}$ and $\vec{B}$ is obtuse, as in Fig. 3.37(b), then the directed length of the projection is considered negative, for its sense is opposite to that of $\vec{B}$. Since $\cos \theta < 0$ in this case, $\vec{A} \cdot \vec{B} < 0$ also, and the computation $\vec{A} \cdot \vec{B}/\|\vec{B}\|$ for the projection will lead to a negative number, as it should.

● Remark 3

When the initial and terminal points of $\vec{A}$ are projected onto the points Q and R, respectively, of a line through vector $\vec{B}$, we call the vector with initial point Q and terminal point R the *vector projection* of $\vec{A}$ on $\vec{B}$'s direction.

In Fig. 3.37(a) $\overrightarrow{QR}$ has the direction of $\vec{B}$, while in Fig. 3.37(b) $\overrightarrow{QR}$ has the direction of $-\vec{B}$. To get the vector projection we take a unit vector in $\vec{B}$'s direction, namely $\vec{B}/\|\vec{B}\|$, and multiply it by the directed length of $\overrightarrow{QR}$:

$$\text{vector projection} = \overrightarrow{QR} = \left(\vec{A} \cdot \frac{\vec{B}}{\|\vec{B}\|}\right)\frac{\vec{B}}{\|\vec{B}\|} = \frac{\vec{A} \cdot \vec{B}}{\|\vec{B}\|^2}\vec{B}.$$

This vector has the same sense as $\vec{\mathbf{B}}$ if $\vec{\mathbf{A}}\cdot\vec{\mathbf{B}} > 0$, Fig. 3.37(a), and the opposite sense if $\vec{\mathbf{A}}\cdot\vec{\mathbf{B}} < 0$, Fig. 3.37(b).

In addition to Theorem 3, we have two more useful formal properties of the scalar product.

■ THEOREM 5

The commutative law for the scalar product.

HYPOTHESIS: $\vec{\mathbf{A}}$ and $\vec{\mathbf{B}}$ are vectors.

CONCLUSION: $\vec{\mathbf{A}}\cdot\vec{\mathbf{B}} = \vec{\mathbf{B}}\cdot\vec{\mathbf{A}}$.

The proof follows immediately from the definition of the scalar product.

■ THEOREM 6

The distributive law for the scalar product.

HYPOTHESIS: $\vec{\mathbf{A}}, \vec{\mathbf{B}}, \vec{\mathbf{C}}$ are vectors.

CONCLUSION: $(\vec{\mathbf{A}} + \vec{\mathbf{B}})\cdot\vec{\mathbf{C}} = \vec{\mathbf{A}}\cdot\vec{\mathbf{C}} + \vec{\mathbf{B}}\cdot\vec{\mathbf{C}}$.

PROOF: It will suffice to demonstrate that

$$(\vec{\mathbf{A}} + \vec{\mathbf{B}})\cdot\frac{\vec{\mathbf{C}}}{\|\vec{\mathbf{C}}\|} = \vec{\mathbf{A}}\cdot\frac{\vec{\mathbf{C}}}{\|\vec{\mathbf{C}}\|} + \vec{\mathbf{B}}\cdot\frac{\vec{\mathbf{C}}}{\|\vec{\mathbf{C}}\|}, \tag{6}$$

for, if we multiply by $\|\vec{\mathbf{C}}\|$ we reach the desired conclusion. Equation (6) says that the directed length of the projection of $\vec{\mathbf{A}} + \vec{\mathbf{B}}$ on $\vec{\mathbf{C}}$'s direction is to equal the sum of the directed lengths of the projections of $\vec{\mathbf{A}}$ and $\vec{\mathbf{B}}$. But these projections are determined by dropping perpendiculars on $\vec{\mathbf{C}}$'s direction from the initial and terminal points of $\vec{\mathbf{A}}, \vec{\mathbf{B}}$, and $\vec{\mathbf{A}} + \vec{\mathbf{B}}$; see Figs. 3.38(a) and 3.38(b). Since $\vec{\mathbf{A}}, \vec{\mathbf{B}}$, and $\vec{\mathbf{A}} + \vec{\mathbf{B}}$ form a closed figure, the three points P, Q, and R serve as the initial and terminal points of $\vec{\mathbf{A}}, \vec{\mathbf{B}}$, and $\vec{\mathbf{A}} + \vec{\mathbf{B}}$, and the three directed projections are $P'Q', Q'R'$, and $P'R'$. In Figs. 3.38(a) and 3.38(b) we have $P'R' = P'Q' + Q'R'$.

There can be no associative law for scalar products, because three vectors cannot be multiplied scalarly. The expressions $(\vec{\mathbf{A}}\cdot\vec{\mathbf{B}})\cdot\vec{\mathbf{C}}$ and $\vec{\mathbf{A}}\cdot(\vec{\mathbf{B}}\cdot\vec{\mathbf{C}})$ are not defined, and it makes no sense to inquire about their equality. $(\vec{\mathbf{A}}\cdot\vec{\mathbf{B}})$ is a scalar,

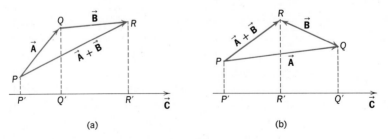

(a)   (b)

Fig. 3.38

for instance, and forming the scalar product of this scalar with vector $\vec{\mathbf{C}}$ to give $(\vec{\mathbf{A}} \cdot \vec{\mathbf{B}}) \cdot \vec{\mathbf{C}}$ is not possible. Only the scalar product of two vectors can be formed.

The scalar product differs from the ordinary product of arithmetic in another important way. In ordinary arithmetic, if a product equals 0, we can conclude that one of the factors must equal 0. This fact makes division possible. For, if $a/c = b_1$, $c \neq 0$, we can prove that there is not a second possible answer for the division problem a/c. Suppose there were a second answer, say $a/c = b_2$ also. Then we would have $a = b_1c$ and $a = b_2c$, so that $b_1c = b_2c$, or $b_1c - b_2c = 0$, or $(b_1 - b_2)c = 0$. But now, if a product is 0, one of the factors must be 0. Since $c \neq 0$, we must conclude that $b_1 - b_2 = 0$, $b_1 = b_2$. There is only one answer to a division problem in ordinary arithmetic.

In scalar product algebra, however, if $\vec{\mathbf{A}} \cdot \vec{\mathbf{B}} = 0$, we cannot conclude that $\vec{\mathbf{A}} = 0$ or $\vec{\mathbf{B}} = \vec{\mathbf{0}}$. It may very well be that $\vec{\mathbf{A}}$ and $\vec{\mathbf{B}}$ are perpendicular. Thus, from $\vec{\mathbf{A}} \cdot \vec{\mathbf{C}} = \vec{\mathbf{A}} \cdot \vec{\mathbf{D}}$, we cannot conclude that $\vec{\mathbf{C}} = \vec{\mathbf{D}}$ by dividing by vector $\vec{\mathbf{A}}$. We can only conclude that $\vec{\mathbf{A}} \cdot \vec{\mathbf{C}} - \vec{\mathbf{A}} \cdot \vec{\mathbf{D}} = 0$, or $\vec{\mathbf{A}} \cdot (\vec{\mathbf{C}} - \vec{\mathbf{D}}) = 0$. Vector $\vec{\mathbf{C}} - \vec{\mathbf{D}}$ might well be perpendicular to $\vec{\mathbf{A}}$; $\vec{\mathbf{C}} - \vec{\mathbf{D}}$ need not be a zero vector.

Before turning to specific examples we need a statement telling how to compute the scalar product when specific vectors are given in $\vec{\mathbf{i}}$, $\vec{\mathbf{j}}$ form.

■ THEOREM 7

Computation of the scalar product.

HYPOTHESIS: $\vec{\mathbf{v}}_1 = a_1\vec{\mathbf{i}} + b_1\vec{\mathbf{j}}$, $\vec{\mathbf{v}}_2 = a_2\vec{\mathbf{i}} + b_2\vec{\mathbf{j}}$.

CONCLUSION: $\vec{\mathbf{v}}_1 \cdot \vec{\mathbf{v}}_2 = a_1a_2 + b_1b_2$.

PROOF: We have already proved this theorem; see Eq. (5). But it may be instructive to give a second proof.

(a) We have $\vec{\mathbf{i}} \cdot \vec{\mathbf{i}} = \|\vec{\mathbf{i}}\| \, \|\vec{\mathbf{i}}\| \cos 0° = 1(1)(1) = 1,$

$$\vec{\mathbf{j}} \cdot \vec{\mathbf{j}} = 1,$$

$$\vec{\mathbf{j}} \cdot \vec{\mathbf{i}} = \vec{\mathbf{i}} \cdot \vec{\mathbf{j}} = \|\vec{\mathbf{i}}\| \, \|\vec{\mathbf{j}}\| \cos 90° = 0.$$

(b) Then

$$\vec{\mathbf{v}}_1 \cdot \vec{\mathbf{v}}_2 = (a_1\vec{\mathbf{i}} + b_1\vec{\mathbf{j}}) \cdot (a_2\vec{\mathbf{i}} + b_2\vec{\mathbf{j}})$$
$$= a_1a_2\vec{\mathbf{i}} \cdot \vec{\mathbf{i}} + a_1b_2\vec{\mathbf{i}} \cdot \vec{\mathbf{j}} + b_1a_2\vec{\mathbf{j}} \cdot \vec{\mathbf{i}} + b_1b_2\vec{\mathbf{j}} \cdot \vec{\mathbf{j}}$$
$$= a_1a_2(1) + a_1b_2(0) + b_1a_2(0) + b_1b_2(1)$$
$$= a_1a_2 + b_1b_2.$$

Theorem 3 and the distributive and commutative laws for the scalar product, Theorems 5 and 6, played vital roles in this computation.

Example 1.   Find the length of $3\vec{\mathbf{i}} + 7\vec{\mathbf{j}}$.

This length could easily be found by using Theorem 3.5-5, but we want to illustrate the scalar product instead.

$$\|3\vec{\mathbf{i}} + 7\vec{\mathbf{j}}\|^2 = (3\vec{\mathbf{i}} + 7\vec{\mathbf{j}}) \cdot (3\vec{\mathbf{i}} + 7\vec{\mathbf{j}})$$
$$= 9\vec{\mathbf{i}} \cdot \vec{\mathbf{i}} + 42\vec{\mathbf{i}} \cdot \vec{\mathbf{j}} + 49\vec{\mathbf{j}} \cdot \vec{\mathbf{j}} = 9 + 49 = 58;$$

$$\|3\vec{\mathbf{i}} + 7\vec{\mathbf{j}}\| = \sqrt{58}.$$

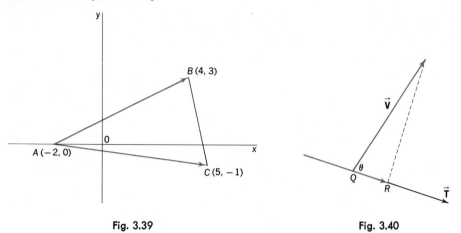

Fig. 3.39   **Fig. 3.40**

Example 2.   Find cos A in triangle $A(-2, 0)$, $B(4, 3)$, $C(5, -1)$. See Fig. 3.39. (a) We have

$$\overrightarrow{AB} = 6\vec{i} + 3\vec{j} \quad \text{and} \quad \overrightarrow{AC} = 7\vec{i} - 1\vec{j}.$$

(b) Then

$$\|\overrightarrow{AB}\|^2 = (6\vec{i} + 3\vec{j})\cdot(6\vec{i} + 3\vec{j})$$
$$= 36\vec{i}\cdot\vec{i} + 36\vec{i}\cdot\vec{j} + 9\vec{j}\cdot\vec{j} = 36 + 9 = 45,$$

and

$$\|\overrightarrow{AC}\|^2 = (7\vec{i} - 1\vec{j})\cdot(7\vec{i} - 1\vec{j}) = 49 + 1 = 50.$$

(c) But

$$\overrightarrow{AB}\cdot\overrightarrow{AC} = \|\overrightarrow{AB}\|\,\|\overrightarrow{AC}\|\cos A,$$

so that

$$\cos A = \frac{\overrightarrow{AB}\cdot\overrightarrow{AC}}{\|\overrightarrow{AB}\|\,\|\overrightarrow{AC}\|} = \frac{(6\vec{i} + 3\vec{j})\cdot(7\vec{i} - 1\vec{j})}{\sqrt{45}\,\sqrt{50}}$$
$$= \frac{42 - 3}{\sqrt{45}\,\sqrt{50}} = \frac{39}{\sqrt{45}\,\sqrt{50}} = \frac{13}{5\sqrt{10}}.$$

Example 3.   Find a vector of length 5 perpendicular to $\vec{T} = 3\vec{i} + 2\vec{j}$.

(a) First we shall find a and b such that $\vec{v} = a\vec{i} + b\vec{j}$ is perpendicular to $\vec{T}$. We have

$$\vec{v}\cdot\vec{T} = 0, \quad (a\vec{i} + b\vec{j})\cdot(3\vec{i} + 2\vec{j}) = 0, \quad 3a + 2b = 0.$$

There are many solutions for one equation in two unknowns, and we need only one solution. A convenient solution is $a = +2$, $b = -3$; $\vec{v} = 2\vec{i} - 3\vec{j}$ is perpendicular to $\vec{T}$.

(b) But $\vec{v}$ is not of length 5. We take $\vec{v}/\|\vec{v}\|$, which is a unit vector perpendicular to $\vec{T}$, and multiply it by 5. The vector we seek is

$$\vec{W} = 5\frac{\vec{v}}{\|\vec{v}\|} = \frac{5}{\sqrt{13}}(2\vec{i} - 3\vec{j}).$$

Another vector of length 5 perpendicular to $\vec{\mathbf{T}}$ is $-\vec{\mathbf{W}}$.

Example 4. Find the directed length of the projection of $\vec{\mathbf{v}} = 3\vec{\mathbf{i}} + 5\vec{\mathbf{j}}$ on the direction of $\vec{\mathbf{T}} = 4\vec{\mathbf{i}} - 1\vec{\mathbf{j}}$. Also find the vector projection. See Fig. 3.40.

(a) The directed length of $\vec{\mathbf{v}}$'s projection on $\vec{\mathbf{T}}$'s direction is

$$\|\vec{\mathbf{v}}\| \cos \theta = \vec{\mathbf{v}} \cdot \frac{\vec{\mathbf{T}}}{\|\vec{\mathbf{T}}\|} = (3\vec{\mathbf{i}} + 5\vec{\mathbf{j}}) \cdot \frac{(4\vec{\mathbf{i}} - 1\vec{\mathbf{j}})}{\sqrt{(4\vec{\mathbf{i}} - 1\vec{\mathbf{j}}) \cdot (4\vec{\mathbf{i}} - 1\vec{\mathbf{j}})}}$$

$$= \frac{12 - 5}{\sqrt{16 + 1}} = \frac{7}{\sqrt{17}}.$$

(b) To get the vector projection, $\overrightarrow{QR}$, we note that a unit vector in $\vec{\mathbf{T}}$'s direction is

$$\frac{\vec{\mathbf{T}}}{\|\vec{\mathbf{T}}\|} = \frac{4\vec{\mathbf{i}} - 1\vec{\mathbf{j}}}{\sqrt{17}}.$$

Since the directed length of the projection is $7/\sqrt{17}$, we have

$$\overrightarrow{QR} = \frac{7}{\sqrt{17}} \frac{4\vec{\mathbf{i}} - 1\vec{\mathbf{j}}}{\sqrt{17}} = \frac{7}{17}(4\vec{\mathbf{i}} - 1\vec{\mathbf{j}}).$$

Example 5. Find the directed length of the projection of $\vec{\mathbf{v}} = 4\vec{\mathbf{i}} + 2\vec{\mathbf{j}}$ on the direction of $\vec{\mathbf{T}} = -6\vec{\mathbf{i}} + 1\vec{\mathbf{j}}$. Also find the vector projection. See Fig. 3.41.

(a) The directed length of $\vec{\mathbf{v}}$'s projection on $\vec{\mathbf{T}}$'s direction is

$$\|\vec{\mathbf{v}}\| \cos \theta = \vec{\mathbf{v}} \cdot \frac{\vec{\mathbf{T}}}{\|\vec{\mathbf{T}}\|} = (4\vec{\mathbf{i}} + 2\vec{\mathbf{j}}) \cdot \frac{(-6\vec{\mathbf{i}} + 1\vec{\mathbf{j}})}{\sqrt{(-6\vec{\mathbf{i}} + 1\vec{\mathbf{j}}) \cdot (-6\vec{\mathbf{i}} + 1\vec{\mathbf{j}})}}$$

$$= \frac{-24 + 2}{\sqrt{36 + 1}} = \frac{-22}{\sqrt{37}}.$$

Note that the angle between $\vec{\mathbf{T}}$ and $\vec{\mathbf{v}}$ is obtuse and that the directed length of the projection is negative, as expected.

(b) To get the vector projection, $\overrightarrow{QR}$, we take the unit vector in $\vec{\mathbf{T}}$'s direction,

$$\frac{\vec{\mathbf{T}}}{\|\vec{\mathbf{T}}\|} = \frac{-6\vec{\mathbf{i}} + 1\vec{\mathbf{j}}}{\sqrt{37}},$$

and multiply by the directed length of $\overrightarrow{QR}$. We have

$$\overrightarrow{QR} = \frac{-22}{\sqrt{37}} \frac{-6\vec{\mathbf{i}} + 1\vec{\mathbf{j}}}{\sqrt{37}} = \frac{22}{37}(6\vec{\mathbf{i}} - 1\vec{\mathbf{j}}).$$

Note that the $\overrightarrow{QR}$ computed has a positive x component and a negative y component, as expected from Fig. 3.41.

Example 6. In Definition 2.8-1 we defined the work done against a force if the force was constant and the displacement directly opposed to the force. Using vector language, we can now describe efficiently a more general case.

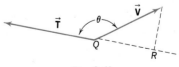

Fig. 3.41

Suppose that the force against which work is done is still constant, and that the vector $\vec{F}$ describes this force, both in magnitude and direction. But this time let the displacement be in a straight line which makes an angle θ with $\vec{F}$. (This would be the case, for instance, if an object were moved against the force of gravity in a nonvertical straight line, as when dragging a weight up a ramp.) Let $\vec{D}$ represent the displacement.

In this case, the physicist defines the work done as the product of the distance moved by the magnitude of that component of $\vec{F}$ which is directly opposed to $\vec{D}$. In Fig. 3.42, this component is $\vec{F}_1$, so that

$$\text{work} = \|\vec{D}\|\,\|\vec{F}_1\| = \|\vec{D}\|\,\|\vec{F}\|\cos\phi = -\|\vec{D}\|\,\|\vec{F}\|\cos\theta = -\vec{D}\cdot\vec{F}.$$

■ DEFINITION 2

Work. If force $\vec{F}$ is constant during the motion of an object displaced in a straight line, the displacement given by $\vec{D}$, then the work done against $\vec{F}$ shall be $-\vec{F}\cdot\vec{D}$.

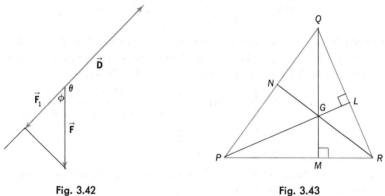

Fig. 3.42   Fig. 3.43

EXERCISES 3.6

1. Decide whether $\vec{U}$ and $\vec{v}$ are perpendicular:
   (a) $\vec{U} = 2\vec{i} - 3\vec{j}$, $\vec{v} = 6\vec{i} + 5\vec{j}$.
   (b) $\vec{U} = \frac{5}{2}\vec{i} + \frac{2}{3}\vec{j}$, $\vec{v} = -\frac{3}{10}\vec{i} - \frac{9}{8}\vec{j}$.
   (c) $\vec{U} = 6\vec{i} + 7\vec{j}$, $\vec{v} = -\frac{7}{2}\vec{i} + 3\vec{j}$.
   (d) $\vec{U} = -\frac{2}{3}\vec{i} - \frac{3}{4}\vec{j}$, $\vec{v} = 6\vec{i} - \frac{16}{3}\vec{j}$.

2. Find a unit vector in $\vec{v}$'s direction if
   (a) $\vec{v} = 4\vec{i} + 3\vec{j}$.   (c) $\vec{v} = \vec{i} + 6\vec{j}$.
   (b) $\vec{v} = -2\vec{i} - 3\vec{j}$.   (d) $\vec{v} = -7\vec{j}$.

3. Find a unit vector perpendicular to the vector of (a) Exercise 2(a), (b) Exercise 2(b), (c) Exercise 2(c), (d) Exercise 2(d).

4. Use vector analysis to find the cosines of the angles of the following triangles:
   (a) $O(0, 0)$, $R(6, 2)$, $S(1, 4)$.   (c) $W(-4, -1)$, $M(3, 0)$, $R(4, 6)$.
   (b) $H(-2, 3)$, $K(2, -1)$, $L(2, 6)$.

5. (a) Find the (directed length of the) projection of $\vec{T}$ on $\vec{v}$'s direction.
   (b) Find the vector projection of $\vec{T}$ on $\vec{v}$'s direction.
      (1) $\vec{T} = 2\vec{i} + 3\vec{j}$, $\vec{v} = 6\vec{i} + 2\vec{j}$.   (3) $\vec{T} = 2\vec{i} + 3\vec{j}$, $\vec{v} = -3\vec{i} - 2\vec{j}$.
      (2) $\vec{T} = -2\vec{i}$, $\vec{v} = -4\vec{i} + 2\vec{j}$.   (4) $\vec{T} = -2\vec{i} + 4\vec{j}$, $\vec{v} = 4\vec{i} - 1\vec{j}$.

6. A particle acted on by the constant force $3\vec{\imath} + \vec{\jmath}$ is displaced in a straight line from $(6, 3)$ to $(1, 2)$. Find the work done against the force.

7. A particle acted on by the resultant of the constant forces $2\vec{\imath} + \vec{\jmath}$ and $-\vec{\imath} + \vec{\jmath}$ is moved in a straight line from $(0, 0)$ to $(1, 5)$. Find the work done against the resultant force.

8. Consult Exercise 3.4-10. In each of the following problems find a vector that bisects the angle between the given vectors:
   (a) $\vec{\jmath}, 3\vec{\imath} - 4\vec{\jmath}$.
   (b) $\vec{\imath}, 4\vec{\imath} + 5\vec{\jmath}$.
   (c) $9\vec{\imath} + 2\vec{\jmath}, 7\vec{\imath} - 6\vec{\jmath}$.
   (d) $3\vec{\imath} - 5\vec{\jmath}, 2\vec{\imath} + 7\vec{\jmath}$.

9. We are given $a = \|\vec{a}\| \neq 0$, $b = \|\vec{b}\| \neq 0$. Use the scalar product directly to show that $(1/a)\vec{a} + (1/b)\vec{b}$ makes equal angles with $\vec{a}$ and $\vec{b}$. (Compare with Exercise 3.4-10.)

10. Let the vectors $\vec{A}$ and $\vec{B}$ determine a parallelogram. Find vectors that represent the diagonals of the parallelogram. Show that the diagonals are perpendicular if and only if the parallelogram is a rhombus.

11. Here is part of a proof of the theorem: The altitudes of a triangle are concurrent (meet in a point). Complete the proof.

    Step (a). Given triangle PQR. Draw altitudes PL and QM, intersecting at G. Draw RG, extended if necessary to intersect PQ at N. The theorem is demonstrated if one can show that RN is perpendicular to PQ. See Fig. 3.43.

    Step (b). In vector language, we are given that $\overrightarrow{QG} \cdot \overrightarrow{PR} = 0$ and that $\overrightarrow{PG} \cdot \overrightarrow{QR} = 0$, and we want to show that $\overrightarrow{RG} \cdot \overrightarrow{PQ} = 0$.
    Step (c). Now

$$\overrightarrow{RG} \cdot \overrightarrow{PQ} = \overrightarrow{RG} \cdot (\overrightarrow{PR} + \overrightarrow{RQ}) = \overrightarrow{RG} \cdot \overrightarrow{PR} + \overrightarrow{RG} \cdot \overrightarrow{RQ}$$
$$= (\overrightarrow{RQ} + \overrightarrow{QG}) \cdot \overrightarrow{PR} + \cdots.$$

12. Let lines L_1 and L_2 have slopes m_1 and $m_2 = -1/m_1$. Use Theorem 3.5-4 to write down vectors $\vec{v}_1$ and $\vec{v}_2$ in the directions of L_1 and L_2, and use vector analysis to show that $L_1 \perp L_2$.

13. Let unit vectors $\vec{u}$ and $\vec{v}$ be obtained by rotating $\vec{\imath}$ about its initial point through angles α and β. Use Theorem 3.5-6 to compute $\vec{u} \cdot \vec{v}$ and get a statement for $\cos(\alpha - \beta)$.

3.7 Curves and Equations

Having prepared part of our vector analysis tool, we return to our study of analytic geometry, keeping in the foreground the correspondence between geometry and algebra.

■ DEFINITION 1

The curve-equation relationship. A curve and equation correspond if the coordinates of each point on the curve satisfy the equation, and if each point whose coordinates satisfy the equation lies on the curve.

To the geometric statement "a point lies on the curve" corresponds the algebraic statement "the coordinates satisfy the equation." The familiar process of computing a table of values when plotting a curve from a given equation is nothing but an attempt to find coordinate pairs that satisfy an equation, and, hence, points that lie on the curve.

The solution of simultaneous equations in algebra corresponds in geometry to finding the points of intersection of the curves that correspond to the equations.

In the algebra we find the pairs of numbers that satisfy both equations; in the geometry we find the points that lie on both curves.

Example 1. In Example 2.7-1A we found the simultaneous solutions of $y = 5 - x^2$ and $y = 5 - 2x$, and thus found that the points of intersection of the corresponding curves were $(2, 1)$ and $(0, 5)$.

Next, let us solve simultaneously $y = 5 - x^2$ and $y = 6 - x$. We are led to the quadratic equation $5 - x^2 = 6 - x$, or to $x^2 - x + 1 = 0$. The quadratic formula tells us that

$$x = \frac{1 + \sqrt{-3}}{2} \qquad \text{or that} \qquad x = \frac{1 - \sqrt{-3}}{2},$$

so that the simultaneous solutions are

$$x = \frac{1 + \sqrt{-3}}{2}, \qquad y = \frac{11 - \sqrt{-3}}{2},$$

and
$$x = \frac{1 - \sqrt{-3}}{2}, \qquad y = \frac{11 + \sqrt{-3}}{2}.$$

A graph shows why the solutions of $y = 5 - x^2$ and $y = 5 - 2x$ are real, whereas those of $y = 5 - x^2$ and $y = 6 - x$ are not. In the first case the corresponding curves intersect. In the second, they do not. See Fig. 3.44.

We shall study the curve-equation relationship systematically in the next 13 sections, starting with the simplest curve, the straight line, and the simplest equation, the first-degree equation.

EXERCISES 3.7

Find the real intersections, if any, of the following pairs of curves. In each case solve the equations simultaneously and plot both curves.

1. $x + 2y = 7$,
   $3x - y = 7$.

2. $4x - y = 7$,
   $5x + 2y = -1$.

3. $2x + 3y = 5$,
   $2x + 3y = 9$.

4. $y = x^2 - 6$,
   $x + 3y = 6$.

5. $x^2 + y^2 = 16$,
   $y = 3x - 2$.

6. $y = x^2 - 6$,
   $y = \frac{1}{2}x - 8$.

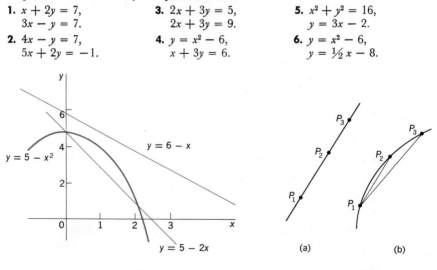

Fig. 3.44   Fig. 3.45

3.8 The Straight Line

Intuitively, we recognize that the straight line is the simplest curve, and we start our detailed investigation of the curve-equation relationship with the straight line and the corresponding "linear" equation.

A characteristic geometric property of the straight line is the following: If a point P_1 on the straight line L is selected and joined to other points on L by drawing straight-line segments, these segments always have the same direction, the direction of the line L itself. Conversely, if a point can be joined to P_1 by a straight-line segment that has the same direction as the line itself, that point lies on L. On the other hand, if a point P_1 on some other curve is selected and straight-line segments are drawn from P_1 to other points on that curve, the straight-line segments obtained do not always have the same direction. See Fig. 3.45.

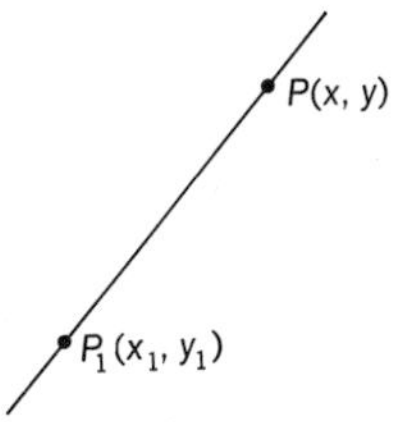

In algebraic language, let $P_1(x_1, y_1)$ be a point on a line L that has finite slope m, and let $P(x, y)$ be any other point on the line; see Fig. 3.46. If we join P to P_1, we get a line segment of slope m:

Fig. 3.46

$$\frac{y - y_1}{x - x_1} = m,$$

or
$$y - y_1 = m(x - x_1), \tag{1}$$

for all points $P(x, y)$ on L other than P_1.

■ THEOREM 1

The point-slope form.

HYPOTHESIS: (a) Line L goes through the point $P_1(x_1, y_1)$.
(b) Line L has slope m.

CONCLUSION: Line L corresponds to the equation
$$y - y_1 = m(x - x_1). \tag{1}$$

PROOF: (a) We have already proved that Eq. (1) holds for all points P on L other than P_1.

(b) By direct substitution we see that Eq. (1) is satisfied by the coordinates of P_1 also, for one gets $y_1 - y_1 = m(x_1 - x_1)$, or $0 = m(0)$.

(c) Now we know that the coordinates of all points on L satisfy Eq. (1), but it may be that points not on L also satisfy this equation. It remains to show that, if the coordinates (x, y) of a point Q satisfy Eq. (1), then Q lies on line L. If $x = x_1$, then $y = y_1$ and point Q coincides with P_1, thus surely lying on L. If $x \neq x_1$, then we shall show that the slope of P_1Q is m, so that Q again lies on L. Indeed, since the coordinates of $Q(x, y)$ satisfy Eq. (1), we can compute

$$\text{slope of } QP_1 = \frac{y - y_1}{x - x_1} = \frac{m(x - x_1)}{x - x_1} = m.$$

For the sake of completeness we need the following theorem.

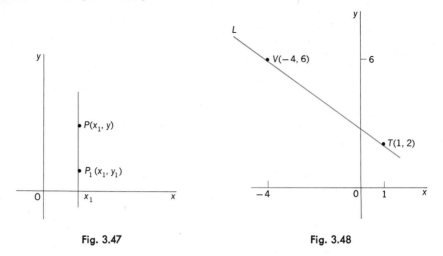

Fig. 3.47   Fig. 3.48

■ THEOREM 2

Equations of vertical lines.

HYPOTHESIS: (a) Line L goes through the point $P_1(x_1, y_1)$.
(b) Line L has infinite slope.

CONCLUSION: Line L corresponds to the equation

$$x = x_1. \tag{2}$$

The proof is left to the reader. See Fig. 3.47.

● **Remark 1**

Theorems 1 and 2 show that any straight line is described either by an equation of Type (1) or by one of Type (2). These equations are first-degree equations. Conversely, every first-degree equation represents a straight line,* for every first-degree equation can be written in the form $Ax + By + C = 0$, with not both A and B zero. If $B \neq 0$ the equation can be rewritten in the forms $By + C = -Ax$, $y + C/B = -(A/B)(x - 0)$, and hence represents the straight line through $(0, -C/B)$ with slope $-(A/B)$. If $B = 0$, then A cannot also be 0, and the equation $Ax + By + C = 0$ can be written $Ax + C = 0$ or $x = -(C/A)$; this equation represents a vertical line.

Example 1. Find the equation of the straight line L that passes through the points $V(-4, 6)$ and $T(1, 2)$. See Fig. 3.48. For L we have

$$m = m_{VT} = \frac{(6) - (2)}{(-4) - (1)} = -\frac{4}{5}.$$

If we consider L to be a line through $V(-4, 6)$ with slope $-\frac{4}{5}$, then, by the point-slope form, L's equation is $y - 6 = -\frac{4}{5}(x + 4)$ or $4x + 5y - 14 = 0$. On the other hand, if we had considered L to be a line through $T(1, 2)$ with slope $-\frac{4}{5}$, L's equation would have been $y - 2 = -\frac{4}{5}(x - 1)$ or $4x + 5y - 14 = 0$ again.

---

* It is for this reason that first-degree equations are often called linear equations.

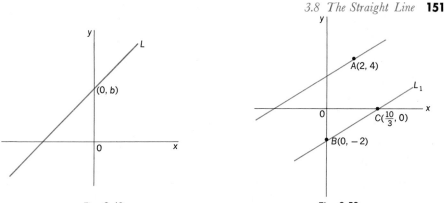

Fig. 3.49

Fig. 3.50

Example 2. Find the equation of the straight line through $(0, b)$ with slope m; see Fig. 3.49.

This is a special case of the point-slope theorem. We have $y - b = m(x - 0)$,

or $$y = mx + b, \tag{3}$$

the "slope-intercept form" for the straight line.

The slope-intercept form points out clearly how the slope of a straight line can be obtained from its equation, for it says that if one has solved for y, m is the coefficient of x. This is repeated as follows.

■ THEOREM 3

The slope of a line L from its equation.

HYPOTHESIS: Line L has the equation $Ax + By + C = 0$, $B \neq 0$.

CONCLUSION: The slope of L is $-(A/B)$, found by solving L's equation for y and taking the coefficient of x.

● Remark 2

The slope of L could also be found by computing dy/dx.

Example 3. Given L_1 with the equation $3x - 5y = 10$. Find the equation of the line L parallel to L_1 and passing through $A(2, 4)$. See Fig. 3.50.

(a) If we solve L_1's equation for y, we get $y = \frac{3}{5}x - 2$. Hence the slope of L_1 is $m_1 = \frac{3}{5}$.

(b) Now L is parallel to L_1 and must have the same slope; $m = \frac{3}{5}$.

(c) Since L passes through $A(2, 4)$, the point-slope form tells us that the equation of L is $y - 4 = \frac{3}{5}(x - 2)$.

Example 4. Given triangle $Q(2, 5)$, $R(-2, -3)$, $S(7, 0)$. Find the equation of the altitude on side RS. See Fig. 3.51.

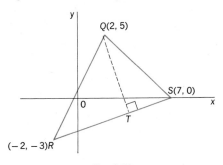

Fig. 3.51

(a) We know that the altitude sought, TQ, is perpendicular to RS.

(b) Now the slope of RS is

$$m_{RS} = \frac{(0) - (-3)}{(7) - (-2)} = \frac{1}{3};$$

hence the slope of TQ is -3.

(c) Since TQ passes through $Q(2, 5)$, the equation of TQ is $y - 5 = -3(x - 2)$.

Example 5.   Find the length of the altitude TQ in the triangle of Example 4.

This length could be determined by finding the coordinates of T (from the equations of RS and TQ), and then by using the formula for the distance between two points. But vector analysis gives us another way of finding TQ that does not require our knowing the coordinates of T or even the equation of TQ.

(a) TQ is the length of the projection of $\overrightarrow{RQ}$ on the direction of $\overrightarrow{TQ}$.

(b) $\overrightarrow{RQ} = 4\vec{i} + 8\vec{j}$.

(c) Next,

$$m_{RS} = \frac{(0) - (-3)}{(7) - (-2)} = \frac{1}{3};$$

therefore $m_{TQ} = -3$. By Theorem 3.5-4, a vector in the direction of $\overrightarrow{TQ}$ is $\vec{v} = -1(1\vec{i} - 3\vec{j}) = -\vec{i} + 3\vec{j}$.*

(d) The projection of $\overrightarrow{RQ}$ on $\overrightarrow{TQ}$'s or $\vec{v}$'s direction is then

$$\|\overrightarrow{TQ}\| = \overrightarrow{RQ} \cdot \frac{\vec{v}}{\|\vec{v}\|} = (4\vec{i} + 8\vec{j}) \cdot \frac{(-1\vec{i} + 3\vec{j})}{\|-1\vec{i} + 3\vec{j}\|}$$

$$= \frac{-4 + 24}{\sqrt{1 + 9}} = \frac{20}{\sqrt{10}} = 2\sqrt{10}.$$

Since the distance from a point to a line is required fairly frequently, let us repeat the work of Example 5 in a more general context.

■ THEOREM 4

The distance from a line to a point.

HYPOTHESIS: (a) Line L has the equation $Ax + By + C = 0$.
   (b) Point P_1 has coordinates (x_1, y_1).

CONCLUSION: The distance from L to P_1 is given by

$$\left| \frac{Ax_1 + By_1 + C}{\sqrt{A^2 + B^2}} \right|.$$

PROOF: (a) Take first the case where $B \neq 0$. One point on L is $S(0, -C/B)$; see Fig. 3.52.

---

* Reference to Fig. 3.51 shows that $-\vec{i} + 3\vec{j}$ is to be preferred to $\vec{i} - 3\vec{j}$ for vector $\overrightarrow{TQ}$, because TQ rises from T to Q.

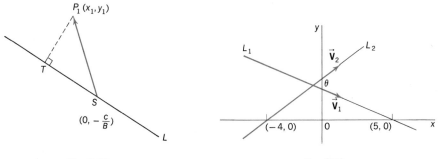

Fig. 3.52   Fig. 3.53

(b) Now the distance sought is TP_1, the projection of $\overrightarrow{SP_1}$ on $\overrightarrow{TP_1}$'s direction.

(c) We have

$$\overrightarrow{SP_1} = (x_1 - 0)\vec{i} + \left(y_1 + \frac{C}{B}\right)\vec{j}.$$

(d) Since the slope of L is $-A/B$, $B \neq 0$, the slope of TP_1 is $+B/A$, and $\vec{v} = 1\vec{i} + (B/A)\vec{j}$ is a vector parallel to TP_1. A more convenient vector parallel to TP_1 is $\vec{W} = A\vec{v} = A\vec{i} + B\vec{j}$.

(e) Then

$$\|\overrightarrow{TP_1}\| = \left|\overrightarrow{SP_1} \cdot \frac{\vec{W}}{\|\vec{W}\|}\right| = \left|\left[x_1\vec{i} + \left(y_1 + \frac{C}{B}\right)\vec{j}\right] \cdot \frac{A\vec{i} + B\vec{j}}{\sqrt{A^2 + B^2}}\right|$$

$$= \left|\frac{Ax_1 + B(y_1 + C/B)}{\sqrt{A^2 + B^2}}\right| = \left|\frac{Ax_1 + By_1 + C}{\sqrt{A^2 + B^2}}\right|.$$

(f) If $B = 0$, line L is vertical. For a point on L, the point S' $(-C/A, 0)$ could be taken, and for the vector $\vec{W}$ in Step (d), the unit vector $\vec{i}$. The details of checking the conclusion in this case are left to the reader.

● **Remark 3**

If the reader expects to use the distance from a point to a line often enough, it would pay to commit the conclusion of this theorem to memory, and perhaps even to agree on direction conventions in order to be able to deal with a directed distance. See Exercise 3.8-24.

Example 6.   Find the acute angle between $L_1: 2x + 5y - 10 = 0$, and $L_2: 3x - 4y + 12 = 0$.

Lines L_1 and L_2 are easily sketched by determining intercept points for each one. See Fig. 3.53.

(a) If we solve the equation of L_1 for y, we find that $m_1 = -\frac{2}{5}$.

(b) Therefore a vector parallel to L_1 is $\vec{W}_1 = 1\vec{i} - \frac{2}{5}\vec{j}$. Another is $\vec{v}_1 = 5\vec{W}_1 = 5\vec{i} - 2\vec{j}$. The diagram leads us to select $\vec{v}_1$ rather than $-\vec{v}_1 = -5\vec{i} + 2\vec{j}$.

(c) Similarly, the slope of L_2 is $\frac{3}{4}$ and a vector parallel to L_2 is $\vec{W}_2 = 1\vec{i} + \frac{3}{4}\vec{j}$. Another is $\vec{v}_2 = 4\vec{W}_2 = 4\vec{i} + 3\vec{j}$.

(d) Now we have

$$\vec{v}_1 \cdot \vec{v}_2 = \|\vec{v}_1\| \, \|\vec{v}_2\| \cos \theta,$$

$$\cos \theta = \frac{\vec{v}_1 \cdot \vec{v}_2}{\|\vec{v}_1\| \, \|\vec{v}_2\|} = \frac{(5\vec{i} - 2\vec{j}) \cdot (4\vec{i} + 3\vec{j})}{\|5\vec{i} - 2\vec{j}\| \, \|4\vec{i} + 3\vec{j}\|}$$

$$= \frac{20 - 6}{\sqrt{29} \, \sqrt{25}} = \frac{14}{5 \sqrt{29}},$$

from which θ can easily be found.

(e) If θ had been closer to $\pi/2$, it might have been difficult to tell from the diagram which angle between L_1 and L_2 was the acute angle. If we had chosen $\vec{v}_1$ and $\vec{v}_2$ in such a way as to determine the obtuse angle, we would have computed a negative number for $\cos \theta$ in Part (d), and could have obtained the acute angle as the supplement of the obtuse angle.

EXERCISES 3.8

1. Find the equations of the sides of the triangle QRS in each of the following cases:
   (a) $Q(0, 0)$, $R(3, 4)$, $S(7, 2)$.   (c) $Q(-1, 2)$, $R(4, 6)$, $S(4, -4)$.
   (b) $Q(-1, 3)$, $R(5, 3)$, $S(1, -4)$.   (d) $Q(-2, 0)$, $R(0, 4)$, $S(6, 5)$.
2. We are given L_1: $2x + y - 8 = 0$ and L_2: $3x - 4y + 8 = 0$.
   (a) Find the equation of a line through $Q(2, 1)$ parallel to L_1.
   (b) Find the equation of a line through $Q(2, 1)$ parallel to L_2.
   (c) Find the equation of a line through $Q(2, 1)$ perpendicular to L_1.
   (d) Find R, the point of intersection of L_1 and L_2.
   (e) Find the equation of the line through R perpendicular to L_2.
3. Repeat Exercise 2 for lines L_1: $3x - 5y - 15 = 0$; L_2: $x = 6$.
4. Find the equation of the altitude on side RS for each triangle of Exercise 1.
5. Find the equation of the perpendicular bisector of side QR for each triangle of Exercise 1.
6. Find the equation of the median drawn through vertex S for each triangle of Exercise 1.
7. Find the cosine of the acute angle between the lines L_1 and L_2 of Exercise 2.
8. Find the cosine of the acute angle between the lines L_1 and L_2 of Exercise 3.
9. Find the cosine of the obtuse angle between the lines $2x - 5y = 10$ and $x + 7y = 7$.
10. One of the angles between $3x + y = 6$ and $x - 2y = -8$ includes the origin. Find the cosine of that angle.
11. (i) Find the length of the altitude on side RS for each triangle of Exercise 1. (ii) Find the area of the triangle.
12. In each case find the distance from the given line to the given point.
    (a) $2x - 3y = 12$; $(0, 4)$.
    (b) The line joining $(1, 7)$ to $(4, 2)$; $(-2, 1)$.
    (c) $5x + 12y = 25$; $(2, 3)$.   (d) $y = 7$; $(2, -4)$.
    (e) $x = -3$; $(1, -1)$.
13. Find the radius of a circle with center at $C(-2, 5)$ if L: $x + 3y = 9$ is a tangent line.
14. Repeat Exercise 13 using $C(0, 4)$ and L: $3x - 5y = 10$.
15. We have used vector analysis to find the cosine of an angle between two given lines. The following theorem for the tangent of an angle between two given lines is often useful.

Theorem 5. On an angle between two lines.

Hypothesis: (a) Neither L_1 nor L_2 is vertical and these lines are not perpendicular.
(b) L_1 and L_2 have inclination angles θ_1 and θ_2 and slopes m_1 and m_2.
(c) θ is the angle obtained by rotating from L_1's position to L_2's in the counterclockwise direction.

Conclusion:

$$\tan \theta = \frac{m_2 - m_1}{1 + m_1 m_2}.$$

Proof: To be carried out by the reader. Draw a diagram for the case where $\theta_2 > \theta_1$ and another for the case where $\theta_2 < \theta_1$. Show that $\theta = \theta_2 - \theta_1$ in one case and $\theta = \pi + \theta_2 - \theta_1$ in the other, but that $\tan \theta = \tan(\theta_2 - \theta_1) = (m_2 - m_1)/(1 + m_1 m_2)$ in both cases.

16. Find the tangent of the
(a) acute angle between $3x - 4y + 8 = 0$ and $2x + y - 8 = 0$;
(b) obtuse angle between $2x - 5y = 10$ and $x + 7y = 7$;
(c) angle between $3x + y = 6$ and $x - 2y = -8$ which includes the origin.

17. Can Theorem 5 be used directly to find the tangent of the acute angle between the lines of Exercise 3 above? Use some of the ideas of the proof of Theorem 5 to find the tangent of this angle.

18. Use Theorem 5 to find
(a) $\tan Q$ in $\triangle QRS$ of Exercise 1(a) above;
(b) $\tan S$ in $\triangle QRS$ of Exercise 1(b) above;
(c) $\tan Q$ in $\triangle QRS$ of Exercise 1(c) above.

19. Show that the fact that a straight line has a first-degree equation is consistent with the fact that the straight line is the only curve whose tangent line never changes its direction. Use derivatives.

20. It is known that the altitudes of a triangle meet in a point. (See Exercise 3.6-11.) Find the equations of the other two altitudes of the triangle of Example 4, and find the coordinates of the point at which all three altitudes intersect.

21. Use the method suggested at the beginning of Example 5 to find the length of altitude TQ.

22. Use analytic methods to prove that the perpendicular bisector of a segment AB is the locus of points equidistant from A and B. (Alternate wording: If a point is equidistant from A and B, then it must lie on the perpendicular bisector of AB, and conversely.) *Suggestion:* Choose coordinate axes so that A has coordinates $(-c, 0)$ and B has coordinates $(c, 0)$.

23. A point moves so that the square of its distance from A is always greater than the square of its distance from B by a constant amount k. Show that the point moves on a straight line perpendicular to AB.

24. Consider Theorem 4. In the case where $B \neq 0$, let us agree to write the equation of L so that $B > 0$. (If $B < 0$, it is necessary only to multiply both members of the equation for L by -1.) Show that if $P_1(x_1, y_1)$ lies above L, then

$$d = \frac{Ax_1 + By_1 + C}{\sqrt{A^2 + B^2}} > 0,$$

and that, if P_1 lies below L, then $d < 0$. *Suggestion:* If $P_1(x_1, y_1)$ lies above L, then a point of L directly below P_1 is $R(x_1, [-Ax_1 - C]/B)$. This means that $y_1 > (-Ax_1 - C)/B$.

25. Show, without plotting, that $Q(6, 0)$ and $R(-2, 12)$ lie above $L: 3x + y - 4 = 0$ but that $S(\frac{1}{2}, 2)$ lies below L.

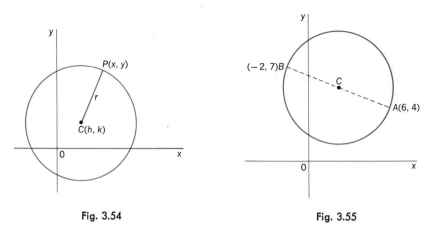

Fig. 3.54   Fig. 3.55

3.9 The Circle

We continue our study of the curve and equation relationship as it applies to the circle.

■ DEFINITION 1

The circle. Let C be a fixed point, called the center, and r a fixed positive number, called the radius. The set of all points at a distance r from C constitutes a circle.

To describe the circle in algebraic language, let us say that the center is the point $C(h, k)$; see Fig. 3.54. If a point $P(x, y)$ lies on the circle, then $PC = r$, or

$$\sqrt{(x - h)^2 + (y - k)^2} = r. \tag{1}$$

We are thus led to the following theorem.

■ THEOREM 1

A circle equation.

HYPOTHESIS: (a) $C(h, k)$ is the center of a circle.
(b) r is the radius of the circle.

CONCLUSION: The equation of the circle is

$$(x - h)^2 + (y - k)^2 = r^2. \tag{2}$$

PROOF: In writing Eq. (1), we have already proved that, if a point lies on the circle, its coordinates satisfy Eq. (2). It remains to show that the only points whose coordinates satisfy Eq. (2) are the points on the circle. Let the coordinates of $Q(x, y)$ satisfy Eq. (2). Then, by using the formula for the distance between two points and Eq. (2) itself, we have

$$QC = \sqrt{(x - h)^2 + (y - k)^2} = \sqrt{r^2} = r,$$

so that Q lies a distance r from the center and is a point of the circle.

Observe that the circle is defined geometrically in terms of its center and radius; algebraically, the coordinates of the center and the radius number play prominent roles in the circle's equation.

Example 1.   Find the equation of a circle if $A(6, 4)$ and $B(-2, 7)$ are the end points of one of its diameters.

(a) The center of the circle must be the midpoint of AB. Hence we have $C(2, 1\frac{1}{2})$; see Fig. 3.55.

(b) Since the radius is half the diameter,

$$r = \tfrac{1}{2}AB = \tfrac{1}{2}\sqrt{64 + 9} = \tfrac{1}{2}\sqrt{73}.$$

(c) Therefore the equation of the circle is

$$(x - 2)^2 + (y - 1\tfrac{1}{2})^2 = 73\tfrac{1}{4},$$

or, if we prefer to multiply out,

$$x^2 - 4x + 4 + y^2 - 11y + 12\tfrac{1}{4} = 73\tfrac{1}{4},$$

or $x^2 + y^2 - 4x - 11y + 16 = 0.$

Example 2.   Find the center and radius of the circle whose equation is

$$x^2 + y^2 + 6x - 8y - 11 = 0.$$

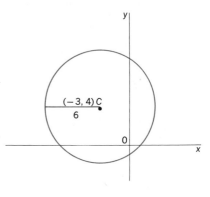

Here we must rewrite the given equation in the form of Eq. (2), which emphasizes the center and radius. To do this, we "complete the square."* First we write

Fig. 3.56

$$(x^2 + 6x + \quad) + (y^2 - 8y + \quad) = 11. \tag{3}$$

The coefficient of the x^2 term is 1; to complete the square for the x terms, we take half the x coefficient and square, getting $[\frac{1}{2}(6)]^2 = 9$. To complete the square for the y terms, we take half the y coefficient and square, getting $[\frac{1}{2}(-8)]^2 = 16$. We then add these numbers to both members of Eq. (3), as follows:

$$(x^2 + 6x + 9) + (y^2 - 8y + 16) = 11 + 9 + 16.$$

Now we recognize the squares we completed,

$$(x + 3)^2 + (y - 4)^2 = 36,$$

and we see that the center is $C(-3, 4)$ while the radius is 6. With this information the circle is sketched in Fig. 3.56.

Example 3.   Find the equation of the circle γ which is tangent to the x axis and concentric with γ_1: $2x^2 + 2y^2 - 11x + 6y - 8 = 0.$

---

* To review the process of "completing the square," observe first that $(x + n)^2 = x^2 + 2nx + n^2$. Now suppose that we are given the first two terms, x^2 and $2nx$, and are asked to give instructions for forming the third term of the square, namely n^2. If we take half of the coefficient of the x term, or $1/2\,(2n) = n$, and then square, we will have the correct third term. Hence the instructions: (a) Make sure that the coefficient of the x^2 term is 1; (b) Take half of the coefficient of the x term, and square.

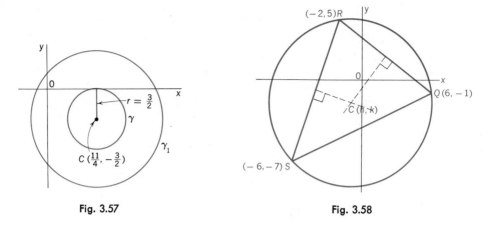

Fig. 3.57   Fig. 3.58

The circles γ and γ_1 have the same center, and so we first complete the square in the equation for γ_1 to find its center.

(a) Divide by 2, because it is easier to complete the square when the coefficient of the x^2 term is 1. This gives

$$(x^2 - 11\tfrac{1}{2}x + \quad) + (y^2 + 3y + \quad) = 4.$$

(b) For the x and y terms, respectively, add

$$[\tfrac{1}{2}(-11\tfrac{1}{2})]^2 = {}^{121}\!/_{16} \qquad \text{and} \qquad [\tfrac{1}{2}(3)]^2 = \tfrac{9}{4}$$

to both members. Thus,

$$\left(x^2 - \frac{11}{2}x + \frac{121}{16}\right) + \left(y^2 + 3y + \frac{9}{4}\right) = 4 + \frac{121}{16} + \frac{9}{4},$$

$$\left(x - \frac{11}{4}\right)^2 + \left(y + \frac{3}{2}\right)^2 = \frac{64 + 121 + 36}{16} = \frac{221}{16}.$$

(c) The circles γ and γ_1 have the center $C_1(11\tfrac{1}{4}, -\tfrac{3}{2})$. Since γ is tangent to the x axis, its radius must be $\tfrac{3}{2}$. See Fig. 3.57. The equation of γ is

$$(x - 11\tfrac{1}{4})^2 + (y + \tfrac{3}{2})^2 = \tfrac{9}{4}.$$

Example 4.   Find the equation of the circle through the points $Q(6, -1)$, $R(-2, 5)$, $S(-6, -7)$. See Fig. 3.58.

(a) Let the equation of the circle be

$$(x - h)^2 + (y - k)^2 = r^2.$$

We must determine the three unknowns, h, k, and r.

(b) Because Q lies on the circle, its coordinates satisfy the equation. Hence

$$(6 - h)^2 + (-1 - k)^2 = r^2$$

or

$$36 - 12h + h^2 + 1 + 2k + k^2 = r^2.$$

(c) Similarly R and S lie on the circle, and we have, for R,

$$(-2 - h)^2 + (5 - k)^2 = r^2 \qquad \text{or} \qquad 4 + 4h + h^2 + 25 - 10k + k^2 = r^2,$$

and for S,

$$(-6 - h)^2 + (-7 - k)^2 = r^2$$

or

$$36 + 12h + h^2 + 49 + 14k + k^2 = r^2.$$

(d) At this point we have three equations for the three unknowns, and we proceed to solve the equations simultaneously. If we subtract the R equation from the Q equation, we obtain

$$-16h + 12k + 8 = 0 \qquad \text{or} \qquad 4h - 3k = 2.$$

(e) Subtracting the S equation from the R equation, we obtain

$$-8h - 24k - 56 = 0 \qquad \text{or} \qquad h + 3k = -7.$$

(f) If we solve Eqs. (d) and (e) simultaneously, we soon find that $h = -1$, $k = -2$, so that C is the point $(-1, -2)$.

(g) From (b) it now follows that

$$r^2 = (6 + 1)^2 + (-1 + 2)^2 = 50.$$

Therefore the circle we seek has the equation

$$(x + 1)^2 + (y + 2)^2 = 50.$$

● **Remark 1**

It is interesting to observe how closely our algebraic solution for the problem followed a solution suggested by a Euclidean theorem. The problem amounts to finding the circle that circumscribes the triangle QRS. Since the center C is equidistant from Q and R, it must lie on the perpendicular bisector of side QR. Similarly C must lie on the perpendicular bisector of side RS. Now it happens that the equation of the perpendicular bisector of QR is $4x - 3y = 2$;* Step (d) above says that $C(h, k)$ lies on this line. The equation of the perpendicular bisector of RS is $x + 3y = -7$; Step (e) says that $C(h, k)$ lies on this line also. When we solve the equations in Step (f), we find C as the point of intersection of the perpendicular bisectors.

Example 5. Find the equations of the circles whose centers lie on $y = x + 1$, which are tangent to the y axis, and which pass through $A(-4, -1)$.

Referring to Fig. 3.59, we see that we can sketch two circles that meet the specifications. Let the equation of such a circle be $(x - h)^2 + (y - k)^2 = r^2$. We have three unknowns to determine: h, k, and r. We shall translate the three specifications stated into three equations for h, k and r, and then solve.

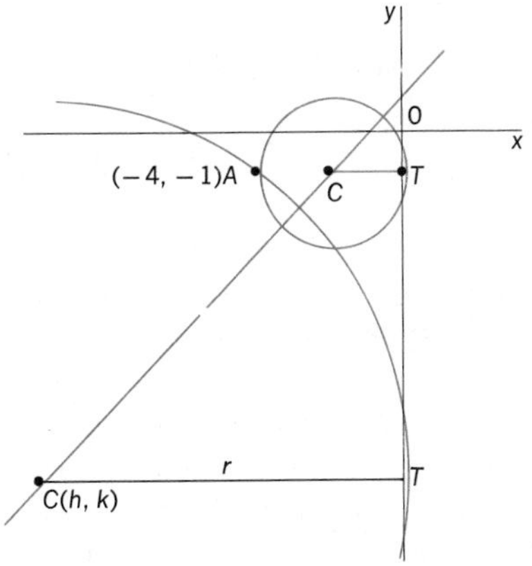

Fig. 3.59

(a) Because $C(h, k)$ lies on $y = x + 1$, we have $k = h + 1$.

(b) Because the circle must be tangent to the y axis, we must have $r = CT = -h$. (Remember that the diagram requires that h be a negative number.)

(c) Because A lies on the circle, we know that

$$(-4 - h)^2 + (-1 - k)^2 = r^2.$$

(d) To solve, we substitute from Parts (a) and (b) into Part (c), obtaining

$$(-4 - h)^2 + (-1 - h - 1)^2 = (-h)^2 \qquad \text{or} \qquad h^2 + 12h + 20 = 0,$$

and then
$$h = -10 \qquad \text{or} \qquad h = -2,$$
$$k = -9 \qquad\qquad\quad k = -1,$$
$$r = 10 \qquad\qquad\quad r = 2.$$

The equations of the circles are

$$(x + 10)^2 + (y + 9)^2 = 100 \qquad \text{and} \qquad (x + 2)^2 + (y + 1)^2 = 4.$$

Example 6.   Prove that an angle inscribed in a semicircle is a right angle.

For algebraic convenience let us choose a coordinate system with origin at the center of the circle and x axis through the end points of the semicircle; see Fig. 3.60. Then if the radius of the circle is r, the theorem we are to demonstrate can be restated as follows.

HYPOTHESIS: $P(x, y)$ is any point on the circle $x^2 + y^2 = r^2$ other than $A(r, 0)$ and $B(-r, 0)$.

CONCLUSION: $PA \perp PB$.

PROOF: To decide whether PA and PB are perpendicular, we can either consider the slopes of PA and PB or $\overrightarrow{PA} \cdot \overrightarrow{PB}$. Let us consider the slopes.

(a) We know that

$$m_{PA} = \frac{y - 0}{x - r}, \qquad m_{PB} = \frac{y - 0}{x + r}.$$

(b) Now $PA \perp PB$ if $m_{PA}m_{PB} = -1$. But

$$m_{PA}m_{PB} = \frac{y^2}{x^2 - r^2} = \frac{r^2 - x^2}{x^2 - r^2} = -1.$$

We were able to replace y^2 by $r^2 - x^2$, because we knew that the coordinates of $P(x, y)$ satisfied the circle's equation.

Example 7.   The set of all points satisfying a geometric condition is called a *locus*. Show that the locus of points whose distance from one fixed point is k times the distance from a second fixed point, $k > 0$ but $k \neq 1$, is a circle.

For algebraic convenience let us place the origin of our coordinate system at one of the fixed points and let us choose for our x axis the line joining the two fixed points; see Fig. 3.61. Thus F_1 has the coordinates $(0, 0)$ and F_2 has the coordinates $(a, 0)$, where a is the distance between the two fixed points. Then

(a) $P(x, y)$ is a point on the curve we are studying if and only if $PO = k\,PF_2$.

(b) Translating into algebra, $P(x, y)$ is on the locus if and only if

$$\sqrt{x^2 + y^2} = k\sqrt{(x - a)^2 + y^2}.$$

(c) Since the radicals and k are positive, we can square and say that $P(x, y)$ is on the locus if and only if

$$x^2 + y^2 = k^2[(x - a)^2 + y^2]$$

or $\quad (k^2 - 1)x^2 + (k^2 - 1)y^2 - 2ak^2x + k^2a^2 = 0.$

We recognize this equation as the equation of a circle, although we would have to complete the square to locate its center.

If we had taken $k = 1$, we would have been looking for the locus of points equidistant from O and F_2 and our answer in (c) would have reduced to the perpendicular bisector of OF_2, the line $x = a/2$.

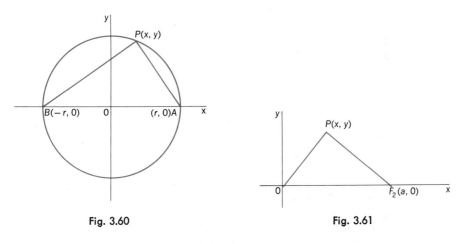

Fig. 3.60   Fig. 3.61

EXERCISES 3.9

1. Consider the following equations. If the corresponding curve is a circle, write down its center and radius and make a sketch. If the coordinates of only one point satisfy the equation, or if the coordinates of no points satisfy the equation, say so.

(a) $x^2 + y^2 - 8x - 6y + 9 = 0.$ (d) $x^2 + y^2 + 4x - 6y + 13 = 0.$
(b) $4x^2 + 4y^2 + 16x - 12y - 7 = 0.$ (e) $x^2 + y^2 + x - 8y + 18 = 0.$
(c) $2x^2 + 2y^2 - 3x + 5y + 2 = 0.$ (f) $3x^2 + 3y^2 - 2x - 12y + 11 = 0.$

2. (a) Find the equation of that circle with center at $(-3, 4)$ which passes through $(4, 2)$.
  (b) The same with center at $(2, -5)$ and through $(-3, 2)$.

3. Find the equation of the circle for which the segment $A(2, 7)$, $B(-3, -1)$ is a diameter.

4. (a) Find the equation of that circle with center at $(1, 3)$ which is tangent to the line $2x - 5y = 16$.
  (b) The same with $(-1, 4)$ as center and $3x + 2y - 12 = 0$ as tangent.

5. Find the equation of the circle that is concentric with $x^2 + y^2 - 3x + 4y - 10 = 0$ and passes through $(-3, 0)$.

6. Find the equation of the circle that is concentric with $2x^2 + 2y^2 + 16x - 7y = 0$ and is tangent to the y axis.

7. Find the equation of the circle that is concentric with $x^2 + y^2 - 8x + 4 = 0$ and tangent to $x + 2y + 6 = 0$.

8. Find the equation of the circle that passes through the points
  (a) $(-3, 0)$, $(5, 4)$, $(6, -3)$.   (b) $(7, -1)$, $(5, 3)$, $(-4, 6)$.

9. We are given the triangle $S(2, 4)$, $T(8, -4)$, $U(-4, -8)$. Find the equation of the circumscribed circle.

10. Find the equation of that circle with center on $3x + 2y = 1$ which passes through $(2, 6)$ and $(6, 4)$.

11. Find the equation of the circle that is tangent to $y = 6$ and to $y = 3$ and whose center lies on $3x + 4y = 12$.

12. Find the equations of those circles which are tangent to the line $y = 2$, pass through $(1, 4)$, and have centers on the line $x - y + 2 = 0$.

13. Find the equations of the circles of radius $\sqrt{10}$ that are tangent to $3x + y = 6$ at $(3, -3)$.

14. Find the equations of the circles that pass through $(0, 0)$ and $(4, 0)$ and are tangent to $x + y = 8$.

15. Prove this converse of the Theorem of Example 6:

Hypothesis: (a) A and B are fixed points.
             (b) P is such that $PA \perp PB$.

Conclusion: P must lie on the circle that has A and B as ends of a diameter.

16. Prove this theorem:

Hypothesis: Point A lies outside circle K.

Conclusion: The point on K that is closest to A lies on the line joining A to the center of K.

17. Prove this theorem:

Hypothesis: Point B lies inside circle K, but is not the center of K.

Conclusion: The point on K that is closest to B lies on the line joining B to the center of K.

18. (a) How close to $(-1, 4)$ would a point traveling on the circle of Exercise 1(a) come?
  (b) How close to $(2, 2)$ would the same point come?

19. Let point A move on the circle $x^2 + y^2 = 4$ and let point B move on the circle $(x - 4)^2 + (y - 5)^2 = 1$. What is the smallest possible value for the distance AB?

20. Find the equation of the line tangent to the circle of Exercise 1(b) at $(0, -\frac{1}{2})$.

21. Two of the tangents to the circle $x^2 + (y - 1)^2 = 10$ pass through $(4, -1)$. Find their equations.

22. Verify that the perpendicular bisectors of sides RQ and RS have the equations stated in Remark 1 of this section.

23. In Remark 1.3-2 we pointed out that the tangent line to a circle at a point P could be taken to be (a) the line perpendicular to the radius or (b) the line whose slope is dy/dx, where $y = f(x)$ describes a portion of the circle containing P. Show that the two definitions are equivalent.

3.10   The Parabola

I

The circle and three other curves have second-degree equations. Here we shall consider the parabola, and, in succeeding sections, the ellipse and the hyperbola.

■ DEFINITION 1

The parabola. The set of all points equidistant from a fixed line (called the directrix) and a fixed point (called the focus) is a parabola.

Simple geometric experiments in which we look for points equidistant from the focus and directrix soon lead us to a curve like the one pictured in Fig. 3.62. Let the distance between the directrix and the focus be called p. Then, as in Fig. 3.63, for any number $q \geq p/2$ we can draw the circle with center at the focus and radius q and also a straight line parallel to the directrix and q units away from it. The points of intersection, P and P', of the circle and line have the same distance q from the focus and directrix and lie on the parabola. In particular, the point V of Fig. 3.62, midway between the focus and directrix, lies on the parabola, because its distances from the focus and directrix are both $p/2$. The points L and L' at a distance p from the focus on the line through the focus parallel to the directrix also lie on the parabola, because the distances from these points to the focus and directrix are all p. It is clear from Figs. 3.62 and 3.63 that the points on the parabola come in pairs which are symmetrically situated with respect to the line through the focus and perpendicular to the directrix. This line is called the axis (of symmetry) of the parabola; the point V at which the axis intersects the parab-

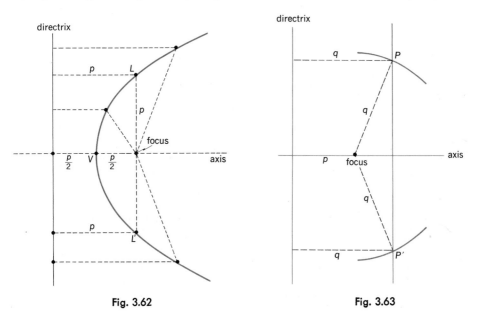

Fig. 3.62   Fig. 3.63

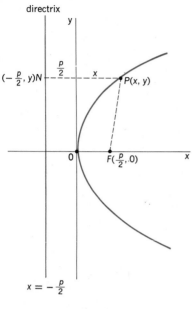

Fig. 3.64

ola is called the vertex; the perpendicular line segment through the focus that joins L to L' is called the latus rectum.

To describe the parabola algebraically, we must refer our diagram to a coordinate system. It seems reasonable to choose the axis of symmetry of the parabola as the x axis. For the y axis we choose the perpendicular line through the vertex, because it turns out that the resulting algebraic equation is then simplest. See Fig. 3.64. The coordinates of the focus will be $(p/2, 0)$ and the equation of the directrix will be $x = -p/2$, because we have agreed that the distance from the directrix to the focus shall be called p.

(a) Let $P(x,y)$ be any point on the parabola. Since P is equidistant from the focus and directrix, we can write $PF = PN$.

(b) Translating into algebra, we have

$$\sqrt{\left(x - \frac{p}{2}\right)^2 + y^2} = x + \frac{p}{2},$$

and simplifying by squaring we find that

$$x^2 - px + \frac{p^2}{4} + y^2 = x^2 + px + \frac{p^2}{4} \qquad \text{or} \qquad y^2 = 2px.$$

Thus we are led to the following theorem.

■ THEOREM 1

An equation for the parabola.

HYPOTHESIS: The directrix of a parabola is the line $x = -p/2$, and $(p/2, 0)$ is the focus.

CONCLUSION: The equation of the parabola is

$$y^2 = 2px. \tag{1}$$

PROOF: We have already shown that, if a point lies on the parabola, its coordinates satisfy Eq. (1). It remains to show that, if the coordinates of a point satisfy Eq. (1), the point is equidistant from the directrix and the focus and thus lies on the parabola. Let $P(x, y)$ be such that Eq. (1) is satisfied. Now for PF and PN we have

$$PF = \sqrt{\left(x - \frac{p}{2}\right)^2 + y^2}, \qquad PN = x + \frac{p}{2}.$$

But because Eq. (1) is satisfied,

$$PF = \sqrt{\left(x - \frac{p}{2}\right)^2 + y^2} = \sqrt{\left(x - \frac{p}{2}\right)^2 + 2px} = \sqrt{x^2 - px + \frac{p^2}{4} + 2px}$$

$$= \sqrt{x^2 + px + \frac{p^2}{4}} = \sqrt{\left(x + \frac{p}{2}\right)^2} = x + \frac{p}{2} = PN.^*$$

This concludes the proof.

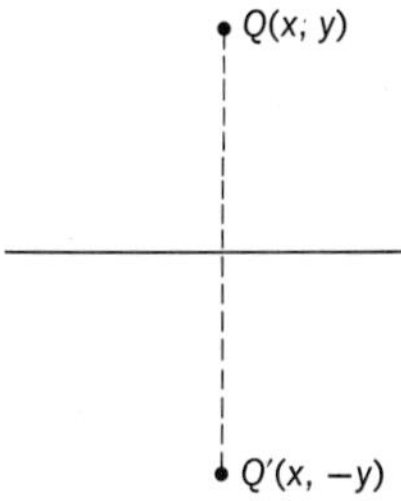

● **Remark 1**

Notice how the equation $y^2 = 2px$ and the graph drawn in Fig. 3.64 agree. The origin lies on the graph; $(0, 0)$ satisfies the equation. The graph has the x axis as its axis of symmetry; when the coordinates $Q(x,y)$ satisfy the equation, so do $Q'(x, -y)$. See Fig. 3.65. Finally, no point of the curve lies to the left of the y axis; when $x < 0$ we have $y^2 < 0$ and y cannot be real.

Fig. 3.65

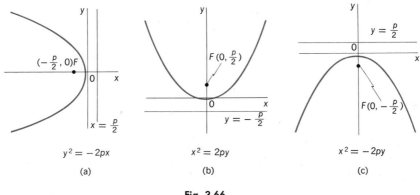

$$y^2 = -2px \qquad x^2 = 2py \qquad x^2 = -2py$$

(a)   (b)   (c)

Fig. 3.66

For this theorem we took a case where the directrix was parallel to the y axis and the focus was a point to its right. This case might be described by saying that the parabola "opened to the right." But there are three other cases that would have been just as easy to discuss. They are shown in Fig. 3.66.

We could learn to associate the different cases with their equations by memorizing, but it would surely be better to do the associating by recognizing that essential properties of the graph can be predicted from the equation. For instance, the equation $x^2 = -2py$ for the graph of Fig. 3.66(c) will be satisfied by the coordinates $(-x, y)$ whenever it is satisfied by (x, y). This means that the points of the graph come in pairs, one to the right of the y axis and the other an equal distance to the left, as in Fig. 3.67; the graph is symmetric with respect to the y axis. The graphs of Figs. 3.66(b) and (c) both have this symmetry. But $x^2 = -2py$, and if

---

* Note that x is positive because $x = y^2/2p$ and that $\sqrt{[x + (p/2)]^2}$ is $x + p/2$ rather than $-x - p/2$.

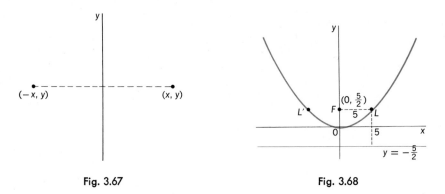

Fig. 3.67   Fig. 3.68

x^2, a square, is to be nonnegative and x is to be real, we must have negative y's. Hence the graph of Fig. 3.66(b), which requires that y be positive, must be ruled out. We take the graph of Fig. 3.66(c) for the equation $x^2 = -2py$.

To review, if its focus point and directrix line are specified, a parabola is determined as the set of points equidistant from that focus and directrix. Two parabolas are congruent if and only if they have the same distance p from focus to directrix. Since the number p has this important geometric property, we expect that the number p should have an important role to play in determining the parabola's equation. It does. Another important geometric property of the parabola is its symmetry. This symmetry also has a role to play in determining the parabola's equation.

Example 1.   Find the focus and directrix of $x^2 = 10y$ and sketch a graph.

(a) Because the point with coordinates $(-x, y)$ lies on the graph whenever the point with coordinates (x, y) does, the y axis is the axis of symmetry for this graph. So far, the parabola can open either upward or downward.

(b) Because $x^2 = 10y$ and y must be nonnegative if x^2 is to be positive and x real, the parabola opens upward rather than downward; see Fig. 3.68.

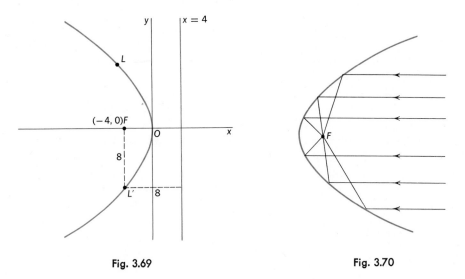

Fig. 3.69   Fig. 3.70

(c) By comparing $x^2 = 10y$ with the standard equation $x^2 = 2py$ we see that $2p = 10$, and that the distance between the focus and the directrix is $p = 5$. Hence the focus has coordinates $(0, \frac{5}{2})$ and the directrix has the equation $y = -\frac{5}{2}$.

(d) In sketching the parabola, it is convenient to use the vertex (the origin) and the ends of the latus rectum (L and L') as key points.

Example 2. A parabola has its vertex at the origin and its focus at $(-4, 0)$. Sketch it, and find its equation.

(a) Since the focus lies at $(-4, 0)$, the directrix must be the line $x = 4$. Points equidistant from the focus and directrix, including O, L, L', can then be found and the graph quickly sketched; see Fig. 3.69.

(b) This graph has x axis symmetry and exists only for negative x. Hence, of the four standard equations, the proper one is $y^2 = -2px$.

(c) We need the value of p to complete the problem. But we know that the distance from the focus to the directrix is $p = 8$. Hence the equation is $y^2 = -16x$.

The parabola occurs frequently in applications. We just scratch the surface when we mention three. There are important "inverse square" forces in physics— the force of gravitation is inversely proportional to the square of the distance; so is the force of attraction between unlike electric charges (Coulomb's law). If one body is attracted to a second by an inverse square force, three curved paths of motion are possible. One of these is a parabola with the second body at the focus; the others are the ellipse and the hyperbola. Which one of the paths the body will follow depends on the velocity vector the first body had when the force field of the second body came into play.

Second, if a cable hangs under its own weight alone, it takes the shape of a curve called the catenary, somewhat like the parabola.* If, however, the cable is weighted so that the net weight per horizontal foot is constant, then the cable will hang in the shape of a parabola.†

Third, reflectors are often parabolic in shape. All waves or rays coming into a parabolic reflector parallel to its axis of symmetry will be reflected in such a way that they pass through the focus point; see Fig. 3.70. Indeed, it is because of this very property that the focus point was given its name. On the other hand, if a source of waves or rays is placed at the focus, those waves or rays that strike the parabolic reflector will be reflected into paths parallel to the axis of the parabola. Automobile headlights, sound and radar detectors, mirrors for telescopes, devices for concentrating the sun's rays,‡ and many other reflectors use this property.

ll

We shall conclude this section by proving the theorem that explains the reflector property of the parabola.

■ THEOREM 2

The parabola as a reflector.

HYPOTHESIS: P is a point on a parabola.

---

* See Exercise 8.6-7.
† See Exercise 3.10-11.
‡ The German word for focus is *Brennpunkt*.

CONCLUSION: The line through P parallel to the axis of symmetry of the parabola and the line joining P to the focus make equal angles with the tangent line at P. $\sphericalangle HPT = \sphericalangle FPU$ in Fig. 3.71.

When these angles are equal, the angles the physicist calls the angles of incidence and reflection are also equal, and we have a reflection at the parabola.

PROOF: (a) Let us draw the coordinate axes so that the equation of the parabola can be taken to be $y^2 = 2px$. The focus will then have coordinates $(p/2, 0)$. If $P(a, b)$ is any point on the parabola, we have $b^2 = 2pa$.

(b) Since we want to prove that $\sphericalangle HPT = \sphericalangle FPU$, we need vectors in the directions of the sides of these angles. We have $\vec{\mathbf{i}} \parallel \overrightarrow{PH}$ to start with.

(c) $\overrightarrow{PF} = (p/2 - a)\vec{\mathbf{i}} + (0 - b)\vec{\mathbf{j}}$.

(d) To get the slope of the tangent line at $P(a, b)$, we note that

$$2y\,\frac{dy}{dx} = 2p, \qquad \frac{dy}{dx} = \frac{p}{y} = \frac{p}{b}.$$

Hence a vector parallel to $\overrightarrow{PT}$ is $1\vec{\mathbf{i}} + (p/b)\,\vec{\mathbf{j}}$; another is $b\vec{\mathbf{i}} + p\vec{\mathbf{j}}$. A vector parallel to $\overrightarrow{PU}$ is $-b\vec{\mathbf{i}} - p\vec{\mathbf{j}}$.

(e) Then

$$\cos HPT = \frac{\vec{\mathbf{i}} \cdot (b\vec{\mathbf{i}} + p\vec{\mathbf{j}})}{\|b\vec{\mathbf{i}} + p\vec{\mathbf{j}}\|} = \frac{b}{\sqrt{b^2 + p^2}}.$$

(f) But, using $b^2 = 2pa$ to replace b^2 at one place,

$$\cos FPU = \frac{\left[\left(\frac{p}{2} - a\right)\vec{\mathbf{i}} - b\vec{\mathbf{j}}\right] \cdot [-b\vec{\mathbf{i}} - p\vec{\mathbf{j}}]}{\left\|\left(\frac{p}{2} - a\right)\vec{\mathbf{i}} - b\vec{\mathbf{j}}\right\| \|-b\vec{\mathbf{i}} - p\vec{\mathbf{j}}\|} = \frac{-b\frac{p}{2} + ab + pb}{\sqrt{\left(\frac{p}{2} - a\right)^2 + b^2}\,\sqrt{b^2 + p^2}}$$

$$= \frac{ab + \frac{p}{2}b}{\sqrt{\left(\frac{p}{2} - a\right)^2 + 2pa}\,\sqrt{b^2 + p^2}} = \frac{b\left(a + \frac{p}{2}\right)}{\sqrt{\frac{p^2}{4} - ap + a^2 + 2pa}\,\sqrt{b^2 + p^2}}$$

$$= \frac{b\left(a + \frac{p}{2}\right)}{\sqrt{\left(\frac{p}{2} + a\right)^2}\,\sqrt{b^2 + p^2}} = \frac{b}{\sqrt{b^2 + p^2}} = \cos HPT.$$

The proof is now complete.

EXERCISES 3.10

1. For each of the following parabolas find the coordinates of the focus and the equation of the directrix, and sketch the graph.
   (a) $y^2 = 40x$.
   (b) $x^2 = 20y$.
   (c) $y^2 = -10x$.
   (d) $x^2 = -\frac{2}{3}y$.

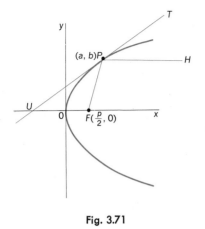

Fig. 3.71

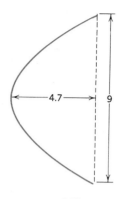

Fig. 3.72

2. Find the equation of the parabola with vertex at the origin,
   (a) focus at $(0, 4)$;
   (b) directrix $x = \frac{3}{2}$;
   (c) ends of latus rectum at $(3, 6)$, $(3, -6)$;
   (d) y axis as axis of symmetry and passing through $(5, -2)$, $(-5, -2)$.
3. Use the definition of the parabola to derive the equation of the parabola with focus at $(0, p/2)$ and directrix $y = -p/2$. This is the parabola of Fig. 3.66(b).
4. Use the definition of the parabola to derive the equation of the parabola with focus at $(4, 1)$ and directrix the y axis. Note that the vertex is not at the origin of coordinates and that the equation now has a first-degree term in y as well as a second-degree term.
5. Use the definition of the parabola to derive the equation of the parabola with focus at $(1, 1)$ and directrix the line $x + y + 2 = 0$. Note that the vertex is at the origin but that the axis of symmetry of the parabola is not one of the coordinate axes, and that the equation now has an xy term.
6. Which point of a parabolic path is closest to the focus? Can you prove this?
7. A reflector is given with the dimensions indicated in Fig. 3.72. Choose coordinate axes in a convenient position, find the equation of the parabola, and locate the focus point.

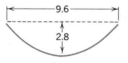

Fig. 3.73

8. The same for the parabolic reflector described in Fig. 3.73.
9. Prove Theorem 2 again by proving that $FU = FP$ in Fig. 3.71.
10. We are given a cable hanging in parabolic shape with end points 100 ft apart horizontally and 30 ft above the lowest point.
   (a) Choose coordinate axes in a convenient position, and find the equation of the parabola.
   (b) Find the height of the cable above the lowest point at a point 10 ft from the end, measured horizontally.
   (c) Find the inclination of the tangent to the cable at an end point.

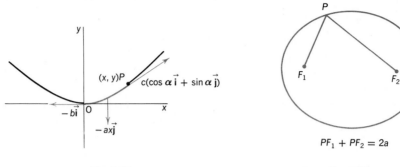

Fig. 3.74   Fig. 3.75

11. Prove that a cable hangs in parabolic shape when it is weighted in such a way that the net weight per horizontal foot is constant.

Step (a). Let the net weight per horizontal foot be a. Let $P(x, y)$ be any point on the cable; see Fig. 3.74. Then the weight of the segment of the cable OP is ax.

Step (b). If the segment OP is to be in equilibrium, the forces acting on it must balance. These forces are:

(1) the weight of the cable segment OP: $-ax\vec{\mathbf{j}}$.
(2) the pull of the remainder of the cable at O: $-b\vec{\mathbf{i}}$, where b is the tension in the cable at O.
(3) the pull of the remainder of the cable at P, assumed to be in the direction of the tangent at P: $c(\cos \alpha \vec{\mathbf{i}} + \sin \alpha \vec{\mathbf{j}})$, where c is the tension in the cable at P and α is the inclination of the tangent line at P.

Step (c). Use the fact that $\tan \alpha = dy/dx$ to show that, when the forces acting on OP balance, we have $dy/dx = (a/b)x$.

Step (d). The curve must be the parabola with equation $\cdots$.

12. A region bounded by a parabola and a line L is called a segment of the parabola. The *base* of the segment is the length of that portion of L which lies within the parabola. The *height* of the segment is the distance between L and that parallel line which is tangent to the parabola. Archimedes proved that the area of any segment is $\frac{4}{3}$ times the area of the triangle that has the same base and height. (a) Prove this theorem in the special case where L is perpendicular to the axis of symmetry of the parabola. (b) Prove this theorem in the more difficult general case.

3.11   The Ellipse

I

■ DEFINITION 1

The ellipse. We are given two fixed, distinct points called foci and a fixed distance, $2a$, greater than the distance between the foci. The set of all points for which the sum of the distances to the foci is precisely $2a$ constitutes an ellipse.

A line segment drawn from a point on the ellipse to a focus is called a focal radius. The definition says that the sum of the lengths of the two focal radii drawn from a point on the ellipse shall be a constant, and we have agreed to call this constant $2a$.

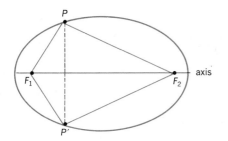

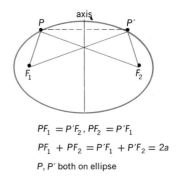

$PF_1 = P'F_1, PF_2 = P'F_2$
$PF_1 + PF_2 = P'F_1 + P'F_2 = 2a$
P, P' both on ellipse

Fig. 3.76

$PF_1 = P'F_2, PF_2 = P'F_1$
$PF_1 + PF_2 = P'F_1 + P'F_2 = 2a$
P, P' both on ellipse

Fig. 3.77

The ellipse can be constructed with the help of a piece of string of length $2a$. Place the ends of the string at the foci, F_1 and F_2, and then place a pencil at a point P in such a way that the string lies taut in the position F_1 to P to F_2; see Fig. 3.75. Point P lies on the ellipse, because $PF_1 + PF_2 = 2a$; if the pencil is now moved, always keeping the string taut, the ellipse will be traced.

Figures 3.76 and 3.77 suggest that the ellipse has two axes of symmetry. One axis is the line through the foci; the other is the perpendicular bisector of the line segment joining the foci. The point of intersection of these axes is the center (of symmetry) of the ellipse; see Fig. 3.78. We shall show immediately that the axis segment which passes through the foci is of length $2a$ and is longer than the other axis segment. The longer axis is called the major axis; its intersections with the ellipse, A_1 and A_2 in Fig. 3.78, are called the major vertices. The shorter axis is called the minor axis; its intersections with the ellipse, B_1 and B_2 in Fig. 3.78, are called the minor vertices.

To show that the major axis is of length $2a$, we observe that for any point P on the ellipse we have $PF_1 + PF_2 = 2a$ and that for A_2 in particular,

$$A_2F_1 + A_2F_2 = 2a.$$

Let us agree to call the distance between the foci $2c$. Then, as Fig. 3.79 suggests, the last equation becomes

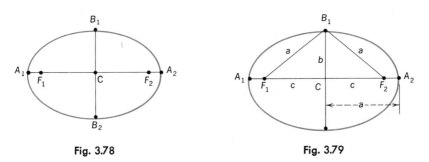

Fig. 3.78

Fig. 3.79

$$(c + CA_2) + (CA_2 - c) = 2a,$$

$$CA_2 = a,$$

and, by symmetry, $A_1A_2 = 2a$, as claimed.

To show that the major axis is longer than the minor axis, draw lines B_1F_1 and B_1F_2, as in Fig. 3.79. Let us agree to call the distance between the minor vertices $2b$ and let us take advantage of the fact that B_1 is on the ellipse to write

$$B_1F_1 + B_1F_2 = 2a.$$

By symmetry, $B_1F_1 = B_1F_2$, so that

$$B_1F_2 = a.$$

Now right triangle CF_2B_1 of Fig. 3.79 tells us that

$$a^2 = b^2 + c^2, \tag{1}$$

from which we conclude that $a > b$ and that the major axis is always longer than the minor axis.

The circle can be considered to be a limiting case for the ellipse. Indeed, if we took the foci closer and closer, and allowed them to coincide in the limit, the string construction for the ellipse would give us a circle. The foci would coincide at the center of the circle and $2a$, the length of the string, would be twice the radius of the circle. From the point of view of Eq. (1), if the foci were allowed to coincide, we would have $c = 0$ and then $a = b$.

To summarize, then, the essential distances associated with the ellipse are

$c =$ distance from the center to a focus

$b =$ distance from the center to a minor vertex

$a =$ distance from the center to a major vertex

$\quad =$ half the sum of the focal radii

$\quad =$ distance from a focus to a minor vertex.

By its very definition an ellipse is determined, except for its position in the plane, by a and c. Two ellipses with the same a and c are congruent. Because c can be determined from a and b through Eq. (1), one can also say that an ellipse is determined, except for its position in the plane, by a and b, its semimajor and semiminor axis lengths. It is to be expected that a, b, and c have prominent roles to play in the ellipse equation.

II

To describe the ellipse algebraically, it is convenient to place the origin of a rectangular coordinate system at the center of the ellipse and to choose the x axis to fall along the major axis, as in Fig. 3.80. Now proceed as follows.

(a) Let $P(x, y)$ be any point on the ellipse; in other words, let

$$PF_1 + PF_2 = 2a.$$

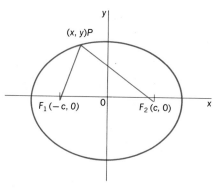

Fig. 3.80

(b) Translating this equation into algebra gives

$$\sqrt{(x + c)^2 + y^2} + \sqrt{(x - c)^2 + y^2} = 2a.$$

(c) Isolate one radical and then square:

$$\sqrt{(x + c)^2 + y^2} = 2a - \sqrt{(x - c)^2 + y^2},$$

$$x^2 + 2cx + c^2 + y^2 = 4a^2 - 4a\sqrt{(x - c)^2 + y^2} + x^2 - 2cx + c^2 + y^2.$$

(d) Isolate the remaining radical, simplify, and square again;

$$4cx - 4a^2 = -4a\sqrt{(x - c)^2 + y^2},$$

$$cx - a^2 = -a\sqrt{(x - c)^2 + y^2},$$

$$c^2x^2 - 2a^2cx + a^4 = a^2(x^2 - 2cx + c^2 + y^2).$$

(e) Finally, collect like terms, and rewrite:

$$a^4 - a^2c^2 = (a^2 - c^2)x^2 + a^2y^2,$$

$$(a^2 - c^2)x^2 + a^2y^2 = a^2(a^2 - c^2),$$

$$\frac{x^2}{a^2} + \frac{y^2}{a^2 - c^2} = 1,$$

or

$$\frac{x^2}{a^2} + \frac{y^2}{b^2} = 1,$$

where we have used Eq. (1). Thus we are led to the following theorem.

■ THEOREM 1

An equation for the ellipse.

HYPOTHESIS: (a) The foci of an ellipse are $(c, 0)$, $(-c, 0)$.
(b) The sum of the focal radii for any point on the ellipse is $2a$, $a > c$.
(c) $b^2 = a^2 - c^2$.

CONCLUSION: The equation of the ellipse is

$$\frac{x^2}{a^2} + \frac{y^2}{b^2} = 1. \tag{2}$$

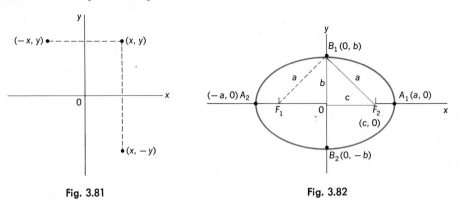

Fig. 3.81   Fig. 3.82

PROOF: We have already shown that, if a point $P(x, y)$ is on the ellipse, so that $PF_1 + PF_2 = 2a$, then the coordinates of P satisfy Eq. (2). But there may be points not on the ellipse whose coordinates also satisfy Eq. (2). For one thing, in deriving Eq. (2) we squared twice, and the careful algebra student knows that in squaring equations one often introduces extraneous solutions. Therefore let $Q(x, y)$ be a point whose coordinates satisfy Eq. (2). Can we show that $QF_1 + QF_2 = 2a$ and thus that Q lies on the ellipse?

Since $Q(x, y)$ satisfies Eq. (2), we can say that

$$y^2 = \frac{b^2}{a^2} (a^2 - x^2). \tag{3}$$

We must also bear in mind that $a^2 = b^2 + c^2$ or $b^2 = a^2 - c^2$, which is Hypothesis (c) above. Now (a):

$$QF_1 = \sqrt{(x + c)^2 + y^2} = \sqrt{(x^2 + 2cx + c^2) + \frac{b^2}{a^2} (a^2 - x^2)}$$

$$= \frac{1}{a}\sqrt{(a^2 - b^2)x^2 + 2a^2cx + a^2(c^2 + b^2)} = \frac{1}{a}\sqrt{c^2x^2 + 2a^2cx + a^4}$$

$$= \frac{1}{a}\sqrt{(cx + a^2)^2} = \frac{1}{a} (cx + a^2).*$$

and (b):

$$QF_2 = \sqrt{(x - c)^2 + y^2} = \sqrt{x^2 - 2cx + c^2 + \frac{b^2}{a^2} (a^2 - x^2)}$$

$$= \frac{1}{a}\sqrt{(a^2 - b^2)x^2 - 2a^2cx + a^2(c^2 + b^2)} = \frac{1}{a}\sqrt{c^2x^2 - 2a^2cx + a^4}$$

$$= \frac{1}{a}\sqrt{(cx - a^2)^2} = \frac{1}{a} (a^2 - cx).\dagger \tag{4}$$

---

* Here in the very last step, it was necessary to select the *positive* square root. x may be negative, but in any event $-a \leq x \leq a$, because otherwise y^2 would be negative; see Eq. (3). We also have $c < a$. Hence $cx + a^2$ is positive.

† Again, in the very last step we were careful to select the positive root.

(c) Hence

$$QF_1 + QF_2 = \frac{1}{a}(cx + a^2) + \frac{1}{a}(a^2 - cx) = \frac{1}{a}(2a^2) = 2a.$$

This concludes the proof of Theorem 1.

Let us check the information we get from the ellipse equation

$$\frac{x^2}{a^2} + \frac{y^2}{b^2} = 1$$

against the information we get directly from the ellipse definition. Because $(-x, y)$ and $(x, -y)$ satisfy the equation whenever (x, y) does, the ellipse is symmetric with respect to both coordinate axes; see Fig. 3.81. From the equation we also see that the x axis intercepts are $A_1(a, 0)$ and $A_2(-a, 0)$, and that the y axis intercepts are $B_1(0, b)$ and $B_2(0, -b)$; see Fig. 3.82. There is no graph for $x > a$ or for $x < -a$, for then we would have $x^2 > a^2$ or $x^2/a^2 > 1$, and thus

$$\frac{y^2}{b^2} = 1 - \frac{x^2}{a^2}$$

would be negative, which is not possible for y real. For a similar reason there is no graph for $y > b$ or $y < -b$. Finally, if we join a focus to a minor vertex we get a right triangle, OF_2B_1 in Fig. 3.82. The hypotenuse is $B_1F_2 = a$, because we know that $b^2 + c^2 = a^2$. This triangle illustrates many of the basic facts for the ellipse.

In this algebraic study of the ellipse we chose to place the x axis along the major axis of the ellipse, but, of course, we could also have placed the y axis along the major axis of the ellipse. The essential facts by which we distinguish the major axis from the minor are (a) that the major axis is the longer axis and (b) that the foci lie on the major axis, not the minor axis.

Example 1. Find the vertices and foci of the ellipse $4x^2 + 25y^2 = 25$ and sketch the graph.

Let us rewrite the equation in the form

$$\frac{4x^2}{25} + y^2 = 1,$$

and then in the form

$$\frac{x^2}{25/4} + \frac{y^2}{1} = 1.$$

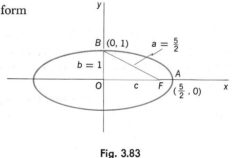

Fig. 3.83

If we set $y = 0$ and then $x = 0$ in this equation we learn that the intercepts are $(\pm \frac{5}{2}, 0)$ and $(0, \pm 1)$. Since the major axis is the longer axis, we see that the major axis lies along the x axis and that $a = \frac{5}{2}$ while $b = 1$. The foci must lie on the major axis, and if we draw the line FB, the triangle BOF will tell us that $c^2 = (\frac{5}{2})^2 - (1)^2$, $c = \sqrt{21}/2$. Hence the foci are $(\pm\sqrt{21}/2, 0)$. See Fig. 3.83.

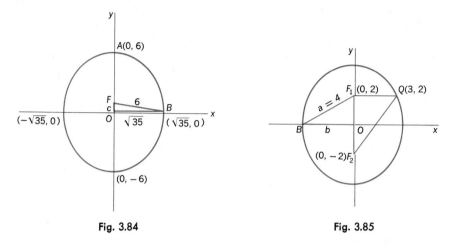

Fig. 3.84   Fig. 3.85

Example 2.   Find the vertices and foci of $x^2/35 + y^2/36 = 1$ and sketch the graph.

Here we see first that the intercepts are $(0, \pm 6)$ and $(\pm\sqrt{35}, 0)$. Thus the major axis lies along the y axis, and $a = 6$ while $b = \sqrt{35}$. This time the foci must lie on the y axis, and if we draw FB, the key triangle BOF tells us that $c^2 = 36 - 35 = 1$. Hence $c = 1$, and the foci are $(0, \pm 1)$. See Fig. 3.84.

Example 3. $F_1(0, 2)$ and $F_2(0, -2)$ are the foci of an ellipse that passes through the point $Q(3, 2)$. Find the equation of the ellipse.

First Solution: See Fig. 3.85.

(a) Because the foci are at $(0, \pm 2)$, the center is at the origin and $c = 2$.

(b) Moreover, the sum of the focal radii must be $2a$, and Q is a point on the ellipse.

$$QF_1 + QF_2 = 2a,$$
$$3 + \sqrt{9 + 16} = 2a,$$
$$a = 4.$$

(c) We could now derive our equation from the definition of the ellipse. If $P(x, y)$ is a point on the ellipse, we could say that $PF_1 + PF_2 = 2a = 8$ and translate into algebra, but it is easier to point out from $\triangle BOF_1$ of Fig. 3.85 that $b^2 = 16 - 4 = 12$.

(d) To allow for the fact that the major axis lies on the y axis, we take for our equation

$$\frac{x^2}{b^2} + \frac{y^2}{a^2} = 1 \quad \text{or} \quad \frac{x^2}{12} + \frac{y^2}{16} = 1.$$

(e) To check, make sure that $Q(3, 2)$ satisfies the equation; $\frac{9}{12} + \frac{4}{16} = 1$.

Second Solution:

(f) As in (a) above, we know that the center is at the origin, the major axis lies on the y axis, $c = 2$, and hence $a^2 = b^2 + 4$.

(g) The equation of the ellipse must be of the form

$$\frac{x^2}{b^2} + \frac{y^2}{a^2} = 1.$$

Since $Q(3, 2)$ is a point of the ellipse,

$$\frac{9}{b^2} + \frac{4}{a^2} = 1,$$

and we have two equations for the two unknowns, a^2 and b^2.

(h) Solving for a^2 and b^2, we find $a^2 = 16$, $b^2 = 12$.

III

The eccentricity of an ellipse helps to describe its shape.

■ DEFINITION 2

The eccentricity of an ellipse is $e = c/a$.

If two ellipses have the same eccentricity, they will be "similar." Their constants a, b, and c will be proportional, and if both ellipses are centered at the origin with major axes in the same direction, it will be possible to associate with each point Q_1 on one ellipse a point Q_2 on the second ellipse such that $\overrightarrow{OQ_2} = k\overrightarrow{OQ_1}$, k the same constant for all pairs of points on the ellipses.* Consider the following example.

Example 4. Ellipses E_1 and E_2 have eccentricity $\frac{2}{3}$. The major vertices of E_1 are $(\pm 6, 0)$, while those of E_2 are $(\pm 12, 0)$. Find the equations of both ellipses and make a sketch.

(a) We are given $c_1/a_1 = \frac{2}{3}$ with $a_1 = 6$ and $c_2/a_2 = \frac{2}{3}$ with $a_2 = 12$. Hence it follows that $c_1 = 4$ and $c_2 = 8$.

(b) From the key triangle, shown in Fig. 3.86, it follows that

$$b_1 = \sqrt{36 - 16} = 2\sqrt{5};$$

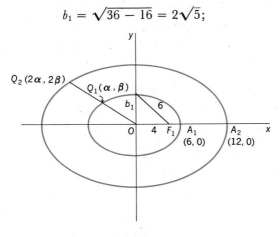

Fig. 3.86

---

* The reader is asked to prove these facts in Exercise 5 at the end of this section.

while for b_2 we would have

$$b_2 = \sqrt{144 - 64} = 4\sqrt{5}.$$

(c) The equations of the ellipses are

$$E_1 : \frac{x^2}{36} + \frac{y^2}{20} = 1 \quad \text{and} \quad E_2 : \frac{x^2}{144} + \frac{y^2}{80} = 1.$$

(d) Observe that if $Q_1(\alpha, \beta)$ lies on E_1 so that

$$\frac{\alpha^2}{36} + \frac{\beta^2}{20} = 1,$$

then $Q_2(2\alpha, 2\beta)$ lies on E_2, for

$$\frac{(2\alpha)^2}{144} + \frac{(2\beta)^2}{80} = \frac{\alpha^2}{36} + \frac{\beta^2}{20} = 1;$$

the coordinates of Q_2 satisfy the equation for E_2. Observe further that $\overrightarrow{OQ_2} = 2\alpha\mathbf{i} + 2\beta\mathbf{j} = 2(\alpha\mathbf{i} + \beta\mathbf{j}) = 2\overrightarrow{OQ_1}$.

Note that $0 < e = c/a < 1$, because $c < a$. If e is close to 0, so that c is small compared to a, then $b = \sqrt{a^2 - c^2}$ will be fairly close to a and the ellipse will be more like a circle. If e is close to unity, so that c is almost as large as a, then b will be small compared with a and the ellipse will be relatively long and thin. The ellipse of Example 2 has eccentricity $\frac{1}{6}$ and is somewhat circle-like; the ellipse of Example 1 has eccentricity $(\sqrt{21}/2) \div (5/2) = \sqrt{21}/5 \approx .9$. It is long and thin by comparison.

In conclusion, we mention a few of the ways the ellipse appears in science and engineering. (a) Many arches are elliptical in shape. (b) As already stated for the parabola, a body traveling in a curved path under the influence of an inverse-square attraction will often travel in an elliptic path. For instance, the planets travel in elliptic orbits with the sun at one focus point. (c) Finally, the ellipse has a reflection property. Any ray originating at one focus will strike the ellipse, reflect as if there were a mirror in the tangential position, and pass through the other focus.

IV

■ **THEOREM 2**

The reflection property for the ellipse.

HYPOTHESIS: P is a point on an ellipse.

CONCLUSION: The focal radii drawn through P make equal angles with the tangent to the ellipse at P.

PROOF: The reader who understood the corresponding theorem for the parabola should be able to prove this theorem in Exercise 3.11-11. See Fig. 3.87.

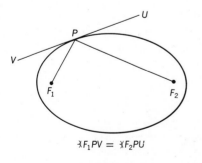

$$\sphericalangle F_1PV = \sphericalangle F_2PU$$

Fig. 3.87

● **Remark 1**

We pointed out earlier that the circle can be considered a limiting case of the ellipse for which c approaches 0. Theorem 2 indicates that the parabola is also a limiting case of the ellipse. For imagine F_1 held fixed and F_2 moved farther and farther away from F_1 in the positive x direction. Then PF_2 would approach a horizontal position and the reflection theorem for the parabola would appear as a limiting case of this theorem.

EXERCISES 3.11

1. Find the coordinates of the major and minor vertices and of the foci, find the eccentricity, and sketch each of the following ellipses.
   (a) $x^2 + 4y^2 = 16$.
   (b) $40y^2 + 49x^2 = 1960$.
   (c) $9y^2 + 36x^2 = 4$.
   (d) $x^2 + 2y^2 = 5$.

2. Find the equation of the ellipse with center at the origin,
   (a) major vertex at $(0, 8)$ and passing through $(6, 0)$.
   (b) focus at $(1, 0)$ and passing through $(4, 0)$.
   (c) focus at $(0, 6)$ and passing through $(0, 7)$.
   (d) focus at $(6, 0)$ and passing through $(0, 7)$.
   (e) focus at $(4, 0)$ and eccentricity $\frac{2}{5}$.
   (f) axes of symmetry in the coordinate-axis directions and passing through $(4, 0)$, $(3, 2)$.
   (g) axes of symmetry in the coordinate-axis directions and passing through $(1, 4)$, $(-2, 1)$.
   (h) major vertex at $(0, 4)$ and eccentricity $\frac{1}{2}$.
   (i) minor vertex at $(0, 4)$ and eccentricity $\frac{1}{2}$.
   (j) focus at $(0, 2)$ and passing through $(\sqrt{3}, 1)$.

3. The latus rectum of an ellipse is a chord drawn through a focus, perpendicular to the major axis. Show that its length is always $2b^2/a$.

4. Find the equation of an ellipse with the same eccentricity as the ellipse of Exercise 1(a) and with major vertex at $(2, 0)$. Sketch both on the same set of axes.

5. Given ellipses E_1 and E_2 with the same eccentricity e, both centered at the origin, and both with major axis on the x axis.
   (a) Show that there is a number k such that

$$\frac{a_2}{a_1} = \frac{b_2}{b_1} = \frac{c_2}{c_1} = k.$$

   (b) Show that, for each point Q_1 on E_1, there is a point Q_2 on E_2 such that $\overrightarrow{OQ_2} = k\overrightarrow{OQ_1}$.

6. An ellipse has foci at $(1, -3)$ and $(1, -1)$, and the sum of the focal radii for points on the ellipse is always 4. Find its equation by translating from the definition of the ellipse into algebra. Note that the center is not at the origin of coordinates and that the equation has first-degree terms as well as second-degree terms.

7. An ellipse has foci at $(2, 1)$ and $(-2, -1)$, and the sum of the focal radii for points on the ellipse is always 6. Find its equation by translating from the definition of the ellipse into algebra. Note that the center is at the origin, but that the axes of the ellipse do not lie on the coordinate axes; the equation does not have first-degree terms, but it does have an xy term.

8. Let $Q(x_1, y_1)$ be a point on the ellipse

$$\frac{x^2}{a^2} + \frac{y^2}{b^2} = 1.$$

Find the equation of the tangent line at Q. Note that the tangents at the vertices are parallel to the axes.

9. (a) Set up an integral for the area of the ellipse $x^2/a^2 + y^2/b^2 = 1$.

(b) Compare this integral with the integral set up for the area of the circle $x^2 + y^2 = a^2$. If πa^2 is the area of the circle, what is the area of the ellipse?

10. An arch for a bridge over a highway is to be a semiellipse of height 20 ft. It is desired to have four traffic lanes of width 10 ft each and a center strip of width 10 ft. How wide would the arch have to be if the outside lanes are to have 13-ft clearance, that is, minimum height 13 ft?

11. Prove Theorem 2.

12. *Conjugate directions.* Work through the following discussion, filling in details where necessary.

Step (a). If we choose different values for d but consider m fixed, then the equation $y = mx + d$ gives us different parallel straight lines of slope m. Let us give the name L_d to the particular line that is obtained for a particular value d. Thus L_1 has the equation $y = mx + 1$.

Step (b). Let L_d intersect the ellipse $x^2/a^2 + y^2/b^2 = 1$ at P_d and Q_d and let M_d be the midpoint of P_d and Q_d. Thus for different choices of d one gets different points M_d. See Fig. 3.88.

Step (c). All points M_d lie on a straight line whose slope is $m' = -b^2/a^2m$. To prove this, let the coordinates of P_d and Q_d be (x_1, y_1) and (x_2, y_2). Then x_1 and x_2 must be the two solutions of

$$(b^2 + a^2m^2)x^2 + 2a^2mdx + (a^2d^2 - a^2b^2) = 0.$$

If we let (x, y) be the coordinates of M_d, we know that $x = \frac{1}{2}(x_1 + x_2)$, and from a theorem on the sum of the roots of a quadratic equation, we show that M_d is the point

$$\left(-\frac{a^2md}{b^2 + a^2m^2}, \frac{b^2d}{b^2 + a^2m^2} \right).$$

Lastly, for different values of d we always get points on the line $y = -(b^2/a^2m)x$.

Step (d). Thus with each direction given we associate a new direction, the direction of the line of the midpoints of the chords parallel to the given direction. The new direction is said to be conjugate to the given one. If a direction has slope m, $m \neq 0$, the slope of the conjugate direction is $m' = -b^2/a^2m$.

Step (e). If the direction of slope m' is conjugate to the direction of slope m, then the direction of slope m is conjugate to the direction of slope m', for

$$m'' = -\frac{b^2}{a^2m'} = m.$$

Step (f). The line of midpoints of chords parallel to a given direction is the line joining the center of the ellipse to the points of tangency of those tangents to the ellipse that have the given direction.

Step (g). The axes of the ellipse are conjugate directions.

Step (h). For a circle, conjugate directions are always perpendicular and conversely.

13. *A construction for the ellipse.* Draw circles of radius a and b, $a > b$, with center at the origin. Draw a line through the origin intersecting the smaller circle at Q and the larger at R, as in Fig. 3.89. Through Q draw a horizontal line and through R a

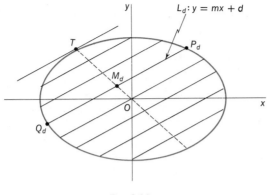

Fig. 3.88

vertical line, intersecting at a point $P(x, y)$. Show that the coordinates of P satisfy the equation $x^2/a^2 + y^2/b^2 = 1$. (*Suggestions:* Let the coordinates of Q and R be (q, y) and (x, r). Use the facts that Q lies on $x^2 + y^2 = b^2$, that R lies on $x^2 + y^2 = a^2$, and that O, Q, and R lie on a line.)

3.12 The Hyperbola

The last of the second-degree curves is the hyperbola.

■ DEFINITION 1

The hyperbola. We are given two fixed, distinct points called foci and a fixed distance, $2a$, less than the distance between the foci. The set of all points for which the absolute value of the difference of the distances to the foci is precisely $2a$ constitutes an hyperbola.

A line drawn from a point on the hyperbola to a focus is called a focal radius. Definition 1 says that the absolute value of the difference of the two focal radii

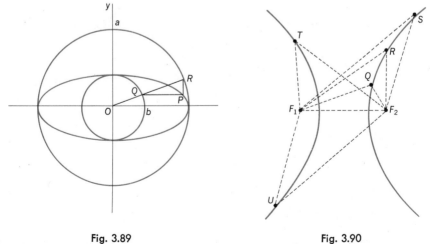

Fig. 3.89   **Fig. 3.90**

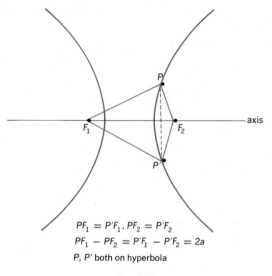

$$PF_1 = P'F_1, PF_2 = P'F_2$$
$$PF_1 - PF_2 = P'F_1 - P'F_2 = 2a$$
P, P' both on hyperbola

Fig. 3.91

drawn to a point on the hyperbola is a constant, and we have agreed to call this constant $2a$.

Let $2c$ be the distance between the foci. Thus, in Fig. 3.90, we have $F_1F_2 = 2c$ and $QF_1 - QF_2 = 2a$, $RF_1 - RF_2 = 2a$, $SF_1 - SF_2 = 2a$, $TF_2 - TF_1 = 2a$,

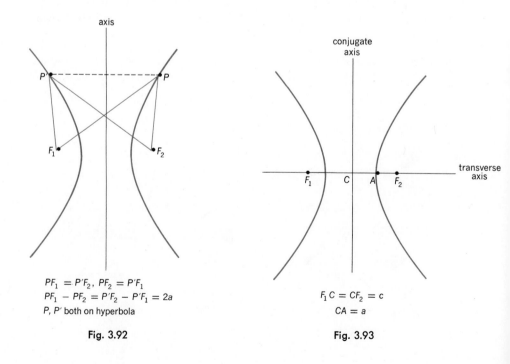

$$PF_1 = P'F_2, PF_2 = P'F_1$$
$$PF_1 - PF_2 = P'F_2 - P'F_1 = 2a$$
P, P' both on hyperbola

Fig. 3.92

$$F_1C = CF_2 = c$$
$$CA = a$$

Fig. 3.93

$UF_2 - UF_1 = 2a.$* The hyperbola will have two axes of symmetry, as Figs. 3.91 and 3.92 indicate, and the point of intersection of these axes is called the center (of symmetry). Of these axes only one actually intersects the hyperbola; it is called the transverse axis and its points of intersection with the hyperbola are called the (transverse) vertices. The foci lie on this axis. The other axis of symmetry is called the conjugate axis for a reason given in Exercise 3.12-13.

It follows from the very definition of the hyperbola that the distance from the center to a transverse vertex is a. For, for any point P on the hyperbola we have

$$PF_1 - PF_2 = \pm 2a,$$

and for the vertex A we have in particular, as in Fig. 3.93,

$$AF_1 - AF_2 = 2a$$
$$(c + CA) - (c - CA) = 2a$$
$$CA = a.$$

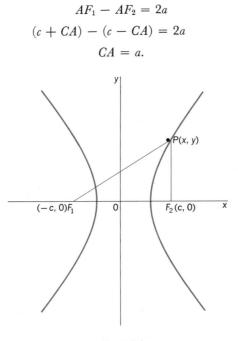

Fig. 3.94

To study the hyperbola algebraically, let us place the origin of a rectangular coordinate system at the center of the hyperbola and choose the x axis to be the transverse axis of the hyperbola. Since the foci are a distance $2c$ apart, their coordinates will be $(\pm c, 0)$. See Fig. 3.94.

(a) Then if $P(x, y)$ is a point of the hyperbola, we must have

$$PF_1 - PF_2 = \pm 2a. \tag{1}$$

(b) Translating into algebra, we have

$$\sqrt{(x + c)^2 + y^2} - \sqrt{(x - c)^2 + y^2} = \pm 2a.$$

* The reader can consider a string construction for the hyperbola in Exercise 3.12-14.

(c) As in the ellipse equation derivation, we simplify patiently by isolating radicals and squaring, as follows:

$$\sqrt{(x+c)^2+y^2} = \pm 2a + \sqrt{(x-c)^2+y^2},$$

$$x^2 + 2cx + c^2 + y^2 = 4a^2 \pm 4a\sqrt{(x-c)^2+y^2} + x^2 - 2cx + c^2 + y^2.$$

$$4cx - 4a^2 = \pm 4a\sqrt{(x-c)^2+y^2},$$

$$cx - a^2 = \pm a\sqrt{(x-c)^2+y^2},$$

$$c^2x^2 - 2a^2cx + a^4 = a^2(x^2 - 2cx + c^2 + y^2).$$

$$(c^2 - a^2)x^2 - a^2y^2 = a^2c^2 - a^4 = a^2(c^2 - a^2),$$

$$\frac{x^2}{a^2} - \frac{y^2}{c^2 - a^2} = 1,$$

or

$$\frac{x^2}{a^2} - \frac{y^2}{b^2} = 1, \qquad \text{where } b^2 = c^2 - a^2.$$

■ THEOREM 1

An equation for the hyperbola.

HYPOTHESIS: (a) The foci of a hyperbola are $(c, 0)$, $(-c, 0)$.
(b) The difference between the focal radii for any point on the hyperbola is $2a$.
(c) $b^2 = c^2 - a^2$.

CONCLUSION: The equation of the hyperbola is

$$\frac{x^2}{a^2} - \frac{y^2}{b^2} = 1. \tag{2}$$

PROOF: We have already shown that if a point lies on the hyperbola, then its coordinates satisfy Eq. (2). It is not an easy matter to show that, if the coordinates of a point satisfy Eq. (2), then the point satisfies Eq. (1) and lies on the hyperbola, but this work is very much like that done for the ellipse and this part of the proof is left to the reader in Exercise 3.12-6.

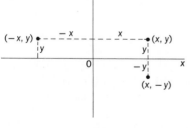

Fig. 3.95

From Eq. (2) for the hyperbola we shall deduce again some of the properties already discussed and some new ones. First, the equation is satisfied by the coordinates $(-x, y)$ and $(x, -y)$ whenever it is satisfied by (x, y). Hence for every point on the hyperbola we also have the points symmetrically situated with respect to the coordinate axes; see Fig. 3.95.

Second, Eq. (2) says that the hyperbola does cross the x axis, but not the y axis. For, if we substitute $y = 0$, we find $x = \pm a$; but if we substitute $x = 0$, we find that y is not real. Further, if we write Eq. (2) in the form

$$y^2 = \frac{b^2}{a^2}(x^2 - a^2), \tag{2a}$$

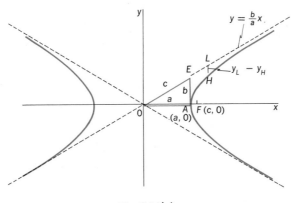

Fig. 3.96(a)

we see that for no x in the interval $-a < x < a$ do we compute real values for y; see Fig. 3.96(a).

Third, rewrite Eq. (2a) in the form

$$y^2 = \frac{b^2}{a^2}x^2\left(1 - \frac{a^2}{x^2}\right), \quad y = \pm\frac{b}{a}x\sqrt{1 - \frac{a^2}{x^2}}. \tag{2b}$$

Because $1 - (a^2/x^2)$ approaches 1 as $|x|$ increases beyond all bounds, we suspect that the larger x is in absolute value the closer the hyperbola graph is to the straight line graphs with equations $y = \pm(b/a)x$. We shall prove in Theorem 2 that this is indeed the case. As we shall see later, such straight lines are called asymptotes.* They will serve as guide lines in drawing the hyperbola. We can, first, start at the intercept point $A(a, 0)$; second, move a distance b perpendicular to the transverse axis from A, thus locating the point $E(a, b)$ whose coordinates satisfy the asymptote equation $y = (b/a)x$; third, sketch the asymptote line; and, fourth, sketch the hyperbola by using the fact that the hyperbola approaches its asymptote lines.

■ **THEOREM 2**

Fig. 3.96(b)

The asymptote for the hyperbola.

HYPOTHESIS: The equation of an hyperbola is

$$\frac{x^2}{a^2} - \frac{y^2}{b^2} = 1.$$

CONCLUSION: The line $y = (b/a)x$ is an asymptote for the hyperbola.

---

* We treat asymptotes in greater detail in Sec. 3.17.

PROOF: Let us write y_H for the ordinate of the upper portion of the hyperbola and y_L for the ordinate of the line. Then, as we see in Fig. 3.96(b), where part of Fig. 3.96(a) is magnified, the distance d between the hyperbola and the line is less than $HL = y_L - y_H$. If we prove that $\lim_{x \to \infty} (y_L - y_H) = 0$, we can be sure that the distance between the hyperbola and the line approaches 0 as we move to the right.*

(a) From Eq. (2a),

$$y_L - y_H = \frac{b}{a} x - \frac{b}{a} \sqrt{x^2 - a^2}.$$

If x increases, we deal with the difference between two increasing numbers. Some such differences approach 0; some do not.

(b) Let us rewrite $y_L - y_H$ by rationalizing:

$$y_L - y_H = \frac{b}{a} \frac{(x - \sqrt{x^2 - a^2})(x + \sqrt{x^2 - a^2})}{x + \sqrt{x^2 - a^2}} = \frac{b}{a} \frac{x^2 - (x^2 - a^2)}{x + \sqrt{x^2 - a^2}}$$

$$= \frac{ab}{x + \sqrt{x^2 - a^2}}.$$

(c) Now if x increases beyond all bounds, we deal in the denominator with the sum of two positive numbers increasing beyond all bounds and such a sum will increase beyond all bounds. We see that $y_L - y_H$ approaches 0 when x grows beyond all bounds. This completes the proof of Theorem 2.

We have described the hyperbola graph algebraically by using a rectangular coordinate system with origin at the center of the hyperbola and x axis along the transverse axis. Other coordinate systems could have been chosen; in particular one could have chosen the y axis to be the transverse axis. But no matter which coordinate system one chooses, remember that the transverse axis is the one that actually intersects the hyperbola at the vertices and on which the foci lie, and that the essential distances associated with the hyperbola are

c = the distance from the center to a focus,

a = half of the constant difference between the focal radii and also the distance from the center to a transverse vertex,

b = the distance one must move from a vertex, perpendicular to the transverse axis, to reach a point on the asymptote.

From the very definition of the hyperbola two hyperbolas with the same c and a are congruent. Because $c^2 = a^2 + b^2$,† however, it can be said that any two of a,

---

* Note that, if $y_1 = x - 2$ and $y_2 = x$, then

$$\lim_{x \to \infty} \frac{y_1}{y_2} = \lim_{x \to \infty} \frac{x - 2}{x} = \lim_{x \to \infty} \left(1 - \frac{2}{x}\right) = 1,$$

but that $\lim_{x \to \infty} (y_2 - y_1) = \lim_{x \to \infty} 2 = 2$. From this illustration we see that, if we only know that $\lim_{x \to \infty} y_L/y_H = 1$, we cannot be sure that $\lim_{x \to \infty} (y_L - y_H) = 0$ without further argument. (Conversely, however, if $\lim_{x \to \infty} (y_2 - y_1) = 0$ and $\lim_{x \to \infty} y_2 \neq 0$, we can be sure that $\lim_{x \to \infty} (y_1/y_2) = 1$.)

† See Hypothesis (c) of Theorem 1, from which $c^2 = a^2 + b^2$. This relationship can be memorized, but it is probably better to read it in each case from a key triangle like $\triangle OAE$ of Fig. 3.96(a).

b, c determine the third and determine the hyperbola except for its location in the plane.

Example 1.   Discuss and sketch the hyperbola whose equation is

$$\frac{x^2}{4} - \frac{y^2}{32} = 1.$$

(a) Upon substituting $y = 0$ in the equation, we find that the transverse vertices are $(\pm 2, 0)$, and thus that the x axis is the transverse axis with $a = 2$. See Fig. 3.97. When we substitute $x = 0$, we do not find a real y.

(b) From the equation we also have $b^2 = 32$. We move a distance $b \doteq \sqrt{32}$ from the vertex $(2, 0)$ in the direction perpendicular to the transverse axis to reach point E, and then we complete the key triangle OAE.

(c) Upon extending the hypotenuse OE and drawing the line symmetrically located with respect to the axes, we get the asymptotes and sketch the hyperbola. Since these asymptotes pass through the origin and rise or fall $\sqrt{32}$ units for a horizontal increase of 2 units, their slopes are $\pm\sqrt{32}/2 = \pm 2\sqrt{2}$, and their equations are $y = \pm 2\sqrt{2}x$.

(d) If we apply the Pythagorean Theorem to the triangle OAE, we find that $c = 6$. The foci are the points $(\pm 6, 0)$.

Example 2.   Discuss and sketch the hyperbola whose equation is

$$-\frac{x^2}{1} + \frac{y^2}{25} = 1.$$

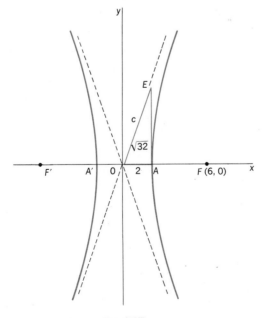

Fig. 3.97

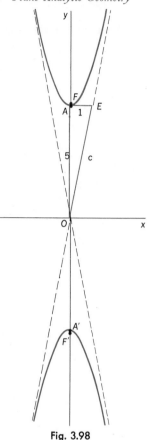

Fig. 3.98

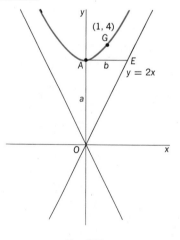

Fig. 3.99

(a) When we substitute $y = 0$, we do not find a real x. However, we find that $(0, \pm 5)$ are points on the hyperbola, so that the transverse axis is the y axis, with $a = 5$. See Fig. 3.98.

(b) The equation tells us that $b^2 = 1$. We move the distance $b = 1$ from $A(0, 5)$ in the direction perpendicular to the transverse axis to reach point E. Then we complete the key triangle OAE.

(c) If we extend hypotenuse OE and draw the line symmetrically located with respect to the axes, we get the asymptotes. Then we can sketch the two wings of the hyperbola fairly quickly. Since the asymptotes pass through $(0, 0)$ and rise or fall 5 units for a horizontal displacement of 1 unit, their equations are $y = \pm 5x$.

(d) Finally, if we apply the Pythagorean Theorem to triangle OAE, we find that $c = \sqrt{26}$. The foci are the points $(0, \pm\sqrt{26})$.

Example 3. A hyperbola has asymptotes $y = \pm 2x$ and passes through the point $G(1, 4)$. Find its equation.

(a) First we sketch the asymptotes from their equations and locate point G in Fig. 3.99. The asymptotes intersect at the origin, which must be the center of the hyperbola.

(b) It is clear from the location of point G with respect to the asymptotes that the hyperbola's transverse axis is the y axis. The equation is of the form

$$-\frac{x^2}{b^2} + \frac{y^2}{a^2} = 1$$

rather than $\qquad \dfrac{x^2}{a^2} - \dfrac{y^2}{b^2} = 1$

because the point $(0, a)$ must satisfy the equation. Since G lies on the hyperbola,

$$-\frac{1}{b^2} + \frac{16}{a^2} = 1.$$

(c) The triangle OAE tells us that the asymptote rises a units for a horizontal run of b units and therefore has slope a/b. But from the given asymptote equation the slope is 2. Thus $a/b = 2$, or $a = 2b$.

(d) Now we have two equations for the unknowns a and b. We substitute $2b$ for a in the last equation of (b) and find that $b^2 = 3$ and $a^2 = 12$, so that the equation of the hyperbola is

$$-\frac{x^2}{3} + \frac{y^2}{12} = 1.$$

II

The eccentricity is again defined to be $e = c/a$, and, as in the case of the ellipse, it is related to the shape of the hyperbola, rather than to its size. In fact, $e = \sec \angle AOE$, where angle AOE of Fig. 3.96(a) is the angle between the transverse axis and the asymptote. Since $c > a$ for the hyperbola, $e = c/a > 1$. When e is close to unity, then angle AOE is small, and the hyperbola fits between two asymptotes that meet at a small angle. This is the case in Example 2, where $e = \sqrt{26}/5 \approx 1.02$. If e is relatively large, the hyperbola fits between asymptotes that meet at a large angle; this is the case in Example 1, where $e = \frac{6}{2} = 3$. When the asymptotes meet at a right angle the hyperbola is called rectangular. In this case we have $a = b$ and $e = c/a = \sec 45° = \sqrt{2}a/a = \sqrt{2}$. See Fig. 3.100.

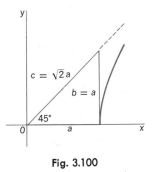

Fig. 3.100

III

The hyperbola appears in many places in nature. First, as already mentioned, a relatively fast-moving body coming under the influence of an inverse-square attractive force will travel in a hyperbolic orbit. Second, the equation $xy = a$ or $y = a/x$ represents a rectangular hyperbola whose asymptotes are the coordinate axes.* This would apply, for example, to the relationship between the pressure and volume of a gas at constant temperature, $PV = $ constant.

As a last application to be touched on here, suppose that a gun is fired at point G and that the report is heard at station S_1 1 sec later than it was heard at station S_2. If we agree for illustrative purposes that sound travels at a speed of 1100 ft per sec, then point G must be 1100 ft closer to S_2 than to S_1. Hence G lies on one wing of a hyperbola whose foci are S_1 and S_2 and for which the difference between the focal radii is $2a = 1100$. If a third station, S_3, also heard the report, then we can say that G lies on a wing of a second hyperbola with foci at S_2 and S_3, and in this way G can be located as an intersection point of the two curves.

---

* We shall study the equations of hyperbolas whose axes are not in the coordinate directions in Sec. 3.14.

EXERCISES 3.12

1. Find the coordinates of the transverse vertices and the foci, the equations of the asymptotes, and the eccentricity, and sketch.
   (a) $x^2 - y^2 = 16$.
   (b) $5x^2 - 4y^2 = 80$.
   (c) $9y^2 - 16x^2 = 144$.
   (d) $2y^2 - x^2 = 20$.
   (e) $4x^2 - 36y^2 = 9$.
   (f) $25y^2 - 16x^2 = 100$.

2. Find the equation of the hyperbola with
   (a) transverse vertices $(\pm 4, 0)$ and foci $(\pm 5, 0)$.
   (b) foci $(0, \pm 6)$ and eccentricity $\frac{3}{2}$.
   (c) transverse vertices $(0, \pm 3)$ and passing through $(2, 4)$.
   (d) foci $(\pm 4, 0)$ and passing through $(5, 3)$.
   (e) center at the origin, transverse axis the x axis, eccentricity 2, and passing through $(4, 1)$.
   (f) transverse vertices $(0, \pm 3)$ and asymptotes $y = \pm \frac{2}{3} x$.
   (g) asymptotes $y = \pm \frac{2}{3} x$ and passing through $(6, 1)$.
   (h) asymptotes $y = \pm \frac{1}{2} x$ and focus at $(0, 4)$.

3. Find the equation of the hyperbola with foci at $(-2, -2)$ and $(-2, 4)$ and for which the difference of the focal radii is 2, working directly from the definition of the hyperbola. Note that the center is not at the origin. The equation has first-degree terms as well as second-degree terms.

4. Find the equation of the hyperbola with foci at $(2, 2)$ and $(-2, -2)$ and for which the difference of the focal radii is 4, working directly from the definition of the hyperbola. Note that the center is at the origin but that the transverse axis is not one of the coordinate axes. The equation does not have first-degree terms but does have an xy term.

5. As for the parabola and the ellipse, a latus rectum is a chord drawn through a focus perpendicular to the axis on which the foci lie. Show that the length of the latus rectum is $2b^2/a$.

6. Complete the proof of Theorem 1 by showing that if a point's coordinates satisfy the equation

$$\frac{x^2}{a^2} - \frac{y^2}{b^2} = 1,$$

then the absolute value of the difference of the distances from this point to the points $(c, 0)$ and $(-c, 0)$ is $2a$, it being understood that $c^2 = a^2 + b^2$.

7. We are given hyperbolas H_1 and H_2 with the same eccentricity e, both with centers at the origin and with transverse axes on the x axis.
   (a) Show that there is a number k such that

$$\frac{a_2}{a_1} = \frac{b_2}{b_1} = \frac{c_2}{c_1} = k.$$

   (b) Prove that, for each point Q_1 on H_1, there is a point Q_2 on H_2 such that $\overrightarrow{OQ_2} = k\overrightarrow{OQ_1}$.

8. Show that the hyperbolas

$$H_1: \frac{x^2}{\alpha^2} - \frac{y^2}{\beta^2} = 1 \quad \text{and} \quad H_2: \frac{y^2}{\beta^2} - \frac{x^2}{\alpha^2} = 1$$

have the same asymptotes, and foci that are the same distances from their common center, but that the transverse axis of one is the conjugate axis of the other. One hyperbola is said to be "conjugate" to the other.

9. Let $Q(x_1, y_1)$ be a point on the hyperbola

$$\frac{x^2}{a^2} - \frac{y^2}{b^2} = 1.$$

Find the equation of the tangent line at Q. Note that the tangents at the transverse vertices are parallel to the conjugate axis.

10. (a) Find the points of intersection of the ellipse

$$\frac{x^2}{36} + \frac{y^2}{20} = 1$$

and the hyperbola $\qquad \dfrac{x^2}{6} - \dfrac{y^2}{10} = 1,$

and show that the curves intersect at right angles.

(b) Show that the ellipse and hyperbola are "confocal," that is, have the same foci.

11. Corresponding to Theorems 3.10-2 and 3.11-2, we have the following theorem. Prove it.

Theorem 3. The reflection property for the hyperbola.

Hypothesis: P is a point on a hyperbola.

Conclusion: The focal radii drawn through P make equal angles with the tangent to the hyperbola at P.

12. Three observation posts are located on a straight line. They use synchronized clocks and want to locate an enemy gun. Post L, the post situated farthest to the left, hears a report 2 sec after Post M does, Post M being 4200 ft from L. Post R, the post situated farthest to the right, 3600 ft from M, hears the report at the same time M does. Assuming that sound travels at the rate of 1100 ft per sec, find the possible locations for the enemy gun. (*Suggestions:* Choose your coordinate axes carefully. In choosing scales on these axes it would be wise to let one of your units represent 100 ft.)

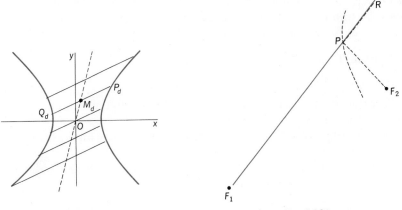

Fig. 3.101   Fig. 3.102

13. *Conjugate directions.* (See Exercise 3.11-12.) As in the case of the ellipse, we define the direction conjugate to a given direction as the direction of the line of the mid-points of the chords of the hyperbola parallel to the given direction. See Fig. 3.101. If the given direction has slope m, $m \neq 0$ and $m \neq \pm b/a$, show that the conjugate direction for the hyperbola $(x^2/a^2) - (y^2/b^2) = 1$ has slope $m' = b^2/a^2 m$. Why don't

the asymptotic directions have conjugates? The transverse and conjugate axes are conjugate, and, indeed, this justifies the choice of the name "conjugate axis."

14. A string construction for the hyperbola. Demonstrate the validity of this proposed construction for a portion of a hyperbola whose foci are to be a distance $2c$ apart and the difference of whose focal radii is to be $2a$. See Fig. 3.102.

   (a) Select two points F_1 and F_2 a distance $2c$ apart.
   (b) Take a straight edge F_1R of length $L > 2a$.
   (c) Take a string of length $L - 2a$ and attach one end to the straight edge at R and the other end to F_2.
   (d) Place a pencil at the one point P of the straight edge which is such that the string runs taut from R to P to F_2.
   (e) Rotate the straight edge about F_1, always keeping the string taut. The point P will trace a portion of the hyperbola.

3.13 Translations

In describing parabolas, ellipses, and hyperbolas algebraically, the coordinate axes were chosen to be axes of symmetry wherever possible, and as a result the corresponding equations were relatively simple. But we often have to consider curves when they are not referred to the axes that lead to the simplest equations. This is the case, for instance, if two curves are being studied at once; it may only be possible to choose the coordinate axes in a convenient position for one of the curves. Suppose, then, that the equation of a curve is known when the curve is referred to a certain set of axes. Can the equation of the curve be stated when the curve is referred to a different set of axes?

We say that the coordinate axes have been "translated" if the new coordinate axes are parallel to the old; see Fig. 3.103. In this section, we shall consider the change made in the equation of a curve when it is referred to a new set of axes obtained by translation from the original axes. In the next section, we shall study rotations of axes and the corresponding changes in equations of curves.

■ THEOREM 1

The equations of translation.

HYPOTHESIS: (a) The x' and y' axes are parallel to the x and y axes, respectively, and have the same positive directions.

(b) The origin of the x', y' axis system is the point with coordinates (h, k) in the x, y axis system.

(c) The coordinates of a point P are (x, y) when referred to the x and y axes and (x', y') when referred to the x' and y' axes.

CONCLUSION:

$$\left. \begin{array}{l} x' = x - h \\ y' = y - k \end{array} \right\} \quad \text{or} \quad \left. \begin{array}{l} x = x' + h, \\ y = y' + k. \end{array} \right\} \tag{1}$$

PROOF: See Fig. 3.104. The proof follows from the vector equation

$$\overrightarrow{OP} = \overrightarrow{OO'} + \overrightarrow{O'P}, \tag{2}$$

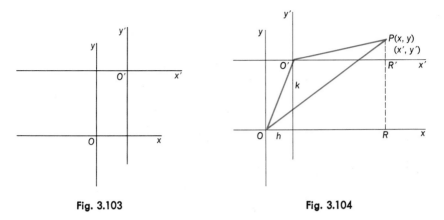

Fig. 3.103   Fig. 3.104

for we have

$$\overrightarrow{OP} = \overrightarrow{OR} + \overrightarrow{RP} = x\vec{i} + y\vec{j}; \quad \overrightarrow{OO'} = h\vec{i} + k\vec{j},$$

$$\overrightarrow{O'P} = \overrightarrow{O'R'} + \overrightarrow{R'P} = x'\vec{i} + y'\vec{j},$$

and upon substitution in Eq. (2), we obtain

$$x\vec{i} + y\vec{j} = (h\vec{i} + k\vec{j}) + (x'\vec{i} + y'\vec{j}).$$

If we equate $\vec{i}$ and $\vec{j}$ coefficients, Eqs. (1) appear.

Example 1. Consider the straight line of slope m passing through the point (h, k); see Fig. 3.105. Its equation is $y - k = m(x - h)$. If we refer the line to new x', y' axes with new origin at (h, k), Eqs. (1) tell us that the line's equation for the new system is to be obtained by replacing x by $x' + h$ and y by $y' + k$. When we do this, we obtain the new equation $y' = mx'$. This is the equation to be expected for a line of slope m through the origin of the x', y' system.

Example 2. Consider the circle of radius r with center (h, k); see Fig. 3.106. The circle's equation is $(x - h)^2 + (y - k)^2 = r^2$. If the circle is referred to new axes with origin at (h, k), the circle's equation in the new system is obtained by replacing x by $x' + h$ and y by $y' + k$, or, what is the same thing, by replacing

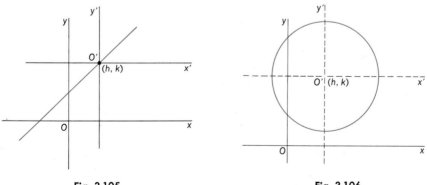

Fig. 3.105   Fig. 3.106

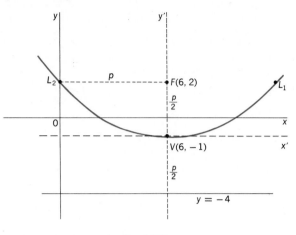

Fig. 3.107

$x - h$ by x' and $y - k$ by y'. The equation of the circle in the new system is $x'^2 + y'^2 = r^2$. This is the equation to be expected for a circle of radius r with center at the origin of the x', y' system.

Example 3.   The focus and directrix of a parabola are $(6, 2)$ and $y = -4$. Find its equation.

(a) In Fig. 3.107 we reason that the vertex must fall midway between the focus and directrix and must therefore be the point $(6, -1)$. The distance from $F(6, 2)$ to the directrix, $y = -4$, is $p = 6$. With the help of the latus rectum points, the parabola is easily sketched; it faces up.

(b) If the parabola were referred to an x'-y' system with origin at its vertex $(6, -1)$, the equation of the parabola would be $x'^2 = 2py' = 12y'$. But we want the equation referred to the original x, y system. Eqs. (1) tell us how the two coordinate systems are related. If we replace x' by $x - 6$ and y' by $y - (-1) = y + 1$, we get $(x - 6)^2 = 12(y + 1)$ as the equation of the parabola in the x, y system.

Example 4.   Find the vertex, focus, and directrix of the parabola $y^2 - 4y + 6x + 22 = 0$ and sketch the graph.

(a) First we complete the square:*

$$y^2 - 4y + = -6x - 22,$$
$$y^2 - 4y + 4 = -6x - 18,$$
$$(y - 2)^2 = -6(x + 3). \tag{3}$$

(b) If we make the coordinate replacements $x + 3 = x'$, $y - 2 = y'$, Eq. (3) becomes

$$y'^2 = -6x', \tag{4}$$

which we recognize to be the equation of a parabola with vertex at the origin of the x', y' system.

(c) Comparison with the Translation Equations (1) tells us that the coordinate replacements $x + 3 = x'$, $y - 2 = y'$ accomplish a translation of axes with the origin of the x', y' system at $(-3, 2)$ in the x, y system.

---

* See the footnote for Example 3.9-2.

(d) Hence, as in Fig. 3.108, we start our sketch by drawing auxiliary x', y' axes through $(-3, 2)$. Then with $(-3, 2)$ as vertex and following Eq. (4), we draw a parabola that faces to the left and for which p, the distance from the focus to the directrix, is 3. The focus falls $\tfrac{3}{2}$ units to the left of the vertex, at $(-\tfrac{9}{2}, 2)$. The directrix lies the same distance to the right of the vertex; its equation is $x = -\tfrac{3}{2}$.

Example 5.   Find the center, transverse vertices, foci, asymptotes, and eccentricity, and sketch the hyperbola whose equation is

$$25x^2 - 4y^2 + 50x - 12y + 116 = 0.$$

(a) We begin by completing the square:

$$25(x^2 + 2x + \quad) - 4(y^2 + 3y + \quad) = -116,$$
$$25(x^2 + 2x + 1) - 4(y^2 + 3y + \tfrac{9}{4}) = -116 + 25 - 9,$$
$$25(x + 1)^2 - 4(y + 3/2)^2 = -100,$$
$$-\frac{(x + 1)^2}{4} + \frac{(y + 3/2)^2}{25} = 1. \tag{5}$$

(b) If we translate axes in such a way that $x + 1$ is replaced by x' and $y + \tfrac{3}{2}$ by y', Eq. (5) becomes

$$-\frac{x'^2}{4} + \frac{y'^2}{25} = 1, \tag{6}$$

which we recognize as that of a hyperbola with center at the origin of the x', y' system.

(c) But the translation equations tell us that the origin of the x', y' system is the point $(-1, -\tfrac{3}{2})$.

(d) Hence, as in Fig. 3.109, we start our sketch by drawing auxiliary x', y' axes through $(-1, -\tfrac{3}{2})$. Then with $(-1, -\tfrac{3}{2})$ as center, and following Eq. (6), we draw a hyperbola whose transverse axis lies along the y' axis and for which

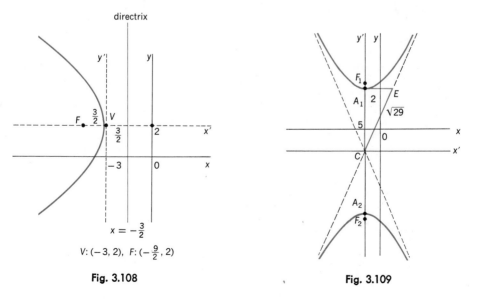

directrix

$x = -\dfrac{3}{2}$

$V: (-3, 2)$, $F: (-\tfrac{9}{2}, 2)$

Fig. 3.108

Fig. 3.109

$a = 5$, $b = 2$. Thus the transverse vertices are 5 units above and below the center $(-1, -\frac{3}{2})$; they have the coordinates $A_1(-1, \frac{7}{2})$ and $A_2(-1, -\frac{13}{2})$. From the triangle CA_1E we read $c = \sqrt{29}$, so that the foci lie $\sqrt{29}$ units above and below $(-1, -\frac{3}{2})$; their coordinates are $F_1(-1, -\frac{3}{2} + \sqrt{29})$ and $F_2(-1, -\frac{3}{2} - \sqrt{29})$. The eccentricity is $e = c/a = \sqrt{29}/5$.

(e) Finally, we observe that the asymptotes pass through $(-1, -\frac{3}{2})$ and either rise or fall 5 units in a horizontal displacement of 2 units, so that their slopes are $\pm\frac{5}{2}$. Their equations are $y + \frac{3}{2} = \pm\frac{5}{2}(x + 1)$.

● **Remark 1**

Although our examples referred to first- and second-degree curves, the translation equations apply to curves in general.

EXERCISES 3.13

1. Find the vertex, focus, and directrix, and sketch each parabola:
   (a) $y^2 - 12x + 48 = 0$.
   (b) $x^2 - 6x - 9y + 27 = 0$.
   (c) $4x^2 + 28x + 32y + 81 = 0$.

2. Find the center, major and minor vertices, foci, and eccentricity, and sketch each ellipse:
   (a) $4x^2 + y^2 - 24x - 8y + 48 = 0$.
   (b) $9x^2 + 16y^2 + 36x - 16y - 104 = 0$.
   (c) $4x^2 + 5y^2 - 40x + 30y + 45 = 0$.

3. Find the center, transverse vertices, foci, asymptotes, and eccentricity, and sketch each hyperbola:
   (a) $x^2 - y^2 + 4y - 20 = 0$.
   (b) $4x^2 - 9y^2 + 16x + 18y + 43 = 0$.
   (c) $4x^2 - 9y^2 - 8x + 12y - 144 = 0$.

4. Find the equation of the
   (a) parabola with vertex at $(1, 4)$ and focus at $(1, 1)$.
   (b) parabola with vertex at $(0, 3)$, axis of symmetry parallel to the x axis, and passing through $(5, 0)$.
   (c) parabola with focus at $(1, 1)$, passing through $(-5, 9)$, and with directrix parallel to the y axis and to the right of it.
   (d) ellipse with vertices $(2, 1)$, $(4, 4)$, $(2, 7)$, $(0, 4)$.
   (e) ellipse with foci at $(-4, -1)$, $(0, -1)$ and sum of focal radii 6.
   (f) ellipse with foci on the y axis, $e = 1/\sqrt{2}$, passing through $(2, 5)$, $(0, 3)$.
   (g) hyperbola with transverse vertices at $(6, 1)$, $(8, 1)$ and eccentricity 2.
   (h) hyperbola with foci at $(-1, 4)$, $(-1, -2)$ and difference of focal radii 4.
   (i) hyperbola with asymptotes $2y - x - 1 = 0$ and $2y + x - 7 = 0$, passing through $(9, 4)$.

5. (a) Sketch $y = x^3$ and $(y - 1) = (x - 2)^3$ on the same set of axes.
   (b) Sketch $y = 2^x$ and $y = 2^{x-1}$ on the same set of axes.

6. We are given three points $Q(-h, y_1)$, $R(0, y_2)$, $S(h, y_3)$; see Fig. 3.110.
   (a) The equation of a parabola with vertical axis of symmetry can be written in the form $y = ax^2 + bx + c$. What conditions must a, b, and c satisfy if the parabola is to go through Q, R, and S?

(b) Show that the area of the region bounded by the parabola, the x axis, $x = -h$, and $x = h$ is $\frac{1}{3} h(y_1 + 4y_2 + y_3)$.*

7. Show that $y^2 = 8x$ and $y^2 = (-16)(x - 6)$ have the same focus and axis of symmetry, and intersect orthogonally.

8. Show that intersecting parabolas with the same focus and axis of symmetry intersect orthogonally. (*Suggestion 1:* Choose as your x axis the common axis of symmetry. Choose as your y axis a line through the vertex of one of the parabolas.) (*Suggestion 2:* Use Theorem 3.10-2.)

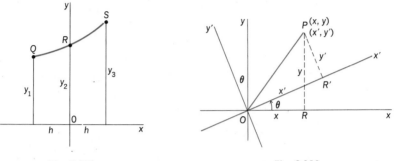

Fig. 3.110   Fig. 3.111

3.14   Rotations

In this section we consider the effect of a rotation of axes on the equation of a curve.

■ THEOREM 1

The equations of rotation.

HYPOTHESIS: (a) The x' and y' axes have the same origin as the x and y axes.

(b) θ is the angle from the x to the x' axis.

(c) The coordinates of a point P are (x, y) when referred to the x and y axes and (x', y') when referred to the x' and y' axes.

CONCLUSION:

$$\begin{aligned} x &= x' \cos \theta - y' \sin \theta, \\ y &= x' \sin \theta + y' \cos \theta. \end{aligned} \tag{1}$$

PROOF: See Fig. 3.111.

(a)

$$\overrightarrow{OP} = \overrightarrow{OR} + \overrightarrow{RP} = x\mathbf{i} + y\mathbf{j}.$$

(b) But also,

$$\overrightarrow{OP} = \overrightarrow{OR'} + \overrightarrow{R'P} = x'\mathbf{i}' + y'\mathbf{j}',$$

where $\mathbf{i}'$ and $\mathbf{j}'$ are unit vectors in the positive x' and y' directions. Thus

$$x\mathbf{i} + y\mathbf{j} = x'\mathbf{i}' + y'\mathbf{j}'.$$

---

* This exercise is referred to in Sec. 6.8.

(c) Now let us take the scalar product of both members of this equation with vector $\vec{i}$. We get

$$x\vec{i}\cdot\mathbf{i} + y\vec{j}\cdot\mathbf{i} = x'\vec{i}'\cdot\mathbf{i} + y'\vec{j}'\cdot\mathbf{i}.$$

(d) Since $\vec{i}$ is a unit vector and $\vec{j}$ and $\vec{i}$ are perpendicular, we have $\vec{i}\cdot\mathbf{i} = 1$ and $\vec{j}\cdot\mathbf{i} = 0$. But

$$\vec{i}'\cdot\mathbf{i} = \|\vec{i}'\| \; \|\vec{i}\| \cos \theta = (1)(1)(\cos \theta),$$

and $$\vec{j}'\cdot\mathbf{i} = \|\vec{j}'\| \; \|\vec{i}\| \cos (\theta + 90°) = (1)(1)(-\sin \theta).$$

Thus Part (c) becomes

$$x = x' \cos \theta - y' \sin \theta.$$

(e) Similarly, if at the end of Part (b) we take the scalar product of both members with $\vec{j}$, we get

$$x\vec{i}\cdot\mathbf{j} + y\vec{j}\cdot\mathbf{j} = x'\vec{i}'\cdot\mathbf{j} + y'\vec{j}'\cdot\mathbf{j}.$$

(f) Now $\vec{i}\cdot\mathbf{j} = 0$ as before; $\vec{j}\cdot\mathbf{j} = 1$ because $\vec{j}$ is a unit vector;

$$\vec{i}'\cdot\mathbf{j} = \|\vec{i}'\| \; \|\vec{j}\| \cos (90° - \theta) = (1)(1) \sin \theta;$$

and $$\vec{j}'\cdot\mathbf{j} = \|\vec{j}'\| \; \|\vec{j}\| \cos \theta = (1)(1) \cos \theta.$$

Therefore $$y = x' \sin \theta + y' \cos \theta.$$

This concludes the proof.

● **Remark 1**

For illustrative purposes in Fig. 3.111 we chose an acute angle for θ and we chose P as a point in the first quadrant for both systems. But the proof does not require that x, y, x' and y' be positive. Further, the cosines of the angles between the axes of x and x', x and y', x' and y, and y and y' will be $\cos \theta$, $\cos (90° + \theta)$, $\cos (90° - \theta)$, and $\cos \theta$ no matter what the size of θ. The proof is valid for all points P and all angles θ.

● **Remark 2**

Equations (1) give x and y in terms of x' and y'. As an algebraic exercise, we can solve for x' and y' in terms of x and y. We multiply the first equation by $\sin \theta$, getting

$$x \sin \theta = x' \sin \theta \cos \theta - y' \sin^2 \theta,$$

and subtract from this the second equation multiplied by $\cos \theta$,

$$y \cos \theta = x' \sin \theta \cos \theta + y' \cos^2 \theta,$$

obtaining as a result

$$x \sin \theta - y \cos \theta = -y' \sin^2 \theta - y' \cos^2 \theta$$
$$= -y'(\sin^2 \theta + \cos^2 \theta),$$
$$y' = -x \sin \theta + y \cos \theta.$$

We leave it to the reader to solve for x', and thus to show that Eqs. (1) can be re-written in the form

$$\left.\begin{array}{l} x' = x \cos \theta + y \sin \theta, \\ y' = -x \sin \theta + y \cos \theta. \end{array}\right\} \tag{2}$$

Example 1. Consider the curve with equation $5x^2 - 6xy + 5y^2 = 8$. This equation is new to us because of its xy term. Let us refer this curve to x', y' axes making a $45°$ angle with the xy axes, and see what its equation is in the new system of coordinates.

The equations of rotation, (1), become

$$\left.\begin{array}{l} x = x' \cos 45° - y' \sin 45° = x'\dfrac{\sqrt{2}}{2} - y'\dfrac{\sqrt{2}}{2} = \dfrac{\sqrt{2}}{2}(x' - y'), \\[3mm] y = x' \sin 45° + y' \cos 45° = x'\dfrac{\sqrt{2}}{2} + y'\dfrac{\sqrt{2}}{2} = \dfrac{\sqrt{2}}{2}(x' + y'). \end{array}\right\} \tag{3}$$

If we replace x and y according to these equations, we get

$$5x^2 - 6xy + 5y^2 = 8,$$
$$5(\tfrac{2}{4})(x' - y')^2 - 6(\tfrac{2}{4})(x' - y')(x' + y') + 5(\tfrac{2}{4})(x' + y')^2 = 8.$$

We multiply both members by 2, expand, and group like terms.

$$5(x'^2 - 2x'y' + y'^2) - 6(x'^2 - y'^2) + 5(x'^2 + 2x'y' + y'^2) = 16,$$
$$4x'^2 + 16y'^2 = 16,$$
$$\frac{x'^2}{4} + \frac{y'^2}{1} = 1.$$

Now we see that our curve is an ellipse. In the x', y' coordinate system, its major and minor vertices are $A_1(2, 0)$, $A_2(-2, 0)$, $B_1(0, 1)$, and $B_2(0, -1)$; the foci are $F_1(\sqrt{3}, 0)$ and $F_2(-\sqrt{3}, 0)$. When referred to these axes, it is relatively easily sketched; see Fig. 3.112.

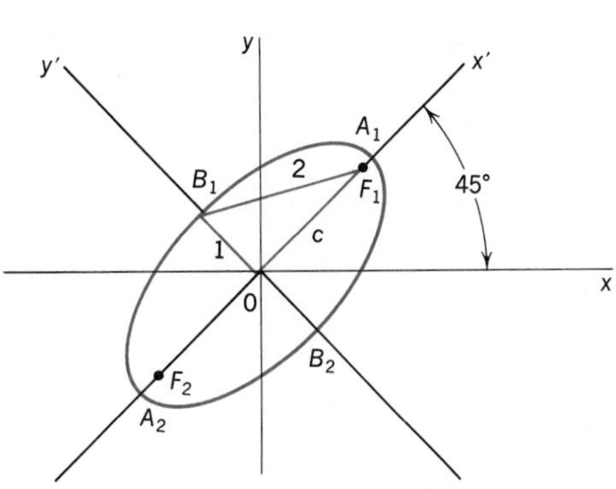

The curve was originally de-scribed to us in terms of the x, y co-ordinate system, however, and we would usually be expected to describe important points in terms of that coordinate system. For the major vertex A_1, for instance, for which $x' = 2$ and $y' = 0$, we see from Eqs. (3) that

Fig. 3.112

$$x = \frac{\sqrt{2}}{2}(2 - 0) = \sqrt{2} \quad \text{and} \quad y = \frac{\sqrt{2}}{2}(2 + 0) = \sqrt{2}.$$

Similarly, for the minor vertex B_1 for which $x' = 0$, $y' = 1$, we have

$$x = \frac{\sqrt{2}}{2}(0 - 1) = -\frac{\sqrt{2}}{2} \quad \text{and} \quad y = \frac{\sqrt{2}}{2}(0 + 1) = \frac{\sqrt{2}}{2}.$$

In the x, y coordinate system the major vertices are $A_1(\sqrt{2}, \sqrt{2})$, $A_2(-\sqrt{2}, -\sqrt{2})$; the minor vertices are $B_1(-\sqrt{2}/2, \sqrt{2}/2)$, $B_2(\sqrt{2}/2, -\sqrt{2}/2)$; the foci are $F_1(\sqrt{6}/2, \sqrt{6}/2)$ and $F_2(-\sqrt{6}/2, -\sqrt{6}/2)$.

A 45° rotation of coordinate axes helped in the analysis of the equation presented in Example 1. But can we be sure that a rotation of axes will always help in the analysis of a second-degree equation that contains an xy term? And if so, what would be a suitable angle of rotation for each case?

To answer these questions let us consider a general second-degree equation

$$Ax^2 + Bxy + Cy^2 + Dx + Ey + F = 0. \tag{4}$$

If we rotate the coordinate axes through an angle θ to form a new x', y' coordinate system, the curve originally described by Eq. (4) will be described by a new equation which we can get by replacing x and y in (4) according to Eqs. (1). In the new coordinate system the equation for the curve is

$$A(x' \cos \theta - y' \sin \theta)^2$$
$$+ B(x' \cos \theta - y' \sin \theta)(x' \sin \theta + y' \cos \theta)$$
$$+ C(x' \sin \theta + y' \cos \theta)^2 + \cdots = 0. \tag{4a}$$

In Eq. (4a) we have written only the second-degree terms. If we multiply out and then group like terms, we get

$$A(x'^2 \cos^2 \theta - 2x'y' \cos \theta \sin \theta + y'^2 \sin^2 \theta)$$
$$+ B(x'^2 \sin \theta \cos \theta + x'y' \cos^2 \theta - x'y' \sin^2 \theta - y'^2 \sin \theta \cos \theta)$$
$$+ C(x'^2 \sin^2 \theta + 2x'y' \sin \theta \cos \theta + y'^2 \cos^2 \theta) + \cdots = 0,$$
$$(A \cos^2 \theta + B \sin \theta \cos \theta + C \sin^2 \theta)x'^2$$
$$+ (-2A \sin \theta \cos \theta + B \cos^2 \theta - B \sin^2 \theta + 2C \sin \theta \cos \theta)x'y'$$
$$+ (A \sin^2 \theta - B \sin \theta \cos \theta + C \cos^2 \theta)y'^2 + \cdots = 0. \tag{4b}$$

Recall that $2 \sin \theta \cos \theta = \sin 2\theta$, $\cos^2 \theta - \sin^2 \theta = \cos 2\theta$, and thus that by the rotation we change from Eq. (4) to

$$A'x'^2 + B'x'y' + C'y'^2 + D'x' + E'y' + F' = 0, \tag{4c}$$

where

$$\begin{aligned}
A' &= A \cos^2 \theta + B \sin \theta \cos \theta + C \sin^2 \theta, \\
B' &= -2A \sin \theta \cos \theta + B \cos^2 \theta - B \sin^2 \theta + 2C \sin \theta \cos \theta \\
&= B \cos 2\theta - (A - C) \sin 2\theta, \\
C' &= A \sin^2 \theta - B \sin \theta \cos \theta + C \cos^2 \theta.
\end{aligned} \tag{5}$$

If we want our new equation (4c) to contain no $x'y'$ term, then we should choose θ so that $B' = 0$, or, by Eq. (5), so that

$$B \cos 2\theta = (A - C) \sin 2\theta$$

$$\tan 2\theta = \frac{B}{A - C}, \qquad A \neq C.$$

If $A = C$, Eq. (5) for B' becomes

$$B' = B \cos 2\theta;$$

then it is apparent that B' will be 0 if $\cos 2\theta = 0$, $2\theta = 90°$, and $\theta = 45°$. We have two theorems.

■ THEOREM 2A

HYPOTHESIS: (a) A curve has a second-degree equation

$$Ax^2 + Bxy + Cy^2 + Dx + Ey + F = 0, \qquad A \neq C.$$

(b) The x', y' system has the same origin as the x, y system, and is arrived at by a rotation through an angle θ, where $\tan 2\theta = B/(A - C)$.

CONCLUSION: When referred to the x', y' system, the equation for the curve will have no $x'y'$ term.

■ THEOREM 2B

HYPOTHESIS: (a) A curve has a second-degree equation

$$Ax^2 + Bxy + Cy^2 + Dx + Ey + F = 0, \qquad A = C.$$

(b) The x', y' system has the same origin as the x, y system and is arrived at by a rotation through 45°.

CONCLUSION: When referred to the x', y' system, the curve will have an equation with no $x'y'$ term.

Example 1A. In the case of Example 1, where a curve had the x, y system equation $5x^2 - 6xy + 5y^2 = 8$, Theorem 2B says that we will get an equation without an $x'y'$ term if we rotate the axes through 45°. That is what we did.

Example 2. Consider the curve with equation

$$2x^2 + 4\sqrt{3}\, xy - 2y^2 = 4. \tag{6}$$

Theorem 2 suggests that we rotate through an angle θ where

$$\tan 2\theta = \frac{4\sqrt{3}}{2 - (-2)} = \sqrt{3},$$

$2\theta = 60°$, $\theta = 30°$. For such a rotation the equations of rotation become

$$\left. \begin{array}{l} x = x' \cos 30° - y' \sin 30° = \tfrac{1}{2}(\sqrt{3}\, x' - y'), \\ y = x' \sin 30° + y' \cos 30° = \tfrac{1}{2}(x' + \sqrt{3}\, y'). \end{array} \right\} \tag{7}$$

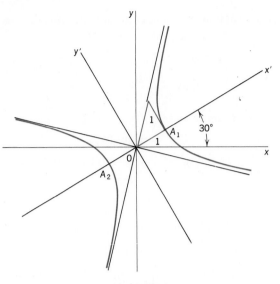

Fig. 3.113

If we substitute for x and y in Eq. (6) according to these equations, multiply by 4, and then collect terms, we obtain

$$2(\tfrac{1}{4})(3x'^2 - 2\sqrt{3}\,x'y' + y'^2) + 4\sqrt{3}\,\tfrac{1}{4}(\sqrt{3}\,x'^2 + 2x'y' - \sqrt{3}\,y'^2)$$
$$- 2(\tfrac{1}{4})(x'^2 + 2\sqrt{3}\,x'y' + 3y'^2) = 4,$$
$$16x'^2 - 16y'^2 = 16,$$
$$\frac{x'^2}{1} - \frac{y'^2}{1} = 1. \tag{6a}$$

The curve is a hyperbola with the x' axis as transverse axis. Using $a = b = 1$, we draw the key triangle, sketch the asymptotes, and then sketch the hyperbola itself. See Fig. 3.113. Since the asymptotes have slope ± 1 when referred to the x', y' axes, their equations are $y' = \pm 1x'$.

The vertex A_1 has x', y' coordinates $(1, 0)$ and, according to Eq. (7), x, y coordinates $x = \tfrac{1}{2}[\sqrt{3}(1) - 0] = \sqrt{3}/2$, $y = \tfrac{1}{2}[1 + \sqrt{3}(0)] = \tfrac{1}{2}$; the x, y coordinates of A_2 are $x = -\sqrt{3}/2$, $y = -\tfrac{1}{2}$.

To write the x, y equations for the asymptotes, we need Eqs. (2), which replace x' and y' as functions of x and y. For $\theta = 30°$, these equations are

$$\left.\begin{array}{l} x' = x\cos 30° + y\sin 30° = \tfrac{1}{2}(\sqrt{3}\,x + y), \\[2mm] y' = -x\sin 30° + y\cos 30° = \tfrac{1}{2}(-x + \sqrt{3}\,y). \end{array}\right\} \tag{7a}$$

Then the asymptote equation $y' = x'$ corresponds to

$$\tfrac{1}{2}(-x + \sqrt{3}\,y) = \tfrac{1}{2}(\sqrt{3}\,x + y)$$

or

$$y = \frac{\sqrt{3} + 1}{\sqrt{3} - 1}x = \frac{\sqrt{3} + 1}{\sqrt{3} + 1}\frac{\sqrt{3} + 1}{\sqrt{3} - 1}x = (2 + \sqrt{3})x.$$

Similarly, the asymptote equation $y' = -x'$ corresponds to

$$\tfrac{1}{2}(-x + \sqrt{3}\,y) = -\tfrac{1}{2}(\sqrt{3}\,x + y),$$

or

$$y = (\sqrt{3} - 2)x.$$

Example 3.   Consider the curve with equation

$$16x^2 - 24xy + 9y^2 - 80x - 190y + 425 = 0. \tag{8}$$

Theorem 2 suggests that we rotate the axes through an angle θ where $\tan 2\theta = -24/(16 - 9) = -24/7$. In order to use the equations of rotation we need the values of $\cos \theta$ and $\sin \theta$. We can get these values from the known value of $\tan 2\theta$ if we first find $\cos 2\theta$ and then use the identities

$$\cos^2 \theta = \frac{1 + \cos 2\theta}{2},$$

$$\sin^2 \theta = \frac{1 - \cos 2\theta}{2}.$$

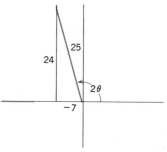

We prefer the first quadrant possibility for θ, and by completing the triangle of Fig. 3.114, we see that

Fig. 3.114

$$\cos 2\theta = \frac{-7}{25}, \qquad \cos^2 \theta = \frac{1 + (-7/25)}{2} = \frac{9}{25}, \qquad \cos \theta = \frac{3}{5};$$

$$\sin^2 \theta = \frac{1 - (-7/25)}{2} = \frac{16}{25}, \qquad \sin \theta = \frac{4}{5}.$$

We finally have for our equations of rotation

$$\left.\begin{aligned} x &= x' \cos \theta - y' \sin \theta = \tfrac{1}{5}(3x' - 4y'), \\ y &= x' \sin \theta + y' \cos \theta = \tfrac{1}{5}(4x' + 3y'). \end{aligned}\right\} \tag{9}$$

When we substitute from Eq. (9) into (8) and collect like terms, we get

$$\tfrac{16}{25}(9x'^2 - 24x'y' + 16y'^2) - \tfrac{24}{25}(12x'^2 - 7x'y' - 12y'^2)$$
$$+ \tfrac{9}{25}(16x'^2 + 24x'y' + 9y'^2) - \tfrac{80}{5}(3x' - 4y') - \tfrac{190}{5}(4x' + 3y') + 425 = 0,$$
$$\tfrac{1}{25}[144 - 288 + 144]x'^2 + \tfrac{1}{25}[-16(24) + 7(24) + 9(24)]x'y'$$
$$+ \tfrac{1}{25}[256 + 288 + 81]y'^2 + [-48 - 152]x' + [64 - 114]y' + 425 = 0,$$
$$25y'^2 - 200x' - 50y' + 425 = 0,$$
$$y'^2 - 8x' - 2y' + 17 = 0. \tag{8a}$$

We recognize Eq. (8a) as that of a parabola with vertex not at the origin. If we complete the square, we can rewrite Eq. (8a) as

$$y'^2 - 2y' + 1 = +8x' - 17 + 1 = +8x' - 16,$$
$$(y' - 1)^2 = +8(x' - 2). \tag{8b}$$

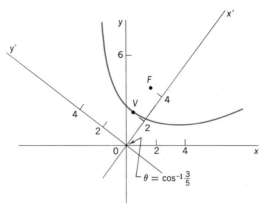

Fig. 3.115

When referred to the x', y' axes, the parabola's vertex is $V(+2, 1)$; its axis of symmetry is parallel to the x' axis; the parabola opens in the positive x' direction; see Fig. 3.115. Equation (8b) tells us that $p = 4$; hence the distance from the vertex to the focus is $p/2 = 2$. The coordinates of the focus are $(+4, 1)$; the directrix is the y' axis itself.

To find the x, y descriptions of V and F, we turn to Eqs. (9). For V we find $x = \frac{1}{5}[3(+2) - 4(1)] = \frac{2}{5}$, $y = \frac{1}{5}[4(+2) + 3(1)] = \frac{11}{5}$. In a similar way we find that the x, y description of F is $(\frac{8}{5}, \frac{19}{5})$.

To find the x, y description of the directrix, $x' = 0$, we need equations that give x' and y' in terms of x and y. These we get from Eqs. (2);

$$x' = x \cos \theta + y \sin \theta = \tfrac{3}{5} x + \tfrac{4}{5} y$$

$$y' = -x \sin \theta + y \cos \theta = -\tfrac{4}{5} x + \tfrac{3}{5} y.$$

Hence for $x' = 0$ we have

$$\tfrac{3}{5} x + \tfrac{4}{5} y = 0 \qquad \text{or} \qquad y = -\tfrac{3}{4} x.$$

Example 4.   The major vertices of an ellipse are the points $A_1(2, 4)$ and $A_2(-2, -4)$; the foci are the points $F_1(\sqrt{2}, 2\sqrt{2})$ and $F_2(-\sqrt{2}, -2\sqrt{2})$. Find the equation of the ellipse.

The center of the ellipse must be $(0, 0)$, the midpoint of A_1A_2. The semimajor axis length is $a = OA_1 = \sqrt{20}$; the distance from the center to a focus is $c = OF_1 = \sqrt{10}$. The distance from the center to a minor vertex would then follow from $b^2 = a^2 - c^2 = 10$. These facts appear in Fig. 3.116. When referred to x', y' axes taken along its major and minor axes, the equation of the ellipse is

$$\frac{x'^2}{20} + \frac{y'^2}{10} = 1,$$

or

$$x'^2 + 2y'^2 = 20. \tag{10}$$

To get the x, y coordinate description of the ellipse we need the relationship between the coordinate systems. From the coordinates of A_1 we see that θ, the

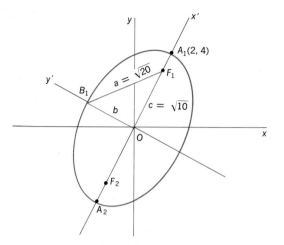

Fig. 3.116

angle through which we rotate in going from the x, y axes to the x', y' axes, is such that $\tan \theta = \frac{4}{2} = 2$. Then

$$\cos \theta = \frac{1}{\sqrt{5}} \quad \text{and} \quad \sin \theta = \frac{2}{\sqrt{5}},$$

and from Eqs. (2) we have

$$x' = x \cos \theta + y \sin \theta = \frac{1}{\sqrt{5}} (1x + 2y),$$

$$y' = -x \sin \theta + y \cos \theta = \frac{1}{\sqrt{5}} (-2x + 1y).$$

(11)

If we substitute from Eqs. (11) into (10), we find that the x, y equation of the ellipse is

$$\tfrac{1}{5}(x + 2y)^2 + 2(\tfrac{1}{5})(-2x + y)^2 = 20,$$

or

$$9x^2 - 4xy + 6y^2 = 100.$$

EXERCISES 3.14

1. Take a new coordinate system by rotating the x, y axes through a suitable angle, find the curve's equation in the new coordinate system, and sketch the graph. If the curve is a parabola, find its vertex, directrix, focus; if an ellipse, its center, major and minor vertices, and foci; if an hyperbola, its center, transverse vertices, foci, and asymptotes. In each case final descriptions should be given in terms of the x, y coordinate system used in stating the problem.
   (a) $x^2 + 2xy + y^2 + 8x - 8y = 0$.
   (b) $9x^2 - 24xy + 16y^2 - 320x - 240y = 0$.
   (c) $7x^2 + 6\sqrt{3}\,xy + 13y^2 = 64$.
   (d) $6x^2 - 6xy + 14y^2 = 45$.
   (e) $xy = a^2$.
   (f) $77x^2 + 120xy + 27y^2 + 117 = 0$.

2. The vertex of a parabola is the origin; the focus is the point $(-2, -2)$. Find its equation.

3. The minor vertices of an ellipse are the points $(2, 1)$, $(-2, -1)$; its eccentricity is $\sqrt{1/6}$. Find its equation.

4. The transverse vertices of an hyperbola are the points $(1, 3)$, $(-1, -3)$; the hyperbola passes through $(0, 5)$. Find its equation.

5. As a fundamental check on the equations of translation and rotation, show that the number computed for the distance between points P_1 and P_2 is not changed if the coordinate system is changed (a) by translation, or (b) by rotation. We say that the distance between two points is invariant under translations and rotations of coordinates.

6. Show that the equation of the straight line $y = (\tan \alpha)x$ becomes $y' = [\tan (\alpha - \theta)]x'$ when the axes are rotated through an angle θ.

7. A rotation of axes through an angle θ followed by a rotation through an angle ϕ is, of course, a rotation through the angle $\theta + \phi$. Show formally that from

$$\left. \begin{array}{l} x' = x \cos \theta + y \sin \theta \\ y' = -x \sin \theta + y \cos \theta \end{array} \right\} \quad \text{and} \quad \left. \begin{array}{l} x'' = x' \cos \phi + y' \sin \phi \\ y'' = -x' \sin \phi + y' \cos \phi \end{array} \right\}$$

there follows

$$\left. \begin{array}{l} x'' = x \cos (\theta + \phi) + y \sin (\theta + \phi) \\ y'' = -x \sin (\theta + \phi) + y \cos (\theta + \phi) \end{array} \right\}.$$

8. (a) Rewrite Eqs. (5) in the form

$$\begin{array}{l} A' = \tfrac{1}{2}[(A + C) + B \sin 2\theta + (A - C) \cos 2\theta], \\ B' = B \cos 2\theta - (A - C) \sin 2\theta, \\ C' = \tfrac{1}{2}[(A + C) - B \sin 2\theta - (A - C) \cos 2\theta]. \end{array}$$

(b) Show that

$$B'^2 - 4A'C' = B^2 - 4AC. \tag{12}$$

$B^2 - 4AC$ is said to be "invariant under rotations."

9. We call $B^2 - 4AC$ the *discriminant* for the conic sections. Show that

$$B^2 - 4AC \begin{cases} < 0 \text{ for ellipses,} \\ = 0 \text{ for parabolas,} \\ > 0 \text{ for hyperbolas,} \end{cases} \tag{13}$$

by considering the equations of these curves in coordinate systems for which the equations do not have mixed terms. According to Exercise 8, Statement (13) would have to hold in any other coordinate system arrived at by rotating axes, because $B^2 - 4AC$ is invariant under rotations. If $B^2 - 4AC < 0$, $B'^2 - 4A'C' < 0$ also.

10. (a) to (f) Check Statement (13) by applying it to the equations of Exercise 1.

11. Show that a curve represented by a second-degree equation in which either the x^2 or y^2 term is missing cannot be an ellipse.

12. From Eqs. (5) show that $A' + C' = A + C$. The quantity $A + C$ is also said to be "invariant under rotations."

3.15 Common Properties of the Parabola, Ellipse, and Hyperbola. Focus-Directrix Definitions

I

The circle, parabola, ellipse, and hyperbola have in common the property that their equations are of the second degree. This is a characteristic property; no other curve has this property, in the sense explained by the following theorem.

■ THEOREM 1

HYPOTHESIS: (a) $\phi(x, y) = Ax^2 + Bxy + Cy^2 + Dx + Ey + F$ does not have linear factors with real coefficients.

(b) The coordinates of more than one point satisfy $\phi(x, y) = 0$.

CONCLUSION: $\phi(x, y) = 0$ is the equation of a circle, a parabola, an ellipse, or a hyperbola.*

PROOF: Any rotation of coordinate axes will replace $\phi(x, y) = 0$ by a new equation, $\tau(x', y') = 0$. But τ will also be of the second degree, and τ will have linear factors if and only if ϕ did.† Hence, if $\phi(x, y) = 0$ has an xy term, we can rotate the coordinate axes through a suitable angle and study instead an equation that has no xy term. Without loss of generality, then, let us consider

$$Ax^2 + Cy^2 + Dx + Ey + F = 0.$$

(a) A and C cannot both vanish, for then the equation would be of the first degree.

(b) If one of A and C vanishes, say $A = 0$, we have, upon completing the square,

$$Cy^2 + Dx + Ey + F = 0,$$

$$C\left(y^2 + \frac{E}{C}y + \frac{E^2}{4C^2}\right) = -Dx - F + \frac{E^2}{4C},$$

$$\left(y + \frac{E}{2C}\right)^2 = -\frac{D}{C}x - \frac{F}{C} + \frac{E^2}{4C^2} = -\frac{D}{C}x + \frac{E^2 - 4FC}{4C^2}.$$

If $D \neq 0$, this equation represents a parabola. If $D = 0$ and $E^2 - 4FC \geq 0$, then the equation reduces to

$$y + \frac{E}{2C} = \pm\frac{1}{2C}\sqrt{E^2 - 4FC}.$$

Here we have one or two straight lines; the original $\phi(x, y)$ must have had linear factors and this case is ruled out by hypothesis. If $D = 0$ and $E^2 - 4FC < 0$, then

---

* Exercise 3.14-9 would help us to state a more detailed conclusion for this theorem.

† If $\phi(x, y)$ can be written as a product of two linear factors, $\phi(x, y) = 0$ represents two straight lines [one if $\phi(x, y)$ is the square of a linear factor]. But in the new coordinate system obtained by rotation, straight lines will still have linear equations and in the description $\tau(x', y') = 0$ for the same two lines, τ will again have to be a product of linear factors.

we have an equation satisfied by the coordinates of no real point, a case again ruled out by hypothesis.

(c) If $AC < 0$, A and C have opposite signs, and upon completing the square we shall get either a hyperbola or two straight lines, the latter case again ruled out in this particular discussion.*

(d) If $AC > 0$, A and C have like signs, and upon completing the square we shall get either (1) an ellipse or circle equation, (2) an equation satisfied only by the coordinates of one point, or (3) an equation satisfied by the coordinates of no point at all. The latter cases are again ruled out.†

We have now outlined the possible cases and this completes our proof.

II

Our definition for the parabola was given in terms of a fixed point and a fixed line; the definitions for the ellipse and hyperbola were a little different, two fixed points being used instead. It is reasonable to inquire whether all three could have been given a common definition.

If P is any point on a parabola, F the focus, and PN the distance from P to the directrix, then

$$PF = PN. \tag{1}$$

We hope to generalize this statement in such a way as to arrive at definitions for the ellipse and hyperbola also. Two simple generalizations are

$$PF = PN + k \tag{2}$$

and
$$PF = kPN, \tag{3}$$

where k is a constant. It is quickly apparent that Eq. (2) leads not to ellipses and hyperbolas but to parabolas again. The addition of the constant k has the net effect of translating the directrix k units.‡

Equation (3) does lead to ellipses and hyperbolas. To determine which line to choose for a directrix and which constant k to try in the ellipse case, let us experiment a little by assuming that a focus-directrix definition like that of Eq. (3) is possible and let us see to what suggestions for directrix line and constant k we are then led.

■ THEOREM 2

HYPOTHESIS: There exist a line $x = d$ and a constant k such that for every point $P(x, y)$ on the ellipse

$$\frac{x^2}{a^2} + \frac{y^2}{b^2} = 1$$

we have $PF_1 = kPN_1$, where PF_1 is the distance from P to the focus $F_1(c, 0)$ and PN_1 is the distance from P to $x = d$.

---

* See Exercise 3.15-9.
† *Ibid.*
‡ See Exercise 3.15-4.

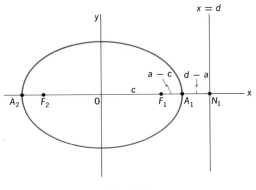

Fig. 3.117

CONCLUSION: (a) The directrix line $x = d$ is the line $x = a/e$.
(b) The ratio k is the eccentricity; $PF_1 = ePN_1$.

PROOF: Consider Fig. 3.117. Since $A_1(a, 0)$ is a point on the ellipse, we know that $A_1F_1 = kA_1N_1$ or

$$a - c = k(d - a).$$

But $A_2(-a, 0)$ is also a point on the ellipse, and so we also know that $A_2F_1 = kA_2N_1$ or

$$a + c = k(d + a).$$

Here we have two equations for d and k. To solve, we can divide equations and thus eliminate k. We find that

$$\frac{a - c}{a + c} = \frac{d - a}{d + a},$$

and then that

$$d = \frac{a^2}{c} = \frac{a}{e}, \qquad k = \frac{c}{a} = e.$$

This completes the proof of our exploratory Theorem 2. Now we know that, *if* a focus-directrix definition like that of Eq. (3) is possible for the ellipse, the directrix line will have to lie perpendicular to the major axis at a distance a/e from the center and the constant of proportionality for the focal and directrix distances will have to be the eccentricity e. Let us prove that a focus-directrix definition is possible for *all* the points of the ellipse, not just for the major vertices dealt with directly in the proof of Theorem 2.

■ **THEOREM 3**

The focus-directrix definition for the ellipse.

HYPOTHESIS: (a) F_1 is a focus of an ellipse; $e = c/a$ is the eccentricity.
(b) The line δ_1 lies perpendicular to the major axis at a distance a^2/c from the center, on the same side of the center as F_1.

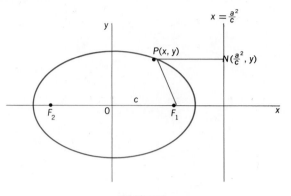

Fig. 3.118

CONCLUSION: (a) For every point P on the ellipse we have $PF_1 = ePN_1$, where PN_1 is the distance from P to the line δ_1.

(b) We have $PF_1 = ePN_1$ only for points on the ellipse.

PROOF: Consider Fig. 3.118 where we have chosen the coordinate axes so that the equation of the ellipse is $x^2/a^2 + y^2/b^2 = 1$, so that F_1 has coordinates $(c, 0)$, and so that the line δ_1 has the equation $x = a^2/c$. Let $P(x, y)$ be any point on the ellipse. To demonstrate Conclusion (a) we shall compute PF_1 and PN_1 and compare them. We have

$$PN_1 = \frac{a^2}{c} - x = \frac{1}{c}(a^2 - cx), \tag{4}$$

and, precisely as in the proof of Theorem 3.11-1, Eq. (3.11-4), where we also computed the distance to the focus $(c, 0)$ from a point on the ellipse graph with the same equation $x^2/a^2 + y^2/b^2 = 1$,

$$PF_1 = \frac{1}{a}(a^2 - cx). \tag{5}$$

It follows from Eqs. (4) and (5) that

$$\frac{PF_1}{PN_1} = \frac{c}{a} = e,$$

which is Conclusion (a).

To demonstrate Conclusion (b), we must show that, if $PF_1 = ePN_1$, then the coordinates of point P satisfy the ellipse equation. But for $PF_1 = ePN_1$, or, better, $(PF_1)^2 = e^2(PN_1)^2$, we can write

$$(x - c)^2 + y^2 = \frac{c^2}{a^2}\left(\frac{a^2}{c} - x\right)^2,$$

$$a^2(x - c)^2 + a^2y^2 = c^2\left(\frac{a^2}{c} - x\right)^2,$$

$$(a^2 - c^2)x^2 + a^2y^2 = a^4 - a^2c^2.$$

$$\frac{x^2}{a^2} + \frac{y^2}{b^2} = 1, \qquad \text{where} \qquad b^2 = a^2 - c^2.$$

This completes the proof of Theorem 3.

Similar facts hold for the hyperbola.

■ THEOREM 4

The focus-directrix definition for the hyperbola.

HYPOTHESIS: (a) F_1 is a focus of an hyperbola; $e = c/a$ is the eccentricity.
(b) The line δ_1 lies perpendicular to the transverse axis at a distance a^2/c from the center, on the same side of the center as F_1.

CONCLUSION: (a) For every point P on the hyperbola we have $PF_1 = ePN_1$, where PN_1 is the distance from P to the line δ_1.
(b) We have $PF_1 = ePN_1$ only for points on the hyperbola.

PROOF: The proof for this theorem is similar to that for the ellipse and is left to the reader as an exercise; see Exercise 3.15-5.

● Remark 1

By symmetry, the ellipse has two directrices, and so does the hyperbola. The ellipse equation

$$\frac{x^2}{a^2} + \frac{y^2}{b^2} = 1$$

can be derived not only in terms of the focus $F_1(c, 0)$ and the directrix $x = a^2/c$, but also in terms of the focus $F_2(-c, 0)$ and the directrix $x = -a^2/c$.

These results can be summarized in a definition that covers the three curves.

■ DEFINITION 1

The focus-directrix definition for the conic sections. An ellipse, parabola, or hyperbola is a locus of points whose distances from a fixed point (focus) and a fixed line (directrix) are, respectively, in a constant ratio $e < 1$, $e = 1$, or $e > 1$, called the eccentricity.

Example 1. Find the equation of the ellipse of eccentricity ⅔ with focus (6, 2) and directrix $x = 11$.

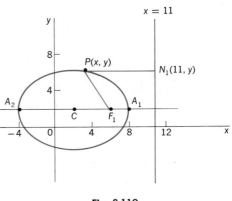

Fig. 3.119

See Fig. 3.119. Definition 1 tells us that for any point $P(x, y)$ on the ellipse we have

$$\frac{PF_1}{PN_1} = \frac{2}{3} \quad \text{or} \quad PF_1 = \frac{2}{3} PN_1.$$

Thus, in algebraic language,

$$\sqrt{(x-6)^2 + (y-2)^2} = \tfrac{2}{3}(11-x),$$

and upon simplifying,

$$9(x-6)^2 + 9(y-2)^2 = 4(11-x)^2,$$
$$9x^2 - 108x + 324 + 9(y-2)^2 = 484 - 88x + 4x^2,$$
$$5x^2 - 20x + 9(y-2)^2 = 160,$$
$$5(x^2 - 4x + 4) + 9(y-2)^2 = 180,$$
$$5(x-2)^2 + 9(y-2)^2 = 180,$$
$$\frac{(x-2)^2}{36} + \frac{(y-2)^2}{20} = 1.$$

The center of the ellipse is at $(2, 2)$ and its major vertices are at $(8, 2)$ and $(-4, 2)$.

Example 2.   Find the directrices for the hyperbola

$$-\frac{x^2}{3} + \frac{y^2}{1} = 1.$$

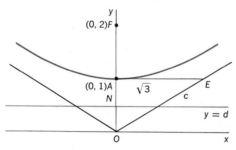

Fig. 3.120

We observe that the center is at the origin and that the points $(0, \pm 1)$ are the transverse vertices, so that $a = 1$. Also, $b = \sqrt{3}$, and with the help of the key triangle AOE we can soon sketch asymptotes and the curve. See Fig. 3.120. From the triangle we read $c = 2$, so that F is the point $(0, 2)$ and $e = c/a = 2/1$.

Let $y = d$ be the equation of the directrix paired with $F(0, 2)$. For any point on the hyperbola, and in particular for the transverse vertex A, the ratio of the distances from F and $y = d$ is e. Hence

$$\frac{AF}{NA} = e,$$

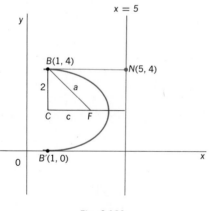

Fig. 3.121

or $\dfrac{1}{1-d} = 2,$ or $d = \dfrac{1}{2}.$

The directrix is the line $y = \tfrac{1}{2}$. By symmetry, the other focus and directrix are $F'(0, -2)$ and $y = -\tfrac{1}{2}$.

Example 3.   Find the equation of the ellipse with minor vertices at $(1, 4)$ and $(1, 0)$ and directrix $x = 5$.

(a) See Fig. 3.121. The center is $C(1, 2)$ and $b = 2$.

(b) The only points on the ellipse that we know are B and B'. For them, as for all points on the ellipse, the ratio of the distances from the focus and the directrix is e; $BF/BN = e$.

(c) Since $BF = a$ and $BN = 4$,

$$\frac{a}{4} = \frac{c}{a} \qquad \text{or} \qquad c = \frac{1}{4}a^2.$$

(d) From triangle BCF we have a second relationship for c and a; $a^2 = c^2 + 4$.

(e) Solving for a gives $a^2 = \frac{1}{16}a^4 + 4$, $a^4 - 16a^2 + 64 = 0$, $(a^2 - 8)^2 = 0$, $a^2 = 8$.

(f) Since the center of the ellipse is $C(1, 2)$ and the major axis is parallel to the x axis, the equation is

$$\frac{(x-1)^2}{8} + \frac{(y-2)^2}{4} = 1.$$

EXERCISES 3.15

1. Find the directrices for each of the following ellipses and hyperbolas.
   (a) $x^2 + 4y^2 = 4$.
   (b) $25x^2 + 9y^2 = 225$.
   (c) $(x-3)^2 + 2(y-1)^2 = 8$.
   (d) $9x^2 + 5y^2 + 36x - 30y + 36 = 0$.
   (e) $x^2 - y^2 = 2$.
   (f) $-9x^2 + 4y^2 = 36$.
   (g) $-\dfrac{(x+1)^2}{9} + \dfrac{(y-2)^2}{16} = 1$.
   (h) $11x^2 - 25y^2 - 44x - 50y = 256$.

2. Find the equation of the ellipse
   (a) with focus $(4, 0)$, corresponding directrix $x = 9$, and eccentricity $\frac{2}{3}$.
   (b) with major vertices $(0, 4)$, $(0, -4)$ and directrices $y = 5, y = -5$.
   (c) with focus $(3, -1)$, corresponding directrix $x = 5$, and passing through $(2, 0)$.

3. Find the equation of the hyperbola
   (a) with focus $(0, 4)$, corresponding directrix $y = 1$, and eccentricity 2.
   (b) with transverse vertices $(3, 0)$, $(-3, 0)$ and directrices $x = +\frac{9}{5}$, $x = -\frac{9}{5}$.
   (c) with focus $(2, 2)$, corresponding directrix $x = 0$, and passing through $(3, 5)$.
   (d) with directrices $x = 0$, $x = 2$, and asymptotes $y - x = 1, y + x = 3$.

4. Consider $F(p/2, 0)$ and PN, the distance from $P(x, y)$ to the line $x = -p/2$. We know from our work on the parabola that a point that moves according to the requirement $PF = PN$ lies on the parabola $y^2 = 2px$. Show that a point that moves according to the requirement $PF = PN + k$ moves along a parabola whose focus is F and whose directrix is $x = -(p/2) - k$.

5. Prove Theorem 4.

6. (a) Sketch a parabola and show its directrix and focus. Which point is closest to the directrix? Which point is closest to the focus? (This point is called the *perihelion point.*)
   (b) Do the same for a hyperbola.
   (c) Do the same for an ellipse.
   (d) For the ellipse case, which point is farthest from a directrix? Which point is farthest from the corresponding focus? (This point is called the *abhelion point.*)

7. The planets move in elliptic paths with the sun at one focus.
   (a) The semimajor axis of the earth's orbit is 92.9 million miles and its eccentricity is .017. How close to the sun does the earth come? What is the greatest possible distance between the sun and the earth?

(b) Answer the questions in (a) for Mercury, whose orbit has a semimajor axis of 36 million miles and eccentricity .206.

8. According to Exercise 3.14-9 the expression $B^2 - 4AC$ helps us to distinguish between parabolas, ellipses, and hyperbolas. In this section we saw that e helps us to distinguish between these curves. It will be instructive to look for a relationship between $B^2 - 4AC$ and e.

Observe first that if one rewrites $x^2/a^2 + y^2/b^2 = 1$ as $b^2x^2 + a^2y^2 = a^2b^2$, $B^2 - 4AC$ changes from $-4/a^2b^2$ to $-4b^2a^2$. This suggests that it would be better to deal with

$$I = \frac{B^2 - 4AC}{(A + C)^2}$$

because Exercises 3.14-9 and 12 assure us that I is invariant with respect to rotations; translations do not affect second-degree terms, and so I is invariant with respect to all rigid motions. Moreover, I and $B^2 - 4AC$ always have the same sign, so that I can serve just as well as $B^2 - 4AC$ to distinguish between the parabolas, ellipses, and hyperbolas. The reader should verify the fact that multiplying a second-degree equation through by any constant does not change I.

Returning to the ellipse $b^2x^2 + a^2y^2 = a^2b^2$ we see that

$$I = \frac{-4a^2b^2}{(a^2 + b^2)^2} = \frac{-4a^2(a^2 - c^2)}{(2a^2 - c^2)^2} = \frac{-4(1 - e^2)}{(2 - e^2)^2}.$$

Fill in the details of this argument, and then show that

$$I = \frac{-4(1 - e^2)}{(2 - e^2)^2}$$

for parabolas and hyperbolas also.

9. (a) Return to the proof of Theorem 1 and discuss Step (c) in greater detail. (b) Do the same for Step (d).

3.16 The Parabola, Ellipse and Hyperbola as Conic Sections

The circle, ellipse, parabola, and hyperbola also have in common the property of being sections of a right circular cone.

Take a circle C. Let A be the line through the center of C perpendicular to the plane of C, and let V be a point on A, not in the plane of C; see Fig. 3.122. Through each point of C draw the line that also passes through V. These lines generate a right circular cone; V is its vertex point and A is its axis. The angle between A and any one of the generating lines is called the *vertex angle*.

A plane section of the cone perpendicular to axis A is a circle; C is such a circle. A plane section that makes a slightly smaller angle with axis A is an ellipse; E is such an ellipse. A plane section that makes with axis A an angle precisely equal to the vertex angle of the cone is a parabola; P is such a parabola. Finally, the lines joining the various points of C to V were understood to be infinite in length, and the cone has an upper nappe as well as a lower nappe. A plane section that makes a still smaller angle with the axis of the cone intersects both nappes of the cone and is a hyperbola; H_1 and H_2 are the two branches of such a hyperbola.

To put the facts in another way, imagine a point source of light placed at V and a circular ring placed at C. The shadow cast by the circular ring will be an ellipse, a parabola, or part of an hyperbola, depending upon the angle θ between the axis of the cone and the plane upon which the shadow is cast. Let α be the vertex angle of the cone. When θ is precisely α, a parabolic shadow is cast. See Fig. 3.123. When $\alpha < \theta < 90°$, the shadow is an ellipse; a hyperbolic shadow is formed when $0° < \theta < \alpha$ or when the plane on which the shadow is cast is parallel to the axis of the cone.

We shall demonstrate some of these facts and leave others to the student and instructor as exercises.

■ THEOREM 1A

The ellipse as a conic section.

HYPOTHESIS: (a) K is a cone with vertex V, axis A, and vertex angle α.

(b) π is a plane intersecting A at an angle θ, $\alpha < \theta < 90°$.

(c) S_1 and S_2 are spheres tangent to K along circles C_1 and C_2, respectively, and also tangent to π at points F_1 and F_2.

CONCLUSION: (a) The intersection of π and K is an ellipse.

(b) F_1 and F_2 are the foci of the ellipse.

PROOF: See Fig. 3.124. Let us give the name E to the curve in which

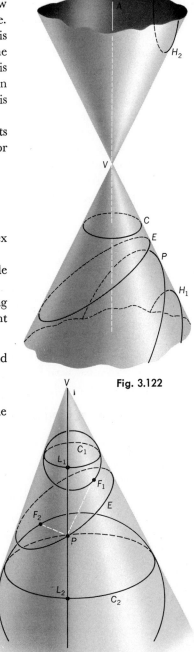

Fig. 3.122

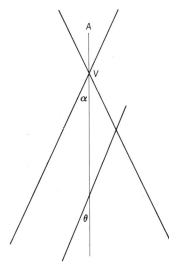

Fig. 3.123

Fig. 3.124

plane π intersects the cone. It will suffice for us to show that for all points P of curve E we get the very same distance sum $PF_1 + PF_2$.

(1) P is a point on the cone. The line PV lies entirely on the cone because it is one of the generating lines of the cone.

(2) The spheres S_1 and S_2 touch the cone along the circles C_1 and C_2. The line PV intersects these circles, say at points L_1 and L_2.

(3) $PF_1 = PL_1$ because both are tangents drawn to a sphere from a common point; such tangents are equal. Similarly, $PF_2 = PL_2$.

(4) Thus $PF_1 + PF_2 = PL_1 + PL_2 = L_1L_2 = $ the distance from C_1 to C_2 as measured along a generator of the cone.

(5) If we had selected any other point Q on curve E, we would have found that $QF_1 + QF_2$ equals the distance from C_1 to C_2 as measured along a different generator of the cone. Since the circles C_1 and C_2 lie in planes perpendicular to the axis of the cone and the cone can be considered as generated by revolution about its axis, the distance from C_1 to C_2 as measured along one generator must be the same as the distance measured along another; $QF_1 + QF_2 = PF_1 + PF_2$.

This concludes the proof of the theorem.

We know that with each focus of the ellipse we can associate a directrix line. Such a line lies in the plane π of the ellipse. It must be the intersection of plane π with some other plane, for a line is the intersection of two planes. Other planes are suggested by Fig. 3.124, namely, the planes determined by circles C_1 and C_2. We shall prove now that the plane in which circle C_1 lies does indeed lead us to the directrix δ_1 associated with focus F_1 and that the plane in which C_2 lies leads us to the directrix δ_2 associated with focus F_2.

■ THEOREM 1B (THEOREM 1A CONTINUED)

HYPOTHESIS: As for Theorem 1A.

CONCLUSION: (c) The directrices of the ellipse are the lines in which plane π is cut by the planes of the circles C_1 and C_2.

(d) The eccentricity of the ellipse is $\cos\theta/\cos\alpha$.

PROOF: Consider Fig. 3.125. Let P be any point on the ellipse, δ_2 the line of intersection of π and the plane of C_2, and PP' the perpendicular drawn from P to δ_2. We want to study the ratio of the distances PF_2 and PP'. We have

(6) $PF_2 = PL_2$ because tangents to S_2 from a common point are equal. (S_2 is not shown in Fig. 3.125.)

(7) But if PG is the perpendicular from P on the plane of C_2, $PL_2 = PG/\cos\alpha$, where α is the vertex angle of the cone, for PG is parallel to the axis of the cone and PL_2 is part of a generator.

(8) On the other hand, $PP' = PG/\cos\theta$, where θ is the angle between plane π and the axis.*

---

* Observe that PP' is perpendicular to δ_2 by definition and that PG is perpendicular to δ_2, because it is perpendicular to the plane of C_2 in which δ_2 lies. Thus the angle $P'PG$ is indeed θ.

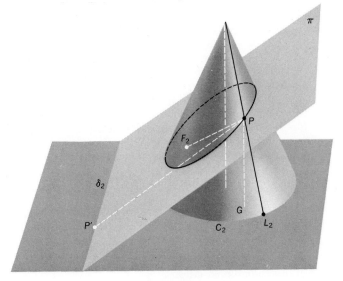

Fig. 3.125

(9) Hence

$$\frac{PF_2}{PP'} = \frac{PL_2}{PP'} = \frac{PG}{\cos \alpha} \div \frac{PG}{\cos \theta} = \frac{\cos \theta}{\cos \alpha}.$$

(10) But θ and α are independent of the particular point P chosen on ellipse E. If Q had been chosen, we would have found

$$\frac{QF_2}{QQ'} = \frac{\cos \theta}{\cos \alpha}.$$

Therefore the line δ_2 is a directrix and the eccentricity is $\cos \theta / \cos \alpha$.

(11) Similar reasoning can now be applied to the sphere S_1 to show that the directrix associated with F_1 is the line of intersection of π and the plane of C_1.

EXERCISES 3.16

1. Consider Theorem 1A. Let θ approach $90°$. What happens to the points F_1 and F_2 at which the spheres S_1 and S_2 touch the plane π?

2. Prove Theorem 2.

Theorem 2. The parabola as a conic section.

Hypothesis: (a) K is a cone with vertex V, axis A, and vertex angle α.
               (b) π is a plane which intersects A at angle α.
               (c) S is a sphere that is tangent to π at point F and also tangent to K along circle C.

Conclusion: (a) The intersection of π and K is a parabola.
             (b) F is the focus of the parabola.
             (c) The directrix of the parabola is the line along which the plane of circle C cuts plane π.

3. Prove Theorem 3.

Theorem 3. The hyperbola as a conic section.

Hypothesis: (a) K is a cone with vertex V, axis A, and vertex angle α.
(b) π is a plane that intersects A at angle θ, $0° < \theta < \alpha$.
(c) S_1 and S_2 are spheres tangent to K along circles C_1 and C_2, respectively, and also tangent to π at points F_1 and F_2.

Conclusion: (a) The intersection of π and K is a hyperbola.
(b) F_1 and F_2 are the foci of the hyperbola.
(c) The directrices of the hyperbola are the lines along which the planes of circles C_1 and C_2 cut π.
(d) The eccentricity of the hyperbola is $\cos \theta / \cos \alpha$.

3.17   Graph Sketching I. Algebraic Clues

We have studied in great detail the curves whose algebraic equations are of the second degree. To study curves of higher degree in the same detailed way would require an expenditure of time prohibitive in this course. We content ourselves with a more general discussion, applicable to most curves we shall meet, even those with nonalgebraic or transcendental equations.

First we want to learn how to predict some of the symmetry properties of a curve from its equation. If every time a point (x, y) is a point of a curve, the point

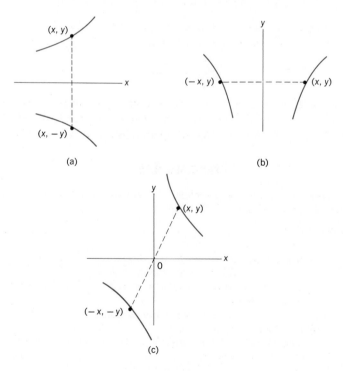

(a)   (b)

(c)

Fig. 3.126

$(x, -y)$ is also a point of the curve, we have symmetry with respect to the x axis. See Fig. 3.126(a). If whenever (x, y) is a point of a curve, the point $(-x, y)$ is also, we have symmetry with respect to the y axis. See Fig. 3.126(b). Finally, if $(-x, -y)$ is a point of the curve whenever (x, y) is, we have symmetry with respect to the origin. See Fig. 3.126(c). These statements are summarized in the following theorem.

■ THEOREM 1

Symmetry criteria.

> HYPOTHESIS: Curve C has the equation $f(x, y) = 0$ and,

$$\left. \begin{array}{ll} \text{in Case (a),} & f(x, -y) = 0 \\ \text{in Case (b),} & f(-x, y) = 0 \\ \text{in Case (c),} & f(-x, -y) = 0 \end{array} \right\} \text{ for those } x \text{ and } y \text{ for which } f(x, y) = 0.$$

> CONCLUSION: Curve C is symmetric with respect to the x axis in Case (a); the y axis in Case (b); and the origin in Case (c).

The converse of this theorem is also true.

We say that two equations, $\phi(x, y) = 0$ and $\tau(x, y) = 0$, are equivalent if the number pairs that satisfy the ϕ equation also satisfy the τ equation, and vice versa. Theorem 1 says, then, in words, that there is x axis symmetry if an equivalent equation is obtained when y is replaced by $-y$; y axis symmetry if an equivalent equation results when x is replaced by $-x$; and origin symmetry if an equivalent equation is formed when x and y are replaced by $-x$ and $-y$.

Example 1A. The curve whose equation is

$$y^2 = \frac{x - 1}{x^2 - 2x - 3}$$

has x axis symmetry, because we get the same equation when we replace y by $-y$.

Example 2. The curve whose equation is $y = 2^x + 2^{-x}$ has y axis symmetry, because the same equation is obtained when x is replaced by $-x$; $y = 2^{-x} + 2^x$ is the same equation.

Example 3A. The curve with equation $y = \frac{1}{3}(x^3 - 9x)$ has origin symmetry, because an equivalent equation results when x is replaced by $-x$ and y by $-y$; the equivalent equation is $-y = \frac{1}{3}(-x^3 + 9x)$.

The *intercepts* are the points at which the curve crosses the coordinate axes. These points are often of importance in sketching a curve. They are found by setting y or x equal to 0 in the equation and solving for the other coordinate.

Example 3B. Discuss the symmetry and intercepts of the curve whose equation is $y = \frac{1}{3}(x^3 - 9x)$, and sketch.

Symmetry: The curve is symmetric with respect to the origin. See Example 3A.

Intercepts: If we rewrite the equation in the form

$$y = \frac{1}{3} x(x^2 - 9) = \frac{1}{3} x(x + 3)(x - 3), \tag{1}$$

we see that $y = 0$ if $x = 0, -3, +3$. The intercepts are $(0, 0), (-3, 0),$ and $(3, 0)$.

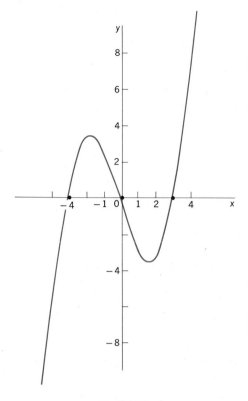

Fig. 3.127

Sketching comments: We shall explain Fig. 3.127. With the help of the intercept points, we break the plane up into several regions and consider these regions one at a time.

(a) Consider the region for which $0 < x < 3$. For any such x, the factor $x - 3$ of Eq. (1) will be negative but the other factors will be positive; for this region we have $y < 0$, and, accordingly, the graph lies below the x axis. From Eq. (1) we learn directly that two points of this region are $(1, -\frac{8}{3})$ and $(2, -\frac{10}{3})$, and we sketch this region roughly.

(b) Consider next the region for which $x > 3$. For such x, all three factors of Eq. (1) are positive and the curve lies above the x axis. Further, as x increases, each factor increases steadily and therefore y increases steadily and rather rapidly. The point $(4, \frac{28}{3})$ helps us to sketch this region.

(c) The region to the left of the x axis is now easily sketched, because there is origin symmetry.

(d) There seems to be a minimum point near $(2, -\frac{10}{3})$. A more detailed computation would place the minimum point nearer to $x = 1.7$. We shall point out in the next section, by using slope ideas, that the minimum point is actually the point $(\sqrt{3}, -2\sqrt{3})$.

After discussing symmetry and intercepts, we discuss asymptotes.

■ DEFINITION 1

The asymptote line: Let w measure directed distance on line L. If the distance between curve C and line L, measured perpendicular to L, approaches 0 when w is positive and grows beyond all bounds or when w is negative and grows beyond all bounds in absolute value, we say that L is an asymptote line for curve C.

See Fig. 3.128.

■ THEOREM 2

A test for a horizontal asymptote.

HYPOTHESIS: $y = f(x)$ is the equation for curve C, and for large positive (or negative) x we have $f(x)$ real and $\lim_{x \to \infty} f(x) = a$ (or $\lim_{x \to -\infty} f(x) = a$).

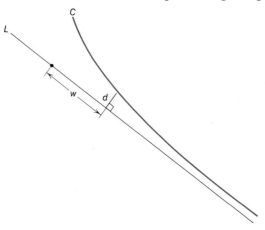

Fig. 3.128

CONCLUSION: $y = a$ is an asymptote line for curve C.

PROOF: See Fig. 3.129, where we have taken the case for which $\lim_{x \to \infty} f(x) = a$. The distance between the curve $y = f(x)$ and the line $L : y = a$ is $d = |f(x) - a|$. By hypothesis, d approaches 0 as we move beyond all bounds to the right on line L.

Theorem 2 is a special case of the more general theorem that follows.

■ THEOREM 3

A test for oblique asymptotes.

HYPOTHESIS: $y = f(x)$ is the equation of curve C, and for large positive (or negative) x we have $f(x)$ real and $\lim_{x \to \infty} [f(x) - ax - b] = 0$ (or $\lim_{x \to -\infty} [f(x) - ax - b] = 0$).

CONCLUSION: $y = ax + b$ is an asymptote line for curve C.

PROOF: The distance d between the curve $y_1 = f(x)$ and the line $y_2 = ax + b$ is proportional to $|f(x) - ax - b|$. Indeed, as Fig. 3.130 indicates, $d = |y_1 - y_2| \cos \alpha = |f(x) - ax - b| \cos \alpha$, where $\tan \alpha = a$. By hypothesis, $|f(x) - ax - b|$ approaches 0 as we move beyond all bounds to the right (or to the left) on line L.

● Remark 1

We have already reasoned in a somewhat similar fashion in working with the asymptotes for the hyperbola; see Theorem 3.12-2.

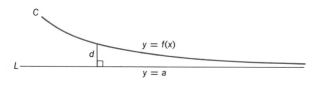

Fig. 3.129

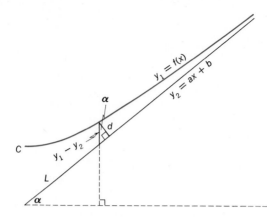

Fig. 3.130

■ THEOREM 4

A test for vertical asymptotes.

HYPOTHESIS: $y = f(x)$ is the equation for curve C, and $f(x)$ is real and increases (or decreases) steadily and continuously, beyond all bounds, as x approaches a from one side.

CONCLUSION: $x = a$ is an asymptote line for curve C.

PROOF: Let us work with the case in which $f(x)$ is positive and increases beyond all bounds as x approaches a from the right; see Fig. 3.131. We must show that the distance d from the line $x = a$ to curve C approaches 0 as y grows beyond all bounds.

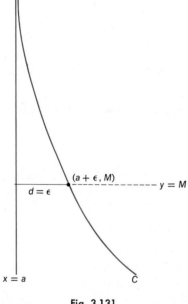

Fig. 3.131

But if any positive number ϵ is specified, no matter how small, there will be a point on C at a distance ϵ from $x = a$, namely, the point $(a + \epsilon, M)$, where M is obtained by taking $M = f(a + \epsilon)$. There is a portion of C above $y = M$ and this portion of C will lie even closer to $x = a$ than ϵ, because the hypothesis tells us that y increases steadily and continuously, growing beyond all bounds as x approaches a from the right. Since ϵ could have been chosen as small as desired, curve C comes as close to $x = a$ as desired, and remains as close as desired, when y grows beyond all bounds. Thus $x = a$ is an asymptote and the proof of Theorem 4 is completed.

Theorems 2, 3, and 4 tell us that to locate horizontal and oblique asymptotes for a graph with equation $y = f(x)$ one should consider $\lim_{x \to \infty} f(x)$ and $\lim_{x \to -\infty} f(x)$.

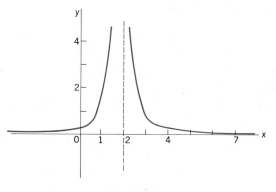

Fig. 3.132

To locate a vertical asymptote, one should ask whether there is a number a such that $\lim_{x \to a^+} f(x) = \infty$ (or such that $\lim_{x \to a^-} f(x) = \infty$ or $\lim_{x \to a^+} f(x) = -\infty$ or $\lim_{x \to a^-} f(x) = -\infty$). For algebraic equations this often means writing the equation in the form $y = \phi(x)/\tau(x)$ and considering values of x near those for which $\tau(x) = 0$.

Of course, if the same curve can be described by an equation of the form $x = g(y)$, one can use theorems analogous to Theorems 2, 3, and 4 in which x and y play interchanged roles.

Example 4.   Consider $y = 1/(x - 2)^2$. When x approaches 2 from either side, y is positive and grows beyond all bounds. Some sample points near $x = 2$ are $(1, 1)$, $(1.5, 4)$, $(1.9, 100)$ and $(3, 1)$ $(2.5, 4)$, $(2.1, 100)$. The line $x = 2$ is a vertical asymptote, because the distance between the curve and the line approaches 0 as the ordinate on the line grows beyond all bounds; see Fig. 3.132.

The line $y = 0$ is a horizontal asymptote, because y approaches 0 as $|x|$ grows beyond all bounds. Some sample points for fairly large x are $(4, .25)$, $(7, .04)$, $(12, .01)$. The distance between the curve and the line approaches 0 as the distance from the origin on the line grows beyond all bounds.

Example 1B.   Consider again the curve whose equation is

$$y^2 = \frac{x - 1}{x^2 - 2x - 3}. \tag{2}$$

Symmetry: The curve is symmetric with respect to the x axis, as in Example 1A.

Intercepts: y^2 is written as a fraction. It can vanish only if its numerator vanishes. The only x intercept is $(1, 0)$; $(0, \sqrt{1/3})$ and $(0, -\sqrt{1/3})$ are y intercepts.

Asymptotes: If we rewrite Eq. (2) in the form

$$y^2 = \frac{x - 1}{(x - 3)(x + 1)}, \tag{2a}$$

we see that, as x approaches 3 or -1, y^2 grows beyond all bounds and that $x = 3$ and $x = -1$ are vertical asymptotes.

If we rewrite Eq. (2) in the form

$$y^2 = \frac{1/x - 1/x^2}{1 - (2/x) - (3/x^2)} \tag{2b}$$

by dividing numerator and denominator by x^2, we see that $y \to 0$ as $x \to \infty$. Hence $y = 0$ is an asymptote also.

Sketching comments: We shall explain Fig. 3.133. Place the intercepts and asymptotes in the diagram.

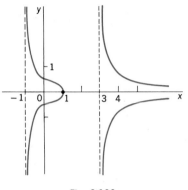

Fig. 3.133

(a) Consider the region $1 < x < 3$, from the intercept $(1, 0)$ to the asymptote $x = 3$. In Eq. (2a), factors $x - 1$ and $x + 1$ are positive here and $x - 3$ is negative. Hence $y^2 < 0$ for this region, y itself is not real, and there is no graph.

(b) Consider the region $-1 < x < 1$, from the intercept $(1, 0)$ to the asymptote $x = -1$. For such x, factor $(x + 1)$ is positive and factors $(x - 1)$ and $(x - 3)$ are negative; thus y^2 is positive and y is real. We already know that the curve passes through $(0, \pm\sqrt{1/3})$ and that $y \to \pm\infty$ as $x \to -1$. With this information we sketch that region.

(c) For the region $x > 3$, to the right of the asymptote $x = 3$, the factors appearing in Eq. (2a) are all positive; this means that $y^2 > 0$ and y is real. The equation tells us directly that $(4, \pm\sqrt{3/5})$ and $(5, \pm\sqrt{1/3})$ are points on the graph, and, knowing that $y \to 0$ as $x \to \infty$ while $y \to \pm\infty$ as $x \to 3$, we sketch this region.

(d) The remaining region, $x < -1$, is empty, for with such x all three factors of Eq. (2a) are negative, so that $y^2 < 0$ and y is not real.

(e) There might be some doubt about the shape of the graph in the neighborhood of $(1, 0)$. Is the graph rounded as shown? Does it come to a point there perhaps? These again are questions that might be answered by detailed computing for values of x near $x = 1$, but they are better answered by considering the tangent to the curve at $(1, 0)$. This we shall do in the next section.

In the last example there were two regions, namely, $x < -1$ and $1 < x < 3$, in which there was no graph. In Example 4 there was no graph for $y \le 0$. It is usually efficient to study the *extent* of the graph before beginning to sketch. This is done by asking for which x the equation will define y as a function of x and for which x it will not, and for which y the equation will define x as a function of y, and for which y it will not.

The next example is a little tricky; it points out the need for considering questions of existence in the neighborhood of a proposed asymptote.

Example 5.   Consider the curve with equation $x^3y^2 + 2x^2y^2 - (x - 2)^3 = 0$. We start by solving for y^2:

$$y^2 = \frac{(x - 2)^3}{x^2(x + 2)}. \tag{3}$$

Symmetry: The same equation is obtained if y is replaced by $-y$; there is symmetry with respect to the x axis.

Intercept: $(2, 0)$; no y intercept.

Asymptotes: It would appear at first that $x = 0$ and $x = -2$ are vertical asymptotes, because y^2 is not finite for either value of x. Actually, for values of x near $x = -2$ and to the left, it will be found that y is real and that $y^2 \to \infty$ as $x \to -2$. However, we shall see that the graph does not exist for values of x near $x = 0$ when we discuss the extent of the graph. Thus $x = -2$ is an asymptote but $x = 0$ is not.

The numerator and denominator of the right member of Eq. (3) are both of the third degree. If we divide numerator and denominator by x^3, we have

$$y^2 = \frac{[1 - (2/x)]^3}{[1 + (2/x)]} \tag{3a}$$

Now we see that $y^2 \to 1$ as $x \to \pm \infty$; therefore $y = \pm 1$ are horizontal asymptotes.

Extent: y^2 cannot be negative if y is to be real. Let us take into account the intercept $(2, 0)$ and the vertical asymptote candidates $x = 0$ and $x = -2$. For the interval $0 < x < 2$, the numerator $(x - 2)^3$ of Eq. (3) is negative while the denominator factors are both positive. Hence there will be no graph in the $0 < x < 2$ region of the plane. The region $-2 < x < 0$ is empty also, because, again, the numerator of Eq. (3) is negative while both denominator factors are again positive. For the region $x > 2$, however, both the numerator and denominator of Eq. (3) are positive; for the region $x < -2$, both the numerator and denominator are negative, so that for both of these regions we have y^2 positive and y real. The graph does exist in the regions $x > 2$ and $x < -2$.

It does not seem to be feasible to solve the original equation for x as we did for y.

Sketching comments: We shall explain Fig. 3.134. Place the proposed intercept and asymptotes in the diagram first. Then

(a) The graph exists in the region $x > 2$, to the right of the intercept at $(2, 0)$. Here $x - 2 < x$ and $x - 2 < x + 2$ so that in Eq. (3) the numerator is

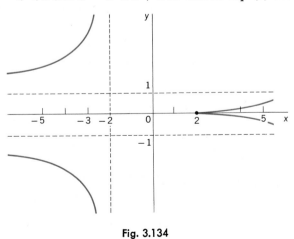

Fig. 3.134

smaller than the denominator and $y^2 < 1$; the curve approaches its horizontal asymptotes from the x axis side. With the help of the points $(3, \pm\sqrt{1/45})$, $(5, \pm\sqrt{27/175})$, we sketch this region.

(b) The regions $0 < x < 2$ and $-2 < x < 0$ are empty.

(c) The graph exists in the region $x < -2$. For negative x we know that $|x - 2| > |x|$ and $|x - 2| > |x + 2|$. Hence for $x < -2$ we shall have $y^2 > 1$ and the curve approaches each horizontal asymptote on the side away from the x axis. Typical points $(-3, \pm\sqrt{125/9})$ and $(-5, \pm\sqrt{343/75})$ help us sketch the curve in this region.

(d) There might be some doubt about the shape of the graph in the neighborhood of $(2, 0)$. Does the graph have a sharp point (cusp) there as shown, or is it rounded there, perhaps? These questions are answered best by studying the tangent to the curve at that point. This we shall do in the next section.

Example 6. Consider the curve with equation $2xy + 2y = (x - 2)^2$. Solving for y, we obtain

$$y = \frac{1}{2}\frac{(x - 2)^2}{x + 1}. \tag{4}$$

Symmetry: None apparent.

Intercepts: $(2, 0)$, $(0, 2)$.

Asymptotes: From Eq. (4) we see that $|y| \to \infty$ as $x \to -1$; $x = -1$ is an asymptote. If we rewrite Eq. (4) in the form

$$y = \frac{1}{2}\frac{x^2 - 4x + 4}{x + 1} = \frac{1}{2}\frac{x - 4 + (4/x)}{1 + (1/x)} \tag{4a}$$

by dividing numerator and denominator by x, we see that $y \to \infty$ as $x \to \infty$; there is no horizontal asymptote. But we can rewrite Eq. (4) in the form

$$y = \frac{1}{2}\left(x - 5 + \frac{9}{x + 1}\right) = \frac{1}{2}(x - 5) + \frac{9}{2(x + 1)} \tag{4b}$$

simply by carrying out the division $(x^2 - 4x + 4) \div (x + 1)$ called for by Eq. (4). Now we see that $y = \frac{1}{2}(x - 5)$ is a second asymptote, because the difference between the ordinate for this line and the ordinate for the curve is $9/2(x + 1)$, which approaches 0 as x grows beyond all bounds; see Theorem 3.

Extent: Equation (4) defines y as a function of x for all $x \neq -1$. If one were to solve the original equation for x in quadratic form, one could write

$$x = 2 + y \pm 2\sqrt{y(y + 6)}.$$

It is apparent from this equation that there can be no graph for $-6 < y < 0$, because x is not real for such y.

Sketching comments: We shall explain Fig. 3.135. We begin by drawing the asymptotes $x = -1$ and $y = \frac{1}{2}(x - 5)$ and the intercepts.

(a) We then consider the region to the right of the intercept $(2, 0)$. Equation (4) says that $y > 0$ when $x > 2$, and we know that our curve approaches $y =$

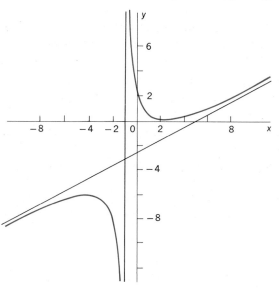

Fig. 3.135

$\frac{1}{2}(x - 5)$ asymptotically. With the help of $(4, \frac{2}{5})$, $(6, \frac{8}{7})$, $(8, 2)$, we sketch this region.

(b) Next, we study the region between the asymptote $x = -1$ and the intercept $(2, 0)$, $-1 < x < 2$. Again y is positive for such x and again the graph lies above the x axis. With the help of $(0, 2)$ and $(-\frac{1}{2}, \frac{25}{4})$, we can sketch this region.

(c) For our last region, we consider $x < -1$. Now Eq. (4) says that $y < 0$, so that the graph lies below the x axis. Keeping in mind the asymptotes and using the points $(-2, -8)$, $(-4, -6)$, $(-8, -\frac{50}{7})$, we sketch this region also. Observe that there is no graph for $-6 < y < 0$, as predicted in our discussion of the extent of the curve.

(d) If the fractions in Eq. (4) are cleared, the fact that Eq. (4) represents a second-degree curve becomes apparent. The curve is a hyperbola. There is symmetry, although not with respect to the coordinate axes, and we might have sketched the curve for the region $x < -1$ by using this symmetry.

The next example points out that translations will sometimes enable us to consider a simpler equation than the one proposed.

Example 7.   Consider the curve C with equation

$$(y - 1)^2 = (x + 2)^3.$$

If we translate axes in such a way that the origin of a new x', y' system is the point $(-2, 1)$, the equation of C becomes

$$y'^2 = x'^3.$$

Let us analyze the curve C from this equation.

Symmetry: The curve is symmetrical with respect to the x' axis, and thus with respect to the line $y = 1$ if we use an x, y axis description.

Intercept: $(0, 0)$ in the x', y' system; thus $(-2, 1)$ in the x, y system.

Asymptotes: None apparent.

Extent: If $x' < 0$, we shall have $y'^2 < 0$ and y' not real. The graph exists only for $x' \geq 0$ and hence only for $x \geq -2$.

Sketching comments: We draw auxiliary x', y' axes with origin at $(-2, 1)$ and explain Fig. 3.136.

(a) The graph exists in the region $x' \geq 0$. With the help of $(1, \pm 1)$, $(2, \pm\sqrt{8})$, $(3, \pm\sqrt{27})$, all in the x', y' system, we sketch the graph.

(b) The question of whether this curve has a sharp point (cusp) or is rounded at $(-2, 1)$ of the x, y system is easily answered by considering slopes, as we shall do in the next section.

● Remark 2

For the most part in our examples we have considered equations that could be solved for y. Curves whose equations can be solved for x can be studied by similar methods, as we shall illustrate in Example 8. Equations that cannot be solved readily for either unknown are more difficult for us to discuss. Some equa-

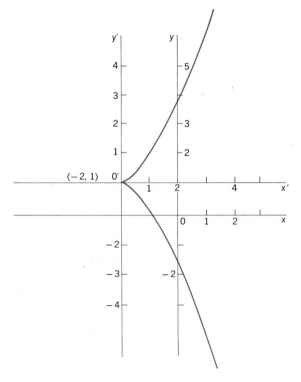

Fig. 3.136

tions of this nature will be considered in Chapter 9, where we study polar coordinates.

Example 8.   Consider the curve with equation $xy^2 - 2y + 4 = 0$. We start by solving for x and write

$$x = \frac{2(y-2)}{y^2} \tag{5}$$

Symmetry: Our symmetry tests do not apply here. We make no symmetry prediction.

Intercepts: Because this fraction can vanish only if its numerator vanishes, we have $x = 0$ only for $y = 2$; $(0, 2)$ is the y axis intercept. There is no x axis intercept, for we cannot set $y = 0$.

Asymptotes: If y approaches 0, $|x|$ will grow beyond all bounds; $y = 0$ is an asymptote. If we rewrite the equation in the form

$$x = \frac{2}{y} - \frac{4}{y^2}, \tag{5a}$$

we see that $x \to 0 - 0 = 0$ when $y \to \pm\infty$; $x = 0$ is another asymptote.

Extent: We can compute x from Eq. (5) for each $y \neq 0$; the graph exists for $y \neq 0$. If we solve the original equation for y, we can write

$$y = \frac{2 \pm \sqrt{4 - 16x}}{2x} = \frac{1 \pm \sqrt{1 - 4x}}{x}.$$

The graph does not exist for $x > \frac{1}{4}$, because real y's are not defined for these x's.

Sketching comments: We shall explain Fig. 3.137. Place the intercept $(0, 2)$ and the asymptotes $y = 0$ and $x = 0$ in the diagram.

(a) Consider the region above the intercept $(0, 2)$. For all $y > 2$ Eq. (5) says that $x > 0$, so that the graph lies to the right of the y axis. We use the points $(\frac{1}{4}, 4)$, $(\frac{2}{9}, 6)$, the fact that $x = 0$ is an asymptote, and the fact that there is no graph for $x > \frac{1}{4}$ to sketch this region.

(b) Consider the region between the intercept $(0, 2)$ and the asymptote $y = 0$. For $0 < y < 2$, we have $y - 2 < 0$ and $y^2 > 0$, so that Eq. (5) requires x to be negative; the curve lies to the left of the y axis. With the help of the point $(-2, 1)$, determined directly from the equation, and the fact that $y = 0$ is an asymptote, this region is then sketched.

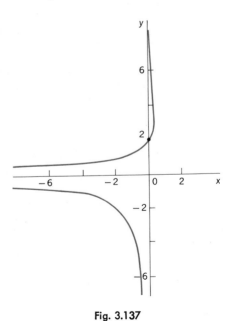

Fig. 3.137

(c) For the region $y < 0$, the numerator for x in Eq. (5) is negative and the denominator is positive, so that again x is negative and the curve lies to the left of the y axis. Our asymptote predictions, together with the points $(-6, -1)$, $(-2, -2)$, $(-\frac{3}{4}, -4)$, all determined directly from Eq. (5), guide us in sketching this region.

EXERCISES 3.17

1. Discuss the symmetry, intercepts, asymptotes, and extent of the curves with the following equations, and sketch. Estimate the coordinates of maximum or minimum points.

(a) $y = x^2(x^2 - 4)$.

(b) $4y = x^3 + 2x^2 - 15x$.

(c) $3y^2 = (x + 2)(x - 6)(x - 1)$.*

(d) $16y^2 = x^3 - 12x^2 + 36x$.†

(e) $16y^2 = x^3 + 12x^2 + 36x$.

(f) $x^2y - 4y = 1$.

(g) $y = \dfrac{(x - 2)^2}{x^2}$.

(h) $y^2 = \dfrac{x^2 - 1}{4 - x^2}$.

(i) $x^2y^2 = 12(x - 3)$.

(j) $x^4y^2 = 6 - x^2$.

(k) $2xy = x^2 + 3$.‡

(l) $9x^2y - 9y - x^3 - 9x^2 = 0$.§

(m) $3x + 6y - y^3 = 0$.

(n) $x^2y - x^2 - y^2 - 1 = 0$.

2. Discuss with the help of the translation equations and sketch.

(a) $2(y + 2)^2 = (x - 1)^3 - 8$.

(b) $y - 4 = (x - 1)^4 - (x - 1)^2$.

3. Propose an equation‖ for curve C if C

(a) has y axis symmetry, intercepts at $(\pm 1, 0)$, $(\pm 2, 0)$, $(0, 3)$, and no asymptotes.

(b) has origin symmetry, intercepts at $(0, 0)$, $(\pm 1, 0)$, and no asymptotes.

(c) has x axis symmetry, intercepts at $(3, 0)$, $(0, 0)$, no asymptotes parallel to the axes, and does not exist for $0 < x < 3$.

(d) has x axis symmetry, intercepts at $(3, 0)$, $(0, 0)$, no asymptotes parallel to the axes, and exists for all x.

(e) has intercepts at $(-1, 0)$, $(2, 0)$, $(0, 1)$, and $x = 4$ as an asymptote.

(f) has intercepts at $(-1, 0)$, $(2, 0)$, and $x = 4$, $y = -1$ as asymptotes.

(g) has x axis symmetry, $(0, \pm 2)$ as the only intercepts, $x = 2$, $x = 4$ as asymptotes.

(h) has x axis symmetry, intercepts at $(1, 0)$, $(-3, 0)$, the coordinate axes as asymptotes, and does not exist for $x > 1$ or for $-3 < x < 0$.

(i) has x axis symmetry, intercepts at $(1, 0)$, $(-3, 0)$, the coordinate axes as asymptotes, and exists for $x \leq 1$.

(j) has origin symmetry, no x axis intercepts, $x = 0$ and $y = 2x$ as asymptotes.

(k) has intercept at $(-2, 0)$, $x = -1$ and $y = x + 3$ as asymptotes.

3.18 Graph Sketching II. The First Derivative

Let (x_1, y_1) be a point on a curve with the equation $y = f(x)$. If $f'(x_1)$ exists, then Definition 1.5-4 tells us that there is a tangent line at (x_1, y_1) with slope precisely $f'(x_1)$. If $f'(x_1)$ does not exist, but if $f'(x) = dy/dx$ does exist for all x near x_1 and if dy/dx grows beyond all bounds as x approaches x_1, then we suspect that there is a

---

* This curve will be discussed further in an exercise at the end of the next section.

† *Ibid.*

‡ *Ibid.*

§ *Ibid.*

‖ The curves are not uniquely determined by the properties given, and two readers who propose different equations may both be correct.

vertical tangent at (x_1, y_1). Just as $dy/dx = 0$ at (x_1, y_1) tells us that there is a tangent parallel to the x axis at (x_1, y_1), so reasoning with the axes interchanged tells us that, when $dx/dy = 0$ at (x_1, y_1), there is a tangent parallel to the y axis at (x_1, y_1).

Example 1. Consider again Example 3.17-7. There in Step (b) of the sketching comments we left unanswered the question of whether the curve $y^2 = x^3$ had a sharp point (cusp) at $(0, 0)$ or was rounded there. If we take $y = +x^{3/2}$, we consider the first-quadrant branch of this curve; $y = -x^{3/2}$ represents the fourth-quadrant branch. Then

$$y = x^{3/2}, \quad \frac{dy}{dx} = \tfrac{3}{2} x^{1/2} \quad \text{and} \quad y = -x^{3/2}, \quad \frac{dy}{dx} = -\tfrac{3}{2} x^{1/2}.$$

In both cases, if x is positive and approaches 0, dy/dx approaches 0; the tangent lines approach the horizontal position, and we have the sharp point of Fig. 3.136.

Example 2. Return to Example 3.17-1B. In Step (e) of the sketching comments there, a question on the shape of the graph in the neighborhood of the intercept point $(1, 0)$ was left unanswered. The equation of the curve was

$$y^2 = \frac{x - 1}{x^2 - 2x - 3}. \tag{1}$$

If we differentiate implicitly with respect to x, we obtain

$$2y \frac{dy}{dx} = \frac{(x^2 - 2x - 3)(1) - (x - 1)(2x - 2)}{(x^2 - 2x - 3)^2} = \frac{-x^2 + 2x - 5}{(x^2 - 2x - 3)^2}$$

or

$$\frac{dy}{dx} = \frac{-x^2 + 2x - 5}{2y(x^2 - 2x - 3)^2}. \tag{2}$$

Equation (1) says that, if x approaches unity from the left, y will approach 0. Equation (2) says that as x approaches unity and y approaches 0, $|dy/dx|$ must grow beyond all bounds. Thus, as one approaches the point $(1, 0)$, the tangent lines approach the vertical position; we suspect that the graph does not have a cusp at $(1, 0)$ but has a vertical tangent and is rounded there. See Fig. 3.133. Indeed, if we had differentiated implicitly with respect to y instead of with respect to x, we would have obtained

$$\frac{dx}{dy} = \frac{2y(x^2 - 2x - 3)^2}{-x^2 + 2x - 5}.$$

At $(1, 0)$ we have $dx/dy = 0$ and a vertical tangent.

We use the first derivative to help us locate maximum and minimum points.

▪ DEFINITION 1

Absolute maximum or minimum point for an interval. Let $y = f(x)$ be defined for an interval. There is an absolute maximum point for this interval at $x = x_1$ if for every other x of this interval $f(x) < f(x_1)$. There is an absolute minimum point for this interval at $x = x_2$ if for every other x of this interval $f(x) > f(x_2)$.*

---

* x_1 or x_2 may be an end point of the interval if the interval has end points.

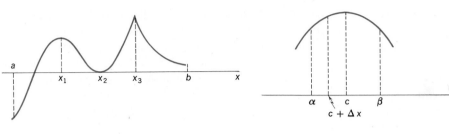

Fig. 3.138   Fig. 3.139

■ DEFINITION 2

Relative maximum or minimum point. Let $y = f(x)$ be defined for an interval and let $x = x_3$ be an interior point of this interval. There is a relative maximum (or minimum) point at $x = x_3$ if this point is an absolute maximum (or minimum) point for some subinterval of which it is an interior point. There is a relative maximum (or minimum) point at an end point of the interval if this end point is an absolute maximum (or minimum) point for some subinterval.

In Fig. 3.138, for instance, we have an absolute minimum for the interval $a \leq x \leq b$ at $x = a$ and an absolute maximum at $x = x_3$. We have relative maxima at $x = x_1$ and $x = x_3$ and relative minima at $x = x_2$, $x = a$, and $x = b$. To justify calling $x = x_1$ a relative maximum point, the subinterval $a < x < x_2$ may be cited. For every x of this subinterval other than x_1 we have $f(x) < f(x_1)$.

■ THEOREM 1

On slopes at relative maxima and minima.

HYPOTHESIS: (a) $f(x)$ has a relative maximum or minimum at $x = c$.
(b) c is an interior point of the interval of definition of $f(x)$.
(c) $f'(c)$ exists.

CONCLUSION: $f'(c) = 0$.

In words, if a function has a relative maximum or minimum at an interior point of an interval, and if it has a derivative there, that derivative must be 0.

PROOF: We shall consider the case where f has a relative maximum at c. The case where f has a relative minimum at $x = c$ is not materially different, and we leave it to the reader as an exercise.

Step (a): We know by hypothesis that there exists a subinterval for $x = c$, say the subinterval $\alpha < x < \beta$ of Fig. 3.139, for every point of which other than $x = c$ we have $f(x) < f(c)$. Stated differently, if $|\Delta x|$ is small enough and not 0, we have $f(c + \Delta x) < f(c)$ or $f(c + \Delta x) - f(c) < 0$.

Step (b): Consider the possibility $\Delta x > 0$. We have

$$\frac{f(c + \Delta x) - f(c)}{\Delta x} < 0$$

because the numerator of this fraction is negative and the denominator positive. Now an expression that takes on only negative values can approach a limit that is negative or 0, but not a limit that is positive. By Hypothesis (c) we know that

$$\lim_{\Delta x \to 0^+} \frac{f(c + \Delta x) - f(c)}{\Delta x}$$

exists, and now we see that

$$\lim_{\Delta x \to 0^+} \frac{f(c + \Delta x) - f(c)}{\Delta x} \leq 0.$$

Step (c): For the possibility $\Delta x < 0$, which is the case illustrated in Fig. 3.139, we have

$$\frac{f(c + \Delta x) - f(c)}{\Delta x} > 0$$

because the numerator of this fraction is negative and the denominator negative. By Hypothesis (c) above we know that

$$\lim_{\Delta x \to 0^-} \frac{f(c + \Delta x) - f(c)}{\Delta x}$$

exists; here we see that

$$\lim_{\Delta x \to 0^-} \frac{f(c + \Delta x) - f(c)}{\Delta x} \geq 0.$$

Step (d): Finally, by Hypothesis (c),

$$f'(c) = \lim_{\Delta x \to 0^-} \frac{f(c + \Delta x) - f(c)}{\Delta x} = \lim_{\Delta x \to 0^+} \frac{f(c + \Delta x) - f(c)}{\Delta x}.$$

Steps (b) and (c) leave us no alternative but to conclude that $f'(c) = 0$.

● **Remark 1**

The converse of Theorem 1 is not true. If $f'(c) = 0$, we can only conclude that $y = f(x)$ has a horizontal tangent at $x = c$; it may or may not have a relative maximum or minimum point there. For $y = f(x) = x^3$, for instance, we find that $f'(x) = 3x^2$ and that $f'(0) = 0$. But $(0, 0)$ is not a maximum or minimum point; see Fig. 3.140.

Example 3. Consider $y = f(x) = |x|$,* Fig. 3.141. We definitely have a relative minimum at $(0, 0)$, and yet we do not have a horizonal tangent there. The

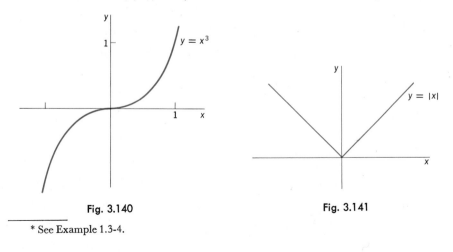

Fig. 3.140   Fig. 3.141

* See Example 1.3-4.

conclusion of Theorem 1 does not hold, because Hypothesis (c) is not satisfied. $f'(x)$ is not defined at $x = 0$.

Example 4. Consider that portion of Fig. 3.138 for which $a \leq x \leq x_1$. At $x = a$ we have a relative minimum point, and yet the tangent there is not horizontal. This time the conclusion of Theorem 1 does not hold, because Hypothesis (b) is not satisfied. The point at which the relative minimum occurs is not an interior point of the interval under consideration.

Remark 1 tells us that, when a curve has slope 0 at a point P, we must distinguish between three possibilities: P may be a maximum point, it may be a minimum point, it may be neither. One way to distinguish between these possibilities is to compute the coordinates of many nearby points. However, it is usually easier to consider slopes. If the slope of a curve is positive throughout an interval, the curve rises there; if the slope is negative, the curve falls there.*

■ THEOREM 2

On testing for maxima and minima.

HYPOTHESIS: (a) $f'(x)$ exists for an interval that includes $x = c$ as an interior point.

(b) $f'(c) = 0$ but $f'(x) = 0$ for no other point of this interval.

(c) For this interval we have four cases.

Case (1):

x	$<c$	$>c$
$f'(x)$	$+$	$-$

Case (2):

x	$<c$	$>c$
$f'(x)$	$-$	$+$

Case (3):

x	$<c$	$>c$
$f'(x)$	$+$	$+$

Case (4):

x	$<c$	$>c$
$f'(x)$	$-$	$-$

CONCLUSION: Case (1): $y = f(x)$ has a relative maximum at $x = c$.
Case (2): $y = f(x)$ has a relative minimum at $x = c$.
Cases (3), (4): $y = f(x)$ has neither a maximum nor a minimum at $x = c$.

PROOF: For Case (1), there exists a subinterval for point c in which the slope of $y = f(x)$ is positive for points to the left of $x = c$, negative for points to the right of $x = c$. Hence, with movement from left to right, the curve rises until $x = c$ is reached and then falls; $x = c$ must be a relative maximum point. Similar reasoning applies to the other cases. See the various parts of Fig. 3.142.

---

* See Theorem 7.5-4 for further discussion of this plausible statement.

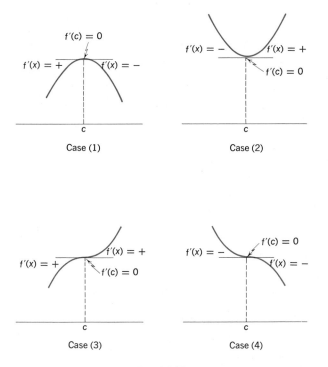

f'(c) = 0

f'(x) = +   f'(x) = −

c

Case (1)

f'(x) = −   f'(x) = +

f'(c) = 0

c

Case (2)

f'(x) = +   f'(x) = +

f'(c) = 0

c

Case (3)

f'(x) = −   f'(c) = 0

f'(x) = −

c

Case (4)

Fig. 3.142

To summarize, when investigating the maximum and minimum points of $y = f(x)$ for a particular interval, the following instructions can be used.

First, look for the solutions of the equation $f'(x) = 0$. If $x = c$ is such a solution, distinguish between the various possibilities for such a point by using Theorem 2.

Second, consider the possibility that a maximum or minimum point might occur at a value of x for which $f'(x)$ is not defined.

Third, consider the possibility that a maximum or minimum point might occur at an end point of the interval.

Example 5.   Discuss and sketch the curve whose equation is

$$y = f(x) = \tfrac{1}{3}(x^3 - 9x).$$

If we write the equation in the forms

$$y = \tfrac{1}{3}x(x^2 - 9) = \tfrac{1}{3}x(x + 3)(x - 3),$$

we can say that there is origin symmetry, that there are intercepts at $(0, 0)$, $(3, 0)$, and $(-3, 0)$, and that there are no asymptote lines. With this information, the graph can be sketched, roughly at least, and this was done in Example 3.17-3B. From the sketch, a relative minimum point somewhere in the interval $0 \le x \le 3$ and a symmetrically placed relative maximum point are expected.

Here let us consider $f'(x)$. The equation for $f'(x)$ is

$$f'(x) = \tfrac{1}{3}(3x^2 - 9) = x^2 - 3.$$

The solutions of $f'(x) = 0$ are $x = \sqrt{3}$ and $x = -\sqrt{3}$, and thus we conclude that the relative minimum point occurs at $(\sqrt{3}, -2\sqrt{3})$, the relative maximum at $(-\sqrt{3}, 2\sqrt{3})$. To illustrate the application of Theorem 2, we cite a suitable subinterval for $x = \sqrt{3}$, say $0 < x < 3$. For this subinterval, we learn from the equation for $f'(x)$ that

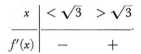

x	$< \sqrt{3}$	$> \sqrt{3}$
$f'(x)$	$-$	$+$

Here we have Case (2) of Theorem 2. With movement from left to right, the graph descends until it reaches $(\sqrt{3}, -2\sqrt{3})$, then rises; $(\sqrt{3}, -2\sqrt{3})$ is a relative minimum point.

There are no points at which $f'(x)$ is not defined, and we did not consider $f(x)$ for an interval with end points. There are no other points to consider in looking for maxima and minima.

Example 6. Discuss and sketch the portion $-1 \leq x \leq 3$ of the curve whose equation is

$$y = f(x) = x^{2/3}(x - 2)^2 = x^{8/3} - 4x^{5/3} + 4x^{2/3}. \tag{3}$$

From Eq. (3) we learn that there will be intercepts at $(0, 0)$ and $(2, 0)$, no symmetry with respect to the axes or the origin, and no vertical or horizontal asymptote lines. Further, we shall always have $y \geq 0$.

The equation for $f'(x)$ is

$$f'(x) = \tfrac{8}{3} x^{5/3} - \tfrac{20}{3} x^{2/3} + \tfrac{8}{3} x^{-1/3} = \tfrac{4}{3} x^{-1/3}(2x^2 - 5x + 2),$$

or

$$f'(x) = \frac{4}{3} \frac{1}{x^{1/3}} (2x - 1)(x - 2). \tag{4}$$

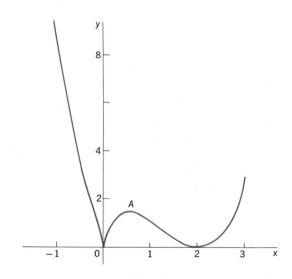

Fig. 3.143

We have $f'(x) = 0$ only for $x = 2$ and $x = \frac{1}{2}$. For $x = 2$ we have $y = 0$, and if we use the subinterval $1 < x < 3$, Eq. (4) tells us that

x	<2	>2
$f'(x)$	$-$	$+$

so that y decreases until $(2, 0)$ is reached, then increases; $(2, 0)$ is a relative minimum point. For $x = \frac{1}{2}$ we have $y = \frac{3}{4}\sqrt[3]{\frac{1}{4}} \approx 1.4$, and if we use the subinterval $\frac{1}{4} < x < 1$, Eq. (4) tells us that

x	$<\frac{1}{2}$	$>\frac{1}{2}$
$f'(x)$	$+$	$-$

The point $A(\frac{1}{2}, \frac{3}{4}\sqrt[3]{\frac{1}{4}})$ is a relative maximum point.

Theorems 1 and 2 have helped us to locate some of the relative maximum and minimum points. But $f'(x)$ does not exist at $x = 0$; the hypotheses of Theorem 1 are not valid at $(0, 0)$. This point is also a relative minimum point, for with the subinterval $-\frac{1}{4} < x < \frac{1}{4}$ in mind we have

x	<0	>0
$f'(x)$	$-$	$+$

y decreases until $(0, 0)$ is reached, then increases.

Finally, we consider the end points. The point $(-1, 9)$ is an absolute maximum point, while the point $(3, \sqrt[3]{9})$ is a relative maximum point. The facts presented in this discussion were used in sketching Fig. 3.143.

EXERCISES 3.18

1. Discuss and sketch the curves whose equations are given below, using information gained from the equations themselves and from the first derivatives.
   (a) $y = 2x^3 - 3x^2 - 12x$.
   (b) $y = -x^3 + 12x^2 - 45x + 54$.
   (c) $y = x^4 - 6x^2 + 8x$.
   (d) $y = 2x^6 - 3x^4$.
   (e) $27y = 2x^5 + 15x^4 + 30x^3$.
   (f) $y = 4 - x^{2/3}$.
   (g) $y = x^{1/3}$ for the interval $-1 \le x \le 1$.
   (h) $y = x^{4/3}$ for the interval $-1 \le x \le 1$.
   (i) $y = 16x^2(x - 1)^{2/3}$ for the interval $-1 \le x \le 2$.
   (j) $y = 1 - |x - 1|$ for the interval $-1 \le x \le 2$. A second description of this curve is

   $$y = f(x) = \begin{cases} x, & -1 \le x \le 1, \\ 2 - x, & 1 \le x \le 2. \end{cases}$$

   (k) $x^4y = 4x^2 - 4$.
   (l) $4x(1 - x)^3y^2 = 1$.

2. Each of the curves whose equation is given below was discussed in Sec. 3.17 at the place indicated. Continue the discussion by locating the maximum and minimum points, if any. Then answer the other questions asked.

(a) $9x^2y - 9y - x^3 - 9x^2 = 0$. Exercise 3.17-1(1). It happens that the curve and its asymptote line $9y = x + 9$ both pass through the intercept point $(-9, 0)$. Which one has the greater slope there?

(b) $2xy = x^2 + 3$. Exercise 3.17-1(k).

(c) $16y^2 = x^3 - 12x^2 + 36x$. Exercise 3.17-1(d). Is the tangent line at $(0, 0)$ vertical or horizontal? Is there a cusp there? What does the slope of the tangent line to the upper branch approach as x approaches 6 from the right? from the left?

(d) $3y^2 = (x + 2)(x - 6)(x - 1) = x^3 - 5x^2 - 8x + 12$. Exercise 3.17-1(c). Is the tangent line at $(6, 0)$ vertical or horizontal? Is there a cusp there?

(e) $xy^2 - 2y + 4 = 0$. Example 3.17-8. At which point is the x coordinate a maximum?

(f) $y^2 = \dfrac{(x - 2)^3}{x^2(x + 2)}$. Example 3.17-5. Is the tangent line at $(2, 0)$ vertical or horizontal? Is there a cusp there?

3. Prove Theorem 1 for the case where $f(x)$ has a relative minimum at $x = c$.

3.19 Graph Sketching III. The Second Derivative

Two curves can pass through the same point and have the same tangent line there but differ greatly in appearance. In Fig. 3.144, for instance, the concave side of curve ATB faces up, while the concave side of curve CTD faces down. The second derivative will help us to distinguish between these possibilities.

■ **DEFINITION 1**

Concavity. The concave side of curve C faces up (expressed more briefly, curve C faces up) in an interval if, throughout this interval, curve C lies above each one of its tangent lines. Curve C faces down in an interval if, throughout this interval, curve C lies below each one of its tangent lines.

Example 1. The curve pictured in Fig. 3.145 faces up for $a \le x \le b$. Two of the tangent lines are shown.

A curve C and its tangent line L have the same slope at the point of tangency T. With movement along L from T, the slope does not change and L continues to rise (or fall) at the same rate. On the other hand, if the slope of C increases with movement in the positive x direction, then it is intuitively clear that along C the rise will be at a faster rate than before, rather than at the same rate (or the fall at a slower rate), and that C will lie above L. In Figs. 3.146(a) and 3.146(b), both L and C had the same slope at T, but the slope of C increased with movement in the

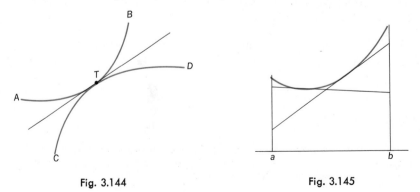

Fig. 3.144   Fig. 3.145

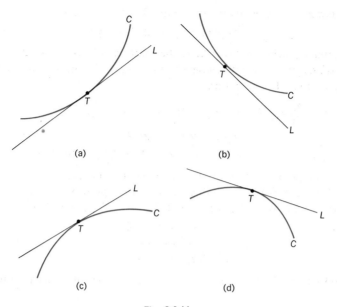

Fig. 3.146

positive x direction while that of L did not, so that C rose above L. In both cases, when the slope increased, the curve faced up.

If the slope of C decreases, however, as in Figs 3.146(c) and 3.146(d), then C will not continue to rise (or fall) at the same rate as L and will fall below L. In both cases, when the slope decreased, the curve faced down.

Because $f'(x)$ or dy/dx is the slope of $y = f(x)$, $f''(x)$ is the rate of change of the slope. Therefore, to say that $f''(x) = d^2y/dx^2 > 0$ in an interval means that the slope is increasing in that interval, and the curve faces up; $f''(x) = d^2y/dx^2 < 0$ would mean that the slope was decreasing in that interval, and the curve faces down. We present these facts as a theorem.*

■ **THEOREM 1A**

On concavity.

HYPOTHESIS: $f''(x) > 0$ (or < 0) and is continuous throughout an interval.

CONCLUSION: The curve $y = f(x)$ faces up (or down) in this interval.

A second theorem may also be stated.

■ **THEOREM 1B**

HYPOTHESIS: (a) The curve $y = f(x)$ faces up (or down) in an interval. (b) f'' exists and is continuous throughout the interval.

CONCLUSION: $f'' \geq 0$ (or ≤ 0) throughout the interval.†

---

* See Theorem 13.10-1A for a proof that does not depend so much on geometric intuition.
† See Theorem 13.10-1B.

Example 2. Let us discuss the graph for the equation

$$y = f(x) = (x - 2)^2(x - 5). \qquad (1)$$

From this equation we learn that the x intercept points are $(2, 0)$ and $(5, 0)$, that there is no symmetry with respect to the axes or the origin, and that there are no asymptote lines. The equation

$$\frac{dy}{dx} = f'(x) = (x - 2)^2(1) + (x - 5)2(x - 2)$$
$$= (x - 2)[(x - 2) + 2(x - 5)] \qquad \cdot$$
$$= 3(x - 2)(x - 4) = 3(x^2 - 6x + 8) \qquad (2)$$

tells us that the points $(2, 0)$ and $(4, -4)$ might be maximum or minimum points, and indeed it turns out that $(2, 0)$ is a maximum point while $(4, -4)$ is a minimum point. For instance, for the interval $3 < x < 5$ we have

x	<4	>4
$f'(x)$	$-$	$+$

which checks with the fact that $(4, -4)$ is a relative minimum point. See Fig. 3.147.

The equation

$$\frac{d^2y}{dx^2} = f''(x) = 3(2x - 6) = 6(x - 3) \qquad (3)$$

says that $f''(x) > 0$ for $x > 3$ and that $f''(x) < 0$ for $x < 3$. According to Theorem 1, $y = f(x)$ faces up for the region $x > 3$ and down for the region $x < 3$. A point like the point $I(3, -2)$, which separates an interval where the curve faces up from an interval where the curve faces down, is called a *point of inflection*, and is often of great value for graph-sketching purposes.

■ **DEFINITION 2**

Point of inflection. The point P is a point of inflection of curve C if C faces in one direction in a region immediately to the left of P, and in the opposite direction in a region immediately to the right of P.

● **Remark 1**

The tangent line to a curve at a point of inflection, I, always crosses the curve because the curve must face up on one side of I and be above the tangent there, while the curve must face down and be below the tangent on the other side. See Fig. 3.148.

The curve $y = f(x)$ changes the direction in which it faces at a point of inflection, I. Hence, if f'' is continuous in an interval including I, Theorem 1B says that $f'' \geq 0$ on one side of I and $f'' \leq 0$ on the other. This can only happen if $f'' = 0$ at I.

■ **THEOREM 2**

On points of inflection.

HYPOTHESIS: (a) $y = f(x)$ has a point of inflection at $x = c$.

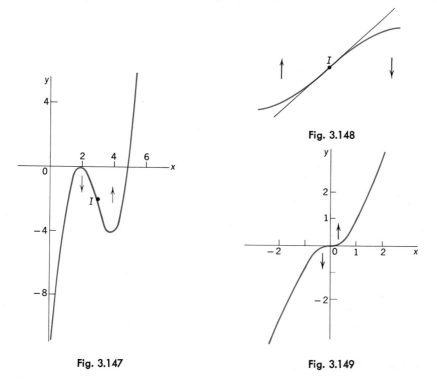

Fig. 3.148

Fig. 3.147

Fig. 3.149

(b) f'' is continuous in an interval that includes $x = c$ as an interior point.
CONCLUSION: $f''(c) = 0$.

● **Remark 2**

The converse of Theorem 2 is not true. It does not always happen that $x = c$ is a point of inflection when $f''(c) = 0$. Notice that $y = f(x) = x^4$ does not have a point of inflection at $(0, 0)$, even though $d^2y/dx^2 = f''(x) = 12x^2$ and $f''(0) = 0$. Indeed, the graph faces up for $x > 0$ and also for $x < 0$; $(0, 0)$ is actually a minimum point. At a point of inflection, the graph must change the direction in which it faces.

Example 3.   Let us discuss the graph for the equation $y = f(x) = x^{5/3}$. From this equation we learn that there is an intercept at $(0, 0)$, and origin symmetry, but no asymptote lines. From the equation

$$\frac{dy}{dx} = f'(x) = \frac{5}{3}x^{2/3},$$

we learn that there will be a horizontal tangent at $(0, 0)$; but further investigation, for the interval $-1 < x < 1$, for instance, shows that there is not a maximum or minimum point at the origin. Indeed, we have

x	<0	>0
$f'(x)$	$+$	$+$

Finally, the equation

$$\frac{d^2y}{dx^2} = f''(x) = \frac{10}{9} x^{-1/3} = \frac{10}{9} \frac{1}{\sqrt[3]{x}}$$

tells us that the graph faces up for $x > 0$ and down for $x < 0$. There is a point of inflection at the origin, even though f'' is not defined there. The conclusion of Theorem 2 does not hold, because Part (b) of the hypothesis of that theorem was not satisfied. The graph is sketched in Fig. 3.149.

We can summarize our discussion of Theorem 2 with the following working instructions for locating points of inflection. First, solve the equation $f''(x) = 0$. If $x = c$ is a solution of this equation, decide whether there is a point of inflection at $x = c$ by deciding whether $f''(x)$ changes sign as x passes through c. Second, consider those values of x for which $f''(x)$ is not continuous, if any; they may also determine points of inflection.

In a region that contains a horizontal tangent, there will be a maximum at the point of zero slope if the graph faces down and a minimum if the graph faces up. This is the case, for instance, in Fig. 3.147. Instead of a first derivative test to distinguish between the maximum and minimum possibilities,* the following theorem can often be used.

■ THEOREM 3

On testing for maxima and minima.

HYPOTHESIS: (a) $f''(x)$ is continuous for an interval that includes $x = c$ as an interior point.
   (b) $f'(c) = 0$.
   (c) For this interval we have $f''(x) < 0$ (or > 0).

CONCLUSION: $f(x)$ has a relative maximum (or minimum) at $x = c$.†

PROOF: If $f''(x) < 0$, $y = f(x)$ faces down and lies below the horizontal tangent at $x = c$. This point is a relative maximum point. A similar argument is valid if $f''(x) > 0$.

Example 4.   Consider the curve with equation

$$y = f(x) = 4 \frac{x}{3 + x^4}. \tag{4}$$

From the equation itself we learn that there is origin symmetry, that $(0, 0)$ is the only intercept point, and, since $3 + x^4$ cannot be 0 for any real x, that there are no vertical asymptote lines. However, the computation

$$\lim_{x \to \infty} f(x) = \lim_{x \to \infty} 4 \frac{x}{3 + x^4} = \lim_{x \to \infty} 4 \frac{1}{(3/x) + x^3} = 0$$

---

* See Theorem 3.18-2.
† See Theorem 13.10-2 for a more complete statement.

tells us that $y = 0$ is a horizontal asymptote. Equation (4) defines a y for each real x so that there are no x intervals for which the curve does not exist. It does not seem to be feasible to solve Eq. (4) for x to see if there are y intervals for which the curve does not exist.

By differentiation, we learn from Eq. (4) that

$$\frac{dy}{dx} = f'(x) = 4\frac{(3 + x^4)1 - x(4x^3)}{(3 + x^4)^2} = 12\frac{1 - x^4}{(3 + x^4)^2} \tag{5}$$

$$\frac{d^2y}{dx^2} = f''(x) = 12\frac{(3 + x^4)^2(-4x^3) - (1 - x^4)2(3 + x^4)(4x^3)}{(3 + x^4)^4}$$

$$\frac{d^2y}{dx^2} = f''(x) = -48x^3\frac{(3 + x^4) + 2(1 - x^4)}{(3 + x^4)^3} = -48\frac{x^3(5 - x^4)}{(3 + x^4)^3}. \tag{6}$$

There are horizontal tangents at $A(1, 1)$ and $B(-1, -1)$, because Eq. (5) says that $dy/dx = 0$ at these points. The second derivative tells us that A is a maximum point and B a minimum point; for instance, according to Eq. (6) we have $f''(1) = -3$ so that there is an interval about $x = 1$ for which $f''(x) < 0$; the graph faces down in this interval and A is a maximum point.

We also learn from Eq. (6) that $f''(x) = 0$ at each of $O(0, 0)$, $I(\sqrt[4]{5}, \frac{1}{2}\sqrt[4]{5})$, $J(-\sqrt[4]{5}, -\frac{1}{2}\sqrt[4]{5})$. Each one of these points is a point of inflection. Thus, for the point I we can cite the interval $1 < x < 2$. For points of this interval to the left of I, $x < \sqrt[4]{5}$, we have $x^4 < 5$, $5 - x^4 > 0$, and $f''(x) < 0$ according to Eq. (6); the graph faces down. For points to the right of I, $x > \sqrt[4]{5}$, we have $f''(x) > 0$; the graph faces up as one would expect if the graph is to approach the x axis asymptotically.

The symmetry, intercept, asymptote, extent of the curve, maximum and minimum points and points of inflection all appear in Fig. 3.150.

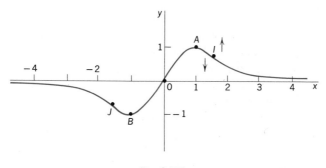

Fig. 3.150

EXERCISES 3.19

1. Show that a parabola with equation $y = ax^2 + bx + c$ faces up or down everywhere according as $a > 0$ or $a < 0$.

2. Discuss and sketch the curves whose equations are given below, using information gained from the equations themselves and from the equations for dy/dx and d^2y/dx^2:

(a) $y = x^3 - 6x^2 + 9x$.
(b) $y = x^3 - 3x^2 + 4x - 2$.

(g) $y = \tfrac{1}{3} x(4 - x)^{1/3}$.
(h) $yx^4 = 12(3 - x^2)$.

(c) $y = \tfrac{1}{5} (x^4 - 4x^3)$.

(i) $y = \dfrac{(x - 3)^2}{(x - 1)^2}$.

(d) $y = \tfrac{1}{8} (3x^5 - 15x^4 + 20x^3)$.
(e) $y = \tfrac{1}{100} (x^5 - 5x^4)$.
(f) $y = x^{1/3}$ (See Exercise 1(g) of Sec. 3.18).

(j) $y^2 x = 3(4 - x)$.

3. Let us consider the cubic curve $\gamma\colon y = ax^3 + bx^2 + cx + d$.
   (a) Show that

   $$I\left(-\frac{b}{3a}, q\right), \qquad \text{where} \quad q = \frac{2b^3}{27a^2} - \frac{bc}{3a} + d,$$

   is always a point of inflection for γ, and that there is no other.
   (b) Show that γ has one maximum point and one minimum point if and only if $b^2 - 3ac > 0$.
   (c) In the case where γ has a maximum point M and a minimum point N, show that the abscissa for I is the average of the abscissas for M and N. (It may be useful to remember that the sum of the roots of a quadratic equation can be found from the coefficients of the equation.)
   (d) The conclusion reached in the foregoing part (c) and many specific exercises suggest that the cubic γ is symmetric with respect to its point of inflection. Prove this by showing that (1) if coordinates are translated so that the origin of the x', y' system is the point $I(-b/3a, q)$, the equation of γ becomes

   $$y' = ax'\left(x'^2 - \frac{b^2 - 3ac}{3a^2}\right);$$

   and (2) γ is symmetric with respect to the origin of the x', y' system.

3.20 Families of Curves

I

In many applications families of curves must be described and studied. For instance, in describing the motion of a fluid, the terms "flow lines" or "stream lines" are often used. The "level lines" on a topographic map are the lines of constant height. In describing a temperature distribution, we speak of the "isothermal lines," the lines of constant temperature.

A *parameter* is a number used to distinguish between the various members of a set, in this case between the various curves of a family of curves. Thus, the height h is usually the parameter for the level lines on a topographic map; we speak of the level curve all of whose points have height $h = 1010$, as distinguished from the curve for which $h = 1020$. Again, a temperature distribution is often presented in map form in weather reports. The temperature T is the parameter; the isothermal curve $T = 30°$ is the curve at all of whose points the temperature is $30°$, as distinguished perhaps from the curve at all of whose points $T = 35°$. In illustrating the technique of describing families of curves, we shall use curves with which we are already familiar.

Example 1. The equation $y = 2x + b$ describes a family of parallel lines of slope 2. The parameter is b, the y intercept. If $b = 1$, for instance, we get the

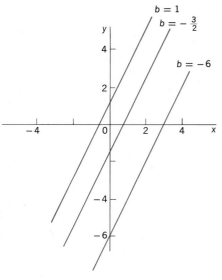

Fig. 3.151

family member $b = 1$: $y = 2x + 1$; if $b = -\frac{3}{2}$, the family member is $b = -\frac{3}{2}$: $y = 2x - \frac{3}{2}$. In Fig. 3.151 we have indicated the nature of the family by sketching several representative members. If one were to ask which member of the family passed through $(2, -2)$, the answer would be $b = -6 : y = 2x - 6$. This is so because the requirement that the coordinates $x = 2$ and $y = -2$ shall satisfy the equation $y = 2x + b$ leads to the computation $-2 = 4 + b$, $b = -6$.

Example 2. The equation

$$(y - 1)^2 = a(x - 3) \qquad (1)$$

describes a family of parabolas with vertex at $(3, 1)$ and symmetric with respect to the line $y = 1$. The parameter is a. For $a = 2$, the family member is $(y - 1)^2 = 2(x - 3)$, which opens to the right. For $a = -4$, the family member is $(y - 1)^2 = -4(x - 3)$, which opens to the left. For $a = 0$, the family member is $y = 1$, an exceptional member of the family. The family is sketched in Fig. 3.152.

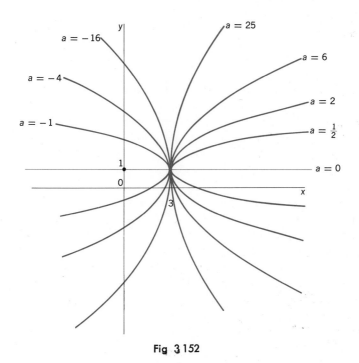

Fig 3.152

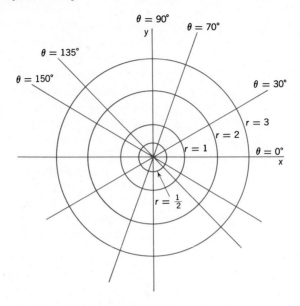

Fig. 3.153

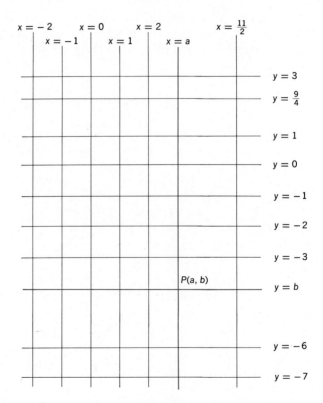

Fig. 3.154

If asked to find the member of the family passing through the origin, we would require that Eq. (1) be satisfied for the coordinates $x = 0$ and $y = 0$. This is the case if $a = -\frac{1}{3}$.

Example 3. Here we shall consider two families at once. Let F_1 be the family of circles with center at the origin, and let F_2 be the family of straight lines through the origin. We can describe F_1 by the equation

$$x^2 + y^2 = r^2, \qquad (2)$$

using the radius r as parameter. For F_2 we choose

$$(\cos \theta)\, y = (\sin \theta)\, x, \qquad 0 \leq \theta < 180°, \qquad (3)$$

using the inclination angle θ as parameter. For the choice $\theta = 90°$, we have $x = 0$, the y axis; for $\theta = 135°$, $y = -x$. Families F_1 and F_2 sketched in Fig. 3.153 are *orthogonal* families; that is, wherever a member of one family meets a member of the other family, they meet at right angles.

● **Remark 1**

Through each point of the plane, except the origin, pass one member of family F_1 and one member of family F_2. Thus with each point of the plane, except the origin, we can associate two numbers, an r number determined by the circle of family F_1 passing through the point and a θ number determined by the line of family F_2 passing through the point. As we stated in Sec. 3.1, a coordinate system sets up a correspondence between the points of a plane and pairs of numbers. If we modified the definitions of F_1 and F_2 slightly so that two different points did not correspond to the same r, θ number pair, we would have a new coordinate system, called the *polar coordinate system*.

Indeed, the rectangular coordinate system most familiar to us can be looked at from a similar point of view. We have a family F_1 of vertical straight lines with equations $x = a$, where the parameter a represents the directed distance from a special member of the family called $x = 0$, and a second family F_2 of horizontal straight lines with equations $y = b$, where the parameter b represents the directed distance from a special member of the family called $y = 0$; see Fig. 3.154. One member of each family passes through each point P of the plane and two numbers may be associated with P, one the parameter number describing the F_1 member through P and the other the parameter number describing the F_2 member through P.

Example 4. Let us look for the family of ellipses with common foci $(\pm 2, 0)$. For such an ellipse we have $c = 2$, $b^2 = a^2 - 4$, and the equation

$$\frac{x^2}{a^2} + \frac{y^2}{a^2 - 4} = 1;$$

see Fig. 3.155. Let us take the equation of this family in the form

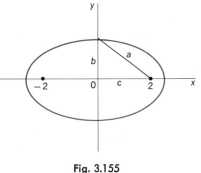

Fig. 3.155

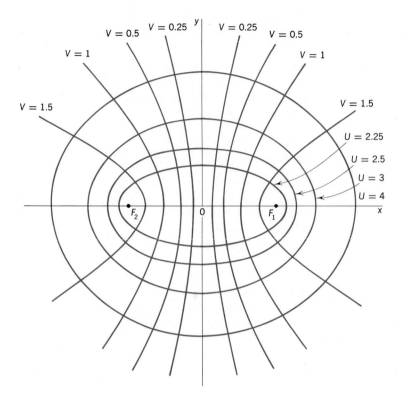

Fig. 3.156

$$F_1: \quad \frac{x^2}{U^2} + \frac{y^2}{U^2 - 4} = 1, \qquad U > 2,$$

where the parameter U can be interpreted geometrically as the semimajor axis. Several members of this family are sketched in Fig. 3.156.

Next let us look for the family of hyperbolas with the same common foci $(\pm 2, 0)$. For such a hyperbola, we have $c = 2$, $a^2 + b^2 = 4$, as Fig. 3.157 suggests, and the equation

$$\frac{x^2}{a^2} - \frac{y^2}{4 - a^2} = 1.$$

Let us take the equation of this family of hyperbolas in the form

$$F_2: \quad \frac{x^2}{V^2} - \frac{y^2}{4 - V^2} = 1, \qquad 0 < V < 2,$$

where the parameter V can be interpreted geometrically as the semitransverse axis. Several members of this family are sketched in Fig. 3.156.

It would appear from Fig. 3.156 that the families of confocal ellipses and hyperbolas are orthogonal families. They are, as can be demonstrated in Exercise

4 below. These families of curves also deter- mine a coordinate system, the *elliptic coordinate system*.

● **Remark 2**

Orthogonal families of curves are impor- tant in many applications, and a problem that is treated in Chapter 14 is this: if we are given a family of curves, find a second family orthogonal to the first.

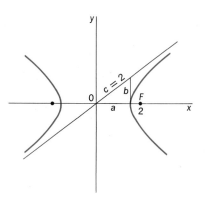

II

Families of curves that pass through the points of intersection of two given curves are often discussed. The following theorem will illustrate this.

Fig. 3.157

■ **THEOREM 1**

HYPOTHESIS: (a) Line L_1 has equation $A_1x + B_1y + C_1 = 0$.
(b) Line L_2 has equation $A_2x + B_2y + C_2 = 0$.
(c) L_1 and L_2 intersect at Q.

CONCLUSION: All members of the family of lines with equation

$$(A_1x + B_1y + C_1) + k(A_2x + B_2y + C_2) = 0,$$

parameter k, pass through Q.

PROOF: Let the coordinates of point Q be (x^*, y^*). Then, because Q lies on L_1 and on L_2,

$$A_1x^* + B_1y^* + C_1 = 0 \quad \text{and} \quad A_2x^* + B_2y^* + C_2 = 0.$$

To decide whether a line L_k with equation

$$(A_1x + B_1y + C_1) + k(A_2x + B_2y + C_2) = 0$$

passes through Q, it is simply necessary to see whether the coordinates of Q satisfy the equation of L_k. Do we have

$$(A_1x^* + B_1y^* + C_1) + k(A_2x^* + B_2y^* + C_2) = 0?$$

Yes, we do, because:

$$0 \quad + k \quad (0) \quad = 0.$$

Theorem 1 is really just a special case of Theorem 2.

■ **THEOREM 2**

HYPOTHESIS: (a) Curve C_1 has equation $f_1(x, y) = 0$.
(b) Curve C_2 has equation $f_2(x, y) = 0$.
(c) C_1 and C_2 intersect at $Q_1, Q_2, \cdots$.

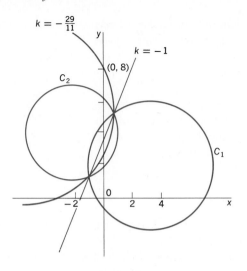

Fig. 3.158

CONCLUSION: All members of the family of curves with equation

$$f_1(x, y) + k[f_2(x, y)] = 0,$$

parameter k, pass through Q_1, Q_2, $\cdots$.

PROOF: The proof of this theorem is very much like that of Theorem 1. We leave it to the reader as an exercise.

Example 5. Given circle C_1 with equation

$$x^2 + y^2 - 6x - 4y - 3 = 0 \qquad \text{or} \qquad (x - 3)^2 + (y - 2)^2 = 16$$

and circle C_2 with equation

$$x^2 + y^2 + 4x - 8y + 11 = 0 \qquad \text{or} \qquad (x + 2)^2 + (y - 4)^2 = 9;$$

see Fig. 3.158. According to Theorem 2, all members of the family of curves with equation

$$(x^2 + y^2 - 6x - 4y - 3) + k(x^2 + y^2 + 4x - 8y + 11) = 0 \qquad (4)$$

pass through the points of intersection of C_1 and C_2. Which member of this family also passes through the point $(0, 8)$? If Eq. (4) is to be satisfied for $x = 0$ and $y = 8$, we must have

$$(0 + 64 - 0 - 32 - 3) + k(0 + 64 + 0 - 64 + 11) = 0 \qquad \text{or} \qquad k = -\tfrac{29}{11}.$$

It is the circle with equation

$$(x^2 + y^2 - 6x - 4y - 3) - \tfrac{29}{11}(x^2 + y^2 + 4x - 8y + 11) = 0$$

or
$$9x^2 + 9y^2 + 91x - 94y + 176 = 0$$

which passes through the intersections of C_1, C_2, and $(0, 8)$.

What is the equation of the straight line through the intersection of C_1 and C_2? A straight line has a first-degree equation, and if a choice of parameter k in Eq. (4) is to lead to a linear equation, it is necessary that the second-degree terms be eliminated. Only the choice $k = -1$ can do this. The straight line with equation

$$(x^2 + y^2 - 6x - 4y - 3) - 1(x^2 + y^2 + 4x - 8y + 11) = 0$$

or
$$5x - 2y + 7 = 0$$

passes through the intersection of C_1 and C_2.

Notice that we dealt with the intersections of C_1 and C_2 without knowing the coordinates of these points. In this particular case, considerable detailed work would be necessary to find these coordinates.

EXERCISES 3.20

1. Sketch several members of each of the following families of curves. Also answer the questions asked.

   (a) $y - 1 = m(x - 3)$, parameter m. Which member of this family is parallel to $x - y = 6$? Is the line $x = 3$ a member of this family? Find a description of the family of all lines through $(3, 1)$.

   (b) $3x + 2y = c$, parameter c. Which member of this family passes through $(1, 1)$?

   (c) $kx + \sqrt{4 - k^2}y = 4$, parameter k, $-2 \le k \le 2$. Prove that the family member L_k is tangent to the circle $x^2 + y^2 = 4$ at the point T_k $(k, \sqrt{4 - k^2})$.

   (d) $(x - 2)^2 + (y + 1)^2 = r^2$, parameter r, $r \ge 0$. Which member of this family is tangent to the y axis?

   (e) $(x - u)^2 + y^2 = 4$, parameter u. Which lines are tangent to all members of the family?

   (f) $y^2 = 4(x - c)$, parameter c. Which member of this family has focus at the origin?

   (g) $\dfrac{x^2}{4} + \dfrac{(y - k)^2}{k^2} = 1$, parameter k, $k \ne 0$. Which lines are tangent to all the members of this family?

   (h) $\dfrac{x^2}{4k} - \dfrac{y^2}{4k} = 1$, parameter k, $k \ne 0$. What do all these hyperbolas have in common?

   (i) $y = x^n$ for $0 \le x \le 2$, parameter $n > 0$.

   (j) $y = x^n$ for $0 < x \le 2$, parameter $n < 0$.

   (k) $x^n + y^n = 1$ for $0 \le x \le 1$, parameter $n \ge 1$. As n grows beyond all bounds, what graph is approached for $0 \le x < 1$?

2. Find an equation for each of the following families of curves.

   (a) The family of straight lines with x intercept $(3, 0)$.

   (b) The family of straight lines perpendicular to $2x - 3y = 7$.

   (c) The family of circles of radius 1 tangent to the x axis and above it.

   (d) The family of circles with centers on $y = x$ and passing through the origin.

   (e) The family of parabolas with vertices at $(0, 0)$ and foci on the x axis.

   (f) The family of parabolas with y axis as axis of symmetry and focus at the origin.

   (g) The family of ellipses with center at the origin, foci on the x axis, and eccentricity $= \frac{1}{2}$.

   (h) The family of ellipses with major vertices at $(3, 0)$ and $(-3, 0)$.

   (i) The family of ellipses with axes of symmetry along the coordinate axes and area 5. (Assume the formula πab for the area of an ellipse, where a and b are the semimajor and semiminor axes.)

(j) The family of hyperbolas with transverse vertices at $(2, 0)$ and $(-2, 0)$.

(k) The family of hyperbolas with foci at $(0, 4)$ and $(0, -4)$.

3. Sketch the following pairs of orthogonal families. Describe the families.

(a) F_1: $x^2 + y^2 - cx = 0$; F_2: $x^2 + y^2 - ky = 0$.

(b) F_1: $x^2 = cy$; F_2: $x^2 + 2y^2 = k$, $k > 0$.

(c) F_1: $y^2 = -2kx + k^2$, $k > 0$; F_2: $y^2 = 2jx + j^2$, $j > 0$.

4. Prove that an ellipse and hyperbola with the same foci intersect at right angles. (This shows that the families F_1 and F_2 of Example 4 are orthogonal families. Theorem 3.11-2 and Exercise 3.12-11 make possible a short geometric proof.)

5. Consider the parabolas of Exercise 3(c) above.

(a) Show that the parabolas of both families have a common focus.

(b) Show that a parabola of family F_1 always intersects a parabola of family F_2 at right angles.

6. Prove Theorem 2.

7. (a) Find the equation of a family of lines through the intersection of L_1: $3x + 2y - 6 = 0$ and L_2: $5x - 4y + 20 = 0$.

(b) Which member of the family passes through the origin?

(c) Which member of the family is perpendicular to L_1?

8. We are given circles C_1: $x^2 + y^2 + 3x - 7y = 0$ and C_2: $x^2 + y^2 - 2x - 6 = 0$.

(a) Find the equation of the circle through the points of intersection of C_1 and C_2 and through $(6, 0)$.

(b) Find the equation of the line through the points of intersection of C_1 and C_2.

9. We are given the curves C_1: $y^2 = +2x$ and C_2: $y^2 = -2(x - 2)$. Sketch C_1 and C_2 and a few members of the family of curves with equation $(y^2 - 2x) + k(y^2 + 2x - 4) = 0$. Describe the family.

The Trigonometric Functions

I

Radian Measure

Angles can be compared in different ways. One familiar system takes a unit angle, called the degree, as the ninetieth part of a right angle; a subdivision called the minute, as the sixtieth part of a degree; and a further subdivision, called the second, as the sixtieth part of a minute. Another system, more common in France than in the United States, starts with a unit angle that is the hundredth part of a right angle and proceeds to subdivide into one-hundredth parts rather than into one-sixtieth parts.

It is the radian measure system, however, that is of essential importance for our purposes.

■ DEFINITION 1

The radian measure for an angle. Place the vertex of the angle at the center of a circle. Let s be the length of the arc subtended, r the radius. Then the number $\theta = s/r$ is the radian measure of the angle. See Fig. 4.1(a).

● Remark 1

If a larger circle had been selected, the radius and subtended arc would both have been larger, but in the same ratio, so that the same number θ would have been assigned to the angle. Note also that if two observers measure distances in different units, they will both report the same radian description for a given angle. In Fig. 4.1(a), for instance, one observer might report $r = 6$ in., $s = 4$ in., $\theta = \frac{2}{3}$. An-

253

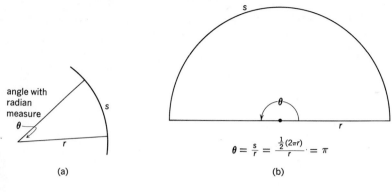

Fig. 4.1

other observer might report $r = 15.24$ cm and $s = 10.16$ cm, but he would also conclude that $\theta = 10.16/15.24 = \frac{2}{3}$.

The correspondence between the degree, minute, second system and the radian measure system can be made to depend on the fact that a straight angle is described by $180°$ in one system and by the number $\pi r / r = \pi$ in the other; see Fig. 4.1(b). By taking proportions we can work with other angles; for instance, the angle described by $60°$ in one system is described by $\pi/3$ in the other; the angle described by the number 1 in the radian system is described by $57°\ 17'\ 45''$* in the other system.

II

The Definitions of the Trigonometric Functions

■ **DEFINITION 2**

If given the real number t,

(a) place an angle with radian measure t "in standard position," that is, with the vertex at the origin of a rectangular coordinate system, and the initial side in the positive x direction. If t is a positive number, the terminal side of the angle is reached by rotating from the positive x direction in the counterclockwise direction. If t is a negative number, the terminal side is reached by rotating in the clockwise direction. In Fig. 4.2, t was taken to be a positive number.

(b) select a point $P(x, y)$, not the vertex, on the terminal side. Let $r = \sqrt{x^2 + y^2}$; observe that $r > 0$.

(c) take

$$\sin t = \frac{y}{r}, \qquad \csc t = \frac{r}{y},$$

$$\cos t = \frac{x}{r}, \qquad \sec t = \frac{r}{x},$$

$$\tan t = \frac{y}{x}, \qquad \cot t = \frac{x}{y}.$$

---

* To the nearest second. Conversion tables are common; see Tables 1, 3, and 6 at the back of this book, for instance.

The instructions furnished for computing the numbers sin t and cos t can be carried out for all real numbers t. The numbers tan t and sec t are not defined for $t = \pi/2$ or $t = 3\pi/2$ or $t = \pi/2 + n\pi$, n any positive or negative integer or 0, because for these t the coordinate x selected in Step (b) of the definition will be 0 and then the instructions of Step (c) cannot be carried out. For similar reasons the numbers csc t and cot t are not defined for $t = n\pi$, n any integer or 0.

● **Remark 2**

If, in Step (b) of Definition 2, two observers select different points on the terminal side of the angle, they will use proportional x's, y's, and r's and hence arrive at the same numbers for the trigonometric functions of t.

● **Remark 3**

If $0 < t < \pi/2$, then Definition 2 is equivalent to this definition: Let ABC be a right triangle with angle A of radian measure t; see Fig. 4.3. Then

$$\sin t = \frac{\text{opp}}{\text{hyp}} = \frac{a}{c}, \qquad \csc t = \frac{\text{hyp}}{\text{opp}} = \frac{c}{a},$$

$$\cos t = \frac{\text{adj}}{\text{hyp}} = \frac{b}{c}, \qquad \sec t = \frac{\text{hyp}}{\text{adj}} = \frac{c}{b},$$

$$\tan t = \frac{\text{opp}}{\text{adj}} = \frac{a}{b}, \qquad \cot t = \frac{\text{adj}}{\text{opp}} = \frac{b}{a}.$$

This definition is perhaps more useful for solving right triangles, but Definition 2 is more general; t is not restricted there to the domain $0 < t < \pi/2$.

● **Remark 4**

It is to be emphasized that the domain of definition for the sine and cosine functions is the set of all real *numbers*. We compute sin t or cos t for a real *number* t. For certain applications one might discuss a trigonometric function for an angle A, but when one writes an expression like sin A one really means sin t, where t is the number that describes the radian measure of angle A. Similarly, we compute cot t for a real number t other than 0 or an integer multiple of π. The reader will observe later that there are many applications in which one computes sin t in con-

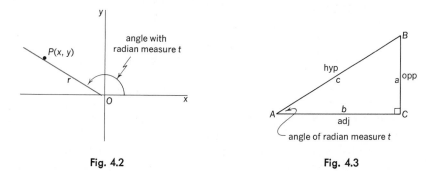

Fig. 4.2   Fig. 4.3

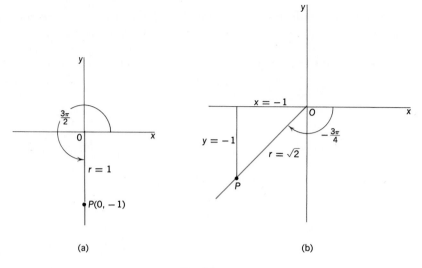

(a)   (b)

Fig. 4.4

texts that have nothing to do with angles. The study of periodically repetitive phenomena is one such application.

Example 1A.   We shall compute sin t, cos t, csc t and cot t for the number t = $3\pi/2$. The angle in standard position with radian measure $3\pi/2$ is such that there is a point P on the terminal side for which $x = 0, y = -1, r = 1$; see Fig. 4.4(a). Hence

$$\sin \frac{3\pi}{2} = \frac{y}{r} = -1, \qquad \csc \frac{3\pi}{2} = \frac{r}{y} = -1,$$

$$\cos \frac{3\pi}{2} = \frac{x}{r} = 0, \qquad \cot \frac{3\pi}{2} = \frac{x}{y} = 0,$$

but tan $3\pi/2$ and sec $3\pi/2$ are not defined.

Example 1B.   We shall compute the values of the trigonometric functions for the negative number $t = -3\pi/4$. The angle in standard position with radian measure $-3\pi/4$ is such that there is a point P on the terminal side for which $x = -1, y = -1, r = \sqrt{2}$; see Fig. 4.4(b). Hence

$$\sin\left(-\frac{3\pi}{4}\right) = \frac{y}{r} = \frac{-1}{\sqrt{2}} = -\frac{\sqrt{2}}{2} \qquad \csc\left(-\frac{3\pi}{4}\right) = \frac{r}{y} = -\sqrt{2}$$

$$\cos\left(-\frac{3\pi}{4}\right) = \frac{x}{r} = \frac{-1}{\sqrt{2}} = -\frac{\sqrt{2}}{2} \qquad \sec\left(-\frac{3\pi}{4}\right) = \frac{r}{x} = -\sqrt{2}$$

$$\tan\left(-\frac{3\pi}{4}\right) = \frac{y}{x} = \frac{-1}{-1} = 1 \qquad \cot\left(-\frac{3\pi}{4}\right) = \frac{x}{y} = 1.$$

Example 2.   For which numbers t, $0 \le t < 2\pi$, is sin $t = -\frac{1}{2}$? Since, by definition, sin $t = y/r$, we must have $y/r = -\frac{1}{2}$, $y = -\frac{1}{2}r$, where y and r refer to a point selected on the terminal side of the angle of radian measure t. Two cases are possible, as sketched in Fig. 4.5. If we use the theorem of Euclid which says

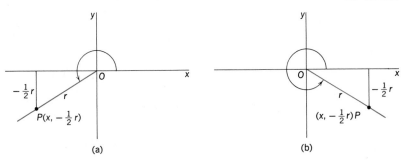

(a)   (b)

Fig. 4.5

that the side opposite an angle of measure $\pi/6$ is half the hypotenuse, we conclude in Fig. 4.5(a) that

$$t = \pi + \frac{\pi}{6} = \frac{7\pi}{6}$$

and in Fig. 4.5(b) that

$$t = 2\pi - \frac{\pi}{6} = \frac{11\pi}{6}.$$

● **Remark 5**

If two numbers are such that the corresponding angles in standard position have the same terminal side, then the same point P could be selected in Step (b) of Definition 2 in both cases, and the trigonometric function values for both numbers must be the same. Thus, in particular,

$$\sin(t + 2\pi) = \sin t, \qquad \cos(t + 2\pi) = \cos t;$$

see Fig. 4.6.

■ **DEFINITION 3**

Periodic functions. If there is a positive number p such that $f(x + p)$ is defined whenever $f(x)$ is defined and $f(x + p) = f(x)$, and if no smaller positive number has this property, we say that the function f is periodic with period p.

The functions $\sin t$ and $\cos t$ are periodic with period 2π.

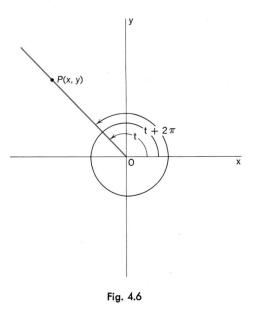

Fig. 4.6

● **Remark 6**

Each trigonometric function assigns positive numbers to some numbers t and assigns negative numbers to other t's, depending on the coor-

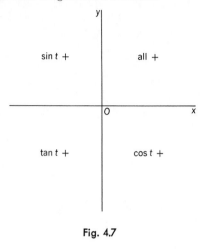

Fig. 4.7

dinates x and y of the point P selected in Definition 2; the number $r = \sqrt{x^2 + y^2}$ is always positive. If t is such that the terminal side of the corresponding angle in standard position falls in the first quadrant, all the trigonometric functions are positive. If the terminal side falls in the second quadrant, then $x < 0$ and $y > 0$; thus $\sin t > 0$ but $\cos t < 0$ and $\tan t < 0$. These statements for $\sin t$, $\cos t$, and $\tan t$, and similar statements for the other quadrants, are summarized in Fig. 4.7.

III

A Working Rule for Computing Trigonometric Function Values

In actual practice, trigonometric tables are used to evaluate the trigonometric functions for most numbers t. A working rule for this purpose is stated here. Other working rules are often presented; if the reader can use a different working rule properly, he need not change over to this one.

Let trig t stand for $\sin t$, or $\cos t$, or $\cot t$, and so on, as the occasion demands.
(a) Consider the angle T, of radian measure t, placed in standard position.
(b) If the terminal side of T has a coordinate axis direction, use Definition 2 directly.
(c) If the terminal side of T does not have a coordinate axis direction, determine the auxiliary or reference angle S formed by that terminal side and the nearest half of the x axis. See Fig. 4.8. Let s be the radian measure of S.
(d) Determine the sign of trig t according to the quadrant of the terminal side of T. (See Remark 6 above.)
(e) Determine the absolute value of trig t by taking $|\text{trig } t| = \text{trig } s$.
Example 3A. Let $t = 5\pi/4$. The reference angle S will then have radian measure $\pi/4$; see Fig. 4.9(a). Since the terminal side of T lies in the third quadrant,

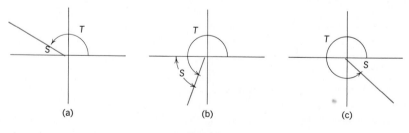

(a)   (b)   (c)

Fig. 4.8

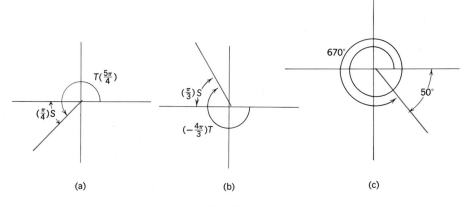

(a) (b) (c)

Fig. 4.9

$$\sin \frac{5\pi}{4} = -\sin \frac{\pi}{4} = -\frac{\sqrt{2}}{2},$$

$$\cos \frac{5\pi}{4} = -\cos \frac{\pi}{4} = -\frac{\sqrt{2}}{2},$$

$$\tan \frac{5\pi}{4} = +\tan \frac{\pi}{4} = 1.$$

Example 3B. Let $t = -4\pi/3$. The reference angle S will then have radian measure $\pi/3$; see Fig. 4.9(b). Since the terminal side of T lies in the second quadrant,

$$\sin\left(-\frac{4\pi}{3}\right) = +\sin \frac{\pi}{3} = \frac{\sqrt{3}}{2}$$

$$\cos\left(-\frac{4\pi}{3}\right) = -\cos \frac{\pi}{3} = -\frac{1}{2}$$

$$\tan\left(-\frac{4\pi}{3}\right) = -\tan \frac{\pi}{3} = -\sqrt{3}.$$

Example 4. To evaluate $\cos 670°$ we observe first that $\cos 670° = \cos 310°$, because the cosine function has the period $2\pi (=360°)$. Next, the terminal side for the angle $310°$ lies in the fourth quadrant, as in Fig. 4.9(c). Thus $\cos 310° > 0$, and since the reference angle is a $50°$ angle, we have

$$\cos 670° = \cos 310° = +\cos 50° = .64279;$$

but $\qquad\quad \sin 670° = \sin 310° = -\sin 50° = -.76604.$

IV
Trigonometric Graphs

Many of the properties of the trigonometric functions can be presented by their graphs. If we compute tables of values for the sine, cosine, and tangent func-

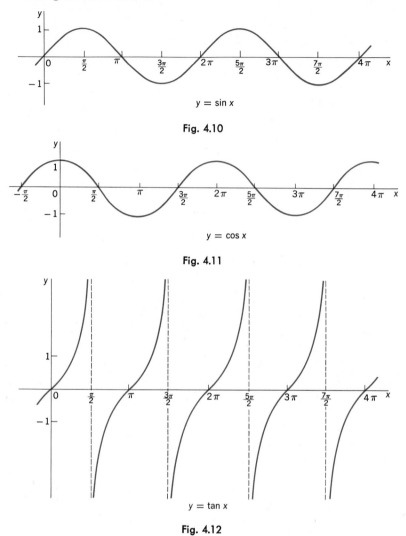

$$y = \sin x$$

Fig. 4.10

$$y = \cos x$$

Fig. 4.11

$$y = \tan x$$

Fig. 4.12

tions from Definition 2 or from a working rule based on Definition 2, we get the graphs of Figs. 4.10, 4.11, and 4.12.*

In Fig. 4.10 we see the repetitive property of the sine function; the graph for the interval $2\pi \le x \le 4\pi$ is a repetition of the graph for the interval $0 \le x \le 2\pi$. We see also that the maximum and minimum values for sin x are 1 and -1.

■ DEFINITION 4

The amplitude of a periodic function. Consider a periodic function for an interval of length one period. The amplitude of the periodic function is half the difference between its absolute maximum and minimum values.

---

* Such tables of values are computed in Exercise 4.1-4.

The function sin x has amplitude 1. The graph of $y = \sin x$ for the interval $0 \leq x \leq 2\pi$ can be considered as consisting of four congruent quarters. First, y increases steadily from 0 to 1 as x increases from 0 to $\pi/2$. Second, as x increases from $\pi/2$ to π, y decreases from 1 to 0 just as it rose earlier; for we have sin $(\pi - x) = \sin x$. Third, y continues to decrease to its lowest value, -1, as x increases further to $3\pi/2$; this quarter is congruent to the first because sin $(x + \pi) = -\sin x$. Fourth, as x increases to 2π, y increases to 0; this quarter is congruent to the second because sin $(x + \pi) = -\sin x$ again.

In Fig. 4.11 we see that the cosine function has period 2π and amplitude 1 just as the sine function does. As for the sine graph, the graph of $y = \cos x$ for the interval $0 \leq x \leq 2\pi$ consists of four congruent quarters, but the cosine graph has a maximum point at $x = 0$ while the sine graph has its maximum point at $x = \pi/2$. The cosine curve can be obtained from the sine curve by moving the sine curve $\pi/2$ units in the negative x-direction, as we see from the identity cos $x = \sin (x + \pi/2)$.

Figure 4.12 points out that the tangent function has period π; tan $(x + \pi) = \tan x$. We are also reminded that the tangent function is unbounded; $y = \tan x$ has the lines $x = \pi/2 + n\pi$, $n = 0, \pm1, \pm2, \cdots$, as asymptotes.

There are many repetitive phenomena in the world about us. A pendulum swings back and forth with a regular period; a weight bobs up and down at the end of a spring with a regular period; a string may vibrate in a certain repetitive fashion to produce a musical sound; we describe an alternating electric current as surging first in one direction, then in the other, and repeating the cycle in a regular fashion. The sine and cosine functions have a simple repetitive property, and they are our primary tool for describing periodic motions. We attempt to describe even very complicated periodic motions as combinations of simpler sine and cosine motions. The tangent function also has a periodic property, but, because it is unbounded, it is less useful as a tool for describing natural phenomena.

The functions sin x and cos x have amplitude 1 and period 2π. The following theorem explains how one can write relatively simple functions with other amplitudes and periods.

■ **THEOREM 1**

The amplitude and period of the sine and cosine functions.

Hypothesis: a and b are real constants, $\neq 0$.

Conclusion: $f(x) = a \sin bx$ and $\phi(x) = a \cos bx$ have amplitude $|a|$ and period $2\pi/b$.

Proof: For absolute extreme values, $f(x) = a \sin bx$ and $\phi(x) = a \cos bx$ both have the numbers $|a|$ and $-|a|$. As a result, each one has amplitude $|a|$. Further,

$$f\left(x + \frac{2\pi}{b}\right) = a \sin b\left(x + \frac{2\pi}{b}\right) = a \sin (bx + 2\pi) = a \sin bx = f(x).$$

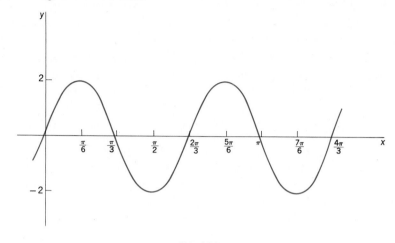

Fig. 4.13

If we had $f(x + p) = f(x)$ for a positive number $p < 2\pi/b$, then we would have $\sin(bx + bp) = \sin bx$ for all x or, equivalently, $\sin(w + bp) = \sin w$ for all w, with $bp < 2\pi$. But here we would have a contradiction, for $\sin w$ has period 2π. Thus $2\pi/b$ is the smallest positive number p with the property $f(x + p) = f(x)$, and is the period of $f(x) = a \sin bx$. By the same argument, $\phi(x) = a \cos bx$ also has the period $2\pi/b$.

Example 5. $y = 2 \sin 3x$ has amplitude 2 and period $2\pi/3$. To sketch the interval $0 \le x \le 2\pi/3$ for this graph roughly but quickly, we first lay off a $2\pi/3$ unit on the x axis, and break it into quarters. Then $y = 0$ at $x = 0$, and for the first quarter, $0 < x < \pi/6, y$ rises to its maximum height, 2; in the second quarter, $\pi/6 < x < \pi/3, y$ descends to 0; in the third quarter, $\pi/3 < x < \pi/2, y$ descends to its lowest value, -2; and in the fourth quarter, $\pi/2 < x < 2\pi/3, y$ returns to 0. More intervals of length $2\pi/3$ can be sketched in similar fashion. See Fig. 4.13.

Example 6. A 60-cycle alternating current has period $\frac{1}{60}$, since it repeats its cycle 60 times in one second. If we assume that this current has maximum value M and can be described by a formula of the type $y = M \cos bx$, then we must have $2\pi/b = \frac{1}{60}$, $b = 120\pi$. The formula is $y = M \cos 120\pi x$. In Fig. 4.14 the graph is sketched for an interval of two periods' length by essentially the same procedure as

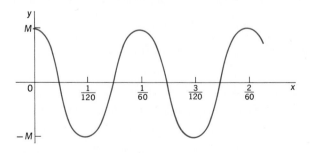

Fig. 4.14

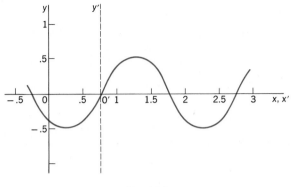

Fig. 4.15

that used in Example 5. The major point of difference is that this cosine graph has a maximum point at $x = 0$, whereas that sine graph had an x intercept at $x = 0$.

Example 7. The graph of $y = \frac{1}{2}\sin \pi(x - \frac{3}{4})$ can be sketched by observing that a translation of axes to a new system with the origin at $(\frac{3}{4}, 0)$ will change the equation to $y' = \frac{1}{2}\sin \pi x'$. Now Theorem 1 says that the curve has amplitude $\frac{1}{2}$ and period $2\pi/\pi = 2$. In Fig. 4.15 the curve was sketched for the interval $\frac{3}{4} \leq x \leq 1\frac{1}{4}$ and then extended back to $x = -\frac{1}{4}$ by using its periodic property.

V

Identities

We use trigonometric identities when we want to use a different description for a function with which we have to work. The identities we shall find most useful are listed here.

(1) (a) $\tan t = \dfrac{\sin t}{\cos t}$,   (c) $\sec t = \dfrac{1}{\cos t}$,

(b) $\cot t = \dfrac{\cos t}{\sin t} = \dfrac{1}{\tan t}$,   (d) $\csc t = \dfrac{1}{\sin t}$.

(2) (a) $\sin (-\theta) = -\sin \theta$,   (b) $\cos (-\theta) = \cos \theta$.

(3) (a) $\sin (\pi - \theta) = \sin \theta$,   (b) $\cos (\pi - \theta) = -\cos \theta$.

(4) (a) $\sin^2 t + \cos^2 t = 1$,

(b) $\tan^2 t + 1 = \sec^2 t$,

(c) $\cot^2 t + 1 = \csc^2 t$.

(5) (a) $\sin (u \pm v) = \sin u \cos v \pm \cos u \sin v$,

(b) $\cos (u \pm v) = \cos u \cos v \mp \sin u \sin v$.

(6) (a) $\sin 2t = 2 \sin t \cos t$,   (c) $\cos 2t = 2 \cos^2 t - 1$,

(b) $\cos 2t = \cos^2 t - \sin^2 t$,   (d) $\cos 2t = 1 - 2 \sin^2 t$.

(7) (a) $\sin^2 t = \dfrac{1 - \cos 2t}{2}$,   (b) $\cos^2 t = \dfrac{1 + \cos 2t}{2}$.

EXERCISES 4.1

1. Find the radian-measure description that corresponds to each of the degree, minute descriptions given. In those cases where the radian measure is not an easy fractional part of π, use the fact that one degree and one minute correspond respectively to .01745 and .00029 in the radian system, or use conversion tables.

   (a) 90°.
   (b) 45°.
   (c) 135°.

   (d) 315°.
   (e) 270°.
   (f) 450°.

   (g) 4°.
   (h) 18° 20′.
   (i) 14° 17′.

2. Find the degree, minute description that corresponds to each of the radian-measure descriptions given. In those cases where the radian measure is not an easy fractional part of π, use the fact that .01745 and .00029 correspond respectively to one degree and one minute in the degree, minute system, or use conversion tables.

   (a) $\dfrac{\pi}{6}$.

   (b) $\dfrac{5\pi}{6}$.

   (c) $\dfrac{11\pi}{6}$.

   (d) $\dfrac{\pi}{4}$.

   (e) $\dfrac{5\pi}{4}$.

   (f) $\dfrac{9\pi}{4}$.

   (g) .17744.

   (h) 3.15904.

   (i) .42819.

3. Check the entries in the following table:

θ	0	$\dfrac{\pi}{6}$	$\dfrac{\pi}{4}$	$\dfrac{\pi}{3}$	$\dfrac{\pi}{2}$
$\sin\theta$	$\dfrac{\sqrt{0}}{2}$	$\dfrac{\sqrt{1}}{2}$	$\dfrac{\sqrt{2}}{2}$	$\dfrac{\sqrt{3}}{2}$	$\dfrac{\sqrt{4}}{2}$
$\cos\theta$	$\dfrac{\sqrt{4}}{2}$	$\dfrac{\sqrt{3}}{2}$	$\dfrac{\sqrt{2}}{2}$	$\dfrac{\sqrt{1}}{2}$	$\dfrac{\sqrt{0}}{2}$

   This table may be of help in remembering these useful numerical facts.

4. Prepare the following tables of values, useful in sketching the graphs of $y = \sin x$, $y = \cos x$, and $y = \tan x$.

x	0	$\dfrac{\pi}{6}$	$\dfrac{\pi}{4}$	$\dfrac{\pi}{3}$	$\dfrac{\pi}{2}$	$\dfrac{2\pi}{3}$	$\dfrac{3\pi}{4}$	$\dfrac{5\pi}{6}$	π	$\dfrac{7\pi}{6}$	$\dfrac{5\pi}{4}$	$\dfrac{4\pi}{3}$	$\dfrac{3\pi}{2}$	$\dfrac{5\pi}{3}$	$\dfrac{7\pi}{4}$	$\dfrac{11\pi}{6}$	2π
$\sin x$																	
$\cos x$																	
$\tan x$																	

5. Find the values of the other trigonometric functions for t if

   (a) $\sin t = \frac{2}{3}$.
   (b) $\cos t = -1$.

   (c) $\tan t = 2$.
   (d) $\sin t = -\frac{3}{5}$.

   (e) $\cos t = -\frac{1}{4}$.
   (f) $\tan t = 0$.

   If there are two possible cases, work out both.

6. On one set of axes sketch
   (a) $y = 1 \sin x$, $y = 2 \sin x$, $y = 1 \sin 2x$, $0 \le x \le 2\pi$.
   (b) $y = 1 \cos x$, $y = 2 \cos x$, $y = 1 \cos 2x$, $0 \le x \le 2\pi$.

7. Determine the amplitude and period and then sketch for an interval of length two periods.
   (a) $y = 3 \cos 4x$.
   (b) $y = \frac{1}{2} \cos \frac{1}{2}x$.
   (c) $y = 1 \cos \pi x$.
   (d) $y = 2 \sin \frac{1}{3}x$.
   (e) $y = \frac{1}{3} \sin 4\pi x$.
   (f) $y = 4 \sin \frac{1}{3}\pi x$.
   (g) $y = 2 \cos (x - \pi/4)$.
   (h) $y = 2 \sin 3\pi(x + \frac{1}{6})$.

8. On one set of axes sketch
   (a) $y = 1 \sin x$, $y = \sin^2 x$, $0 \le x \le 2\pi$.
   (b) $y = \sin x$, $y = \sin 2x$, $y = \sin x + \sin 2x$, $0 \le x \le 2\pi$.
   (c) $y = \cos \pi x$, $y = \sin \frac{1}{2}\pi x$, $y = \cos \pi x - \sin \frac{1}{2}\pi x$, $0 \le x \le 4$.

9. Find an expression of the form $f(x) = a \sin bx$ or $f(x) = a \cos bx$ to meet the following specifications:
   (a) amplitude 3, period 4π, $f(0) = 0$.
   (b) amplitude .5, period .1, $f(0) = .5$.
   (c) amplitude .02, period $\frac{1}{512}$, $f(0) = 0$.

10. Demonstrate Identities (1) directly from Definition 2.

11. The same for Identities (2).

12. Assume the validity of the identities for $\sin (u + v)$ and $\cos (u + v)$ and Identities (1) and (2). Demonstrate
    (a) the identities for $\sin (u - v)$, $\cos (u - v)$
    (b) Identities (4)
    (c) Identities (3)
    (d) the identities $\sin (\theta + n\pi) = (-1)^n \sin \theta$
    $$\cos (\theta + n\pi) = (-1)^n \cos \theta,$$
    where n is an integer
    (e) the identities $\sin \left(\theta + \frac{n\pi}{2}\right) = (-1)^{(n-1)/2} \cos \theta$
    $$\cos \left(\theta + \frac{n\pi}{2}\right) = -(-1)^{(n-1)/2} \sin \theta,$$
    where n is an odd integer.

13. Assume the validity of the identities for $\sin (u + v)$ and $\cos (u + v)$ and Identity (4a). Demonstrate Identities (6) and (7).

14. Show that $a \cos t + b \sin t$ can be rewritten as $\sqrt{a^2 + b^2} \cos (t - \alpha)$, where $\cos \alpha = a/\sqrt{a^2 + b^2}$, $\sin \alpha = b/\sqrt{a^2 + b^2}$.

4.2 The Derivatives of sin x and cos x

The slope of the tangent line at a point $P(x, y)$ of the graph $y = \sin x$, Fig. 4.10, can be studied just as the slopes of the tangent lines for other graphs are studied. First a point $Q(x + \Delta x, y + \Delta y)$ on the graph near P is selected; then the slope of the secant line PQ is determined; finally the fact that the tangent line at P is, by definition, the line approached by the secant lines PQ as Q approaches P, is used. Similarly, if the position of a particle on a straight line at time t is given by $x = \sin t$, the speed at time t can be computed just as for other motions; average speeds are computed for intervals and then the fact that the instantaneous speed is defined as a limit of average speeds is used. To compute $f'(x)$ for $f(x) = \sin x$, then, the very same definition for $f'(x)$ that we have always used is applied, although naturally the details appearing in work with a trigonometric function can be expected to differ from those appearing in work with algebraic functions.

■ THEOREM 1

The derivative of sin x.

HYPOTHESIS: $y = f(x) = \sin x$ for all real x.

CONCLUSION: $dy/dx = f'(x) = \cos x$ for all real x.

PROOF: Choose $\Delta x \neq 0$. Then

(a) $y + \Delta y = f(x + \Delta x) = \sin (x + \Delta x) = \sin x \cos \Delta x + \cos x \sin \Delta x.$*

(b) $\Delta y = f(x + \Delta x) - f(x) = \sin x \cos \Delta x + \cos x \sin \Delta x - \sin x$
$$= \sin x(\cos \Delta x - 1) + \cos x \sin \Delta x.$$

(c) $\dfrac{\Delta y}{\Delta x} = \dfrac{f(x + \Delta x) - f(x)}{\Delta x} = \sin x \, \dfrac{\cos \Delta x - 1}{\Delta x} + \cos x \, \dfrac{\sin \Delta x}{\Delta x}.$

(d) $\dfrac{dy}{dx} = f'(x) = \lim\limits_{\Delta x \to 0} \dfrac{f(x + \Delta x) - f(x)}{\Delta x}$
$$= \sin x \left(\lim_{\Delta x \to 0} \frac{\cos \Delta x - 1}{\Delta x} \right) + \cos x \left(\lim_{\Delta x \to 0} \frac{\sin \Delta x}{\Delta x} \right).$$

(e) We shall show in Lemmas 1 and 2 immediately below that
$$\lim_{\Delta x \to 0} \frac{\sin \Delta x}{\Delta x} = 1 \quad \text{and} \quad \lim_{\Delta x \to 0} \frac{\cos \Delta x - 1}{\Delta x} = 0.$$

Then we could conclude from (d) that $f'(x) = \cos x$, and the proof would be complete.

■ LEMMA 1

HYPOTHESIS: $$\phi(t) = \frac{\sin t}{t}.$$

CONCLUSION: $$\lim_{t \to 0} \phi(t) = \lim_{t \to 0} \frac{\sin t}{t} = 1.$$

PROOF: $\phi(t)$ is not defined for $t = 0$, but it is defined for all other t, and we assert that if ϕ is computed for values of t approaching 0 the corresponding values of ϕ will approach unity. That this is a plausible result would follow from a five-place table for $\sin t$ that uses radian measure. From such a table we have prepared the following data.

t	.20	.10	.05	.02	.01
$\sin t$	.19867	.09983	.04998	.02000	.01000
$\dfrac{\sin t}{t}$	.9934	.9983	.9996	1.000	1.000

* We used the identity for the sine of a sum of two numbers.

Our proof is based on Fig. 4.16. Let angle ACD, of radian measure t, $0 < t < \pi/2$, be placed with vertex at the center of a circle of radius 1. Let AB be drawn perpendicular to CD and AE tangent to the circle at A. Then

$$\text{area } ACB < \text{area } ACD < \text{area } ACE. \tag{1}$$

But
$$\text{area } ACB = \tfrac{1}{2}(CB)(BA) = \tfrac{1}{2}(\cos t)(\sin t),$$

and
$$\text{area } ACE = \frac{1}{2}(AE)(AC) = \frac{1}{2}(\tan t)(1) = \frac{1}{2}\frac{\sin t}{\cos t},$$

while area ACD is that of a sector of a circle and hence the $t/2\pi$ part of the area of the complete circle, so that

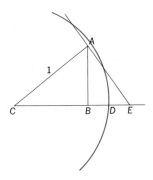

$$\text{area } ACD = \frac{t}{2\pi}\,\pi(1)^2 = \frac{1}{2}t.$$

Hence Inequality (1) can be rewritten as

$$\frac{1}{2}\cos t \sin t < \frac{1}{2}t < \frac{1}{2}\frac{\sin t}{\cos t}. \tag{2}$$

Now multiply each member by the positive number $2/\sin t$; we get

Fig. 4.16

$$\cos t < \frac{t}{\sin t} < \frac{1}{\cos t}. \tag{3}$$

If $t \to 0$, we know that $\cos t \to 1$ and that $1/\cos t \to 1$ also.[*] Thus $t/\sin t$, which lies between $\cos t$ and $1/\cos t$, must approach 1. But if $t/\sin t \to 1$, so does $\sin t/t \to 1$.

It is also necessary to consider $\sin t/t$ for t approaching 0 through negative values. But because $\sin (-t) = -\sin t$, we have

$$\frac{\sin (-t)}{-t} = \frac{\sin t}{t},$$

and the limit in this case must be the same as in the case already studied. This completes the proof of Lemma 1.

■ LEMMA 2

HYPOTHESIS:
$$\psi(t) = \frac{1 - \cos t}{t}.$$

CONCLUSION:
$$\lim_{t \to 0} \psi(t) = \lim_{t \to 0} \frac{1 - \cos t}{t} = 0.$$

PROOF: We make Lemma 2 depend on Lemma 1. We have

$$\frac{1 - \cos t}{t} = \frac{(1 - \cos t)}{t}\frac{(1 + \cos t)}{(1 + \cos t)}$$

$$= \frac{1 - \cos^2 t}{t(1 + \cos t)} = \frac{\sin^2 t}{t(1 + \cos t)} = \frac{\sin t}{t}\frac{\sin t}{1 + \cos t}.$$

---

[*] See Exercise 4.2-10.

But, by Lemma 1, $\sin t/t \to 1$ as $t \to 0$ and $\sin t/(1 + \cos t) \to 0/2 = 0$; hence the limit approached by $(1 - \cos t)/t$ is 0. This completes the proof of Lemma 2, and, with it, the proof of Theorem 1.

We know now how to find the rate of change for a sine function of period 2π, but what about the rate of change for a sine function of different period? This and still more general situations are covered by the next theorem.

■ THEOREM 2

HYPOTHESIS: (a) $y = \sin u$, where $u = f(x)$ for x of domain D.
(b) $du/dx = f'(x)$ exists for x of D.

CONCLUSION: $dy/dx = \cos u \, du/dx$ for x of D.

In words, the derivative of the sine of a function is the cosine of that function multiplied by the derivative of the function.

PROOF: We use the Chain Rule* which says, in a situation like this, that

$$\frac{dy}{dx} = \frac{dy}{du}\frac{du}{dx}.$$

Here we have

$$\frac{dy}{du} = \cos u,$$

so that

$$\frac{dy}{dx} = \cos u \frac{du}{dx},$$

which is our conclusion.

We could find $f'(x)$ for $f(x) = \cos x$ by the Δ process, but we prefer to take advantage of the fact that the graphs for $y = \cos x$ and $y = \sin x$ are translations, one of the other.

■ THEOREM 3

The derivative of cos u.

HYPOTHESIS: (a) $y = \cos u$, where $u = f(x)$ for x of domain D.

(b) $\dfrac{du}{dx} = f'(x)$ exists for x of D.

CONCLUSION: $\dfrac{dy}{dx} = - \sin u \dfrac{du}{dx}$ for x of D.

In words, the derivative of the cosine of a function is the product of -1, the sine of the function, and the derivative of the function. In particular,

$$\frac{d(\cos x)}{dx} = - \sin x \frac{d(x)}{dx} = - \sin x.$$

---

* Theorem 1.7-1

PROOF: (a) By the identity for a sine of a sum of two numbers,*

$$y = \cos u = \sin\left(u + \frac{\pi}{2}\right).$$

(b) By Theorem 2,

$$\frac{dy}{dx} = \cos\left(u + \frac{\pi}{2}\right)\frac{du}{dx}.$$

(c) By the identity for a cosine of the sum of two numbers,

$$\frac{dy}{dx} = -\sin u \frac{du}{dx}.$$

Example 1.   For $y = a \sin bx$,

$$\frac{dy}{dx} = a(\cos bx)(b) = ab \cos bx;$$

For $z = a \cos bx$,

$$\frac{dz}{dx} = a(-\sin bx)(b) = -ab \sin bx.$$

Example 2.   If

$$v = \sin^3 2t = (\sin 2t)^3,$$

then

$$\frac{dv}{dt} = 3(\sin 2t)^2 \frac{d(\sin 2t)}{dt}$$

$$= 3(\sin 2t)^2(\cos 2t)(2) = 6 \sin^2 2t \cos 2t.$$

Example 3.   Let y be defined as a function of x implicitly by the equation

$$x \cos y + y \sin x = \frac{\pi}{2}. \tag{4}$$

We differentiate both members of this identity with respect to x, using the product rule, and we find that

$$x\frac{d(\cos y)}{dx} + \cos y \frac{d(x)}{dx} + y\frac{d(\sin x)}{dx} + \sin x \frac{d(y)}{dx} = 0,$$

$$x(-\sin y)\frac{dy}{dx} + \cos y + y \cos x + \sin x \frac{dy}{dx} = 0,$$

$$(-x \sin y + \sin x)\frac{dy}{dx} = -\cos y - y \cos x,$$

$$\frac{dy}{dx} = \frac{-\cos y - y \cos x}{-x \sin y + \sin x} = \frac{\cos y + y \cos x}{x \sin y - \sin x}. \tag{5}$$

---

* Observe that $\sin[u + (\pi/2)] = \sin u \cos \pi/2 + \cos u \sin \pi/2$
$$= \sin u\,(0) + \cos u\,(1) = \cos u.$$

If x and y are interpreted as graph coordinates, then the point $(\pi/2, 0)$ lies on the graph with Eq. (4). Equation (5) says that the slope of the tangent line there is -1; the equation of that tangent line is

$$y - 0 = -1\left(x - \frac{\pi}{2}\right).$$

Example 4.   We can check our knowledge of the derivatives of sin x and cos x against the graphs for these functions. For $y = f(x) = \sin x$ we have $dy/dx = f'(x) = \cos x$. For $0 \le x < \pi/2$ and for $3\pi/2 < x \le 2\pi$ this derivative is positive and the graph rises; see Fig. 4.10. For $\pi/2 < x < 3\pi/2$, this derivative is negative and the graph falls. At $x = \pi/2$ and at $x = 3\pi/2, f'(x) = 0$; at $(\pi/2, 1)$ $y = \sin x$ has a maximum point, while at $(3\pi/2, -1)$ it has a minimum point.

The second derivative is $d^2y/dx^2 = f''(x) = -\sin x$. For $0 < x < \pi$ this second derivative is negative and the graph faces down; for $\pi < x < 2\pi, f''(x) > 0$ and the graph faces up. At $(\pi, 0), f''(x) = 0$; we have a point of inflection.

Example 5.   *Simple harmonic motion.*   Consider a particle P moving on the x axis, its position at time t given by

$$x = b \sin 2\pi kt.$$

The amplitude and period of the motion are b and $2\pi/2\pi k = 1/k$, and the velocity at time t is given by

$$v = \frac{dx}{dt} = 2\pi kb \cos 2\pi kt.$$

Let us follow P through one cycle of its motion.

At time $t = 0$, we have $x = 0$; P is at the origin. As t increases to $t = 1/4k$ during the first quarter-cycle, v changes from $2\pi kb$ to 0; v is positive and P moves to the right. At $t = 1/4k$, $v = 0$ and $x = b$; the particle stops at $x = b$. As t increases to $t = 2/4k$ and then to $t = 3/4k$, v changes from 0 to $-2\pi kb$ and back to 0; v is negative and P moves to the left, passing through $x = 0$ at $t = 2/4k$ and stopping at $x = -b$ at $t = 3/4k$. As t increases to $t = 4/4k = 1/k$, v increases from 0 to $2\pi kb$, P moves to the right, reaching $x = 0$ at $t = 1/k$, ready to start another cycle of its motion. Since the period is $1/k$, P moves through k cycles in unit time and the motion has frequency k.

Now consider the acceleration,

$$a = \frac{dv}{dt} = -4\pi^2k^2b \sin 2\pi kt = -4\pi^2k^2x.$$

Let F be the force that causes the motion; then

$$F = ma = -4\pi^2k^2mx.$$

In words, F is proportional to the displacement x and oppositely directed. There are many such forces in nature; when such a force acts on a particle, the resulting motion, of the form $x = b \sin 2\pi kt$ or $x = b \cos 2\pi kt$ or a linear combination of these, is periodic.* We mention just two such forces. If a weight at the end of a

---

* We shall show in Exercise 4.2-5 that $F = -4\pi^2mk^2x$ if $x = b \sin 2\pi kt + c \cos 2\pi kt$. Later, in Sec. 14.8, it will be shown that, if $F = -4\pi^2mk^2x$, x not only can, but *must* be of the form $b \sin 2\pi kt + c \cos 2\pi kt$, where b and c are suitably chosen constants.

spring is displaced from the equilibrium position, the spring pulls back on the weight with a force directly proportional to the displacement and oppositely directed (Hooke's law); if the weight is released, it will bob up and down periodically.* If a floating cylindrical body is pushed down from its equilibrium position, Archimedes' Law says that the body is buoyed up by a force equal to the weight of the displaced liquid. But this weight is proportional to the volume of the displaced liquid and, since the body is cylindrical, to the displacement. Again we have a force proportional to the displacement and oppositely directed; if the floating body is released, it will bob up and down in periodic motion.

To say that $d(\sin x)/dx = \cos x$ is the same as to say that a function whose derivative with respect to x is $\cos x$ must be of the form $\sin x + C$;

$$\int \cos x \, dx = \sin x + C.$$

Similarly, Theorems 2 and 3 can be rewritten in the integral form

$$\int \cos u \, \frac{du}{dx} \, dx = \sin u + C. \tag{6}$$

$$\int \sin u \, \frac{du}{dx} \, dx = -\cos u + C. \tag{7}$$

Example 6. $\int \sin 3x \, dx = \frac{1}{3} \int \sin 3x \, (3) \, dx = -\frac{1}{3} \cos 3x + C.$
Example 7. $\int \sin^7 2x \cos 2x \, dx = ?$
Bearing in mind the fact that

$$\int (u)^7 \, \frac{du}{dx} \, dx = \frac{(u)^8}{8} + C,$$

we write

$$\int (\sin 2x)^7 (\cos 2x) \, dx = \frac{1}{2} \int (\sin 2x)^7 (2 \cos 2x) \, dx$$

$$= \frac{1}{2} \frac{(\sin 2x)^8}{8} + C = \frac{1}{16} \sin^8 2x + C.$$

Example 8

$$\int \frac{\sin 2t}{\cos^3 2t} \, dt = ?$$

Bearing in mind the fact that

$$\int (u)^{-3} \, \frac{du}{dt} \, dt = \frac{(u)^{-2}}{-2} + C,$$

we write

$$\int \frac{\sin 2t}{\cos^3 2t} \, dt = \int (\cos 2t)^{-3} \sin 2t \, dt = -\frac{1}{2} \int (\cos 2t)^{-3} (-2 \sin 2t) \, dt$$

$$= -\frac{1}{2} \frac{(\cos 2t)^{-2}}{-2} + C = \frac{1}{4} \frac{1}{\cos^2 2t} + C.$$

---

* We assume here that no force of friction acts.

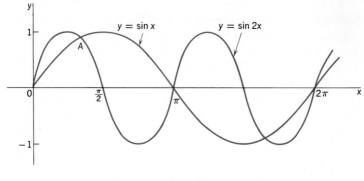

Fig. 4.17

Example 9.   Find the smaller of the areas bounded by $y = f_1(x) = \sin x$ and $y = f_2(x) = \sin 2x$. The function $y = \sin x$ has amplitude 1 and period 2π; $y = \sin 2x$ has amplitude 1 and period π. The two curves are sketched in Fig. 4.17. We want the area of the region bounded by points O and A. First, we locate these points by solving the equations $y = \sin x$ and $y = \sin 2x$ simultaneously. Thus:

$$\sin 2x = \sin x,$$
$$2 \sin x \cos x = \sin x,$$
$$2 \sin x \cos x - \sin x = 0,$$
$$\sin x(2 \cos x - 1) = 0;$$

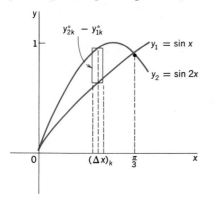

Fig. 4.18

either $\sin x = 0$ or $2 \cos x - 1 = 0$. If $\sin x = 0$, we have $x = 0$, π, $2\pi, \cdots$; if $\cos x = \frac{1}{2}$, we have $x = \pi/3$, $5\pi/3, \cdots$. Point A has coordinates $(\pi/3, \sqrt{3}/2)$.

Second, we consider the region in question as a sum of vertical subregions formed by subdividing the x interval, $0 \le x \le \pi/3$, into n parts of widths $(\Delta x)_1$, $(\Delta x)_2, \cdots$, $(\Delta x)_n$; see Fig. 4.18. Let x_k^* be a number of the kth subinterval, y_{1k}^* and y_{2k}^* the corresponding ordinates. Then

area of subregion $\approx [y_{2k}^* - y_{1k}^*](\Delta x)_k$

$\qquad\qquad\qquad = [f_2(x_k^*) - f_1(x_k^*)](\Delta x)_k$

area of region $\approx \sum_{k=1}^{n} [f_2(x_k^*) - f_1(x_k^*)](\Delta x)_k$

area of region $= \displaystyle\int_{x=0}^{\pi/3} [f_2(x) - f_1(x)] \, dx = \int_{x=0}^{\pi/3} (\sin 2x - \sin x) \, dx.$

$\qquad\qquad\quad = (-\tfrac{1}{2} \cos 2x + \cos x) \, \big|_0^{\pi/3}$

$\qquad\qquad\quad = \left(-\dfrac{1}{2} \cos \dfrac{2\pi}{3} + \cos \dfrac{\pi}{3} \right) - \left(-\dfrac{1}{2} \cos 0 + \cos 0 \right)$

$\qquad\qquad\quad = (\tfrac{1}{4} + \tfrac{1}{2}) - (-\tfrac{1}{2} + 1) = \tfrac{1}{4}.$

EXERCISES 4.2

1. (a) $y = 3 \sin 2x + 4 \cos 2x, \dfrac{dy}{dx} = ?$

(b) $s = a \sin 2\pi(t - \frac{1}{8}), \dfrac{ds}{dt} = ?$

(c) $y = 2 \sin^4 \pi x, \dfrac{dy}{dx} = ?$

(d) $L = a\sqrt{\cos^5 4t}, \dfrac{dL}{dt} = ?$

(e) $y = x \sin x, \dfrac{dy}{dx} = ?$

(f) $y = \sin^2 2x \cos^3 2x, \dfrac{dy}{dx} = ?$

(g) $x = \dfrac{\sin t}{1 - \cos t}, \dfrac{dx}{dt} = ?$

(h) $y = \dfrac{\sqrt{\sin t}}{t}, \dfrac{dy}{dt} = ?$

(i) $\sin x + \cos y = .1, \dfrac{dy}{dx} = ?$

(j) $\sin (x + y) + x + 2y = \pi + 1, \dfrac{dy}{dx} = ?$

2. (a) $\displaystyle\int \cos ax \, dx = ?$
(b) $\displaystyle\int (a \sin 3x + b \cos 3x) \, dx = ?$
(c) $\displaystyle\int \sqrt{\sin x} \cos x \, dx = ?$
(d) $\displaystyle\int (8 \sin^3 2x + 6 \sin^2 2x) \cos 2x \, dx = ?$

(e) $\displaystyle\int \dfrac{1}{\sin^2 ax} \cos ax \, dx = ?$

(f) $\displaystyle\int \cos^n bx \sin bx \, dx = ?$ when $n > 0$.

(g) $\displaystyle\int \dfrac{1}{\sqrt{\cos^3 x}} \sin x \, dx = ?$

(h) $\displaystyle\int \dfrac{1}{\cos^n bx} \sin bx \, dx = ?$ when $n \neq 1$.

3. Use the Δ process to show that $f'(x) = -\sin x$ if $f(x) = \cos x$.
4. Use information deduced from the equations for y, dy/dx, and d^2y/dx^2 to sketch
(a) $y = \cos x$.   (d) $y = 2 \sin x + \sin 2x$.
(b) $y = \cos^2 x$.   (e) $y = x + \cos x$.
(c) $y = \sin^3 x$.
5. Show that for the straight-line motion described by $x = b \sin 2\pi k t + c \cos 2\pi k t$, where x gives the position at time t, the acceleration is proportional to the displacement from the origin and oppositely directed.

6. (a) Consider the simple harmonic motion $x = b \cos 2\pi kt$. Show that the magnitude of the velocity is a maximum whenever the particle passes the origin, for instance at time $t = 1/4k$, and find the kinetic energy, $\frac{1}{2}mv^2$, at that moment.
  (b) Find the work done in extending a spring from $x = 0$ to $x = b$ if the restoring force is given by $F = -4\pi^2k^2mx$, where x is the displacement from the origin.

7. (a) Find the area under one arch of the curve $y = \sin x$.
  (b) Find the area under one arch of the curve $y = \cos x$.
  (c) Find the area of one of the regions bounded by $y = \sin \pi x$ and $y = 2x$.
  (d) Find the area of one of the regions bounded by $y = \sin x$ and $y = \cos x$.
  (e) Find the area under one arch of $y = \sin^2 x$. (*Suggestion:* In evaluating the integral that you set up, you may want to replace $\sin^2 x$ by $(1 - \cos 2x)/2$.

8. We saw in Example 9 that $y = \sin x$ and $y = \sin 2x$ intersect at $(\pi/3, \sqrt{3}/2)$. Find the cosine of their acute angle of intersection.

9. A particle of mass m is at rest at the point $(d, 0)$ at the time $t = 0$. Let the force described by $a \sin bt \, \mathbf{i}$ act on the particle for $t \geq 0$. Find the particle's speed and location at time $t \geq 0$.

10. In the proof of Lemma 1 we used the fact that $\cos t \to 1$ when $t \to 0$. To prove this, explain why
  (a) $1 - \cos t \geq 0$,

  (b) $1 - \cos t = \dfrac{\sin^2 t}{1 + \cos t} \leq \sin^2 t$ for $-\dfrac{\pi}{2} \leq t \leq \dfrac{\pi}{2}$,

  (c) $\sin^2 t \leq 4t^2$ for $-\dfrac{\pi}{3} \leq t \leq \dfrac{\pi}{3}$. [Use the first part of Inequality (2) for $t > 0$. Observe that $(-t)^2 = t^2$ and $\sin^2 (-t) = \sin^2 t$.]

  (d) $0 \leq 1 - \cos t \leq 4t^2$ for $-\dfrac{\pi}{3} \leq t \leq \dfrac{\pi}{3}$,

  (e) $1 - \cos t \to 0$ when $t \to 0$.

4.3   The Derivatives of tan x, sec x, cot x, and csc x

The derivatives of the four remaining commonly used trigonometric functions are easily found once the derivatives of the sine and cosine functions are known.

■ THEOREM 1

HYPOTHESIS: $u = f(x)$ and $du/dx = f'(x)$ have domain D.

CONCLUSION:

(a)
$$\frac{d}{dx}(\tan u) = \sec^2 u \, \frac{du}{dx}$$

for those x of D for which $\tan u$ is defined.

(b)
$$\frac{d}{dx}(\sec u) = \sec u \tan u \, \frac{du}{dx}$$

for those x of D for which $\sec u$ is defined.

(c)
$$\frac{d}{dx}(\cot u) = -\csc^2 u \, \frac{du}{dx}$$

for those x of D for which cot u is defined.

(d) $$\frac{d}{dx}(\csc u) = -\csc u \cot u \frac{du}{dx}$$

for those x of D for which csc u is defined.

PROOF: We write $\tan u = \dfrac{\sin u}{\cos u}$, and then

$$\frac{d}{dx}(\tan u) = \frac{\cos u[d \sin u/dx] - \sin u[d \cos u/dx]}{\cos^2 u}$$

$$= \frac{\cos^2 u(du/dx) + \sin^2 u(du/dx)}{\cos^2 u}$$

$$= \frac{1}{\cos^2 u}\frac{du}{dx} = \sec^2 u \frac{du}{dx}.$$

Thus the first part of the conclusion is demonstrated. We leave the remaining parts to the reader as exercises.

● **Remark 1**

In considering the derivatives of the trigonometric functions, three families can be formed:

Family 1	*Family 2*	*Family 3*
$\dfrac{d}{dx}(\sin x) = \cos x.$	$\dfrac{d}{dx}(\tan x) = \sec^2 x.$	$\dfrac{d}{dx}(\cot x) = -\csc^2 x.$
$\dfrac{d}{dx}(\cos x) = -\sin x.$	$\dfrac{d}{dx}(\sec x) = \sec x \tan x.$	$\dfrac{d}{dx}(\csc x) = -\csc x \cot x.$
$\sin^2 x + \cos^2 x = 1.$	$\tan^2 x + 1 = \sec^2 x.$	$\cot^2 x + 1 = \csc^2 x.$

With each family we have included an identity that can frequently be used to rewrite one function of the family in terms of the other. It is also helpful to notice that the derivatives of the three "co-functions"—namely, cosine, cotangent, and cosecant—are precisely the three that have the factor (-1).

Example 1. If $y = \sec 3x$,

$$\frac{dy}{dx} = (\sec 3x \tan 3x)(3) = 3 \sec 3x \tan 3x.$$

Example 2. If $y = \cot^{3/2} ax$, or $y = (\cot ax)^{3/2}$, then

$$\frac{dy}{dx} = \frac{3}{2}(\cot ax)^{1/2}\frac{d}{dx}(\cot ax) = \frac{3}{2}(\cot ax)^{1/2}(-\csc^2 ax)(a)$$

$$= -\tfrac{3}{2} a \cot^{1/2} ax \csc^2 ax.$$

Example 3. If y is defined implicitly by the equation

$$\tan x + \sec y = x + y + 1,$$

then upon differentiating with respect to x we get

$$\sec^2 x + \sec y \tan y \frac{dy}{dx} = 1 + \frac{dy}{dx},$$

$$\frac{dy}{dx} = \frac{1 - \sec^2 x}{\sec y \tan y - 1} = \frac{-\tan^2 x}{\sec y \tan y - 1} = \frac{\tan^2 x}{1 - \sec y \tan y}.$$

The conclusions of Theorem 1 can also be stated in integral form. We have

(1) $\dfrac{d}{dx}(\tan u) = \sec^2 u \dfrac{du}{dx}$ $\leftrightarrow$ $\displaystyle\int \sec^2 u \frac{du}{dx}\, dx = \tan u + C.$

(2) $\dfrac{d}{dx}(\sec u) = \sec u \tan u \dfrac{du}{dx}$ $\leftrightarrow$ $\displaystyle\int \sec u \tan u \frac{du}{dx}\, dx = \sec u + C.$

(3) $\dfrac{d}{dx}(\cot u) = -\csc^2 u \dfrac{du}{dx}$ $\leftrightarrow$ $\displaystyle\int \csc^2 u \frac{du}{dx}\, dx = -\cot u + C.$

(4) $\dfrac{d}{dx}(\csc u) = -\csc u \cot u \dfrac{du}{dx}$ $\leftrightarrow$ $\displaystyle\int \csc u \cot u \frac{du}{dx}\, dx = -\csc u + C.$

Example 4. $\int \sec^2 5x\, dx = \frac{1}{5}\int \sec^2 5x (5)\, dx = \frac{1}{5}\tan 5x + C.$
Example 5

$$\int \csc ax \cot ax\, dx = \frac{1}{a}\int \csc ax \cot ax (a)\, dx = -\frac{1}{a}\csc ax + C.$$

Example 6. $\int \cot^4 x \csc^2 x\, dx = ?$

For the cosecant and cotangent family we know that, constants aside, csc x cot x can serve as the derivative of csc x or that $\csc^2 x$ can serve as the derivative of cot x. Here we use the latter fact, and bearing in mind also that

$$\int (u)^4 \frac{du}{dx}\, dx = \frac{u^5}{5} + C,$$

we write

$$\int \cot^4 x \csc^2 x\, dx = \int (\cot x)^4 \csc^2 x\, dx = -\int (\cot x)^4 (-\csc^2 x)\, dx$$

$$= -\frac{(\cot x)^5}{5} + C.$$

Example 7. $I = \int \sec^3 x \tan x\, dx = ?$

In the secant and tangent family we recognize that sec x tan x can serve as the derivative of sec x or that $\sec^2 x$ can serve as the derivative of tan x. In this problem, the former fact is easier to apply. We have

$$I = \int (\sec x)^2 \sec x \tan x\, dx.$$

Then, since

$$\int (u)^2 \frac{du}{dx}\, dx = \frac{(u)^3}{3} + C,$$

we have
$$I = \frac{(\sec x)^3}{3} + C.$$

Example 8
$$I = \int \frac{\sec^2 2x}{(1 + \tan 2x)^2} \, dx = ?$$

Here we write
$$I = \int (1 + \tan 2x)^{-2} \sec^2 2x \, dx,$$

and then, bearing in mind the fact that
$$\int (u)^{-2} \frac{du}{dx} \, dx = \frac{(u)^{-1}}{-1} + C,$$

we continue with
$$I = \frac{1}{2} \int (1 + \tan 2x)^{-2}(2 \sec^2 2x) \, dx = \frac{1}{2} \frac{(1 + \tan 2x)^{-1}}{-1} + C$$

$$= -\frac{1}{2(1 + \tan 2x)} + C.$$

Example 9.   We shall conclude this set of formal integration examples with an integration that can be carried out in three different ways. Consider
$$I = \int \cos x \sin x \, dx.$$

First, in the sine and cosine family we can use the fact that cos x is the derivative of sin x or the fact that $-\sin x$ is the derivative of cos x. The former gives
$$I = \int (\sin x)^1 \cos x \, dx = \frac{(\sin x)^2}{2} + C,$$

and the latter gives
$$I = \int (\cos x)^1 \sin x \, dx = - \int (\cos x)^1(-\sin x) \, dx = -\frac{(\cos x)^2}{2} + C.$$

Finally, if we use a double-angle identity, we have
$$I = \int \sin x \cos x \, dx = \frac{1}{2} \int \sin 2x \, dx = \frac{1}{4} \int \sin 2x \, (2) \, dx = -\frac{1}{4} \cos 2x + C.$$

It might seem to the reader at first that we have three different answers for the same problem. But by using the identities $\sin^2 x = 1 - \cos^2 x$ and $\cos 2x = 2 \cos^2 x - 1$, the answers can be shown to be equivalent.

Example 10.   Find the area of the region bounded by the y axis, $y = \sec^2 x$, and $y = 8 \cos x$.

First we solve the given equations simultaneously to find the points of intersection of the curves. We have $\sec^2 x = 8 \cos x$, $1/\cos^2 x = 8 \cos x$, $\cos^3 x = \frac{1}{8}$, cos x

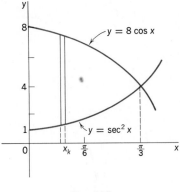

Fig. 4.19

$= \frac{1}{2}$, $x = \pi/3$; the curves intersect at $(\pi/3, 4)$. Figure 4.19 suggests that the region be subdivided by vertical lines. If x_k^* is a number of the kth subinterval of $0 \le x \le \pi/3$, we can say that

$$\text{area of } k\text{th subregion} \approx (8 \cos x_k^* - \sec^2 x_k^*)(\Delta x)_k,$$

$$\text{area of region} \approx \sum_{k=1}^{n} (8 \cos x_k^* - \sec^2 x_k^*)(\Delta x)_k,$$

$$\text{area of region} = \int_{x=0}^{\pi/3} (8 \cos x - \sec^2 x) \, dx = (8 \sin x - \tan x) \Big|_0^{\pi/3}$$

$$= 8\left(\frac{\sqrt{3}}{2}\right) - \sqrt{3} = 3\sqrt{3}.$$

EXERCISES 4.3

1. (a) Demonstrate Conclusion (b) of Theorem 1.
   (b) Demonstrate Conclusion (c) of Theorem 1.
   (c) Demonstrate Conclusion (d) of Theorem 1.

2. (a) From the fact that $\lim\limits_{\Delta x \to 0} \dfrac{\sin \Delta x}{\Delta x} = 1$, show that $\lim\limits_{\Delta x \to 0} \dfrac{\tan \Delta x}{\Delta x} = 1$.

   (b) Use the Δ process to show that $\dfrac{d(\tan x)}{dx} = \sec^2 x.$*

3. Find the first derivative in each of the following cases:
   (a) $L = 4 \tan 3t$.
   (b) $y = \csc 2t + \cot 2t$.

   (c) $y = \sec^3 x$.

   (d) $y = \dfrac{\tan ax}{\sec ax + 1}$.

   (e) $x = (\sec 3t + \tan 3t)^2$.

   (f) $y = \sqrt[3]{\cot 2\pi x}$.

   (g) $y = \sec^2 x \tan^3 x$.
   (h) $v = \cot 2t \csc^2 2t$.

   (i) $y = \dfrac{\csc ax}{\csc ax + 1}$.

   (j) $u = \sqrt{\tan^2 v - 1}$.

   (k) $v = \dfrac{1}{\sqrt{1 + \sec^2 u}}$.

   (l) $s = x \tan \dfrac{1}{x}$.

---

* The identity $\tan (A + B) = (\tan A + \tan B)/(1 - \tan A \tan B)$ might be useful.

4. Find dy/dx in each of the following cases:
   (a) $y \tan x - x \tan y = 1$.
   (b) $\sec (x + y) = y$.
   (c) $\sec^2 x + \csc^2 y = 3$.

5. Evaluate each of the following indefinite integrals:

   (a) $\int \sec^2 \dfrac{1}{2} x \, dx$.

   (b) $\int \csc^2 2x \, dx$.

   (c) $\int \cot 3t \csc 3t \, dt$.

   (d) $\int \tan^3 2x \sec^2 2x \, dx$.

   (e) $\int \dfrac{\sec^2 x}{\sqrt{\tan x + 2}} \, dx$.

   (f) $\int \tan^n ax \sec^2 ax \, dx, \ n \neq -1$.

   (g) $\int \sec^5 x \tan x \, dx$.

   (h) $\int \dfrac{\tan x}{\sec^5 x} \, dx$.

   (i) $\int \sec^n ax \tan ax \, dx, \ n \neq 0$.

   (j) $\int \dfrac{\csc^2 2t}{\cot^4 2t} \, dt$.

   (k) $\int \sqrt{\cot^3 x} \csc^2 x \, dx$.

   (l) $\int \cot^n x \csc^2 x \, dx, \ n \neq -1$.

   (m) $\int \csc^4 ax \cot ax \, dx$.

   (n) $\int \csc^n ax \cot ax \, dx, \ n \neq 0$.

6. Evaluate each of the following definite integrals:

   (a) $\displaystyle\int_0^{\pi/6} \sec 2x \tan 2x \, dx$.

   (b) $\displaystyle\int_{-\pi/4}^{\pi/4} \sec^2 x \tan x \, dx.$*

   (c) $\displaystyle\int_{\pi/6}^{\pi/2} \csc^3 x \cot x \, dx$.

   (d) $\displaystyle\int_{\pi/4}^{\pi/2} \dfrac{\csc^2 x}{(\cot x + 1)^3} \, dx$.

7. Figure 4.12 suggests that the graph of $y = \tan x$ has no maximum or minimum points but does have points of inflection at the x intercepts. Demonstrate these facts.

8. (a) On one set of axes sketch $y = \cos$ and $y = \sec x = 1/\cos x$.
   (b) The graph of $y = \sec x$ has a minimum point for the region $-\pi/2 < x < \pi/2$, but no point of inflection. Demonstrate these facts.

9. $y = \sec^2 x$ and $y = 2 \tan x$ intersect just once in the region $0 \leq x < \pi/2$. Find this point of intersection and show that the graphs are tangent there.

10. Let $y = f(x) = \tan^2 x - \tan x, \ -\pi/2 < x < \pi/2$. Get what information you can from the equations for $f(x), f'(x),$ and $f''(x)$ and make a sketch.

11. Find the area of a region bounded by the y axis, $y = 2 \tan^2 x$, and $y = \sec^2 x$.

12. In Example 10 the equations were chosen so that the point of intersection would be easy to use. But the problem would not have been essentially more difficult if we had had to deal with $y = 7 \cos x$ instead of $y = 8 \cos x$. Find the area in this case.

4.4   Inverse Functions. Inverse Trigonometric Functions

I

When describing a correspondence between two sets of numbers, say T numbers and V numbers, we may wish on one occasion to explain how a V number is assigned each time a suitable T number is specified and on another occasion to explain how a T number is assigned each time a suitable V number is specified. For instance, the volume of some mercury in a circuit-breaking device might be considered as a function of the temperature: $V = f(T)$; if the temperature rises, the volume of the mercury increases, the mercury expands, and a circuit is changed.

---

* Can the answer be predicted without detailed work?

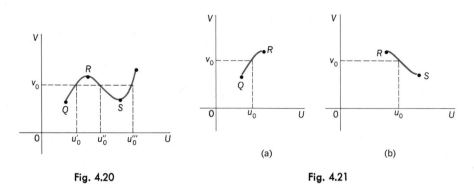

Fig. 4.20   Fig. 4.21

But if the same mercury were placed in a thermometer, the temperature would be considered as a function of the volume of the mercury when reading the thermometer: $T = \phi(V)$. As we shall soon see in a little greater detail, the functions f and ϕ are called inverse functions.

If given a function or correspondence $v = f(u)$ which associates a number v of range set S_v with each number u of domain set S_u, simple illustrations point out that it is not always possible to describe the same pairing of u and v numbers with a statement of the form $u = \phi(v)$ using domain set S_v and range set S_u. Thus, for the function $v = f(u)$ whose graph is given in Fig. 4.20, the same number v_0 of the range set S_v is assigned to all three numbers u_0', u_0'', u_0''' of the domain set S_u. If we were to try to write $u = \phi(v)$ with domain S_v and range S_u we would not know, without further restrictions, whether to assign u_0', u_0'', or u_0''' when v_0 is specified. In general, if we wish to invert the statement $v = f(u)$ with domain S_u and range set S_v, we must at least make sure that there is no number v_0 of S_v assigned by f to more than one number of S_u. This we can do by restricting our consideration of $v = f(u)$ to a domain on which f is steadily increasing or steadily decreasing,* as in Figs. 4.21(a) and 4.21(b).

Example 1.   Consider
$$v = f(u) = u^2, \text{ domain } S_u : 0 \le u \le 2, \text{ range } S_v : 0 \le v \le 4; \qquad (1)$$
see Fig. 4.22(a). Here f increases steadily for this domain S_u, and to any number v of S_v we can assign the specific number u of S_u to which v corresponds in Statement (1) by choosing
$$u = \phi(v) = \sqrt{v}, \text{ domain } S_v : 0 \le v \le 4; \text{ range } S_u : 0 \le u \le 2; \qquad (2)$$
see Fig. 4.22(b). We might say that Statement (1) defines v as a function of u while Statement (2) defines u as a function of v. Observe that the two graphs are symmetric with respect to the line $u = v$; see Exercise 4.4-11.

Example 2.   Consider
$$v = f(u) = \sin u, \text{ domain } S_u : -\frac{\pi}{2} \le u \le \frac{\pi}{2}, \text{ range } S_v : -1 \le v \le 1; \qquad (3)$$
see Fig. 4.23(a). The function f increases steadily for this domain S_u, and to any number v of S_v we can assign one number u of S_u by selecting that number u for

---

* To be more precise, f increases steadily for its domain S_u if whenever u_1 and u_2 belong to S_u and $u_1 < u_2$, we have $f(u_1) < f(u_2)$; f decreases steadily if $f(u_1) > f(u_2)$.

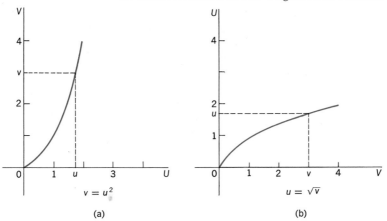

$$v = u^2$$

(a)

$$u = \sqrt{v}$$

(b)

Fig. 4.22

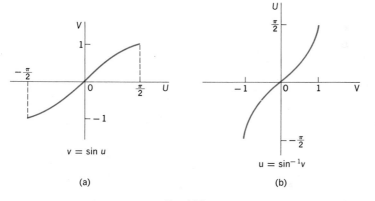

$$v = \sin u$$

(a)

$$u = \sin^{-1} v$$

(b)

Fig. 4.23

which Statement (3) holds. Thus to $v = \sqrt{3}/2$ we assign $u = \pi/3$ and to $v = -\frac{1}{2}$ we assign $u = -\pi/6$. In this way we can define u as a function of v and write

$$u = \phi(v) = \sin^{-1} v, \text{ domain } S_v : -1 \le v \le 1, \text{ range } S_u : -\frac{\pi}{2} \le u \le \frac{\pi}{2}; \quad (4)$$

see Fig. 4.23(b). Observe that the two graphs are again symmetric with respect to the line $u = v$. In Remarks 3 and 4, which appear later in this section, we shall explain the reason for the inverse function notation used in Statement (4).

Example 3. Consider the steadily increasing but discontinuous function whose graph is sketched in Fig. 4.24. For each number u of the domain set S_u: $a \le u \le b$ a number v of the range set S_v is assigned, and to no two different numbers of S_u is the same number of S_v assigned, but S_v is not a single connected

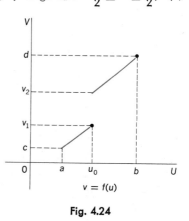

$$v = f(u)$$

Fig. 4.24

interval the way S_u is. There is no number u of S_u to which a number v of $v_1 < v < v_2$ is assigned. If we want the range set for f, which is the domain set for the inverse function, to be a single connected interval, it would appear to be sufficient to take f to be a continuous function. There is an Intermediate Value Theorem for continuous functions that tells us that, if v^* is a number that lies between the maximum and minimum values of $f(u)$ for the interval $S_u : a \leq u \leq b$, then there is a number u^* of S_u for which f assigns the number v^*; $v^* = f(u^*)$. This intuitively plausible theorem is discussed further in Sec. 7.4.

To summarize, we present a definition.

■ **DEFINITION 1**

Inverse function. Let the function $v = f(u)$ with domain S_u and range S_v be continuous and steadily increasing (or steadily decreasing). Let $u = \phi(v)$ with domain S_v and range S_u be the function that assigns to each number v of S_v the number u such that $v = f(u)$. We say that ϕ with domain S_v is the function inverse to f with domain S_u.

■ **THEOREM 1**

On inverse functions.

A.   HYPOTHESIS: (a) $v = f(u)$, with domain S_u and range S_v, is such that f is continuous and steadily increasing (or steadily decreasing) for S_u.

(b) $u = \phi(v)$, with domain S_v and range S_u, is the function inverse to f.

CONCLUSION: (a) ϕ is continuous and steadily increasing (or steadily decreasing) for S_v.

B. HYPOTHESIS: (c) For u_0 of S_u, $f'(u_0)$ exists and $f'(u_0) \neq 0$.

CONCLUSION: For $v_0 = f(u_0)$ of S_v, $\phi'(v_0)$ exists and $\phi'(v_0) = \dfrac{1}{f'(u_0)}$.

We give a plausibility argument based on a geometric argument at this point in the text and an analytic proof in Exercise 4.4-12.

PLAUSIBILITY ARGUMENT: Sketch a graph for $v = f(u)$ for u of S_u and one for $u = \phi(v)$ for v of S_v as in Figs. 4.25(a) and 4.25(b). Since to each point $P_0 (u_0, v_0)$ of the one graph there corresponds the point $Q_0(v_0, u_0)$ of the other and these points are symmetrically situated with respect to the line $u = v,$* these graphs are symmetric with respect to the line $u = v$.

Step (1): By Hypothesis (a), $v = f(u)$ is continuous for S_u; this means that there are no gaps in Fig. 4.25(a), and if we select nearby points $P_0(u_0, v_0)$ and $P_1(u_0 + \Delta u, v_0 + \Delta v)$, we find that P_1 approaches P_0 as Δu approaches 0. By symmetry, there are no gaps in Fig. 4.25(b) either, and if we select nearby points $Q_0(v_0, u_0)$ and $Q_1(v_0 + \Delta v, u_0 + \Delta u)$, we find that Q_1 approaches Q_0 as Δv approaches 0. Thus ϕ is continuous for S_v when f is continuous for S_u.

Step (2): That ϕ increases steadily when f does, follows from an argument by contradiction. Suppose that for two numbers v_1 and v_2 of S_v such that $v_1 < v_2$ we

---

* See Exercise 4.4-11.

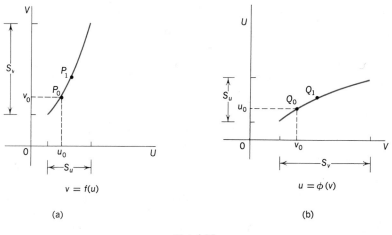

Fig. 4.25

have $\phi(v_1) \geq \phi(v_2)$ instead of $\phi(v_1) < \phi(v_2)$. If $u_1 = \phi(v_1)$ and $u_2 = \phi(v_2)$, so that $u_1 \geq u_2$, we have $v_1 = f(u_1)$ and $v_2 = f(u_2)$ and then $v_1 \geq v_2$, because f increases steadily by Hypothesis (a). But this contradicts our earlier statement that $v_1 < v_2$, and we must conclude that $\phi(v_1) < \phi(v_2)$. We have now demonstrated Conclusion (a).

Step (3): If, as in Hypothesis (c), $f'(u_0)$ exists and $f'(u_0) \neq 0$, then $v = f(u)$ has a nonhorizontal tangent line at $P_0(u_0, v_0)$ with slope $f'(u_0)$ and inclination α such that $\tan \alpha = f'(u_0)$. By symmetry, $u = \phi(v)$ has a tangent line at $Q_0(u_0, v_0)$ with inclination angle $(\pi/2) - \alpha$; see Figs. 4.26(a) and 4.26(b).* Thus the tangent line at Q_0 has slope

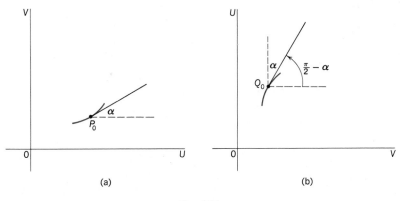

Fig. 4.26

---

* Since $f(u)$ increases steadily by hypothesis, we have $f'(u_0) \geq 0$ and α acute. If $f(u)$ had deceased steadily, we would have had $f'(u_0) \leq 0$ and α obtuse. In that case $u = \phi(v)$ would have had at Q_0 a tangent line with inclination $[(\pi/2)-\alpha] + \pi$. But

$$\tan \left[\left(\frac{\pi}{2} - \alpha \right) + \pi \right] = \tan \left(\frac{\pi}{2} - \alpha \right),$$

so that the proofs in the two cases are not materially different.

$$\tan\left(\frac{\pi}{2} - \alpha\right) = \cot \alpha = \frac{1}{\tan \alpha} = \frac{1}{f'(u_0)}.$$

We have now demonstrated Conclusion (b) in the case where f is a steadily increasing function. The reasoning is not materially different in the case in which f is a steadily decreasing function.

● **Remark 1**

Let $v = f(u)$ with domain S_u be continuous and steadily increasing (or decreasing) on S_u and let $u = \phi(v)$ with domain S_v be the inverse function. By Definition 1, if u of S_u and v of S_v satisfy one of $v = f(u)$ and $u = \phi(v)$, they satisfy the other. By Theorem 1, $u = \phi(v)$ is continuous and steadily increasing (or decreasing) on S_v. But then Definition 1 allows us to say that f with domain S_u is the function inverse to ϕ with domain S_v. When ϕ is inverse to f, f is inverse to ϕ (for the appropriate domains).

● **Remark 2**

Rewriting the equation $v = f(u)$ or $F(u, v) = v - f(u) = 0$ in the form $u = \phi(v)$ is really a matter of illustrating the Implicit Function Theorem mentioned in Sec. 1.9. In Remark 1.9-2 we demonstrated Conclusion (b) above from that point of view.

● **Remark 3**

In function notation, when $v = f(u)$ with domain S_u and $u = \phi(v)$ with domain S_v are inverse, we have

$$v = f(u) = f(\phi(v)), \qquad v \text{ in } S_v \tag{5}$$

and
$$u = \phi(v) = \phi(f(u)), \qquad u \text{ in } S_u. \tag{6}$$

In words, Eq. (5) says that the composite function $f(\phi(v))$ assigns to each number v of S_v the number $1v$ itself. One might say, symbolically, that $f\phi = 1$, and, reasoning in similar fashion with Eq. (6), that $\phi f = 1$. This suggests, symbolically, the following convention.

■ **NOTATION CONVENTION 1**

If the functions f with domain S_u and ϕ with domain S_v are inverse, we shall write $\phi = f^{-1}$ or $f = \phi^{-1}$.

● **Remark 4**

In adopting this notation convention we have created a source of ambiguity. We do not mean to suggest that $\phi(x) = f^{-1}(x) = 1/f(x)$; it is not intended in inverse function notation to say that, for example,

$$\sin^{-1} x = \frac{1}{\sin x} = \csc x.$$

With a little experience the reader will learn to tell from the context whether the inverse function notation or the negative exponent notation is intended.

‖

Now let us turn to the trigonometric functions and their inverses.

We point out, as in Example 2, that $y = \sin x$ with domain $-\pi/2 \leq x \leq \pi/2$ and range $-1 \leq y \leq 1$ is continuous and steadily increasing, so that an inverse function can be defined.

■ **DEFINITION 2**

The inverse sine function. For $-1 \leq x \leq 1$, $\sin^{-1} x$ shall be that number y, $-\pi/2 \leq y \leq \pi/2$, such that $\sin y = x$.*

To illustrate again, $\sin^{-1} \sqrt{2}/2 = \pi/4$ because $-\pi/2 \leq \pi/4 \leq \pi/2$ and $\sin \pi/4 = \sqrt{2}/2$, while $\sin^{-1}(-\sqrt{2}/2) = -\pi/4$ because $-\pi/2 \leq -\pi/4 \leq \pi/2$ and $\sin(-\pi/4) = -\sqrt{2}/2$. Because $\sin x$ has the derivative $\cos x$ for each x of $-\pi/2 \leq x \leq \pi/2$ and $\cos x$ vanishes only for $x = -\pi/2$ and $x = \pi/2$, the graph of $y = \sin x$ has a tangent at each point of $-\pi/2 \leq x \leq \pi/2$ and horizontal tangents only at the end points. By symmetry, the graph of $y = \sin^{-1} x$ has a tangent at each point of the interval $-1 \leq x \leq 1$, but the tangents at the end points are vertical. Hence, as Theorem 1B states, $y = \sin^{-1} x$ has a derivative for each x of $-1 < x < 1$.

Example 4. Let us evaluate $\cos(\sin^{-1} a)$, $|a| \leq 1$. First, we write $\sin^{-1} a = b$; that is, b is the number, $-\pi/2 \leq b \leq \pi/2$, such that $\sin b = a$.

Now we seek $\cos b$. But

$$\cos b = \pm \sqrt{1 - \sin^2 b} = \pm \sqrt{1 - a^2}.$$

We take the plus sign because $\cos b$ must be nonnegative if $-\pi/2 \leq b \leq \pi/2$; $\cos(\sin^{-1} a) = \sqrt{1 - a^2}$.

■ **THEOREM 2**

The derivative of the inverse sine function.

HYPOTHESIS: $u(x)$ and $u'(x)$ have domain D.

CONCLUSION:
$$\frac{d(\sin^{-1} u)}{dx} = \frac{1}{\sqrt{1 - u^2}} \frac{du}{dx}$$

for those x of D for which $u^2 < 1$.

PROOF: Write $y = \sin^{-1} u$. Then y must be a number, $-\pi/2 \leq y \leq \pi/2$, such that $\sin y = u$. If we differentiate implicitly with respect to x, we get

$$\cos y \frac{dy}{dx} = \frac{du}{dx}, \qquad \frac{dy}{dx} = \frac{1}{\cos y} \frac{du}{dx}.$$

But, as in Example 4, if $y = \sin^{-1} u$, then

$$\cos y = \sqrt{1 - \sin^2 y} = \sqrt{1 - u^2}.$$

Hence
$$\frac{dy}{dx} = \frac{1}{\sqrt{1 - u^2}} \frac{du}{dx}.$$

---

* Suggestion: for "$\sin^{-1} x$" read "the number whose sine is x" or "inverse sine x."

Example 5.   If $y = \sin^{-1} x$,

$$\frac{dy}{dx} = \frac{1}{\sqrt{1 - x^2}}.$$

If $y = \sin^{-1} (2x)$,

$$\frac{dy}{dx} = \frac{1}{\sqrt{1 - (2x)^2}} \, (2) = \frac{2}{\sqrt{1 - 4x^2}}.$$

The function $y = \tan x$, $-\pi/2 < x < \pi/2$, is continuous and steadily increasing. Hence an inverse function exists. See Figs. 4.27(a) and 4.27(b).

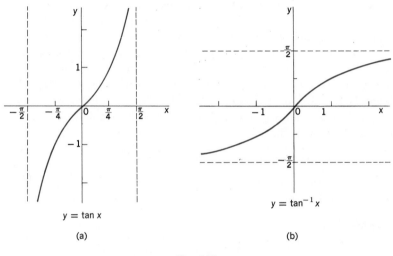

$y = \tan x$

(a)

$y = \tan^{-1} x$

(b)

Fig. 4.27

■ **DEFINITION 3**

The inverse tangent function. For all real x, $\tan^{-1} x$ shall be the number y, $-\pi/2 < y < \pi/2$, such that $\tan y = x$.*

Since $d \tan x/dx = \sec^2 x$ exists for all x of $-\pi/2 < x < \pi/2$ and is never 0, the graph of $y = \tan x$ has a nonhorizontal tangent at each point of that interval. By symmetry, there is a nonvertical tangent at each point of the graph of $y = \tan^{-1} x$; $\tan^{-1} x$ is differentiable for all x.

Example 6.   For $y = f(x) = \tan x$, $-\pi/2 < x < \pi/2$, we have $f(0) = \tan (0) = 0$, $f(\pi/4) = \tan (\pi/4) = 1$, $f(-\pi/6) = \tan (-\pi/6) = -1/\sqrt{3}$. For $y = f^{-1}(x) = \tan^{-1} x$ we have $f^{-1}(0) = \tan^{-1} (0) = 0$, $f^{-1}(1) = \tan^{-1} 1 = \pi/4$, $f^{-1}(-1/\sqrt{3}) = \tan^{-1} (-1/\sqrt{3}) = -\pi/6$. In detail, the very last result is valid, because $-\pi/6$ is the number that lies between $-\pi/2$ and $\pi/2$ and is such that $\tan (-\pi/6) = -1/\sqrt{3}$.

---

* Suggestion: for "$\tan^{-1} x$" read "the number whose tangent is x" or "inverse tan x."

■ **THEOREM 3**

The derivative of the inverse tangent function.

Hypothesis: $u(x)$ and $u'(x)$ have domain D.

Conclusion: $\dfrac{d(\tan^{-1} u)}{dx} = \dfrac{1}{1 + u^2}\dfrac{du}{dx}$ for x of D.

Proof: Write $y = \tan^{-1} u$. Then y must be a number, $-\pi/2 < y < \pi/2$ such that $\tan y = u$. If we differentiate implicitly with respect to x we get

$$\sec^2 y \frac{dy}{dx} = \frac{du}{dx}, \qquad \frac{dy}{dx} = \frac{1}{\sec^2 y}\frac{du}{dx}.$$

But if $\tan y = u$, then $\sec^2 y = 1 + \tan^2 y = 1 + u^2$. Hence

$$\frac{dy}{dx} = \frac{1}{1 + u^2}\frac{du}{dx},$$

as the theorem states.

Example 7.   If $y = \tan^{-1} x$,

then $\dfrac{dy}{dx} = \dfrac{1}{1 + x^2}.$

If $y = \tan^{-1} ax$, then

$$\frac{dy}{dx} = \frac{1}{1 + (ax)^2}\,(a) = \frac{a}{1 + a^2 x^2}.$$

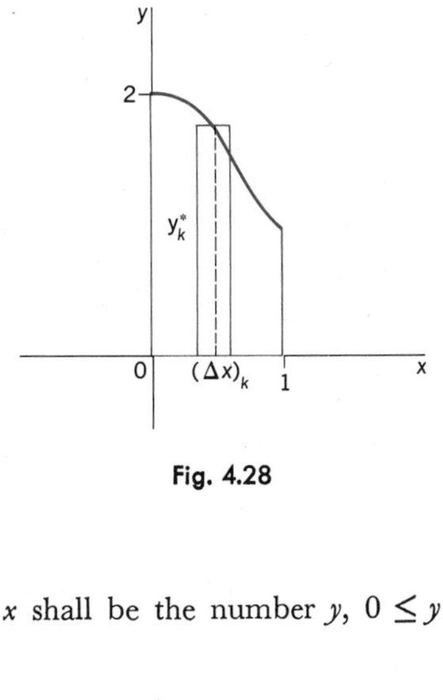

Fig. 4.28

■ **DEFINITION 4**

The inverse secant function. For $|x| \geq 1$, $\sec^{-1} x$ shall be the number y, $0 \leq y < \pi/2$ or $\pi/2 < y \leq \pi$ such that $\sec y = x$.

We shall not use this function as frequently as we use $\sin^{-1} x$ and $\tan^{-1} x$, and the computation of its derivative is left to the reader as an exercise. The inverse functions $\cot^{-1} x$ and $\cos^{-1} x$ are also touched upon briefly in exercises.

III

We conclude this section by restating in integral language the differentiation formulas appearing in the conclusions of Theorems 2 and 3.

$$\int \frac{1}{\sqrt{1 - x^2}}\, dx = \sin^{-1} x + C, \qquad \int \frac{1}{\sqrt{1 - u^2}}\frac{du}{dx}\, dx = \sin^{-1} u + C. \quad (7)$$

$$\int \frac{1}{1 + x^2}\, dx = \tan^{-1} x + C, \qquad \int \frac{1}{1 + u^2}\frac{du}{dx}\, dx = \tan^{-1} u + C. \quad (8)$$

Example 8.   Find the area of the region bounded by $y = 2/(1 + x^2)$, the y axis, the x axis, and $x = 1$. The region in question is sketched in Fig. 4.28. Form

n subregions by drawing vertical lines, and let x_k^* be an x of the kth subinterval with corresponding ordinate y_k^*. Then

$$\text{area of subregion} \approx (y_k^*)(\Delta x)_k = \frac{2}{1 + (x_k^*)^2}\,(\Delta x)_k,$$

$$\text{area of region} \approx \sum_{k=1}^{n} \frac{2}{1 + (x_k^*)^2}\,(\Delta x)_k,$$

$$\text{area of region} = \int_{x=0}^{1} \frac{2}{1 + x^2}\,dx$$

$$= 2 \int_{x=0}^{1} \frac{1}{1 + x^2}\,dx = 2\,\tan^{-1} x\,\Big|_0^1 = 2\,(\tan^{-1} 1 - \tan^{-1} 0)$$

$$= 2\left(\frac{\pi}{4} - 0\right) = \frac{\pi}{2}.$$

If the right boundary of the region had been $x = 1.2$ instead of $x = 1$, we would have had $2\,\tan^{-1} 1.2$ as our answer. From a table for the trigonometric functions with argument described in radian measure, we would have read $\tan\,(.876) \approx 1.2$ or $\tan^{-1} 1.2 \approx .876$, $2\,\tan^{-1} 1.2 \approx 1.752$.

EXERCISES 4.4

1. Consider $v = f(u) = \frac{1}{2} u + 6$ with domain $S_u : 0 \le u \le 6$ and range $S_v : 6 \le v \le 9$. Show that there is an inverse function $u = f^{-1}(v)$ with domain S_v and range S_u, and find it. Sketch $v = f(u)$ on u, v axes and $u = f^{-1}(v)$ on v, u axes.

2. Consider $v = f(u) = 9 - (u - 1)^2$ for the domain $S_u : -2 \le u \le 1$ and for the domain $S_u' : 0 \le u \le 3$. For which one of these domains can an inverse function be found? Find it. Sketch $v = f(u)$ and $u = f^{-1}(v)$ for the appropriate u and v domains.

3. Evaluate

(a) $\sin^{-1} \dfrac{\sqrt{3}}{2}$.

(b) $2 \sin^{-1}\left(-\dfrac{\sqrt{2}}{2}\right)$.

(c) $\tan^{-1}(\sqrt{3})$.

(d) $\dfrac{3}{\tan^{-1}(-1)}$.

(e) $\sin\,(\sin^{-1} .9)$.

(f) $\cos\,[\sin^{-1}(-.3)]$.

(g) $\tan\,[\tan^{-1}(-.3)]$.

(h) $\sec\,(\tan^{-1} 6)$.

(i) $\sin^{-1} \sin\,(.7)$.

(j) $\tan^{-1} \tan\,(-1)$.

(k) $\sin^{-1} \cos \dfrac{\pi}{3}$.

(l) $\sin^{-1} \sin\left(\dfrac{3\pi}{5}\right)$.

4. Find $\dfrac{dy}{dx}$ for

(a) $y = \sin^{-1} 4x$.

(b) $y = 6 \sin^{-1} (x - 2)$.

(c) $y = 3 \tan^{-1} \frac{1}{2} x$.

(d) $y = \tan^{-1} \dfrac{1}{x}$.

(e) $y = x \sin^{-1} x$.

(f) $y = \frac{1}{2} \sqrt{4 - x^2} + \sin^{-1} \frac{1}{2} x$.

(g) $y = \dfrac{\tan^{-1} x}{x}$.

(h) $y = \dfrac{1}{1 + a^2 x^2} + \tan^{-1} ax$.

5. Evaluate

(a) $\displaystyle\int_{-1/2}^{1/2} \dfrac{1}{\sqrt{1 - x^2}}\, dx$.

(b) $\displaystyle\int_{-1/2}^{1/2} \dfrac{x}{\sqrt{1 - x^2}}\, dx$.

(c) $\displaystyle\int_{0}^{\sqrt{3}} \dfrac{x}{\sqrt{1 + x^2}}\, dx$.

(d) $\displaystyle\int_{0}^{\sqrt{3}} \dfrac{1}{1 + x^2}\, dx$.

(e) $\displaystyle\int_{0}^{1/2} \dfrac{1}{1 + 4x^2}\, dx$.

(f) $\displaystyle\int_{0}^{1/2} \dfrac{1}{4 + x^2}\, dx$.

(g) $\displaystyle\int_{0}^{1/2a} \dfrac{1}{\sqrt{1 - a^2 x^2}}\, dx$.

(h) $\displaystyle\int_{0}^{a/4} \dfrac{1}{\sqrt{a^2 - x^2}}\, dx$.

6. Show that

$$\frac{d}{dx}(\sec^{-1} x) = \begin{cases} \dfrac{1}{x\sqrt{x^2 - 1}}, & x > 1, \\[2ex] -\dfrac{1}{x\sqrt{x^2 - 1}}, & x < -1. \end{cases}$$

7. (a) Consider $f(x) = \cos x$ for the interval $0 \le x \le \pi$ and write out a definition for the inverse function. Sketch $y = \cos x$ for $0 \le x \le \pi$ and $y = \cos^{-1} x$ for $-1 \le x \le 1$.

(b) Show that $\cos^{-1} x = \pi/2 - \sin^{-1} x$ for $0 \le x \le 1$.

(c) Show that $\cos^{-1} x = \pi/2 - \sin^{-1} x$ for $-1 \le x \le 0$.

(d) Find $\dfrac{d(\cos^{-1} x)}{dx}$.

8. (a) Consider $\cot x$ for $-\pi/2 < x < 0$ and $0 < x \le \pi/2$. Write out a definition for $\cot^{-1} x$. Sketch $y = \cot x$ for $-\pi/2 < x \le \pi/2$ and $y = \cot^{-1} x$ for all real x.

(b) Show that $\cot^{-1} x = \tan^{-1} \dfrac{1}{x}$ for $x > 0$.

(c) Show that $\cot^{-1} x = \tan^{-1} \dfrac{1}{x}$ for $x < 0$.

(d) Find $\dfrac{d(\cot^{-1} x)}{dx}$.

9. Show that $y = \sin^{-1} x$ and $y = \frac{2}{3} \tan^{-1} 2x$ intersect at $(\frac{1}{2}, \pi/6)$. Find the cosine of their acute angle of intersection.

10. (a) Discuss and sketch $y = 1/\sqrt{1 - x^2}$.

(b) Find the area of the region bounded by the x axis, the y axis, the curve, and $x = \sqrt{2}/2$.

11. Show that the line $u = v$ in the u, v plane is the perpendicular bisector of the line segment joining (u_0, v_0) to (v_0, u_0).

12. The text gave a plausibility discussion for Theorem 1 based primarily on a geometric symmetry argument. Fill in the details of the following analytic proof.

Step (1). Show as in Step (2) of the text discussion that ϕ increases steadily when f does.

Step (2). To show that ϕ is continuous for v of S_v we must show that, if v_0 is a number of S_v and if $v \to v_0$, then $\phi(v) \to \phi(v_0)$. In this event there could be no gap in the graph for $u = \phi(v)$ at $v = v_0$. Consider first the case where v approaches v_0 through values of v less than v_0, so that v increases as it approaches v_0. Because ϕ increases steadily by Step (1) above, $\phi(v)$ increases as v approaches v_0 and $u = \phi(v)$ either approaches $u_0 = \phi(v_0)$, which is what we want to happen, or else $u = \phi(v)$ approaches a number u^* less than u_0. Show that the latter case leads to a contradiction by considering the numbers u that lie between u_0 and u^* and the v's that correspond to these u's and that would have to lie between v_0 and $v^* = f(u^*)$. Consider also the case where v approaches v_0 through values of v greater than v_0, so that v decreases as v approaches v_0.

Step (3). To show that $\varphi'(v_0) = 1/f'(u_0)$ when $f'(u_0) \neq 0$, note that the point (v_0, u_0) on the graph $u = \varphi(v)$ corresponds to the point (u_0, v_0) on the graph of $v = f(u)$ and that the point $(v_0 + \Delta v, u_0 + \Delta u)$, with $\Delta v \neq 0$ corresponds to the point $(u_0 + \Delta u, v_0 + \Delta v)$, $\Delta u \neq 0$, because both functions are steadily increasing. Then

$$f'(u_0) = \lim_{\Delta u \to 0} \frac{\Delta v}{\Delta u}, \text{ and } \varphi'(v_0) = \lim_{\Delta v \to 0} \frac{\Delta u}{\Delta v} = \lim_{\Delta v \to 0}\left[1 \Big/ \left(\frac{\Delta v}{\Delta u}\right)\right] = \lim_{\Delta u \to 0}\left[1 \Big/ \left(\frac{\Delta v}{\Delta u}\right)\right]$$

$$= 1 \Big/ \lim_{\Delta u \to 0} \frac{\Delta v}{\Delta u} = 1/f'(u_0).$$

Here we used the fact that $\Delta u \to 0$ when $\Delta v \to 0$, a restatement of the result of Step (2) above.

13. (a) The functions $x = \sin y$ with domain $-\pi/2 \leq y \leq \pi/2$ and $y = \sin^{-1} x$ with domain $-1 \leq x \leq 1$ are inverse functions. Derive the statement

$$\frac{d(\sin^{-1} x)}{dx} = \frac{1}{\sqrt{1 - x^2}} \qquad \text{for } -1 < x < 1$$

from Conclusion (b) of Theorem 1.

(b) The same as Part (a) for the functions $x = \tan y$ with domain $-\pi/2 < y < \pi/2$ and $y = \tan^{-1} x$ with domain the set of all real x, and the statement

$$\frac{d(\tan^{-1} x)}{dx} = \frac{1}{1 + x^2} \qquad \text{for all real } x.$$

The Logarithmic
and Exponential Functions

5.1   On Filling a Gap in Our Formal Integration Knowledge

We can evaluate $\int t^2 \, dt$, $\int t^{-2} \, dt$, and, in general, $\int t^n \, dt$ if $n \neq -1$. Let us consider the exceptional case, $\int (1/t) \, dt$. The definite integral $\int_{t=1}^{x} (1/t) \, dt$, $x > 0$, would arise, for instance, if one looked for the area of the region bounded by $y = 1/t$, the t axis, $t = 1$, and $t = x$; see Fig. 5.1.* Let us write

$$f(x) = \int_{t=1}^{x} \frac{1}{t} \, dt, \qquad x > 0. \tag{1}$$

Each time a number $x > 1$ is specified, $f(x)$ will assign a positive number which will be arrived at by subdividing the interval $1 \leq t \leq x$ into n subintervals of lengths $(\Delta t)_1, (\Delta t)_2, \cdots, (\Delta t)_n$, choosing a t_k^* in the kth subinterval, forming the sum

$$\sum_{k=1}^{n} \frac{1}{t_k^*} (\Delta t)_k,$$

and taking

$$\lim_{n \to \infty} \sum_{k=1}^{n} \frac{1}{t_k^*} (\Delta t)_k,$$

it being assumed that the largest $(\Delta t)_k$ approaches 0 as n grows beyond all bounds. If $x = 1$ is specified, f will assign the number $f(1) = 0$, because the integral of Statement (1) will then have identical upper and lower boundaries. If a number

---

*We restrict x to positive values because the integrand, $1/t$, is not defined for $t = 0$ and we would not want to consider a region whose base included the point $t = 0$.

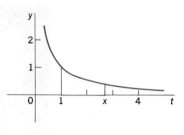

Fig. 5.1

$x, 0 < x < 1$ is specified, the function f will assign a negative number which will be arrived at by writing

$$f(x) = \int_{t=1}^{x} \frac{1}{t}\, dt = -\int_{t=x}^{1} \frac{1}{t}\, dt$$

and by working with the interval $x \leq t \leq 1$ as we did before with the interval $1 \leq t \leq x$.

Is $f(x)$ a function that we have already met? It is not a function of the form x^n; it is not a familiar trigonometric function. But perhaps by experimenting with it and discovering more of its properties we may be led to an intelligent guess for $f(x)$.

The technique of substitution is often useful in working with integrals. We shall show that, if one substitutes properly for the variable t in $\int_{t=a}^{b} f(t)\, dt$, one gets a new definite integral of the same value. Of course, when using this technique one hopes to learn more from the new form for the integral than from the original form.

■ THEOREM 1

On change of variable for definite integrals.

HYPOTHESIS: (a) $f(t)$ is continuous for $a \leq t \leq b$ and $\int_{t=a}^{b} f(t)\, dt = A$.

(b) $\tau(u)$ is steadily $\begin{cases} \text{increasing} \\ \text{decreasing} \end{cases}$ and $\tau'(u)$ is continuous for $\begin{cases} \alpha \leq u \leq \beta \\ \beta \leq u \leq \alpha \end{cases}$, with $\tau(\alpha) = a$, $\tau(\beta) = b$.

CONCLUSION:
$$\int_{u=\alpha}^{\beta} f(\tau(u)) \frac{d\tau}{du}\, du = A.$$

In words, start with a definite integral described in terms of t. Replace t wherever it occurs in the integrand by a steadily increasing (or steadily decreasing) function $\tau(u)$ with continuous derivative, and introduce the factor $d\tau/du$. Replace the t boundaries for the t integral by the corresponding u boundaries. We now have a definite integral described in terms of u, and it is asserted that this integral has the same value as the original t integral.

PROOF: Since $f(t)$ is continuous for $a \leq t \leq b$, there is a $\phi(t)$ such that $\phi'(t) = f(t)$ for $a \leq t \leq b$; see Theorem 2.6-6. The Fundamental Theorem of the Integral Calculus, Theorem 2.6-5, then says that

$$\int_{t=a}^{b} f(t)\, dt = A = \phi(b) - \phi(a).$$

Now let us consider the effect of substituting $\tau(u)$ for t in $\phi(t)$. The composite function $\phi(\tau(u))$, $\alpha \leq u \leq \beta$, is such that

$$\frac{d\phi(\tau(u))}{du} = \frac{d\phi(t)}{du} = \frac{d\phi}{dt}\frac{dt}{du} = f(t)\frac{dt}{du} = f(\tau(u))\frac{d\tau}{du},$$

and the Fundamental Theorem of the Integral Calculus says that we can write

$$\int_{u=\alpha}^{\beta} f(\tau(u)) \frac{d\tau}{du} du = \phi(\tau(u)) \Big|_{u=\alpha}^{\beta} = \phi(\tau(\beta)) - \phi(\tau(\alpha))$$

$$= \phi(b) - \phi(a) = A.$$

This is our conclusion. The reader can work through a proof that deals more directly with the definition of the definite integral when he gets to Chapter 7; see Exercise 7.6-3.

Example 1.   We know that

$$\int_{t=0}^{1} f(t)\, dt = \int_{t=0}^{1} t\, dt = \frac{1}{2} t^2 \Big|_{t=0}^{1} = \frac{1}{2}.$$

But suppose that we find it desirable to substitute for t by writing $t = \tau(u) = 4u^2$, $0 \le u \le \frac{1}{2}$. Observe that $\tau'(u) = 8u$ is continuous and that $\tau(u)$ increases steadily for $0 \le u \le \frac{1}{2}$, that $\tau(0) = 0$, $\tau(\frac{1}{2}) = 1$. Since the hypotheses of Theorem 1 are satisfied, we can accept the conclusion; the original integral can be replaced by

$$\int_{u=0}^{1/2} f(\tau(u)) \frac{d\tau}{du} du = \int_{u=0}^{1/2} (4u^2)(8u)\, du = 32 \int_{u=0}^{1/2} u^3\, du$$

$$= 8u^4 \Big|_{u=0}^{1/2} = \frac{1}{2}.$$

● **Remark 1**

The hypothesis requirement of Theorem 1 that τ be steadily increasing or steadily decreasing did not appear in the proof and is not necessary, although in actual practice the substitutions we use will have this property in almost all cases. The reader can investigate this matter further in Exercises 3 and 4 at the end of this section.

Now let us return to Eq. (1):

$$f(x) = \int_{t=1}^{x} \frac{1}{t}\, dt, \qquad x > 0.$$

We have, for $a > 0$ and $b > 0$,

$$f(a) = \int_{t=1}^{a} \frac{1}{t}\, dt \qquad \text{and} \qquad f(b) = \int_{t=1}^{b} \frac{1}{t}\, dt.$$

What can we say about $f(ab)$? We can write

$$f(ab) = \int_{t=1}^{ab} \frac{1}{t}\, dt = \int_{t=1}^{a} \frac{1}{t}\, dt + \int_{t=a}^{ab} \frac{1}{t}\, dt.$$

The first integral of the last member is easily recognized; it is $f(a)$. To recognize the second integral, let us try to rewrite it so that its lower boundary is 1. Write $t = \tau(u) = au$, $1 \le u \le b$,* and observe that $\tau(u)$ increases steadily for $1 \le u \le b$,

---

* Or, if $b < 1$, write $t = \tau(u) = au$, $b \le u \le 1$.

that $\tau'(u) = a$ is continuous, and that $\tau(1) = a$, $\tau(b) = ab$. Then, by the conclusion of Theorem 1,

$$\int_{t=a}^{ab} \frac{1}{t}\, dt = \int_{u=1}^{b} \frac{1}{au}\, (a)\, du = \int_{u=1}^{b} \frac{1}{u}\, du = f(b).$$

Thus we have found, when $a > 0$, $b > 0$, that

$$f(ab) = f(a) + f(b). \tag{2}$$

An alert reader will soon recognize that we have already encountered a function with this property, for we know that

$$\log ab = \log a + \log b$$

when $a > 0$, $b > 0$. Moreover, $\log x$, like $f(x)$, has a domain $x > 0$, assigns positive numbers to domain numbers x such that $x > 1$, assigns the number 0 to $x = 1$, and assigns negative numbers to domain numbers x such that $0 < x < 1$. Hence we begin to suspect that $f(x)$ might be $\log x$ or at least related to it. Let us experiment further. What can be said of $f(a/b)$?

First, using Eq. (2), we can say that if $a > 0$, $b > 0$

$$f\!\left(\frac{a}{b}\right) = f\!\left(a\,\frac{1}{b}\right) = f(a) + f\!\left(\frac{1}{b}\right)$$

$$= f(a) + \int_{t=1}^{1/b} \frac{1}{t}\, dt.$$

Now let us try the substitution $t = \tau(v) = 1/v$, $1 \le v \le b$.* Observe that τ is steadily decreasing for $1 \le v \le b$, that $\tau'(v) = -1/v^2$ is continuous for $1 \le v \le b$, and that $\tau(1) = 1$, $\tau(b) = 1/b$. Hence, by Theorem 1,

$$f\!\left(\frac{a}{b}\right) = f(a) + \int_{v=1}^{b} \frac{1}{1/v}\left(-\frac{1}{v^2}\right) dv$$

$$= f(a) - \int_{v=1}^{b} \frac{1}{v}\, dv = f(a) - f(b). \tag{3}$$

Since $\log a/b = \log a - \log b$, we now suspect still more strongly that it is the logarithm function that will help us fill the gap in our ability to integrate $\int t^n\, dt$.

EXERCISES 5.1

1. If $f(x) = \int_{t=1}^{x} \frac{1}{t}\, dt$, show that $f(a^n) = nf(a)$ for $a > 0$.

2. Show directly that $\int_{t=0}^{3} t\, dt = \frac{9}{2}$. Try the substitution $t = \tau(u) = 4 - (u-2)^2 = 4u - u^2$, $0 \le u \le 1$, and show again that the value of the integral is $\frac{9}{2}$.

3. It was stated in Remark 1 that the requirement in Hypothesis (b) of Theorem 1 that τ be steadily increasing or steadily decreasing was not used directly in the proof of the

---

* Or, if $b < 1$, try $t = \tau(v) = 1/v$, $b \le v \le 1$.

theorem and was not necessary. Return to the integral of Exercise 2. Consider the substitution $t = \tau(u) = 4u - u^2$, $0 \leq u \leq 3$. Observe that $\tau'(u) = 4 - 2u$ is continuous for $0 \leq u \leq 3$ and that $\tau(0) = 0$, $\tau(3) = 3$, but that τ is not steadily increasing for $0 \leq u \leq 3$. Use this substitution according to the instructions of the conclusion of Theorem 1, nevertheless, and show that one still gets the correct answer.

4. We continue the discussion of Remark 1.

   (a) Show directly that $\int_{t=-2}^{1} \sqrt{1-t}\,dt = \tfrac{2}{3}\,(3)^{3/2}$.

   (b) Consider the substitution $t = \tau(u) = 2 - u^2$, $-2 \leq u \leq -1$. Observe that $\tau(u)$ is steadily increasing for $-2 \leq u \leq -1$, $\tau'(u) = -2u$ is continuous for $-2 \leq u \leq -1$, and that $\tau(-2) = -2$, $\tau(-1) = 1$. Use this substitution and evaluate the integral again.

   (c) Consider the substitution $t = \tau(u) = 2 - u^2$, $-2 \leq u \leq 1$. Observe that $\tau(u)$ is not steadily increasing for $-2 \leq u \leq 1$, but that $\tau'(u) = -2u$ is continuous for $-2 \leq u \leq 1$ and that $\tau(-2) = -2$, $\tau(1) = 1$. Why does this substitution make no sense for this problem? This exercise suggests that, if the steadily increasing (or steadily decreasing) requirement of Hypothesis (b) of Theorem 1 is to be dropped, one must add the requirement that $f(\tau(u))$ be continuous for $\alpha \leq u \leq \beta$ (or $\beta \leq u \leq \alpha$).

5.2   The Logarithm Function. Review

Before investigating whether

$$\frac{d}{dt}\,\log t = \frac{1}{t},$$

in which case we would have

$$\int \frac{1}{t}\,dt = \log t + C,$$

we shall review briefly the definition of logarithm and some of the properties of this function.

Most students first encounter logarithms as a computational aid. To illustrate the ideas behind these computations, assume that a table of values for the function 10^x is available and consider the following two examples.

Example 1A. $4(2.1) \approx 10^{0.6021}10^{0.3222} = 10^{0.9243} \approx 8.4.$

Example 2A. $\sqrt[3]{8.12} = (8.12)^{1/3} \approx (10^{0.9096})^{1/3} = 10^{0.3032} \approx 2.01.$

It is not essential that 10 be used as the base, for the laws of exponents apply in the same form to the powers of every other positive number except 1. A second number for which we have tabular aid is an irrational number whose first 8 significant digits are 2.7182818. To be able to refer to this number quickly, we give it the name e.

Example 1B. $4(2.1) \approx e^{1.38629}e^{0.74194} = e^{2.12823} \approx 8.4.$

Example 2B. $\sqrt[3]{8.12} \approx (8.12)^{1/3} \approx (e^{2.09433})^{1/3} = e^{0.69811} \approx 2.01.$

We refer to exponents frequently in this method of computing by using powers of a base number, and we find it convenient to give a name to the exponent we use when trying to write a given number as a power of the base number.

■ DEFINITION 1

The logarithm of a number. Let $N > 0$, and let $b > 0$, $b \neq 1$. The logarithm of N to the base b, written $\log_b N$, is the exponent we must use when writing N as a power of b; in symbols, $N = b^{\log_b N}$.

We shall use the number e as our base for logarithms almost exclusively for a reason that will be apparent when we return to the computation of $d(\log t)/dt$; we shall usually write $\log N$ for $\log_e N$.

Example 3.   We write $\log_{10} 10 = 1$, because $10 = 10^1$; in words, if we write 10 as a power of 10, the proper exponent is 1. Also, $\log_{10} 1 = 0$, because $1 = 10^0$; $\log_{10} \sqrt{10} = \frac{1}{2}$, because $\sqrt{10} = 10^{1/2}$.

Example 4.   We write $\log e = 1$, because $e = e^1$. Also $\log 1/e^2 = -2$, because $1/e^2 = e^{-2}$; -2 is the exponent of that power of e which equals $1/e^2$.

Example 5.   If $\log x = \frac{2}{3}$, then $\frac{2}{3}$ is the exponent of that power of e which equals x; that is, $x = e^{2/3}$.

■ THEOREM 1

The laws of logarithms.

HYPOTHESIS: $a > 0$, $c > 0$.

CONCLUSION: (a) $\log_b ac = \log_b a + \log_b c$.

(b) $\log_b \dfrac{a}{c} = \log_b a - \log_b c$.

(c) $\log_b a^n = n \log_b a$.

PROOF: Logarithms are exponents, and the foregoing conclusions are restatements in logarithm language of the laws of exponents. We present a proof of Conclusion (b). Proofs of Conclusions (a) and (c) are left to the reader as exercises.

Since $\log_b a$ is the exponent of that power of b which equals a, $a = b^{\log_b a}$. Similarly, $c = b^{\log_b c}$. But then

$$\frac{a}{c} = \frac{b^{\log_b a}}{b^{\log_b c}} = b^{\log_b a - \log_b c}.$$

This last equation says that, if we write a/c as a power of b, we are to use the exponent $\log_b a - \log_b c$; that is,

$$\log_b \frac{a}{c} = \log_b a - \log_b c.$$

■ THEOREM 2

The relationship between logarithms to base e and those to base 10.

HYPOTHESIS: $N > 0$.

CONCLUSION: $$\log_{10} N = \frac{1}{\log 10} \log N.$$

PROOF: If N is written as a power of e, the exponent is log N;

$$N = e^{\log N}. \tag{1}$$

If N is written as a power of 10, the exponent is $\log_{10} N$; $N = 10^{\log_{10} N}$. But 10 itself can be written as a power of e; $10 = e^{\log 10}$. Thus we have

$$N = 10^{\log_{10} N} = (e^{\log 10})^{\log_{10} N} = e^{\log 10 \, \log_{10} N}. \tag{2}$$

Two powers of e with different exponents cannot be equal; therefore Eqs. (1) and (2) together say that log N = log 10 $\log_{10} N$, or that

$$\log_{10} N = \frac{1}{\log 10} \log N.$$

Since log $10 \approx 2.30259$, Theorem 2 says in greater detail that

$$\log_{10} N \approx \frac{1}{2.30259} \log N \approx .43429 \log N. \tag{3}$$

Example 6.   From the fact that log $7 \approx 1.94591$ we can compute

$$\log_{10} 7 \approx .43429 \log 7 \approx (.43429)(1.94591) \approx .84509.*$$

Example 7.   According to Theorem 1,

$$\log_{10} 10N = \log_{10} 10 + \log_{10} N = 1 + \log_{10} N,$$

and $$\log_{10} \frac{N}{10} = \log_{10} N - \log_{10} 10 = \log_{10} N - 1.$$

These facts make possible the system of "characteristics" and "mantissas" that is used in working with logs to the base 10:

$$\log_{10} 2 \approx 0.30103,$$
$$\log_{10} 20 = \log_{10} [10(2)] = \log_{10} 10 + \log_{10} 2 \approx 1 + 0.30103,$$
$$\log_{10} 0.2 = \log_{10} [2/10] = \log_{10} 2 - \log_{10} 10 \approx 0.30103 - 1.$$

In a table of $\log_{10} N$, it is necessary to write down only the values of $\log_{10} N$ for $1 \leq N \leq 10$. Logarithms of larger or smaller numbers are quickly obtained by using the characteristics, the logarithms of the integer powers of 10.

Example 8.   Tables of log N are also usually written for $1 \leq N \leq 10$, as in Table IV of the Appendix, but now it is harder to find the logarithms of larger or smaller numbers, because the logarithms of the integer powers of 10 are not themselves integers. We have

$$\log 3.28 \approx 1.18784,$$

$$\log 32.8 = \log 3.28 + \log 10 \approx 1.18784 + 2.30259 = 3.49043,$$

$$\log 0.0328 = \log \frac{3.28}{100} = \log 3.28 - 2 \log 10 \approx 1.18784 - 2(2.30259)$$

$$= 1.18784 - 4.60518 = -3.41734 = 0.58266 - 4.$$

---

* This result is as accurate as can be expected in using two 5-decimal approximations.

Example 9. If $\log N \approx 4.58803$, then

$$\log N \approx 2.30259 + 2.28544 \qquad \text{and} \qquad N \approx 10(9.83) = 98.3.$$

If $\log N \approx 0.20371 - 1$, then

$$\log N \approx 0.20371 + 1.30259 - 1.30259 - 1,$$

$$\log N \approx 1.50630 - 2.30259 \qquad \text{and} \qquad N \approx \frac{4.51}{10} = 0.451.$$

In this work we formed the logarithm of 10, 2.30259, wherever possible, because it is easy to multiply or divide by 10 in our base-10 decimal-number system.

EXERCISES 5.2

1. Prove Conclusions (a) and (c) of Theorem 1.

2. (a) $\log e^2 = ?$ (c) $\log e^3 \sqrt{e} = ?$

    (b) $\log \sqrt[3]{e} = ?$ (d) $\log \dfrac{1}{\sqrt{e}} = ?$

3. Write N as a power of e if
    (a) $\log N = 3.$ (c) $3 \log N - 4 = 0.$
    (b) $2 \log N + 3 = 0.$

4. Given $\log 9 \approx 2.19722$. Find
    (a) $\log 90.$ (d) $\log 0.09.$
    (b) $\log 900.$ (e) $\log 3.$
    (c) $\log 0.9.$ (f) $\log_{10} 9.$

5. Given $\log 7 \approx 1.94591$, $\log 8 \approx 2.07944$. Find N if
    (a) $\log N \approx 4.24850.$ (c) $\log N \approx 0.47426 - 3.$
    (b) $\log N \approx 6.68462.$ (d) $\log N \approx 0.64332 - 1.$

6. Use Table IV of the Appendix to find
    (a) $\log 3.42.$ (d) $\log 4.49.$
    (b) $\log 342.$ (e) $\log 44.9.$
    (c) $\log .00342.$ (f) $\log .0449.$

7. Use Table IV of the Appendix to find N if
    (a) $\log N = 1.61343.$ (d) $\log N = 2.00148.$
    (b) $\log N = 6.21860.$ (e) $\log N = 13.51441.$
    (c) $\log N = -0.68916.$ (f) $\log N = -2.60369.$

8. Use Table IV of the Appendix to compute
    (a) $1.55 \, e^{0.12345}.$
    (b) $24.7 \, e^{-0.12345}.$
    (c) $0.23 \, e^{2.02}.$

5.3 The Derivative of the Logarithm Function

I

Let us return now to the question of whether or not

$$f(x) = \int_{t=1}^{x} \frac{1}{t} \, dt$$

is the logarithm function or closely related to it. To state the question differently, if $y = \log_b t$, will $dy/dt = 1/t$ or will dy/dt at least be close enough to $1/t$ in form to enable us to state precisely which function $f(x)$ is? We do not know a priori whether logarithms taken to base 10 or some other base will be more useful, therefore we shall use logarithms to the base b and not commit ourselves too soon.

Let us investigate dy/dx, then, when $y = \log_b x$. Because of the definition of the derivative, we take

$$y = \log_b x, \qquad x > 0,$$
$$y + \Delta y = \log_b (x + \Delta x), \qquad \Delta x \neq 0, x + \Delta x > 0,$$
$$\Delta y = \log_b (x + \Delta x) - \log_b x,$$

and, using the law of logarithms having to do with fractions, we obtain

$$\Delta y = \log_b\left(\frac{x + \Delta x}{x}\right) = \log_b\left(1 + \frac{\Delta x}{x}\right).$$

Next
$$\frac{\Delta y}{\Delta x} = \frac{\log_b(1 + \Delta x/x)}{\Delta x}. \tag{1}$$

If we let $\Delta x \to 0$ when $\Delta y/\Delta x$ is written in this form, we cannot find the limit approached, because the denominator and the numerator both approach 0. We must rewrite Eq. (1) if we are to find $\lim_{\Delta x \to 0} \Delta y/\Delta x$. Since we suspect that dy/dx may turn out to be closely related to $1/x$, we try writing

$$\frac{\Delta y}{\Delta x} = \frac{x}{x}\frac{1}{\Delta x}\log_b\left(1 + \frac{\Delta x}{x}\right) = \frac{1}{x}\frac{x}{\Delta x}\log_b\left(1 + \frac{\Delta x}{x}\right) = \frac{1}{x}\log_b\left(1 + \frac{\Delta x}{x}\right)^{x/\Delta x}, \tag{2}$$

using the law of logarithms having to do with powers at the last step. Now, from Eq. (2), we have

$$\frac{dy}{dx} = \lim_{\Delta x \to 0} \frac{\Delta y}{\Delta x} = \frac{1}{x} \lim_{\Delta x \to 0} \log_b\left(1 + \frac{\Delta x}{x}\right)^{x/\Delta x}. \tag{3}$$

This result forces us to consider $\lim_{\Delta x \to 0} [1 + (\Delta x/x)]^{x/\Delta x}$ or, if we write $w = \Delta x/x$, $\lim_{w \to 0} (1 + w)^{1/w}$. If to start with, we try some numerical experiments, we note that

w	1	0.5	0.05	0.01	-0.5	-0.05	-0.01
$(1 + w)^{1/w}$	2	2.25	2.65	2.70	4	2.79	2.73

We suspect, then, that $\lim_{w \to 0} (1 + w)^{1/w}$ exists and is a number that lies between 2.70 and 2.73. In Exercise 5.3-9 we shall outline a proof of the fact that $\lim_{w \to 0} (1 + w)^{1/w}$ exists. Because this limit is important, its computation has been pushed quite far—to many thousand decimal places in recent years. To summarize, we can say that this limit defines a number, called e, whose value, approximated to five decimal places, is 2.71828.

$$e = \lim_{w \to 0} (1 + w)^{1/w} = 2.71828\cdots. \tag{4}$$

Now let us return to Eq. (3) and conclude our investigation of $d(\log_b x)/dx$. We have Eq. (3) or

$$\frac{dy}{dx} = \lim_{\Delta x \to 0} \frac{\Delta y}{\Delta x} = \frac{1}{x} \lim_{w \to 0} \log_b (1 + w)^{1/w}. \tag{3a}$$

The definition of logarithm is such that, intuitively, we recognize the logarithm as a continuous function; if $N > 0$ changes gradually, then $\log N$ changes gradually, or without jumps. If $(1 + w)^{1/w}$ approaches e, then $\log_b (1 + w)^{1/w}$ approaches $\log_b e$. Thus Eq. (3a) becomes

$$\frac{dy}{dx} = \frac{1}{x} \log_b e. \tag{5}$$

If the base number of the logarithm system is chosen to be e itself, then $\log_e e = 1$ and Eq. (5) becomes

$$\frac{dy}{dx} = \frac{1}{x}. \tag{6}$$

For no other choice of base could we have obtained such a simple result. If, for instance, we were to choose 10 as base, we would have

$$\frac{d}{dx} (\log_{10} x) = \frac{1}{x} \log_{10} e \approx (.43429) \frac{1}{x}.$$

We have proved the following theorem.

■ **THEOREM 1**

The derivative of the logarithm function.

HYPOTHESIS: $y = f(x) = \log x, \qquad x > 0.$

CONCLUSION: $\dfrac{dy}{dx} = f'(x) = \dfrac{1}{x}.$

By using the chain rule we can rewrite this result in a more general form.

■ **THEOREM 2**

HYPOTHESIS: $u(x) > 0$ for x of domain D and $u'(x)$ exists for x of D.

CONCLUSION: $\dfrac{d}{dx} (\log u) = \dfrac{1}{u} \dfrac{du}{dx}$ for x of D.

In words, the conclusion says that *the derivative of the logarithm of a function is the reciprocal of that function multiplied by its derivative.*

PROOF: Let $y = \log u$. Then

$$\frac{dy}{dx} = \frac{dy}{du} \frac{du}{dx} = \frac{1}{u} \frac{du}{dx}.$$

Example 1. $y = \log \sqrt{1 + x^2}$; $dy/dx = ?$ It is easier to differentiate $y = \frac{1}{2} \log (1 + x^2)$. We get

$$\frac{dy}{dx} = \frac{1}{2} \frac{1}{1 + x^2} (2x) = \frac{x}{1 + x^2}.$$

Example 2.   If $y = \log (\sec x + \tan x)$,

$$\frac{dy}{dx} = \frac{1}{\sec x + \tan x} (\sec x \tan x + \sec^2 x)$$

$$= \frac{\sec x (\tan x + \sec x)}{\sec x + \tan x} = \sec x.$$

Example 3.   Let us discuss the graph of $y = \log x$. Since the logarithm function is defined only for $x > 0$, the graph exists only for these x. We shall have an x intercept when $y = 0$, that is, when $\log x = 0$, or when $x = e^0 = 1$. From the equation $dy/dx = 1/x$ we see that the slope is always positive. The graph rises steadily, but at an ever-decreasing rate because $1/x$ decreases as x increases. Finally, from the equation $d^2y/dx^2 = -1/x^2$ we see that $d^2y/dx^2 < 0$; the graph must always face down.

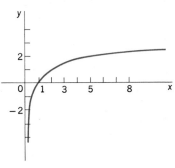

Fig. 5.2

We start to sketch our graph at the intercept point $(1, 0)$. See Fig. 5.2. If we sketch to the right, we know that the graph rises steadily while facing down, and the easily computed points $(e, 1)$, $(e^2, 2)$ help us with this portion of the graph. For the region to the left of $x = 1$, we know that $y < 0$; for, if $x < 1$, then $1/x > 1$ and $\log 1/x$ is positive, while

$$y = \log x = \log \frac{1}{1/x} = \log 1 - \log \frac{1}{x} = 0 - \log \frac{1}{x}$$

is negative. In fact, as x approaches 0, $1/x$ and $\log 1/x$ increase beyond all bounds and $y = -\log 1/x$ decreases beyond all bounds; the y axis is an asymptote. The specific points $(1/e, -1)$ and $(1/e^2, -2)$ help with this portion of the graph.

Example 4.   Find dy/dx if

$$y = \sqrt{\frac{(x - 3)(x^2 + 4)^3}{(x^2 + 1)(x - 2)^3}}.$$

We could differentiate explicitly, using the power, product, and quotient rules; but, since logarithms can help in analyzing powers, products, and quotients, we shall first rewrite the problem by taking the logarithm of y and then we shall differentiate implicitly. (The name *logarithmic differentiation* is usually given to this technique.)

We have

$$\log y = \log \left[\frac{(x - 3)(x^2 + 4)^3}{(x^2 + 1)(x - 2)^3} \right]^{1/2} = \frac{1}{2} \log \frac{(x - 3)(x^2 + 4)^3}{(x^2 + 1)(x - 2)^3}$$

$$= \frac{1}{2} [\log (x - 3) + 3 \log (x^2 + 4) - \log (x^2 + 1) - 3 \log (x - 2)].$$

Then, differentiating implicitly with respect to x, we obtain

$$\frac{1}{y} \frac{dy}{dx} = \frac{1}{2} \left[\frac{1}{x - 3} + 3 \frac{1}{x^2 + 4} (2x) - \frac{1}{x^2 + 1} (2x) - 3 \frac{1}{x - 2} \right].$$

Since we want a statement for dy/dx, we write

$$\frac{dy}{dx} = \frac{y}{2}\left[\frac{1}{x-3} + \frac{6x}{x^2+4} - \frac{2x}{x^2+1} - \frac{3}{x-2}\right].$$

Example 5.   Find dy/dx if $y = x^x$. We have dealt with problems of the form x^n, n constant, but this is different. Since logarithms can help in analyzing powers, we try logarithmic differentiation. We have $\log y = \log x^x = x \log x$. Then, by implicit differentiation, using the product rule,

$$\frac{1}{y}\frac{dy}{dx} = x\frac{1}{x} + 1 \log x,$$

$$\frac{dy}{dx} = y(1 + \log x) = x^x(1 + \log x).$$

● **Remark 1**

Note that we cannot expect logarithms to help us deal with sums or differences. There are simple replacements for $\log ab$, $\log a/b$, and $\log (a^b)$, but not for $\log (a + b)$ or $\log (a - b)$.

II

Theorems 1 and 2 can be rewritten in integral form, and in fact these integrals motivated our discussion. We have the statements:

$$\int \frac{1}{x}\,dx = \log x + C, \qquad x > 0, \tag{7a}$$

$$\int \frac{1}{x}\,dx = \log (-x) + C, \qquad x < 0, \tag{7b}$$

$$\int \frac{1}{u}\frac{du}{dx}\,dx = \log u + C, \qquad u > 0, \tag{8a}$$

$$\int \frac{1}{u}\frac{du}{dx}\,dx = \log (-u) + C, \qquad u < 0. \tag{8b}$$

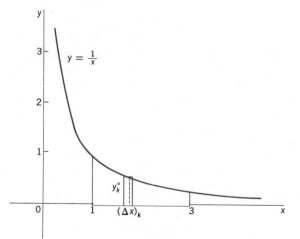

Fig. 5.3

Statements (7a) and (8a) are direct restatements of Theorems 1 and 2. Statements (7b) and (8b) follow from the others. To derive Eq. (7b), for instance, write

$$\int \frac{1}{x}\, dx = \int \frac{1}{-x}\,(-1)\, dx = \log{(-x)} + C.$$

We used the fact that $-x$ is positive when x is negative and substituted $-x$ for u in Eq. (8a).

Example 6.   Find the area of the region bounded by $y = 1/x$, the x axis, $x = 1$, and $x = 3$. See Fig. 5.3. Divide the region given into n subregions of widths $(\Delta x)_1, (\Delta x)_2, \cdots, (\Delta x)_n$ by drawing vertical lines and let x_k^* be an x of the kth subregion, y_k^* the corresponding y. Then

$$\text{area of } k\text{th subregion} \approx y_k^*(\Delta x)_k = \frac{1}{x_k^*}\,(\Delta x)_k,$$

$$\text{area of region} \approx \sum_{k=1}^{n} \frac{1}{x_k^*}\,(\Delta x)_k,$$

$$\text{area} = \int_{x=1}^{3} \frac{1}{x}\, dx$$

$$= \log x \,\Big|_{x=1}^{3} = \log 3 - \log 1 \approx 1.099 - 0 = 1.099.$$

Example 7.   Find the area of the region bounded by $y = 1/x$, the x axis, $x = -3$, and $x = -1$. See Fig. 5.4. Divide the given region into n subregions of widths $(\Delta x)_1, (\Delta x)_2, \cdots, (\Delta x)_n$ by drawing vertical lines and let x_k^* be an x of the kth subregion, y_k^* the corresponding y. Then, because $-y_k^*$ is positive,

$$\text{area of } k\text{th subregion} \approx (-y_k^*)(\Delta x)_k = -\frac{1}{x_k^*}\,(\Delta x)_k,$$

$$\text{area of region} \approx \sum_{k=1}^{n} \left(-\frac{1}{x_k^*}\right)(\Delta x)_k,$$

$$\text{area} = -\int_{x=-3}^{-1} \frac{1}{x}\, dx.$$

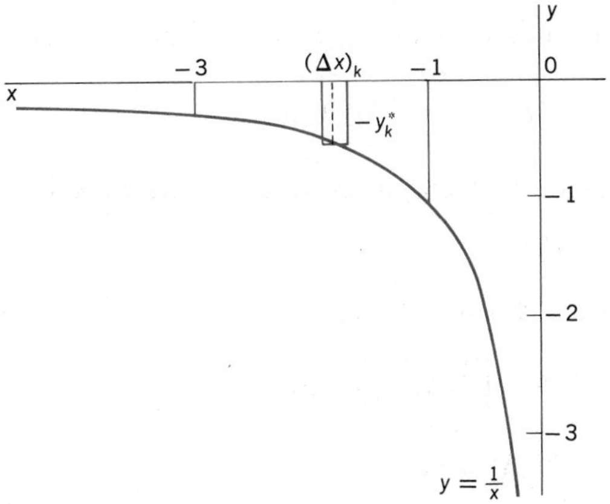

Fig. 5.4

We would not have real numbers if we took log x for $x < 0$, and so we continue with

$$\text{area} = -\int_{x=-3}^{-1} \frac{1}{-x}(-1)\,dx = -\log(-x)\Big|_{x=-3}^{-1}$$

$$= -(\log 1 - \log 3) = \log 3 \approx 1.099.$$

In effect, we used Eq. (7b) instead of (7a).

Example 8.   As in Example 2.8-4, consider some gas at pressure 14 psi in a cylinder of radius 1 in. and height 5 in. Suppose this time that a piston compresses the gas isothermally from height 5 to height $\frac{1}{2}$. How much work did the piston do? (Assume that in an isothermal compression or expansion the pressure and volume are related by $PV = $ constant.)

Since $P = 14$ when $V = \pi(1)^2 5 = 5\pi$, we have $PV = C = 14(5\pi) = 70\pi$, and we can say that

$$P = \frac{70\pi}{V}.$$

The face area of the piston is π sq in., so that the force pressing against the piston at any height h is

$$F = P\left(\frac{\text{lb}}{\text{sq in.}}\right)\pi \text{ sq in.} = P\pi \text{ lb.}$$

Note also that V and h are related:

$$V = (\text{cross-sectional area})h = \pi h, \qquad h = \frac{1}{\pi}V;$$

Fig. 5.5

see Fig. 5.5.

Now break the interval $\frac{1}{2} \le h \le 5$ into n subintervals of widths $(\Delta h)_1$, $(\Delta h)_2, \cdots, (\Delta h)_n$ and let h_k^* be an h of the kth subinterval, P_k^* the corresponding P. We have

distance moved by piston during kth subinterval

$$= (\Delta h)_k \text{ in.} = \frac{1}{\pi}(\Delta V)_k \text{ in.,}$$

force against which piston works during kth subinterval

$$\approx P_k^*\pi \text{ lb,}$$

work done during kth subinterval $= (\text{force})(\text{distance})$

$$\approx (P_k^*\pi)\left[\frac{1}{\pi}(\Delta V)_k\right] \text{in.-lb}$$

$$\approx P_k^*(\Delta V)_k \text{ in.-lb,}$$

work done in all $\approx \displaystyle\sum_{k=1}^{n} P_k^*(\Delta V)_k$

$$= \int_{V=1/2\pi}^{5\pi} P \, dV = \int_{V=1/2\pi}^{5\pi} 70\pi \, \frac{1}{V} \, dV$$

$$= 70\pi \log V \Big|_{V=1/2\pi}^{5\pi} = 70\pi (\log 5\pi - \log \tfrac{1}{2}\pi)$$

$$= 70\pi \log \frac{5\pi}{1/2\pi} = 70\pi \log 10$$

$$\approx 506.37 \text{ in.-lb} \approx 42.20 \text{ ft-lb}.$$

Example 9. For

$$I_1 = \int \frac{x}{(x^2 + 1)^2} \, dx$$

we write $\quad I_1 = \displaystyle\int (x^2 + 1)^{-2} x \, dx = \tfrac{1}{2} \int (x^2 + 1)^{-2} \, 2x \, dx$

$$= \frac{1}{2} \frac{(x^2 + 1)^{-1}}{-1} + C = -\frac{1}{2} \frac{1}{x^2 + 1} + C.$$

But for $\quad I_2 = \displaystyle\int \frac{x}{x^2 + 1} \, dx$

we write

$$I_2 = \int \frac{1}{x^2 + 1} \, x \, dx = \frac{1}{2} \int \frac{1}{x^2 + 1} \, 2x \, dx = \frac{1}{2} \log (x^2 + 1) + C.$$

Example 10. For $I = \int \tan x \, dx$, we write

$$I = \int \frac{\sin x}{\cos x} \, dx = \int \frac{1}{\cos x} \sin x \, dx = - \int \frac{1}{\cos x} (-\sin x) \, dx$$

$$= -\log \cos x + C.^{*}$$

EXERCISES 5.3

1. Find dy/dx. Keep in mind the possibility of rewriting logarithms of products, quotients, and powers.

(a) $y = x \log x$.

(b) $y = 6 \log 2x + 4 \log 3x$.

(c) $y = \log \dfrac{x + 1}{x^2 + 1}$.

(d) $y = \log (2x - 3)^5$.

(e) $y = \log (x^2 \sqrt{2x - 3})$.

(f) $y = \log \sqrt[3]{\dfrac{x + 2}{2x + 1}}$.

(g) $y = \log \log x$.

(h) $y = \log^2 x$.

(i) $y = \log \sin x$.

(j) $y = \log \cos^2 x$.

---

* For $\cos x > 0$. If x were such that $\cos x < 0$, we would have written

$$I = -\log (-\cos x) + C.$$

(k) $y = \log (\csc x - \cot x)$.

(q) $y = \dfrac{(x + 5) \sqrt{2x - 1}}{\sqrt[3]{x^2 + 4}}$.

(l) $y = \log (\tan x + 1)$.

(r) $y = x^{\log x}$.

(m) $y = \dfrac{\log x}{x^2}$.

(s) $y = \cos x \cos 2x \cos 3x \cos 4x$.

(n) $y = 2 \tan^{-1} x + x \log (1 + x^2)$.

(t) $y = \dfrac{\sqrt[3]{x - 1} \log x}{\sqrt{x + 1}}$.

(o) $y = 4^x$.

(u) $\log xy + x + y = 2$.

(p) $y = (\sin x)^x$.

(v) $\log \dfrac{y}{x} + xy = 1$.

2. Integrate

(a) $\displaystyle\int \dfrac{1}{x + 2}\, dx$.

(f) $\displaystyle\int \dfrac{1}{\sqrt{1 - x^2}}\, dx$.

(k) $\displaystyle\int \dfrac{\sec^2 x}{\sqrt{\tan x}}\, dx$.

(b) $\displaystyle\int \dfrac{1}{(x + 2)^2}\, dx$.

(g) $\displaystyle\int \dfrac{1}{1 + t^2}\, dt$.

(l) $\displaystyle\int \dfrac{\cos \theta}{\sin \theta + 1}\, d\theta$.

(c) $\displaystyle\int \dfrac{1}{1 - 2t}\, dt$.

(h) $\displaystyle\int \dfrac{t}{1 + t^2}\, dt$.

(m) $\displaystyle\int \dfrac{\sin x}{1 - \cos x}\, dx$.

(d) $\displaystyle\int \dfrac{x}{1 - x^2}\, dx$.

(i) $\displaystyle\int \cot x\, dx$.

(n) $\displaystyle\int \dfrac{\csc^2 x}{1 + \cot x}\, dx$.

(e) $\displaystyle\int \dfrac{x}{\sqrt{1 - x^2}}\, dx$.

(j) $\displaystyle\int \dfrac{\sec^2 x}{\tan x}\, dx$.

3. Discuss and sketch the graph for the equation

(a) $y = \log (1 + x^2)$.

(b) $y = \dfrac{\log x}{x}$.

4. We can derive the product rule by logarithmic differentiation. If $y = uv$, then

$$\log y = \log u + \log v, \quad \frac{1}{y}\frac{dy}{dx} = \frac{1}{u}\frac{du}{dx} + \frac{1}{v}\frac{dv}{dx}, \quad \frac{dy}{dx} = \frac{y}{u}\frac{du}{dx} + \frac{y}{v}\frac{dv}{dx},$$

$$\frac{dy}{dx} = v\frac{du}{dx} + u\frac{dv}{dx}.$$

(a) Derive the quotient rule: $\dfrac{d(u/v)}{dx} = \dfrac{v(du/dx) - u(dv/dx)}{v^2}$.

(b) Derive the power rule: $\dfrac{d(u^n)}{dx} = n(u)^{n-1}\dfrac{du}{dx}$.

5. Find the area of the region bounded by $y = \tan x$, the x axis, and $x = \pi/3$.

6. Find the area of the region bounded by $y = 1/x$, $y = 1/x^2$, and $x = 3$.

7. The areas of two of the regions described below can be determined. Find these areas.

(a) region bounded by $y = \dfrac{1}{1 - x}$, the x axis, $x = 2$, and $x = 4$.

(b) region bounded by $y = \dfrac{1}{1 - x}$, the x axis, $x = 0$, and $x = 2$.

(c) region bounded by $y = \dfrac{1}{1 - x}$, the x axis, $x = -3$, and $x = 0$.

8. A gas in a cylinder at pressure P_A and volume V_A is compressed to pressure P_B and volume V_B, the pressure and volume satisfying the relationship $PV = \text{const}$ throughout the compression. How much work was done?

9. Read carefully the following outline for a proof of the fact that $\lim_{w \to 0} (1 + w)^{1/w}$ exists.

Step (a). If we write $w = 1/n$, then $w \to 0$ from above as $n \to \infty$. If we write $w = -1/n$, then $w \to 0$ from below as $n \to \infty$. We shall first consider $\lim_{n \to \infty} (1 + 1/n)^n$. Second, when this limit has been demonstrated to exist, we shall consider $\lim_{n \to \infty} (1 - 1/n)^{-n}$, and show that this limit is the same as the first. In this way the existence of $\lim_{w \to 0} (1 + w)^{1/w}$ will be demonstrated. We shall restrict ourselves at first to integer values for n.

Step (b). Consider, then, $u_n = (1 + 1/n)^n$. We have $u_1 = (1 + 1)^1 = 2$; $u_2 = (1 + \frac{1}{2})^2 = 2.25$; $u_3 = (1 + \frac{1}{3})^3 = \frac{64}{27} \approx 2.37 \cdots$. We shall show that $u_{n+1} \geq u_n$ for all n; that is, that the sequence of u_n numbers is steadily increasing. We shall also show that $u_n < 3$ for every n. Then, intuitively, if a bounded sequence of numbers increases steadily, that sequence must approach a limit less than, or equal to, its bound.

Step (c). By the Binomial Theorem we have

$$u_n = \left(1 + \frac{1}{n}\right)^n = 1 + \frac{n}{1}\left(\frac{1}{n}\right) + \frac{n(n-1)}{1(2)}\left(\frac{1}{n}\right)^2 + \frac{n(n-1)(n-2)}{1(2)(3)}\left(\frac{1}{n}\right)^3$$

$$+ \frac{n(n-1)(n-2)(n-3)}{1(2)(3)(4)}\left(\frac{1}{n}\right)^4 + \cdots + \frac{n(n-1)(n-2)\cdots 1}{1(2)(3)\cdots(n)}\left(\frac{1}{n}\right)^n$$

$$u_n = 1 + 1 + \frac{1}{2!}\left(1 - \frac{1}{n}\right) + \frac{1}{3!}\left(1 - \frac{1}{n}\right)\left(1 - \frac{2}{n}\right) + \frac{1}{4!}\left(1 - \frac{1}{n}\right)\left(1 - \frac{2}{n}\right)\left(1 - \frac{3}{n}\right)$$

$$+ \cdots + \frac{1}{n!}\left(1 - \frac{1}{n}\right)\left(1 - \frac{2}{n}\right)\cdots\left(1 - \frac{n-1}{n}\right), \qquad (9)$$

where $k!$ is an abbreviation for $(1)(2)(3)\cdots(k-1)(k)$. To continue, for u_{n+1} we would have a similar expression with n replaced by $n + 1$:

$$u_{n+1} = 1 + 1 + \frac{1}{2!}\left(1 - \frac{1}{n+1}\right) + \frac{1}{3!}\left(1 - \frac{1}{n+1}\right)\left(1 - \frac{2}{n+1}\right)$$

$$+ \frac{1}{4!}\left(1 - \frac{1}{n+1}\right)\left(1 - \frac{2}{n+1}\right)\left(1 - \frac{3}{n+1}\right) + \cdots.$$

Because

$$\frac{1}{n+1} < \frac{1}{n},$$

we have

$$\left(1 - \frac{k}{n+1}\right) > \left(1 - \frac{k}{n}\right).$$

· The terms of u_{n+1} are greater than those of u_n and there is also one extra positive term. We conclude that $u_{n+1} > u_n$.

Step (d). Because $1 - k/n < 1$ we can deduce from Eq. (9) that

$$u_n < 1 + 1 + \frac{1}{2!} + \frac{1}{3!} + \frac{1}{4!} + \cdots + \frac{1}{n!}.$$

Because $\quad \dfrac{1}{3!} = \dfrac{1}{(2)(3)} < \dfrac{1}{(2)(2)} \quad$ and $\quad \dfrac{1}{4!} = \dfrac{1}{(2)(3)(4)} < \dfrac{1}{(2)(2)(2)},$

we deduce next that

$$u_n < 1 + 1 + \frac{1}{2} + \frac{1}{2^2} + \frac{1}{2^3} + \cdots + \frac{1}{2^{n-1}} = 1 + 1 + \left(\frac{1}{2} + \frac{1}{4} + \frac{1}{8} + \cdots + \frac{1}{2^{n-1}}\right).$$

Here we recognize a well-known geometric series, and we see that

$$u_n < 1 + 1 + (1) = 3.$$

Thus we have shown that the u_n's are a steadily increasing, bounded sequence and have a limit. That limit is called e.

Step (e). We should also consider the case where $w \to 0$ through negative values. If we let $w = -1/n$ and let $n \to \infty$, we are led to consider $\lim_{n \to \infty} (1 - 1/n)^{-n}$. But

$$v_n = \left(1 - \frac{1}{n}\right)^{-n} = \left(\frac{n-1}{n}\right)^{-n} = \left(\frac{n}{n-1}\right)^{n}.$$

Writing $n - 1 = m$, we have

$$v_n = \left(\frac{m+1}{m}\right)^{m+1} = \left(1 + \frac{1}{m}\right)^{m+1} = \left(1 + \frac{1}{m}\right)^{m}\left(1 + \frac{1}{m}\right)^{1}.$$

If $n \to \infty$, so does m, and we see that

$$\lim_{n \to \infty} v_n = \lim_{m \to \infty} v_n = \lim_{m \to \infty} \left(1 + \frac{1}{m}\right)^{m}\left(1 + \frac{1}{m}\right) = e(1) = e.$$

Step (f). A more complete proof would now take into account the fact that we restricted n to integer values. Show that, if n is a positive integer and $n < t < n + 1$, then

$$\left(1 + \frac{1}{n+1}\right)^{n} < \left(1 + \frac{1}{t}\right)^{t} < \left(1 + \frac{1}{n}\right)^{n+1},$$

or

$$\frac{\left(1 + \dfrac{1}{n+1}\right)^{n+1}}{\left(1 + \dfrac{1}{n+1}\right)^{1}} < \left(1 + \frac{1}{t}\right)^{t} < \left(1 + \frac{1}{n}\right)^{n}\left(1 + \frac{1}{n}\right)^{1}.$$

Here $(1 + 1/n)^n$ and $[1 + 1/(n+1)]^{n+1}$ are known to come as close to e as desired for large enough n, while $1 + 1/n$ and $1 + 1/(n+1)$ come as close to unity as desired.

5.4 The Exponential Function and Its Derivative

The logarithmic and exponential functions are inverse functions;

$$y = f(x) = \log x, \text{ domain } S_x : x > 0, \text{ range } S_y : \text{ all real } y \qquad (1)$$

means that y is the proper exponent to use when writing a positive number x as a power of e; in symbols,

$$x = f^{-1}(y) = e^{y}, \text{ domain } S_y : \text{ all real } y, \text{ range } S_x : x > 0. \qquad (2)$$

The logarithm function can be said to carry a particular positive x into a certain y, Eq. (1); it is the exponential function that carries that number y back into the original x, Eq. (2). In this section we shall investigate some of the properties of the exponential function.

■ **THEOREM 1A**

HYPOTHESIS: $y = e^x$, x any real number.

CONCLUSION: $$\frac{dy}{dx} = e^x.$$

■ **THEOREM 1B**

HYPOTHESIS: $u(x)$ and $u'(x)$ exist for x of domain D.

CONCLUSION: $$\frac{d}{dx} e^u = e^u \frac{du}{dx} \qquad \text{for } x \text{ of } D.$$

In words, the conclusion says that the derivative of an exponential function is the *very same exponential function* multiplied by the derivative of the exponent.

PROOF: Theorem 1A is a special case of Theorem 1B. We shall prove the latter. From $y = e^u$, logarithmic differentiation gives us

$$\log y = \log e^u = u \log e = u,$$

$$\frac{1}{y} \frac{dy}{dx} = \frac{du}{dx}, \qquad \frac{dy}{dx} = y \frac{du}{dx} = e^u \frac{du}{dx}.$$

Example 1. If $y = 16e^{-3t}$, then

$$\frac{dy}{dt} = 16e^{-3t}(-3) = -48e^{-3t}.$$

If $x = ze^{-3z^2}$, we use the product rule and write

$$\frac{dx}{dz} = z \frac{d}{dz}(e^{-3z^2}) + e^{-3z^2} \frac{d(z)}{dz} = ze^{-3z^2}(-6z) + e^{-3z^2}(1) = e^{-3z^2}(1 - 6z^2). \qquad -$$

Example 2. Let us discuss and sketch the graph of $y = e^x$. Because the exponential and logarithmic functions are inverse functions, one way to draw the graph of $y = e^x$ would be to take the graph of $y = \log x$ and interchange the x and y axes. Compare Fig. 5.2 with Fig. 5.6 here.

We shall discuss the graph of $y = e^x$ directly. First, $y = e^x > 0$ for all x. This we show by considering the various possibilities for x. If x is a positive integer, then y is an integral power of e and surely positive. If $x = p/q$, p and q positive integers, then, by definition, e^x is the positive number whose qth power is e^p. If x is a positive irrational number, then x can be approximated as closely as desired by rational numbers of the form p/q, and since the exponential function is continuous, e^x can be approximated as closely as desired by numbers of the form $e^{p/q}$, already known to be positive. If $x = 0$, then $y = e^0 = 1$.

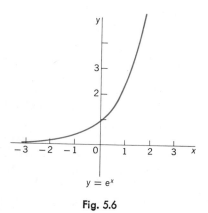

$y = e^x$

Fig. 5.6

Lastly, if x is negative, then $x = -z$ where z is positive, $e^x = e^{-z} = 1/e^z$, and e^x is positive because it is the reciprocal of a positive number.

Further, if $x > 0$ and x grows beyond all bounds, y will grow beyond all bounds. But if $x \to -\infty$, then $z = -x$ will approach $+\infty$ and $y = e^x = e^{-z} = 1/e^z$ will approach 0. The x axis is an asymptote.

From $dy/dx = e^x > 0$ we see that the graph rises steadily; there is a tangent at every point, never horizontal and never vertical. From $d^2y/dx^2 = e^x > 0$, we see that the graph always faces up. The graph was sketched in Fig. 5.6, coordinates of specific points having been determined from a table for the function e^x.

Example 3. Let us discuss and sketch a "normal probability" graph, $y = e^{-x^2}$. From the equation itself we see that the graph will be symmetric with respect to the y axis, because $(-x, y)$ will lie on the graph whenever (x, y) does. Further, we can write $y = 1/e^{x^2}$ and $y \to 0$ as $x \to \pm\infty$; the x axis is an asymptote. From the equation $dy/dx = -2xe^{-x^2}$ we conclude that dy/dx exists for all x and vanishes only at $(0, 1)$. For d^2y/dx^2 we have

$$\frac{d^2y}{dx^2} = -2[xe^{-x^2}(-2x) + e^{-x^2}] = -2e^{-x^2}[1 - 2x^2].$$

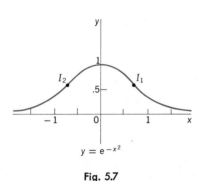

$y = e^{-x^2}$

Fig. 5.7

At $(0, 1)$, $d^2y/dx^2 = -2 < 0$; the graph faces down and we have a maximum point as in Fig. 5.7. We shall have $d^2y/dx^2 = 0$ when $x^2 = \frac{1}{2}$, thus at $I_1 (\sqrt{\frac{1}{2}}, e^{-1/2})$ and $I_2 (-\sqrt{\frac{1}{2}}, e^{-1/2})$. At these points d^2y/dx^2 changes sign, as we see in the table

x	$< \sqrt{\frac{1}{2}}$	$> \sqrt{\frac{1}{2}}$
y''	$-$	$+$

and we conclude that I_1 and I_2 are points of inflection.

Example 4. The function $y = a \cos bt$, $a > 0$ and $b > 0$, is periodic with period $2\pi/b$. It attains the same maximum value, $y = a$, at $t = 0, 2\pi/b, 4\pi/b$, and so on. It can describe a simple harmonic motion. But, in nature, repetitive phenomena actually lose strength gradually and "damp out." A weight will not bob up and down at the end of a spring indefinitely; the system gradually loses energy because of friction, and the maximum displacement gradually decreases. The function $y = e^{-at} \cos bt$ can describe a "damped harmonic motion." We find that $y = 0$ at regular intervals and that y is alternately positive and negative, but that the maximum displacements gradually decrease.

In particular, let us discuss $y = e^{-.2t} \cos 2\pi t$ for $t \geq 0$. The function $\bar{y} = \cos 2\pi t$ has amplitude 1 and period $2\pi/2\pi = 1$. It vanishes at $t = \frac{1}{4}, \frac{3}{4}, \frac{5}{4}, \frac{7}{4}, \cdots$ and attains its maximum and minimum values at $t = 0, \frac{1}{2}, 1, \frac{3}{2}, 2, \cdots$ (see Fig. 5.8). For the function $y = e^{-.2t} \cos 2\pi t = e^{-.2t}\bar{y}$, we see that y vanishes wherever $\bar{y}$ does. But at the places where $\bar{y}$ attains its maximum and minimum values, $+1$ and -1, y takes on smaller values, as shown in Table 5.1.

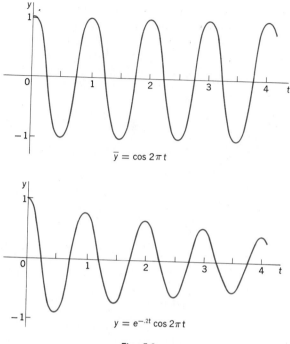

$\bar{y} = \cos 2\pi t$

$y = e^{-.2t} \cos 2\pi t$

Fig. 5.8

TABLE 5.1

t	0	0.5	1	1.5	2	2.5	3	3.5	4
$\bar{y}$	1	-1	1	-1	1	-1	1	-1	1
y	1	-0.90	0.82	-0.74	0.67	-0.61	0.55	-0.50	0.45

The graph for y is sketched roughly from these data for $0 \le t \le 4$. As $t \to \infty$, $e^{-.2t} = 1/e^{.2t} \to 0$, and y approaches 0 in the sense that $|y|$ will become, and remain, less than any positive number specified, no matter how small.

However, y does not attain its maximum and minimum values at precisely $t = 0, \frac{1}{2}, 1, \frac{3}{2}, 2$, and so on, as $\bar{y}$ did, but slightly before these values of t. This is one reason for saying that in Fig. 5.8 we have an easily drawn but only approximate sketch for y. The reader can discuss this matter further in Exercise 5.4-5.

● **Remark 1**

For $y = e^{kx}$ we have $dy/dx = ke^{kx}$. Thus $y = e^{kx}$ is a function whose rate of change is proportional to the function itself. There are many situations in nature where a quantity changes at a rate proportional to the quantity itself. To describe such a quantity, we would have to use exponential functions.

Example 5.   Let us consider a population problem. Assume that N, the number of bacteria in a certain test tube at time t, changes at a rate proportional to N itself.* If the constant of proportionality is k, and if there are N_0 bacteria at time $t = 0$, find a formula for N at any time t, and find the time required for the bacteria to double in number.

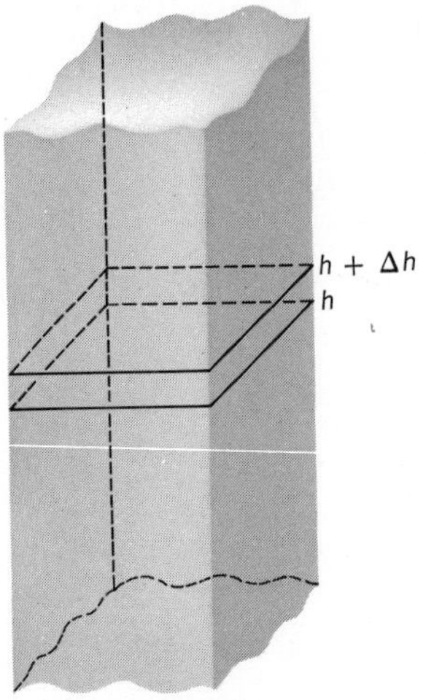

We are told that

$$\frac{dN}{dt} = kN \qquad \text{or} \qquad \frac{1}{N}\frac{dN}{dt} = k.$$

If we integrate with respect to t, we get

$$\log N = kt + C. \qquad (3)$$

We were also told that $N = N_0$ when $t = 0$. Hence, in Eq. (3), $\log N_0 = 0 + C$, or $C = \log N_0$, and rewriting Eq. (3) we have

$$\log N = kt + \log N_0,$$

or $\log N - \log N_0 = kt$, $\quad \log \dfrac{N}{N_0} = kt$, $\quad \dfrac{N}{N_0} = e^{kt}$,

and thus $\qquad\qquad N = N_0 e^{kt}$,

which is a formula for N as a function of t. Finally, N will be $2N_0$ when $2N_0 = N_0 e^{kt}$, so that

Fig. 5.9

$$e^{kt} = 2, \qquad kt = \log 2, \qquad t = \frac{\log 2}{k}.$$

The bacteria will double in number in $(\log 2)/k$ units of time.

The equation $dN/dt = kN$, which we studied here, is called a derivative equation or a differential equation. Chapter 14 of this text is devoted to a more detailed discussion of differential equations.

Example 6.   Consider a column of air of cross-sectional area 1 sq in.; see Fig. 5.9. If the weight of the air in the column above level h is w lb, then we say that the pressure p at height h is w lb psi. We shall find the rate at which p changes with respect to h.

If we increase h by Δh, the pressure at level $h + \Delta h$ will be the weight of the air in the column above level $h + \Delta h$, and the decrease in pressure will be the weight of the air in the column between the two levels. The volume of this air is $\Delta h(1)^2 = \Delta h$, and if $\bar{p}$ is the average weight density of the air between the levels, then

$$\Delta p = -\bar{p}\,\Delta h. \qquad (4)$$

But we are assuming that the temperature is constant and under this condition the density of the gas is in turn proportional to the pressure; hence Eq. (4) becomes

$$\Delta p = -k\bar{p}\,\Delta h \qquad \text{or} \qquad \frac{\Delta p}{\Delta h} = -k\bar{p},$$

---

* This is a reasonable assumption to make; other influences kept constant, twice as many "births" would be expected when twice as many bacteria are present.

where $\bar{p}$ is the average pressure for the interval h to $h + \Delta h$. Now if $\Delta h \to 0$, $\bar{p} \to p$ and we have

$$\frac{dp}{dh} = -kp;$$

the rate of change of p is proportional to p itself.

The formula for p as a function of h must be exponential. Indeed, we have

$$\frac{1}{p}\frac{dp}{dh} = -k,$$

and integrating with respect to h we get

$$\log p = -kh + C.$$

Now let $p = p_0$ when $h = 0$; then $\log p_0 = 0 + C$, $C = \log p_0$, and

$$\log p = -kh + \log p_0.$$

Rewriting, we obtain

$$\log p - \log p_0 = -kh, \qquad \log \frac{p}{p_0} = -kh, \qquad \frac{p}{p_0} = e^{-kh}, \qquad p = p_0 e^{-kh}.$$

We conclude this section by pointing out that the conclusions of Theorems 1A and 1B can be written in integral form, as follows:

$$\int e^x \, dx = e^x + C, \tag{5}$$

and

$$\int e^u \frac{du}{dx} \, dx = e^u + C. \tag{6}$$

In words, Eq. (6) might read, "To get an exponential function multiplied by the derivative of its exponent, that very same exponential function must be differentiated."

Example 7

$$\int e^{kx} \, dx = \frac{1}{k} \int e^{kx} k \, dx = \frac{1}{k} e^{kx} + C \qquad \text{if } k \neq 0.$$

We provided the derivative of the exponent by introducing the constants k and $1/k$.

Example 8

$$\int e^{-\pi t^2} t \, dt = -\frac{1}{2\pi} \int e^{-\pi t^2}(-2\pi t) \, dt = -\frac{1}{2\pi} e^{-\pi t^2} + C.$$

● **Remark 2**

We would like very much to evaluate the integral $\int e^{-x^2} \, dx$, because statisticians find areas under the normal probability graph very important, but this integral is not a special case of the integral appearing in Eq. (6) and we cannot handle it yet.

EXERCISES 5.4

1. Find dy/dx for

(a) $y = e^{-.2x}$.

(b) $y = ae^{bx^2}$.

(c) $y = ax^n e^{bx}$.

(d) $y = e^{ax} \sin bx$.

(e) $y = \dfrac{e^{2x}}{x^2}$.

(f) $y = \dfrac{e^x + e^{-x}}{e^x - e^{-x}}$.

(g) $ye^{ax} + xe^{ay} = 1$.

(h) $e^{x+y} = e^x + e^y$.

(i) $y = e^{e^x}$.

2. Integrate

(a) $\int e^{-4x}\, dx$.

(b) $\int \dfrac{1}{e^{4x}}\, dx$.

(c) $\int (e^{-2x})^2\, dx$.

(d) $\int e^{-x^3} x^2\, dx$.

(e) $\int e^{\sqrt{x}}\, \dfrac{1}{\sqrt{x}}\, dx$.

(f) $\int \dfrac{e^x}{e^x + 1}\, dx$.

3. Discuss and sketch $y = e^{-x}$.

4. Choose b so that $y = e^{-bx^2}$ will have a point of inflection at $x = 1$.

5. Return to Example 4. Show that the maximum and minimum values of $y = e^{-.2t} \cos 2\pi t$ occur at those t for which $\tan 2\pi t = -1/10\pi$. (This means $t \approx k/2 - .005$, $k = 0, 1, 2, \cdots$.)

6. Find the area of the region bounded by $y = e^{-2x}$, the coordinate axes, and $x = b > 0$. For which value of b will this area be $\frac{1}{4}$? What value would the area approach if b were chosen larger and larger, exceeding any finite bound that might be named?

7. Find the area of the region bounded by the x axis, $y = (a/2)(e^{x/a} + e^{-x/a})$, $x = -h$, and $x = +h$.

8. Consider the following population problem. Let N be the number of atoms of a certain radioactive element in a container at time t. Let $N = N_0$ at time $t = 0$, and let this element disintegrate in such a way that N decreases at a rate proportional to N itself, k the constant of proportionality. This is a reasonable assumption to make; for, when there are twice as many atoms present, one would expect twice as many disintegrations in unit time, and hence twice the rate of loss. Find a formula for N as a function of t and find the time required for N to decrease to half its original value.

9. Let a metal rod have length L_0 at temperature $T = 0$, and let the length change at a rate proportional to the length itself as the temperature changes. This is a reasonable assumption, because a longer rod will expand more than a shorter rod. Find a formula for the length of the rod at any temperature. What must the constant of proportionality be for a certain metal if a rod of length L_0 at $T = 0$ has a length $1.0012L_0$ at $T = 100$?

10. A beam of light passing through a liquid loses intensity, I, as the distance, x, it has moved through the liquid increases. The rate of change of I is proportional to I itself, with a constant of proportionality, $-k$, which depends on the liquid used, among other things. What must k be if a beam of intensity 1 at $x = 0$ has an intensity .01 at $x = 10$?

11. Newton's law of cooling says that a body at temperature T loses heat at a rate proportional to the difference between T and T^*, the temperature of the surrounding medium. Then T decreases at a rate proportional to $T - T^*$. Assuming that T^* is constantly $74°$, that T was $110°$ at time $t = 0$, and the constant of proportionality is .02, find a formula for T as a function of time.

12. A 10-gal container of the solution of a certain salt will be saturated when 20 lb of the salt are in solution. We start with pure water at time $t = 0$, add 20 lb of the salt, and stir steadily. Let N be the number of pounds of the salt already dissolved at time t. Assume that the rate at which more salt is dissolved is $.02(20 - N)$. Find a formula for N as a function of t. When will 10 lb of the salt be dissolved?

13. In electrical circuit theory (and elsewhere) we frequently want to find functions y that satisfy an equation of the form

$$a\frac{d^2y}{dt^2} + b\frac{dy}{dt} + cy = 0, \qquad a, b, c \text{ constants.} \tag{7}$$

Equation (7) requires that a sum of terms shall vanish; this can happen if it is possible to rewrite Eq. (7) so that like terms appear, some with negative coefficients and others with positive coefficients. The function $y = e^{mt}$ is such that dy/dt and d^2y/dt^2 are constant multiples of y, and hence it seems reasonable to try $y = e^{mt}$ as a solution of Eq. (7). Find two values of m for which $y = e^{mt}$ would be a solution of Eq. (7).

14. A particle of mass m is at rest at the origin at time $t = 0$. It moves on the x axis under the influence of a force in the positive x direction of magnitude $k(1 - e^{-t})$, k constant. Derive the formulas

$$v = \frac{k}{m}(e^{-t} + t - 1)$$

and $\qquad x = \frac{k}{m}\left(-e^{-t} + \frac{t^2}{2} - t + 1\right)$

for the particle's speed and position at any later time.

15. We have pointed out that $y = f(x) = \log x$, $x > 0$, and $x = \phi(y) = e^y$, all real y, are inverse functions. Use these functions to illustrate Conclusion (b) of Theorem 4.4-1.

16. Fill in the details of the following argument, in which we explain how great a force is required to cause slipping when a rope is wrapped around a rough cylindrical post, as in the docking of ships.

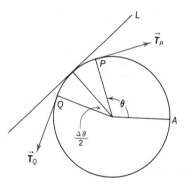

Fig. 5.10

Step (a). Let the tension at A, one end of the rope, be T_0.

Step (b). Let the central angle θ of Fig. 5.10 be measured by the arc starting at A, and consider a portion of the rope, $\overparen{PQ}$, just before slipping takes place in the direction P to Q. We shall analyze the various forces acting on segment $\overparen{PQ}$ by considering the components along and perpendicular to L, the tangent at the midpoint of $\overparen{PQ}$.

Step (c). The tension at P, $\vec{T}_P$, has magnitude $T(\theta)$ and components $T(\theta)$ cos $(\Delta\theta/2)$, $T(\theta)$ sin $(\Delta\theta/2)$ along and perpendicular to L.

Step (d). The tension at Q, $\vec{T}_Q$, has magnitude $T(\theta + \Delta\theta)$ and components $T(\theta + \Delta\theta)$ cos $(\Delta\theta/2)$, $T(\theta + \Delta\theta)$ sin $(\Delta\theta/2)$ along and perpendicular to L.

Step (e). Those components perpendicular to L give rise to a frictional force of magnitude

$$k\left[T(\theta)\sin\frac{\Delta\theta}{2} + T(\theta + \Delta\theta)\sin\frac{\Delta\theta}{2}\right]$$

which helps the component of $\vec{T}_P$ along L balance that of $\vec{T}_Q$ along L; k is the "coefficient of friction."

Step (f). Equating components along L, because $\overparen{PQ}$ is in equilibrium, we have

$$T(\theta + \Delta\theta)\cos\frac{\Delta\theta}{2} = T(\theta)\cos\frac{\Delta\theta}{2} + k\sin\frac{\Delta\theta}{2}[T(\theta) + T(\theta + \Delta\theta)].$$

Step (g). Dividing by $\Delta\theta$ and letting $\Delta\theta$ approach 0, we get

$$\cos\frac{\Delta\theta}{2}\left[\frac{T(\theta+\Delta\theta)-T(\theta)}{\Delta\theta}\right] = k\,\frac{\sin(\Delta\theta/2)}{\Delta\theta}[T(\theta)+T(\theta+\Delta\theta)],$$

$$\frac{dT}{d\theta} = kT.*$$

Again, a rate of change is proportional to the expression itself.

Step (h). Now from

$$\frac{1}{T}\frac{dT}{d\theta} = k,$$

it follows that $T = T_0\,e^{k\theta}$. When k is of suitable magnitude, T is very much larger than T_0 for large θ.

5.5 The Hyperbolic Functions and Their Derivatives

!

Certain combinations of the exponential functions occur so frequently that they are given names. They can then be referred to easily.

■ DEFINITION 1

The hyperbolic functions.

(A) $\cosh x = \dfrac{e^x + e^{-x}}{2}$ for all x. (D) $\coth x = \dfrac{\cosh x}{\sinh x}$, $x \neq 0$.

(B) $\sinh x = \dfrac{e^x - e^{-x}}{2}$ for all x. (E) $\operatorname{sech} x = \dfrac{1}{\cosh x}$ for all x.

(C) $\tanh x = \dfrac{\sinh x}{\cosh x}$ for all x. (F) $\operatorname{csch} x = \dfrac{1}{\sinh x}$, $x \neq 0$.

From these definitions, certain identities for the hyperbolic functions follow. These identities resemble trigonometric identities, and we list the two sets of identities side by side.

■ THEOREM 1

Identities for the hyperbolic functions.

HYPOTHESIS: x is a number for which the hyperbolic or trigonometric functions concerned are defined.

---

* Observe that

$$\lim_{\Delta\theta\to 0}\cos\frac{\Delta\theta}{2} = 1,$$

$$\lim_{\Delta\theta\to 0}\frac{\sin(\Delta\theta/2)}{\Delta\theta} = \lim_{\Delta\theta\to 0}\frac{1}{2}\frac{\sin(\Delta\theta/2)}{\Delta\theta/2} = \frac{1}{2}\lim_{w\to 0}\frac{\sin w}{w} = \frac{1}{2},$$

and

$$\lim_{\Delta\theta\to 0}[T(\theta)+T(\theta+\Delta\theta)] = 2T(\theta).$$

CONCLUSION:

Hyperbolic Identities	Trigonometric Identities
(A) $\cosh(-x) = \cosh x.$	(A') $\cos(-x) = \cos x.$
(B) $\sinh(-x) = -\sinh x.$	(B') $\sin(-x) = -\sin x.$
(C) $\cosh^2 x - \sinh^2 x = 1.$	(C') $\cos^2 x + \sin^2 x = 1.$
(D) $1 - \tanh^2 x = \operatorname{sech}^2 x.$	(D') $1 + \tan^2 x = \sec^2 x.$
(E) $\coth^2 x - 1 = \operatorname{csch}^2 x.$	(E') $\cot^2 x + 1 = \csc^2 x.$
(F) $\cosh(x+y) = \cosh x \cosh y$ $+ \sinh x \sinh y.$	(F') $\cos(x+y) = \cos x \cos y$ $- \sin x \sin y.$
(G) $\sinh(x+y) = \sinh x \cosh y$ $+ \cosh x \sinh y.$	(G') $\sin(x+y) = \sin x \cos y$ $+ \cos x \sin y.$
(H) $\cosh 2x = \cosh^2 x + \sinh^2 x.$	(H') $\cos 2x = \cos^2 x - \sin^2 x.$
(I) $\sinh 2x = 2 \sinh x \cosh x.$	(I') $\sin 2x = 2 \sin x \cos x.$

PROOF: We shall demonstrate some of these identities and leave others to the reader as exercises.

To demonstrate Identity (A), we write

$$\cosh(-x) = \frac{e^{-x} + e^{-(-x)}}{2} = \frac{e^{-x} + e^x}{2} = \frac{e^x + e^{-x}}{2} = \cosh x.$$

To demonstrate Identity (C), we have

$$\cosh^2 x - \sinh^2 x = \frac{(e^x + e^{-x})^2}{4} - \frac{(e^x - e^{-x})^2}{4}$$
$$= \tfrac{1}{4}[(e^{2x} + 2 + e^{-2x}) - (e^{2x} - 2 + e^{-2x})]$$
$$= \tfrac{1}{4}(4) = 1.$$

Lastly, to demonstrate Identity (F), we compute:

$$\cosh x \cosh y + \sinh x \sinh y = \left(\frac{e^x + e^{-x}}{2}\right)\left(\frac{e^y + e^{-y}}{2}\right) + \left(\frac{e^x - e^{-x}}{2}\right)\left(\frac{e^y - e^{-y}}{2}\right)$$
$$= \tfrac{1}{4}(e^{x+y} + e^{x-y} + e^{-x+y} + e^{-x-y} + e^{x+y} - e^{x-y} - e^{-x+y} + e^{-x-y})$$
$$= \tfrac{1}{2}(e^{x+y} + e^{-x-y}) = \cosh(x+y).$$

The derivatives of the hyperbolic functions follow from their definitions, and again we also list the corresponding trigonometric facts.

■ THEOREM 2

The derivatives of the hyperbolic functions.

HYPOTHESIS: $u(x)$ and $u'(x)$ have domain $D.$

CONCLUSION: For those x for which the hyperbolic or trigonometric functions concerned are defined, we have

Hyperbolic Derivatives	*Trigonometric Derivatives*

(A) $\dfrac{d}{dx} \cosh x = \sinh x,$ (A') $\dfrac{d}{dx} (\cos x) = -\sin x.$

$\dfrac{d}{dx} \cosh u = \sinh u \dfrac{du}{dx}.$

(B) $\dfrac{d}{dx} \sinh x = \cosh x,$ (B') $\dfrac{d}{dx} (\sin x) = \cos x.$

$\dfrac{d}{dx} \sinh u = \cosh u \dfrac{du}{dx}.$

(C) $\dfrac{d}{dx} \tanh x = \operatorname{sech}^2 x,$ (C') $\dfrac{d}{dx} (\tan x) = \sec^2 x.$

$\dfrac{d}{dx} \tanh u = \operatorname{sech}^2 u \dfrac{du}{dx}.$

(D) $\dfrac{d}{dx} \operatorname{sech} x = -\operatorname{sech} x \tanh x,$ (D') $\dfrac{d}{dx} (\sec x) = \sec x \tan x.$

$\dfrac{d}{dx} \operatorname{sech} u = -\operatorname{sech} u \tanh u \dfrac{du}{dx}.$

(E) $\dfrac{d}{dx} \coth x = -\operatorname{csch}^2 x,$ (E') $\dfrac{d}{dx} (\cot x) = -\csc^2 x.$

$\dfrac{d}{dx} \coth u = -\operatorname{csch}^2 u \dfrac{du}{dx}.$

(F) $\dfrac{d}{dx} \operatorname{csch} x = -\operatorname{csch} x \coth x,$ (F') $\dfrac{d}{dx} (\csc x) = -\csc x \cot x.$

$\dfrac{d}{dx} \operatorname{csch} u = -\operatorname{csch} u \coth u \dfrac{du}{dx}.$

● **Remark 1**

For most readers it will suffice to remember the derivatives of $\cosh x$ and $\sinh x$ and to look up or work out the derivatives of the others as required.

PROOF: Again we prove some of these statements and leave others as exercises. To prove Identity (A) we have

$$\frac{d}{dx} (\cosh u) = \frac{d}{dx} \frac{e^u + e^{-u}}{2} = \frac{1}{2}\left[e^u \frac{du}{dx} - e^{-u} \frac{du}{dx} \right] = \sinh u \frac{du}{dx}.$$

To prove Identity (C) we first have

$$\frac{d}{dx} (\tanh u) = \frac{d}{dx} \frac{\sinh u}{\cosh u} = \frac{\cosh u \cosh u (du/dx) - \sinh u \sinh u (du/dx)}{\cosh^2 u},$$

using Identities (A) and (B). Then, using Identity (C) of Theorem 1,

$$\frac{d}{dx}(\tanh u) = \frac{\cosh^2 u - \sinh^2 u}{\cosh^2 u}\frac{du}{dx} = \frac{1}{\cosh^2 u}\frac{du}{dx} = \operatorname{sech}^2 u\,\frac{du}{dx}.$$

Example 1. We can discuss the graph for $y = \cosh x$ in two different ways. First, we are already familiar with the graph of $y = e^x$. The graph for $y = e^{-x}$ and that for $y = e^x$ are symmetric with respect to the y axis, because, if the point (a, b) lies on one, the point $(-a, b)$ lies on the other. These graphs are sketched in Fig. 5.11. Finally, the equation $y = \cosh x = \frac{1}{2}(e^x + e^{-x})$ says that the hyperbolic cosine ordinates are averages of the corresponding ordinates of the e^x and e^{-x} curves. At

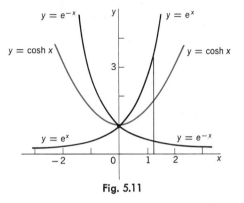

Fig. 5.11

any x, the graph for $\cosh x$ will be found precisely midway between those for e^x and e^{-x}. This graph is called the *catenary*.

We can also discuss the graph $y = \cosh x$ directly. The graph must be symmetric with respect to the y axis because $\cosh(-x) = \cosh x$. Because e^x and $e^{-x} = 1/e^x$ are positive for all x, so is $\cosh x$; the graph lies above the x axis. Further, the difference between the ordinates for $y = \cosh x = \frac{1}{2}(e^x + e^{-x})$ and $y = \frac{1}{2}e^x$ is $\frac{1}{2}e^{-x}$ or $\frac{1}{2}(1/e^x)$, and this difference approaches 0 when x grows beyond all bounds. From

$$\frac{dy}{dx} = \sinh x = \frac{e^x - e^{-x}}{2} = \frac{e^x - 1/e^x}{2} = \frac{e^{2x} - 1}{2e^x},$$

we conclude that $dy/dx = 0$ if $e^{2x} = 1$, $x = 0$. From $d^2y/dx^2 = \cosh x$, we conclude that $d^2y/dx^2 > 0$ for all x, that the graph always faces up, and that $(0, 1)$ is a minimum point. There can be no points of inflection, because the graph cannot change over from facing up to facing down.

Example 2. Let us discuss the graph for $y = \sinh x$ directly. When $y = 0$,

$$\sinh x = \frac{e^x - e^{-x}}{2} = \frac{1}{2}\left(e^x - \frac{1}{e^x}\right) = \frac{e^{2x} - 1}{2e^x} = 0, \qquad e^{2x} = 1, \qquad x = 0;$$

$(0, 0)$ is the only intercept point. Because $\sinh(-x) = -\sinh x$, the point $(-a, -b)$ lies on the graph whenever (a, b) does, and the graph is symmetric with respect to the origin. Further, the difference between the ordinates for $y = \sinh x = \frac{1}{2}(e^x - e^{-x})$ and $y = \frac{1}{2}e^x$ is

$$-\frac{1}{2}e^{-x} = -\frac{1}{2}\frac{1}{e^x}$$

and this difference approaches 0 when x grows beyond all bounds.

From $dy/dx = \cosh x$, we conclude that the slope is always positive and that the graph always rises; there can be no maximum or minimum points. Since $y = \sinh x = 0$ at $x = 0$ and the graph always rises, we must have $y > 0$ for $x > 0$ and $y < 0$ for $x < 0$. Finally, from $d^2y/dx^2 = \sinh x$, we conclude that the graph faces up for $x > 0$, down for $x < 0$. There is a point of inflection at $(0, 0)$, and the slope at this point is $dy/dx = \cosh 0 = 1$. The graph is sketched in Fig. 5.12, individual points having been plotted with the help of tabulated data as required.

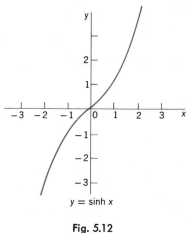

$y = \sinh x$

Fig. 5.12

● **Remark 2**

The conclusion of Theorem 2 can be restated in integral form. Thus we have

$$\int \sinh x \, dx = \cosh x + C, \qquad (1)$$

$$\int \sinh u \, \frac{du}{dx} \, dx = \cosh u + C, \qquad (1a)$$

$$\int \cosh x \, dx = \sinh x + C, \qquad (2)$$

$$\int \cosh u \, \frac{du}{dx} \, dx = \sinh u + C. \qquad (2a)$$

Because $y = \sinh x$ always rises, the hyperbolic sine function does not associate the same y with two different x's and an inverse function is defined. Similarly, because $d(\tanh x)/dx = \operatorname{sech}^2 x > 0$ for all x, $y = \tanh x$ rises for all x and again an inverse function is defined. However,

$$\tanh x = \frac{\sinh x}{\cosh x} = \frac{e^x - e^{-x}}{e^x + e^{-x}} = \frac{e^x - 1/e^x}{e^x + 1/e^x} = \frac{1 - 1/e^{2x}}{1 + 1/e^{2x}};$$

we see that $-1 < \tanh x < 1$ and that $\tanh x$ approaches 1 when x grows beyond all bounds. The reader is asked to continue this discussion and to draw a graph for $y = \tanh x$ in Exercise 5.5-10.

‖

■ **DEFINITION 2**

The inverse hyperbolic functions. For any x, $y = \sinh^{-1} x$ is the number whose hyperbolic sine is x; $\sinh y = x$. For $-1 < x < 1$, $y = \tanh^{-1} x$ is the number whose hyperbolic tangent is x; $\tanh y = x$.

■ **THEOREM 3**

Some identities for the inverse hyperbolic functions.

HYPOTHESIS A: x is a real number.

CONCLUSION: $\sinh^{-1} x = \log (x + \sqrt{x^2 + 1})$.

HYPOTHESIS B: $-1 < x < 1$.

CONCLUSION: $\tanh^{-1} x = \frac{1}{2} \log \dfrac{1 + x}{1 - x}$.

PROOF: We shall prove Theorem 3A and leave the proof of Theorem 3B as an exercise.

Write $y = \sinh^{-1} x$ or $\sinh y = x$. Then, from $(e^y - e^{-y})/2 = x$ we get

$$e^y - e^{-y} = 2x, \qquad e^y - \frac{1}{e^y} = 2x, \qquad e^{2y} - 2xe^y - 1 = 0,$$

and by the quadratic formula,

$$e^y = \frac{2x \pm \sqrt{4x^2 + 4}}{2} = x \pm \sqrt{x^2 + 1}. \tag{3}$$

But $x^2 + 1 > x^2$ and $\sqrt{x^2 + 1} > |x|$. Since e^y must be positive, of the two possibilities that appear at first in Eq. (3) we must choose

$$e^y = x + \sqrt{x^2 + 1}.$$

Finally, taking logarithms, $y = \log(x + \sqrt{x^2 + 1})$, which was to be demonstrated.

■ THEOREM 4

The derivatives of the inverse hyperbolic functions.

HYPOTHESIS: $u(x)$ and $u'(x)$ have domain D.

CONCLUSION: (a) $\dfrac{d \sinh^{-1} u}{dx} = \dfrac{1}{\sqrt{1 + u^2}} \dfrac{du}{dx}$ for x of D.

(b) $\dfrac{d \tanh^{-1} u}{dx} = \dfrac{1}{1 - u^2} \dfrac{du}{dx}$ for x of D for which $-1 < u < 1$.

PROOF: We shall demonstrate Conclusion (a) and leave the demonstration of Conclusion (b) to an exercise. We write $y = \sinh^{-1} u$ or $\sinh y = u$. Then by implicit differentiation,

$$\cosh y \frac{dy}{dx} = \frac{du}{dx}, \qquad \frac{dy}{dx} = \frac{1}{\cosh y} \frac{du}{dx}.$$

Now $\cosh^2 y - \sinh^2 y = 1$, so that $\cosh^2 y = 1 + \sinh^2 y$, and since $\cosh y$ must be positive, we have $\cosh y = \sqrt{1 + \sinh^2 y}$. Thus

$$\frac{dy}{dx} = \frac{1}{\sqrt{1 + \sinh^2 y}} \frac{du}{dx} = \frac{1}{\sqrt{1 + u^2}} \frac{du}{dx}.$$

III

We conclude this section by explaining why the trigonometric functions are sometimes called the "circular" functions and the functions we have studied in this section are called the "hyperbolic" functions.

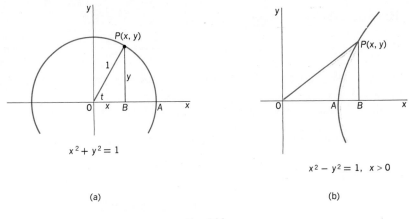

Fig. 5.13

Consider Figs. 5.13(a) and (b). We assert that for any number $t \geq 0$ we can find a point $P(x, y)$ on

the *circle* $x^2 + y^2 = 1$, for which	the *hyperbola* $x^2 - y^2 = 1$, for which
$x = OB = \cos t$,	$x = OB = \cosh t$,
$y = BP = \sin t$,	$y = BP = \sinh t$,
$t = 2(\text{area } OAP)$;	$t = 2(\text{area } OAP)$.

That the points with coordinates $(\cos t, \sin t)$ lie on the circle $x^2 + y^2 = 1$ follows from the identity $\cos^2 t + \sin^2 t = 1$. That the area of sector OAP is $\frac{1}{2} t$ follows from the formula for the area of a sector of a circle with central angle of radian measure t.

On the other hand, we can be sure that the points with coordinates $(\cosh t, \sinh t)$ lie on the hyperbola $x^2 - y^2 = 1$, because we have the identity $\cosh^2 t - \sinh^2 t = 1$. In greater detail, since $\cosh t \geq 1$ for all t, we see that the points $(\cosh t, \sinh t)$ lie on the right wing of the hyperbola. The fact that the area OAP is $t/2$ in this case also will follow readily from an integral computation. We guide the reader through this work in Exercise 5.5-14.

EXERCISES 5.5

1. Complete the proof of Theorem 1 by demonstrating these identities:

   (B) $\sinh(-x) = -\sinh x$.

   (G) $\sinh(x + y) = \sinh x \cosh y + \cosh x \sinh y$.

   (D) $1 - \tanh^2 x = \mathrm{sech}^2 x$.

   (E) $\coth^2 x - 1 = \mathrm{csch}^2 x$.

   (H) $\cosh 2x = \cosh^2 x + \sinh^2 x$.

   (I) $\sinh 2x = 2 \sinh x \cosh x$.

2. Write e^x and e^{-x} in terms of $\cosh x$ and $\sinh x$.

3. Complete the proof of Theorem 2 by demonstrating the following differentiation facts:

   (B) $\dfrac{d}{dx} \sinh x = \cosh x$.

   (E) $\dfrac{d}{dx} \coth x = -\mathrm{csch}^2 x$.

   (D) $\dfrac{d}{dx} \mathrm{sech}\, x = -\mathrm{sech}\, x \tanh x$.

   (F) $\dfrac{d}{dx} \mathrm{csch}\, x = -\mathrm{csch}\, x \coth x$.

4. (a) $y = 2 \sinh 3x + 3 \cosh 3x;$ $\dfrac{dy}{dx} = ?$ (e) $L = \dfrac{\cosh ax + 1}{\sinh ax + 1};$ $\dfrac{dL}{dx} = ?$

(b) $V = \tanh^3 ax;$ $\dfrac{dV}{dx} = ?$ (f) $y = \log \cosh t;$ $\dfrac{dy}{dt} = ?$

(c) $x = t \sinh t;$ $\dfrac{dx}{dt} = ?$ (g) $x \cosh y + y \sinh x = 1;$ $\dfrac{dy}{dx} = ?$

(d) $y = \sinh 2x \cosh^2 2x;$ $\dfrac{dy}{dx} = ?$ (h) $\cosh (x + y) = x - y;$ $\dfrac{dy}{dx} = ?$

5. Integrate

(a) $\int (4 \cosh x + 3 \sinh x) \, dx.$ (d) $\displaystyle\int \dfrac{\sinh 2x}{\cosh 2x + 1} \, dx.$

(b) $\int \operatorname{sech}^2 x \, dx.$ (e) $\displaystyle\int \dfrac{\sinh 2x}{(\cosh 2x + 1)^2} \, dx.$

(c) $\int \sinh^3 x \cosh x \, dx.$

6. Find the area of the region bounded by $y = a \cosh bx$, the coordinate axes, and $x = c$.

7. Find the area of the region bounded by $y = \cosh x$, $y = \sinh 2x$, and the y axis.

8. (a) Show that $y = \alpha \sin kt + \beta \cos kt$ is a solution of $d^2y/dt^2 = -k^2y$.
(If $F = ma = m(d^2y/dt^2)$ is proportional to the displacement and oppositely directed, a periodic motion results.)
(b) Show that $y = \alpha \sinh kt + \beta \cosh kt$ is a solution of $d^2y/dt^2 = k^2y$.
(If $F = ma = m(d^2y/dt^2)$ is proportional to the displacement and similarly directed, a nonperiodic motion results.)

9. If $k > 0$, for what choice of α and β will $\lim_{t \to \infty} (\alpha \sinh kt + \beta \cosh kt) = 0$? What will the limit be for other choices of α and β? If a particle's position at time t is given by the formula $y = \alpha \sinh kt + \beta \cosh kt$, what can be said about its position for large t?

10. Discuss and sketch the graph for $y = \tanh x$.

11. Draw the graphs of $y = \cosh x$ and $y = \operatorname{sech} x$ on the same set of axes. Where are the points of inflection of $y = \operatorname{sech} x$?

12. Complete the proof of Theorem 3 by proving Theorem 3B.

13. Complete the proof of Theorem 4 by demonstrating Conclusion (b).

14. Let $P(\cosh t, \sinh t)$, $t > 0$, be a point on the hyperbola $x^2 - y^2 = 1$; let $A(1, 0)$ be a transverse vertex. We shall outline a computation for the area of region OAP. Fill in the details.

See Fig. 5.14. We shall compute areas OBP and ABP and subtract to find the area of OAP. We have

Step (a). Area $OBP = \frac{1}{2}(OB)(BP) = \frac{1}{2} \cosh t \sinh t = \frac{1}{4} \sinh 2t$.

Step (b). If the region ABP is subdivided by vertical lines, with $(\Delta x)_k$ the width of the kth subregion and y_k^* a representative ordinate for that subregion, then we can say that

$$\text{area of the } k\text{th subregion} \approx y_k^* \, (\Delta x)_k,$$

$$\text{area of } ABP = \int_{x=1}^{\cosh t} y \, dx = \int_{x=1}^{\cosh t} \sqrt{x^2 - 1} \, dx.$$

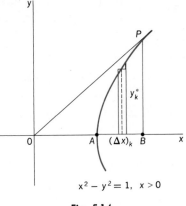

$$x^2 - y^2 = 1, \quad x > 0$$

Fig. 5.14

Step (c). To change the form of this integral, make the substitution $x = \cosh v$, $0 \leq v \leq t$. Then

$$\text{area of } ABP = \int_{v=0}^{t} \sinh^2 v \, dv.$$

Step (d). Through identities for $\cosh 2v$,

$$\text{area of } ABP = \tfrac{1}{2} \int_{v=0}^{t} (\cosh 2v - 1) \, dv,$$

$$\text{area of } ABP = \tfrac{1}{4} \sinh 2t - \tfrac{1}{2} t.$$

Step (e). Area of $OAP = \tfrac{1}{2} t$.

5.6   On the Logarithm Function Defined as an Integral

At the beginning of this chapter we investigated the integral $\int_{t=1}^{x} (1/t) \, dt$. Some of the properties of this integral reminded us of the function $\log x$, and we found that we could write

$$\int_{t=1}^{x} \frac{1}{t} \, dt = \log x$$

if we used logarithms to the base e.

It could very well happen, however, that an integral in which someone was interested could not be expressed in terms of functions already known, and that this integral thus defined a new function. The statistician, for instance, finds that areas under the normal probability graph are very important; he wants to study the integral

$$\frac{1}{\sqrt{2\pi}} \int_{t=0}^{x} e^{-t^2/2} \, dt$$

for different values of $x \geq 0$. This integral cannot be evaluated in terms of previously known functions. It defines a new function,

$$\phi(x) = \frac{1}{\sqrt{2\pi}} \int_{t=0}^{x} e^{-t^2/2} \, dt, \qquad x \geq 0, \tag{1}$$

sometimes called the error integral function. For each $x \geq 0$, Eq. (1) leads to a specific value of ϕ, and the properties of ϕ are deduced from that equation. Two properties thus deduced are

$$\phi(0) = 0 \quad \text{and} \quad \phi'(x) = \frac{1}{\sqrt{2\pi}} e^{-x^2/2}.$$

If we had not already been familiar with the logarithm function, we would have had to define a new function in the following manner.

■ DEFINITION 1

Alternate definition for the logarithm function.

$$\log x = \int_{t=1}^{x} \frac{1}{t}\, dt, \qquad x > 0. \tag{2}$$

Then we would have had to work out the properties of the new function from this definition. By methods like those used in Sec. 5.1 we would have showed that $\log ab = \log a + \log b$, that $\log a/b = \log a - \log b$, and that $\log (a)^c = c \log a$ for all real c. From

$$\frac{d}{dx} \log x = \frac{1}{x}$$

it would follow that $\log x$ is continuous (since it is differentiable) for its domain $x > 0$ and that it is a steadily increasing function for its domain, because its derivative is always positive there. Accordingly there is an inverse function and we can write

$$y = f(x) = \log x, \text{ domain} : x > 0, \text{ range} : \text{all real } y$$

with inverse function

$$x = \phi(y), \text{ domain} : \text{all real } y, \text{ range} : x > 0.$$

In particular, for each real number y we have a corresponding number $x > 0$ such that

$$y = \log x = \log [\phi(y)]. \tag{3}$$

But, if we now give the name e to the number such that $\log e = 1$, we can also write

$$\log e^y = y \log e = y. \tag{4}$$

Equations (3) and (4) together say that $\phi(y) = e^y$, for the logarithm function is steadily increasing and we could not have two different numbers with logarithm both equal to y. Thus we could arrive at the exponential function as the function inverse to the logarithm function:

$$x = \phi(y) = e^y, \text{ domain} : \text{all real } y, \text{ range} : x > 0.$$

In this way of ordering the topics one first computes the logarithm function values from Eq. (2) and then computes the exponential function values as those of the function inverse to the logarithm function.

We did not study the topics in that order, but this procedure does have a basic advantage. If one starts with the exponential function and computes the values of the logarithm function as those of the function inverse to the exponential function, as we did, there is the difficulty of defining what is meant by e^x when x is a real but irrational number. We tacitly assumed that this could be done, but it is not an elementary matter.

We shall further illustrate the derivation of facts about the logarithm function from its integral definition in the example and theorem that follow.

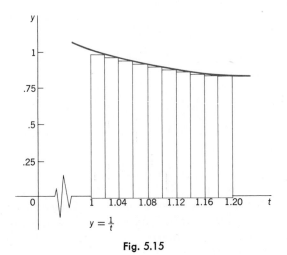

Fig. 5.15

Example 1. We shall compute log 1.2, accurate to two decimal places. We know that $\log 1.2 = \int_1^{1.2} (1/t)\, dt$ and that log 1.2 is thus the area of the region bounded by the t axis, $y = 1/t$, $t = 1$, and $t = 1.2$; see Fig. 5.15. Break this region into 10 subregions by drawing equally spaced vertical lines as shown. If for each subregion we approximate by taking a rectangle whose height is the right boundary ordinate, as shown, then we get an estimate that is too small. If we take a rectangle whose height is the left boundary ordinate, not shown, we get an estimate that is too large. These approximations and the estimates for log 1.2 are given in Table 5.2. (The numbers appearing in the third and fifth columns are values of $1/t$ and are taken from a table of reciprocals.) We conclude from these computations that $.1806 < \log 1.2 < .1840$, so that, to two decimal places, $\log 1.2 \approx .18$. With the help of a computing machine and some approximation refinements, more accurate statements for log 1.2 could be obtained.

It is clear that $\sqrt{x}$, $\sqrt[3]{x}$, and, indeed, x^a for $0 < a < 1$ all increase beyond all bounds when x increases beyond all bounds, but we can easily show that none of them increases as rapidly as x itself does. For, we can write

$$\lim_{x \to \infty} \frac{x^a}{x} = \lim_{x \to \infty} \frac{1}{x^{1-a}} = 0 \qquad \text{for } 0 < a < 1.$$

TABLE 5.2

Subregion boundaries	Base	Minimum height	Area under- estimate	Maximum height	Area over- estimate
1 ↔ 1.02	.02	.9804	.019608	1.0000	.020000
1.02 ↔ 1.04	.02	.9615	.019230	.9804	.019608
1.04 ↔ 1.06	.02	.9434	.018868	.9615	.019230
1.06 ↔ 1.08	.02	.9259	.018518	.9434	.018868
1.08 ↔ 1.10	.02	.9091	.018182	.9259	.018518
1.10 ↔ 1.12	.02	.8929	.017858	.9091	.018182
1.12 ↔ 1.14	.02	.8772	.017544	.8929	.017858
1.14 ↔ 1.16	.02	.8621	.017242	.8772	.017544
1.16 ↔ 1.18	.02	.8475	.016950	.8621	.017242
1.18 ↔ 1.20	.02	.8333	.016666	.8475	.016950
			.180666		.184000

Numerical computations like $\log 7.39 \approx \log e^2 = 2$ and $\log 403 \approx \log e^6 = 6$ would make it appear that the function $\log x$ also does not increase as rapidly as x does. But much more can be said, as Theorem 5.6-1 shows. Not only does $\log x$ not increase as rapidly as x when x increases, but $\log x$ increases less rapidly than $\sqrt{x}$, $\sqrt[3]{x}$, or x^a, where a can be any positive number, no matter how small. For large enough x, even $x^{0.000001}$ will be so much larger than $\log x$ that the quotient $(\log x)/x^{0.000001}$ will be as close to 0 as desired.

■ THEOREM 1

On the relative sizes of $\log x$ *and* x *for large* x.

HYPOTHESIS: $a > 0$.

CONCLUSION:
$$\lim_{x \to \infty} \frac{\log x}{x^a} = 0.$$

PROOF: (a) To get an estimate for the size of $\log w$ for $w > 1$, we can observe that $1/t < 1$ for $t > 1$ and that if we interpret $\int_{t=1}^{w} 1/t \, dt$ and $\int_{t=1}^{w} 1 \, dt$ to be areas under the graphs $y = 1/t$ and $y = 1$, the latter area must be the larger. For $w > 1$

$$\log w = \int_{t=1}^{w} \frac{1}{t} \, dt < \int_{t=1}^{w} 1 \, dt = w - 1 < w.$$

Of course, we also have $\log w > 0$ for $w > 1$, so that

$$0 < \log w < w \qquad \text{for } w > 1. \tag{5}$$

(b) But $x^{a/2} > 1$ for $x > 1$ and, if we take $w = x^{a/2}$ in Eq. (5), we can write

$$0 < \log x^{a/2} < x^{a/2}$$

$$0 < \frac{a}{2} \log x < x^{a/2}$$

$$0 < \frac{a}{2} \frac{\log x}{x^a} < \frac{x^{a/2}}{x^a}$$

$$0 < \frac{\log x}{x^a} < \frac{2}{a} \frac{1}{x^{a/2}}. \tag{6}$$

(c) Since $\lim_{x\to\infty} 1/x^{a/2} = 0$, the conclusion of Theorem 1 follows from Statement (6).

■ THEOREM 2

On the relative sizes of e^x and x for large x.

HYPOTHESIS: $a > 0$.

CONCLUSION: $$\lim_{x\to\infty} \frac{x^a}{e^x} = 0.$$

PROOF: We make the proof of this theorem depend on Theorem 1. If we write $x = \log y$, or $e^x = y$, then $y \to \infty$ when $x \to \infty$, and we can say that

$$\lim_{x\to\infty} \frac{x^a}{e^x} = \lim_{y\to\infty} \frac{(\log y)^a}{y} = \lim_{y\to\infty} \left(\frac{\log y}{y^{1/a}}\right)^a. \tag{7}$$

But Theorem 1 says that $y^{1/a}$, and indeed any power of y with positive exponent, grows large much more rapidly than $\log y$ does; that is,

$$\lim_{y\to\infty} \frac{\log y}{y^{1/a}} = 0.$$

Hence, from Eq. (7), the conclusion of this theorem follows.

This theorem says that for large x, e^x is much larger than any power of x with constant exponent, no matter how large that exponent.

On The Evaluation of Integrals

In his later work the reader will often encounter integrals that we have not yet considered. We shall devote this chapter to the evaluation of integrals, so that it will not be necessary later to interrupt the work at hand for this purpose.

6.1 Review

The integrals we are already familiar with state our differentiation rules in integral language. At this point the reader should be able to recognize integrals of the following types:

$$(1) \quad \int x^n \, dx = \frac{x^{n+1}}{n+1} + C, \qquad n \neq -1.$$

$$(1a) \quad \int (u)^n \frac{du}{dx} \, dx = \frac{(u)^{n+1}}{n+1} + C, \qquad n \neq -1.$$

$$(2) \quad \int x^{-1} \, dx = \int \frac{1}{x} \, dx$$
$$= \log x + C, \qquad x > 0.$$
$$= \log (-x) + C, \qquad x < 0.$$

$$(2a) \quad \int \frac{1}{u} \frac{du}{dx} \, dx = \log u + C, \qquad u > 0.$$
$$= \log (-u) + C, \qquad u < 0.$$

$$(3) \quad \int e^x \, dx = e^x + C.$$

$$(3a) \quad \int e^u \frac{du}{dx} \, dx = e^u + C.$$

$$(4) \quad \int \sin x \, dx = -\cos x + C.$$

$$(4a) \quad \int \sin u \frac{du}{dx} \, dx = -\cos u + C.$$

$$(5) \quad \int \cos x \, dx = \sin x + C.$$

$$(5a) \quad \int \cos u \frac{du}{dx} \, dx = \sin u + C.$$

329

(6) $\displaystyle\int \sec^2 x \, dx = \tan x + C.$

(6a) $\displaystyle\int \sec^2 u \frac{du}{dx} \, dx = \tan u + C.$

(7) $\displaystyle\int \sec x \tan x \, dx = \sec x + C.$

(7a) $\displaystyle\int \sec u \tan u \frac{du}{dx} \, dx = \sec u + C.$

(8) $\displaystyle\int \csc^2 x \, dx = -\cot x + C.$

(8a) $\displaystyle\int \csc^2 u \frac{du}{dx} \, dx = -\cot u + C.$

(9) $\displaystyle\int \csc x \cot x \, dx = -\csc x + C.$

(9a) $\displaystyle\int \csc u \cot u \frac{du}{dx} \, dx$
$= -\csc u + C.$

(10) $\displaystyle\int \frac{1}{\sqrt{1-x^2}} \, dx = \sin^{-1} x + C.$

(10a) $\displaystyle\int \frac{1}{\sqrt{1-u^2}} \frac{du}{dx} \, dx = \sin^{-1} u + C.$

(11) $\displaystyle\int \frac{1}{1+x^2} \, dx = \tan^{-1} x + C.$

(11a) $\displaystyle\int \frac{1}{1+u^2} \frac{du}{dx} \, dx = \tan^{-1} u + C.$

(12) $\displaystyle\int \sinh x \, dx = \cosh x + C.$

(12a) $\displaystyle\int \sinh u \frac{du}{dx} \, dx = \cosh u + C.$

(13) $\displaystyle\int \cosh x \, dx = \sinh x + C.$

(13a) $\displaystyle\int \cosh u \frac{du}{dx} \, dx = \sinh u + C.$

EXERCISES 6.1

Integrate if possible. If the integral stated is not of one of the types (1)–(13), say so.

1. $\displaystyle\int \left(4x^2 + \frac{6}{x} - \frac{3}{x^2}\right) dx.$

2. $\displaystyle\int (6 \sin 2x - 4 \cos 2x) \, dx.$

3. $\displaystyle\int \frac{x}{1 + 4x^2} \, dx.$

4. $\displaystyle\int 3e^{-.01x} \, dx.$

5. $\displaystyle\int \sec^4 x \tan x \, dx.$

6. $\displaystyle\int \csc^2 3t \, dt.$

7. $\displaystyle\int \left(\frac{3}{\sqrt{x}} - 5\sqrt{x^3}\right) dx.$

8. $\displaystyle\int \frac{1}{\sqrt{1 - 4u^2}} \, du.$

9. $\displaystyle\int \sec^2 ax \, dx.$

10. $\displaystyle\int \frac{t}{(1 + t^2)^3} \, dt.$

11. $\displaystyle\int (3 \cosh 3x - \sinh 3x) \, dx.$

12. $\displaystyle\int \sqrt{1 - x^2} \, dx.$

13. $\displaystyle\int \sec \frac{1}{2} z \tan \frac{1}{2} z \, dz.$

14. $\displaystyle\int (2t + 1)^4 \, dt.$

15. $\displaystyle\int \frac{\cos x}{\sin x + 2} \, dx.$

16. $\displaystyle\int (e^x + 1)^5 e^x \, dx.$

17. $\displaystyle\int e^{\sqrt{x}} \, dx.$

18. $\displaystyle\int \sqrt{x^3 + 1} \, x \, dx.$

19. $\displaystyle\int \cosh^3 x \sinh x \, dx.$

20. $\displaystyle\int \sqrt[3]{x^2 + 1} \, x \, dx.$

21. $\displaystyle\int \csc ax \cot ax \, dx.$

22. $\displaystyle\int \frac{3}{2t + 1} \, dt.$

23. $\displaystyle\int \frac{1}{1 + 4x^2} \, dx.$

24. $\displaystyle\int \frac{\sin y}{(\cos y + 1)^2} \, dy.$

6.2 Trigonometric Integrals

I

We can handle those trigonometric integrals that are already in one of the forms (4) to (9) listed in Sec. 6.1, or in the form $\int (u)^n(du/dx)\, dx$, where u is a trigonometric expression. We try to convert other trigonometric integrals to one of these forms by using identities.

Remember that the trigonometric functions can be grouped in three families and that for each family we have one of the Pythagorean identities.

Family 1	*Family 2*	*Family 3*
$\dfrac{d \sin x}{dx} = \cos x.$	$\dfrac{d \tan x}{dx} = \sec^2 x.$	$\dfrac{d \cot x}{dx} = -\csc^2 x.$
$\dfrac{d \cos x}{dx} = -\sin x.$	$\dfrac{d \sec x}{dx} = \sec x \tan x.$	$\dfrac{d \csc x}{dx} = -\csc x \cot x.$
$\sin^2 x + \cos^2 x = 1.$	$\sec^2 x = \tan^2 x + 1.$	$\csc^2 x = \cot^2 x + 1.$

In the sine-cosine family, for instance, if the factor $\cos x$ is part of the integrand, we can handle powers of $\sin x$; if the factor $\sin x$ is part of the integrand, we can handle powers of $\cos x$. For we have

$$
\begin{aligned}
\int (\sin x)^n \cos x \, dx &= \frac{(\sin x)^{n+1}}{n+1} + C, \quad n \neq -1 \\
&= \log \sin x + C, \quad n = -1 \text{ and } \sin x > 0 \\
&= \log(-\sin x) + C, \quad n = -1 \text{ and } \sin x < 0
\end{aligned} \Bigg\} . \quad (1)
$$

$$
\begin{aligned}
\int (\cos x)^n \sin x \, dx &= -\int (\cos x)^n(-\sin x)\, dx \\
&= -\frac{(\cos x)^{n+1}}{n+1} + C, \quad n \neq -1 \\
&= -\log \cos x + C, \quad n = -1 \text{ and } \cos x > 0 \\
&= -\log(-\cos x) + C, \quad n = -1 \text{ and } \cos x < 0
\end{aligned} \Bigg\} . \quad (2)
$$

By using the identity $\sin^2 x + \cos^2 x = 1$, it may be possible to rewrite other integrands that contain $\sin x$ or $\cos x$ as a factor in such a way that integrals of the form (1) or (2) are obtained.

Example 1

$$
\begin{aligned}
\int \sin^3 x \, dx &= \int \sin^2 x \sin x \, dx \\
&= \int (1 - \cos^2 x) \sin x \, dx \\
&= \int \sin x \, dx - \int (\cos x)^2 \sin x \, dx
\end{aligned}
$$

$$= -\int -\sin x \, dx + \int (\cos x)^2(-\sin x) \, dx$$

$$= -\cos x + \frac{\cos^3 x}{3} + C.$$

Here we separated out the factor $\sin x$ as part of the integrand immediately and then tried to convert the rest of the integrand to powers of $\cos x$, because we knew that $-\sin x$ was the derivative of $\cos x$.

Example 2. $\int \cos^3 2x \sin^2 2x \, dx$. Here we shall separate out the factor $\cos 2x$ as part of the integrand and try to convert the rest of the integrand to powers of $\sin 2x$. We have

$$\int \cos^3 2x \sin^2 2x \, dx = \int \sin^2 2x \cos^2 2x \cos 2x \, dx$$

$$= \int \sin^2 2x(1 - \sin^2 2x) \cos 2x \, dx$$

$$= \int (\sin 2x)^2 \cos 2x \, dx - \int (\sin 2x)^4 \cos 2x \, dx$$

$$= \tfrac{1}{2} \int (\sin 2x)^2(2 \cos 2x) \, dx - \tfrac{1}{2} \int (\sin 2x)^4(2 \cos 2x) \, dx$$

$$= \frac{1}{2} \frac{(\sin 2x)^3}{3} - \frac{1}{2} \frac{(\sin 2x)^5}{5} + C$$

$$= \tfrac{1}{30} (\sin 2x)^3[5 - 3 \sin^2 2x] + C.$$

Similar strategies should be tried first in the other families also. In the tangent-secant family, for instance, we try to arrange to have the factor $\sec^2 x$ as part of the integrand and the rest of the integral as a sum of powers of $\tan x$; or else we try to have the factor $\sec x \tan x$ as part of the integrand and the rest of the integrand as a sum of powers of $\sec x$.

Example 3. Consider $\int \sec^4 x \tan^2 x \, dx$. We shall try to separate out the factor $\sec^2 x$ and then to write the rest of the integrand as a sum of powers of $\tan x$. We have

$$\int \sec^4 x \tan^2 x \, dx = \int \tan^2 x \sec^2 x \sec^2 x \, dx$$

$$= \int \tan^2 x(\tan^2 x + 1) \sec^2 x \, dx$$

$$= \int (\tan x)^4 \sec^2 x \, dx + \int (\tan x)^2 \sec^2 x \, dx$$

$$= \frac{\tan^5 x}{5} + \frac{\tan^3 x}{3} + C.$$

Example 4. Consider $\int \csc x \cot^5 x \, dx$. Here we shall try to separate out the factor $\csc x \cot x$ and to write the rest of the integrand as a sum of powers of $\csc x$. We have

$$\int \csc x \cot^5 x \, dx = \int \cot^4 x \csc x \cot x \, dx$$

$$= \int (\cot^2 x)^2 \csc x \cot x \, dx$$

$$= \int (\csc^2 x - 1)^2 \csc x \cot x \, dx$$

$$= \int (\csc^4 x - 2 \csc^2 x + 1) \csc x \cot x \, dx$$

$$= -\int (\csc x)^4 (-\csc x \cot x) \, dx$$

$$+ 2 \int (\csc x)^2 (-\csc x \cot x) \, dx - \int - \csc x \cot x \, dx$$

$$= -\tfrac{1}{5}(\csc x)^5 + \tfrac{2}{3}(\csc x)^3 - \csc x + C.$$

‖

The strategy just considered cannot be used in every case. In $\int \cos^4 2x \sin^2 2x \, dx$, for instance, we can separate off the factor $\sin 2x$, but then we cannot rewrite the rest of the integrand as a sum of powers of $\cos 2x$. We have

$$\int \cos^4 2x \sin^2 2x \, dx = \int \cos^4 2x \sin 2x \sin 2x \, dx$$

$$= \int \cos^4 2x \sqrt{1 - \cos^2 2x} \sin 2x \, dx.$$

Because the square root of a sum or difference cannot be rewritten as a sum or difference of square roots, we cannot bring the problem to the form (2).

In the sine-cosine family this difficulty wlil arise whenever we are forced to deal only with even powers of the sine and cosine. Let us look, then, for a replacement for $\sin^2 x$. The replacement $\sin^2 x = 1 - \cos^2 x$ is useless for our present purpose, because it will be no easier to deal with $\cos^2 x$ than with $\sin^2 x$. Another identity in which the expression $\sin^2 x$ occurs in the *double-angle identity*

$$\cos 2x = \cos^2 x - \sin^2 x$$

$$= 2 \cos^2 x - 1$$

$$= 1 - 2 \sin^2 x.$$

From the third of these alternate forms we can see that $2 \sin^2 x = 1 - \cos 2x$, or

$$\sin^2 x = \frac{1 - \cos 2x}{2}, \tag{3}$$

and, similarly, from the second of the alternate forms,

$$\cos^2 x = \frac{1 + \cos 2x}{2}. \tag{4}$$

Identities (3) and (4) will be of great value to us.*

Example 5

$$\int \sin^2 x \, dx = \int \frac{1 - \cos 2x}{2} \, dx = \frac{1}{2} \int 1 \, dx - \frac{1}{2} \int \cos 2x \, dx$$

$$= \frac{1}{2} x - \frac{1}{4} \int \cos 2x(2) \, dx = \frac{1}{2} x - \frac{1}{4} \sin 2x + C.$$

Example 6. Consider now $\int \cos^4 x \sin^2 x \, dx$. This will be a long problem, but it will review the ideas of this section. Since we do not have an odd power of $\sin x$ or $\cos x$, we cannot employ the identity $\sin^2 x + \cos^2 x = 1$ to advantage, and instead we use the half-angle identities. We have

$$I = \int \cos^4 x \sin^2 x \, dx = \int (\cos^2 x)^2 \sin^2 x \, dx$$

$$= \int \left(\frac{1 + \cos 2x}{2}\right)^2 \left(\frac{1 - \cos 2x}{2}\right) dx$$

$$= \frac{1}{8} \int (1 + \cos 2x)(1 - \cos^2 2x) \, dx$$

$$= \frac{1}{8} \int (1 + \cos 2x - \cos^2 2x - \cos^3 2x) \, dx,$$

or $\quad I = \frac{1}{8}\left[\int 1 \, dx + \int \cos 2x \, dx - \int \cos^2 2x \, dx - \int \cos^3 2x \, dx \right]. \tag{5}$

In the last of these integrals we have an odd power, and we can separate off the factor $\cos 2x$ to advantage. We obtain

$$\int \cos^3 2x \, dx = \int \cos^2 2x \cos 2x \, dx = \int (1 - \sin^2 2x) \cos 2x \, dx$$

$$= \frac{1}{2} \int \cos 2x \, (2) \, dx - \frac{1}{2} \int (\sin 2x)^2 (2 \cos 2x) \, dx$$

$$= \frac{1}{2} \sin 2x - \frac{1}{2} \frac{(\sin 2x)^3}{3}.$$

For the third integral of Eq. (5) we must use the half-angle identity again. Thus,

$$\int \cos^2 2x \, dx = \int \frac{1 + \cos 4x}{2} \, dx = \frac{1}{2} \int 1 \, dx + \frac{1}{2} \int \cos 4x \, dx$$

$$= \frac{1}{2} x + \frac{1}{8} \int \cos 4x \, (4) \, dx = \frac{1}{2} x + \frac{1}{8} \sin 4x.$$

---

* The reader is advised to remember these identities in words: "To get the square of the sine of any number, take 1 minus the cosine of twice the number and divide by 2." When looked at from this point of view, these identities are called the *half-angle identities*.

Returning now to Statement (5), we can write

$$\int \cos^4 x \sin^2 x \, dx$$

$$= \tfrac{1}{8}[x + \tfrac{1}{2}\sin 2x - \tfrac{1}{2}x - \tfrac{1}{8}\sin 4x - \tfrac{1}{2}\sin 2x + \tfrac{1}{6}\sin^3 2x] + C$$

$$= \tfrac{1}{16}x - \tfrac{1}{64}\sin 4x + \tfrac{1}{48}\sin^3 2x + C.$$

III

Other identities we sometimes find useful are

$$\sin 2x = 2 \sin x \cos x. \tag{6}$$
$$\sin (x + y) = \sin x \cos y + \cos x \sin y, \tag{7a}$$
$$\sin (x - y) = \sin x \cos y - \cos x \sin y. \tag{7b}$$
$$\cos (x + y) = \cos x \cos y - \sin x \sin y, \tag{8a}$$
$$\cos (x - y) = \cos x \cos y + \sin x \sin y. \tag{8b}$$

Identity (6) enables us to replace the product $\sin x \cos x$. The other four identities help us with problems in which the sine and cosine of different expressions are dealt with simultaneously.

Example 7. Consider again the integral of Example 6. Since $\sin x \cos x = \tfrac{1}{2}\sin 2x$, we can also write

$$I = \int \cos^4 x \sin^2 x \, dx = \int (\sin x \cos x)^2 \cos^2 x \, dx$$

$$= \int \left(\frac{\sin 2x}{2}\right)^2 \frac{1 + \cos 2x}{2} \, dx$$

$$= \tfrac{1}{8} \int \sin^2 2x \, dx + \tfrac{1}{8} \int (\sin 2x)^2 \cos 2x \, dx.$$

Here the first integral can be rewritten by using a half-angle identity and the second is almost of the form $\int (u)^2 (du/dx) \, dx$. We leave it to the reader to complete the work.

Example 8. $\int \cos mx \cos nx \, dx = ?,\ m^2 \neq n^2$. The product $\cos mx \cos nx$ suggests the identities for the cosine of a sum and difference of two numbers, Identities (8a) and (8b). We can write

$$\cos (mx + nx) = \cos mx \cos nx - \sin mx \sin nx,$$
$$\cos (mx - nx) = \cos mx \cos nx + \sin mx \sin nx.$$

Adding, we find that

$$\cos (mx + nx) + \cos (mx - nx) = 2 \cos mx \cos nx$$
$$\cos mx \cos nx = \tfrac{1}{2}[\cos (m + n)x + \cos (m - n)x],$$

and thus a product can be replaced by a sum. We have now

$$\int \cos mx \cos nx \, dx = \tfrac{1}{2} \int \cos (m + n)x \, dx + \tfrac{1}{2} \int \cos (m - n)x \, dx$$

$$= \frac{1}{2} \frac{1}{m + n} \int [\cos (m + n)x](m + n) \, dx$$

$$+ \frac{1}{2} \frac{1}{m - n} \int [\cos (m - n)x](m - n) \, dx$$

$$= \frac{1}{2} \frac{1}{m + n} \sin (m + n)x + \frac{1}{2} \frac{1}{m - n} \sin (m - n)x + C.$$

IV

Two integrals of the tangent-secant family of frequent occurrence are $\int \tan x \, dx$ and $\int \sec x \, dx$. The first we have already met in Example 5.3-10. To repeat,

$$\int \tan x \, dx = \int \frac{\sin x}{\cos x} \, dx = -\int \frac{1}{\cos x} (-\sin x) \, dx$$

$$= \begin{cases} -\log \cos x + C = \log \sec x + C & \text{if } \cos x > 0 \\ -\log (- \cos x) + C = \log (- \sec x) + C & \text{if } \cos x < 0. \end{cases} \quad (9)$$

For the second, we found in Example 5.3-2 that

$$\frac{d}{dx} \log (\sec x + \tan x) = \frac{1}{\sec x + \tan x} (\sec x \tan x + \sec^2 x)$$

$$= \frac{\sec x(\tan x + \sec x)}{\sec x + \tan x} = \sec x,$$

so that

$$\int \sec x \, dx = \log (\sec x + \tan x) + C, \quad (10)$$

assuming, as was done tacitly in the differentiation, that $\sec x + \tan x > 0$.

To conclude this section we show how Eq. (10) might have been derived *ab initio*. There are several ways of deriving this formula, none especially obvious. We can write

$$\sec x = \frac{1}{\cos x} = \frac{\cos x}{\cos^2 x} = \frac{\cos x}{1 - \sin^2 x} = \frac{\cos x}{(1 - \sin x)(1 + \sin x)}.$$

It is reasonable now to inquire whether a fraction with denominator

$$(1 - \sin x)(1 + \sin x)$$

might not have been the sum of two fractions with denominators $1 - \sin x$ and $1 + \sin x$. (Indeed, we shall deal later with this sort of rewriting of fractions in greater detail.) We have, then, perhaps after a little trial and error,

$$\sec x = \frac{1}{2} \cos x \left[\frac{1}{1 + \sin x} + \frac{1}{1 - \sin x} \right].$$

Thus

$$\int \sec x \, dx = \frac{1}{2} \int \frac{1}{1 + \sin x} \cos x \, dx + \frac{1}{2} \int \frac{1}{1 - \sin x} \cos x \, dx$$

$$= \frac{1}{2} \log (1 + \sin x) - \frac{1}{2} \log (1 - \sin x) + C$$

$$= \frac{1}{2} \log \frac{1 + \sin x}{1 - \sin x} + C$$

$$= \frac{1}{2} \log \left(\frac{1 + \sin x}{1 - \sin x} \frac{1 + \sin x}{1 + \sin x} \right) + C$$

$$= \frac{1}{2} \log \frac{(1 + \sin x)^2}{\cos^2 x} + C$$

$$= \log \frac{1 + \sin x}{\cos x} + C = \log (\sec x + \tan x) + C.$$

Formulas for the cosecant-cotangent family that correspond to Eqs. (9) and (10) are

$$\int \cot x \, dx = \begin{cases} \log \sin x + C & \text{if } \sin x > 0 \\ \log (- \sin x) + C & \text{if } \sin x < 0, \end{cases} \tag{11}$$

$$\int \csc x \, dx = \begin{cases} - \log(\csc x + \cot x) + C & \text{if } \csc x + \cot x > 0 \\ - \log(- \csc x - \cot x) + C & \text{if } \csc x + \cot x < 0. \end{cases} \tag{12}$$

EXERCISES 6.2

Integrate

1. $\int \sin^3 x \cos x \, dx.$

2. $\int \sin^3 x \cos^2 x \, dx.$

3. $\int \sin^3 x \cos^3 x \, dx.$

4. $\int \dfrac{\sin 2x}{\cos^2 2x} \, dx.$

5. $\int \dfrac{\sin^2 2x}{\cos^2 2x} \, dx.$

6. $\int \dfrac{\sin^3 2x}{\cos^2 2x} \, dx.$

7. $\int \cos^2 ax \, dx.$

8. $\int \cos^3 ax \, dx.$

9. $\int \cos^4 ax \, dx.$

10. $\int \cos^5 ax \, dx.$

11. $\int \sin^2 x \cos^2 x \, dx.$

12. $\int \sin^4 x \, dx,$

13. $\int \sin^4 x \cos^2 x \, dx.$

14. $\int (\sin ax + \cos ax)^2 \, dx.$

15. $\int (1 + \cos x)^2 \, dx.$

16. $\int \tan^3 x \sec^2 x \, dx.$

17. $\int \tan^3 x \sec^4 x \, dx.$

18. $\int \tan^3 x \sec^m x \, dx.$

19. $\int \tan^4 x \sec^4 x \, dx.$

20. $\int \tan^m x \sec^4 x \, dx.$

21. $\int \tan ax \, dx.$

22. $\int \tan^2 ax \, dx.$

23. $\int \tan^3 ax \, dx.$

24. $\int \sec ax \, dx.$

25. $\int \sec^2 ax \, dx.$

26. $\int \dfrac{\sin^2 x}{\cos x} \, dx.$

27. $\int \cot^4 ax \, dx.$

28. $\int \cot^3 x \csc^m x \, dx.$

29. $\int \csc^4 x \cot^m x \, dx.$

30. $\int (\tan x + \cot x)^2 \, dx.$

31. Finish Example 7.

32. Start with the trigonometric statements

$$\sec x = \frac{1}{\cos x} = \frac{1}{\cos^2 (x/2) - \sin^2 (x/2)} = \frac{\sec^2 (x/2)}{1 - \tan^2 (x/2)}$$

$$= \sec^2 (x/2) \left\{ \frac{1}{[1 + \tan (x/2)][1 - \tan (x/2)]} \right\}$$

and work out a formula for $\int \sec x \, dx$.

33. Verify Eq. (12) for $\int \csc x \, dx$.

34. Let m and n be positive integers. Show that

(a) $\displaystyle\int_{-1}^{1} \cos n\pi x \cos m\pi x \, dx = \begin{cases} 0 \text{ if } m \neq n, \\ 1 \text{ if } m = n. \end{cases}$

(b) $\displaystyle\int_{-1}^{1} \cos n\pi x \sin m\pi x \, dx = 0.$

(c) $\displaystyle\int_{-1}^{1} \sin n\pi x \sin m\pi x \, dx = \begin{cases} 0 \text{ if } m \neq n, \\ 1 \text{ if } m = n. \end{cases}$

These formulas are used in the Fourier series expansions.

6.3   Trigonometric Substitutions

I

We pointed out in Sec. 5.1, when we experimented with the definite integral $\int_{t=1}^{z} 1/t \, dt$, that a change of variable might well enable one to rewrite a definite integral in a new form that was easier to handle than the original form. Here is the theorem we proved at that time, Theorem 5.1-1.

■ THEOREM 1

On change of variable for definite integrals.

HYPOTHESIS: (a) $f(t)$ is continuous for $a \leq t \leq b$ and $\int_{t=a}^{b} f(t)dt = A$.

(b) $\tau(u)$ is steadily $\begin{cases} \text{increasing} \\ \text{decreasing} \end{cases}$ and $\tau'(u)$ is continuous for $\begin{cases} \alpha \leq u \leq \beta \\ \beta \leq u \leq \alpha, \end{cases}$

with $\tau(\alpha) = a, \tau(\beta) = b$.

CONCLUSION: $\int_{u=\alpha}^{\beta} f(\tau(u)) \dfrac{d\tau}{du} \, du = A.$

Let us work out a theorem on a change of variable for an indefinite integral.

When we consider $\int f(t) \, dt$ we have a certain interval in mind and we look for a function $\phi(t)$ such that $\phi'(t) = f(t)$ for this interval. Thus we might say that

$$\int t \, dt = \frac{t^2}{2} + C \qquad \text{for all } t$$

and that $\displaystyle\int \frac{1}{\sqrt{1 - t^2}} \, dt = \sin^{-1} t + C \qquad \text{for } 0 \leq t \leq \frac{1}{2}.$

If we do not see how to find a function $\phi(t)$ such that $\phi'(t) = f(t)$ for $a \leq t \leq b$, we can substitute for t, replace the antidifferentiation problem $\int f(t)dt$ by another antidifferentiation problem, and try again. Let $\tau(u)$ be as described in Hypothesis (b) of Theorem 1. Then consider the u integral

$$\int f(\tau(u)) \frac{d\tau}{du} du$$

whose integrand is arrived at (1) by replacing t wherever it occurred in the original integrand by $\tau(u)$ and (2) by multiplying by $dt/du = d\tau/du$. If for this new integral we can find an antiderivative function, say $\Phi(u)$, then we have an antiderivative function for the original integration problem also. For we took $t = \tau(u)$ for $\alpha \leq u \leq \beta$ in such a way that there is an inverse function, $u = \tau^{-1}(t)$ for $a \leq t \leq b$, and if we replace u in $\Phi(u)$ by $\tau^{-1}(t)$, then the resulting function of t, $\phi(t) = \Phi(\tau^{-1}(t))$ will be such that $\phi'(t) = f(t)$ or $\int f(t)dt = \phi(t) + C$.

■ THEOREM 2

On change of variable for indefinite integrals.

HYPOTHESIS: (a) $f(t)$ is continuous for $a \leq t \leq b$.

(b) $\tau(u)$ is steadily $\begin{cases} \text{increasing} \\ \text{decreasing} \end{cases}$ for $\begin{cases} \alpha \leq u \leq \beta \\ \beta \leq u \leq \alpha \end{cases}$ and $\tau'(u)$ is continuous there, with $\tau(\alpha) = a$, $\tau(\beta) = b$.

(c) $\int f(\tau(u)) \dfrac{d\tau}{du} du = \Phi(u) + C.$

(d) $\phi(t) = \Phi(\tau^{-1}(t)).$

CONCLUSION: $\int f(t)\, dt = \phi(t) + C.$

PROOF: By Hypothesis (c) we know that

$$\frac{d\Phi}{du} = f(\tau(u)) \frac{d\tau}{du}.$$

For $\phi(t) = \Phi(u) = \Phi(\tau^{-1}(t))$ we then have, by the chain rule,

$$\frac{d\phi}{dt} = \frac{d\phi}{du} \frac{du}{dt} = \frac{d\Phi}{du} \frac{du}{dt} = \left[f(\tau(u)) \frac{d\tau}{du} \right] \frac{du}{dt}.$$

But we are using inverse functions, and hence we know that $(d\tau/du)(du/dt) = (dt/du)(du/dt) = 1$; see Example 1.9-6 or Theorem 4.4-1.

Hence $\dfrac{d\phi}{dt} = f(t).$

To repeat, we have learned that if the direct integration of $\int f(t)\, dt$ seems to be difficult, a suitable substitution $t = \tau(u)$ will lead to a new integral whose integrand is obtained (1) by replacing t in $f(t)$ wherever it occurs by $\tau(u)$ and (2) by multiplying by $d\tau/du$, and that a solution of the new integral leads immediately to a solution of the original one. This concludes our work on substitutions in indefinite integrals.

II

The Pythagorean identities,

$$1 - \sin^2 \theta = \cos^2 \theta, \tag{1}$$

$$\sec^2 \theta - 1 = \tan^2 \theta, \tag{2}$$

$$\tan^2 \theta + 1 = \sec^2 \theta, \tag{3}$$

often help us to rewrite algebraic expressions of the second degree to advantage. For an expression of the form $a^2 - x^2$, $a > 0$, Identity (1) is suggested, because it replaces a number minus a square. If we let $x = a \sin \theta$, we can say that

$$\sqrt{a^2 - x^2} = \sqrt{a^2 - a^2 \sin^2 \theta} = \sqrt{a^2(1 - \sin^2 \theta)} = a \cos \theta.*$$

Similarly, for an expression of the form $x^2 - a^2$, $a > 0$, Identity (2) is suggested, because it replaces a square minus a number. If we let $x = a \sec \theta$, we can say that

$$\sqrt{x^2 - a^2} = \sqrt{a^2 \sec^2 \theta - a^2} = \sqrt{a^2(\sec^2 \theta - 1)} = a \tan \theta.†$$

Finally, if we want to rewrite an expression of the form $x^2 + a^2$, $a > 0$, we can try $x = a \tan \theta$ and use Identity (3). We have

$$\sqrt{x^2 + a^2} = \sqrt{a^2 \tan^2 \theta + a^2} = \sqrt{a^2(\tan^2 \theta + 1)} = a \sec \theta.‡$$

In each of these cases a binomial was replaced by a monomial, and since a root or power of a sum or difference cannot be simplified as easily as the same root or power of a monomial, we have gained something. In making a trigonometric substitution, we may also gain by bringing to bear the techniques of Sec. 6.2.

Example 1.   Consider

$$I = \int \frac{x}{\sqrt{x^2 - a^2}} \, dx, \qquad x > a > 0.$$

If we write

$$I = \int (x^2 - a^2)^{-1/2} x \, dx = \tfrac{1}{2} \int (x^2 - a^2)^{-1/2} 2x \, dx,$$

we see that we have an integral of the form $\int (u)^n du/dx \, dx$ and that no trigonometric substitution is necessary. Thus,

$$I = \frac{1}{2} \frac{(x^2 - a^2)^{1/2}}{1/2} + C = \sqrt{x^2 - a^2} + C.$$

Example 2.   Consider

$$\int \frac{1}{\sqrt{x^2 - a^2}} \, dx, \qquad x > a > 0.$$

---

* If $\cos \theta > 0$. If $\cos \theta < 0$, $\sqrt{a^2 \cos^2 \theta} = -a \cos \theta$.
† If $\tan \theta > 0$. If $\tan \theta < 0$, $\sqrt{a^2 \tan^2 \theta} = -a \tan \theta$.
‡ If $\sec \theta > 0$. If $\sec \theta < 0$, $\sqrt{a^2 \sec^2 \theta} = -a \sec \theta$.

This time the problem is not of the form $\int (u)^n \, du/dx \, dx$, and since we deal with an expression that is a square minus a number, we try to take advantage of the identity $\sec^2 \theta - 1 = \tan^2 \theta$. Let $x = a \sec \theta$ with $0 < \theta < \pi/2$ and $\theta = \sec^{-1}(x/a)$ with $x > a > 0$. Then

$$\frac{dx}{d\theta} = a \sec \theta \tan \theta,$$

$$x^2 - a^2 = a^2 \sec^2 \theta - a^2 = a^2(\sec^2 \theta - 1) = a^2 \tan^2 \theta.$$

Thus

$$\int \frac{1}{\sqrt{x^2 - a^2}} \, dx = \int \frac{1}{a \tan \theta} \, a \sec \theta \tan \theta \, d\theta = \int \sec \theta \, d\theta$$

$$= \log (\sec \theta + \tan \theta) + C.$$

Because $0 < \theta < \pi/2$, we have $\tan \theta > 0$, and in fact

$$\tan^2 \theta = \sec^2 \theta - 1 = \frac{x^2}{a^2} - 1 = \frac{x^2 - a^2}{a^2},$$

$$\tan \theta = \frac{+\sqrt{x^2 - a^2}}{a}. *$$

Hence

$$\int \frac{1}{\sqrt{x^2 - a^2}} \, dx = \log \left(\frac{x}{a} + \frac{\sqrt{x^2 - a^2}}{a} \right) + C = \log \left(\frac{x + \sqrt{x^2 - a^2}}{a} \right) + C$$

$$= \log (x + \sqrt{x^2 - a^2}) - \log a + C$$

$$= \log (x + \sqrt{x^2 - a^2}) + C'.$$

Example 3. Consider

$$I = \int \frac{\sqrt{7 - x^2}}{x^2} \, dx, \qquad 0 < x \le \sqrt{7}.$$

This problem is not of the form $\int (u)^n du/dx \, dx$, but we do recognize that $7 - x^2$ is a number minus a square and we try the substitution $x = \sqrt{7} \sin \theta$ for $0 < \theta \le \pi/2$, $\theta = \sin^{-1}(x/\sqrt{7})$ for $0 < x \le \sqrt{7}$, in order to take advantage of the identity $1 - \sin^2 \theta = \cos^2 \theta$. We can write $dx/d\theta = \sqrt{7} \cos \theta$, $7 - x^2 = 7 - 7 \sin^2 \theta = 7(1 - \sin^2 \theta) = 7 \cos^2 \theta$, so that

$$\int \frac{\sqrt{7 - x^2}}{x^2} \, dx = \int \frac{\sqrt{7} \cos \theta}{7 \sin^2 \theta} \sqrt{7} \cos \theta \, d\theta = \int \cot^2 \theta \, d\theta.$$

For this trigonometric integral we can write

$$I = \int (\csc^2 \theta - 1) \, d\theta = -\cot \theta - \theta + C.$$

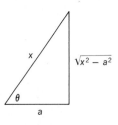

Fig. 6.1

* We could also have computed $\tan \theta$ from the triangle of Fig. 6.1.

Fig. 6.2   Fig. 6.3

Since we deal with $0 < \theta \le \pi/2$, $\cot \theta$ must be positive, as is x. We compute

$$\cot^2 \theta = \csc^2 \theta - 1 = \frac{7}{x^2} - 1 = \frac{7 - x^2}{x^2},$$

$$\cot \theta = \frac{\sqrt{7 - x^2}}{x}, \quad *$$

and then

$$I = -\frac{\sqrt{7 - x^2}}{x} - \sin^{-1} \frac{x}{\sqrt{7}} + C.$$

Example 4.   As a last illustration, consider

$$I = \int \frac{x^2}{(x^2 + a^2)^2} \, dx, \qquad a > 0.$$

Again we do not have an integral of the form $\int (u)^n \, du/dx \, dx$, but we do have a quadratic function to deal with, and we take advantage of the identity $\tan^2 \theta + 1 = \sec^2 \theta$. If we try $x = a \tan \theta$ for $-\pi/2 < \theta < \pi/2$, $\theta = \tan^{-1}(x/a)$ for all real x, we write $dx/d\theta = a \sec^2 \theta$, $x^2 + a^2 = a^2 \tan^2 \theta + a^2 = a^2(\tan^2 \theta + 1) = a^2 \sec^2 \theta$. Then

$$I = \int \frac{a^2 \tan^2 \theta}{a^4 \sec^4 \theta} a \sec^2 \theta \, d\theta = \frac{1}{a} \int \frac{\tan^2 \theta}{\sec^2 \theta} \, d\theta = \frac{1}{a} \int \sin^2 \theta \, d\theta.$$

Now we use a half-angle identity,

$$I = \frac{1}{2a} \int (1 - \cos 2\theta) \, d\theta = \frac{1}{2a}\left(\theta - \frac{1}{2} \sin 2\theta\right) + C. \tag{4}$$

For the $\sin 2\theta$ term we write

$$\frac{1}{2} \sin 2\theta = \sin \theta \cos \theta = \frac{x}{\sqrt{x^2 + a^2}} \frac{a}{\sqrt{x^2 + a^2}} = \frac{ax}{x^2 + a^2},$$

using the facts that for $-\pi/2 < \theta < \pi/2$, (a) $\cos \theta > 0$ and (b) $\tan \theta = x/a$ and $\sin \theta$ have the same sign as x.† Hence our answer is

$$I = \frac{1}{2a}\left(\tan^{-1} \frac{x}{a} - \frac{ax}{x^2 + a^2}\right) + C. \tag{5}$$

If we had been asked to evaluate

$$\int_{x=0}^{a} \frac{x^2}{(x^2 + a^2)^2} \, dx,$$

---

* For $0 < \theta < \pi/2$ we can also compute $\cot \theta$ from the triangle of Fig. 6.2.
† For $0 < \theta < \pi/2$ we can compute $\sin \theta$ and $\cos \theta$ from the triangle of Fig. 6.3.

we could have proceeded as above and substituted for $x = a$ and $x = 0$ in Eq. (5), but it would have been easier to change the boundaries when changing the variable of integration and to use Eq. (4) instead. From $x = a \tan \theta$ we see that $x = 0$ and $x = a$ correspond to $\theta = 0$ and $\theta = \pi/4$, so that, by Eq. (4),

$$\int_{x=0}^{a} \frac{x^2}{(x^2 + a^2)^2}\, dx = \frac{1}{2a} \int_{\theta=0}^{\pi/4} (1 - \cos 2\theta)\, d\theta = \frac{1}{2a}\left(\theta - \frac{1}{2}\sin 2\theta\right)\Big|_{\theta=0}^{\pi/4}$$

$$= \frac{1}{2a}\left[\left(\frac{\pi}{4} - \frac{1}{2}\right) - (0)\right] = \frac{1}{8a}(\pi - 2).$$

EXERCISES 6.3

Integrate each of the following:

1. $\displaystyle\int \frac{x^2}{\sqrt{a^2 - x^2}}\, dx.$

2. $\displaystyle\int \frac{x^3}{\sqrt{x^2 - 9}}\, dx.$

3. $\displaystyle\int x\sqrt{1 - x^2}\, dx.$

4. $\displaystyle\int \frac{1}{x^2 - a^2}\, dx.$

5. $\displaystyle\int \frac{1}{\sqrt{(x^2 + 4)^3}}\, dx.$

6. $\displaystyle\int \frac{x}{\sqrt{(x^2 + a^2)^3}}\, dx.$

7. $\displaystyle\int \frac{x}{\sqrt{x^2 - 5}}\, dx.$

8. $\displaystyle\int \frac{1}{x^2 + a^2}\, dx.$

9. $\displaystyle\int x^3\sqrt{8 - x^2}\, dx.$

10. $\displaystyle\int x^3\sqrt{x^2 + 16}\, dx.$

11. $\displaystyle\int \frac{x^3}{(x^2 - a^2)^2}\, dx.$

12. $\displaystyle\int \frac{\sqrt{a^2 - x^2}}{x}\, dx.$

Evaluate each of the following:

13. $\displaystyle\int_{x=0}^{3} \frac{1}{\sqrt{x^2 + 3}}\, dx.$

14. $\displaystyle\int_{x=2}^{3} x^3\sqrt{x^2 - 4}\, dx.$

15. $\displaystyle\int_{x=-.1}^{+.1} \frac{x}{\sqrt{x^2 + a^2}}\, dx.$

16. $\displaystyle\int_{x=a/2}^{a} \frac{\sqrt{(a^2 - x^2)^3}}{x^2}\, dx.$

17. Find the area of a quarter circle of radius a by integration.

18. (a) Check the result of Example 3 by differentiation.
    (b) Check the result (5) of Example 4 by differentiation.

19. *On hyperbolic function substitutions.* Instead of Identities (1), (2), and (3), the following could be used:

$$1 - \tanh^2 u = \operatorname{sech}^2 u. \tag{1a}$$

$$\cosh^2 u - 1 = \sinh^2 u. \tag{2a}$$

$$\sinh^2 u + 1 = \cosh^2 u. \tag{3a}$$

In fact, we used such a substitution in Exercise 5.5-14. Try hyperbolic substitutions in
(a) Exercise 13 above.   (b) Exercise 9 above.

6.4 Partial Fractions

We have already used trigonometric identities to rewrite trigonometric integrands that we did not recognize at first. In this section we shall work out certain algebraic identities having to do with fractions, so that we can replace fractional integrands we might not be able to handle directly.

I

A quotient of two polynomials is called a *rational function*. If the numerator is of lower degree than the denominator, we say that we have a *proper rational function*. If the numerator is not of lower degree than the denominator, long division will always enable us to write our rational function as a polynomial plus a proper rational function, so that for the most part we shall restrict our attention to proper rational functions.

Example 1

$$\frac{x + 1}{x^2 - 3x + 4}$$

is a proper rational function.

Example 2

$$f(x) = \frac{x^3 + 2x + 5}{x^2 - 3x + 4}$$

is not a proper rational function, but by long division we can write

$$f(x) = (x + 3) + \frac{7x - 7}{x^2 - 3x + 4}$$

so that $f(x)$ is the sum of a polynomial and a proper rational function.

The following theorem makes possible the technique we wish to employ.

■ THEOREM 1

HYPOTHESIS: (a) $v(x)$ is a polynomial of degree n.

(b) $\dfrac{u(x)}{v(x)}$ is a proper rational function in simplest form.

(c) $v(x) \equiv (x - a)^r v_1(x)$ where $v_1(x)$ is a polynomial and $v_1(a) \neq 0$.*

CONCLUSION: There exists a number A and a polynomial $u_1(x)$ of degree less than $n - 1$ such that

$$\frac{u(x)}{v(x)} \equiv \frac{u(x)}{(x - a)^r v_1(x)} \equiv \frac{A}{(x - a)^r} + \frac{u_1(x)}{(x - a)^{r-1} v_1(x)}. \tag{1}$$

---

* The sign $\equiv$ means "identically equal to."

● **Remark 1**

Note that $v_1(x)$ is of degree $n - r$ and that $(x - a)^{r-1} v_1(x)$ is of degree $n - 1$, so that

$$\frac{u_1(x)}{(x - a)^{r-1}v_1(x)}$$

is a proper rational function whose denominator is of lower degree than that of the proper rational function with which we started.

PROOF: It is our task to exhibit the proper A and $u_1(x)$. We shall allow Eq. (1) itself to suggest the proper A and $u_1(x)$, and then we shall show that when the A and $u_1(x)$ suggested are used, Identity (1) is indeed valid.

If we add the fractions of the right member of Eq. (1), we obtain

$$\frac{u(x)}{(x - a)^r v_1(x)} \equiv \frac{Av_1(x) + (x - a)u_1(x)}{(x - a)^r v_1(x)}.$$

The denominators are identical; we want to choose A and $u_1(x)$, so that the numerators will also be identical:

$$u(x) \equiv Av_1(x) + (x - a)u_1(x). \tag{2}$$

Since an identity is to hold for all x, we expect it to hold for $x = a$ in particular. Hence

$$u(a) = Av_1(a) + 0,$$

and we must choose

$$A = \frac{u(a)}{v_1(a)}. \tag{3}$$

Having decided on a choice for A, we return to Eq. (2) and solve for $u_1(x)$:

$$(x - a)u_1(x) \equiv u(x) - Av_1(x) \equiv u(x) - \frac{u(a)}{v_1(a)} v_1(x)$$

$$\equiv \frac{1}{v_1(a)} [v_1(a)u(x) - u(a)v_1(x)],$$

$$u_1(x) \equiv \frac{1}{v_1(a)} \frac{v_1(a)u(x) - u(a)v_1(x)}{x - a}. \tag{4}$$

It might appear at first that the function required by Eq. (4) for $u_1(x)$ is not a polynomial. But observe that for the numerator of this function,

$$\phi(x) = v_1(a)u(x) - u(a)v_1(x),$$

we have

$$\phi(a) = v_1(a)u(a) - u(a)v_1(a) = 0.$$

Therefore, by the Remainder Theorem of algebra, $\phi(x)$ is divisible by $x - a$ and $u_1(x)$ is a polynomial. Moreover, since $u(x)$ and $v_1(x)$ are both of degree less than n, the $u_1(x)$ required by Eq. (4) will be of degree less than $n - 1$.

Now we show that the Identity (1) holds when we add fractions and substitute from Eqs. (3) and (4) for A and $u_1(x)$:

$$\frac{A}{(x-a)^r} + \frac{u_1(x)}{(x-a)^{r-1}v_1(x)} \equiv \frac{Av_1(x) + (x-a)u_1(x)}{(x-a)^r v_1(x)}$$

$$\equiv \frac{1}{v(x)}\left\{\frac{u(a)}{v_1(a)}v_1(x) + \frac{1}{v_1(a)}[v_1(a)u(x) - u(a)v_1(x)]\right\}$$

$$\equiv \frac{u(x)}{v(x)}.$$

This concludes the proof.

Example 3.   Let us integrate

$$\int \frac{x+2}{x^3 + x^2 - 6x}\,dx.$$

We have

$$x^3 + x^2 - 6x = x(x^2 + x - 6) = x(x-2)(x+3),$$

and then according to Theorem 1, with $r = 1$, there exist constants A, B, and C such that

$$\frac{x+2}{x^3+x^2-6x} \equiv \frac{x+2}{x(x-2)(x+3)} \equiv \frac{A}{x} + \frac{Bx+C}{(x-2)(x+3)}.$$

If we apply Theorem 1 to the second fraction of the right member, we see that there exist constants D and E such that

$$\frac{Bx+C}{(x-2)(x+3)} \equiv \frac{D}{x-2} + \frac{E}{x+3}.$$

In all, then, the original fraction can be written as a sum of fractions,

$$\frac{x+2}{x(x-2)(x+3)} \equiv \frac{A}{x} + \frac{D}{x-2} + \frac{E}{x+3}. \tag{5}$$

To evaluate the constants A, D, and E, we can proceed just about as we did in the proof of Theorem 1. Combine the fractions of the right member to get

$$\frac{x+2}{x(x-2)(x+3)} \equiv \frac{A(x-2)(x+3) + Dx(x+3) + Ex(x-2)}{x(x-2)(x+3)}.$$

We must choose A, D, and E so that the numerators are identical:

$$x+2 \equiv A(x-2)(x+3) + Dx(x+3) + Ex(x-2).$$

The last identity is to hold for all x. In particular, for $x = 0$,

$$2 = -6A + 0 + 0 \qquad \text{or} \qquad A = -\tfrac{1}{3}.$$

For $x = 2$,

$$4 = 0 + 10D + 0 \qquad \text{or} \qquad D = \tfrac{2}{5}.$$

For $x = -3$,

$$-1 = 0 + 0 + 15E \qquad \text{or} \qquad E = -\tfrac{1}{15}.$$

Hence Eq. (5) becomes

$$\frac{x+2}{x(x-2)(x+3)} = -\frac{1}{3}\frac{1}{x} + \frac{2}{5}\frac{1}{x-2} - \frac{1}{15}\frac{1}{x+3},$$

and then

$$\int \frac{x+2}{x^3 + x^2 - 6x}\, dx = -\frac{1}{3} \int \frac{1}{x}\, dx + \frac{2}{5} \int \frac{1}{x-2}\, dx - \frac{1}{15} \int \frac{1}{x+3}\, dx,$$

$$= -\tfrac{1}{3} \log x + \tfrac{2}{5} \log (x-2) - \tfrac{1}{15} \log (x+3) + C.^*$$

Example 4. Let us integrate

$$\int \frac{x^3 + 5}{x^2 - 25}\, dx.$$

Here our integrand is not a proper rational function, and we use long division to rewrite it. We get

$$\frac{x^3 + 5}{x^2 - 25} \equiv x + \frac{25x + 5}{x^2 - 25},$$

and then we apply Theorem 1 to the fraction:

$$\frac{25x + 5}{x^2 - 25} \equiv \frac{25x + 5}{(x+5)(x-5)} \equiv \frac{A}{x+5} + \frac{B}{x-5}.$$

To determine the A and B whose existence is asserted by the theorem, we must have

$$\frac{25x + 5}{(x+5)(x-5)} \equiv \frac{A(x-5) + B(x+5)}{(x+5)(x-5)},$$

$$25x + 5 \equiv A(x-5) + B(x+5).$$

If the last identity is to hold for the particular values $x = 5$ and $x = -5$, we must have

$$x = \quad 5: \qquad 130 = 0 + 10B \qquad \text{or} \qquad B = 13,$$

$$x = -5: \qquad -120 = -10A + 0 \qquad \text{or} \qquad A = 12.$$

Hence

$$\frac{x^3 + 5}{x^2 - 25} \equiv x + \frac{12}{x+5} + \frac{13}{x-5},$$

and

$$\int \frac{x^3 + 5}{x^2 - 25}\, dx = \int x\, dx + 12 \int \frac{1}{x+5}\, dx + 13 \int \frac{1}{x-5}\, dx$$

$$= \tfrac{1}{2} x^2 + 12 \log (x+5) + 13 \log (x-5) + C.\dagger$$

---

* Assuming that we are interested in x for which x, $x + 3$, and $x - 2$ are all positive.
† Assuming that we are interested in x for which $x + 5$ and $x - 5$ are both positive.

Example 5.   Integrate

$$\int \frac{3x^2 - 10x + 14}{(x - 2)^3(x + 1)}\, dx.$$

If we apply Theorem 1 with $r = 3$ to this integrand, we can say that there are constants A, B, C, and D such that

$$\frac{3x^2 - 10x + 14}{(x - 2)^3(x + 1)} \equiv \frac{A}{(x - 2)^3} + \frac{Bx^2 + Cx + D}{(x - 2)^2(x + 1)}.$$

If we apply Theorem 1 with $r = 2$, we can rewrite the last fraction:

$$\frac{Bx^2 + Cx + D}{(x - 2)^2(x + 1)} \equiv \frac{E}{(x - 2)^2} + \frac{Fx + G}{(x - 2)(x + 1)}.$$

If we use Theorem 1 once more, we finally say that there are constants A, E, H, and J such that

$$\frac{3x^2 - 10x + 14}{(x - 2)^3(x + 1)} \equiv \frac{A}{(x - 2)^3} + \frac{E}{(x - 2)^2} + \frac{H}{x - 2} + \frac{J}{x + 1}. \tag{6}$$

Let us combine the fractions of the right member:

$$\frac{3x^2 - 10x + 14}{(x - 2)^3(x + 1)}$$

$$\equiv \frac{A(x + 1) + E(x - 2)(x + 1) + H(x - 2)^2(x + 1) + J(x - 2)^3}{(x - 2)^3(x + 1)}.$$

The constants A, E, H, and J must be such that

$$3x^2 - 10x + 14$$
$$\equiv A(x + 1) + E(x - 2)(x + 1) + H(x - 2)^2(x + 1) + J(x - 2)^3.$$

In particular, for $x = -1$,

$$27 = 0 + 0 + 0 - 27J \quad \text{or} \quad J = -1,$$

and for $x = 2$,

$$6 = 3A + 0 + 0 + 0 \quad \text{or} \quad A = 2.$$

It is not quite so easy to evaluate the other constants. If we let $x = 0$ and then $x = 1$, and use our known values for A and J, we obtain

$$x = 0: \quad 14 = A - 2E + 4H - 8J \quad \text{or} \quad -E + 2H = 2$$
$$x = 1: \quad 7 = 2A - 2E + 2H - 1J \quad \text{or} \quad -E + H = 1.$$

Now we solve two equations for the two unknowns E and H and find that $H = 1$, $E = 0$ so that Eq. (6) becomes

$$\frac{3x^2 - 10x + 14}{(x - 2)^3(x + 1)} \equiv \frac{2}{(x - 2)^3} + \frac{1}{x - 2} - \frac{1}{x + 1}.$$

Then we have

$$\int \frac{3x^2 - 10x + 14}{(x - 2)^3(x + 1)} \, dx = 2 \int \frac{1}{(x - 2)^3} \, dx + \int \frac{1}{x - 2} \, dx - \int \frac{1}{x + 1} \, dx$$

$$= -\frac{1}{(x - 2)^2} + \log (x - 2) - \log (x + 1) + C.*$$

We chose the particular values $x = 0$ and $x = 1$ when determining the constants E and H because they were easy to compute with, but other choices for x could also have been used.†

||

It will often happen in factoring the denominator of a proper rational function that a quadratic factor appears. In that case the following theorem may be applied.

■ THEOREM 2

HYPOTHESIS: (a) $v(x)$ is a polynomial of degree n.
(b) $u(x)/v(x)$ is a proper rational function in simplest form.
(c) $v(x) \equiv (ax^2 + bx + c)^r v_2(x)$, where $v_2(x)$ is a polynomial and neither root of $ax^2 + bx + c = 0$ is a root of $v_2(x) = 0$.

CONCLUSION: There exist numbers A and B and a polynomial $u_2(x)$, of degree less than $n - 2$, such that

$$\frac{u(x)}{v(x)} \equiv \frac{u(x)}{(ax^2 + bx + c)^r v_2(x)}$$

$$\equiv \frac{Ax + B}{(ax^2 + bx + c)^r} + \frac{u_2(x)}{(ax^2 + bx + c)^{r-1}v_2(x)}. \tag{7}$$

PROOF: The proof of this theorem can be made to depend on Theorem 1. The reader is guided through the proof of the $r = 1$ case in Exercise 6.4-16.

Example 6.   Consider

$$I = \int \frac{3x^2 + x + 6}{x^4 + 3x^2 + 2} \, dx.$$

The integrand is a proper rational function and the $r = 1$ case of Theorem 2 asserts that there are constants A, B, C, and D such that

$$\frac{3x^2 + x + 6}{x^4 + 3x^2 + 2} \equiv \frac{3x^2 + x + 6}{(x^2 + 1)(x^2 + 2)} \equiv \frac{Ax + B}{x^2 + 1} + \frac{Cx + D}{x^2 + 2}. \tag{8}$$

We add the fractions of the right member and compare numerators:

$$3x^2 + x + 6 \equiv (Ax + B)(x^2 + 2) + (Cx + D)(x^2 + 1).$$

---

* Assuming that we are interested in x for which $x - 2$ and $x + 1$ are both positive.
† See Exercise 6.4-15.

Substituting individual values for x will not lead us directly to values for A, B, C, and D this time, and instead we compare coefficients:

$$3x^2 + x + 6 \equiv (A + C)x^3 + (B + D)x^2 + (2A + C)x + (2B + D).$$

$$
\begin{array}{lll}
x^3 \text{ coefficients:} & 0 = A + C \\
x^2 \text{ coefficients:} & 3 = B + D \\
x \text{ coefficients:} & 1 = 2A + C \\
\text{constant terms:} & 6 = 2B + D
\end{array}
\right\}
\Rightarrow
\left\{
\begin{array}{l}
A = 1 \\
C = -1 \\
B = 3 \\
D = 0.
\end{array}
$$

Hence for Identity (8) we have

$$\frac{3x^2 + x + 6}{x^4 + 3x^2 + 2} \equiv \frac{x + 3}{x^2 + 1} - \frac{x}{x^2 + 2}$$

and then
$$
I = \int \frac{x + 3}{x^2 + 1}\, dx - \int \frac{x}{x^2 + 2}\, dx
$$

$$
= \int \frac{x}{x^2 + 1}\, dx + 3 \int \frac{1}{x^2 + 1}\, dx - \int \frac{x}{x^2 + 2}\, dx
$$

$$
= \tfrac{1}{2} \log\,(x^2 + 1) + 3 \tan^{-1} x - \tfrac{1}{2} \log\,(x^2 + 2) + C
$$

$$
= \frac{1}{2} \log \frac{x^2 + 1}{x^2 + 2} + 3 \tan^{-1} x + C.
$$

III

We can summarize the working instructions for rewriting fractions that we have developed from Theorems 1 and 2 as follows:

(a) If the integrand is an improper rational function, use long division to rewrite it as the sum of a polynomial and a proper rational function.

(b) Factor the denominator of the proper rational function.

(c) For each linear factor, $(x - a)^r$, write a sum of partial fractions of the form

$$\frac{A}{(x - a)^r} + \frac{B}{(x - a)^{r-1}} + \cdots + \frac{F}{(x - a)^2} + \frac{G}{x - a}.$$

(d) For each quadratic factor, $(x^2 + ax + b)^q$, write a sum of partial fractions of the form

$$\frac{Ax + B}{(ax^2 + bx + c)^q} + \frac{Cx + D}{(ax^2 + bx + c)^{q-1}} + \cdots + \frac{Jx + K}{(ax^2 + bx + c)^2} + \frac{Lx + M}{ax^2 + bx + c}.$$

Example 7. Constants $A, B, \cdots, G$ can be determined such that

$$\frac{1}{(x^2 + a^2)^2(x - b)^3} \equiv \frac{Ax + B}{(x^2 + a^2)^2} + \frac{Cx + D}{x^2 + a^2} + \frac{E}{(x - b)^3} + \frac{F}{(x - b)^2} + \frac{G}{x - b}.$$

● **Remark 2**

In effect, we have shown that, if $R(x)$ is a rational function whose denominator is one of certain types, then the integration of $\int R(x)\, dx$ can be carried out in terms of rational functions, logarithmic functions of the forms $\log (x - a)$ and $\log (ax^2 + bx + c)$, and inverse tangent functions of the form $\tan^{-1}(ax + b)$. It can be shown that for all rational functions $R(x)$ the integration of $\int R(x) \, dx$ can still be carried out in terms of these few functions.*

EXERCISES 6.4

Integrate

1. $\int \dfrac{1}{x^2 - a^2} \, dx.$

5. $\int \dfrac{4x + 12}{x^2(x + 2)^2} \, dx.$

8. $\int \dfrac{1}{x^4 - 1} \, dx.$

2. $\int \dfrac{x^3 + 1}{x^2 - 4} \, dx.$

6. $\int \dfrac{3x^2 - 2x + 1}{x^5 - 2x^4 + x^3} \, dx.$

9. $\int \dfrac{x^3 + 2x^2 + 9x + 2}{x^4 + 10x^2 + 9} \, dx.$

3. $\int \dfrac{4x^2 - 11x + 3}{x^3 - 4x^2 + 3x} \, dx.$

7. $\int \dfrac{x + 4}{x(x^2 + 4)} \, dx.$

10. $\int \dfrac{x^4 + 2x^3 + 2x + 1}{x(x^2 + 1)^2} \, dx.$

4. $\int \dfrac{2x^2 - 9x + 10}{2x^2 - 5x + 3} \, dx.$

Evaluate

11. $\int_5^7 \dfrac{5x}{x^2 - 3x - 4} \, dx.$

13. $\int_1^2 \dfrac{x^2 + 6}{x^2 - 3x} \, dx.$

12. $\int_{-3}^{-1} \dfrac{x + 2}{x(x - 2)^2} \, dx.$

14. $\int_1^2 \dfrac{x^3 - 1}{x^4 + x^2} \, dx.$

15. In Example 5 we found that the constants H and E were respectively 1 and 0 by using the particular values $x = 0$ and $x = 1$. Use other particular values for x to determine H and E.

16. Fill in where necessary and justify the various steps of this proof of Theorem 2 for the case $r = 1.$†

Step (a). If $b^2 - 4ac = 0$, there exists a number α such that $ax^2 + bx + c = a(x - \alpha)^2$. But then $v(x) = (x - \alpha)^2 av_2(x)$ and Theorem 1, applied twice, says that there exist constants A and B and a polynomial $u_2(x)$, of degree less than $n - 2$, such that

$$\frac{u(x)}{v(x)} \equiv \frac{A'}{(x - \alpha)^2} + \frac{B'}{(x - \alpha)} + \frac{u_2(x)}{v_2(x)}.$$

This identity can be rewritten in the form of Eq. (7).

Step (b). If $b^2 - 4ac \ne 0$, then $ax^2 + bx + c = 0$ has two distinct roots, say α and β:

$$ax^2 + bx + c = a(x - \alpha)(x - \beta).$$

But then

$$v(x) = (x - \alpha)(x - \beta)av_2(x),$$

---

* See, for instance, the classic text of E. Goursat, *A Course in Mathematical Analysis*, translated by E. R. Hedrick, vol. 1, pp. 208ff. Reprinted by Dover Publications, New York, 1959.

† There is no essentially different idea involved in proving Theorem 2 for general r by the same method.

and Theorem 1, applied twice, says that there exist constants A' and B' and a polynomial $u_2(x)$, of degree less than $n - 2$, such that

$$\frac{u(x)}{v(x)} \equiv \frac{A'}{x - \alpha} + \frac{B'}{x - \beta} + \frac{u_2(x)}{v_2(x)}.$$

This identity can be rewritten in the form of Eq. (7).

Step (c). In the case where α and β are not real, they are complex conjugate numbers. It can then be shown that A' and B' are complex conjugates and that $u_2(x)$ has real coefficients, so that the numerators in Eq. (7) are real.

17. Example 8. *An application to chemistry*

Suppose that, in a certain chemical reaction, materials α and β unite in the ratio of 2 grams to 3 grams, and form material γ. Suppose that we start with 8 grams of α and 9 grams of β and that, under the conditions of this experiment, the rate at which γ is formed at time t is proportional to the product of the amounts of α and β present at time t. Now if x grams of γ have already been formed at time t, then $\frac{2}{5}x$ grams of α and $\frac{3}{5}x$ grams of β must have been used up, and there remain $8 - \frac{2}{5}x$ grams of α and $9 - \frac{3}{5}x$ grams of β. Thus

$$\frac{dx}{dt} = C\left(8 - \frac{2}{5}x\right)\left(9 - \frac{3}{5}x\right) = K(20 - x)(15 - x), \tag{9}$$

where C and $K = 6C/25$ are constants determined by chemical experiment. We can rewrite Eq. (9) as

$$\frac{1}{(20 - x)(15 - x)} \frac{dx}{dt} = K,$$

and then, by our partial fraction technique, as

$$\left(-\frac{1}{5}\frac{1}{20 - x} + \frac{1}{5}\frac{1}{15 - x}\right)\frac{dx}{dt} = K.$$

Integrating with respect to t, we get

$$\int -\frac{1}{20 - x}\frac{dx}{dt}\,dt + \int \frac{1}{15 - x}\frac{dx}{dt}\,dt = \int 5K\,dt$$

or

$$\log(20 - x) - \log(15 - x) = 5Kt + C', \tag{10}$$

where C' is a constant of integration.

But at time $t = 0$, no γ was yet present; $x = 0$. Hence in Eq. (10),

$$\log 20 - \log 15 = C' \quad \text{or} \quad C' = \log \tfrac{20}{15} = \log \tfrac{4}{3},$$

and Eq. (10) reads

$$\log(20 - x) - \log(15 - x) = 5Kt + \log \tfrac{4}{3},$$

$$\log \frac{3(20 - x)}{4(15 - x)} = 5Kt,$$

$$\frac{3(20 - x)}{4(15 - x)} = e^{5Kt}.$$

At any time t there are

$$x = 15\,\frac{e^{5Kt} - 1}{e^{5Kt} - .75} \tag{11}$$

grams of γ. As a common-sense check, 6 grams of α will ultimately combine with the 9 grams of β originally present to give 15 grams of γ; note that Eq. (11) says that $x \to 15$ as t grows beyond all bounds.

6.5   More Substitutions

We have already observed how trigonometric substitutions help to change certain integrals to more easily recognized forms. We shall use the theorems on change of variable in integration, Theorems 6.3-1 and 6.3-2, in other problems also.

I

If an integrand contains fractional powers of $a + bx$, a substitution of the form $a + bx = y^n$, n suitably chosen according to the exponents appearing in the problem, will help us to rewrite the integrand so that integer powers of y appear instead of the fractional power of $a + bx$.

Example 1.   To integrate

$$I = \int \frac{x}{\sqrt{x-2}} \, dx, \qquad x > 2,$$

we try the substitution $y = \sqrt{x-2}$ for $x > 2$, $x - 2 = y^2$, $x = y^2 + 2$ for $y > 0$. Since $dx/dy = 2y$,

$$I = \int \frac{y^2 + 2}{y} \, 2y \, dy = 2 \int (y^2 + 2) \, dy = 2\left(\frac{y^3}{3} + 2y\right) + C$$

$$= 2[\tfrac{1}{3} (x-2)^{3/2} + 2(x-2)^{1/2}] + C = \tfrac{2}{3} (x-2)^{1/2}(x+4) + C.$$

Example 2.   To integrate

$$I = \int \frac{1}{\sqrt{x} + \sqrt[3]{x}} \, dx, \qquad x > 0,$$

we try the substitution $x = y^6$ for $y > 0$, $y = x^{1/6}$ for $x > 0$, so that $dx/dy = 6y^5$, $\sqrt{x} = y^3$, and $\sqrt[3]{x} = y^2$. We have

$$I = \int \frac{1}{y^3 + y^2} \, 6y^5 \, dy = 6 \int \frac{y^3}{y+1} \, dy = 6 \int \left(y^2 - y + 1 - \frac{1}{y+1}\right) dy,$$

using long division at the last step. Then

$$I = 6\left[\frac{y^3}{3} - \frac{y^2}{2} + y - \log(y+1)\right] + C$$

$$= 2\sqrt{x} - 3\sqrt[3]{x} + 6\sqrt[6]{x} - 6\log(\sqrt[6]{x} + 1) + C.$$

II

An analogous substitution may help to rationalize an integrand containing $\sqrt{a^2 + x^2}$, $\sqrt{a^2 - x^2}$, or $\sqrt{x^2 - a^2}$.

Example 3.   Consider

$$I = \int \frac{\sqrt{a^2 - x^2}}{x} \, dx, \qquad 0 < x \le a.$$

The trigonometric substitution $x = a \sin \theta$ is suggested by the integrand, but the substitution $\sqrt{a^2 - x^2} = y$ for $0 < x \le a$, $x = \sqrt{a^2 - y^2}$ for $0 \le y < a$ can also be tried. We have $x^2 = a^2 - y^2$ and, then, by implicit differentiation,

$$2x \frac{dx}{dy} = -2y \qquad \text{or} \qquad \frac{dx}{dy} = -\frac{y}{x},$$

so that
$$I = \int \frac{y}{x} \frac{dx}{dy} \, dy = \int \frac{y}{x} \left(-\frac{y}{x} \right) dy = -\int \frac{y^2}{a^2 - y^2} \, dy.$$

Either by observation or long division we get

$$I = \int \left(1 - \frac{a^2}{a^2 - y^2} \right) dy,$$

and then by partial fractions,

$$I = \int \left(1 - \frac{a}{2} \frac{1}{a-y} - \frac{a}{2} \frac{1}{a+y} \right) dy = y + \frac{a}{2} \log \frac{a-y}{a+y} + C$$

$$= \sqrt{a^2 - x^2} + \frac{a}{2} \log \frac{a - \sqrt{a^2 - x^2}}{a + \sqrt{a^2 - x^2}} + C.$$

Example 4.   Consider

$$I = \int x^{2n+1} \sqrt{x^2 + a^2} \, dx, \qquad x \ge 0,$$

where n is a positive integer or 0 and $2n + 1$ is an odd integer. The trigonometric substitution $x = a \tan \theta$ is suggested, but we can also try the algebraic substitution $\sqrt{x^2 + a^2} = y$ for $x \ge 0$, $x = \sqrt{y^2 - a^2}$ for $y \ge a$. We have $x^2 = y^2 - a^2$, and thus, by implicit differentiation,

$$x \frac{dx}{dy} = y.$$

Then

$$I = \int (x^2)^n \sqrt{x^2 + a^2} \, x \, dx = \int (y^2 - a^2)^n \, yx \frac{dx}{dy} \, dy = \int (y^2 - a^2)^n \, y^2 \, dy.$$

This integrand can be written in polynomial form and the integration is straight-forward.

If n had been a negative integer, the number $x = 0$ would have had to be excluded from any interval considered, but the computation would have been essentially the same and our last integrand for y would have been a rational function to which the ideas of the last section could have been applied.

Finally, if we had wished to consider the integral I for an x interval of negative numbers, we could have substituted $x = -w$ for $w > 0$, $w = -x$ for $x < 0$ and then proceeded with the w integral as before. An x interval that was partly positive and partly negative could have been separated into an interval of nonnegative numbers and an interval of negative numbers.

● **Remark 1**

We would not have been able to use an algebraic substitution to advantage in considering the integral

$$\mathcal{J} = \int x^{2n} \sqrt{x^2 + a^2}\, dx,$$

where $2n$ is an even integer. The same substitution as the one used in Example 4 would have led us to

$$\mathcal{J} = \int x^{2n-1} \sqrt{x^2 + a^2}\, x\, dx = \int (y^2 - a^2)^{(2n-1)/2} yx \frac{dx}{dy}\, dy = \int (y^2 - a^2)^{(2n-1)/2} y^2 dy.$$

We still have a radical to deal with, and are no better off than before.

● **Remark 2**

In general, as the reader can show in Exercise 6.5-26, the integral

$$\int x^{kn-1} (ax^n + b)^{p/q}\, dx$$

will be rationalized by the substitution $y = (ax^n + b)^{1/q}$, $x = [(y^q - b)/a]^{1/n}$. Here it is understood that $a \neq 0$ and $n \neq 0$, that q is a positive integer, p is a positive or negative integer, k is an integer or 0, and that appropriate x- and y-domain intervals are used. In Examples 3 and 4 we worked with the case $n = 2$, in Example 1 with the case $n = 1$.

III

Sometimes the fact that a particular expression occurs several times suggests that a substitution be made for that expression. It might also pay to replace an expression that occurs only once but seems to be making an integrand hard to handle.

Example 5.   Consider

$$I = \int \frac{1}{e^x + 2e^{-x}}\, dx.$$

Since $e^{-x} = 1/e^x$, and e^x really occurs twice, we try the substitution $e^x = y$ for all real x, $x = \log y$ for $y > 0$. We have $dx/dy = 1/y$, and hence

$$I = \int \frac{1}{y + 2(1/y)} \frac{1}{y}\, dy = \int \frac{1}{y^2 + 2}\, dy. \tag{1}$$

Now we have almost the standard inverse tangent integral. We can say that

$$I = \frac{1}{2} \int \frac{1}{(y^2/2) + 1}\, dy = \frac{1}{2} \int \frac{1}{(y/\sqrt{2})^2 + 1}\, dy$$

$$= \frac{\sqrt{2}}{2} \int \frac{1}{(y/\sqrt{2})^2 + 1} \frac{1}{\sqrt{2}}\, dy = \frac{\sqrt{2}}{2} \tan^{-1} \frac{y}{\sqrt{2}} + C.$$

We can achieve the same result through the trigonometric substitution $y = \sqrt{2}\tan\theta$ in Eq. (1). In any event,

$$I = \frac{1}{\sqrt{2}}\tan^{-1}\frac{e^x}{\sqrt{2}} + C.$$

Example 6. Consider

$$\mathcal{J} = \int\frac{1}{2+\tan x}\,dx, \qquad \tan^{-1}(-2) < x < \pi/2.$$

Since $\sec^2 x$ is not present, $\mathcal{J}$ seems to be difficult to handle in the tangent-secant family. A change to sines and cosines could be made, but that does not lead to an immediately recognized integral, either. Let us try the substitution $\tan x = y$ for $\tan^{-1}(-2) < x < \pi/2$, $x = \tan^{-1} y$ for $y > -2$. Since

$$\frac{dx}{dy} = \frac{1}{1+y^2},$$

we have

$$\mathcal{J} = \int\frac{1}{2+y}\frac{1}{1+y^2}\,dy.$$

Here partial fractions are suggested. If we write

$$\frac{1}{2+y}\frac{1}{1+y^2} = \frac{A}{2+y} + \frac{By+C}{1+y^2},$$

we soon find that $A = \frac{1}{5}$, $B = -\frac{1}{5}$, $C = \frac{2}{5}$, so that

$$\mathcal{J} = \frac{1}{5}\int\frac{1}{2+y}\,dy - \frac{1}{5}\int\frac{y}{1+y^2}\,dy + \frac{2}{5}\int\frac{1}{1+y^2}\,dy$$
$$= \tfrac{1}{5}\log(2+y) - \tfrac{1}{10}\log(1+y^2) + \tfrac{2}{5}\tan^{-1}y + C$$
$$= \tfrac{1}{5}\log(2+\tan x) - \tfrac{1}{5}\log\sec x + \tfrac{2}{5}x + C.$$

EXERCISES 6.5

Integrate

1. $\int\dfrac{\sqrt{x}}{x+1}\,dx.$

2. $\int\dfrac{x+1}{\sqrt{x}}\,dx.$

3. $\int\dfrac{1}{\sqrt{2x-1}}\,dx.$

4. $\int\dfrac{x^2}{\sqrt{2x-1}}\,dx.$

5. $\int\dfrac{\sqrt{x}}{1-\sqrt{x}}\,dx.$

6. $\int\dfrac{\sqrt[3]{x}}{1+\sqrt[3]{x}}\,dx.$

7. $\int\dfrac{(4+x)^{3/2}}{x}\,dx.$

8. $\int\dfrac{dx}{x+2\sqrt{x}-8}.$

9. $\int x\sqrt{a^2-x^2}\,dx.$

10. $\int x^3\sqrt{a^2-x^2}\,dx.$

11. $\int\dfrac{\sqrt{x^2-1}}{x}\,dx.$

12. $\int\dfrac{\sqrt{a^2+x^2}}{x^2}\,dx.$

13. $\int\dfrac{(a^2+x^2)^{3/2}}{x}\,dx.$

14. $\int\dfrac{e^{2x}}{e^x+e^{-x}}\,dx.$

15. $\int\dfrac{5\tan x}{\tan x-2}\,dx.$

16. $\int\dfrac{dx}{x^{2/3}(x^{2/3}+1)}.$

17. $\int\dfrac{x^5}{\sqrt{x^3+8}}\,dx.$

18. $\int\dfrac{\sqrt{x}}{\sqrt{1-x}}\,dx.*$

19. $\int\dfrac{\sqrt{a-x}}{\sqrt{a}-\sqrt{x}}\,dx.$

---
* *Suggestion:* Look for a trigonometric substitution that will rationalize both radicals.

Evaluate

20. $\displaystyle\int_0^1 x(1-x)^{2/3}\,dx.$

23. $\displaystyle\int_{x=a}^{2a} x^3\sqrt{x^2-a^2}\,dx.$

21. $\displaystyle\int_{-2}^1 \frac{1}{(x+7)\sqrt{2-x}}\,dx.$

24. $\displaystyle\int_0^{16} \sqrt{4-\sqrt{x}}\,dx.$

22. $\displaystyle\int_4^{16} \frac{1}{\sqrt{x}-\sqrt[4]{x}}\,dx.$

25. $\displaystyle\int_{-1}^8 \sqrt{2+x^{1/3}}\,dx.$

26. Show that the integral $\int x^{kn-1}(ax^n+b)^{p/q}\,dx$ will be rationalized by the substitution $y=(ax^n+b)^{1/q},\ x=[(y^q-b)/a]^{1/n}.$ Here $n\neq 0$ and $a\neq 0$, q is a positive integer, p is a positive or negative integer, k is an integer or 0, and it is understood that appropriate x- and y-domain intervals are used.

6.6 Integration by Parts

This section will deal with the product rule of differentiation, stated in integral form. If du/dx and dv/dx are continuous functions of x, then

$$\frac{d(uv)}{dx}=u\frac{dv}{dx}+v\frac{du}{dx}\qquad\text{or}\qquad u\frac{dv}{dx}=\frac{d(uv)}{dx}-v\frac{du}{dx}$$

is an identity; if we integrate both members with respect to x, we get

$$\int u\frac{dv}{dx}\,dx=\int \frac{d(uv)}{dx}\,dx-\int v\frac{du}{dx}\,dx.$$

The first integral of the right member has the value uv, because uv is a function whose derivative with respect to x is $d(uv)/dx$. Therefore the following theorem may be stated.

■ THEOREM 1

Integration by parts.

HYPOTHESIS: du/dx and dv/dx are continuous functions of x for a suitable interval.

CONCLUSION: $\displaystyle\int u\frac{dv}{dx}\,dx=uv-\int v\frac{du}{dx}\,dx.$

Theorem 1 tells us that the integration of an expression that can be written as a product of one function and the derivative of another can be made to depend on a second integration in which the two functions interchange roles. Often the second integral can be dealt with more easily than the first.

The first decision one makes in applying this theorem to a particular integral is that of deciding which factor of the integrand should be called the factor u and which one the factor dv/dx. We usually choose for the dv/dx factor the most difficult factor for which v can be found.

Example 1. Consider $I=\int x\cos x\,dx.$ Here we try

$$\frac{dv}{dx}=\cos x,\qquad u=x$$

(rather than $dv/dx = x$, $u = \cos x$). With this choice we write

$$v = \sin x, \qquad \frac{du}{dx} = 1.$$

Then, by Theorem 1,

$$I = \int x \cos x \, dx = x \sin x - \int \sin x \, (1) \, dx.$$

The original integral has been replaced by a second integral which we recognize:

$$I = x \sin x + \cos x + C.$$

Not only can integration by parts be useful when the integrand consists of two factors of different types, as in Example 1, but it can also be useful when the integrand consists of only one factor.

Example 2.   Consider $I = \int \sin^{-1}x \, dx$. Let us write

$$I = \int \sin^{-1} x \, (1) \, dx$$

and then

$$\frac{dv}{dx} = 1, \qquad u = \sin^{-1} x,$$

so that

$$v = x \quad \text{and} \quad \frac{du}{dx} = \frac{1}{\sqrt{1 - x^2}}.$$

Thus

$$I = x \sin^{-1} x - \int x \, \frac{1}{\sqrt{1 - x^2}} \, dx.$$

Again we are led to an easier integral than the one we started with, and we have

$$I = x \sin^{-1} x + \tfrac{1}{2} \int (1 - x^2)^{-1/2}(-2x) \, dx$$

$$= x \sin^{-1} x + \sqrt{1 - x^2} + C.$$

Sometimes the technique of integration by parts is applied more than once.

Example 3.   Consider $I = \int x^2 e^{ax} \, dx$. Again we choose as our dv/dx factor the most difficult factor for which we can find v:

$$\frac{dv}{dx} = e^{ax}, \qquad u = x^2.$$

Then

$$v = \frac{1}{a} e^{ax}, \qquad \frac{du}{dx} = 2x,$$

so that

$$I = \frac{1}{a} x^2 e^{ax} - \int \frac{1}{a} e^{ax} 2x \, dx = \frac{1}{a} x^2 e^{ax} - \frac{2}{a} \int x e^{ax} \, dx.$$

The new integral seems to be easier than the original one, so that we are encouraged to try integration by parts again. This time we can write

$$\frac{dv}{dx} = e^{ax} \qquad \text{and} \qquad u = x,$$

so that
$$v = \frac{1}{a} e^{ax} \quad \text{and} \quad \frac{du}{dx} = 1.$$

Then
$$I = \frac{1}{a} x^2 e^{ax} - \frac{2}{a} \left[\frac{1}{a} x e^{ax} - \frac{1}{a} \int e^{ax} \, 1 \, dx \right] = \frac{1}{a} x^2 e^{ax} - \frac{2}{a^2} x e^{ax} + \frac{2}{a^3} e^{ax} + C.$$

It may happen that the very integral with which we start appears a second time during the integration by parts, in which case we can solve for that integral by elementary algebra.

Example 4. The function $e^{-ax} \cos bx$ can describe a damped-out periodic motion. Consider $I = \int e^{-ax} \cos bx \, dx$. If we choose
$$\frac{dv}{dx} = \cos bx \quad \text{and} \quad u = e^{-ax},$$

then we can write
$$v = \frac{1}{b} \sin bx \quad \text{and} \quad \frac{du}{dx} = -ae^{-ax},$$

so that by Theorem 1
$$I = (e^{-ax})\left(\frac{1}{b} \sin bx\right) - \int \frac{1}{b} \sin bx \, (-ae^{-ax}) \, dx$$
$$= \frac{1}{b} e^{-ax} \sin bx + \frac{a}{b} \int e^{-ax} \sin bx \, dx.$$

The new integral seems to be of about the same order of difficulty as the original integral, but, if we repeat the integration by parts, using this time
$$\frac{dv}{dx} = \sin bx \quad \text{and} \quad u = e^{-ax},$$

so that
$$v = -\frac{1}{b} \cos bx \quad \text{and} \quad \frac{du}{dx} = -ae^{-ax},$$

then we have
$$I = \frac{1}{b} e^{-ax} \sin bx + \frac{a}{b} \left[(e^{-ax})\left(-\frac{1}{b} \cos bx\right) - \int \left(-\frac{1}{b} \cos bx\right)(-ae^{-ax}) \, dx \right],$$
$$= \frac{1}{b} e^{-ax} \sin bx - \frac{a}{b^2} e^{-ax} \cos bx - \frac{a^2}{b^2} \int e^{-ax} \cos bx \, dx,$$

or
$$I = \frac{1}{b} e^{-ax} \sin bx - \frac{a}{b^2} e^{-ax} \cos bx - \frac{a^2}{b^2} I.$$

If we solve this linear equation for our unknown I, we get
$$I + \frac{a^2}{b^2} I = \frac{1}{b} e^{-ax} \sin bx - \frac{a}{b^2} e^{-ax} \cos bx,$$
$$b^2 I + a^2 I = be^{-ax} \sin bx - ae^{-ax} \cos bx,$$
$$(b^2 + a^2)I = e^{-ax}(b \sin bx - a \cos bx),$$
$$I = \frac{e^{-ax}}{a^2 + b^2} (b \sin bx - a \cos bx).$$

Example 5. The integral $I = \int \sec^3 x \, dx$ is hard to work with if only the ideas of Sec. 6.2 are used. For instance, if we write $I = \int \sec x \sec^2 x \, dx$ and say that $\sec^2 x$ is $d(\tan x)/dx$, we are unable to rewrite $\sec x$ as a power of $\tan x$ or a sum of such powers. But let us write $I = \int \sec x \sec^2 x \, dx$ again and try integration by parts, using the parts

$$\frac{dv}{dx} = \sec^2 x, \qquad u = \sec x,$$

so that

$$v = \tan x, \qquad \frac{du}{dx} = \sec x \tan x.$$

Then

$$I = \sec x \tan x - \int \tan x \sec x \tan x \, dx$$

$$= \sec x \tan x - \int \sec x \tan^2 x \, dx.$$

Here again we have an integral that is hard to work with if only the ideas of Sec. 6.2 are used. But if we use the replacement $\tan^2 x = \sec^2 x - 1$, we obtain

$$I = \sec x \tan x - \int \sec x (\sec^2 x - 1) \, dx$$

$$= \sec x \tan x - I + \int \sec x \, dx.$$

The original integral appeared a second time. Solving for I, we have

$$2I = \sec x \tan x + \int \sec x \, dx,$$

$$2I = \sec x \tan x + \log (\sec x + \tan x) + C',$$

$$I = \tfrac{1}{2}[\sec x \tan x + \log (\sec x + \tan x)] + C.$$

To summarize, the application of the technique of integration by parts is indicated immediately in problems where the integrand consists of two factors of different types. In such cases we usually split the integrand into a dv/dx factor and a u factor by choosing the dv/dx factor as the most inclusive factor for which a v can be found. But integration by parts can be applied in many different situations, and, indeed, might even be called a method of "last resort," to be considered when other methods have failed.

● Remark 1

Two different students might try the same dv/dx and u analysis in a given problem, using different v's, however, for the same dv/dx. The first student might write

$$\int u \frac{dv}{dx} \, dx = uv - \int v \frac{du}{dx} \, dx. \tag{1}$$

If the second student took $v_2 = v + c$ as his v function, just as good a choice since both come from the same dv/dx, he would write

$$\int u \frac{dv}{dx} dx = uv_2 - \int v_2 \frac{du}{dx} dx. \tag{2}$$

These results are not different, for, continuing with Eq. (2), we have

$$\int u \frac{dv}{dx} dx = u(v + c) - \int (v + c) \frac{du}{dx} dx$$

$$= uv + uc - \int v \frac{du}{dx} dx - c \int \frac{du}{dx} dx$$

$$= uv + uc - \int v \frac{du}{dx} dx - cu$$

$$= uv - \int v \frac{du}{dx} dx,$$

which agrees with Eq. (1).

EXERCISES 6.6

1. $\int x \sin x \, dx$.

2. $\int t \cosh 2t \, dt$.

3. $\int y \sec^2 y \, dy$.

4. $\int \frac{x}{e^x} dx$.

5. $\int x \sin^2 ax \, dx$.

6. $\int x^2 \sinh x \, dx$.

7. $\int t^3 \cos t \, dt$.

8. A. $\int \log x \, dx$.
   B. $\int \log (x + 1) \, dx$.*

9. $\int x^n \log x \, dx, n \neq -1$.

10. $\int x^{-1} \log x \, dx$.

11. $\int \tan^{-1} x \, dx$.

12. $\int x \tan^{-1} x \, dx$.

13. $\int x^2 \tan^{-1} x \, dx$.

14. $\int x \sin^{-1} x \, dx$.

15. $\int \frac{\log y}{(y - 1)^2} dy$.

16. $\int \frac{te^t}{(t + 1)^2} dt$.

17. $\int (\log x)^2 \, dx$.

18. $\int e^{ax} \sin bx \, dx$.

19. $\int \csc^3 t \, dt$.

20. $\int \sqrt{1 + x^2} \, dx$.

21. $\int \frac{x^2}{\sqrt{1 + x^2}} dx$.

22. $\int \frac{\sqrt{x}}{\sqrt{x - a}} dx$.

23. (a) Use a trigonometric substitution to integrate $\int \sqrt{x^2 - a^2} \, dx$.
    (b) Show that $P(\cosh u, \sinh u)$ is a point of $x^2 - y^2 = 1$ for each u. Let $u \geq 0$ and let A be the point $(1, 0)$. Show that the area bounded by OP, OA, and $x^2 - y^2 = 1$ is $\frac{1}{2} u$. (This fact was arrived at in a different way in Exercise 5.5-14.)

6.7 Tables of Integrals. Review List of Integrals

I

It is a matter of common-sense efficiency to keep a record of formal integration results that will be needed fairly frequently and that would require considerable repeated effort if derived each time. On the other hand, not all integrals can be

---

* *Suggestion:* Consider Remark 1.

listed in any table of formal integration results. The student who can make substitutions, use algebraic and trigonometric identities, and integrate by parts will often be able to rewrite an integral so that it takes on a form that appears in his table of integrals.

One result that requires a fair amount of computation and that is well worth recording in a reference table of integrals is given in Examples 1 and 2 below.

Example 1. Consider

$$I = \int \frac{dx}{\sqrt{x^2 - 6x + 11}}.$$

First we rewrite our quadratic expression by completing the square:

$$x^2 - 6x + 11 = (x^2 - 6x + 9) + 11 - 9 = (x - 3)^2 + 2,$$

so that

$$I = \int \frac{1}{\sqrt{(x - 3)^2 + 2}} \, dx.$$

Now a trigonometric substitution is suggested: Let $x - 3 = \sqrt{2} \tan \theta$ for $-\pi/2 < \theta < \pi/2$, $\theta = \tan^{-1} [(x - 3)/\sqrt{2}]$ for all real x. Since

$$\frac{dx}{d\theta} = \sqrt{2} \sec^2 \theta \qquad \text{and} \qquad (x - 3)^2 + 2 = 2 \tan^2 \theta + 2 = 2 \sec^2 \theta,$$

we write

$$I = \int \frac{1}{\sqrt{2} \sec \theta} \sqrt{2} \sec^2 \theta \, d\theta = \int \sec \theta \, d\theta = \log (\sec \theta + \tan \theta) + C_1.$$

But from the fact that $\tan \theta = (x - 3)/\sqrt{2}$ we see that

$$\sec^2 \theta = 1 + \tan^2 \theta = 1 + \frac{(x - 3)^2}{2} = \frac{1}{2} (x^2 - 6x + 11),$$

so that

$$\sec \theta = \frac{1}{\sqrt{2}} \sqrt{x^2 - 6x + 11}.$$

Hence

$$I = \log \left(\frac{\sqrt{x^2 - 6x + 11}}{\sqrt{2}} + \frac{x - 3}{\sqrt{2}} \right) + C_1$$

$$= \log (\sqrt{x^2 - 6x + 11} + x - 3) + C.$$

Rather than repeat the computation with different coefficients, let us write it out once and for all.

Example 2. Consider

$$I = \int \frac{dx}{\sqrt{ax^2 + bx + c}}, \qquad a > 0.$$

Again we rewrite our quadratic expression by completing the square and then we use a trigonometric substitution. First we have

$$ax^2 + bx + c = a\left(x^2 + \frac{b}{a}x + \phantom{\frac{b^2}{4a^2}}\right) + c$$

$$= a\left(x^2 + \frac{b}{a}x + \frac{b^2}{4a^2}\right) + c - \frac{b^2}{4a}$$

$$= a\left(x + \frac{b}{2a}\right)^2 + \frac{4ac - b^2}{4a} = a\left[\left(x + \frac{b}{2a}\right)^2 + \frac{4ac - b^2}{4a^2}\right]$$

so that

$$I = \frac{1}{\sqrt{a}} \int \frac{1}{\sqrt{\left(x + \frac{b}{2a}\right)^2 + \frac{4ac - b^2}{4a^2}}}\, dx. \tag{1}$$

Now there are essentially three possibilities for the "discriminant," $q = 4ac - b^2$. If $q = 0$, then

$$I = \frac{1}{\sqrt{a}} \int \frac{1}{x + b/2a}\, dx = \frac{1}{\sqrt{a}} \log\left(x + \frac{b}{2a}\right) + C.*$$

If $q = 4ac - b^2 > 0$, we try the trigonometric substitution

$$x + \frac{b}{2a} = \frac{\sqrt{q}}{2a} \tan\theta \quad \text{for } -\frac{\pi}{2} < \theta < \frac{\pi}{2}, \quad \theta = \tan^{-1}\frac{2ax + b}{\sqrt{q}} \quad \text{for all } x.$$

Then

$$\left(x + \frac{b}{2a}\right)^2 + \frac{q}{4a^2} = \frac{q}{4a^2}(\tan^2\theta + 1) = \frac{q}{4a^2}\sec^2\theta,$$

and

$$\frac{dx}{d\theta} = \frac{\sqrt{q}}{2a}\sec^2\theta,$$

so that

$$I = \frac{1}{\sqrt{a}} \int \frac{1}{(\sqrt{q}/2a)\sec\theta}\, \frac{\sqrt{q}}{2a}\sec^2\theta\, d\theta$$

$$= \frac{1}{\sqrt{a}} \int \sec\theta\, d\theta = \frac{1}{\sqrt{a}} \log(\sec\theta + \tan\theta) + C_1.$$

But then, returning to the x's, we have

$$\tan\theta = \frac{2a}{\sqrt{q}}\left(x + \frac{b}{2a}\right) = \frac{1}{\sqrt{q}}(2ax + b)$$

and

$$\sec^2\theta = 1 + \tan^2\theta = 1 + \frac{1}{q}(2ax + b)^2 = \frac{1}{q}(q + 4a^2x^2 + 4abx + b^2)$$

$$= \frac{1}{q}(4a^2x^2 + 4abx + 4ac) = \frac{4a}{q}(ax^2 + bx + c),$$

---

* See Exercise 6.7-2. We have assumed $x + b/2a > 0$.

so that

$$I = \frac{1}{\sqrt{a}} \log \left[\frac{2\sqrt{a}}{\sqrt{q}} \sqrt{ax^2 + bx + c} + \frac{2a}{\sqrt{q}} \left(x + \frac{b}{2a} \right) \right] + C_1$$

$$= \frac{1}{\sqrt{a}} \log \left[\frac{2\sqrt{a}}{\sqrt{q}} \left(\sqrt{ax^2 + bx + c} + \sqrt{a}x + \frac{b}{2\sqrt{a}} \right) \right] + C_1$$

$$= \frac{1}{\sqrt{a}} \log \left(\sqrt{ax^2 + bx + c} + \sqrt{a}x + \frac{b}{2\sqrt{a}} \right) + C. \tag{2}$$

II

The third possibility for q is $q = 4ac - b^2 < 0$. In this case $b^2 - 4ac = -q$ would be positive and Eq. (1) should be rewritten as

$$I = \frac{1}{\sqrt{a}} \int \frac{1}{\sqrt{[x + (b/2a)]^2 - (b^2 - 4ac)/4a^2}} \, dx.$$

Now the integration is possible only if $[x + (b/2a)]^2 > (b^2 - 4ac)/4a^2$; let us take $x + (b/2a) > \sqrt{-q}/2a$. If we use the trigonometric substitution

$$x + \frac{b}{2a} = \frac{\sqrt{-q}}{2a} \sec \theta \qquad \text{for } 0 < \theta < \frac{\pi}{2},$$

$$\theta = \sec^{-1} \frac{2ax + b}{\sqrt{-q}} \qquad \text{for } x > -\frac{b}{2a} + \frac{\sqrt{-q}}{2a},$$

we have

$$\left(x + \frac{b}{2a} \right)^2 - \frac{-q}{4a^2} = \frac{-q}{4a^2} (\sec^2 \theta - 1) = \frac{-q}{4a^2} \tan^2 \theta,$$

and

$$\frac{dx}{d\theta} = \frac{\sqrt{-q}}{2a} \sec \theta \tan \theta,$$

so that

$$I = \frac{1}{\sqrt{a}} \int \frac{1}{(\sqrt{-q}/2a) \tan \theta} \frac{\sqrt{-q}}{2a} \sec \theta \tan \theta \, d\theta = \frac{1}{\sqrt{a}} \int \sec \theta \, d\theta$$

$$= \frac{1}{\sqrt{a}} \log (\sec \theta + \tan \theta) + C_2$$

again. This time

$$\sec \theta = \frac{2a}{\sqrt{-q}} \left(x + \frac{b}{2a} \right) = \frac{1}{\sqrt{-q}} (2ax + b)$$

and

$$\tan^2 \theta = \sec^2 \theta - 1 = \frac{1}{-q} (4a^2 x^2 + 4abx + b^2 + q)$$

$$= \frac{1}{-q} (4a^2 x^2 + 4abx + 4ac)$$

$$= \frac{4a}{-q} (ax^2 + bx + c),$$

so that

$$I = \frac{1}{\sqrt{a}} \log \left[\frac{2a}{\sqrt{-q}} \left(x + \frac{b}{2a} \right) + \frac{2\sqrt{a}}{\sqrt{-q}} \sqrt{ax^2 + bx + c} \right] + C_2$$

and again

$$I = \frac{1}{\sqrt{a}} \log \left(\sqrt{ax^2 + bx + c} + \sqrt{a}\,x + \frac{b}{2\sqrt{a}} \right) + C.$$

To summarize, a typical integral table entry would read

$$\int \frac{dx}{\sqrt{ax^2 + bx + c}} = \frac{1}{\sqrt{a}} \log \left(\sqrt{ax^2 + bx + c} + \sqrt{a}\,x + \frac{b}{2\sqrt{a}} \right)$$
$$+ C, \qquad a > 0. \tag{2a}$$

Note that for the integral of Example 1 we have $a = 1$, $b = -6$, $c = 11$. Hence Eq. (2a) says that

$$\int \frac{dx}{\sqrt{x^2 - 6x + 11}} = \log \left(\sqrt{x^2 - 6x + 11} + x - 3 \right) + C,$$

which agrees with the computation of Example 1.

III

No course of study could consider all known devices for formal integration. Often, therefore, a table entry will give an inquirer a result he has not derived for himself, or perhaps a result based on a device he once used but has since forgotten.

Example 3.   Consider

$$I = \int \frac{1}{(1 + 2y) \sqrt{1 - y^2}} \, dy, \qquad -\frac{1}{2} < y < 1,$$

an integral not listed in some tables. The radical suggests the substitution $y = \sin t$ for $-\pi/6 < t < \pi/2$, $t = \sin^{-1} y$ for $-\frac{1}{2} < y < 1$.
Since

$$\frac{dy}{dt} = \cos t \qquad \text{and} \qquad 1 - y^2 = 1 - \sin^2 t = \cos^2 t,$$

$$I = \int \frac{1}{(1 + 2\sin t)\cos t} \cos t \, dt = \int \frac{1}{1 + 2\sin t} \, dt.$$

We have here a trigonometric integral of a type not studied in Sec. 6.2,* but an entry found in most tables of integrals is

$$\int \frac{dx}{a + b\sin x} = \frac{1}{\sqrt{b^2 - a^2}} \log \frac{a \tan (x/2) + b - \sqrt{b^2 - a^2}}{a \tan (x/2) + b + \sqrt{b^2 - a^2}}, \qquad b > a.$$

---

* This integral can be worked out with the help of the substitution $\tan \frac{1}{2} t = z$, $t = 2 \tan^{-1} z$.

Hence, taking $a = 1$ and $b = 2$, we have

$$I = \frac{1}{\sqrt{3}} \log \frac{\tan \frac{1}{2} t + 2 - \sqrt{3}}{\tan \frac{1}{2} t + 2 + \sqrt{3}} + C.$$

Since a trigonometric replacement for $\tan \frac{1}{2} t$ is given by the identity

$$\tan \frac{1}{2} t = \frac{1 - \cos t}{\sin t}$$

and since $\sin t = y$, we have

$$\tan \frac{1}{2} t = \frac{1 - \sqrt{1 - y^2}}{y},$$

and the answer can be rewritten

$$I = \frac{1}{\sqrt{3}} \log \frac{1 - \sqrt{1 - y^2} + (2 - \sqrt{3})y}{1 - \sqrt{1 - y^2} + (2 + \sqrt{3})y} + C.$$

IV

For the sake of conciseness, arrangers of tables of integrals often use "reduction formulas." A whole sequence of related integrals is described by referring each one to the previous one. Thus, for example, rather than devote many lines to statements for $\int \sin x \, dx$, $\int \sin^2 x \, dx$, $\int \sin^3 x \, dx$, $\int \sin^4 x \, dx, \cdots$, the following entries might be printed in a table:

$$\int \sin x \, dx = -\cos x + C, \tag{3}$$

$$\int \sin^n x \, dx = -\frac{\sin^{n-1} x \cos x}{n} + \frac{n-1}{n} \int \sin^{n-2} x \, dx, \qquad n \neq 0. \tag{4}$$

Example 4.   Here we shall work out the reduction formula (4). If we write

$$I = \int \sin^n x \, dx = \int \sin^{n-1} x \sin x \, dx$$

and then use integration by parts with

$$\frac{dv}{dx} = \sin x, \qquad u = \sin^{n-1} x,$$

so that $\qquad v = -\cos x, \qquad \dfrac{du}{dx} = (n-1) \sin^{n-2} x \cos x,$

then $\qquad I = \sin^{n-1} x(-\cos x) - \displaystyle\int (-\cos x)(n-1) \sin^{n-2} x \cos x \, dx$

$$= -\sin^{n-1} x \cos x + (n-1) \int \sin^{n-2} x \cos^2 x \, dx.$$

But we can replace $\cos^2 x$ by $1 - \sin^2 x$, so that we continue with

$$I = -\sin^{n-1} x \cos x + (n-1) \int \sin^{n-2} x \, dx - (n-1) \int \sin^n x \, dx.$$

Again, we have the integral with which we started, and so

$$I = -\sin^{n-1} x \cos x + (n-1) \int \sin^{n-2} x \, dx - (n-1)I,$$

$$nI = -\sin^{n-1} x \cos x + (n-1) \int \sin^{n-2} x \, dx,$$

$$\int \sin^n x \, dx = -\frac{1}{n} \sin^{n-1} x \cos x + \frac{n-1}{n} \int \sin^{n-2} x \, dx. \tag{5}$$

Example 5. We shall use the reduction formula (4) to evaluate

$$Q = \int_0^{\pi/2} \sin^{10} x \, dx.$$

We have, by Eq. (4), for $n = 10$,

$$Q = -\tfrac{1}{10} \sin^9 x \cos x \Big|_0^{\pi/2} + \tfrac{9}{10} \int_0^{\pi/2} \sin^8 x \, dx = \tfrac{9}{10} \int_0^{\pi/2} \sin^8 x \, dx.$$

Now, by Eq. (4), with $n = 8$, we get

$$Q = \tfrac{9}{10}\left[-\tfrac{1}{8} \sin^7 x \cos x \Big|_0^{\pi/2} + \tfrac{7}{8} \int_0^{\pi/2} \sin^6 x \, dx \right]$$

$$= \frac{9 \cdot 7}{10 \cdot 8} \int_0^{\pi/2} \sin^6 x \, dx.$$

Continuing to reduce our integral with the help of Eq. (4), we get

$$Q = \frac{9 \cdot 7 \cdot 5}{10 \cdot 8 \cdot 6} \int_0^{\pi/2} \sin^4 x \, dx,$$

$$Q = \frac{9 \cdot 7 \cdot 5 \cdot 3}{10 \cdot 8 \cdot 6 \cdot 4} \int_0^{\pi/2} \sin^2 x \, dx,$$

and then $\quad Q = \dfrac{9 \cdot 7 \cdot 5 \cdot 3 \cdot 1}{10 \cdot 8 \cdot 6 \cdot 4 \cdot 2} \displaystyle\int_0^{\pi/2} 1 \, dx = \dfrac{9 \cdot 7 \cdot 5 \cdot 3 \cdot 1}{10 \cdot 8 \cdot 6 \cdot 4 \cdot 2} \dfrac{\pi}{2}.$

▽

In the exercise lists of the earlier sections of this chapter the reader could often tell which integration technique to use simply by noticing which integration techniques were being studied in the section at hand. In these exercises we present a mixed list so that he will get practice in "diagnosing" integrals.

EXERCISES 6.7

1. Integrate. Start by completing the square.

(a) $\displaystyle\int \frac{1}{x^2 + 4x + 13}\, dx.$

(e) $\displaystyle\int \frac{1}{x^2 + 12x + 12}\, dx.$

(b) $\displaystyle\int \frac{1}{9x^2 - 12x + 11}\, dx.$

(f) $\displaystyle\int \frac{1}{(x^2 + x + 1)^{3/2}}\, dx.$

(c) $\displaystyle\int \frac{1}{\sqrt{3 + 2x - x^2}}\, dx.$

(g) $\displaystyle\int \sqrt{x^2 + 6x + 25}\, dx.$

(d) $\displaystyle\int \frac{1}{\sqrt{12x - 4x^2 - 6}}\, dx.$

2. In Example 2, consider the case $q = 4ac - b^2 = 0$ and show that Formula (2a) gives a correct answer in this case also.

3. Let $X = ax^2 + bx + c$, $q = 4ac - b^2$. Demonstrate the formulas

(a) $\displaystyle\int \frac{1}{X}\, dx = \frac{2}{\sqrt{q}} \tan^{-1} \frac{2ax + b}{\sqrt{q}} + C, \qquad a > 0,\, q > 0.$

(b) $\displaystyle\int \frac{1}{X^{3/2}}\, dx = \frac{2(2ax + b)}{q\sqrt{X}} + C, \qquad a > 0,\, q > 0.$

(c) $\displaystyle\int \frac{1}{X}\, dx = \frac{1}{\sqrt{-q}} \log \left| \frac{2ax + b - \sqrt{-q}}{2ax + b + \sqrt{-q}} \right| + C, \qquad a > 0,\, q < 0.$

(d) $\displaystyle\int \frac{dx}{\sqrt{X}} = \frac{1}{\sqrt{-a}} \sin^{-1} \left(\frac{-2ax - b}{\sqrt{-q}} \right) + C, \qquad a < 0 \text{ and } q < 0.$

4. In Exercises 1(a) to 1(f), integrate by referring to one of the formulas of Exercise 3.

5. (a) Demonstrate the formulas

$$\int \cos x\, dx = \sin x,$$

$$\int \cos^n x\, dx = \frac{1}{n} \cos^{n-1} x \sin x + \frac{n - 1}{n} \int \cos^{n-2} x\, dx, \qquad n \neq 0.$$

(b) Use the reduction formula of Part (a) to write out $\int \cos^7 x\, dx$.

(c) Evaluate $\int_0^\pi \cos^8 x\, dx$.

6. (a) Demonstrate the formulas

$$\int \tan x\, dx = -\log \cos x,$$

$$\int \tan^n x\, dx = \frac{\tan^{n-1} x}{n - 1} - \int \tan^{n-2} x\, dx, \qquad n \neq 1.$$

(b) Use the reduction formula of Part (a) to write out $\int \tan^7 x\, dx$.

(c) Evaluate $\int_0^{\pi/8} \tan^6 2x\, dx$.

7. (a) Let $a \neq 0$, $n \neq -\frac{3}{2}$. Demonstrate the formulas

$$\int \sqrt{ax + b}\, dx = \frac{2}{3a} (ax + b)^{3/2},$$

$$\int x^n \sqrt{ax + b}\, dx = \frac{2}{a(2n + 3)} \left[x^n (ax + b)^{3/2} - nb \int x^{n-1} \sqrt{ax + b}\, dx \right].$$

(b) Use the reduction formula of Part (a) to write out $\int x^2 \sqrt{x+1}\ dx$.

(c) Evaluate $\int_2^3 x^n (x-2)^{1/2}\ dx$ for $n = 0, 1, 2$.

In each of the following:

(a) Decide which technique or techniques of integration could be used;

(b) Carry out the integration yourself;

(c) Use a table of integrals if this is feasible.

8. $\int \cot^3 y \csc y\ dy$.

9. $\int \dfrac{x^2}{\sqrt{9-x^2}}\ dx$.

10. $\int 3e^{-t^2/2}\ t\ dt$.

11. $\int x e^{-2x}\ dx$.

12. $\int \dfrac{x^2+2}{x^2-7x+12}\ dx$.

13. $\int \cos^3 2t \sin 2t\ dt$.

14. $\int y \log(y+1)\ dy$.

15. $\int \dfrac{\sqrt{t}}{3+\sqrt{t}}\ dt$.

16. $\int \sqrt{x^2+10}\ x\ dx$.

17. $\int \dfrac{\sqrt{5-x^2}}{x}\ dx$.

18. $\int \sinh 2t \cosh 2t\ dt$.

19. $\int \sin 2t \cosh 2t\ dt$.

20. $\int y^3 \sqrt{y^2-a^2}\ dy$.

21. $\int (\sin ax + 1)^2\ dx$.

22. $\int \dfrac{e^{2x}-e^x}{e^x+1}\ dx$.

23. $\int \tan^{1/2} t \sec^4 t\ dt$.

24. $\int \dfrac{4}{x^3-4x^2+4x}\ dx$.

25. $\int \dfrac{3x}{\sqrt{x+2}}\ dx$.

26. $\int \dfrac{x^3-5x^2+7x+1}{x^2}\ dx$.

27. $\int \left(\cos 2x + \dfrac{2}{\cos 2x}\right)^2\ dx$.

28. $\int \tanh 3y\ dy$.

29. $\int \dfrac{x+4}{x^3+4x}\ dx$.

30. $\int e^{-.1x} \cos \pi x\ dx$.

31. $\int \dfrac{y \sqrt{y^2+4}}{y^2+5}\ dy$.

32. $\int \dfrac{\sin^3 x}{\sqrt{\cos x}}\ dx$.

33. $\int \dfrac{1}{1+t^{2/3}}\ dt$.

34. $\int \dfrac{x+2}{\sqrt{x^2+2x-3}}\ dx$.

35. $\int \dfrac{\log z}{z}\ dz$.

36. $\int \dfrac{4}{\sqrt{e^t}}\ dt$.

37. $\int \log(x + \sqrt{x^2+1})\ dx$.

38. $\int \dfrac{1}{1-\cos x}\ dx$.

39. $\int \dfrac{1}{x^3-1}\ dx$.

40. $\int \log(x^2+a^2)\ dx$.

41. Derive Wallis' formula,

$$\frac{\pi}{2} = \lim_{n \to \infty} \frac{2}{1} \frac{2}{3} \frac{4}{3} \frac{4}{5} \frac{6}{5} \frac{6}{7} \cdots \frac{2n}{2n-1} \frac{2n}{2n+1},$$

as follows:

Step (a). As in Example 5, show that

$$\int_0^{\pi/2} \sin^{2n} x \, dx = \frac{(2n-1)(2n-3)\cdots 1}{(2n)(2n-2)\cdots 2} \frac{\pi}{2},$$

n a positive integer, and that

$$\int_0^{\pi/2} \sin^{2n+1} x \, dx = \frac{(2n)(2n-2)\cdots 2}{(2n+1)(2n-1)\cdots 3},$$

so that, by division,

$$\frac{\pi}{2} = \frac{2 \cdot 2 \cdot 4 \cdot 4 \cdot 6 \cdot 6 \cdots (2n)(2n)}{1 \cdot 3 \cdot 3 \cdot 5 \cdot 5 \cdot 7 \cdots (2n-1)(2n+1)} \frac{\displaystyle\int_0^{\pi/2} \sin^{2n} x \, dx}{\displaystyle\int_0^{\pi/2} \sin^{2n+1} x \, dx}.$$

Step (b). Observe that for $0 \le x \le \pi/2$ we have $0 \le \sin x \le 1$, and then

$$0 \le \sin^{2n+1} x \le \sin^{2n} x \le \sin^{2n-1} x \le 1.$$

Explain why

$$0 < \int_0^{\pi/2} \sin^{2n+1} x \, dx \le \int_0^{\pi/2} \sin^{2n} x \, dx \le \int_0^{\pi/2} \sin^{2n-1} x \, dx.$$

Step (c). From Formula (4) show that

$$\int_0^{\pi/2} \sin^{2n+1} x \, dx = \frac{2n}{2n+1} \int_0^{\pi/2} \sin^{2n-1} x \, dx,$$

and from Step (b) that

$$1 \le \frac{\displaystyle\int_0^{\pi/2} \sin^{2n} x \, dx}{\displaystyle\int_0^{\pi/2} \sin^{2n+1} x \, dx} \le 1 + \frac{1}{2n}.$$

Step (d). Now from Step (a) derive Wallis' formula.

6.8   A Numerical Method for Definite Integrals. The Parabolic Rule

Not all antidifferentiation questions can be answered in terms of functions already known. For instance, using a finite number of functions already studied, we cannot write down an expression whose derivative is e^{-x^2}. Indeed, by using definite integrals whose integrands are expressions for which we do not know antiderivatives, we can define new functions that may prove to be of major importance. Recall that the function log x could have been defined as a definite integral:

$$\log x = \int_{t=1}^{x} \frac{1}{t}\, dt.$$

If we want to consider $\int_a^b f(x)\, dx$, with $f(x) \geq 0$ and continuous for $a \leq x \leq b$, and we do not know a function $\phi(x)$ such that $\phi'(x) = f(x)$ for a $\leq x \leq b$, we can fall back on the idea that the region of the x, y plane bounded by $y = f(x)$, the x axis, $x = a$ and $x = b$ has an area $\int_a^b f(x)\, dx$ and we can attempt to approximate that area in various ways. This region is indicated in Fig. 6.4. One fairly simple way to approximate to the area is to divide the interval $a \leq x \leq b$ into subintervals, erect vertical lines at the division points, and approximate to the areas of the sub-regions by using rectangles. For the heights of the various rectangles, the ordinates at the midpoints of the subintervals might be chosen (see Fig. 6.5).

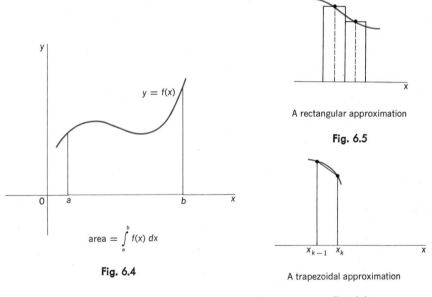

A rectangular approximation

Fig. 6.5

$y = f(x)$

area $= \int_a^b f(x)\, dx$

Fig. 6.4

A trapezoidal approximation

Fig. 6.6

We could also approximate to the area of a subregion by using a trapezoid, as in Fig. 6.6.* In effect, for each subinterval, we replace the curve by a straight line; we replace $y = f(x)$ by $y = ax + b$ with properly chosen constants a and b. A reader might ask next whether replacing $y = f(x)$ by $y = ax^2 + bx + c$ with properly chosen constants a, b, and c might not lead to an approximation better enough to warrant the extra effort. The parabolic rule, sometimes called Simp-son's rule, does just this. We divide the interval $a \leq x \leq b$ into an *even* number of subintervals of equal width Δx. For each *pair* of subregions, say the kth and $(k + 1)$st,

---

* See Exercise 6.8-2.

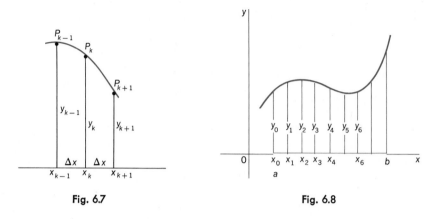

Fig. 6.7   Fig. 6.8

we replace curve $y = f(x)$ by the parabola through P_{k-1}, P_k, P_{k+1} with equation $y = ax^2 + bx + c$, three points being necessary to determine the three constants a, b, and c (see Fig. 6.7). But it was demonstrated in Exercise 3.13-6 that the area of two subregions under such a parabola is $\frac{1}{3} \Delta x(y_{k-1} + 4y_k + y_{k+1})$. Thus for the first and second subregions the approximating parabolic area would be $\frac{1}{3} \Delta x$ $(y_0 + 4y_1 + y_2)$; for the third and fourth, $\frac{1}{3} \Delta x(y_2 + 4y_3 + y_4)$; for the fifth and sixth, $\frac{1}{3} \Delta x(y_4 + 4y_5 + y_6)$; and so on. See Fig. 6.8. Adding up, we have

$$\int_a^b f(x)\, dx \approx \frac{1}{3} \Delta x(y_0 + 4y_1 + 2y_2 + 4y_3 + 2y_4 + 4y_5 + 2y_6 + \cdots).$$

Let us restate this result.

■ WORKING RULE 1

The parabolic rule for approximating $\int_a^b f(x)\, dx$. Let $f(x)$ be continuous for $a \le x \le b$. Then

(a) break the interval $a \le x \le b$ into $2m$ equal parts of width $\Delta x = (b - a)/2m$ each, choosing subdivision points $x_0 = a$, $x_1 = a + \Delta x$, $x_2 = a + 2\,\Delta x,\cdots$, $x_{2m} = a + 2m\,\Delta x = b$.

(b) compute $y_k = f(x_k)$, $k = 0, 1, 2, \cdots, 2m$.

(c) take

$$\int_a^b f(x)\, dx \approx \frac{1}{3} \Delta x(y_0 + 4y_1 + 2y_2 + 4y_3 + 2y_4 + \cdots + 2y_{2m-2}$$

$$+ 4y_{2m-1} + y_{2m}) \tag{1}$$

Example 1.   Let us follow through a parabolic rule approximation for the integral $\int_1^{1.2} 1/x\, dx$. (This integral represents $\log 1.2$.) Divide the interval $1 \le x \le 1.2$ into 10 equal subintervals, $\Delta x = .02$, and draw up a table of values for $y = f(x) = 1/x$ (Table 6.1). We read the following data from a table of reciprocals:

TABLE 6.1

k	0	1	2	3	4	5	6	7	8	9	10
x_k	1.0	1.02	1.04	1.06	1.08	1.10	1.12	1.14	1.16	1.18	1.2
y_k	1.	.9804	.9615	.9434	.9259	.9091	.8929	.8772	.8621	.8475	.8333

If we add up for the pairs of subregions according to Formula (1), we have

$$\int_1^{1.2} \frac{1}{x}\, dx \approx \tfrac{1}{3}(.02)[1. + 4(.9804) + 2(.9615) + 4(.9434) + 2(.9259)$$

$$+ 4(.9091) + 2(.8929) + 4(.8772) + 2(.8621)$$

$$+ 4(.8475) + .8333]$$

$$\approx \tfrac{1}{3}(.02)[27.3485] \approx .182323.$$

Note that in a five-decimal-place table, the value for log 1.2 is given as .18232.

Example 2.   Consider $\int_{.5}^2 e^{-x^2}\, dx$.

We use six subdivisions of width .25 each and read $y = e^{-x^2}$ from a table for the exponential function for two-decimal-place arguments. See Table 6.2.

TABLE 6.2

k	0	1	2	3	4	5	6
x_k	.5	.75	1.00	1.25	1.50	1.75	2
x_k^2	.25	.56	1.00	1.56	2.25	3.06	4
y_k	.779	.571	.368	.210	.105	.047	.018

Then Formula (1) says that

$$\int_{.5}^2 e^{-x^2}\, dx \approx \tfrac{1}{3}(.25)[.779 + 4(.571) + 2(.368) + 4(.210)$$

$$+ 2(.105) + 4(.047) + .018]$$

$$\approx \tfrac{1}{3}(.25)[5.055] \approx 0.42.$$

● **Remark 1**

In our discussion leading to Working Rule 1 we considered $\int_a^b f(x)\, dx$ with $f(x)$ continuous and ≥ 0 for $a \leq x \leq b$, but in Working Rule 1 itself we only required that $f(x)$ be continuous for $a \leq x \leq b$. The motivation for adopting Working Rule 1, even when $f(x)$ is negative for some or all numbers of $a \leq x \leq b$, is as follows. Since $f(x)$ is continuous for $a \leq x \leq b$, there is a lower bound number for it, and this number is negative; there is a number B, $B > 0$, such that $f(x)$

$\geq -B$ for $a \leq x \leq b$. But then $g(x) = f(x) + B$ is continuous and ≥ 0 for $a \leq x \leq b$ so that Working Rule 1 is applicable to $\int_a^b g(x) \, dx$. We would write

$$\int_a^b f(x) \, dx = \int_a^b [g(x) - B] \, dx = \int_a^b g(x) \, dx - \int_a^b B \, dx$$
$$\approx \tfrac{1}{3} \Delta x[g(x_0) + 4g(x_1) + 2g(x_2) + 4g(x_3) + \cdots]$$
$$- \tfrac{1}{3} \Delta x[B + 4B + 2B + 4B + \cdots]$$
$$\approx \tfrac{1}{3} \Delta x[\{g(x_0) - B\} + 4\{g(x_1) - B\}$$
$$+ 2\{g(x_2) - B\} + 4\{g(x_3) - B\} + \cdots]$$
$$\approx \tfrac{1}{3} \Delta x[f(x_0) + 4f(x_1) + 2f(x_2) + 4f(x_3) + \cdots].$$

This instruction for approximating to $\int_a^b f(x) \, dx$ is precisely the instruction furnished by Working Rule 1.

Example 3.   Let us use the parabolic rule to approximate $\int_{-.5}^{.3} x/(1 + x) \, dx$. We shall use eight subdivisions of width $\Delta x = .1$ each and compute entries to two-decimal-place accuracy, as shown in Table 6.3.

TABLE 6.3

k	0	1	2	3	4	5	6	7	8
x_k	$-.5$	$-.4$	$-.3$	$-.2$	$-.1$	0	.1	.2	.3
$1 + x_k$	.5	.6	.7	.8	.9	1	1.1	1.2	1.3
$\dfrac{x_k}{1 + x_k}$	$-1.$	$-.67$	$-.43$	$-.25$	$-.11$	0.	.09	.17	.23

The parabolic rule now says that

$$\int_{-.5}^{.3} \frac{x}{1 + x} \, dx \approx \tfrac{1}{3}(.1)[(-1) + 4(-.67) + 2(-.43) + 4(-.25) + 2(-.11)$$
$$+ 4(0.) + 2(.09) + 4(.17) + (.23)]$$
$$\approx \tfrac{1}{3}(.1)[-4.67] \approx -.156^-.$$

For the sake of comparison, observe that

$$\int_{-.5}^{.3} \frac{x}{1 + x} \, dx = \int_{-.5}^{.3} \left[1 - \frac{1}{1 + x} \right] dx = [x - \log(1 + x)]_{-.5}^{.3}$$
$$= (.3 - \log 1.3) - (-.5 - \log .5) = -.15551,$$

using the five-place logarithm table of the Appendix (Table IV).

Many modern computing machines are really remarkably fast adding machines. They approximate to an integral by breaking the interval of integration into many very small subintervals, approximating for the subintervals according to a set scheme, and then adding up.

EXERCISES 6.8

1. Use the parabolic rule to approximate each of the following definite integrals:

(a) $\displaystyle\int_{1}^{1.5} \frac{1}{x}\, dx.$

(d) $\displaystyle\int_{.05}^{.15} \frac{\sin x}{x}\, dx.$

(b) $\displaystyle\int_{0}^{1} \sqrt{0.2 + x^3}\, dx.$

(e) $\displaystyle\int_{0.8}^{1.2} (\log x)\,(\sin x)\, dx.$

(c) $\displaystyle\int_{.4}^{1.2} \frac{e^x}{x}\, dx.$

2. Show that the area of the trapezoid sketched in Fig. 6.9 is $\frac{1}{2}(y_{k-1} + y_k)\, \Delta x.$ Make plausible the following rule.

Working Rule 2. *The trapezoidal rule for approximating $\int_a^b f(x)\, dx$.*

    Step (a). Break the interval $a \le x \le b$ into n equal parts of width Δx each.
    Step (b). Compute $y_k = f(x_k)$, $k = 0, 1, 2, 3, \cdots, n$; $x_0 = a$, $x_n = b$.
    Step (c). Then

$$\int_a^b f(x)\, dx \approx \Delta x[\tfrac{1}{2}y_0 + y_1 + y_2 + y_3 + \cdots + y_{n-2} + y_{n-1} + \tfrac{1}{2}y_n].$$

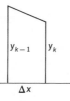

Fig. 6.9

3. Use the trapezoidal rule to approximate to each of the definite integrals of Exercise 1.

4. Evaluate $\int_{-h}^{h} y\, dx$ for $y = c$, (a) by using the antidifferentiation technique and (b) by breaking the interval $-h \le x \le h$ into two equal parts and using the parabolic rule. (c) From this show that the parabolic rule gives the exact value for the integral of a constant.

5. (a), (b) Do the same calculation as in Exercise 4 (a) and (b) for $y = ax + b$.
(c) From this show that the parabolic rule gives the exact value for the integral of a first-degree polynomial.

6. (a), (b) Do the same calculation as in Exercise 4 (a) and (b) for $y = ax^3 + bx^2 + cx + d$.
(c) From this show that the parabolic rule gives the exact value for the integral of a third-degree polynomial.

On the Underlying Theory

So far in this course we have accepted certain key words on an intuitive basis, without stating explicitly what we meant by them. The word "approach" was such a word; as Δx "approached" 0, $\Delta y/\Delta x$ would "approach" a number called dy/dx. Also, certain cornerstone statements were accepted, because they seemed to be intuitively reasonable. For instance, for a "continuous" function $f(x)$ we accepted the fact that sums of the form $\sum_{k=1}^{n} f(x_k^*)(\Delta x)_k$ would approach specific limits as n grew beyond all bounds and as the largest $(\Delta x)_k$ approached 0, partly because this agreed with our experience with plane areas. But we must learn to be very cautious about relying on statements and ideas that are "intuitively clear." A statement that agrees perfectly with one man's experience and thus is "intuitively clear" to him, may not be so clear to another man who has had different experience.

In this chapter we shall examine important words and statements more closely, and try to learn how to use the English and mathematical languages more carefully. We shall not undertake a thorough and complete study of fundamentals. For one thing, a certain level of mathematical maturity, which few beginning students could be expected to have, is required. But it is to be hoped that the work presented here will contribute significantly to the student's mathematical background and will help bring him to a level of mathematical maturity that will permit him to take more rigorous courses after he has finished this one.

The inequality and absolute value notations will be used frequently in the work of this chapter and the student is invited to refer to Secs. A1 and A2 of the Appendix when necessary. Certain facts are listed here for the sake of easy reference.

(a) If a number, positive or negative, is added to both members of an inequality, the inequality is preserved; if $a < b$, then $a + c < b + c$ for any number c.

(b) If both members of an inequality are multiplied or divided by a positive number, the inequality is preserved; if $a < b$, then $ca < cb$ for any number $c > 0$.

(c) If both members of an inequality are multiplied or divided by a negative number, the inequality is reversed; if $a < b$, then $ca > cb$ for any number $c < 0$.

(d) If the absolute value of a number q is less than a positive number a, then q lies between $-a$ and a, and conversely; $|q| < a$ and $-a < q < a$ are equivalent statements.

(e) If a and b differ by less than a positive number c, then $|a - b| < c$ or $-c < a - b < c$, and it will follow that $b - c < a < b + c$, $a - c < b < a + c$.

(f) The absolute value of a product is the product of the absolute values; $|ab| = |a||b|$.

(g) The absolute value of a sum is less than, or equal to, the sum of the absolute values; $|a + b| \leq |a| + |b|$.

7.1 On the Concept of Limit

Consider again a body that falls a distance $s = 16t^2$ in time t, and the question of determining its instantaneous velocity at the time $t = 1$. We reasoned as follows:

(a) At time $t = 1$ we have $s = 16$. At time $t = 1 + \Delta t$, $\Delta t \neq 0$ and $1 + \Delta t \geq 0$, we have $s = 16(1 + \Delta t)^2 = 16 + 32 \, \Delta t + 16 \, \Delta t^2$.

(b) For the interval I, $1 \leq t \leq 1 + \Delta t$ if $\Delta t > 0$ and $1 + \Delta t \leq t \leq 1$ if $\Delta t < 0$, we have

$$\text{distance traveled} = \Delta s = 32 \, \Delta t + 16 \, \Delta t^2.$$

(c) For interval I,

$$\text{average speed} = \frac{\Delta s}{\Delta t} = \frac{32 \, \Delta t + 16 \, \Delta t^2}{\Delta t}.$$

Then since we could not define the instantaneous speed directly, we agreed to take the definition:

instantaneous speed at $t = 1$ is $\lim_{\Delta t \to 0}$ (average speed for interval I).

We then computed

(d) At $t = 1$,

$$\text{instantaneous speed} = \lim_{\Delta t \to 0} \frac{\Delta s}{\Delta t} = \lim_{\Delta t \to 0} \frac{32 \, \Delta t + 16 \, \Delta t^2}{\Delta t} = 32.$$

Just what did we mean when we said that "the average speed for the interval approached the instantaneous speed as the length of the interval approached 0"? In algebraic language, what did we mean by

$$\lim_{\Delta t \to 0} \frac{32 \, \Delta t + 16 \, \Delta t^2}{\Delta t} = 32?$$

In slightly different form, what does the statement

$$\lim_{x \to 0} \frac{32x + 16x^2}{x} = 32 \tag{1}$$

mean? A similar question would be: What does the statement

$$\lim_{x \to 1} \frac{x^2 + x - 2}{x - 1} = 3 \tag{2}$$

mean?

In Statements (1) and (2) we are not trying to say what value $(32x + 16x^2)/x$ has when $x = 0$ or what value $(x^2 + x - 2)/(x - 1)$ has when $x = 1$, for these functions simply are not defined for those particular values of x. Instead, we are trying to give some information about the values these functions assign when x is near 0 in one case and near unity in the other. Statement (1) says that the closer x is to 0, the closer $(32x + 16x^2)/x$ is to 32; Statement (2) says that the closer x is to 1, the closer $(x^2 + x - 2)/(x - 1)$ is to 3. In general, when we say that

$$\lim_{x \to a} f(x) = L, \tag{3}$$

we mean that the closer x is to a, the closer $f(x)$ is to L. Note that we make no statement about $f(a)$; it may not even exist, and, if it does exist, it does not have to be the number L.*

The words "near" and "close" appeared in key roles in the last paragraph. Let us try now to be more explicit. To say that "$f(x)$ is close to L" is the same as to say that "$|f(x) - L|$ is close to 0." But how can we make precise the meaning of the phrase "close to 0"? Is .1 "close to 0"? No, .1 is not acceptable as a criterion of "close to 0," because we can easily think of situations where .1 would have to be considered as quite different from 0. Neither are .01, .001, or. 0001 acceptable. In fact, there are objections to accepting any single number as a criterion of "close to 0." First, it is conceivable that a real-life situation might arise where this number and the number zero had quite different roles to play. Second, no matter what *single* number is specified, there are always other numbers between that number and 0. Why not select one of these still smaller numbers instead? When we say, then, that $f(x)$ approaches L we shall mean that $|f(x) - L|$ becomes, and remains, less than *every* positive challenge number that might be presented to us.

But, surely, when a challenge number ϵ is specified, we cannot be expected to show that $|f(x) - L| < \epsilon$ for all x. We must exclude $x = a$, for which particular value of x we are not trying to make a statement, and we must exclude those x's that are too far from $x = a$. For instance, in Statement (2) above, we cannot be expected to show that $(x^2 + x - 2)/(x - 1)$ is closer to 3 than a challenge number $\epsilon = .01$ for an x as far from $x = 1$ as $x = 7$. We can only expect to show that $|f(x) - L| < \epsilon$ for the x's of a certain neighborhood of $x = a$, and the smaller the challenge number ϵ, the smaller this neighborhood of $x = a$ will have to be.

The ideas we have presented thus far can be stated in the following definition.

■ DEFINITION 1A

The definition of $\lim_{x \to a} f(x) = L$. We say that $\lim_{x \to a} f(x) = L$ if, for every positive challenge number ϵ, no matter how small, there is a neighborhood of $x = a$ such that $|f(x) - L| < \epsilon$ for all x of this neighborhood other than $x = a$ itself.

---

* See Exercise 7.1-7(a).

Note again that this definition does not even require that a itself be a number of the domain of function f. The number $f(a)$ may or may not exist, and, if it does exist, we may or may not have $f(a) = L$.

It remains to make more precise the meaning of the word "neighborhood." Let us agree that by a neighborhood of a we mean the interior of an interval with its center at a and width > 0. If the half-width of the neighborhood or interval is $\delta > 0$, then the neighborhood consists of the numbers x such that $a - \delta < x < a + \delta$ or, subtracting a from each member of the inequality, $-\delta < x - a < \delta$, or, using absolute value notation, $|x - a| < \delta$. Now our limit definition can be written in the following form.

■ DEFINITION 1

The definition of $\lim_{x \to a} f(x) = L$. We say that $\lim_{x \to a} f(x) = L$ if, for every positive challenge number ϵ, no matter how small, there is a positive number δ such that $|f(x) - L| < \epsilon$ for all x of the neighborhood $a - \delta < x < a + \delta$ other than $x = a$ itself.

● Remark 1

The number δ, which is the half-width of the neighborhood that must be exhibited, will depend on the ϵ specified. The smaller the ϵ, the smaller the δ we must expect to exhibit.

As the reader studies the examples of Definition 1 that follow, he should bear in mind that we are trying to practice using the more precise language of Definition 1. We are not interested at the moment in getting new results.

Example 1

$$\lim_{x \to 1} \frac{x^2 + x - 2}{x - 1} = 3.$$

Let the special challenge number $\epsilon = .01$ be specified. We must exhibit a neighborhood of $x = 1$ for all of whose points, except $x = 1$ itself, we shall have $(x^2 + x - 2)/(x - 1)$ closer to 3 than .01, or

$$\left| \frac{x^2 + x - 2}{x - 1} - 3 \right| < .01.$$

In order to have some idea of which neighborhood to exhibit, let us work with

$$\frac{x^2 + x - 2}{x - 1} - 3 = \frac{(x + 2)(x - 1)}{x - 1} - 3.$$

Since we do not have to prove anything when $x = 1$, we consider only the $x \neq 1$ possibility and write

$$\frac{x^2 + x - 2}{x - 1} - 3 = (x + 2) - 3 = x - 1 \qquad \text{if } x \neq 1. \tag{4}$$

In other words

$$\left| \frac{x^2 + x - 2}{x - 1} - 3 \right|$$

will be less than .01 if $|x - 1| < .01$, $x = 1$ excluded. But another way of writing $|x - 1| < .01$ is $-.01 < x - 1 < .01$ or $1 - .01 < x < 1 + .01$. We have furnished a neighborhood of $x = 1$, namely, $.99 < x < 1.01$, which meets the special challenge $\epsilon = .01$.

But we have to be able to meet *every* challenge. It would be futile to go on to $\epsilon = .001$, .0001, and other special cases for ϵ; we would never finish. We therefore reason with the symbol ϵ itself. Given any positive challenge number ϵ at all, we must exhibit a neighborhood of $x = 1$ for all of whose points, except $x = 1$ itself, we shall have

$$\left| \frac{x^2 + x - 2}{x - 1} - 3 \right| < \epsilon.$$

But Eq. (4) tells us that $|[(x^2 + x - 2)/(x - 1)] - 3|$ will be less than ϵ if $|x - 1| < \epsilon$, $x = 1$ excluded. To say that $|x - 1| < \epsilon$ is to say that $-\epsilon < x - 1 < \epsilon$, or that $1 - \epsilon < x < 1 + \epsilon$. Hence we can exhibit a suitable neighborhood of $x = 1$, namely, $1 - \epsilon < x < 1 + \epsilon$, and the limit statement is demonstrated. As Remark 1 pointed out, the neighborhood half-width δ must be expected to depend on the ϵ specified. In this case, we have shown that we may select $\delta = \epsilon$ or anything smaller.

Example 2

$$\lim_{x \to 0} \frac{32x + 16x^2}{x} = 32.$$

Let an $\epsilon > 0$ be specified, no matter how small. We must exhibit a neighborhood of $x = 0$ for all of whose points, except $x = 0$ itself, we shall have

$$\left| \frac{32x + 16x^2}{x} - 32 \right| < \epsilon.$$

Consider first the difference $(32x + 16x^2)/x - 32$. We can say that

$$\frac{32x + 16x^2}{x} - 32 = 32 + 16x - 32 = 16x \qquad \text{for } x \neq 0.$$

Hence $|[(32x + 16x^2)/x] - 32|$ will be less than ϵ if $|16x| < \epsilon$, or if $|x| < \epsilon/16$, $x = 0$ excluded. A suitable neighborhood of $x = 0$ is $|x| < \epsilon/16$ or $-\epsilon/16 < x < \epsilon/16$. In this case we can use $\delta = \epsilon/16$ as neighborhood half-width, or anything smaller.

Example 3

$$\lim_{x \to 3} (x^2 + x) = 12.$$

Let an $\epsilon > 0$ be specified, no matter how small. We must exhibit a neighborhood of $x = 3$ for all of whose points, except perhaps $x = 3$ itself, we shall have $|(x^2 + x) - 12| < \epsilon$.

Let us study the difference $(x^2 + x) - 12$. We can say that

$$(x^2 + x) - 12 = (x + 4)(x - 3).$$

Roughly, first, if x is close to 3, then $x + 4$ will be close to 7, thus less than 8. If we choose $|x - 3| < \epsilon/8$ we shall have

$$|(x + 4)(x - 3)| = |x + 4| \, |x - 3| < 8 \frac{\epsilon}{8} = \epsilon.$$

Now, more precisely, let N_1 be the neighborhood $3 - 1 < x < 3 + 1$ or $2 < x < 4$. If we add 4 to all members of this inequality, we shall have $6 < x + 4 < 8$, and thus

$$|x + 4| < 8 \qquad (5)$$

for any x of N_1. Then let N_2 be the neighborhood $3 - \epsilon/8 < x < 3 + \epsilon/8$. If we subtract 3 from all members of this inequality, we see that, for any x of N_2, we have $-\epsilon/8 < x - 3 < \epsilon/8$, or

$$|x - 3| < \frac{\epsilon}{8}. \qquad (6)$$

Now let N be the smaller of the two neighborhoods N_1 and N_2. Any x of N lies in both N_1 and N_2, and for any x of N we have both Eqs. (5) and (6). Hence, for any x of N, we shall have

$$|(x^2 + x) - 12| = |(x + 4)(x - 3)| = |x + 4| \, |x - 3| < 8\frac{\epsilon}{8} = \epsilon.$$

We have exhibited a suitable neighborhood of $x = 3$, namely N.

We did not have to prove that $|(x^2 + x) - 12| < \epsilon$ for $x = 3$ itself to justify the original limit statement, but it happens that $|(x^2 + x) - 12| < \epsilon$ for $x = 3$ also.

Example 4

$$\lim_{\theta \to 0} \sin \theta = 0.$$

Let an $\epsilon > 0$ be specified, no matter how small. We must exhibit a neighborhood of $\theta = 0$ for all of whose points, except $\theta = 0$ itself, we shall have $|\sin \theta - 0| < \epsilon$.

Consider $0 < \theta < \pi/2$. If we take an angle of radian measure θ in standard position and select a point on the terminal side at a distance 1 from the origin, then $\sin \theta$ is the y coordinate of this point from the definition of the sine function. See Fig. 7.1. But $y <$ chord AB, because the hypotenuse of a right triangle is always its longest side; chord $AB <$ arc AB, because a straight line is always the shortest distance between two of its points. Finally, arc $AB = \theta$ by the definition of radian measure. Thus $0 < \sin \theta < \theta$.

If we have $-\pi/2 < \theta < 0$, then $0 < -\theta < \pi/2$ and from what was shown above $0 < \sin(-\theta) < (-\theta)$, or $0 < -\sin \theta < -\theta$, or, multiplying by -1, $\theta < \sin \theta < 0$. Hence for any θ of $-\pi/2 < \theta < \pi/2$, except $\theta = 0$ itself, we have $|\sin \theta| < |\theta|$.

Thus if we choose the neighborhood $|\theta| < \epsilon$ or $-\epsilon < \theta < \epsilon$, we shall have $|\sin \theta - 0| < |\theta| < \epsilon$ for all θ of the neighborhood, and we have exhibited a suitable neighborhood as required. To justify the original limit statement, it is not necessary that $|\sin \theta - 0| < \epsilon$ for $\theta = 0$ itself, but this happens to be the case.

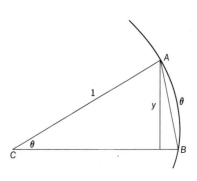

Fig. 7.1

Example 5.   Consider a "taxi-fare" function, or "step" function,

$$f(x) = \begin{cases} 25, & 0 \le x < \tfrac{1}{5}, \\ 30, & \tfrac{1}{5} \le x < \tfrac{2}{5}, \\ 35, & \tfrac{2}{5} \le x < \tfrac{3}{5}. \end{cases}$$

See Fig. 7.2. We have $f(\tfrac{1}{5}) = 30$, but does $\lim_{x \to 1/5} f(x)$ exist?

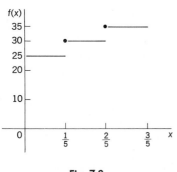

Fig. 7.2

The limit asked for does not exist. For, no matter what neighborhood of $x = \tfrac{1}{5}$ we try to exhibit, this neighborhood will contain x's that are less than $\tfrac{1}{5}$ and for which $f(x) = 25$; it will also contain x's that are greater than $\tfrac{1}{5}$ and for which $f(x) = 30$. If, therefore, an $\epsilon < 2.5$ is specified, we will not be able to find a number L such that $|f(x) - L| < \epsilon$ for all x's of the neighborhood except $x = \tfrac{1}{5}$. Unless we choose L within ϵ of 25, we shall have trouble with the x's that are less than $\tfrac{1}{5}$. Unless we choose L within ϵ of 30, we shall have trouble with the x's that are greater than $\tfrac{1}{5}$. We cannot choose an L to meet both requirements.

Example 6.   Consider

$$f(x) = \frac{1}{1 + 2^{1/x}}, \qquad x \ne 0.$$

Does $\lim_{x \to 0} f(x)$ exist?

Again the limit does not exist. No matter what neighborhood of $x = 0$ we try to exhibit, this neighborhood will contain points that are slightly to the right of $x = 0$ and other points that are slightly to the left. For the sake of concreteness, if $0 < x < .1$, we shall have $1/x > 10$, $2^{1/x} > 2^{10}$, $1 + 2^{1/x} > 1 + 2^{10}$, and

$$f(x) = \frac{1}{1 + 2^{1/x}} < \frac{1}{1 + 2^{10}} = \frac{1}{1025} < .001.$$

On the other hand, if $-.1 < x < 0$, we shall have $1/x < -10$, $2^{1/x} < 2^{-10} = 1/2^{10}$, $1 + 2^{1/x} < 1 + 1/2^{10}$, and

$$f(x) = \frac{1}{1 + 2^{1/x}} > \frac{1}{1 + 1/2^{10}} = \frac{2^{10}}{2^{10} + 1} = \frac{1024}{1025} > .999.$$

Now, in any neighborhood of $x = 0$, there are some x's that lie in $0 < x < .1$ and for which $f < .001$; there are other x's that lie in $-.1 < x < 0$ and for which $f > .999$. If an ϵ like .25 is specified, we cannot find a number L such that $|f(x) - L| < \epsilon$ for *all* x's of the neighborhood except $x = 0$ itself.

Example 7.   Consider

$$f(x) = \sin \frac{1}{x}, \qquad x \ne 0.$$

What can we say about $\lim_{x \to 0} f(x)$?

It is a fact that $f(1/n\pi) = \sin n\pi = 0$ for every integer $n \neq 0$, and that therefore in every neighborhood of $x = 0$, no matter how small, we can find points for which $f(x) = 0$ by choosing $x = 1/n\pi$ with n large enough. For such points we surely have $|f(x) - 0|$ less than any ϵ that might be proposed. But if an $\epsilon < 1$ is specified, we cannot find a neighborhood of $x = 0$ for *all* of whose points, except $x = 0$ itself, we shall have $|f(x) - 0| < \epsilon$, because between $1/n\pi$ and $1/(n+1)\pi$ we have $1/(n + \frac{1}{2})\pi$ and

$$f\left(\frac{1}{[n + 1/2]\pi}\right) = \sin (n + \tfrac{1}{2})\pi = \pm 1.$$

In different words, $|f(x) - 0|$ becomes less than ϵ as x approaches 0, but does not *remain* less than ϵ; $\lim_{x \to 0} f(x)$ is not 0, and in fact does not exist at all, because a similar argument would apply if we tried to show that $\lim_{x \to 0} f(x) = q$, where q is any other number between -1 and 1.

EXERCISES 7.1

1. Show that, for any x of the neighborhood $1 - \epsilon/2 < x < 1 + \epsilon/2$, we have $|(2x + 3) - 5| < \epsilon$. Write down a limit statement that is thus justified.
2. Show that, for any x of the neighborhood $-1 - \epsilon/3 < x < -1 + \epsilon/3$, we have $|(3x + 4) - 1| < \epsilon$. Write down a limit statement that is thus justified.
3. Find a neighborhood of $x = 2$ for all of whose points we shall have $|(2x + 7) - 11| < \epsilon$. Write down a limit statement that is thus justified.
4. Find a neighborhood of $x = 2$ for all of whose points except $x = 2$ itself we shall have

$$\left|\frac{x^2 + x - 6}{x - 2} - 5\right| < \epsilon.$$

   Write down a limit statement that is thus justified.
5. Justify each of the following statements by using Definition 1.

   (a) $\lim_{x \to 5} x^2 = 25$.

   (b) $\lim_{x \to 1} x^3 = 1$.

   (c) $\lim_{x \to 0} \cos x = 1$.

   (d) $\lim_{x \to 0} |x| = 0$.

   (e) $\lim_{t \to 2} \dfrac{t^2 + 2t - 8}{t - 2} = 6$.

   (f) $\lim_{t \to 0} \dfrac{3t + 3t^2 + t^3}{t} = 3$.

   (g) $\lim_{x \to 1} \dfrac{x^2 + x - 2}{x^2 + 2x - 3} = \dfrac{3}{4}$.

   (h) $\lim_{x \to 4} \sqrt{x} = 2$.

   (i) $\lim_{x \to 0} x \sin \dfrac{1}{x} = 0$.

6. Is the statement "$\lim_{x \to 1} f(x)$ exists" true or false in the following cases? Discuss each case.

   (a) $f(x) = \begin{cases} x^2, & 0 \le x < 1, \\ 2 - x^2, & x > 1. \end{cases}$

   (b) $f(x) = \begin{cases} x^2, & 0 \le x < 1, \\ x, & x > 1. \end{cases}$

   (c) $f(x) = \begin{cases} x + 1, & 0 \le x \le 1, \\ \dfrac{1}{x}, & x > 1. \end{cases}$

7. Decide whether the following propositions are valid or not, and explain why.

(a) *Hypothesis:* (a) $f(x) = g(x)$ for all $x \neq 0$,
   (b) $f(0) \neq g(0)$,
   (c) $\lim_{x \to 0} f(x) = c$.

   Conclusion: $\lim_{x \to 0} g(x) = c$.

(b) *Hypothesis:* (a) $f(x) = g(x)$ for $-.1 < x < .1$,
   (b) $f(x) \neq g(x)$ for other x,
   (c) $\lim_{x \to 0} f(x) = c$.

   Conclusion: $\lim_{x \to 0} g(x) = c$.

(c) *Hypothesis:* (a) $f(x) = g(x)$ for $-.00001 < x < .00001$,
   (b) $f(x) \neq g(x)$ for other x,
   (c) $\lim_{x \to 0} f(x) = c$.

   Conclusion: $\lim_{x \to 0} g(x) = c$.

(d) *Hypothesis:* (a) For $x > 0$, $g(x) = f(x)$,
   (b) For $x < 0$, $g(x) = -f(x)$,
   (c) $\lim_{x \to 0} f(x) = 0$.

   Conclusion: $\lim_{x \to 0} g(x) = 0$.

(e) *Hypothesis:* (a) For $x > 0$, $g(x) = f(x)$,
   (b) For $x < 0$, $g(x) = -f(x)$,
   (c) $\lim_{x \to 0} f(x) = 1$.

   Conclusion: $\lim_{x \to 0} g(x)$ exists.

7.2   On the Concept of Limits. Some Theorems

I

We often use the phrase "becomes infinite." For instance, we might say that as x approaches 0, $f(x) = 1/x^2$ becomes infinite; in symbols,

$$\lim_{x \to 0} \frac{1}{x^2} = \infty.$$

Another illustration would be

$$\lim_{x \to \infty} \frac{1}{x+1} = 0.$$

Let us try to make precise the meanings of these statements.

A first explanation of the statement "a function becomes infinite" might be that "the function grows large, very large." But what criterion is there for the word "large"? Is $(10)^9$ a good criterion? Sometimes it is, but we can easily think of situations where a billion is not large. There would be objections to accepting any *single* number as a criterion of "large" or "very large." Again, the useful idea is the idea of surpassing *all* possible challenges, not just one.

■ DEFINITION 1

The definition of $\lim_{x \to a} f(x) = \infty$. We say that $\lim_{x \to a} f(x) = \infty$ if for every positive challenge number B, no matter how large, there is a positive number δ such that $f(x) > B$ for all x of the neighborhood $a - \delta < x < a + \delta$ other than $x = a$ itself.

Note again that a may or may not be a number of the domain of the function f, and that if $f(a)$ does exist, we may or may not have $f(a) > B$.

● Remark 1

In Definition 1 the half-width of the neighborhood that we exhibit will depend on the size of the challenge number B.

● Remark 2

When we say that $\lim_{x \to a} f(x)$ exists, we mean that there is a finite number L such that $\lim_{x \to a} f(x) = L$. The case $\lim_{x \to a} f(x) = \infty$ is excluded when one says that $\lim_{x \to a} f(x)$ exists.

Example 1

$$\lim_{x \to 0} \frac{1}{x^2} = \infty.$$

Suppose first that a specific challenge number $B = (10)^8$ is presented. We shall show that there is a neighborhood of $x = 0$ for all of whose points, except $x = 0$ itself, we shall have $1/x^2 > 10^8$. But $1/x^2$ will be $> 10^8$ if $x^2 < 1/10^8$, $x = 0$ excepted, and thus if $-1/10^4 < x < 1/10^4$, $x = 0$ excepted. We have found a suitable neighborhood of $x = 0$, namely, $-1/10^4 < x < 1/10^4$.

However, Definition 1 says that we must meet every possible challenge, not just one. Thus if a positive challenge number B is presented, no matter how large, we must exhibit a neighborhood of $x = 0$ for all of whose points, except $x = 0$ itself, we shall have $1/x^2 > B$. But we shall have $1/x^2 > B$ if $x^2 < 1/B$, $x = 0$ excepted, or if $-\sqrt{1/B} < x < \sqrt{1/B}$, $x = 0$ excepted. We have exhibited a suitable neighborhood of $x = 0$, namely, $-\sqrt{1/B} < x < \sqrt{1/B}$.

Another frequently used statement is made precise in the following definition.

■ DEFINITION 2

The definition of $\lim_{x \to \infty} f(x) = L$. We that say $\lim_{x \to \infty} f(x) = L$ if for every positive challenge number ϵ, no matter how small, there is a positive number B such that $|f(x) - L| < \epsilon$ for all $x > B$.

● Remark 3

An alternate reading for "$\lim_{x \to \infty} f(x) = L$" is: "$f(x)$ approaches L as x grows beyond all bounds."

● Remark 4

The size of the number B of Definition 2 will depend on the challenge number ϵ.

Example 2

$$\lim_{x \to \infty} \frac{1}{x} = 0.$$

Let any positive number ϵ be specified, no matter how small. We must find a number B so large that for all $x > B$, we shall have $1/x$ closer to 0 than ϵ; that is, $|1/x - 0|$ shall be less than ϵ for all $x > B$. But $1/x$ will be less than ϵ if $x > 1/\epsilon$. We have found a large enough number B; let $B = 1/\epsilon$. Then when $x > B$, we shall have $|1/x - 0| < \epsilon$.

II

We shall conclude our study of limits by proving several theorems that we have used many times in the past, their validity having been assumed with little if any question by the average reader because they seemed to agree so well with his experience, or because the notation used seemed to suggest that the theorems were valid. The proofs of these theorems will now be based on deductive reasoning. Among other things, if we know the numbers approached by several functions, these theorems will enable us to predict the number approached by a more complex function built up from the original ones by adding, subtracting, multiplying, dividing, and finding roots.

■ **THEOREM 1**

HYPOTHESIS: There is a neighborhood N of $x = a$ for which $f(x) = c$, except perhaps for $x = a$ itself.

CONCLUSION: $\lim_{x \to a} f(x) = c$.

PROOF: Let $\epsilon > 0$ be specified, no matter how small. We must exhibit a neighborhood of $x = a$ for all of whose points, except perhaps a itself, we shall have $|f(x) - c| < \epsilon$. But N itself is such a neighborhood. For all x of N, except perhaps $x = a$, we have $|f(x) - c| = |c - c| = 0$, so that we surely have $|f(x) - c| < \epsilon$ for these x.

■ **THEOREM 2**

HYPOTHESIS: There is a neighborhood N of $x = a$ for which $f(x) = x$, except perhaps for $x = a$ itself.

CONCLUSION: $\lim_{x \to a} f(x) = a$.

PROOF: Let $\epsilon > 0$ be specified, no matter how small. We must exhibit a neighborhood of $x = a$ for all of whose points, except perhaps a itself, we shall have $|f(x) - a| < \epsilon$. But $|f(x) - a| < \epsilon$ means $|x - a| < \epsilon$ in this case, or $-\epsilon < x - a < \epsilon$ or $a - \epsilon < x < a + \epsilon$. We can choose the neighborhood $a - \epsilon < x < a + \epsilon$, or, if this neighborhood does not lie entirely within the neighborhood N of the hypothesis, we can choose a new neighborhood within $a - \epsilon < x < a + \epsilon$ that does lie entirely within N. For such a neighborhood we have $|x - a| < \epsilon$ or $|f(x) - a| < \epsilon$, except perhaps for $x = a$ itself.

■ **THEOREM 3**

The uniqueness of the limit.

> HYPOTHESIS: (a) $\lim\limits_{x \to a} f(x) = L$.
>
> (b) $\lim\limits_{x \to a} f(x) = M$.
>
> CONCLUSION: $L = M$.

In words, if f approaches a limit at all as x approaches a, it can only approach one limit.

PROOF: We shall give a proof by contradiction. If L and M are distinct, then $L - M \neq 0$. Let the positive challenge number $\epsilon = |L - M|/3$ be presented. Then, by Hypothesis (a), there is a neighborhood N_1 of $x = a$ for all of whose points, except perhaps for $x = a$ itself, we have

$$|f(x) - L| < \epsilon = \frac{|L - M|}{3}. \tag{1}$$

By Hypothesis (b), there is a neighborhood N_2 of $x = a$ for all of whose points, except perhaps for $x = a$ itself, we have

$$|f(x) - M| < \epsilon = \frac{|L - M|}{3}. \tag{2}$$

Neighborhoods N_1 and N_2 have points in common other than $x = a$; let x^* be such a common point. Now Eq. (1) says that $f(x^*)$ lies closer to L than the number $1/3$ of the way from L to M, while Eq. (2) says that $f(x^*)$ lies closer to M than the number $\frac{1}{3}$ of the way from M to L; see Fig. 7.3. We have a contradiction.

Fig. 7.3

■ **THEOREM 4**

Limits of sums, differences, products, quotients, roots.

> HYPOTHESIS: (a) $\lim\limits_{x \to a} f(x) = L$.
>
> (b) $\lim\limits_{x \to a} g(x) = M$.
>
> CONCLUSION: (a) $\lim\limits_{x \to a} [f(x) + g(x)] = L + M$.
>
> (b) $\lim\limits_{x \to a} [f(x) - g(x)] = L - M$.
>
> (c) $\lim\limits_{x \to v} [f(x) \, g(x)] = LM$.

HYPOTHESIS: (c) $M \neq 0$.

CONCLUSION: (d) $\lim\limits_{x \to a} \dfrac{f(x)}{g(x)} = \dfrac{L}{M}$.

HYPOTHESIS: (d) q is an odd positive integer.

CONCLUSION: (e) $\lim\limits_{x \to a} \sqrt[q]{f(x)} = \sqrt[q]{L}$.

HYPOTHESIS: (e) r is an even positive integer and $L > 0$.

CONCLUSION: (f) $\lim\limits_{x \to a} \sqrt[r]{f(x)} = \sqrt[r]{L}$.

An alternate reading for this theorem is: If $f(x)$ and $g(x)$ approach L and M as x approaches a, then $f(x) + g(x)$ approaches $L + M$, $f(x)g(x)$ approaches LM, and so on.

We shall illustrate this theorem before proceeding to the proofs of the various parts of the conclusion.

Example 3

$$\lim_{\Delta t \to 0} \left(\frac{3t^2\, \Delta t + 3t\, \Delta t^2 + \Delta t^3}{\Delta t} \right) = ?$$

First, this limit statement will say nothing about the value of

$$\frac{3t^2\, \Delta t + 3t\, \Delta t^2 + \Delta t^3}{\Delta t}$$

for $\Delta t = 0$; it will make a statement about the values of that function for Δt near 0. Therefore we write

$$\frac{3t^2\, \Delta t + 3t\, \Delta t^2 + \Delta t^3}{\Delta t} = 3t^2 + 3t\, \Delta t + \Delta t^2, \qquad \Delta t \neq 0.$$

Now, by Theorems 1 and 2, we have

$$\lim_{\Delta t \to 0} 3t^2 = 3t^2, \qquad \lim_{\Delta t \to 0} 3t = 3t, \qquad \text{and} \qquad \lim_{\Delta t \to 0} \Delta t = 0.$$

Then by Conclusion (c) of Theorem 4,

$$\lim_{\Delta t \to 0} (3t\, \Delta t) = \left(\lim_{\Delta t \to 0} 3t \right)\left(\lim_{\Delta t \to 0} \Delta t \right) = 3t(0),$$

and $\qquad \lim\limits_{\Delta t \to 0} \Delta t^2 = \left(\lim\limits_{\Delta t \to 0} \Delta t \right)\left(\lim\limits_{\Delta t \to 0} \Delta t \right) = (0)(0).$

Finally, by Conclusion (a) of Theorem 4,

$$\lim_{\Delta t \to 0} (3t^2 + 3t\, \Delta t + \Delta t^2) = \lim_{\Delta t \to 0} 3t^2 + \lim_{\Delta t \to 0} 3t\, \Delta t + \lim_{\Delta t \to 0} \Delta t^2$$

$$= 3t^2 + 0 + 0.$$

Example 4

$$\lim_{x \to 2} \frac{x + 4}{x - 3} = ?$$

We conclude from Theorems 2 and 1 that $\lim_{x \to 2} x = 2$, $\lim_{x \to 2} 4 = 4$ and from Conclusion (a) of Theorem 4 that $\lim_{x \to 2} (x + 4) = 2 + 4 = 6$. From Theorems 2 and 1 and Conclusion (b) of Theorem 4 we conclude that $\lim_{x \to 2} (x - 3) = 2 - 3 = -1$. Then by Conclusion (d) of Theorem 4 we conclude that

$$\lim_{x \to 2} \frac{x + 4}{x - 3} = \frac{6}{-1} = -6.$$

Example 5

$$\lim_{x \to 2} \sqrt{x^2 + x} = ?$$

We know that $\lim_{x \to 2} x = 2$ by Theorem 2, that $\lim_{x \to 2} x^2 = \lim_{x \to 2} (xx) = (\lim_{x \to 2} x)(\lim_{x \to 2} x) = 2(2) = 4$ by Conclusion (c) of Theorem 4, that $\lim_{x \to 2} (x^2 + x) = \lim_{x \to 2} x^2 + \lim_{x \to 2} x = 4 + 2 = 6$ by Conclusion (a) of Theorem 4, and that $\lim_{x \to 2} \sqrt{x^2 + x} = \sqrt{6}$ by Conclusion (f) of Theorem 4.

III

PROOF OF CONCLUSION (a) OF THEOREM 4:   Let an $\epsilon > 0$ be specified, no matter how small. We must exhibit a neighborhood of $x = a$ for all of whose points, except $x = a$ itself, we shall have

$$|[f(x) + g(x)] - [L + M]| < \epsilon.$$

The difference we must study can be rewritten. We must find a neighborhood of $x = a$ for which

$$|[f(x) - L] + [g(x) - M]| < \epsilon, \qquad x \neq a.$$

It would suffice to find a neighborhood of $x = a$ for which

$$|f(x) - L| + |g(x) - M| < \epsilon, \qquad x \neq a,$$

for the absolute value of a sum is less than, or equal to, the sum of the absolute values:

$$|[f(x) - L] + [g(x) - M]| < |f(x) - L| + |g(x) - M|,$$

and if the right member is less than ϵ, then surely the left member is. But according to Hypothesis (a), for any positive challenge number that may be presented we can find a neighborhood of $x = a$ for all of whose points, except $x = a$, we shall have $|f(x) - L|$ less than that challenge number. Take this challenge number to be $\epsilon/2$ and let N_1 be a corresponding neighborhood of $x = a$;

$$|f(x) - L| < \frac{\epsilon}{2} \qquad \text{for } x \text{ in } N_1 \text{ but } x \neq a. \tag{3}$$

Similarly let N_2 be a neighborhood of $x = a$ for which

$$|g(x) - M| < \frac{\epsilon}{2} \qquad \text{for } x \text{ in } N_2 \text{ but } x \neq a. \tag{4}$$

Then let N be the smaller of N_1 and N_2; any point of N lies in both N_1 and N_2 and Eqs. (3) and (4) both apply. Now, for any x of N except $x = a$ we have

$$|[f(x) + g(x)] - [L + M]| = |[f(x) - L] + [g(x) - M]|$$
$$\leq |f(x) - L| + |g(x) - M|$$
$$< \frac{\epsilon}{2} + \frac{\epsilon}{2} = \epsilon.$$

We have exhibited the neighborhood we were supposed to exhibit.

IV

PROOF OF CONCLUSION (c) OF THEOREM 4: We shall demonstrate first the special case where one of the functions approaches 0 and then show how Conclusion (c) can be made to follow from this special case. Consider, then, the following lemma.

■ LEMMA 1

HYPOTHESIS: (a) $\lim\limits_{x \to a} f(x) = L$,

(b) $\lim\limits_{x \to a} h(x) = 0$.

CONCLUSION: $\lim\limits_{x \to a} [f(x)h(x)] = 0$.

PROOF: Let an $\epsilon > 0$ be specified, no matter how small. We must exhibit a neighborhood of $x = a$ for all of whose points, except $x = a$ itself, we shall have $|f(x)h(x) - 0| < \epsilon$. Hypothesis (a) says that $|f(x) - L|$ can be made as small as desired. Let N_1 be a neighborhood of $x = a$ for all of whose points, except $x = a$ itself, we have $|f(x) - L| < 1$ or $L - 1 < f(x) < L + 1$, and

$$|f(x)| < |L| + 1.$$

Then we use Hypothesis (b) to say that there exists a neighborhood, N_2, of $x = a$ for all of whose points, except $x = a$, we have

$$|h(x) - 0| < \frac{\epsilon}{|L| + 1}.$$

Finally, if N is the smaller of N_1 and N_2, for any point of N except $x = a$, we have

$$|f(x)h(x)| = |f(x)| \, |h(x)| < (|L| + 1) \frac{\epsilon}{|L| + 1} = \epsilon.$$

This is the neighborhood of $x = a$ we were to exhibit, and the proof of Lemma 1 is thus concluded.

To return to the proof of Conclusion (c) of Theorem 4, we note that it would suffice to show that

$$\lim\limits_{x \to a} [f(x)g(x) - LM] = 0.$$

But we can rewrite $f(x)g(x) - LM$ in such a way as to make this difference depend on the differences $f(x) - L$ and $g(x) - M$. Indeed,

$$f(x)g(x) - LM = f(x)g(x) - f(x)M + f(x)M - LM,$$

or $\qquad f(x)g(x) - LM = f(x)[g(x) - M] + M[f(x) - L]. \qquad (5)$

But by Hypothesis (a) of Theorem 4, $\lim_{x \to a} [f(x) - L] = 0$, and by Lemma 1, $\lim_{x \to a} \{M[f(x) - L]\} = 0$. Similarly by Hypothesis (b) of Theorem 1, $\lim_{x \to a} [g(x) - M] = 0$, and by Lemma 1, $\lim_{x \to a} \{f(x)[g(x) - M]\} = 0$. Finally, by Conclusion (a) of Theorem 4, it follows that

$$\lim_{x \to a} \{f(x)[g(x) - M] + M[f(x) - L]\}$$
$$= \lim_{x \to a} \{f(x)[g(x) - M]\} + \lim_{x \to a} \{M[f(x) - L]\} = 0 + 0 = 0,$$

and then Eq. (5) gives us our result.

The reader will find some guidance for the proofs of the other conclusions of Theorem 4 in Exercises 7.2-7, 7.2-8, 7.2-9, and 7.2-10.

V

● **Remark 5**

In the statement of Theorem 4 we can replace $\lim_{x \to a}$ by $\lim_{x \to \infty}$ and change the proofs accordingly. We shall not do that here, but the reader can work through one such modified proof in Exercise 7.2-11.

Example 6

$$\lim_{x \to \infty} \frac{x + 1}{x^2 + 3x - 5} = ?$$

A limit statement of this type ultimately calls for establishing a point set of the form $x > B$, B a positive number, for all of whose points we shall have a certain inequality. However, $x = 0$ cannot be a member of such a point set, and the division of numerator and denominator by x^2 is therefore permissible. Thus

$$\lim_{x \to \infty} \frac{x + 1}{x^2 + 3x - 5} = \lim_{x \to \infty} \frac{1/x + 1/x^2}{1 + 3/x - 5/x^2}.$$

We showed in Example 2 that $\lim_{x \to \infty} 1/x = 0$. Then, by Conclusion (c) of Theorem 4 and by Theorem 1,

$$\lim_{x \to \infty} \frac{3}{x} = (\lim_{x \to \infty} 3)(\lim_{x \to \infty} \frac{1}{x}) = 3(0) = 0,$$

and $\qquad \lim_{x \to \infty} \frac{1}{x^2} = (\lim_{x \to \infty} \frac{1}{x})(\lim_{x \to \infty} \frac{1}{x}) = 0(0) = 0,$

while $\qquad \lim_{x \to \infty} \frac{5}{x^2} = (\lim_{x \to \infty} 5)(\lim_{x \to \infty} \frac{1}{x^2}) = 5(0) = 0.$

But by Conclusions (a) and (b) of Theorem 4 and by Theorem 1,

$$\lim_{x \to \infty} \left(\frac{1}{x} + \frac{1}{x^2}\right) = 0 + 0 = 0,$$

and
$$\lim_{x \to \infty} \left(1 + \frac{3}{x} - \frac{5}{x^2}\right) = 1 + 0 - 0 = 1.$$

Finally, by Conclusion (d) of Theorem 4,
$$\lim_{x \to \infty} \frac{1/x + 1/x^2}{1 + 3/x - 5/x^2} = \frac{0}{1} = 0.$$

EXERCISES 7.2

1. Show that for any x of the neighborhood $2 - 1/\sqrt{B} < x < 2 + 1/\sqrt{B}$ other than $x = 2$ itself, we have $1/(x - 2)^2 > B$. Write down a limit statement that is thus justified.

2. Find a neighborhood of $x = 3$ for all of whose points except $x = 3$ itself we shall have $6/(x - 3)^2 > B$, B any positive number. Write down a limit statement that is thus justified.

3. Show that for any x of the point set $x > 3/2\epsilon - \frac{1}{2}$ we shall have
$$\left|\frac{3}{2x + 1} - 0\right| < \epsilon,$$

ϵ a positive number. Write down a limit statement that is thus justified.

4. Find a point set of the form $x > B$ for all of whose points we shall have
$$\left|\frac{x}{x - 1} - 1\right| < \epsilon.$$

Write down a limit statement that is thus justified.

5. Justify each of the following statements by using Definition 1 or Definition 2.

   (a) $\lim\limits_{x \to 0} \dfrac{1}{x^4} = \infty$.

   (c) $\lim\limits_{x \to \infty} \dfrac{1}{x^2 + 1} = 0$.

   (b) $\lim\limits_{x \to 2} \dfrac{x}{(x - 2)^2} = \infty$.

   (d) $\lim\limits_{x \to \infty} \dfrac{2x + 1}{x - 1} = 2$.

6. Determine each of the following limits. Cite Theorems 1, 2, and 4 each time you use them in your work.

   (a) $\lim\limits_{x \to 2} \dfrac{x^2 + 3x}{x - 4}$.

   (g) $\lim\limits_{x \to 3} \dfrac{2x - 2}{(x - 3)^2}$.

   (b) $\lim\limits_{x \to 1} \sqrt[3]{1 - 2x^2}$.

   (h) $\lim\limits_{x \to 0} \dfrac{\tan x}{x}$.*

   (c) $\lim\limits_{s \to 0} s \sqrt{\dfrac{1}{1 + s}}$.

   (i) $\lim\limits_{x \to 0} \dfrac{1 - \cos x}{x}$.†

   (d) $\lim\limits_{x \to -2} \dfrac{x + 2}{|x - 2|}$.

   (j) $\lim\limits_{x \to 0} \dfrac{1 - \cos x}{x^2}$.‡

   (e) $\lim\limits_{\Delta t \to 0} \dfrac{-2t\,\Delta t - \Delta t^2}{\Delta t(t^2)(t + \Delta t)^2}$.

   (k) $\lim\limits_{x \to 0} x \sin x$.

   (f) $\lim\limits_{x \to \infty} \dfrac{x^2 + 1}{x^2 - 1}$.

---

* You may use here the fact that $\lim_{\theta \to 0} (\sin \theta)/\theta = 1$.
† *Ibid.*
‡ *Ibid.*

7. Write out a proof of Conclusion (b), Theorem 4. (*Suggestion:* Follow the proof of Conclusion (a) given in the text.)

8. Write out a proof of Conclusion (d), Theorem 4.
   Suggestion: It will suffice to show that

$$\lim_{x \to a} \frac{1}{g(x)} = \frac{1}{M},$$

for then the fact that

$$\frac{f(x)}{g(x)} = [f(x)]\left[\frac{1}{g(x)}\right]$$

can be used together with Conclusion (c). Start by showing that

$$\left|\frac{1}{g(x)} - \frac{1}{M}\right| = \frac{1}{|M|\,|g(x)|}\,|g(x) - M|.$$

Then assert that there is a neighborhood of $x = a$, call it N_1, for all of whose points, except $x = a$ itself,

$$|g(x)| > \frac{|M|}{2}.$$

Next assert that there is a neighborhood of $x = a$, call it N_2, for all of whose points, except $x = a$ itself,

$$|g(x) - M| < \frac{|M|^2}{2}\,\epsilon.$$

9. Write out a proof of Conclusion (e) of Theorem 4.
   Suggestion: Step (a). Point out that $v = u^q$ with domain all u, and $u = v^{1/q}$ with domain all v, are inverse functions, that the first is steadily increasing and that the second must be also.
   Step (b). Demonstrate Conclusion (e) in the special case where $L = 0$. Explain why, for any $\epsilon > 0$, there is a neighborhood of $x = a$ for all of whose points, except perhaps $x = a$ itself, one has $-\epsilon^q < f(x) < \epsilon^q$ and hence $-\epsilon < \sqrt[q]{f(x)} < \epsilon$.
   Step (c). Show that it suffices to demonstrate Conclusion (e) in the special case $L = 1$ in order to complete the proof. For, if $L \ne 0$ and $L \ne 1$, one can write $k(x) = (1/L) f(x)$, observe that $\lim_{x \to a} k(x) = 1$, and apply the result for the special case where the limit is 1.
   Step (d). Now demonstrate Conclusion (e) in the special case $L = 1$. Show that for any $\epsilon > 0$ there is a neighborhood N of $x = a$ for all of whose points, except perhaps $x = a$ itself, one has $1 - \epsilon < f(x) < 1 + \epsilon$, $\sqrt[q]{1 - \epsilon} < \sqrt[q]{f(x)} < \sqrt[q]{1 + \epsilon}$. Show that $1 + \epsilon < (1 + \epsilon)^q$ or $\sqrt[q]{1 + \epsilon} < 1 + \epsilon$, and that $1 - \epsilon > (1 - \epsilon)^q$ or $1 - \epsilon < \sqrt[q]{1 - \epsilon}$. Hence show that $1 - \epsilon < \sqrt[q]{f(x)} < 1 + \epsilon$ for x of N other than $x = a$.

10. (a) The proof of Conclusion (f) of Theorem 4 can be modeled after the one suggested for Conclusion (e) in Exercise 9, because, even though r is an even integer this time, $v = u^r$ with domain $u \ge 0$ and $u = v^{1/r}$ with domain $v \ge 0$ are steadily increasing functions. Step (b) in Exercise 9 can be eliminated.
   (b) Consider $f(x) = -x^2$. Show that $\lim_{x \to 0} f(x) = 0$. What is the largest possible domain for $k(x) = \sqrt{f(x)}$? Show that $\lim_{x \to 0} \sqrt{f(x)}$ does not exist even though $\sqrt{\lim_{x \to 0} f(x)}$ does exist and is 0.
   (c) Demonstrate this addition to Conclusion (f) of Theorem 4.
   Hypothesis: (f) r is an even positive integer, $L = 0$

(g) $f(x) \geq 0$ for all x of a neighborhood of $x = a$, except perhaps for $x = a$ itself.

Conclusion: (g) $\lim\limits_{x \to a} \sqrt[r]{f(x)} = 0$.

11. Write out a proof of this extension of Conclusion (a) of Theorem 4.

Hypothesis: (a) $\lim\limits_{x \to \infty} f(x) = L$.

(b) $\lim\limits_{x \to \infty} g(x) = M$.

Conclusion: (a) $\lim\limits_{x \to \infty} [f(x) + g(x)] = L + M$.

Suggestion: Modify the proof of Conclusion (a) given in the text by replacing neighborhoods of $x = a$ by point sets of the form $x > B$. Thus Eq. (3) will become

$$|f(x) - L| < \frac{\epsilon}{2} \qquad \text{for } x > B_1; \tag{3a}$$

Eq. (4) will become

$$|g(x) - M| < \frac{\epsilon}{2} \qquad \text{for } x > B_2; \tag{4a}$$

and B^* can be chosen to be the larger of B_1 and B_2. For $x > B^*$ it can ultimately be shown that

$$|[f(x) + g(x)] - [L + M]| < \epsilon.$$

12. (a) Write out a definition of the statement $\lim_{x \to a} f(x) = -\infty$.
(b) Give an example.

13. (a) Write out a definition of the statement $\lim_{x \to -\infty} f(x) = L$.
(b) Give an example.

14. (a) Write out a definition of the statement $\lim_{x \to \infty} f(x) = \infty$.
(b) Give an example.

15. Sometimes we want to convey information about the values of $f(x)$ for x near a but only on one side of a. The statement $\lim_{x \to a^+} f(x) = L$ is such a statement.*

Definition 3. $\lim_{x \to a^+} f(x) = L$ if for every positive challenge number ϵ, no matter how small, there is a positive number δ such that $|f(x) - L| < \epsilon$ for all x of the upper half-neighborhood $a < x < a + \delta$.

(a) From Definition 3, prove that $\lim\limits_{x \to 0^+} \sqrt{x} = 0$.

(b) Write out a definition for the statement $\lim\limits_{x \to a^-} f(x) = L$.†

(c) From your definition of Part (b), prove that $\lim\limits_{x \to 5^-} \sqrt{5 - x} = 0$.

(d) Write out definitions for the statements $\lim\limits_{x \to a^+} f(x) = \infty$, $\lim\limits_{x \to a^-} f(x) = \infty$.

(e) Prove that $\lim\limits_{x \to 0^+} \dfrac{1}{x} = \infty$; $\lim\limits_{x \to 0^-} \dfrac{1}{x} = -\infty$.

(f) Prove that, if $\lim\limits_{x \to a} f(x) = L$, then $\lim\limits_{x \to a^+} f(x) = \lim\limits_{x \to a^-} f(x) = L$.

(g) Prove that, if $\lim\limits_{x \to a^+} f(x) = \lim\limits_{x \to a^-} f(x) = L$, then $\lim\limits_{x \to a} f(x) = L$.

16. We showed in Example 7.1-6 that $\lim_{x \to 0} f(x)$ does not exist when $f(x) = 1/(1 + 2^{1/x})$, $x \neq 0$. Do $\lim_{x \to 0^+} f(x)$ and $\lim_{x \to 0^-} f(x)$ exist?

---

* An alternate reading: "$f(x)$ approaches L as x approaches a from above."
† An alternate reading: "$f(x)$ approaches L as x approaches a from below."

17. There is a difference between the statements (1) "$f(x)$ is unbounded in every neighborhood of $x = a$" and (2) "$\lim_{x \to a} f(x) = \infty$". (a) Consider $f(x) = (1/x) \sin(1/x)$. Show that for every positive number B, no matter how large, and every neighborhood N of $x = 0$, no matter how small, there will be numbers x of N of the form $x = 1/(2n + \frac{1}{2})\pi$, n an integer, such that $f(x) > B$. This shows that $f(x)$ is unbounded in every neighborhood of $x = 0$. (b) Show that there will also be numbers x of N of the form $x = 1/n\pi$, n an integer, such that $f(x) = 0$. Explain why the statement "$\lim_{x \to 0} f(x) = \infty$" is not valid for this f.

18. Complete the details for this alternate proof of Theorem 3. Let $\epsilon > 0$ be specified, no matter how small. By hypothesis, there are neighborhoods N_1 and N_2 of $x = a$ such that $|f(x) - L| < \epsilon/2$ for x of N_1 other than $x = a$ and $|f(x) - M| < \epsilon/2$ for x of N_2 other than $x = a$. But for x of N_1 and N_2, other than $x = a$, we have $|L - M| = |[L - f(x)] + [f(x) - M)]| \le |L - f(x)| + |f(x) - M| < \epsilon/2 + \epsilon/2 = \epsilon$. It follows that $|L - M| = 0$, thus that $L = M$, because $|L - M|$ must be nonnegative and 0 is the only nonnegative number that is less than every specified positive ϵ.

7.3 The Concept of Continuity

I

We have spoken of continuous functions and used their properties frequently, especially in studying integration. Unless a particular function was fairly complicated, most students could tell whether that function was continuous or not at a given point by using an intuitive definition for the word "continuous." Thus, most students would predict that $f(x) = x^2$ was continuous everywhere (see Fig. 7.4), but that the step function considered in Example 7.1-5 was discontinuous at $x = \frac{1}{5}$.

If pressed for an explanation of his decision on the continuity of a given function at a given place, a beginning student might reply, "$f(x)$ was continuous at $x = a$, because, as x changed gradually through $x = a$, $f(x)$ changed gradually also, making no jumps and leaving no gaps."

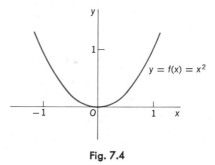

Fig. 7.4

Such a statement has merit, but we can present our ideas more precisely if we use the language we developed in studying limits. A jump of size ϵ at $x = a$ would be impossible if we required that the difference between $f(x)$ and $f(a)$ be less than ϵ, or $|f(x) - f(a)| < \epsilon$, for *all* x of a neighborhood of $x = a$. Since we want to rule out all jumps, we shall require that $|f(x) - f(a)| < \epsilon$ for all challenge numbers $\epsilon > 0$, no matter how small.

■ DEFINITION 1

Continuity of $f(x)$ at $x = a$. The function $f(x)$ is continuous at $x = a$ if (1) $f(a)$ exists, and if (2) for every $\epsilon > 0$, no matter how small, there is a neighborhood of $x = a$ such that $|f(x) - f(a)| < \epsilon$ for all x of the neighborhood.

When the definition of limit given in Sec. 7.1 is borne in mind, our definition of continuity can be written in a shorter form:

■ DEFINITION 1A

Continuity of $f(x)$ at $x = a$. The function $f(x)$ is continuous at $x = a$ if (1) $f(a)$ exists, and if (2) $\lim_{x \to a} f(x) = f(a)$.

Example 1. $y = f(x) = x^2$ is continuous for all x. See Fig. 7.4. For, if a is any real number, (1) $f(a) = a^2$ exists, and (2)

$$\lim_{x \to a} f(x) = \lim_{x \to a} x^2 = (\lim_{x \to a} x)(\lim_{x \to a} x) = (a)(a) = a^2 = f(a).$$

We used the theorem on the limit of a product.

Example 2. $y = f(x) = |x|$ is continuous at $x = 0$. See Fig. 7.5. First, $f(0)$ exists; indeed $f(0) = |0| = 0$. Second, $\lim_{x \to 0} f(x) = 0 = f(0)$. For, if an $\epsilon > 0$ is specified, no matter how small, we can find a neighborhood of $x = 0$ for all of whose points $|f(x) - f(0)| < \epsilon$. Such a neighborhood is $-\epsilon < x < \epsilon$. For these x we have

$$|f(x) - f(0)| = |\,|x| - 0\,| = |x| < \epsilon.$$

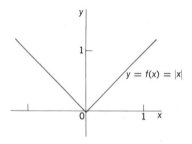

$y = f(x) = |x|$

Fig. 7.5

Example 3.   If

$$y = f(x) = \frac{x^2 + 2x}{x}, \qquad x \neq 0,$$

we can say that $\lim_{x \to 0} f(x) = \lim_{x \to 0}(x + 2) = 2$; see Fig. 7.6(a). If we extend the original definition of $f(x)$ to read

$$f_1(x) = \begin{cases} \dfrac{x^2 + 2x}{x}, & x \neq 0, \\[2mm] 2, & x = 0, \end{cases}$$

then we shall have a function continuous at $x = 0$. See Fig. 7.6(b). If, however, we extend the original definition to read

$$f_2(x) = \begin{cases} \dfrac{x^2 + 2x}{x}, & x \neq 0, \\[2mm] 3, & x = 0, \end{cases}$$

then we shall have a discontinuous function at $x = 0$, for we shall have $\lim_{x \to 0} f_2(x) \neq f_2(0)$. See Fig. 7.6(c).

Example 4.   The definition of

$$y = f(x) = \frac{1}{(x - 1)^2}, \qquad x \neq 1,$$

cannot be extended to $x = 1$ in such a way as to make f continuous there (see Fig. 7.7), because

$$\lim_{x \to 1} \frac{1}{(x - 1)^2} = \infty,$$

and we cannot choose a finite number for $f(1)$ which would be such that $\lim_{x \to 1} f(x) = f(1)$.

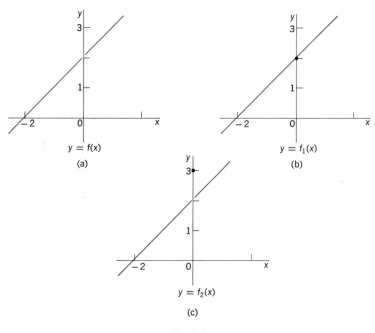

y = f(x)

(a)

y = f₁(x)

(b)

y = f₂(x)

(c)

Fig. 7.6

Example 5.   Consider the step function of Example 7.1-5. This function is defined at $x = \frac{1}{5}$, but is discontinuous there. The function cannot be redefined at this point in such a way as to be made continuous there, because $\lim_{x \to 1/5} f(x)$ does not exist. It is not just a question of making $f(\frac{1}{5})$ agree with $\lim_{x \to 1/5} f(x)$.

Example 6.   The function

$$f(x) = \begin{cases} 1, & x \text{ rational,} \\ 0, & x \text{ irrational,} \end{cases}$$

is everywhere discontinuous, because, in any neighborhood that might be considered, there will be both rational and irrational x and therefore places where $f(x) = 1$ and other places where $f(x) = 0$. The function $f(a)$ exists for any a, but, when an $\epsilon < \frac{1}{2}$ is specified, there is no neighborhood of $x = a$ for *all* of whose points $|f(x) - f(a)| < \epsilon$.

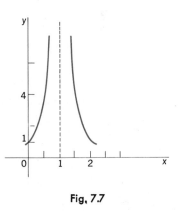

Fig. 7.7

∥

Let us discuss, now, three methods of deciding whether a specific function is continuous at a specific place. First, we can refer directly to the definition of continuity, Definition 1 or 1A.

Second, we can use the following theorem, which tells us that a function built up from continuous functions by addition, subtraction, multiplication, division, and the finding of roots must itself be continuous.

■ **THEOREM 1**

HYPOTHESIS: (a) $f(x)$ is continuous at $x = a$.
(b) $g(x)$ is continuous at $x = a$.

CONCLUSION: (a) $f(x) + g(x)$ is continuous at $x = a$.
(b) $f(x) - g(x)$ is continuous at $x = a$.
(c) $f(x)g(x)$ is continuous at $x = a$.

HYPOTHESIS: (c) $g(a) \neq 0$.

CONCLUSION: (d) $f(x)/g(x)$ is continuous at $x = a$.

HYPOTHESIS: (d) q is an odd positive integer.

CONCLUSION: (e) $\sqrt[q]{f(x)}$ is continuous at $x = a$.

HYPOTHESIS: (e) r is an even positive integer and $f(a) > 0$.

CONCLUSION: (f) $\sqrt[r]{f(x)}$ is continuous at $x = a$.

PROOF OF CONCLUSION (a): We must show two things for the new function $h(x) = f(x) + g(x)$. First, we must be sure that $h(a)$ exists. It does exist, because by hypothesis $f(a)$ and $g(a)$ exist, and then

$$h(a) = f(a) + g(a).$$

Second, we must show that $\lim_{x \to a} h(x) = h(a)$. But

$$\lim_{x \to a} h(x) = \lim_{x \to a} f(x) + \lim_{x \to a} g(x)$$

because the limit of a sum is the sum of the limits,* and

$$\lim_{x \to a} f(x) = f(a), \qquad \lim_{x \to a} g(x) = g(a)$$

by Hypotheses (a) and (b) of this theorem. Hence

$$\lim_{x \to a} h(x) = f(a) + g(a) = h(a).$$

This concludes the proof of Conclusion (a). We assign the proof of Conclusion (c) in Exercise 7.3-6, but omit proofs of the other conclusions because they present no new ideas.

Example 7.   We shall show that every rational function is continuous at every point at which it is defined. First, $f(x) = x$ is continuous at $x = a$, where a is any real number, because $f(a) = a$ exists and because

$$\lim_{x \to a} f(x) = \lim_{x \to a} x = a = f(a).$$

---

* Conclusion (a) of Theorem 7.2-4.

Second, $f(x) = x^n$, n a positive integer, is continuous for all x by repeated applications of Conclusion (c) of Theorem 1. Third, $f(x) = c$, c a constant, is continuous because $f(a) = c$ exists and

$$\lim_{x \to a} f(x) = \lim_{x \to a} c = c = f(a).$$

With this, $f(x) = cx^n$ is continuous, because it is a product of continuous functions. Fourth, if $f(x)$ is a polynomial, it is a sum of terms of the form cx^n and continuous by repeated applications of Conclusion (a). Finally, if $f(x)$ is a rational function, it is a quotient of polynomials, and it would be continuous at any point at which it was defined by Conclusion (d).

In the third method of deciding continuity in a specific situation, we refer to another theorem.

■ THEOREM 2

Differentiability implies continuity.

HYPOTHESIS: $f(a)$ and $f'(a)$ exist.

CONCLUSION: $f(x)$ is continuous at $x = a$.

PROOF: The hypothesis tells us that

$$f'(a) = \lim_{\Delta x \to 0} \frac{f(a + \Delta x) - f(a)}{\Delta x}$$

exists. We would like to show that $\lim_{x \to a} f(x) = f(a)$ or that $\lim_{\Delta x \to 0} f(a + \Delta x) = f(a)$. For such a limit statement, the possibility $\Delta x = 0$ need not be considered. Hence we can say that

$$f(a + \Delta x) - f(a) = \Delta x \frac{f(a + \Delta x) - f(a)}{\Delta x}, \qquad \Delta x \neq 0,$$

and then, since the limit of a product is the product of the limits,[*] we have

$$\lim_{\Delta x \to 0} [f(a + \Delta x) - f(a)] = \left[\lim_{\Delta x \to 0} \Delta x \right] \left[\lim_{\Delta x \to 0} \frac{f(a + \Delta x) - f(a)}{\Delta x} \right]$$
$$= (0)[f'(a)] = 0.$$

This means that $\lim_{\Delta x \to 0} f(a + \Delta x) = f(a)$.

● **Remark 1**

Theorem 2 assures us that every differentiable function is continuous, but these are not the only continuous functions. There are continuous functions that are not differentiable. For instance, Example 2 above points out that $f(x) = |x|$ is continuous at $x = 0$, but we saw in Example 1.3-4 that $f(x)$ was not differentiable at $x = 0$.

We conclude with the following remark.

---

[*] Conclusion (c) of Theorem 7.2-4.

● **Remark 2**

One cannot tell, in general, what $\lim_{x \to a} f(x)$ will be by examining $f(a)$. There are cases where $f(a)$ does not even exist; in some of these cases $\lim_{x \to a} f(x)$ exists, in others not. In Example 5, $f(\frac{1}{5})$ exists, and indeed $f(\frac{1}{5}) = 30$, but we still cannot find $\lim_{x \to 1/5} f(x)$. In the case of the function $f_2(x)$ mentioned at the end of Example 3, we have $f_2(0) = 3$, and this time $\lim_{x \to 0} f_2(x)$ does exist, but it does not equal 3. However, Definition 1 does tell us that *if $f(x)$ is known to be continuous at $x = a$*, then one can get $\lim_{x \to a} f(x)$ from a knowledge of $f(a)$: $\lim_{x \to a} f(x) = f(a)$.

EXERCISES 7.3

1. Consider $f(x) = 3x + 1$. Show that it is continuous at $x = 2$ by showing that $f(2)$ exists and that, for any $\epsilon > 0$, there is a neighborhood of $x = 2$ for all of whose points $|f(x) - f(2)| < \epsilon$.

2. Consider $f(x) = 1/(3x + 1)$. Show that it is continuous at $x = 3$ by showing that $f(3)$ exists and that, for any $\epsilon > 0$, there is a neighborhood of $x = 3$ for all of whose points $|f(x) - f(3)| < \epsilon$.

3. Consider $f(x) = \sqrt{x - 1}$. Show that it is continuous at $x = 2$ by showing that $f(2)$ exists and that, for any $\epsilon > 0$, there is a neighborhood of $x = 2$ for all of whose points $|f(x) - f(2)| < \epsilon$.

4. Decide whether the following functions are continuous at the points indicated. Explain.

(a) $f(x) = x^2 + 3x + 1$; $x = 4$.

(b) $f(x) = \dfrac{x^2 + 3x - 5}{x^3 + 2x^2 - x - 2}$; $x = 2$.

(c) $f(x) = \dfrac{x^2 + 3x - 5}{x^3 + 2x^2 - x - 2}$; $x = -2$.

(d) $f(x) = \begin{cases} x, & 0 \le x \le 1 \\ 2 - x, & 1 < x \end{cases}$; $x = 1$.

(e) $f(x) = \begin{cases} x^2, & 0 \le x \le 1 \\ x, & 1 < x \end{cases}$; $x = 1$.

(f) $f(x) = \begin{cases} \dfrac{x^2 - 9}{x - 3}, & x \ne 3 \\ 5, & x = 3 \end{cases}$; $x = 3$.

5. The following functions are not completely defined. Complete the definitions so that they will be continuous at the points where they were not originally defined; or, if this cannot be done, say so. Explain.

(a) $f(x) = \begin{cases} \dfrac{x^2 - 3x + 2}{2x - 4}, & x \ne 2; \\ ?, & x = 2. \end{cases}$

(b) $f(x) = \begin{cases} \dfrac{x + 2}{x^3 + 2x^2 + x + 2}, & x \ne -2; \\ ?, & x = -2. \end{cases}$

(c) $f(x) = \begin{cases} \dfrac{x - 2}{x^3 + 2x^2 + x + 2}, & x \ne -2; \\ ?, & x = -2. \end{cases}$

(d) $f(x) = \begin{cases} \dfrac{\sin x}{x}, & x \neq 0; \\ ? \,, & x = 0. \end{cases}$

(g) $f(x) = \begin{cases} \dfrac{1}{1 + 2^{1/x}}, & x \neq 0; \\ ? \,, & x = 0. \end{cases}$

(e) $f(x) = \begin{cases} \sin \dfrac{1}{x}, & x \neq 0; \\ ? \,, & x = 0. \end{cases}$

(h) $f(x) = \begin{cases} \csc x - \cot x, & x \neq 0; \\ ? \,, & x = 0. \end{cases}$

(f) $f(x) = \begin{cases} x \sin \dfrac{1}{x}, & x \neq 0; \\ ? \,, & x = 0. \end{cases}$

6. Prove Conclusion (c) of Theorem 1.

7. Show that $f(x) = x^{1/3}$ is continuous at $x = 0$ but that $f'(0)$ does not exist.

8. Show that the following function is continuous at $x = 0$:

$$f(x) = \begin{cases} 0 \text{ if } x = 0, \\ 0 \text{ if } x \text{ is irrational}, \\ 1/n^2 \text{ if } x \neq 0, \text{ is rational, and is } m/n \text{ when written as a quotient of integers in simplest form.} \end{cases}$$

Suggestion: In deciding whether $|f(x) - f(0)| < \epsilon$ for all points of a neighborhood of $x = 0$, reason separately with those x that are rational and those x that are not.

9. The following theorem is an extension of Theorem 1; roughly, it says that a continuous function of a continuous function is continuous. Complete the details of the proof.

Theorem 3. *Continuity for composite functions.*

Hypothesis: (a) $f(x)$ is continuous at $x = a$, and $f(a) = b$.

(b) $g(u)$ is continuous at $u = b$.

Conclusion: $h(x) = g(f(x))$ is continuous at $x = a$.

Proof: (1) $h(a) = g(f(a)) = g(b)$ exists.

(2) Let $\epsilon > 0$ be specified. There is a neighborhood N_1 of $u = b$ such that $|g(u) - g(b)| < \epsilon$ for all u of N_1. Let the description of N_1 be $b - \delta < u < b + \delta$ or $|u - b| < \delta$.

(3) There is a neighborhood N of $x = a$ such that $|f(x) - b| < \delta$ for all x of N.

(4) Write $u = f(x)$ and combine the above steps to conclude that $|h(x) - h(a)| < \epsilon$ for all x of N.

7.4 Some Properties of Continuous Functions

I

In this section we shall state and discuss properties of continuous functions which we have already used and which we shall use frequently in the future. We cannot prove these theorems here, even though most of them seem intuitively obvious, primarily because we have not organized carefully our ideas about the real number system and therefore do not know how to go about proving the existence of numbers with specified properties.*

---

* Note that the conclusions of the first three theorems begin with the phrase "there exists a number . . . ."

■ THEOREM 1

On boundedness for continuous functions.

   HYPOTHESIS: $f(x)$ is continuous for the closed interval $a \leq x \leq b$.

   CONCLUSION: There exists a number M with the property

$$|f(x)| \leq M \qquad \text{for } a \leq x \leq b.$$

In words, a function that is continuous on a closed interval is bounded there.

   Example 1. $f(x) = 1/x$ is continuous for the closed interval $1 \leq x \leq 2$ because $f'(x) = -1/x^2$ exists for each point of that interval and differentiability implies continuity. According to Theorem 1, $f(x)$ should be bounded for that interval. Indeed, a bound number M is easily exhibited:

$$|f(x)| \leq 1 \qquad \text{for } 1 \leq x \leq 2.$$

   On the other hand, the interval $0 < x < 1$ is not closed, because it does not include its end points, but $f(x) = 1/x$ is continuous at each point of that interval also, because $f'(x) = -1/x^2$ exists for each point of that interval. However, $f(x)$ is not bounded on this open interval. For, no matter how large a number M is specified, there will be points of the open interval $0 < x < 1$, namely, $0 < x < 1/M$, for which $f(x) = 1/x > M$. This example shows that the weaker hypothesis, that f be continuous on an interval, would not be sufficient to enable one to conclude that f was bounded there.

   Suppose that we extend the definition of $f(x)$ by taking

$$f_1(x) = \begin{cases} \dfrac{1}{x} & \text{when } x \neq 0, \\ 0 & \text{when } x = 0. \end{cases}$$

See Fig. 7.8. Now we can consider the closed interval $0 \leq x \leq 1$. We see that $f_1(x)$ is not bounded on this closed interval, for, again, no matter what large number M is specified, we can always find x's of $0 \leq x \leq 1$ for which $f(x) > M$; we need only choose $0 < x < 1/M$. The conclusion of Theorem 1 does not hold this time, because

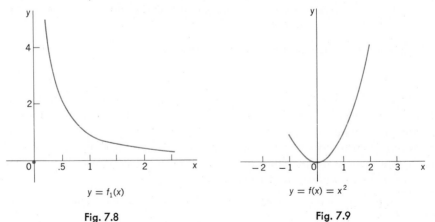

$$y = f_1(x) \qquad\qquad\qquad y = f(x) = x^2$$

Fig. 7.8   **Fig. 7.9**

$f_1(x)$ is not continuous for the interval $0 \leq x \leq 1$; $f_1(x)$ is discontinuous at $x = 0$. This example shows that the weaker hypothesis, that f be defined over a closed interval, would not be sufficient to enable one to conclude that f was bounded there.

If a function does not increase beyond all bounds, it makes sense to ask next if it achieves a highest value.

■ THEOREM 2

On achieving extreme values with a continuous function.

HYPOTHESIS: $f(x)$ is continuous for the closed interval $a \leq x \leq b$.

CONCLUSION: (a) There exists a number w_1, $a \leq w_1 \leq b$, such that $f(w_1) \geq f(x)$ for all x of $a \leq x \leq b$.

(b) There exists a number w_2, $a \leq w_2 \leq b$, such that $f(w_2) \leq f(x)$ for all x of $a \leq x \leq b$.

In words, a function that is continuous on a closed interval will achieve a maximum value and a minimum value on that interval.

Example 2.   Consider $f(x) = x^2$, Fig. 7.9. This function is continuous for the closed interval $-1 \leq x \leq 2$, and according to Theorem 2 will achieve a maximum value and a minimum value for this interval. Indeed, it achieves its maximum value at $x = 2$ and its minimum value at $x = 0$.

If, however, we consider $f(x) = x^2$ for the interval $-1 \leq x < 2$, which is not closed because it does not include one of its boundaries, then $f(x)$ will not achieve a maximum value on the interval, even though it is continuous there. For, no matter what point w_1 is alleged to be the point at which f achieves its maximum, we can always find x's in the interval closer to $x = 2$ than w_1 is. For such x's it will not be true that $f(w_1) \geq f(x)$. The conclusion of Theorem 2 did not hold because the interval was not closed.

Example 3.   Consider the function

$$f(x) = \begin{cases} x & \text{when } 0 \leq x < 2, \\ 1 - x & \text{when } 2 \leq x \leq 3. \end{cases}$$

See Fig. 7.10. This function is defined for the closed interval $0 \leq x \leq 3$, but does not achieve a maximum value for the interval. The conclusion of Theorem 2 is not valid, because $f(x)$ is discontinuous at $x = 2$.

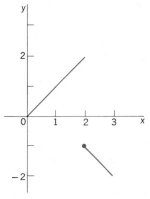

Having inquired about extreme values, we next inquire about intermediate values.

■ THEOREM 3

Fig. 7.10

On achieving intermediate values with a continuous function.

HYPOTHESIS: (a) $f(x)$ is continuous for $a \leq x \leq b$.

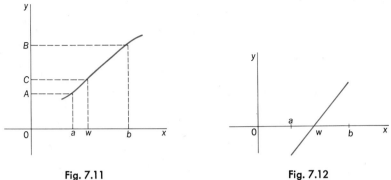

Fig. 7.11   Fig. 7.12

(b) $f(a) = A, f(b) = B$.
(c) C is any number between A and B.

CONCLUSION: There exists a number w, $a < w < b$, such that $f(w) = C$.

In words, a function continuous for a closed interval achieves all values between the values achieved at the end points of the interval. See Fig. 7.11. This theorem is used in many places; for instance, in algebra when we reason that the
equation $f(x) = 0$, $f(x)$ continuous for $a \le x \le b$, must have at least one root between $x = a$ and $x = b$ if $f(x)$ is negative at $x = a$ and positive at $x = b$. See Fig.
7.12.

Example 4.   Consider again the function f defined in Example 3 for the
closed interval $0 \le x \le 3$. We have $f(0) = 0$ and $f(3) = -2$. The value $-\frac{1}{2}$
would be an intermediate one, but f does not achieve this value for any x of $0 \le x$
≤ 3. The conclusion of Theorem 3 is not valid because f is discontinuous at $x = 2$.

In Exercise 7.4-4 we ask the reader to furnish an example of an intermediate
value that is not achieved because the function is discontinuous at an end point
of the interval in question.

‖

We conclude this discussion of the properties of continuous functions by
introducing the concept of uniform continuity and stating a theorem on its occurrence. It is this property of uniform continuity that makes continuous functions so
useful to us in integration work.

Consider $f(x) = x^2$. We know that f is continuous at each point $x = a$ of the
interval $1 \le x \le 2$, and that this means that if an $\epsilon > 0$ is specified, no matter how
small, there is a neighborhood of $x = a$ for all of whose points $|f(x) - f(a)| < \epsilon$.
Let us specify such a neighborhood in detail. We compute, to start with, that

$$|f(x) - f(a)| = |x^2 - a^2| = |x + a| \, |x - a|.$$

Now let N_1 be the following neighborhood of $x = a$: $a - 1 < x < a + 1$. Adding a
to all members of this inequality, we can see that for any x of N_1 we have $2a - 1$
$< x + a < 2a + 1$, and thus that $|x + a| < 2a + 1$ for any x of N_1. Then let N_2 be
the following neighborhood of $x = a$:

$$a - \frac{\epsilon}{2a + 1} < x < a + \frac{\epsilon}{2a + 1}.$$

If N_a is the smaller of N_1 and N_2, any x of N_a is a point of both N_1 and N_2, and we can say that

$$|f(x) - f(a)| = |x + a| \, |x - a| < (2a + 1)\left(\frac{\epsilon}{2a + 1}\right) = \epsilon, \qquad x \text{ in } N_a.$$

The neighborhood we seek is N_a. Actually, we must be able to meet all challenge numbers $\epsilon > 0$, no matter how small, and since N_2 will be smaller than N_1 when ϵ is small, we can take N_a to be N_2 without real loss of generality. Thus N_a, a neighborhood suitable for an ϵ challenge at $x = a$, is of half-width $\delta_a = \epsilon/(2a + 1)$.

If we test for continuity at $x = 1$, a neighborhood of half-width $\delta_1 = \epsilon/3$ is suitable for an ϵ challenge. If we test at $x = 1.5$, $\delta_{1.5} = \epsilon/4$ is suitable for an ϵ challenge. If we test at $x = 2$, $\delta_2 = \epsilon/5$ is suitable for an ϵ challenge. So far, then, at different points of the interval we would use neighborhoods of different sizes to meet an ϵ challenge. However, the smallest of these neighborhoods for different $x = a$'s is the one of half-width $\epsilon/5$, and if $|f(x) - f(a)| < \epsilon$ for the x's of a neighborhood of half-width $\epsilon/(2a + 1)$, it is surely true that $|f(x) - f(a)| < \epsilon$ for the x's of a smaller neighborhood of the same point. Therefore it is possible to say that a neighborhood of half-width $\delta = \epsilon/5$ would suffice for an ϵ challenge at *any* point of the interval $1 \le x \le 2$. In symbols, whenever $a - \epsilon/5 < x < a + \epsilon/5$, or $|x - a| < \delta = \epsilon/5$ for $1 \le x$, $a \le 2$, we have $|f(x) - f(a)| < \epsilon$. We have replaced a set of neighborhoods of different sizes by a set all of the *same* size, and that is why the adjective "uniform" is used in this work.

■ DEFINITION 1

Uniform continuity over an interval. Let $f(x)$ be defined over a given interval, and let a be any point of that interval. Let $\epsilon > 0$ be specified, no matter how small. If there is a neighborhood half-width number δ, the same δ to serve for all choices of a, such that $|f(x) - f(a)| < \epsilon$ whenever x is in the given interval ·and $|x - a| < \delta$, then we shall say that f is uniformly continuous over that interval. *

● Remark 1

Let us stress by repetition the fact that the neighborhood half-width number δ will depend on ϵ; the smaller the ϵ challenge, the smaller the uniformly suitable neighborhood half-width will have to be. But the δ is *not* to depend on a; the *same* half-width is to suffice at all points of the interval. In our preliminary computation with $f(x) = x^2$ and the interval $1 \le x \le 2$, a uniformly suitable half-width was $\delta = \epsilon/5$.

● Remark 2

Notice that one can speak of continuity at a point or of continuity over an interval, but one can only speak of uniform continuity over an interval. There is no uniformizing to be done when one works only with continuity at one point.

---

* This definition can be restated a little more concisely.

Definition 1A. Let $f(x)$ be defined over a given interval. Let $\epsilon > 0$ be specified, no matter how small. If there is a number δ, $\delta = \delta(\epsilon)$, such that $|f(x) - f(z)| < \epsilon$ whenever x and z are points of the interval and $|x - z| < \delta$, then we shall say that f is uniformly continuous on that interval.

■ THEOREM 4

On uniform continuity for continuous functions.

HYPOTHESIS: $f(x)$ is continuous for the closed interval $a \leq x \leq b$.

CONCLUSION: $f(x)$ is uniformly continuous over $a \leq x \leq b$.

In our work with $f(x) = x^2$ above we illustrated this theorem by showing that that function is uniformly continuous for the closed interval $1 \leq x \leq 2$. We exhibited a uniformly suitable neighborhood half-width, $\delta = \epsilon/5$. Here is another, and last, example.

Example 5.   Consider $f(x) = 1/x$. We know that f is continuous at $x = a$, $a > 0$, because $f'(x) = -1/x^2$ exists for all $x \neq 0$. Therefore, when a positive ϵ challenge number is specified, no matter how small, there exists a neighborhood of $x = a$ for all of whose points we have $|f(x) - f(a)| < \epsilon$. Let us find such a neighborhood.

Because

$$|f(x) - f(a)| = \left|\frac{1}{x} - \frac{1}{a}\right| = \left|\frac{a - x}{ax}\right| = \frac{1}{a}\frac{1}{|x|}|a - x|,$$

we can reason as follows. Let N_1 be the neighborhood

$$a - \frac{a}{2} < x < a + \frac{a}{2} \quad \text{or} \quad \frac{a}{2} < x < \frac{3a}{2}.$$

For x of this neighborhood we have

$$\frac{2}{3a} < \frac{1}{x} < \frac{2}{a} \quad \text{and thus} \quad \frac{1}{|x|} < \frac{2}{a},$$

so that $|f(x) - f(a)| < \dfrac{1}{a}\dfrac{2}{a}|a - x| = \dfrac{2}{a^2}|x - a|$ for x of N_1.

Now let N_2 be the following neighborhood of $x = a$, for which $|x - a| < (a^2/2)\epsilon$:

$$a - \frac{a^2}{2}\epsilon < x < a + \frac{a^2}{2}\epsilon.$$

Since we have to meet challenges for positive ϵ's, no matter how small, we can assume without loss of generality that ϵ is so small that N_2 is smaller than N_1 and that any x of N_2 can be considered to be in N_1. Then

$$|f(x) - f(a)| < \frac{2}{a^2}|x - a| < \frac{2}{a^2}\frac{a^2}{2}\epsilon = \epsilon \quad \text{for } x \text{ of } N_2.$$

For $x = a > 0$, a neighborhood of half-width $\delta_a = \frac{1}{2}a^2\epsilon$ is suitable for an ϵ challenge.

Now consider the closed interval $.1 \leq x \leq 1$. For different $x = a$'s selected from this interval, the different suitable neighborhood half-widths will vary from $\delta_{.1} = \frac{1}{2}(.1)^2\epsilon = .005\epsilon$ to $\delta_1 = \frac{1}{2}(1)^2\epsilon = .5\epsilon$. If we select $\delta = .005\epsilon$, we will have a *uniformly* acceptable neighborhood half-width for an ϵ challenge. Whenever x and *a* are such that $.1 \leq x, a \leq 1$ and $|x - a| < \delta = .005\epsilon$, we can be sure that

$$\left| \frac{1}{x} - \frac{1}{a} \right| < \epsilon.$$

This shows that the function $f(x) = 1/x$, known to be continuous for the closed interval $.1 \leq x \leq 1$, is uniformly continuous there.

The interval $0 < x \leq 1$ is not closed, however, because it does not contain its end point 0. We shall show below that $f(x) = 1/x$ is not uniformly continuous for $0 < x \leq 1$ even though it is continuous at every point of $0 < x \leq 1$. This example will thus explain that the weaker hypothesis, that f be continuous on an interval, would not be sufficient to enable one to conclude that f was uniformly continuous on that interval.

In the first place, observe that we cannot modify directly the argument used for the interval $.1 \leq x \leq 1$ and make it apply for the interval $0 < x \leq 1$. The suitable half-width numbers $\delta_a = \frac{1}{2} a^2\epsilon$ of that argument have no positive lower bound if *a* can be selected anywhere in the interval $0 < x \leq 1$, and hence we cannot select a *uniformly* acceptable positive δ by taking the smallest of the δ_a's used for the various *a*'s of the interval.

But this, of itself, does not mean that uniform continuity cannot be established by a different argument. We shall show that $f(x)$ is not uniformly continuous for $0 < x \leq 1$ by giving a proof by contradiction. Suppose that $f(x) = 1/x$ is uniformly continuous for $0 < x \leq 1$. Then, for any positive ϵ specified, there would be a positive δ such that $|f(x) - f(a)| < \epsilon$ whenever $0 < x, a \leq 1$ and $|x - a| < \delta$. * In particular, for the choices $a = \delta$ and $0 < x < \delta$ we have $0 < x, a \leq 1$, and $|x - a| < \delta$ so that $|1/x - 1/a| < \epsilon$ would follow. But there is a contradiction here, because $1/a = 1/\delta$ is now fixed and *x* of the subinterval $0 < x < \delta$ can be chosen so close to 0 that $1/x$ will be as large as desired, thus making $|1/x - 1/a|$ larger, rather than smaller, than ϵ.

EXERCISES 7.4

1. In Example 1 we exhibited a function that was everywhere defined in a closed interval but was unbounded there. Can you exhibit another function with the same property?

2. Exhibit a function that is continuous on a nonclosed interval but that does not achieve a minimum value on that interval.

3. Exhibit a function that is defined on a closed interval but does not achieve a minimum there, because it is not continuous on that interval.

4. Exhibit a function defined over the closed interval $2 \leq x \leq 5$ with $f(2) = 0, f(5) = 4$, which fails to achieve the intermediate value 2, because it is discontinuous at one of the end points of the interval.

5. According to Theorem 4, $f(x) = 1/x$ is uniformly continuous for the interval $1 \leq x \leq 2$. Let $\epsilon > 0$ be specified. Prove the uniform continuity yourself by exhibiting a uniformly suitable neighborhood half-width δ; that is, show that for any *x* and *a* such that $1 \leq x, a \leq 2$ and $|x - a| < \delta$, we shall have $|f(x) - f(a)| < \epsilon$.

6. The same as Exercise 5 for $f(x) = x^2 + x$ over the interval $0 \leq x \leq 1$.

7. The same as Exercise 5 for $f(x) = x^3$ over the interval $-1 \leq x \leq 0$.

---

* We can assume that $\delta < 1$; if δ were originally ≥ 1, we could replace it by any smaller δ we wanted to use.

7.5   The Theorem of Mean Value

In this section we shall consider the Theorem of Mean Value. This theorem is used to help demonstrate a surprising number of basic statements.

I

First let us consider the theorem from a geometric standpoint. It seems plausible to assert that a function which vanishes at the end points of an interval will have a horizontal tangent at some point of the interval; see Fig. 7.13. This is, in good part, what Rolle's Theorem, a special case of the Theorem of Mean Value, asserts. If we rotate the diagram, we see that a more general statement is possible. It would now seem plausible to assert that, if a secant line is drawn through two points of a curve, there must be an intermediate point at which the tangent line is parallel to the secant line; see Fig. 7.14. This is, in good part, the assertion made by the Theorem of Mean Value.

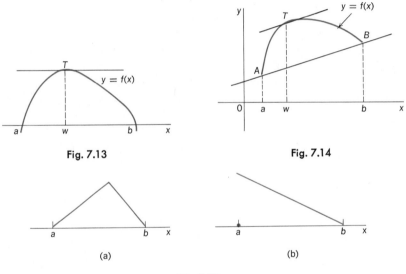

Fig. 7.13   **Fig. 7.14**

(a)   (b)

Fig. 7.15

If we return to the first assertion and look for exceptions, we shall soon see how to state Rolle's Theorem. In Fig. 7.15(a) we have a function that vanishes at the end points of an interval, and yet we cannot find an intermediate point at which the tangent is horizontal. But there is a point within the interval at which this graph has no tangent at all, and we surmise that we ought to exclude functions that are not differentiable everywhere within the interval. If we require differentiability, then we automatically require continuity.* In Fig. 7.15(b) we have another function that vanishes at the end points of an interval, but for which we cannot find an intermediate point with a horizontal tangent. We see that we must also exclude a function if it is discontinuous at an end point of the interval.

Now we are ready to state and prove Rolle's Theorem.

---
* Theorem 7.3-2.

■ THEOREM 1

Rolle's Theorem.

HYPOTHESIS: (a) $f(x)$ is continuous for $a \leq x \leq b$.
(b) $f'(x)$ exists for $a < x < b$.
(c) $f(a) = f(b) = 0$.

CONCLUSION: There exists a number w, $a < w < b$, such that $f'(w) = 0$.

PROOF: The case where $f(x) \equiv 0$ throughout the interval is easily treated, because then $f'(x) \equiv 0$ throughout the interval and any interior point of the interval could serve as the point w called for in the conclusion.

Consider, then, the case where $f(x)$ is not identically zero for the interval, but is positive for some values of x.* Since $f(x)$ is continuous for a closed interval by Hypothesis (a), f achieves a maximum value somewhere inside the interval.† Let a maximum value be achieved at w. But $f'(w)$ exists by Hypothesis (b), and then by Theorem 3.18-1, we conclude that $f'(w) = 0$. See Fig. 7.13.

The Theorem of Mean Value would not appear to be essentially different from Rolle's Theorem, one diagram seeming to be a rotation of the other. Indeed, we shall make the proof of the Theorem of Mean Value depend directly on Rolle's Theorem. In Fig. 7.14, the conclusion reached is that there will be an interior point T at which the tangent is parallel to the chord AB. Since the coordinates of A and B are $[a, f(a)]$ and $[b, f(b)]$, this means that

$$f'(w) = \frac{f(b) - f(a)}{b - a} \quad \text{or} \quad f(b) - f(a) = f'(w)(b - a).$$

■ THEOREM 2

The Theorem of Mean Value.

HYPOTHESIS: (a) $f(x)$ is continuous for $a \leq x \leq b$.
(b) $f'(x)$ exists for $a < x < b$.

CONCLUSION: There exists a number w, $a < w < b$, such that

$$f(b) = f(a) + f'(w)(b - a).$$

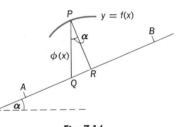

Fig. 7.16

PROOF: In the proof of Rolle's Theorem, we located the point T by maximizing the length of the perpendicular drawn from the curve to the x axis. By analogy, we should consider here the perpendicular drawn from the curve to the chord AB. But it is easier to consider the vertical distance from the curve to the chord, and this is just as good, for the two distances are proportional; in Fig. 7.16 we have $PR = (\cos \alpha)PQ$ and α depends only on the slope of line AB, not on the point P under

---

* If $f(x)$ is never positive but is negative for some x of the interval, we would reason in what follows with minima instead of maxima.

† See Theorem 7.4-2. Note that the maximum cannot occur at an end point, because $f(a) = f(b) = 0$ while f is positive for some x's.

consideration. Hence, if the perpendicular distance achieves a maximum at a point T, the vertical distance will also achieve a maximum at that point.

The line AB goes through point $A[a, f(a)]$ and has slope $[f(b) - f(a)]/(b - a)$; its equation is

$$y - f(a) = \frac{f(b) - f(a)}{b - a}(x - a)$$

or

$$y = f(a) + \frac{f(b) - f(a)}{b - a}(x - a).$$

Therefore the vertical distance from the curve $y = f(x)$ to the chord AB, which distance we shall call $\phi(x)$, is the difference in ordinates:

$$\phi(x) = f(x) - f(a) - \frac{f(b) - f(a)}{b - a}(x - a). \tag{1}$$

Now $f(x)$ and $x - a$ are continuous for $a \le x \le b$; $\phi(x)$ is therefore a sum of continuous functions for $a \le x \le b$ and is continuous there also. For $\phi(x)$ we can compute

$$\phi'(x) = f'(x) - \frac{f(b) - f(a)}{b - a}; \tag{2}$$

$\phi'(x)$ exists for $a < x < b$ because $f'(x)$ does. Finally, the definition of $\phi(x)$ as a difference of ordinates requires that $\phi(a) = \phi(b) = 0$, because the chord and curve intersect at A and B.* Therefore the hypotheses of Rolle's Theorem are valid for $\phi(x)$, and there must be a number w, $a < w < b$, for which $\phi'(w) = 0$. But Eq.(2) says that for this w,

$$f'(w) = \frac{f(b) - f(a)}{b - a}.$$

This concludes the proof.

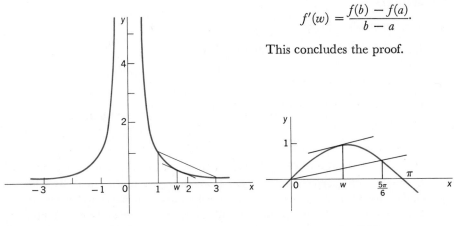

Fig. 7.17   Fig. 7.18

---

* Direct computation in Eq. (1) also shows that this is the case. For instance,

$$\phi(b) = f(b) - f(a) - \frac{f(b) - f(a)}{b - a}(b - a) = f(b) - f(a) - [f(b) - f(a)] = 0.$$

Example 1. The function $f(x) = 1/x^2$ is differentiable and continuous for all $x \neq 0$; $f'(x) = -2/x^3$. The Theorem of Mean Value applies, then, to the interval $1 \leq x \leq 3$ and asserts the existence of a number w, $1 < w < 3$, such that $f(3) = f(1) + f'(w)(3 - 1)$. Indeed, we have $\frac{1}{9} = 1 + (-2/w^3)(2), -\frac{8}{9} = -4/w^3$, $w^3 = \frac{9}{2}$, $w = \sqrt[3]{\frac{9}{2}} \approx 1.65$. See Fig. 7.17. We could not have applied the theorem for the interval $-1 \leq x \leq 1$, because f is not continuous for this interval.

Example 2. The function $f(x) = \sin x$ is differentiable and continuous for all x; $f'(x) = \cos x$. The Theorem of Mean Value applies, then, to the interval $0 \leq x \leq 5\pi/6$ and asserts the existence of a number w, $0 < w < 5\pi/6$, such that $f(5\pi/6) = f(0) + f'(w)(5\pi/6 - 0)$. Indeed, we have $\frac{1}{2} = 0 + \cos w \, (5\pi/6)$, $\cos w = 3/5\pi \approx .1910$, $w \approx 1.38$. See Fig. 7.18 and Table II of the Appendix.

Example 3. The function $f(x) = \sqrt{x}$ is continuous for $0 \leq x \leq 1$ and differentiable for $0 < x \leq 1$; $f'(x) = 1/(2\sqrt{x})$. The Theorem of Mean Value applies for this interval because Hypothesis (b) of that theorem does not require differentiability at the end points of the interval. The theorem asserts the existence of a number w, $0 < w < 1$, such that $f(1) = f(0) + f'(w)(1 - 0)$. Indeed,

$$1 = 0 + \frac{1}{2\sqrt{w}}(1 - 0), \quad 2\sqrt{w} = 1, \quad w = \frac{1}{4}.$$

$\parallel$

Now we turn to two basic theorems whose proofs can be made to depend on the Theorem of Mean Value. First, in antidifferentiation work, the fact that two functions with the same derivative could differ only by a constant was crucial. Otherwise, knowing dy/dx to be $f(x)$ and knowing a function $F(x)$ such that $F'(x) = f(x)$, we could not be sure that y was of the form $F(x) + C$.*

We start with a special case of the theorem we want.

■ **THEOREM 3A**

HYPOTHESIS: $f'(x) = 0$ for $a \leq x \leq d$.

CONCLUSION: $f(x) = $ constant for $a \leq x \leq d$.

PROOF: Let b be such that $a < b \leq d$. Since differentiability implies continuity, the hypotheses of the Theorem of Mean Value are valid for $a \leq x \leq b$. That theorem then asserts that there exists a w, $a < w < b \leq d$, such that

$$f(b) = f(a) + f'(w)(b - a). \tag{3}$$

But by the hypothesis of this theorem, $f'(w) = 0$, and then Eq. (3) says that $f(b) = f(a)$. In words, f has the same value at any point of the interval that it has at the beginning of the interval; f is constant for the interval.

Now the more general theorem follows immediately.

---

* See Theorem 2.1-1.

■ THEOREM 3

On the uniqueness of the antiderivative.

HYPOTHESIS: $f'(x) = g'(x)$ for $a \leq x \leq d$.

CONCLUSION: $f(x) - g(x) = $ const for $a \leq x \leq d$.

PROOF: Consider the function $\phi(x) = f(x) - g(x)$. By hypothesis, $\phi'(x) = f'(x) - g'(x) = 0$ for $a \leq x \leq d$. Hence Theorem 3A applies and asserts that $\phi(x)$ is constant for $a \leq x \leq d$. This proves our theorem.

In the past we have often spoken of increasing and decreasing functions.

■ THEOREM 4

On increasing functions.

HYPOTHESIS: (a) $f(x)$ is continuous for $c \leq x \leq d$.
(b) $f'(x) > 0$ for $c < x < d$.

CONCLUSION: $f(x)$ is an increasing function for the interval $c \leq x \leq d$.

PROOF: Let a and b be any two points of the interval $c \leq x \leq d$ such that $b > a$. Since f' exists for $a < x < b$ and f is continuous for $a \leq x \leq b$, the hypotheses of the Theorem of Mean Value are satisfied and we can say that there exists a number w, $c \leq a < w < b \leq d$ such that

$$f(b) = f(a) + f'(w)(b - a). \tag{4}$$

Now $b - a$ is positive because $b > a$, and $f'(w)$ is positive by hypothesis. Therefore, Eq. (4) says that $f(b) > f(a)$. But this is what characterizes an increasing function; $f(b) > f(a)$ whenever $b > a$.

● Remark 1

We leave to the reader in an exercise at the end of this section the statement and proof of a corresponding theorem on decreasing functions. We also consider a theorem on nondecreasing functions in another exercise.

III

The proofs of Theorems 3A and 4 point to a fruitful way of looking at the conclusion of the Theorem of Mean Value. Equation (4) compares f's values at two different places. If we know $f(a)$, then $f(b)$ will be $f(a)$ plus a correction. This correction, in turn, depends on the difference between b and a and the value of the derivative at some intermediate point.

Example 4.   Let us furnish an estimate for $\sqrt{101}$. We know that $\sqrt{100} = 10$, and we shall use the Theorem of Mean Value, for it is our strategy to compare the values of a function at two places. We write $f(x) = \sqrt{x}$ and choose the interval $100 \leq x \leq 101$. Since $f'(x) = 1/(2\sqrt{x})$ exists for this interval, the theorem applies and asserts that there exists a w, $100 < w < 101$, such that $f(101) = f(100) + f'(w)(101 - 100)$, or

$$\sqrt{101} = 10 + \frac{1}{2\sqrt{w}}. \tag{5}$$

Since $100 < w < 101$, we can say that $10 < \sqrt{w} < 11$.* Then $1/\sqrt{w}$ lies between $\frac{1}{11}$ and $\frac{1}{10}$, and $1/(2\sqrt{w})$ lies between $\frac{1}{22}$ and $\frac{1}{20}$. Finally, Eq. (5) says that $10 + \frac{1}{22} < \sqrt{101} < 10 + \frac{1}{20}$, or $10.045 < \sqrt{101} < 10.05$.

EXERCISES 7.5

1. Decide whether the Theorem of Mean Value applies to the functions listed below for the intervals indicated. If it does, find the intermediate point whose existence is asserted by the theorem. If the theorem does not apply, explain why it does not.

   (a) $f(x) = x^2$, $-1 \le x \le 1$.

   (b) $f(x) = 1 - |x|$, $-1 \le x \le 1$.

   (c) $f(x) = \dfrac{x}{x-1}$, $0 \le x \le 2$.

   (d) $f(x) = \dfrac{x}{x-1}$, $2 \le x \le 4$.

   (e) $f(x) = \log x$, $1 \le x \le 2$.

   (f) $f(x) = e^{-x}$, $-1 \le x \le 1$.

   (g) $f(x) = \tan^{-1} x$, $0 \le x \le 1$.

   (h) $f(x) = \sqrt[3]{x}$, $-8 \le x \le 1$.

   (i) $f(x) = \sqrt[3]{x}$, $0 \le x \le 1$.

2. Use the Theorem of Mean Value to get estimates for

   (a) $\sqrt{9.02}$.

   (b) $\sqrt{15.96}$.

   (c) $\sqrt[3]{8.06}$.

   (d) $\log 1.01$.

   (e) $\tan^{-1} 1.02$.

3. State and prove a theorem on decreasing functions analogous to Theorem 4.

4. A nondecreasing function, to be distinguished from an increasing function, is one for which $f(b) \ge f(a)$ whenever $b > a$. Prove this theorem on nondecreasing functions:
   Hypothesis: (a) $f(x)$ is continuous for $c \le x \le d$.
   (b) $f'(x) \ge 0$ for $c < x < d$.
   Conclusion: $f(x)$ is a nondecreasing function for $c \le x \le d$.

5. Illustrate Theorem 4 by considering $f(x) = x^2$ for $0 \le x \le 1$.

7.6 On the Existence of the Definite Integral

In Sec. 2.4 we defined the definite integral by means of a limiting process.

▪ NOTATION CONVENTION 1

The definite integral. The symbol $\int_{x=a}^{b} f(x)\,dx$, $b > a$ stands for the number arrived at in the following way: (a) divide the interval $a \le x \le b$ into n subintervals, the kth subinterval of length $(\Delta x)_k$. (b) Let x_k^* be any point in the kth subinterval. (c) Form the sum $\sum_{k=1}^{n} f(x_k^*)(\Delta x)_k$. (d) Find $\lim_{n \to \infty} \sum_{k=1}^{n} f(x_k^*)(\Delta x)_k$, it being understood that the largest of the $(\Delta x)_k$'s approaches 0 as n grows beyond

---

* The number 11 was chosen for the sake of arithmetic simplicity. We could choose a smaller number, like 10.5, and have a sharper estimate.

all bounds, and that the same limit is approached no matter how the subintervals and the points x_k^* within them are chosen.

It seemed reasonable to assume that this limit would exist if the integrand $f(x)$ were continuous for $a \leq x \leq b$, and we proceeded on that assumption. Let us examine the matter further.

I

In this section we shall be concerned with the following theorem.

■ THEOREM 1

On the existence of the definite integral.

HYPOTHESIS: $f(x)$ is continuous for $a \leq x \leq b$.

CONCLUSION: $\int_{x=a}^{b} f(x)\, dx$ exists.

DISCUSSION: Let x_k' and x_k'' be the points of the kth subinterval at which f achieves its minimum and maximum values for that subinterval. (Theorem 7.4-2 assures us that these points exist.) Let x_k^* be any point of the kth subinterval. Then, we have $f(x_k') \leq f(x_k^*) \leq f(x_k'')$ for each k and

$$\underline{S_n} = \sum_{k=1}^{n} f(x_k')(\Delta x)_k \leq \sum_{k=1}^{n} f(x_k^*)(\Delta x)_k \leq \sum_{k=1}^{n} f(x_k'')(\Delta x)_k = \overline{S_n}.$$

If we succeed in showing that $\lim_{n\to\infty} (\overline{S_n} - \underline{S_n}) = 0$, it being understood that the maximum subinterval width approaches 0, then it will follow that if one of $\overline{S_n}$, $\sum_{k=1}^{n} f(x_k^*)(\Delta x)_k$, and $\overline{S_n}$ approaches a limit, all three sums approach the same limit. Let a positive ϵ challenge number be presented. We want to show that $|\overline{S_n} - \underline{S_n}| < \epsilon$ for all partitions of $a \leq x \leq b$ with maximum $(\Delta x)_k$ small enough.

We can write

$$\overline{S_n} - \underline{S_n} = [f(x_1'')(\Delta x)_1 + f(x_2'')(\Delta x)_2 + \cdots + f(x_n'')(\Delta x)_n]$$
$$- [f(x_1')(\Delta x)_1 + f(x_2')(\Delta x)_2 + \cdots + f(x_n')(\Delta x)_n],$$
$$\overline{S_n} - \underline{S_n} = [f(x_1'') - f(x_1')](\Delta x)_1 + [f(x_2'') - f(x_2')](\Delta x)_2$$
$$+ \cdots + [f(x_n'') - f(x_n')](\Delta x)_n. \tag{1}$$

By hypothesis, $f(x)$ is continuous for $a \leq x \leq b$, and by Theorem 7.4-4 it is uniformly continuous for that interval. This means that if any positive challenge number is specified, no matter how small, we can exhibit a neighborhood half-width δ such that $|f(x) - f(z)|$ is less than that positive challenge number for any z and x of the interval within δ of each other: $a \leq z,\, x \leq b,\, |x - z| < \delta$. Let the positive challenge number $\epsilon/(b - a)$ be specified; then there is a corresponding neighborhood half-width number δ. Consider partitions of $a \leq x \leq b$ for which the greatest of the $(\Delta x)_k$'s will be less than this δ. Since x_k'' and x_k' both lie in the same *k*th subinterval, and thus within δ of each other, we can be sure that $|f(x_k'') - f(x_k')|$ $< \epsilon/(b - a)$ for each k. Now we return to Eq. (1) and write

$$\overline{S}_n - \underline{S}_n < \frac{\epsilon}{b - a} (\Delta x)_1 + \frac{\epsilon}{b - a} (\Delta x)_2 + \frac{\epsilon}{b - a} (\Delta x)_3 + \cdots + \frac{\epsilon}{b - a} (\Delta x)_n$$

$$= \frac{\epsilon}{b - a} [(\Delta x)_1 + (\Delta x)_2 + (\Delta x)_3 + \cdots + (\Delta x)_n] = \frac{\epsilon}{b - a} (b - a) = \epsilon.$$

The definitions of $\overline{S}_n$ and $\underline{S}_n$ are such that $\overline{S}_n - \underline{S}_n \geq 0$. Hence we have shown that $\lim_{n\to\infty} (\overline{S}_n - \underline{S}_n) = 0$, and we know that if one of $\underline{S}_n$, $\sum_{k=1}^{n} f(x_k^*)(\Delta x)_k$, and $\overline{S}_n$ approaches a limit as the greatest $(\Delta x)_k$ of the partition approaches 0, all approach the same limit.

II

It remains to show that one of $\underline{S}_n$ and $\overline{S}_n$ approaches a limit as the greatest $(\Delta x)_k$ of the partition of $a \leq x \leq b$ approaches 0.

If we suspect that a sequence of numbers $u_1, u_2, u_3, \cdots$ approaches a specific number U, we ask, "If a positive ϵ is specified, no matter how small, is there a number N such that $|u_n - U| < \epsilon$ for all $n \geq N$?" But how can one show that a sequence $u_1, u_2, u_3, \cdots$ approaches a limit if the specific number U being approached is not known? For this purpose mathematicians use a theorem of Cauchy.* The theorem seems plausible; roughly, it says that if the numbers of a sequence approach each other as we go farther and farther out in the sequence, then the numbers of the sequence are approaching a limit. We state Cauchy's Theorem without proof.†

■ THEOREM 2

Cauchy's criterion for a convergent sequence.

HYPOTHESIS: When an $\epsilon > 0$ is specified, no matter how small, there exists a number N such that $|u_m - u_n| < \epsilon$ for all $m, n > N$.

CONCLUSION: There exists a number U such that $\lim_{n\to\infty} u_n = U$.

Now we shall return to the lower sum numbers $\underline{S}_n = \sum_{k=1}^{n} f(x_k')(\Delta x)_k$ and use the idea presented by Cauchy's Theorem. Let a positive challenge number ϵ be presented, no matter how small. We want to show how to choose δ, the allowable maximum $(\Delta x)_k$ for an interval partition, so that we shall have $|\underline{S}_m - \underline{S}_n| < \epsilon$ whenever $\underline{S}_m$ and $\underline{S}_n$ refer to partitions of $a \leq x \leq b$ for which the maximum $(\Delta x)_k$ $< \delta$. If we succeed, we shall claim that the $\underline{S}_n$'s have a limit.

---

* Augustin Cauchy, 1789–1857, one of the first mathematicians to organize analysis on a basis presently considered sufficiently rigorous.

† Our primary difficulty in organizing a proof is again caused by the fact that we have not carefully organized our ideas about the real number system and that, therefore, the phrase "there exists a number such that . . ." will cause trouble.

We already know that $\lim_{n \to \infty} (\overline{S_n} - \underline{S_n}) = 0$, it being understood that the largest $(\Delta x)_k$ approaches 0. Hence we can find a positive number δ such that

$$\overline{S_n} - \underline{S_n} < \frac{\epsilon}{2} \quad \text{and} \quad \overline{S_m} - \underline{S_m} < \frac{\epsilon}{2}, \tag{2}$$

whenever the partitions to which these sums refer have maximum $(\Delta x)_k < \delta$. From these two partitions of $a \le x \le b$ into n parts and m parts, we form one new finer partition into j parts by uniting the two original sets of subdivision points into one new set. Then we consider the one or more subintervals of the new subdivision corresponding to the kth subinterval of the original subdivision into n parts. Where $\underline{S_n}$ and $\overline{S_n}$ used the minimum and maximum values of f for this whole subinterval, $\underline{S_j}$ will use the minimum values of f for parts of this subinterval. Since a minimum for a part of a subinterval is always greater than, or equal to, the minimum for the whole subinterval and is, of course, always less than, or equal to, the maximum for the whole subinterval, we can say that

$$\underline{S_n} \le \underline{S_j} \le \overline{S_n}, \tag{3a}$$

and, similarly,

$$\underline{S_m} \le \underline{S_j} \le \overline{S_m}. \tag{3b}$$

To conclude, we put all our inequalities together. From Eqs. (3a) and (2) it follows that

$$|\underline{S_j} - \underline{S_n}| \le |\overline{S_n} - \underline{S_n}| < \frac{\epsilon}{2}. \tag{4a}$$

From Eqs. (3b) and (2), it follows that

$$|\underline{S_j} - \underline{S_m}| \le |\overline{S_m} - \underline{S_m}| < \frac{\epsilon}{2}. \tag{4b}$$

From Eqs. (4a) and (4b) it follows that

$$|\underline{S_m} - \underline{S_n}| = |(\underline{S_m} - \underline{S_j}) + (\underline{S_j} - \underline{S_n})| \le |\underline{S_m} - \underline{S_j}| + |\underline{S_j} - \underline{S_n}|$$

$$= |\underline{S_j} - \underline{S_m}| + |\underline{S_j} - \underline{S_n}| < \frac{\epsilon}{2} + \frac{\epsilon}{2} = \epsilon.$$

We have now concluded our discussion of the fact that the $\underline{S_n}$ numbers have a limit when the number n of subintervals into which the interval $a \le x \le b$ is partitioned increases beyond all bounds, the size of the largest $(\Delta x)_k$ approaching 0. From our earlier discussion, the $\overline{S_n}$ numbers would approach the same limit, as would any set of intermediate numbers, and it is this limit number that is $\int_a^b f(x) \, dx$ in the case where $f(x)$ is continuous for $a \le x \le b$.

● **Remark 1**

The continuous functions are not the only integrable functions. We shall leave to advanced calculus courses the question of describing the integrable functions in greater detail.

EXERCISES 7.6

1. (a) Prove that

$$\cos \phi + \cos 2\phi + \cos 3\phi + \cdots + \cos n\phi = \frac{1}{2}\left[\frac{\sin (n + 1/2) \phi}{\sin (\phi/2)} - 1\right].$$

Suggestion: Prove first that

$$\sin (k + \tfrac{1}{2})\phi - \sin (k - \tfrac{1}{2})\phi = 2 \sin \tfrac{1}{2} \phi \cos k\phi.$$

Write this formula out for $k = 1, 2, 3, 4, \cdots, n - 1, n$, and add.

(b) Evaluate $\int_{x=0}^{b} \cos x \, dx$ directly from the definition of the definite integral.
Suggestion: Divide the interval $0 \le x \le b$ into n equal parts by using subdivision points $x_0 = 0$, $x_1 = 1 \, \Delta x$, $x_2 = 2 \, \Delta x$, $x_3 = 3 \, \Delta x$, $\cdots$, $x_n = n \, \Delta x = b$. For each subinterval, evaluate $\cos x$ at the right end point and form the sum $\sum_{k=1}^{n} (\cos x_k)\Delta x$. Use the formula of Part (a).

2. In this exercise we consider a subdivision into unequal subintervals. Evaluate $\int_{x=1}^{2} (1/x^2)$ dx directly from the definition of the definite integral.
Suggestion: Divide the interval $1 \le x \le 2$ into n parts by using subdivision points $x_0 = 1$, $x_1 = \sqrt[n]{2} = c$, $x_2 = c^2$, $x_3 = c^3$, $\cdots$, $x_{n-1} = c^{n-1}$, $x_n = c^n = 2$. Then

$$(\Delta x)_k = c^{k-1}(c - 1), \qquad k = 1, 2, \cdots, n.$$

Form $\sum_{k=1}^{n} f(x_k)(\Delta x)_k$ and evaluate $\lim_{n \to \infty} \sum_{k=1}^{n} f(x_k)(\Delta x)_k$. You will need the formula for the sum of n terms of a geometric progression and the fact that $\lim_{n \to \infty} \sqrt[n]{2} = 1$.

3. Here we prove Theorem 5.1-1, the theorem on change of variable for a definite integral. Fill in the details.

(a) Subdivide the interval $\alpha \le u \le \beta$ by choosing $\alpha = u_0 < u_1 < u_2 < \cdots < u_n = \beta$. With each u_k associate $t_k = \tau(u_k)$ and thus subdivide the interval $a \le t \le b$.

(b) There is a number u_k^* such that $u_{k-1} \le u_k^* \le u_k$ and $t_k - t_{k-1} = \tau'(u_k^*) (u_k - u_{k-1})$. Why? Write $t_k^* = \tau(u_k^*)$.

(c) Explain why

$$f(t_k^*)(t_k - t_{k-1}) = f(\tau(u_k^*)) \, \tau'(u_k^*)(u_k - u_{k-1})$$

$$\sum_{k=1}^{n} f(t_k^*)(\Delta t)_k = \sum_{k=1}^{n} f(\tau(u_k^*))\tau'(u_k^*)(\Delta u)_k$$

$$\int_{t=a}^{b} f(t) \, dt = \int_{u=\alpha}^{\beta} f(\tau(u)) \frac{d\tau}{du} \, du.$$

7.7 On the Evaluation of Definite Integrals. The Fundamental Theorem of Integral Calculus

I

We know now that $\int_{a}^{b} f(x) \, dx$ exists if $f(x)$ is continuous, but how is it to be evaluated? We can go directly to Definition 7.6-1, as we did in Examples 1, 2, and 3 of Sec. 2.4 and Exercises 1 and 2 of the last section, but such summation work is tedious and may require considerable ingenuity. If we know an antiderivative function for $f(x)$, then the evaluation can be carried out relatively simply. See Theorem 2.6-5.

■ THEOREM 1

The Fundamental Theorem of the Integral Calculus.

HYPOTHESIS: (a) $f(x)$ is continuous for $a \leq x \leq b$.
(b) $\phi'(x) = f(x)$ for $a \leq x \leq b$.

CONCLUSION: $\int_{x=a}^{b} f(x) \, dx = \phi(b) - \phi(a)$.

PROOF: Divide the interval $a \leq x \leq b$ into n parts by using subdivision points $x_0 = a < x_1 < x_2 < x_3 < \cdots < x_{n-1} < x_n = b$. Let $(\Delta x)_k = x_k - x_{k-1}$, $k = 1, 2, \cdots, n$. Now consider the function $\phi(x)$, taken over the first subinterval, $x_0 \leq x \leq x_1$. By Hypothesis (b) ϕ' exists for this subinterval, and continuity for ϕ would follow from the fact that there is differentiability.* Hence the Theorem of Mean Value applies and we can say that there exists a number of the first subinterval, which we shall call x_1^*, such that $\phi(x_1) - \phi(x_0) = \phi'(x_1^*)(x_1 - x_0)$. By Hypothesis (b), this can be rewritten

$$\phi(x_1) - \phi(x_0) = f(x_1^*)(\Delta x)_1, \qquad x_0 < x_1^* < x_1. \tag{1}$$

But similar statements hold for the other subintervals;

$$\left.\begin{array}{ll} \phi(x_2) - \phi(x_1) = f(x_2^*)(\Delta x)_2, & x_1 < x_2^* < x_2, \\ \phi(x_3) - \phi(x_2) = f(x_3^*)(\Delta x)_3, & x_2 < x_3^* < x_3, \\ \quad\vdots & \quad\vdots \\ \phi(x_{n-1}) - \phi(x_{n-2}) = f(x_{n-1}^*)(\Delta x)_{n-1}, & x_{n-2} < x_{n-1}^* < x_{n-1}, \\ \phi(x_n) - \phi(x_{n-1}) = f(x_n^*)(\Delta x)_n, & x_{n-1} < x_n^* < x_n. \end{array}\right\} \tag{1a}$$

Adding Eqs. (1) and (1a), we obtain

$$\phi(x_n) - \phi(x_0) = \sum_{k=1}^{n} f(x_k^*)(\Delta x)_k,$$

or, since $x_0 = a$ and $x_n = b$,

$$S_n = \sum_{k=1}^{n} f(x_k^*)(\Delta x)_k = \phi(b) - \phi(a). \tag{2}$$

Thus we find that $\lim_{n \to \infty} S_n = \phi(b) - \phi(a)$ when we use this special choice of intermediate points, it being understood that the largest $(\Delta x)_k$ approaches 0. But when $f(x)$ is continuous, we get the same result for $\int_{x=a}^{b} f(x) \, dx$ whether we use maximum values, minimum values, or intermediate values for f in the various subintervals. Hence

$$\int_{x=a}^{b} f(x) \, dx = \phi(b) - \phi(a).$$

---

* Theorem 7.3-2.

II

We shall also demonstrate Theorem 2.6-6 again, without reference to any one special application for definite integrals like the area application. This theorem might be interpreted as a sort of converse of Theorem 1 of the present section.

■ **THEOREM 2**

HYPOTHESIS: (a) $f(x)$ is continuous for $a \leq x \leq b$.
(b) $\phi(x) = \int_{t=a}^{x} f(t) \, dt$ for $a \leq x \leq b$.

CONCLUSION: $\phi'(x) = f(x)$ for $a \leq x \leq b$.

In proving this theorem we shall make use of the First Mean Value Theorem for Integrals, a theorem used frequently enough to warrant mention for its own sake.

■ **THEOREM 3**

The First Mean Value Theorem for Integrals.

HYPOTHESIS: $f(x)$ is continuous for $a \leq x \leq b$.

CONCLUSION: There exists a number w, $a < w < b$, such that

$$\int_{x=a}^{b} f(x) \, dx = f(w)(b - a).$$

PROOF OF THEOREM 3: Because f is continuous for the interval $a \leq x \leq b$, there must exist points c and d of the interval at which f achieves its minimum value m and its maximum value M for the closed interval.* Now from the definition of the definite integral as a limit of a sum it follows that

$$\int_{x=a}^{b} f(x) \, dx \leq \int_{x=a}^{b} M \, dx. \tag{3}$$

Indeed, if we use the same subdivision of the interval $a \leq x \leq b$ for both integrals, we have $f(x_k^*)(\Delta x)_k \leq M(\Delta x)_k$ for each subinterval, and then Eq. (3) follows. Similarly,

$$\int_{x=a}^{b} m \, dx \leq \int_{x=a}^{b} f(x) \, dx.$$

Hence

$$m(b - a) \leq \int_{x=a}^{b} f(x) \, dx \leq M(b - a),$$

and we conclude that there must be a number q, $m \leq q \leq M$, such that

$$\int_{x=a}^{b} f(x) \, dx = q(b - a).$$

---

* Theorem 7.4-2.

But by the Intermediate Value Theorem for continuous functions,* there exists a number w, w between c and d and hence $a \le w \le b$, with the property $f(w) = q$. This concludes the proof of Theorem 3.

PROOF OF THEOREM 2:   We shall compute $\phi'(x)$ from the definition of the derivative:

$$\phi'(x) = \lim_{\Delta x \to 0} \frac{\phi(x + \Delta x) - \phi(x)}{\Delta x}.$$

Since $\phi(x) = \int_{t=a}^{x} f(t)\, dt$ and $\phi(x + \Delta x) = \int_{t=a}^{x+\Delta x} f(t)\, dt,$

we can write

$$\phi(x + \Delta x) - \phi(x) = \int_{t=a}^{x+\Delta x} f(t)\, dt - \int_{t=a}^{x} f(t)\, dt,$$

or, quoting Theorem 2.6-4,

$$\phi(x + \Delta x) - \phi(x) = \int_{t=x}^{x+\Delta x} f(t)\, dt. \tag{4}$$

Now the First Mean Value Theorem for Integrals says that there exists a w, $x < w < x + \Delta x$, such that

$$\phi(x + \Delta x) - \phi(x) = \int_{t=x}^{x+\Delta x} f(t)\, dt = f(w)\, \Delta x, \tag{5}$$

or $$\frac{\phi(x + \Delta x) - \phi(x)}{\Delta x} = f(w), \qquad x < w < x + \Delta x.$$

But $w \to x$ when $\Delta x \to 0$; since f is a continuous function for $a \le x \le b$, we can say that

$$\lim_{\substack{w \to x \\ \Delta x \to 0}} f(w) = f(x).$$

Hence $$\phi'(x) = \lim_{\Delta x \to 0} \frac{\phi(x + \Delta x) - \phi(x)}{\Delta x} = \lim_{\Delta x \to 0} f(w) = f(x).$$

Our work was written throughout with a positive Δx in mind. If Δx were negative, the very same ideas could be used. For Eqs. (4) and (5), for instance, we could write

$$\phi(x + \Delta x) - \phi(x) = -\int_{t=x+\Delta x}^{x} f(t)\, dt \tag{4a}$$

and

$$\phi(x + \Delta x) - \phi(x) = -f(w)[x - (x + \Delta x)], \qquad x + \Delta x < w < x \tag{5a}$$
$$= f(w)\, \Delta x.$$

This concludes the proof of Theorem 2.

---

* Theorem 7.4-3.

● **Remark 1**

The number $f(w)$ which appears in the conclusion of Theorem 3,

$$\int_a^b f(x)\, dx = f(w)(b - a), \tag{6}$$

is called the mean value of $f(x)$ for the interval $a \le x \le b$. Equation (6) then says, in words, that the integral of f over an interval is the product of the mean value of f for that interval by the length of the interval. Indeed, it is for this reason that Theorem 3 is called a mean value theorem.

■ **DEFINITION 1**

If $f(x)$ is continuous for $a \le x \le b$, then the number $\int_a^b f(x)\, dx/(b - a)$ is called the *mean value* (or average value) of $f(x)$ for the interval $a \le x \le b$.

● **Remark 2**

In the case where $f(x) \ge 0$ for $a \le x \le b$, Eq. (6) can be interpreted to say that the area of the region bounded by $y = f(x)$, the x axis, $x = a$, and $x = b$ is equal to the area of the rectangle with the same base, but height equal to $\bar{f}$, the average value of $f(x)$ for the interval $a \le x \le b$; see Fig. 7.19. In slightly different words, $\bar{f}$, the average or mean value of $f(x)$ for $a \le x \le b$, is the height of that rectangle with base $a \le x \le b$ which has the same area as the region bounded by $y = f(x)$, the x axis, $x = a$, and $x = b$.

● **Remark 3**

It is interesting to compare Definition 1 for the average value of f over an interval with the definition of the average value of a finite set of numbers. In elementary statistics, $\bar{\bar{f}}$, the average value of the n numbers $f_1, f_2, \cdots f_n$ is taken to be

$$\bar{\bar{f}} = \frac{1}{n}(f_1 + f_2 + \cdots + f_n) = \frac{1}{n}\sum_{k=1}^{n} f_k. \tag{7}$$

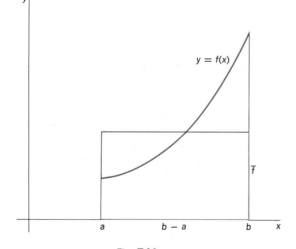

Fig. 7.19

Definition 1 says that $\bar{f}$, the average value of $f(x)$ for the interval $a \le x \le b$, is

$$\bar{f} = \frac{1}{b-a} \int_a^b f(x)\, dx. \tag{8}$$

Let us subdivide the interval $a \le x \le b$ into n equal parts of length $(\Delta x)_1 = (\Delta x)_2 = \cdots = (\Delta x)_n = (b-a)/n$ each, and let us take for our representative points for the various subintervals the numbers x_k^*. Then, since the definite integral of Eq. (8) is the limit approached by $\sum_{k=1}^n f(x_k^*)(\Delta x)_k$, no matter what the manner of subdivision and the choice of representative points, so long as the largest $(\Delta x)_k$ approaches zero, we can rewrite Eq. (8) in the forms

$$\bar{f} = \frac{1}{b-a} \lim_{n \to \infty} \sum_{k=1}^n f(x_k^*)(\Delta x)_k$$

$$\bar{f} = \frac{1}{b-a} \lim_{n \to \infty} \sum_{k=1}^n f(x_k^*) \frac{b-a}{n}$$

$$\bar{f} = \lim_{n \to \infty} \frac{1}{n} \sum_{k=1}^n f(x_k^*). \tag{9}$$

At the last step we observed that $b-a$ and n were independent of k when rewriting the summation. Compare Eqs. (7) and (9). Equation (9) instructs us to select n representative values for f, somewhat evenly spaced, to average them in the sense of Eq. (7), and to find a limit.

EXERCISES 7.7

1. Evaluate $\int_0^b \cos x\, dx$ by using Theorem 1. Compare with Exercise 7.6-1.

2. Evaluate $\int_1^2 1/x^2\, dx$ by using Theorem 1. Compare with Exercise 7.6-2.

3. (a) Show that $2/\pi$ is the mean value of $f(x) = \cos x$ for the interval $0 \le x \le \pi/2$.
(b) Sketch $y = \cos x$ and $y = 2/\pi$ for $0 \le x \le \pi/2$ on the same set of axes.

4. (a) Show that $\tfrac{1}{2}$ is the mean value of $f(x) = 1/x^2$ for $1 \le x \le 2$. (b) Sketch $y = 1/x^2$ and $y = \tfrac{1}{2}$ for $1 \le x \le 2$ on the same set of axes.

5. *Deviations from the average.* (a) $\bar{\bar{f}} = 1/n \sum_{k=1}^n f_k$, the mean value of the n numbers $f_1, f_2, \cdots, f_n$, has the characteristic property that some of the deviations of the f_k's from $\bar{\bar{f}}$ are positive, some are negative, and that the sum of the deviations, $\sum_{k=1}^n (f_k - \bar{\bar{f}})$, is 0. Prove that $\bar{\bar{f}}$ has this property and that no other number has this property.
(b) In somewhat analogous fashion, $\bar{f} = \int_a^b f(x)\, dx/(b-a)$, the mean value of $f(x)$ for the interval $a \le x \le b$, has the property that $f(x) > \bar{f}$ for some x of $a \le x \le b$, that $f(x) < \bar{f}$ for other x of $a \le x \le b$ and that

$$\int_a^b [f(x) - \bar{f}]\, dx = 0.$$

Prove that $\bar{f}$ has this property and that no other number does. Show that this means that A_1, the area of the region or regions to the right of $x = a$ and to the left of $x = b$, which lie above the line $y = \bar{f}$ and below $y = f(x)$, is equal to A_2, the area of the region or regions that lie below the line $y = \bar{f}$ and above $y = f(x)$.

More Applications

8.1 Maximum and Minimum Problems

We have already discussed the problem of determining maximum and minimum points of graphs in Secs. 3.18 and 3.19. In this section we shall apply our results to the problem of determining maximum and minimum values of functions that arise in various geometric, physical, and economic situations. Many of the applications are important for their own sake, but our primary goal is to give the student practice in applying the theorems on extreme values to concrete situations.

From Theorems 3.18-1, 3.18-2, and 3.19-3 we can draw the following set of working instructions for a problem in which a function is to be maximized or minimized.

(a) Write down specifically which quantity Q is to be minimized or maximized.

(b) Write down from the given material or work out, if necessary, a statement in which Q is described as a function of one variable x; include in this statement a clause explaining for which x the quantity Q is defined. If at first Q is a function of several variables, it will be necessary to eliminate all but one of these variables either explicitly or implicitly.*

(c) Determine dQ/dx and then those critical x for which $dQ/dx = 0$.

(d) Test Q for a maximum or minimum value at each of the critical x's. This will usually be done either by using the first derivative table test (Theorem 3.18-2) or the second derivative test (Theorem 3.19-3).

---

* It is only common sense to point out that the student should draw clear diagrams wherever possible to help him understand the various functional correspondences involved. The student who does not put his diagrams on paper is really carrying them in his head, and that is rarely an efficient procedure in complex situations.

423

(e) Consider the possibility of an extreme value for Q at an end point of the interval for which Q is defined or at a point at which dQ/dx is not defined.

Example 1.   A farmer has 80 running ft of fencing available with which to construct a rectangular enclosure along the side of his barn. What should the dimensions of the rectangle be if the area enclosed is to be a maximum?

Consider Fig. 8.1(a). The area of the rectangular enclosure is to be maximized, and we write down a formula for that area:

$$A = xy.$$

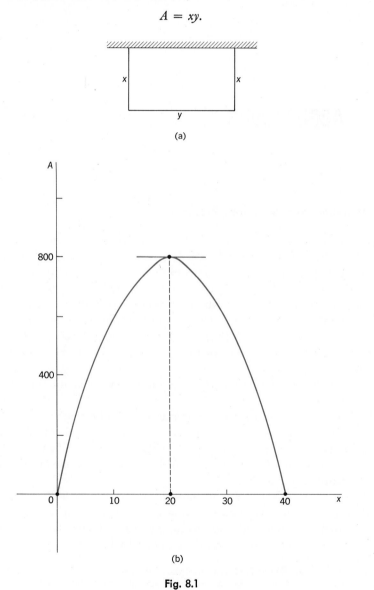

(a)

(b)

Fig. 8.1

Because 80 ft of fencing will be used, we can say that

$$2x + y = 80 \quad \text{or} \quad y = 80 - 2x,$$

so that we can write A as a function of one variable:

$$A = x(80 - 2x) = 80x - 2x^2, \qquad 0 \le x \le 40. \tag{1}$$

The physical conditions of the problem tell us that this expression for A makes sense only for the x interval indicated; if x were greater than 40 the farmer would have to use more fencing than the 80 ft available. Next,

$$\frac{dA}{dx} = 80 - 4x, \tag{2}$$

and dA/dx will vanish if $x = 20$. It would appear that the farmer ought to use dimensions $x = 20$ and $y = 40$.

To check, we observe that $d^2A/dx^2 = -4$, which tells us that when A is plotted as a function of x, as in Fig. 8.1(b), the graph faces down everywhere and that A thus takes on a maximum value at $x = 20$. The first derivative table test would read

x	<20	>20
$\dfrac{dA}{dx}$	$+$	$-$

,

and would lead to the same conclusion.

We see immediately from Fig. 8.1(b) or from Eq. (1) that A is not larger at the end points of the interval $0 \le x \le 40$ than at $x = 20$, and from Eq. (2) that there is no x of this interval for which dA/dx does not exist.

Example 2. We are given heat sources at points A and B, 8 units apart, with the source at A twice as strong as that at B. If the heat received at a point is inversely proportional to the square of the distance from the heat source and directly proportional to the strength of that source, at what point on the line segment joining A to B will the heat received be a minimum?

Consider Fig. 8.2(a). The total heat received at P, which we shall call H, is to be a minimum. According to the hypothesis, the heat received at P from source B is

$$H_B = k\frac{1}{(8 - r)^2};$$

that received from source A is

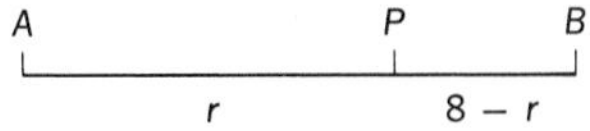

$$H_A = k\frac{2}{r^2}.$$

Fig. 8.2(a)

Therefore,

$$H = k\frac{1}{(8 - r)^2} + k\frac{2}{r^2} = k(8 - r)^{-2} + 2kr^{-2}, \qquad 0 < r < 8.$$

Next we differentiate the quantity that is to be minimized;

$$\frac{dH}{dr} = k(-2)(8-r)^{-3}(-1) + 2k(-2)r^{-3} = k\left[\frac{2}{(8-r)^3} - \frac{4}{r^3}\right]. \qquad (3)$$

We see that

$$\frac{dH}{dr} = 0 \quad \text{if} \quad \frac{2}{(8-r)^3} = \frac{4}{r^3},$$

$$\left(\frac{r}{8-r}\right)^3 = 2 \quad \text{or} \quad \frac{r}{8-r} = \sqrt[3]{2},$$

$$r = \sqrt[3]{2}\,(8-r), r = \frac{8\sqrt[3]{2}}{1+\sqrt[3]{2}} \approx 4.46.$$

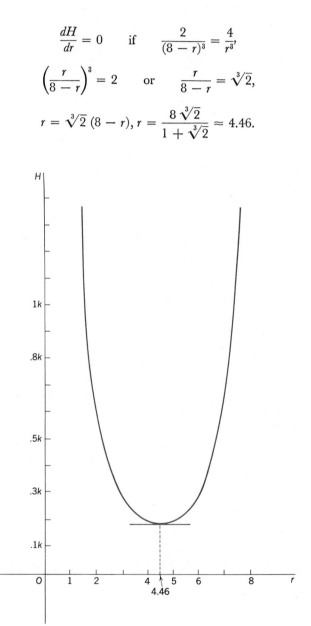

Fig. 8.2(b)

To check this critical value of r, we shall use the second derivative test. We write

$$\frac{d^2H}{dr^2} = -6k(8-r)^{-4}(-1) + 12kr^{-4} = \frac{6k}{(8-r)^4} + \frac{12k}{r^4},$$

which is surely positive for all r of the interval $0 < r < 8$, since we deal with even powers. When $d^2H/dr^2 > 0$ at an r for which $dH/dr = 0$, we have a minimum value. From Eq. (3) we see that there is no r of the domain $0 < r < 8$ for which dH/dr does not exist, and in this problem there is no question of whether H has a smaller value at an end point of the interval than at the point where $dH/dr = 0$. The point on the line segment AB at which the heat received is a minimum is the point 4.46 units from A. See Fig. 8.2(b).

Example 3. We have a fixed number of square feet of lumber with which to construct an open box of maximum volume, it being specified that the box is to have square ends. What should be the ratio of the length of the base to the height of the box?

Consider Fig. 8.3, and note that the quantity to be maximized is

$$V = xy^2. \tag{4}$$

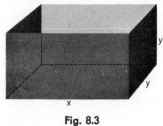

Fig. 8.3

But the surface area is fixed by the restriction on the lumber available for the box, say A sq ft. Since the box is to have no top,

$$2y^2 + 3xy = A, \qquad 0 < y \le \sqrt{\frac{A}{2}}.* \tag{5}$$

We could solve for x in Eq. (5) and substitute in Eq. (4), thus arriving at an explicit statement for V in terms of y, but for the sake of illustration we shall work implicitly, and consider x to be a function of y, determined implicitly by Eq. (5).

Since it is V that is to be maximized, we form, from Eq. (4),

$$\frac{dV}{dy} = x\,2y + \frac{dx}{dy}y^2.$$

But the dx/dy needed here can be obtained by differentiating both members of Eq. (5) with respect to y, thus:

$$4y + 3\left(x + \frac{dx}{dy}y\right) = 0 \qquad \text{or} \qquad \frac{dx}{dy} = -\frac{4y+3x}{3y}, \qquad y \ne 0.$$

Then for dV/dy we have

$$\frac{dV}{dy} = 2xy - \frac{(4y+3x)}{3y}y^2 = xy - \frac{4y^2}{3} = y\left(x - \frac{4y}{3}\right); \tag{6}$$

---

* The square ends have area y^2 each; the bottom, back and front have area xy each. We cannot have $y = 0$ because then Eq. (5) cannot be satisfied for any choice of x. We can have $y = \sqrt{A/2}$ if we are willing to consider $x = 0$.

dV/dy will vanish if $x = 4y/3$, or $x/y = 4/3$. Observe that we cannot consider the possibility $y = 0$ and that there is no y of $0 < y \leq \sqrt{A/2}$ for which dV/dy does not exist. When $x = \frac{4}{3}y$, we learn from Eq. (5) that $y = \sqrt{A/6}$.

From the third member of Eq. (6) we see that

$$\frac{d^2V}{dy^2} = x + y\frac{dx}{dy} - \frac{8}{3}y = x - \frac{1}{3}(4y + 3x) - \frac{8}{3}y = -4y.$$

Since $d^2V/dy^2 < 0$ for all y of $0 < y \leq \sqrt{A/2}$, the graph for V as a function of y would face down for all y of this interval and there would be a maximum value for V if x and y were chosen so that $x/y = \frac{4}{3}$. When $y = \sqrt{A/2}$, at the end point of the interval under consideration, we compute $x = 0$ from Eq. (5) and hence $V = 0$ there. There is no absolute maximum at the end point of the interval.

Example 4.   One hypothesis which will account for the law of refraction of light in physics is the hypothesis that a light ray will travel in the path that requires least time.

Let a light ray travel from point A in medium 1 to point B in medium 2 with velocity v_1 in the first medium, v_2 in the second; see Fig. 8.4. For different choices of the point P at which the light ray will cross the intersurface, we get different total times required for the trip from A to B. We want to minimize that time.

The time required to traverse the path AP at velocity v_1 is AP/v_1, and the time required to traverse PB at velocity v_2 is PB/v_2. Hence the time required for the trip from A to B is

$$T = \frac{1}{v_1}[a^2 + x^2]^{1/2} + \frac{1}{v_2}[b^2 + (c - x)^2]^{1/2}, \qquad 0 \leq x \leq c.$$

But now

$$\frac{dT}{dx} = \frac{1}{v_1}\frac{1}{2}[a^2 + x^2]^{-1/2}(2x) + \frac{1}{v_2}\frac{1}{2}[b^2 + (c - x)^2]^{-1/2}\,2(c - x)^1(-1),$$

or

$$\frac{dT}{dx} = \frac{1}{v_1}\frac{x}{\sqrt{a^2 + x^2}} - \frac{1}{v_2}\frac{c - x}{\sqrt{b^2 + (c - x)^2}}. \tag{7}$$

If we give the names i and r to the angles that the incident and refracted rays make

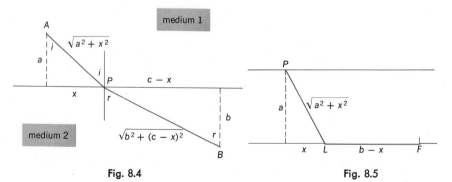

Fig. 8.4   Fig. 8.5

with the normal to the intersurface, as is usually done in physics books, we can say that

$$\frac{dT}{dx} = \frac{1}{v_1} \sin i - \frac{1}{v_2} \sin r.$$

It follows now that $dT/dx = 0$ if

$$\frac{\sin i}{\sin r} = \frac{v_1}{v_2}. \tag{8}$$

This is the law of refraction.

When we compute the second derivative from Eq. (7) we find that

$$\frac{d^2T}{dx^2} = \frac{1}{v_1} \frac{a^2}{(a^2 + x^2)^{3/2}} + \frac{1}{v_2} \frac{b^2}{[b^2 + (c - x)^2]^{3/2}}.$$

Because d^2T/dx^2 is positive for $0 \leq x \leq c$, we know that we have minimized T when we use Eq. (8).

Note that the graph for T as a function of x faces up for $0 \leq x \leq c$ and that for such a graph we cannot have an absolute minimum at an end point of the interval when there is an interior point for which $dT/dx = 0$. Note also from Eq. (7) that there is no x of $0 \leq x \leq c$ for which dT/dx is not defined.

Example 5A. Suppose that we have a power house, P, situated on one bank of a straight river a feet wide and a factory, F, situated on the other bank, b feet downstream, $b = 2a$. We want to lay a cable from P to F at minimum cost. If underwater cable costs \$1 per ft and land cable costs \$.50 per ft, what path should we choose for the cable?

Consider Fig. 8.5. The cost of the underwater cable PL will be $1\sqrt{a^2 + x^2}$; that of the land cable LF will be $\frac{1}{2}(b - x)$. The quantity to be minimized is

$$C = [a^2 + x^2]^{1/2} + \tfrac{1}{2}(b - x), \qquad 0 \leq x \leq b = 2a.$$

We have

$$\frac{dC}{dx} = \frac{x}{\sqrt{a^2 + x^2}} - \frac{1}{2},$$

and then $dC/dx = 0$ if

$$\frac{x}{\sqrt{a^2 + x^2}} = \frac{1}{2}, \qquad 4x^2 = a^2 + x^2, \qquad x = \frac{1}{\sqrt{3}} a.$$

We really minimize C with this x, because

$$\frac{d^2C}{dx^2} = \frac{a^2}{(a^2 + x^2)^{3/2}} > 0.$$

Note that the graph for C as a function of x faces up for $0 \leq x \leq b$ and that for such a graph we cannot have an absolute minimum at an end point of the interval when we have an interior point for which $dC/dx = 0$. Note also that there is no x of $0 \leq x \leq b$ for which dC/dx is not defined.

Example 5B.   Consider the same problem with one modification. Let us suppose that the cost of laying land cable in a heavily industrialized area is $1.50 per ft instead of $.50, as before. Now what path should we choose for the cable? Common sense would say that the cable should go directly from P to F underwater if land cable is more expensive than water cable, but let us illustrate our theory.

Reasoning as before, the quantity to be minimized is

$$C = [a^2 + x^2]^{1/2} + \tfrac{3}{2}(b - x), \qquad 0 \leq x \leq b = 2a,$$

and

$$\frac{dC}{dx} = \frac{x}{\sqrt{a^2 + x^2}} - \frac{3}{2}. \tag{9}$$

When we set $dC/dx = 0$, we get

$$\frac{x}{\sqrt{a^2 + x^2}} = \frac{3}{2}, \qquad 4x^2 = 9(a^2 + x^2), \qquad x^2 = -\frac{9}{5}a^2.$$

We cannot find an x of the interval $0 \leq x \leq b$ for which $dC/dx = 0$. We check Eq. (9) to be sure that the derivative dC/dx exists for all x of the interval. After that we investigate the end points of our interval and find that C is a minimum when $x = b$. See Fig. 8.6, where we have sketched C quickly as a function of x. Note that Eq. (9) requires that $dC/dx < 0$ for all x of $0 \leq x \leq b$, because $x = \sqrt{x^2} < \sqrt{a^2 + x^2}$, so that $x/\sqrt{a^2 + x^2} < 1$. Note also that again we have

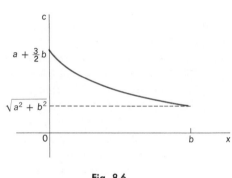

Fig. 8.6

$$\frac{d^2C}{dx^2} = \frac{a^2}{(a^2 + x^2)^{3/2}} > 0$$

for all x of $0 \leq x \leq b$, so that the curve faces up.

In this problem an extreme value occurred at the end of an interval. In Exercise 36, the extreme value occurs at a point at which the derivative is not defined.

● **Remark 1**

If we have $f(x) \geq 0$ for $I\colon a \leq x \leq b$, then $kf(x)$, where k is a positive constant, $\sqrt{f(x)}$, and $[f(x)]^2$ will all attain maximum and minimum values for I at the very same points that f does. This will enable one to replace a given function by a simpler function in certain discussions. To illustrate, it may be easier to discuss

$$g(x) = [f(x)]^2 = \frac{x^3 + 4}{x^2} = x + \frac{4}{x^2}$$

on the interval $1 \leq x \leq 5$ than $f(x) = \sqrt{x^3 + 4}/x$ itself. The student can demonstrate this remark and generalize it in Exercise 40.

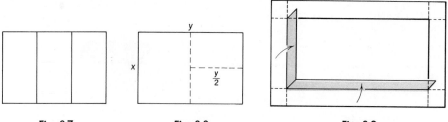

Fig. 8.7   Fig. 8.8   Fig. 8.9

EXERCISES 8.1

1. Which rectangle of perimeter 24 has the greatest area?

2. A farmer wants to build a rectangular enclosure of area 800 sq ft, including two interior fences, as shown in Fig. 8.7. What dimensions should he choose if the length of fencing required is to be a minimum?

3. Consider the floor plan indicated in Fig. 8.8. The total area is to be 750 sq ft, and exterior walls cost twice as much as interior walls. What dimensions should be chosen to minimize the cost of the walls?

4. An open channel with rectangular cross section of fixed area is to be designed so that the contact between the liquid and the walls will be a minimum when the channel is full. Find the ratio of the width to the depth.

5. A box manufacturer wishes to make an open box of maximum volume from a rectangular piece of cardboard of dimensions 8 by 12 by cutting out (or doubling under) a square at each corner, and then folding. What should be the size of the square cutout? See Fig. 8.9.

6. A printer is to use a page of area 80 sq in. with margins of 1 in. at the top and sides and $1\frac{1}{2}$ in. at the bottom. What dimensions should he choose for the page to make the area of printed matter a maximum?

7. What should be the dimensions of a circular sector of perimeter 12 if the area is to be a maximum?

8. An open box with square ends and volume 2304 cu in. is to be constructed. What should the dimensions be if the surface area is to be a minimum?

9. An aquarium is to be 6 ft high and is to have a volume of 750 cu ft. The base, ends, and back are to be made of slate, but the front is to be made of a plate glass, which costs 1.5 times as much as the slate per sq ft. What dimensions should be chosen to make the cost of raw materials a minimum?

10. Assume that the strength of a rectangular beam varies jointly as the width and the square of the depth. Which rectangular beam cut from a circular log of radius 10 in. will have the maximum strength?

11. A post-office regulation says that no package can be accepted if the sum of its length and cross-section perimeter exceeds 60 in. What are the dimensions of the circular cylinder package of largest volume that can be mailed?

12. A trough is to be made from a long sheet of tin of width W by folding into thirds. Through what angle should the sides be turned up to achieve maximum carrying capacity? See Fig. 8.10.

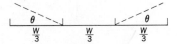

Fig. 8.10

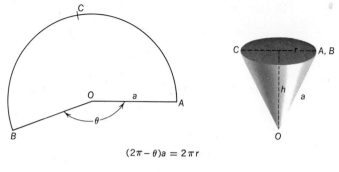

$$(2\pi - \theta)a = 2\pi r$$

Fig. 8.11

13. What is the maximum possible area for an isosceles triangle with two sides equal to *a*?

14. Of all the cylinders which can be inscribed in a sphere of radius *a*, which one has maximum volume?

15. A cylindrical container, open at the top, is to hold 30 cu in. What should the dimensions be if the material used is to be a minimum?

16. A closed cylindrical can is to hold 1 quart. What should be the ratio of radius to height if the surface area is to be a minimum?

17. A cylindrical can is to hold V cu in., V a constant. Assume that tin costs .01 cents per sq in. and that it costs .01 cents per running inch to solder the seams. (There will be one linear seam for the lateral surface area, one circular seam at the top, and one circular seam at the bottom.) The sum of the cost of material and the cost of soldering is to be a minimum. Find an equation satisfied by the critical value for the radius.

18. The speed of signaling in a marine cable is proportional to $x^2 \log (1/x)$, where x is the ratio of the radius of the core of the cable to that of the entire cable. For which x is the greatest speed attained?

19. A conical filter of maximum volume is to be formed from a piece of circular filter paper of radius *a* by cutting out (or folding under) a circular sector. See Fig. 8.11.
(a) Find the radius of the base and the height of this largest filter.
(b) Find the central angle of the sector that is to be cut out of the original circle.

20. A picture of height 8 ft is mounted on a museum wall, with the base of the picture 10 ft above the floor. How far from the wall should an observer stand if he wants the picture to subtend the greatest possible angle at his eye? (Assume that the observer's eye is 5 ft from the floor.)

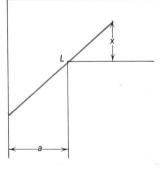

Fig. 8.12

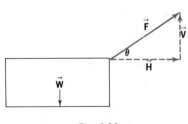

Fig. 8.13

21. There is a wall a ft high and a second, higher wall b ft behind the first one.
    (a) What is the length of the shortest pole that has one end on the ground, passes over the first wall, and reaches the second wall?
    (b) How high up the second wall will it reach?

22. A beam L ft long is to be rolled in horizontal position from a corridor a ft wide around a corner into a second corridor. What will be the maximum protrusion into the second corridor, neglecting the width of the beam and assuming that it is kept as close to the wall of the first corridor and the corner as possible? See Fig. 8.12.

23. A force $\vec{F}$ of fixed magnitude is available for dragging a weight W along the ground, the coefficient of friction being μ. At what angle from the horizontal should the force be directed if it is to have maximum forward-pulling effect? Does the answer depend on W or $\|\vec{F}\|$? *Suggestions:* Note that the force $\vec{F}$ has horizontal and vertical components, $\vec{H}$ and $\vec{V}$. The frictional drag is $\mu\,(\|\vec{W}\| - \|\vec{V}\|)$. The net forward component is the difference between $\|\vec{H}\|$ and this drag. See Fig. 8.13.

24. (a) Show that the law of reflection of light, angle of incidence equal to angle of reflection, can be explained by the same hypothesis as the one used to predict the law of refraction of light in Example 4. See Fig. 8.14.
    (b) Towns A and B, situated inland on the same side of a straight river, want to erect a jointly owned pumping station P on the river. Where should P be located if the length of pipe to be used from P to A and from P to B is to be a minimum?

25. Island A is 8 miles off a straight coast and B is 18 miles down the coast. Some freight is to be moved from A to B on a regular schedule, each trip to be made as quickly as possible. If the freight can be moved at the rate of 7 miles per hr on water and at 25 miles per hr on land, how far from B should a dock be built for the landing of the freight? See Fig. 8.15.

26. Suppose that in Exercise 25 poor roads reduce the rate at which the freight can be moved on land to 5 miles per hr. The best route from A to B is then obvious by common sense, but go through the analysis for the sake of illustration.

27. The minimum distance from a point Q to a line L is achieved along a path perpendicular to L. Similarly, the minimum or maximum distance from a point Q to a circle K is achieved along a path perpendicular to K. Consider the curve C with equation $y = f(x)$, $a \le x \le b$, and let $f'(x)$ exist for $a < x < b$. Let $Q(c, d)$ be a point not on C. Show that if the distance from Q to C achieves a maximum or minimum at a nonterminal point of C, that extreme value is achieved along a path that is perpendicular to C.

28. (a) If we are given two spheres of radius 1 and radius 2, with centers 6 units apart, at what point on the line joining the centers should a source of light be placed if the sum of the areas illuminated on the two spheres is to be a maximum? (The surface area of a segment of height h on a sphere of radius r is $2\pi r h$.)
    (b) Repeat Part (a) using 4 as the radius of the larger sphere.

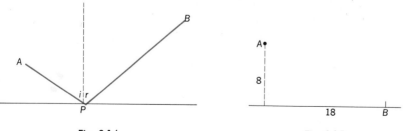

Fig. 8.14   Fig. 8.15

29. Suppose that the box manufacturer of Exercise 5 is requested by a customer to make boxes of height no greater than 1.25. With this extra limitation, what should be the size of the square cut out of the 8 by 12 piece of cardboard to make an open box of maximum volume?

30. There is a refinery at A and an oil well at B, which can be reached by traveling 10 miles along a straight highway from A and then 6 miles perpendicular to the highway. If pipe line along the highway costs b dollars per mile while pipe line across country interferes with farming and costs $1.1b$ dollars per mile, how should the pipe line be laid out to achieve minimum cost?

31. For which points on the circle $x^2 + y^2 = 25$ will the sum of the distances from $(1, 0)$ and $(-1, 0)$ be a minimum?

32. (a) In measuring the same length twice a man reported lengths L_1 and L_2. Show that for $L = (L_1 + L_2)/2$ the sum of the squares of the differences between L and L_1 and L and L_2 will be a minimum.

(b) Given observations $L_1, L_2, \cdots, L_n$. What number L will be such that the sum of the squares of the differences between L and the various L_k's, $k = 1, 2, \cdots, n$, will be a minimum?

(c) Show that $F(a) = \int_0^1 (x - a)^2 \, dx$ will be a minimum for $a = \frac{1}{2}$.

(d) Show that $G(a) = \int_0^1 (x - a)^k \, dx$ will be a minimum for $a = \frac{1}{2}$ if k is an even positive integer and that $G(\frac{1}{2}) = 0$ if k is an odd positive integer.

33. At a price of $1.00, a dealer can sell 1000 articles that cost him 60 cents each. For each cent that he lowers the price, he can increase the number sold by 50. What price will maximize his profit?

34. A manufacturer estimates that his weekly cost of production is given by the formula $C = 8000 + 7x + .0001x^2$, where x is the number of articles manufactured.* If he sets the selling price of his article at y, he estimates that each week he can sell $x = 11,000 - 500y$ articles.† How many articles should he try to manufacture each week and what selling price should he set for his article if he wants to maximize his profit?

35. A river steamer can carry 600 passengers. The owner estimates that he will get x passengers for a day's outing if he charges y per ticket, where $x = 1400 - 400y$. What price should he charge to maximize his income?

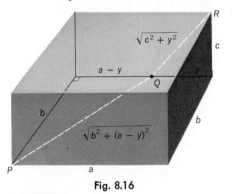

Fig. 8.16

36. A manufacturer estimates his overhead at $1000 per week, the cost of raw materials at $1 per article, and the cost of labor at $2 per article if he manufactures 3000 articles a week or less. However, if he manufactures more than 3000 articles, he must begin to pay "time and a half" or $3 per article for labor on the articles manufactured in excess of 3000. Write down the cost per article as a function of the number of articles manufactured. Draw the graph of this function. For what number of articles is the cost per article a minimum?

---

* The "overhead" is $8000 per week; the cost of materials and direct labor is $7 per article; the term $.0001x^2$ becomes significant only for large x and says, in effect, that the plant is of a certain size and becomes inefficient if the manufacturer attempts too much production.

† This formula is based on an estimate of 4000 sales at a price of $14 and a loss of 500 sales for each $1 increase in selling price.

37. (a) At which point on the graph of $y = x^4 - 2x^3 + 4x - 3$ is the slope a relative maximum? (b) At which point is the slope decreasing most rapidly?

38. A particle is displaced a distance $s = 3 \sin 2t + 1 \cos t$ at time t. For which t, $0 \le t \le 2\pi$, will the acceleration be increasing most rapidly? decreasing most rapidly?

39. We are given a rectangular parallelepiped with sides a, b, c, $a > b > c$. Show that, if motion is restricted to the sides of the parallelepiped, the shortest distance from a vertex to the opposite vertex is $\sqrt{a^2 + b^2 + c^2 + 2bc}$. See Fig. 8.16.

40. (a) Prove this theorem.

Hypothesis: (a) $\alpha \le f(x) \le \beta$ for $a \le x \le b$.
 (b) $\varphi(u)$ is steadily increasing for $\alpha \le u \le \beta$.
 (c) $g(x) = \varphi(f(x))$ for $a \le x \le b$.
Conclusion: (a) $g(x_1) < g(x_2)$ if $f(x_1) < f(x_2)$, $a \le x_1, x_2 \le b$.
 (b) $f(x_1) < f(x_2)$ if $g(x_1) < g(x_2)$, $a \le x_1, x_2 \le b$.

(b) Show that $f(x)$ and $g(x)$ attain maximum and minimum values for $a \le x \le b$ at the very same places.

(c) Show that Remark 1 of this article is demonstrated by choosing $\varphi(u) = ku$, $\varphi(u) = \sqrt{u}$, and $\varphi(u) = u^2$.

(d) Show that $g(x) = \sin^{-1}[x^2/(x^2 + 1)]$ and $f(x) = x^2/(x^2 + 1)$ attain maximum and minimum values for $-1 \le x \le 2$ at the very same places.

8.2 Related Rates

Let x and dx/dt, y and dy/dt be functions of the time t for a t domain D. If we are given, or can deduce, a relationship between x and y valid for t of D, and if we can differentiate implicitly with respect to t, we get a relationship between dx/dt and dy/dt. We can also deal with functions of a variable other than the time, for instance, temperature.

Example 1. A conical icicle, whose height is always 12 times the radius of its base, is being formed by the dripping of water. If the volume is increasing at the rate of 1 cu cm per hr, at what rate is the height increasing when the height is 8 cm?

We are given that $dV/dt = 1$ and we are asked to find dh/dt. We know that we can get a relationship between dV/dt and dh/dt if we start with a relationship between V and h. Hence we start with

$$V = \tfrac{1}{3} \pi r^2 h$$

because we deal with a cone, and write

$$V = \frac{1}{3} \pi \left(\frac{1}{12} h \right)^2 h = \frac{1}{3(12)^2} \pi (h)^3$$

because we are told that $r = \tfrac{1}{12} h$ always. We have here, essentially, an identity in t for $t \ge 0$, and if we differentiate both members with respect to t, we obtain

$$\frac{dV}{dt} = \tfrac{1}{144} \pi h^2 \frac{dh}{dt}.$$

But now, when $h = 8$,

$$1 = \frac{1}{144} \pi (8)^2 \frac{dh}{dt} \quad \text{or} \quad \frac{dh}{dt} = \frac{144}{64\pi} = \frac{9}{4\pi} \approx .72 \text{ cm per hr.}$$

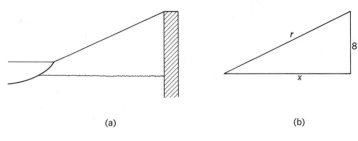

(a)   (b)

Fig. 8.17

Example 2.   A dock stands 8 ft above the deck of a boat. The boat is being pulled into the dock by means of a rope attached to the deck at the front of the boat. If 2 ft of rope are drawn in each minute, at what rate is the boat moving toward the dock when the boat is 15 ft away?

See Fig. 8.17. We are given that $dr/dt = -2$ and we are to find dx/dt when $x = 15$. We start with a relationship between x and r, because the rates of x and r are to be related. We have

$$(x)^2 = (r)^2 - 64, \qquad t \geq 0. \tag{1}$$

If we differentiate with respect to t, we get

$$2(x)^1 \frac{dx}{dt} = 2(r)^1 \frac{dr}{dt} - 0 \qquad \text{or} \qquad x\frac{dx}{dt} = r\frac{dr}{dt}. \tag{2}$$

When $x = 15$, Eq. (1) says that $r = 17$, and then Eq. (2) says that

$$15\frac{dx}{dt} = 17(-2) \qquad \text{or} \qquad \frac{dx}{dt} = -\frac{34}{15} \approx -2.27 \text{ ft per min.}$$

The boat is advancing toward the deck at the rate of 2.27 ft per min when the boat is 15 ft away.

Example 3.   A particle moves on the parabolic path $y^2 = 4(x + 1)$. At the instant it passes through the point $(3, 4)$ its x component of velocity, dx/dt, is $+1$. What is the y component of its velocity at that instant? The focus of this parabola is the origin. At what rate is the focal radius rotating at this instant?

Consider Fig. 8.18. We are given that $dx/dt = 1$ at $(3, 4)$ and asked for dy/dt and then $d\theta/dt$. The equation of the parabola is a relationship between x and y valid for all t under consideration, because the particle moves along the parabola. When we differentiate $y^2 = 4(x + 1)$ with respect to t we get

$$2(y)^1 \frac{dy}{dt} = 4\frac{dx}{dt}.$$

Hence at $(3, 4)$ we have

$$\frac{dy}{dt} = \frac{2}{y}\frac{dx}{dt} = \frac{2}{4}(1) = \frac{1}{2}.$$

If we are to find the rate of change of θ we must first state a relationship for θ itself. We have

$$\tan \theta = \frac{y}{x} \qquad \text{or} \qquad \theta = \tan^{-1}\frac{y}{x}.$$

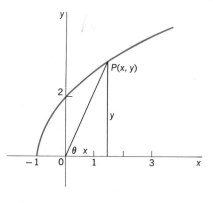

Fig. 8.18

for points of a neighborhood of $(3, 4)$. Then

$$\frac{d\theta}{dt} = \frac{1}{1 + (y^2/x^2)} \frac{d}{dt}\left(\frac{y}{x}\right) = \frac{1}{1 + (y^2/x^2)} \frac{x(dy/dt) - y(dx/dt)}{x^2} = \frac{x(dy/dt) - y(dx/dt)}{x^2 + y^2}.$$

Therefore, at $(3, 4)$

$$\frac{d\theta}{dt} = \frac{3(\frac{1}{2}) - 4(1)}{3^2 + 4^2} = -.1.$$

The focal radius is rotating in the clockwise direction at a rate of .1 radian per unit of time at the instant the particle is at $(3, 4)$.

● **Remark 1**

The reader should be careful to distinguish between quantities that are constant throughout the discussion and those that vary but assume specific values at a specific time. Thus, in Example 2, the height of the dock above the deck is constant throughout the discussion; it was labeled as the constant 8. The distance from the boat to the dock, however, varies as the rope is drawn in. That distance was labeled x, even though we were especially interested in the specific value $x = 15$. To form a rate of change of x at the specific t for which $x = 15$, one must consider x for a t interval which includes that specific t.

EXERCISES 8.2

1. A stone is dropped into a still pond. Concentric circular ripples spread out, the radius of the disturbed region increasing at the rate of a ft per sec. At what rate does the area of the disturbed region increase when its radius is b ft?

2. The volume of a spherical balloon is increasing at the rate of 3 cu ft per min. At what rate is the radius increasing when the radius is 8 ft?

3. Assume that water condenses on the surface of a spherical drop of water in such a way that the volume increases at a rate equal to k times the surface area. What can be said about the rate at which the radius of the drop increases?

4. Sand drops onto a conical pile at the rate of 3 cu ft per min. If the height of the pile is constantly 1.8 times the radius of its base, at what rate is the height increasing when the pile is already 9 ft high?

5. A cylinder is expanding in such a way that the height and radius both increase at the rate of 1 percent per day. At what rate is the volume increasing?

6. We are given an empty conical filter of height 24 cm and with radius of the top 7 cm. See Fig. 8.19. A solution is poured in at the rate of 2 cu cm per min and filters through at a rate per minute equal to $\frac{1}{100}$ of the surface area of the filter in contact with the solution. At what rate is the height of the solution in the filter rising when that height is already 10 cm? How high will the solution ultimately rise in the filter? (The curved surface of a cone of radius r and height h is $\pi r \sqrt{r^2 + h^2}$.)

7. We are given a cylindrical tank of radius 5 ft and length 20 ft, lying on its side as in Fig. 8.20(a). Oil is being pumped in at the rate of 1 cu ft per min. At what rate is the level of the oil rising when the oil is already 2 ft deep in the tank? *Suggestion 1:* The area of segment ABD in Fig. 8.20(b) is $25[(\pi/2) - \sin^{-1}(x/5)] - x\sqrt{25 - x^2}$. *Suggestion 2:* Rotate Fig. 8.20(b) through 90° to form Fig. 8.20(c). Write K for the area of ABD. Why is $dV/dt = 20\ dK/dt = 20\ (dK/dx)\ (dx/dt)$? What can you deduce from Theorem 2.3-1?

8. The force of repulsion F between two charges of like sign is inversely proportional to the square of the distance r between them, and is 5 units when $r = 3$ cm. The charges are brought nearer to each other at the rate of 1 cm per min. At what rate is F increasing when $r = 1.5$?

9. A particle of mass 2 units is moving with velocity 60 ft per sec and constant acceleration 32 ft per sec². At what rate is its kinetic energy increasing? [Kinetic energy $= \frac{1}{2}(\text{mass})(\text{velocity})^2$.]

10. The "thin lens equation" is

$$\frac{1}{s} + \frac{1}{s'} = \frac{1}{f},$$

where s is the object distance, s' the image distance, and f the focal length. An object is 30 cm away from a thin lens of focal length 10 cm and is moving toward the lens at the rate of 2 cm per sec. Find the image distance and the rate at which it is changing.

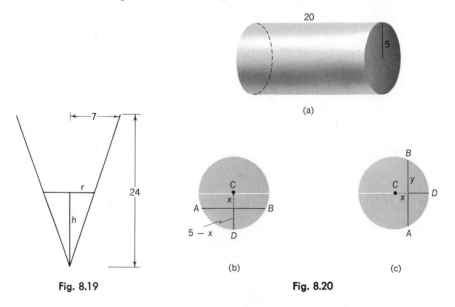

(a)

(b)

(c)

Fig. 8.19   Fig. 8.20

11. The pressure and volume of a gas are related by the formula $PV^{\gamma} = $ const. If at volume V_1 we have pressure P_1, and if then the volume is changing at the rate of 3 cu cm per sec, at what rate is the pressure changing at that time?

12. A ladder 12 ft long leans against a wall. The foot of the ladder is pulled away from the wall at the rate of $\frac{1}{2}$ ft per min. What is the height of the top of the ladder, and at what rate is it falling when the foot of the ladder is 4 ft from the wall?

13. A beacon is located on an island 2 miles off a straight coast. The beacon rotates with an angular velocity of $\frac{1}{2}$ revolution per min. At what rate does the ray of light move along the coast at a point 5 miles from the point opposite the island?

14. A man 6 ft tall is 12 ft from a lamppost that is 20 ft high. The man is walking directly away from the lamppost at a rate of 4.4 ft per sec. At what rate is the length of his shadow increasing?

15. An airplane is assumed to be flying in a straight line at a constant elevation of 3000 ft. An observer, directly under the path of the plane, noted that, when his angle of elevation for sighting the plane was $60°$, this angle was decreasing at the rate of $5°$ per sec. What was the airplane's speed then?

16. A weight is attached to one end of a rope which passes over a pulley 20 ft above the ground. A man who keeps his hand 4 ft off the ground grasps the other end of the rope and walks away at the rate of 2 ft per sec. When the man is 12 ft from the point directly under the pulley, the weight is off the ground and rising. At what rate is it rising?

17. Point Q lies on a hill which makes an angle of $5°$ with a horizontal direction H. Ball B is dropped from a point 100 ft directly above Q, its height at time t given by $h = 100 - 16t^2$. The sun's rays make a $45°$ angle with H, the ball's shadow, P, lying directly downhill from Q as in Fig. 8.21. At what rate will P be moving up the hill at $t = 2$?

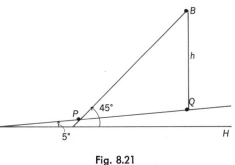

Fig. 8.21

18. A particle moved on the circular path $x^2 + y^2 = 25$. As it moved through the point $(-3, 4)$, its x component of velocity, dx/dt, was 8. What was the y component of its velocity, and what was its speed?

19. A particle moved on the elliptic path

$$\frac{(x - 1)^2}{4} + \frac{y^2}{3} = 1$$

in the clockwise direction with speed 5 at the moment it passed through the point $(2, \frac{3}{2})$.
(a) Find dx/dt and dy/dt, the x and y components of the velocity, at that moment.
(b) One of the foci of the ellipse is the origin. Find the rate at which the focal radius drawn to the origin was rotating as the particle passed through $(2, \frac{3}{2})$.

20. At a certain moment the equal sides of an isosceles triangle were 4 cm and increasing at the rate of .1 cm per min. The included angle was $\pi/6$ and decreasing at the rate of .02 radians per min. At what rate was the area of the triangle changing?

21. Given forces of magnitudes F_1 and F_2 which are increasing at the rate of 1 percent per hr, these forces having an included angle θ which is increasing at the rate of 2 percent per hr. At what rate is the magnitude of the resultant of these forces changing at a moment when $F_1 = 4$ lb, $F_2 = 6$ lb, and $\theta = \pi/3$?

22. A cylindrical tank of radius 1 ft is standing upright. Water is pouring out through a tap at the bottom of radius ½ in., the velocity of the flow being $v = \sqrt{2gh}$, where h is the height of the water in the tank and g is the constant 32.2 ft per sec². At what rate is the water level in the tank dropping when the water in the tank is 3 ft deep? *Suggestion:* Show that $-\Delta V$, the volume of water passing through the tap in time Δt, is approximately $\sqrt{2gh}\,\pi(\frac{1}{24})^2\,\Delta t$, so that

$$\frac{dV}{dt} = -\frac{\pi\sqrt{2gh}}{(24)^2}.$$

8.3   Differentials. Approximate Increments

If we are given $y = f(x)$, we have already stated what we meant by dy/dx, namely,

$$\frac{dy}{dx} = \lim_{\Delta x \to 0}\frac{\Delta y}{\Delta x} = \lim_{\Delta x \to 0}\frac{f(x + \Delta x) - f(x)}{\Delta x};$$

dy/dx is defined as the limit of a fraction. The notation for the derivative, dy/dx, suggests, however, that we expect to find it useful to define new quantities dx and dy such that dy/dx can also be found by dividing dy by dx. In this section we shall define these new quantities, and we shall consider their application to approximate increment problems. In a later section we shall consider their application to the computation of derivatives of functions defined parametrically.

■ DEFINITION 1

The differentials. Let $y = f(x)$ and $dy/dx = f'(x)$ be defined for x of domain D. To each nonzero dx such that the interval from x to $x + dx$ is in D we assign $dy = f'(x)\,dx$.

Example 1.   Consider $y = f(x) = \sin x$ and $dy/dx = f'(x) = \cos x$ for all x. If dx is any number, not equal to 0, then $dy = f'(x)\,dx = \cos x\,dx$.

Example 2.   Consider $Q = \tan^{-1} t$ and $Q'(t) = 1/(1 + t^2)$ for all t. For any number $dt \neq 0$ we have $dQ = Q'(t)\,dt = [1/(1 + t^2)]\,dt$.

● Remark 1

Definition 1 meets one requirement suggested by our differentiation notation: if y is a differentiable function of x, and we take dx and dy and form $dy \div dx$, we get $f'(x)$ or dy/dx. Our definition for differentials is also consistent with our integral notation. If $t = \tau(u)$ and $dt/du = \tau'(u)$ have domain D, then for u of D we have $dt = (dt/du)\,du$ or $dt = (d\tau/du)\,du$, and the integral notation suggests that $\int f(t)\,dt$ and $\int f(\tau(u))(dt/du)\,du$ ought to have the same meaning, for, formally, we have merely replaced dt by $(dt/du)\,du$. These integrals do have the same meaning. To repeat what was said in Theorem 6.3-2 from our present point of view, $\int f(t)\,dt$ means a set of functions whose derivatives with respect to t are all $f(t)$; let $dF/dt = f(t)$ so that $F(t) + C$ is such a set of functions. When we replace t by $\tau(u)$ wherever it occurs in $F(t)$ to form the composite function $F(\tau(u))$, the Chain Rule enables us to say that

$$\frac{dF(\tau(u))}{du} = \left[\frac{dF(t)}{dt}\right]_{t=\tau(u)} \frac{dt}{du}$$

$$\frac{dF(\tau(u))}{du} = [f(t)]_{t=\tau(u)} \frac{dt}{du} = f(\tau(u)) \frac{dt}{du},$$

so that $\int f(\tau(u))(dt/du)du = F(\tau(u)) + C$. The same function F is used to describe both $\int f(t) \, dt$ and $\int f(\tau(u))(dt/du) \, du$.

When we look for a graphical interpretation of our differential definition, we are led to one of our applications for differentials.

■ THEOREM 1

Differentials as tangent increments.

HYPOTHESIS: (a) f and f' have domain D; x of D determines the point Q on the graph of $y = f(x)$.

(b) $dx, \neq 0$ and such that the interval from x to $x + dx$ is in D, determines an increment in x at Q.

CONCLUSION: dy is the corresponding increment in y achieved by the tangent to $y = f(x)$ at Q.

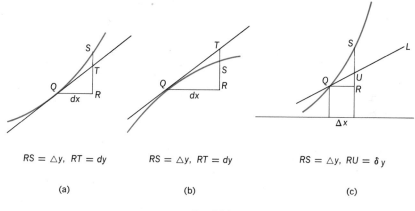

RS = Δy, RT = dy   RS = Δy, RT = dy   RS = Δy, RU = δy

(a)   (b)   (c)

Fig. 8.22

In symbols, if $dx = \Delta x$, then $dy = (\Delta y)_{\text{tan}}$, where by $(\Delta y)_{\text{tan}}$ we mean Δy for the tangent line.

PROOF: See Fig. 8.22(a). The slope of QT, the tangent line at Q, is dy/dx, evaluated at Q. But the slope of QT is also

$$\frac{\text{rise}}{\text{run}} = \frac{RT}{QR}.$$

Thus $\quad \dfrac{RT}{QR} = \dfrac{dy}{dx},\quad$ and $\quad (\Delta y)_{\text{tan}} = RT = \dfrac{dy}{dx} QR = \dfrac{dy}{dx} dx = dy.$

● **Remark 2**

Thus, for an x increment $\Delta x \equiv dx$, the curve increment is $RS = \Delta y$, while the tangent increment is $RT = (\Delta y)_{\text{tan}} = dy$. If, as in Fig. 8.22(a), the graph faces up, then the tangent will lie below the curve and $dy < \Delta y$. If the graph faces down, as in Fig. 8.22(b), then the tangent will lie above the graph and $dy > \Delta y$.

It would seem intuitively clear that the tangent line at a point approximates the curve better than any other line through that point could. The following theorem throws some light on the question of why we get the best straight-line approximation when we take the tangent line.

■ **THEOREM 2**

HYPOTHESIS: $y = f(x)$ and $dy/dx = f'(x)$ have domain D.

CONCLUSION: At x of D we have

$$\lim_{\Delta x \to 0} \frac{\Delta y - dy}{\Delta x} = 0.$$

PROOF: Take $dx = \Delta x \neq 0$. Then

$$\frac{\Delta y - dy}{\Delta x} = \frac{\Delta y}{\Delta x} - \frac{1}{\Delta x}\left(\frac{dy}{dx}\,dx\right) = \frac{\Delta y}{\Delta x} - \frac{dy}{dx},$$

and

$$\lim_{\Delta x \to 0}\left(\frac{\Delta y}{\Delta x} - \frac{dy}{dx}\right) = \frac{dy}{dx} - \frac{dy}{dx} = 0.$$

● **Remark 3**

Draw an arbitrary line L through point Q, and use L to form a proposed approximate increment $RU = \delta y$; see Fig. 8.22(c). Even for this arbitrary line L we have $\Delta y - \delta y = US$ and

$$\lim_{\Delta x \to 0} (\Delta y - \delta y) = 0.$$

But Theorem 2 says that if L is the tangent line, then more is true. Not only does $\Delta y - \delta y$ approach 0 as Δx approaches 0, but $(\Delta y - dy)/\Delta x$ approaches 0; in other words, if L is the tangent line, then $\Delta y - dy$ approaches 0 faster than Δx itself does.

Conversely, we have

$$\lim_{\Delta x \to 0} \frac{\Delta y - \delta y}{\Delta x} = 0$$

only if δy, the increment for the straight line L, is the tangent line increment dy. For, from

$$\lim_{\Delta x \to 0} \frac{\Delta y - \delta y}{\Delta x} = 0$$

there follows

$$\lim_{\Delta x \to 0} \frac{\delta y}{\Delta x} = \lim_{\Delta x \to 0} \frac{\Delta y}{\Delta x} = f'(x).$$

Since $\lim_{\Delta x \to 0} (\delta y / \Delta x)$ is the slope of line L, this equation says that line L has the same slope as the tangent line at Q; L must be the tangent line.

● **Remark 4**

The conclusion of Theorem 2 can be rewritten in a fruitful way. Let

$$\epsilon = \frac{\Delta y - dy}{\Delta x}.$$

Then ϵ approaches 0 as Δx approaches 0 and we have

$$\epsilon \, \Delta x = \Delta y - dy \qquad \text{or} \qquad \Delta y = dy + \epsilon \, \Delta x. \tag{1}$$

Unless $dy/dx = 0$, $\epsilon \, \Delta x$ is smaller than dy when Δx is small, for both factors of $\epsilon \, \Delta x$ are small, whereas only one factor of $dy = (dy/dx) \, \Delta x$ is. If $dy/dx \neq 0$, then Eq. (1) says that dy is the principal part of Δy and that $\epsilon \, \Delta x$ is the correction to be used when dy is taken in the place of Δy.*

Example 3. The radius of a circle is reported to be 2 when in reality it is 2.01. Approximately what error will there be in the computed area of the circle if $r = 2$ is used in the computation?

We know that $A = \pi r^2$ and we are asked for an approximate value of ΔA when $r = 2$ and $\Delta r = .01$. We have

$$\frac{dA}{dr} = 2\pi r \qquad \text{and} \qquad dA = \frac{dA}{dr} \, dr = 2\pi r \, dr.$$

Thus, if we take dA as our approximate increment for A, we obtain

$$\Delta A \approx dA = 2\pi(2)(.01) = .04\pi.$$

For the sake of comparison, note that when $r = 2$, $A = 4\pi$, and that when $r = 2.01$, $A = \pi(2.01)^2 = 4.0401\pi$, so that the exact value for ΔA is $.0401\pi$.

Example 4. From the table entry $\log 4 = 1.38629$, determine an approximate value for $\log 4.01$.

We are given $y = f(x) = \log x$ and $\log 4$. If we knew the Δy that corresponded to $\Delta x = .01$ when $x = 4$, we could find $\log (4.01)$ by adding this Δy to $\log 4$. But

$$\frac{dy}{dx} = \frac{1}{x} = \frac{1}{4} \qquad \text{and} \qquad dy = \frac{dy}{dx} \, dx = \frac{1}{4}(.01).$$

If we use dy as our approximate increment, we have

$$\Delta y \approx dy = .0025 \qquad \text{and} \qquad \log 4.01 \approx 1.38629 + .0025 = 1.38879.$$

For the sake of comparison, a table entry for $\log 4.01$ is precisely 1.38879. Actually, however, we know that our approximate increment is slightly large because

$$\frac{d^2 y}{dx^2} = -\frac{1}{x^2} < 0,$$

so that the graph faces down at $x = 4$, and the tangent line lies above the graph. Our differential, dy, represents the tangent line increment rather than the $y = \log x$ increment. We have a case like that of Fig. 8.22(b).

---

* See Exercises 8.3-17 and 8.3-18.

Example 5. If the motion of a simple pendulum of length L has small amplitude, the period is $T = 2\pi\sqrt{L/g}$, where we shall take g to be 32.2 ft per sec². Thus a pendulum of length 4 ft would have a period of

$$T = 2\pi \sqrt{4/32.2} \text{ sec} \approx 2.21 \text{ sec}.$$

If the pendulum now expands, that is, if L increases, then T increases. Approximately what change in L is allowable if T is not to change by more than .0001?

We are given $\Delta T = .0001$ and asked for a corresponding approximate increment in L when $L = 4$. But

$$T = \frac{2\pi}{\sqrt{g}} L^{1/2} \quad \text{and} \quad \frac{dT}{dL} = \frac{\pi}{\sqrt{g}} \frac{1}{\sqrt{L}} = \frac{\pi}{2\sqrt{g}},$$

so that

$$dT = \frac{dT}{dL} \Delta L = \frac{\pi}{2\sqrt{g}} \Delta L.$$

Thus

$$.0001 = \Delta T \approx dT = \frac{\pi}{2\sqrt{g}} \Delta L,$$

$$\Delta L \approx \frac{.0002\sqrt{g}}{\pi} \approx .00036.$$

EXERCISES 8.3

1. Approximately what change is there in the computed area of a square if the side changes from 10 to 10.02? Exactly what change?

2. A square of side approximately 10 cm is to have its area accurate to within .01 sq cm. Approximately what error in the side is permissible?

3. Given a circle of radius 5. Approximately what change in radius will cause a change in area of .04?

4. A cube expands so that its edge changes from 8 to 8.03. Approximately what is the change in volume? Is this approximate increment smaller or larger than the actual increment?

5. A spherical ball bearing of radius 4 mm wears down evenly to radius 3.9 mm. Approximately what is the change in mass if it is made of material of density 7.8 grams per cu cm?

In Exercises 6–10, (a) use differentials to find approximate values; (b) state whether the approximate value is too large or too small, and explain why.

6. $\log 1.01$.

7. $\sqrt{100.2}$.

8. $\sqrt[3]{7.97}$.

9. $\sin^{-1} .51$.

10. $\tan^{-1} 1.02$.

11. Table entries state that $\sin .50 = .47943$, $\cos .50 = .87758$. Work out approximate values for (a) $\sin .51$, (b) $\cos .51$.

12. An object is attracted by a magnet r cm away with a force $F = 12/r^2$. Approximately what error will be made in computing F if r is taken to be 3 when it really is 2.97?

13. Consider a formula of Maxwell for λ, the mean free path of a gas molecule: $\lambda = 1/(\sqrt{2}\,\pi n d^2)$. Here n is the number of molecules in a unit volume and d is the "diameter" of the molecule.* A .1-percent change in the estimate for d would correspond to approximately what change in λ?

---

* The phrase "the distance of nearest approach of the centers of two molecules in an impact" would be better than the word "diameter."

14. Stefan's law for the rate of emission of radiant energy from the surface of a body is $R = kT^4$, where R is the rate of emission per unit of area, T is the temperature,* and k is a physical constant depending on the body in question. A 1-percent change in T corresponds to approximately what change in R?

15. When two resistors are in parallel, the equivalent resistance R follows from the individual resistances, R_1 and R_2:

$$\frac{1}{R} = \frac{1}{R_1} + \frac{1}{R_2}.$$

Let $R_1 = 1$, $R_2 = 2$. What can be said about the approximate change in R if the accepted value for R_2 should have to be increased by .01 after a second measurement?

16. Demonstrate the following theorem.

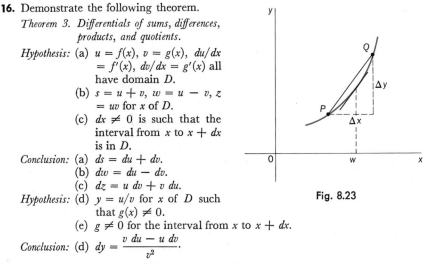

Theorem 3. Differentials of sums, differences, products, and quotients.

Hypothesis: (a) $u = f(x)$, $v = g(x)$, $du/dx = f'(x)$, $dv/dx = g'(x)$ all have domain D.

(b) $s = u + v$, $w = u - v$, $z = uv$ for x of D.

(c) $dx \neq 0$ is such that the interval from x to $x + dx$ is in D.

Conclusion: (a) $ds = du + dv$.

(b) $dw = du - dv$.

(c) $dz = u\,dv + v\,du$.

Hypothesis: (d) $y = u/v$ for x of D such that $g(x) \neq 0$.

(e) $g \neq 0$ for the interval from x to $x + dx$.

Conclusion: (d) $dy = \dfrac{v\,du - u\,dv}{v^2}$.

Fig. 8.23

17. Justify the references to the Theorem of Mean Value in these discussions.

(a) One way of finding an upper bound for the error made in using dy for Δy is this. Observe from Remark 4 that

$$\epsilon = \frac{\Delta y}{\Delta x} - \frac{dy}{dx} = \text{(slope of chord } PQ) - \text{(slope of tangent at } P).$$

But, granted that f' exists for the interval x to $x + \Delta x$, the Theorem of Mean Value says that there is a number w, $x < w < x + \Delta x$, for which $f'(w) = \Delta y / \Delta x$. See Fig. 8.23. Thus

$$\epsilon = f'(w) - f'(x). \tag{2}$$

By taking the maximum value of $|f'(z) - f'(x)|$ for $x < z < x + \Delta x$, we obtain an upper bound for $|\epsilon|$, and then from $\Delta y - dy = \epsilon \Delta x$ an upper bound for $|\Delta y - dy|$.

(b) If it is further true that f'' exists for the interval x to $x + \Delta x$, then the Theorem of Mean Value says that there is a number v, $x < v < x + \Delta x$, for which

$$\epsilon = f''(v)(w - x), \tag{3}$$

so that $|\epsilon| < |f''(v)|\,|\Delta x|$. Now by taking the maximum value of $|f''(z)|\,|\Delta x|$ for $x < z < x + \Delta x$, an upper bound for $|\epsilon|$ is determined.

18. (a) Apply the discussion of Exercise 17(a) to Example 3.

(b) Apply the discussion of Exercise 17(b) to Example 3.

---

* On the Kelvin scale.

8.4 Parametric Representation for Curves

In describing the motion of a particle it is often convenient to state its coordinates as functions of the time. In this way we obtain not only a description of the path on which the particle travels, but, in addition, information about the location of the particle on the path at specific times. Also, even if we are just interested in describing a curve, it is often more convenient to use two simpler equations for x and y in terms of a third variable,

$$x = f(\phi) \quad \text{and} \quad y = g(\phi), \quad \phi \text{ in } D, \tag{1}$$

than it is to use one more difficult equation in x and y in one of the forms

$$y = f(x) \quad \text{or} \quad F(x, y) = 0. \tag{2}$$

The new variable of which x and y are functions is called a parameter. For each number ϕ of the pertinent domain D, Eqs. (1) give us the coordinates of a point of the curve. If we want a description of the curve in one of the forms (2), we must "eliminate the parameter" in the system (1).

The parametric equation description of curves also makes it easier to use the vector analysis tool in studying these curves, as will appear in numerous examples.

Example 1. Consider a particle whose position at time t is given by the equations $x = \cos^2 \pi t$, $y = \sin^2 \pi t$ for all t. Because we know that $\cos^2 \pi t + \sin^2 \pi t = 1$ for all t, we know that the particle moves on the straight-line path $x + y = 1$. Since neither $\cos^2 \pi t$ nor $\sin^2 \pi t$ can be negative, the particle moves on that portion of $x + y = 1$ which lies in the first quadrant; see Fig. 8.24. Indeed, taking into account the periodic properties of these functions and the data in Table 8.1, we see that at $t = 0$ the particle is at $A(1, 0)$; that it moves to $B(0, 1)$, reaching that point at $t = \frac{1}{2}$; that it moves back to A in the next half second; and that it repeats this motion from A to B and back to A once each second.

TABLE 8.1

t	0	$\frac{1}{6}$	$\frac{1}{4}$	$\frac{1}{3}$	$\frac{1}{2}$	$\frac{2}{3}$	$\frac{3}{4}$	$\frac{5}{6}$	1
x	1	$\frac{3}{4}$	$\frac{1}{2}$	$\frac{1}{4}$	0	$\frac{1}{4}$	$\frac{1}{2}$	$\frac{3}{4}$	1
y	0	$\frac{1}{4}$	$\frac{1}{2}$	$\frac{3}{4}$	1	$\frac{3}{4}$	$\frac{1}{2}$	$\frac{1}{4}$	0

To find the speed of the particle at any time, we notice that the components of the velocity are

$$v_x = \frac{dx}{dt} = 2(\cos \pi t)^1 (-\sin \pi t)\pi = -\pi \sin 2\pi t,$$

$$v_y = \frac{dy}{dt} = 2(\sin \pi t)^1 (\cos \pi t)\pi = \pi \sin 2\pi t.$$

Hence the speed of the particle is

$$v = \sqrt{v_x^2 + v_y^2} = \sqrt{2}\, \pi\, |\sin 2\pi t|.$$

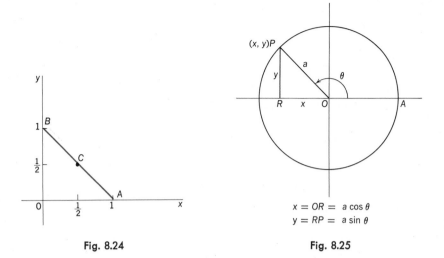

$$x = OR = a \cos \theta$$
$$y = RP = a \sin \theta$$

Fig. 8.24   Fig. 8.25

Because $\sin 2\pi t = 0$ when $t = 0, \frac{1}{2}, 1, \frac{3}{2}, 2, \cdots$, and $|\sin 2\pi t| = 1$ when $t = \frac{1}{4}$, $\frac{3}{4}, \frac{5}{4}, \cdots$, the speed is 0 whenever the particle is at A or B, and the speed is greatest whenever the particle is at $C(\frac{1}{2}, \frac{1}{2})$.

Example 2. The equations $x = a \cos \theta$ and $y = a \sin \theta$, $0 \leq \theta \leq 2\pi$, can serve as parametric equations for the circle of radius a with center at the origin. Indeed, from the identity $\cos^2 \theta + \sin^2 \theta = 1$ we get

$$\frac{x^2}{a^2} + \frac{y^2}{a^2} = 1 \qquad \text{or} \qquad x^2 + y^2 = a^2;$$

see Fig. 8.25. As θ varies from 0 to 2π, the point $P(x, y)$ moves around the circle once in the counterclockwise direction, starting at $A(a, 0)$. See Table 8.2.

TABLE 8.2

θ	0	$\dfrac{\pi}{6}$	$\dfrac{\pi}{4}$	$\dfrac{\pi}{3}$	$\dfrac{\pi}{2}$	π	$\dfrac{3\pi}{2}$	2π
x	a	$.87a$	$.71a$	$.5a$	0	$-a$	0	a
y	0	$.5a$	$.71a$	$.87a$	a	0	$-a$	0

Example 3. Let a projectile be fired from the origin at time $t = 0$ with an initial velocity of magnitude v_0 ft per sec and direction given by elevation angle α, and let it be influenced by the force of gravity alone thereafter. Discuss its motion.

We shall discuss the x and y components of the acceleration separately. Since the force of gravity acts in the negative y direction alone, we can say that $a_x = dv_x/dt = 0$ but that $a_y = dv_y/dt = -g$. Hence

$$v_x = C_1 \qquad \text{and} \qquad v_y = -gt + C_2.$$

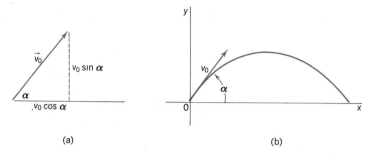

Fig. 8.26

But at $t = 0$ we have $v_x = v_0 \cos \alpha$ and $v_y = v_0 \sin \alpha$, as in Fig. 8.26(a); thus C_1 $= v_0 \cos \alpha$ and $C_2 = v_0 \sin \alpha$, and

$$v_x = \frac{dx}{dt} = v_0 \cos \alpha, \qquad v_y = \frac{dy}{dt} = -gt + v_0 \sin \alpha.$$

Then $\quad x = v_0(\cos \alpha)t + C_3 \quad$ and $\quad y = -\frac{g}{2} t^2 + v_0(\sin \alpha)t + C_4.$

Because the particle is at $(0, 0)$ when $t = 0$, we have $C_3 = C_4 = 0$, and the equations

$$x = v_0(\cos \alpha)t, \qquad y = -\frac{g}{2} t^2 + v_0(\sin \alpha)t \tag{3}$$

furnish the parametric description of the motion.

We can replace the parameter t in Eqs. (3) by solving the first of these equations for t and substituting in the second. We have

$$t = \frac{x}{v_0 \cos \alpha},$$

and then

$$y = -\frac{g}{2} \frac{x^2}{v_0^2 \cos^2 \alpha} + v_0 \sin \alpha \frac{x}{v_0 \cos \alpha}$$

$$= -\frac{g}{2v_0^2 \cos^2 \alpha} x^2 + (\tan \alpha)x.$$

Thus the particle follows a parabolic path; see Fig. 8.26(b). Other properties of the motion are discussed in Exercise 8.4-4.

Example 4. *The cycloid.* Let a circle of radius a roll on a straight line L without slipping or sliding. Let us discuss the path of a point P on the circumference of the circle, and let us start to study P's motion at the instant P touches L. As the

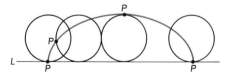

Fig. 8.27

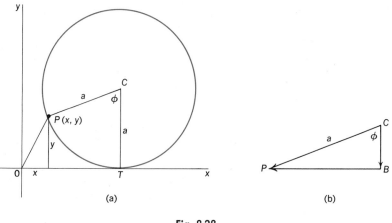

Fig. 8.28

circle rolls to the right, Fig. 8.27, other points on the circumference will touch *L* in turn, and *P* will take new positions. When every other point on the circumference of the circle has touched *L*, then *P* will touch a second time, and after that we shall have the motion repeated. The distance along *L* from the beginning of a cycle to the end of that cycle should be $2\pi a$, the circumference of the circle.

Now let us look for parametric equations that describe *P*'s motion. Let *L* be the *x* axis, and let a point at which *P* touches *L* be the origin. Then let the circle roll forward the arbitrary distance $OT = \overset{\frown}{PT}$, $0 \leq OT \leq 2\pi a$, as in Fig. 8.28(a). In vector notation we can say that

$$\overrightarrow{OP} = x\mathbf{i} + y\mathbf{j}, \tag{4}$$

and also that

$$\overrightarrow{OP} = \overrightarrow{OT} + \overrightarrow{TC} + \overrightarrow{CP}. \tag{5}$$

But $\|\overrightarrow{OT}\| = \overset{\frown}{PT} = a\phi$, $0 \leq \phi \leq 2\pi$, so that $\overrightarrow{OT} = a\phi\mathbf{i}$; for $\overrightarrow{TC}$ we have $\overrightarrow{TC} = a\mathbf{j}$. Further

$$\overrightarrow{CP} = \overrightarrow{CB} + \overrightarrow{BP} = -a \cos \phi\mathbf{j} - a \sin \phi\mathbf{i}$$

as in Fig. 8.28(b).* Hence, by combining Eqs. (4) and (5), we have

$$x\mathbf{i} + y\mathbf{j} = a\phi\mathbf{i} + a\mathbf{j} - a \cos \phi\mathbf{j} - a \sin \phi\mathbf{i}$$
$$= a(\phi - \sin \phi)\mathbf{i} + a(1 - \cos \phi)\mathbf{j}$$

or $\qquad x = a(\phi - \sin \phi) \qquad$ and $\qquad y = a(1 - \cos \phi), \qquad 0 \leq \phi \leq 2\pi, \quad$ (6)

as parametric equations of the curve we seek.

As one check on our work, notice that $y = 0$ when $a(1 - \cos \phi) = 0$, when $\cos \phi = 1$, or $\phi = 0, 2\pi, \cdots$. Two of the points at which the cycloid touches the *x* axis are $\phi = 0$, $(0, 0)$ and $\phi = 2\pi$, $(2\pi a, 0)$. These points are $2\pi a$ units apart on *L* as expected. Note also that when $\phi = \pi$, we get the highest point on the curve, $y = 2a = $ diameter of circle.

---

*The student should show that the expression used for $\overrightarrow{CP}$ is valid for all ϕ, $0 \leq \phi \leq 2\pi$.

To eliminate the parameter in Eqs. (6), we can solve the second of these equations for ϕ and then substitute in the first. We get

$$\cos \phi = 1 - \frac{y}{a} = \frac{a - y}{a} \qquad \text{or} \qquad \phi = \cos^{-1} \frac{a - y}{a}.$$

Now

$$\sin^2 \phi = 1 - \cos^2 \phi = 1 - \frac{(a - y)^2}{a^2} = \frac{2ay - y^2}{a^2}$$

so that

$$x = a \cos^{-1} \frac{a - y}{a} - \sqrt{2ay - y^2}. \tag{7}$$

In writing out Eq. (7) we have assumed that $0 \le \phi \le \pi/2$ in order to proceed quickly. Even without going back to check on the equation for other ϕ, it would appear that the parametric equations (6) will be easier to deal with than Eq. (7).

The student is asked to sketch the cycloid from Eqs. (6) in some detail in Exercise 8.4-5.

Example 5.   We shall find the area of the region bounded by the x axis and one cycle of the cycloid

$$x = a(\phi - \sin \phi) \\ y = a(1 - \cos \phi), \qquad \cdot 0 \le \phi \le 2\pi.$$

See Fig. 8.29.

If we subdivide the x axis interval $0 \le x \le 2\pi a$ into n parts of widths $(\Delta x)_k$, $k = 1, 2, \cdots, n$, choose a number x_k^* in each subinterval, find the corresponding ϕ_k^* and y_k^*, and draw vertical lines at the subdivision points, we can say that

$$\text{area of } k\text{th subregion} \approx y_k^* \, (\Delta x)_k,$$

$$\text{area of region} = \int_{x=0}^{2\pi a} y \, dx. \tag{8}$$

But because the cycloid is described parametrically, we change to the variable ϕ;

$$\text{area of region} = \int_{\phi=0}^{2\pi} y \frac{dx}{d\phi} \, d\phi = \int_{\phi=0}^{2\pi} a(1 - \cos \phi) a(1 - \cos \phi) \, d\phi \tag{9}$$

$$= a^2 \int_{\phi=0}^{2\pi} (1 - 2 \cos \phi + \cos^2 \phi) \, d\phi$$

$$= a^2 \int_{\phi=0}^{2\pi} \left(1 - 2 \cos \phi + \frac{1 + \cos 2\phi}{2} \right) d\phi$$

$$= a^2 [\tfrac{3}{2}\phi - 2 \sin \phi + \tfrac{1}{4} \sin 2\phi]_{\phi=0}^{2\pi} = 3\pi a^2.$$

Note that in a formal sense the change from Eq. (8) to Eq. (9) could be described by saying that the differential dx was replaced by $(dx/d\phi)d\phi$ and that the boundaries were changed from x boundaries for the dx integral to ϕ boundaries for the $d\phi$ integral. See Remark 8.3-1.

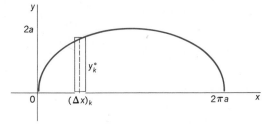

Fig. 8.29

EXERCISES 8.4

1. Sketch from the parametric equations and find an equation in the form $y = f(x)$ or $F(x, y) = 0$.
   (a) $x = 2t + 1$, $y = 1 - t$.
   (b) $x = 2u + 2$, $y = 3u - 1$, $-1 \leq u \leq 2$.
   (c) $x = 2v$, $y = v^2$.
   (d) $x = (u^2/2) - 1$, $y = 2 + 2u$.
   (e) $x = 2 + 3 \cos \theta$, $y = -1 + 3 \sin \theta$, $0 \leq \theta \leq 2\pi$.
   (f) $x = \cos \theta$, $y = 2 \sin \theta$, $0 \leq \theta \leq 2\pi$.
   (g) $x = -1 + 3 \cos \theta$, $y = \sin \theta$, $-\pi \leq \theta \leq \pi$.
   (h) $x = \tan u$, $y = \sec u$, $-\pi/2 < u < \pi/2$.
   (i) $x = 2 \cosh u$, $y = \sinh u$.
   (j) $x = t^2$, $y = t^3$, $-2 \leq t \leq 2$.
   (k) $x = t^3$, $y = 1 - t^2$.
   (l) $x = a \cos^3 \theta$, $y = a \sin^3 \theta$, $0 \leq \theta \leq 2\pi$.
   (m) $x = \sin \phi$, $y = \cos 2\phi$, $0 \leq \phi \leq 2\pi$.
   (n) $x = \sin \phi$, $y = \sin 2\phi$, $0 \leq \phi \leq 2\pi$.

2. A particle moves in a circular path of radius a, center at the origin, with an angular velocity of b revolutions per min. The particle is at $(a, 0)$ when $t = 0$. Find parametric equations to describe its motion.

3. (a) Show that the equations $x = a \cos \theta$ and $y = b \sin \theta$, $a > b > 0$, describe an ellipse with the center at the origin, x axis as the major axis, and semiaxes a and b.
   (b) Derive these parametric equations by referring to Exercise 3.11-13. In Fig. 3.89, let the line OQR make angle θ with the positive x axis.

4. Consider the motion of the projectile described by Eqs. (3) of Example 3.
   (a) Let the distance from the point at which the projectile is fired to the point at which it next crosses the x axis be called its range. Show that the range is given by

   $$R = \frac{v_0^2}{g} \sin 2\alpha.$$

   (b) For which angle of elevation will the range be a maximum? What is that maximum range? How long will it take the projectile to complete this trip of maximum range?
   (c) If the projectile is fired with elevation α (as measured from the horizontal) down a hill that makes an angle β with the horizontal, how far down the hill will it land? Which angle α produces the maximum "downhill range"?

(d) Show that the projectile will pass through the point (x_1, y_1) if the angle α is chosen so that

$$\tan \alpha = \frac{v_0^2 \pm \sqrt{v_0^4 - 2v_0^2 g y_1 - g^2 x_1^2}}{g x_1}.$$

5. Work out a table of values for the equations of the cycloid, Eqs. (6) of Example 4, and sketch for $0 \le \phi \le 2\pi$.

6. A wheel of radius a ft rolls with constant speed b ft per sec on level ground. Write down equations for the motion of a point on the circumference of the wheel. (First, how many cycles does the point complete in 1 sec if the wheel rolls forward b ft in that second?)

7. Find the area of the region included within the hypocycloid of four cusps, $x = a \cos^3 \theta$, $y = a \sin^3 \theta$, $0 \le \theta \le 2\pi$.

8. Find the area of the region included within $x = \sin \phi$, $y = \sin 2\phi$, $0 \le \phi \le \pi$.

9. *The hypocycloid.* If a circle of radius b rolls without slipping or sliding inside a fixed circle of radius a, $a > b$, the path followed by a point on the circumference of the smaller circle is called a hypocycloid. Work through the following derivation of parametric equations for the hypocycloid, filling in details where necessary.

Let the point on the smaller circle which traces out the hypocycloid be called $P(x, y)$. Place the origin of the coordinate system at the center of the larger circle, and choose as the x axis a line through a point on the larger circle touched by P in the course of its motion. Thus, in Fig. 8.30, point P touched point A when our rolling began and $\overset{\frown}{TP} = \overset{\frown}{TA}$, or

$$b\phi = a\theta. \tag{10}$$

In vector notation, $$\overrightarrow{OP} = x\mathbf{i} + y\mathbf{j} \tag{11}$$

and also $$\overrightarrow{OP} = \overrightarrow{OC} + \overrightarrow{CP}. \tag{12}$$

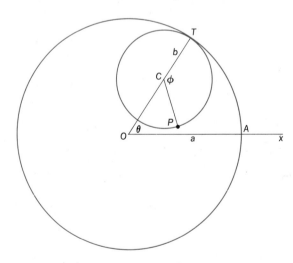

Fig. 8.30

But $\overrightarrow{OC}$ makes angle θ with $\mathbf{i}$ and has length $a - b$, so that

$$\overrightarrow{OC} = (a - b)(\cos \theta \mathbf{i} + \sin \theta \mathbf{j}).* \tag{13}$$

Similarly, $\overrightarrow{CP}$ makes angle $2\pi - (\phi - \theta)$ with $\mathbf{i}$ and has length b, so that

$$\overrightarrow{CP} = b\{\cos [2\pi - (\phi - \theta)]\mathbf{i} + \sin [2\pi - (\phi - \theta)]\mathbf{j}\}$$
$$= b(\cos [\phi - \theta]\mathbf{i} - \sin [\phi - \theta]\mathbf{j}). \tag{14}$$

From Eqs. (10), (11), (12), (13), and (14) we find that

$$\left. \begin{array}{l} x = (a - b) \cos \theta + b \cos \dfrac{a - b}{b} \theta \\[3mm] y = (a - b) \sin \theta - b \sin \dfrac{a - b}{b} \theta \end{array} \right\} \tag{15}$$

are parametric equations of the hypocycloid.

If, in particular, $b = \frac{1}{4}a$, then the circumference of the smaller circle will be one-fourth that of the larger circle and the hypocycloid will touch the larger circle four times. Parametric equations of the hypocycloid of four cusps are

$$x = a \cos^3 \theta \qquad \text{and} \qquad y = a \sin^3 \theta. \tag{16}$$

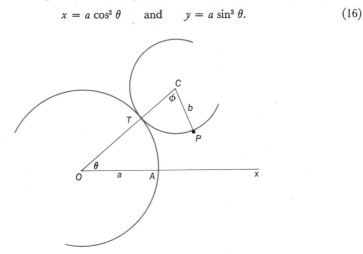

Fig. 8.31

10. (a) *The epicycloid.* If a circle of radius b rolls without slipping or sliding on the outside of a fixed circle of radius a, the path followed by a point on the circumference of the moving circle is called an epicycloid. Show that if the coordinate system indicated in Fig. 8.31 is used, parametric equations for the epicycloid are

$$\left. \begin{array}{l} x = (a + b) \cos \theta - b \cos \dfrac{a + b}{b} \theta, \\[3mm] y = (a + b) \sin \theta - b \sin \dfrac{a + b}{b} \theta. \end{array} \right\} \tag{17}$$

---

* See Theorem 3.5-6.

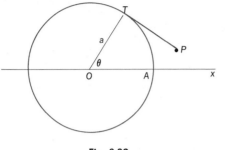

Fig. 8.32

It is understood that in Fig. 8.31 $P(x, y)$ is the point that traces out the epicycloid and that A is a point at which P touched the fixed circle.

(b) The special epicycloid for which $b = a$ is a *cardioid*. Rewrite Eqs. (17) in this case and make a sketch from the new equations.

11. *The involute of a circle.* Let a string, held taut, be unwound without slipping from the circumference of a circle. The path traced by its end point is called the involute of the circle. Work through the following derivation of parametric equations for this curve, filling in details where necessary. Then sketch that portion of this curve for which $0 \leq \theta \leq \pi$.

Let the circle have radius a and choose its center as the origin of coordinates. Choose as the x axis the line through the point on the circle at which $P(x, y)$, the end point of the string, started its motion. Then, in the notation of Fig. 8.32,

$$\widehat{AT} = \|\overrightarrow{TP}\| = a\theta. \tag{18}$$

But

$$\overrightarrow{OP} = x\mathbf{i} + y\mathbf{j} \tag{19}$$

and

$$\overrightarrow{OP} = \overrightarrow{OT} + \overrightarrow{TP}. \tag{20}$$

Since $\overrightarrow{OT}$ is of length a and makes angle θ with $\mathbf{i}$,

$$\overrightarrow{OT} = a(\cos\theta\mathbf{i} + \sin\theta\mathbf{j}). \tag{21}$$

By Eq. (18), $\overrightarrow{TP}$ is of length $a\theta$, and it makes angle $\theta + 3\pi/2$ with $\mathbf{i}$; then

$$\overrightarrow{TP} = a\theta\left(\cos\left[\theta + \frac{3\pi}{2}\right]\mathbf{i} + \sin\left[\theta + \frac{3\pi}{2}\right]\mathbf{j}\right). \tag{22}$$

Combining Eqs. (19), (20), (21), and (22), we have

$$\left.\begin{array}{l} x = a[\cos\theta + \theta\sin\theta] \\ y = a[\sin\theta - \theta\cos\theta] \end{array}\right\} \tag{23}$$

as parametric equations for the involute of the circle.

8.5 Differentials. Derivatives for Curves Defined Parametrically

When y is defined explicitly as a differentiable function of x, $y = f(x)$, we have defined dy to be $f'(x)dx$ or $(dy/dx)\,dx$. It is therefore small wonder that $dy \div dx = dy/dx$. It is important to note, however, that $dy \div dx$ still gives us dy/dx when x and y are differentiable functions of a parameter t.

■ THEOREM 1

Differentials and derivatives in general.

HYPOTHESIS: (a) $x = \phi(t)$, $dx/dt = \phi'(t)$ for t of domain D. $\phi(t)$ has range R.

(b) $y = \tau(t)$, $dy/dt = \tau'(t)$ for t of D.

(c) $\phi'(t)$, $\tau'(t)$ are continuous for t of D and $\phi'(t) \neq 0$ for t of D.

CONCLUSION: The equations $x = \phi(t)$, $y = \tau(t)$ for t of D determine a function $y = f(x)$ for x of R and $f'(x) = dy/dx = dy \div dx$.

PROOF: By hypothesis, dy/dt exists for t of D and $dy = (dy/dt)dt$ for suitably chosen nonzero dt. Similarly, $dx = (dx/dt)\,dt$. Thus

$$dy \div dx = \left(\frac{dy}{dt} dt\right) \div \left(\frac{dx}{dt} dt\right) = \frac{dy}{dt} \div \frac{dx}{dt}.$$

The Intermediate Value Theorem for continuous functions tells us that ϕ' is always positive or always negative for t of D, because ϕ' is continuous and not 0 for those t's. It follows from this that ϕ is steadily increasing or steadily decreasing for t of D and that it is possible to find the function inverse to $x = \phi(t)$ for t in D; this inverse function can be written $t = \phi^{-1}(x)$ for x in R.* But then $y = \tau(t)$ becomes

$$y = \tau(t) = \tau(\phi^{-1}(x)) = f(x), \tag{1}$$

where we have written $f(x) = \tau(\phi^{-1}(x))$ for the sake of abbreviation.

Now observe that if we substitute $x = \phi(t)$ and $y = \tau(t)$ in Eq. (1), we have an identity in t, and if we differentiate with respect to t, using the chain rule, we get

$$\frac{dy}{dt} = \frac{dy}{dx}\frac{dx}{dt} \qquad \text{and} \qquad \frac{dy}{dx} = \frac{dy}{dt} \div \frac{dx}{dt}.$$

Thus $dy \div dx$ and dy/dx have both been shown to be equal to $(dy/dt) \div (dx/dt)$. The conclusion of the theorem is demonstrated.†

Example 1. Consider the parametric description

$$x = a \cos \theta, \qquad y = a \sin \theta, \qquad 0 < \theta < \pi, \tag{2}$$

of the portion of the circle $x^2 + y^2 = a^2$ for which $y > 0$ and $-a < x < a$. We have $dx/d\theta = -a \sin \theta$, thus continuous and not zero for $0 < \theta < \pi$, and we can write

$$dx = \frac{dx}{d\theta} d\theta = -a \sin \theta\, d\theta \tag{3}$$

for suitably chosen $d\theta$. We also have $dy/d\theta = a \cos \theta$, thus continuous for $0 < \theta < \pi$, and we can write

$$dy = \frac{dy}{d\theta} d\theta = a \cos \theta\, d\theta.$$

Then Theorem 1 says that Eqs. (2) determine y as a function of x for $-a < x < a$ and that dy/dx is to be obtained by dividing dy by dx; thus

$$y' = \frac{dy}{dx} = \frac{a \cos \theta\, d\theta}{-a \sin \theta\, d\theta} = -\cot \theta, \qquad 0 < \theta < \pi. \tag{4}$$

---

* See Sec. 4.4 on inverse functions or Sec. 11.7 on the Implicit Function Theorem.

† The case where x and y are defined parametrically really includes the case where y is defined explicitly in terms of x, for we can always replace one equation $y = g(x)$ by the two parametric equations $x = t$, $y = g(t)$. Thus the phrase "derivatives in general" in the title of Theorem 1 is justified.

To find d^2y/dx^2, we observe that if we write $dy/dx = y'$, then $d^2y/dx^2 = dy'/dx$. We use Theorem 1 again; it says that dy'/dx is to be obtained by taking dy' and dividing by dx. From Eq. (4),

$$\frac{dy'}{d\theta} = \csc^2 \theta \qquad \text{and} \qquad dy' = \frac{dy'}{d\theta}\, d\theta = \csc^2 \theta\, d\theta,$$

so that, with the help of Eq. (3), we have

$$\frac{d^2y}{dx^2} = \frac{dy'}{dx} = \frac{\csc^2 \theta\, d\theta}{-a \sin \theta\, d\theta} = -\frac{1}{a} \csc^3 \theta, \qquad 0 < \theta < \pi. \tag{5}$$

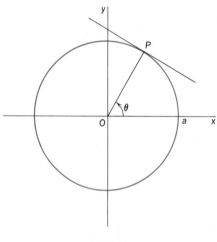

Fig. 8.33

Observe in Fig. 8.33 that the slope of the radius line OP is $\tan \theta$, $\theta \neq \pi/2$, and that the slope of the tangent line at P, as stated by Eq. (4), is $-\cot \theta = -1/\tan \theta$, $\theta \neq \pi/2$. Observe also that Eq. (5) states that $d^2y/dx^2 < 0$ for $0 < \theta < \pi$; the circle does face down for these points. If we had worked with the interval $\pi < \theta < 2\pi$, thus with the portion of the circle for which $y < 0$, we would have made the very same computations and arrived at

$$\frac{dy}{dx} = -\cot \theta, \qquad \pi < \theta < 2\pi, \tag{4a}$$

$$\frac{d^2y}{dx^2} = -\frac{1}{a} \csc^3 \theta, \qquad \pi < \theta < 2\pi. \tag{5a}$$

Equation (5a) says that $d^2y/dx^2 > 0$ for $\pi < \theta < 2\pi$, because $\csc \theta = 1/\sin \theta < 0$ for such θ. In Fig. 8.33 we see that the circle does face up at points for which $y < 0$.

Example 2.   Consider a parametric description of the cycloid:

$$x = a(\phi - \sin \phi), \quad y = a(1 - \cos \phi), \qquad 0 \leq \phi \leq 2\pi.$$

We have

$$\left.\begin{aligned} dx &= \frac{dx}{d\phi}\, d\phi = a(1 - \cos \phi)\, d\phi, \\[2mm] dy &= \frac{dy}{d\phi}\, d\phi = a \sin \phi\, d\phi, \end{aligned}\right\} \tag{6}$$

so that dy divided by dx is

$$y' = \frac{dy}{dx} = \frac{a \sin \phi\, d\phi}{a(1 - \cos \phi)\, d\phi} = \frac{\sin \phi}{1 - \cos \phi}, \qquad 0 < \phi < 2\pi. \tag{7}$$

To get $d^2y/dx^2 = dy'/dx$, we take dy' and divide by dx. From Eq. (7) we learn that

$$dy' = \frac{dy'}{d\phi}\, d\phi = \frac{(1 - \cos \phi) \cos \phi - \sin \phi\, (\sin \phi)}{(1 - \cos \phi)^2}\, d\phi$$

$$= \frac{\cos \phi - 1}{(1 - \cos \phi)^2} \, d\phi$$

$$= -\frac{1}{1 - \cos \phi} \, d\phi.$$

Hence

$$\frac{d^2y}{dx^2} = \frac{dy'}{dx} = \frac{[-1/(1 - \cos \phi)] \, d\phi}{a(1 - \cos \phi) \, d\phi} = -\frac{1}{a} \frac{1}{(1 - \cos \phi)^2}, \quad 0 < \phi < 2\pi. \qquad (8)$$

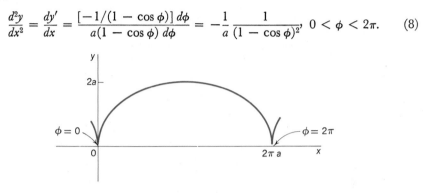

Fig. 8.34

Equation (8) says that for $0 < \phi < 2\pi$ we shall have $d^2y/dx^2 < 0$. Indeed, the cycloid graph does face down for all such points; see Fig. 8.34. Equation (7) does not say what the slope of the tangent line is when $\phi = 0$ or $\phi = 2\pi$, but we can say that

$$\lim_{\phi \to 0} \left| \frac{\sin \phi}{1 - \cos \phi} \right| = \lim_{\phi \to 0} \left| \frac{\sin \phi \, (1 + \cos \phi)}{(1 - \cos \phi)(1 + \cos \phi)} \right|$$

$$= \lim_{\phi \to 0} \left| \frac{1 + \cos \phi}{\sin \phi} \right| = \infty.$$

The tangents at these points seem to be vertical.*

EXERCISES 8.5

1. Find dy/dx and d^2y/dx^2 from the parametric equations given for the curves of Exercise 8.4-1.

2. Find dy/dx and d^2y/dx^2 from the parametric equations for the projectile:

$$x = v_0(\cos \alpha)t \quad \text{and} \quad y = v_0(\sin \alpha)t - \tfrac{1}{2} gt^2.$$

Check by eliminating the parameter and then finding dy/dx and d^2y/dx^2.

3. Find dy/dx and d^2y/dx^2 from:
   (a) $x = a(\cos \theta + \theta \sin \theta)$, $y = a(\sin \theta - \theta \cos \theta)$, the involute of the circle.

---

* To compute dy/dx directly when $\phi = 0$, we would consider $\Delta y/\Delta x$ and then

$$\frac{dy}{dx} = \lim_{\phi \to 0} \frac{y(\phi) - y(0)}{x(\phi) - x(0)} = \lim_{\phi \to 0} \frac{a(1 - \cos \phi)}{a(\phi - \sin \phi)}.$$

See Exercise 13.10-9.

(b) $x = \dfrac{2a}{1 + t^2}, y = \dfrac{2a}{t(1 + t^2)}, t \neq 0$, the cissoid.

(c) $x = \dfrac{3t}{1 + t^3}, y = \dfrac{3t^2}{1 + t^3}, t \neq -1$, the folium.

4. Show that the curve $x = \sin \phi, y = \sin 2\phi$ passes through the origin twice, in two different directions, and find the angle between these directions. [See Exercise 1(n) above.]

5. Sketch the tractrix $x = t - a \tanh (t/a), y = a \operatorname{sech} (t/a)$. Show that the line tangent at the point P with parameter value t has x intercept point $I(t, 0)$. Show that $IP = a$.

8.6   Length of Arc

I

If we are given that portion of the curve $y = f(x)$ which lies between A and B, what do we mean by the length of the arc AB? (See Fig. 8.35.) We can agree on a standard yardstick (or meterstick) as a unit of measure, but how is an arc like AB to be compared with a straight unit of measure?

We shall allow our intuition to guide us to a definition of length of arc. One helpful suggestion is this: (a) place a string along the curve from A to B; (b) straighten the string out without stretching, or "rectify" the string; and (c) compare the string with a ruler. But, in greater detail, how is Step (a) of this suggestion to be accomplished? Subdivide the arc AB into n parts by using points $P_0 = A, P_1, P_2, \cdots, P_n = B$; place pins at these points, and let the string run in straight-line paths from pin to pin. In Fig. 8.36 we illustrate with $n = 3$. Intuition tells us that the straight line is the shortest distance between two points and that therefore the string thus placed is shorter than the arc. But if we take n larger, bringing the subdivision points closer together, the difference between the length of the arc and the length of the string should approach 0. With these intuitive considerations as a guide we form a definition of arc length.

■ DEFINITION 1

The length of an arc. Given an arc. Inscribe in it a set of n chords. Let n grow beyond all bounds, the length of the longest chord approaching 0. If the limit

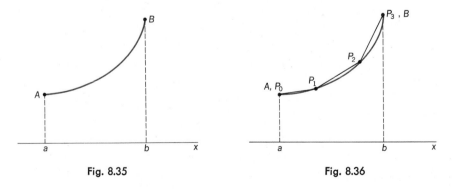

Fig. 8.35   Fig. 8.36

approached by the sum of the lengths of the chords exists, independent of the manner of the inscription of the chords, we shall call that limit the length of the arc.

We shall rewrite Definition 1 in symbols. Let the arc be described by $y = f(x)$, $a \le x \le b$. Let us subdivide the interval by choosing $x_0 = a < x_1 < x_2 < \cdots < x_n = b$, thus determining the points $A = P_0(x_0, y_0)$, $P_1(x_1, y_1), \cdots, P_n(x_n, y_n) = B$ on the arc. Then, as we see in Fig. 8.37, we have

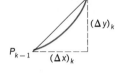

$$\text{length of } k\text{th chord} = \sqrt{(\Delta x)_k{}^2 + (\Delta y)_k{}^2}$$
$$= \sqrt{1 + [(\Delta y)_k/(\Delta x)_k]^2}\,(\Delta x)_k. \qquad (1)$$

But if $f(x)$ is differentiable for $a \le x \le b$, the Theorem of Mean Value applies, and we can say that there exists a w_k, $x_{k-1} < w_k < x_k$, such that

Fig. 8.37

$$f(x_k) - f(x_{k-1}) = f'(w_k)(x_k - x_{k-1})$$

or
$$(\Delta y)_k = f'(w_k)(\Delta x)_k.$$

Hence, returning to Eq. (1), we have

$$\text{length of } k\text{th chord} = \sqrt{1 + [f'(w_k)]^2}\,(\Delta x)_k$$

and
$$\text{sum of lengths of chords} = \sum_{k=1}^{n} \sqrt{1 + [f'(w_k)]^2}\,(\Delta x)_k. \qquad (2)$$

For the sake of abbreviation, write $g(x) = \sqrt{1 + [f'(x)]^2}$. If we require not only that $f'(x)$ shall exist but also that $f'(x)$ shall be continuous, then $g(x)$ will be continuous. But for continuous $g(x)$, if we take n ever larger, the largest $(\Delta x)_k$ approaching 0, we know that $\lim_{n\to\infty} \sum_{k=1}^{n} g(w_k)(\Delta x)_k$ exists and we write $\int_{x=a}^{b} g(x)\,dx$ for it. Thus, according to Definition 1, Eq. (2) leads us to the statement

$$\text{length of arc } AB = \int_{x=a}^{b} \sqrt{1 + [f'(x)]^2}\,dx.$$

We have demonstrated the following theorem.

■ THEOREM 1

On the length of an arc.

HYPOTHESIS: $f'(x)$ is continuous for $a \le x \le b$.

CONCLUSION: The length of the arc of $y = f(x)$, $a \le x \le b$, is given by

$$\int_{x=a}^{b} \sqrt{1 + [f'(x)]^2}\,dx \qquad \text{or by} \qquad \int_{x=a}^{b} \sqrt{1 + \left(\frac{dy}{dx}\right)^2}\,dx.$$

We have chosen a definition of arc length that seems to agree with intuition, but let us check the definition against our experience with the simplest curves we know, namely, the straight lines and circles.

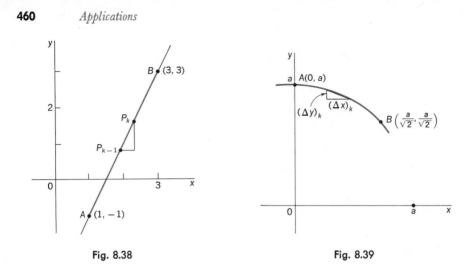

Fig. 8.38   Fig. 8.39

Example 1.   Find the length of that portion of $y = f(x) = 2x - 3$ which lies between $A(1, -1)$ and $B(3, 3)$. See Fig. 8.38. If we use subdivision points $P_0 \equiv A, P_1, P_2, \cdots, P_n \equiv B$, we can say that

$$\text{length of } k\text{th chord} = \sqrt{(\Delta x)_k^2 + (\Delta y)_k^2} = \sqrt{1 + [(\Delta y)_k/(\Delta x)_k]^2}\ (\Delta x)_k$$

$$= \sqrt{1 + [f'(w_k)]^2}\ (\Delta x)_k, \qquad x_{k-1} < w_k < x_k,$$

$$\text{sum of lengths of chords} = \sum_{k=1}^{n} \sqrt{1 + [f'(w_k)]^2}\ (\Delta x)_k,$$

$$\text{length of arc} = \int_{x=1}^{3} \sqrt{1 + [f'(x)]^2}\ dx.$$

To evaluate this integral, we note that $f'(x) = 2$, so that $1 + [f'(x)]^2 = 5$. Thus

$$\text{length of arc} = \int_{x=1}^{3} \sqrt{5}\, dx = \sqrt{5}\, x \Big|_{x=1}^{3} = 2\sqrt{5}.$$

This result agrees with the distance formula computation.

Example 2.   Find the circumference of the circle $x^2 + y^2 = a^2$. We shall follow Definition 1 in computing the length of that eighth of the circle described by $y = f(x) = \sqrt{a^2 - x^2}$, $0 \leq x \leq a/\sqrt{2}$; see Fig. 8.39. We have

$$\text{length of } k\text{th chord} = \sqrt{(\Delta x)_k^2 + (\Delta y)_k^2} = \sqrt{1 + [(\Delta y)_k/(\Delta x)_k]^2}\ (\Delta x)_k$$

$$= \sqrt{1 + [f'(w_k)]^2}\ (\Delta x)_k, \qquad x_{k-1} < w_k < x_k,$$

$$\text{sum of lengths of chords} = \sum_{k=1}^{n} \sqrt{1 + [f'(w_k)]^2}\ (\Delta x)_k,$$

$$\text{length of arc} = \int_{x=0}^{a/\sqrt{2}} \sqrt{1 + (dy/dx)^2}\ dx.$$

But, for this arc,

$$\frac{dy}{dx} = \frac{1}{2}(a^2 - x^2)^{-1/2}(-2x) = \frac{-x}{\sqrt{a^2 - x^2}}$$

so that

$$1 + \left(\frac{dy}{dx}\right)^2 = 1 + \frac{x^2}{a^2 - x^2} = \frac{a^2}{a^2 - x^2}.$$

Thus   length of arc $= \displaystyle\int_{x=0}^{a/\sqrt{2}} \frac{a}{\sqrt{a^2 - x^2}}\, dx$

$$= a \sin^{-1}\frac{x}{a}\Big|_{x=0}^{a/\sqrt{2}} = a\left[\sin^{-1}\frac{1}{\sqrt{2}} - \sin^{-1} 0\right] = \frac{\pi}{4}a.$$

The circumference of the complete circle would then be $2\pi a$.

Note that we have not "proved" that the circumference of the circle is $2\pi a$. We assumed that fact when we said that $\sin^{-1}(1/\sqrt{2}) = (\pi/4)$. This example merely indicates that Definition 1 is consistent with our earlier work on circles.*

Example 3. Find the length of the parabola $y = f(x) = x^2$ from $(0, 0)$ to $(1, 1)$. See Fig. 8.40. Subdividing as usual, we can say that

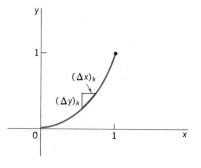

Fig. 8.40

length of kth chord $= \sqrt{(\Delta x)_k^2 + (\Delta y)_k^2} = \sqrt{1 + [(\Delta y)_k/(\Delta x)_k]^2}\,(\Delta x)_k$

$$= \sqrt{1 + [f'(w_k)]^2}\,(\Delta x)_k, \qquad x_{k-1} < w_k < x_k,$$

length of arc $= \displaystyle\int_{x=0}^{1} \sqrt{1 + [f'(x)]^2}\, dx.$

Since $f'(x) = 2x$, we have

$$\text{length of arc} = \int_{x=0}^{1} \sqrt{1 + 4x^2}\, dx.$$

The trigonometric substitution $x = \frac{1}{2}\tan\theta$ leads us to the new form,

$$\text{length of arc} = \int_{\theta=0}^{\tan^{-1} 2} \sec\theta\,\tfrac{1}{2}\sec^2\theta\, d\theta = \tfrac{1}{2}\int_{\theta=0}^{\tan^{-1} 2} \sec^3\theta\, d\theta.$$

This trigonometric integral can be evaluated by using integration by parts,† and we have

---

* We did not work with the first-quadrant quarter of the circle, because dy/dx is not finite at $(a, 0)$; the integral $\int_0^a [a/\sqrt{a^2 - x^2}]\, dx$ has not yet been defined.

† See Example 6.6-5.

$$\text{length of arc} = \left. \tfrac{1}{4}[\sec \theta \tan \theta + \log (\sec \theta + \tan \theta)] \right|_{\theta=0}^{\tan^{-1} 2}$$

$$= \tfrac{1}{4}[(\sqrt{5})(2) + \log (\sqrt{5} + 2) - 0 - 0]$$

$$= \tfrac{1}{2}\sqrt{5} + \tfrac{1}{4} \log (\sqrt{5} + 2)$$

$$\approx 1.48.$$

We used the fact that

$$\sec (\tan^{-1} 2) = \sqrt{1 + [\tan (\tan^{-1} 2)]^2} = \sqrt{1 + 4} = \sqrt{5}.$$

It might be easier in a particular problem to describe a curve by an equation of the form $x = f(y)$, $a \leq y \leq b$, perhaps because dy/dx is infinite at a point of the arc while $dx/dy = 0$ there. This would have been the case, for instance, if we had asked for the length of $y^2 = x$ from $(0, 0)$ to $(1, 1)$ in Example 3 instead of the length of $y = x^2$ between these points.

■ THEOREM 2

On the length of an arc.

HYPOTHESIS: $f'(y)$ is continuous for $a \leq y \leq b$.

CONCLUSION: The length of the arc of $x = f(y)$, $a \leq y \leq b$, is given by

$$\int_{y=a}^{b} \sqrt{1 + [f'(y)]^2} \, dy \qquad \text{or by} \qquad \int_{y=a}^{b} \sqrt{1 + (dx/dy)^2} \, dy.$$

The proof is very much like that of Theorem 1 and is left to the reader.

In Sec. 8.4 we discussed the parametric description of curves. What analytic form does Definition 1 take if a curve is described parametrically?

■ THEOREM 3

On the length of an arc.

HYPOTHESIS: $f'(t)$ and $g'(t)$ are continuous for $a \leq t \leq b$.

CONCLUSION: The length of the arc described by $x = f(t)$, $y = g(t)$, $a \leq t \leq b$, is given by

$$\int_{t=a}^{b} \sqrt{[f'(t)]^2 + [g'(t)]^2} \, dt \qquad \text{or by} \qquad \int_{t=a}^{b} \sqrt{(dx/dt)^2 + (dy/dt)^2} \, dt.$$

PROOF: The arc whose length we want starts at A, corresponding to the parameter value $t = a$, and ends at B, corresponding to the parameter value $t = b$. Let us choose as subdivision points the points corresponding to parameter values $t_0 = a < t_1 < t_2 \cdots < t_n = b$. Then, as we saw in Fig. 8.37, we can say that

$$\text{length of } k\text{th inscribed chord} = \sqrt{(\Delta x)_k^2 + (\Delta y)_k^2}$$

$$= \sqrt{[(\Delta x)_k/(\Delta t)_k]^2 + [(\Delta y)_k/(\Delta t)_k]^2} \, (\Delta t)_k. \qquad (3)$$

But because $f(t)$ is differentiable, the Theorem of Mean Value allows us to say that there exists a w_k, $t_{k-1} < w_k < t_k$, such that

$$(\Delta x)_k = f(t_k) - f(t_{k-1}) = f'(w_k)(t_k - t_{k-1}) = f'(w_k)(\Delta t)_k.$$

Similarly, because the hypothesis also says that $g(t)$ is differentiable, we can say that there exists a v_k, $t_{k-1} < v_k < t_k$, such that

$$(\Delta y)_k = g(t_k) - g(t_{k-1}) = g'(v_k)(t_k - t_{k-1}) = g'(v_k)(\Delta t)_k.$$

Therefore we can rewrite Eq. (3) as

$$\text{length of }k\text{th inscribed chord} = \sqrt{[f'(w_k)]^2 + [g'(v_k)]^2}\,(\Delta t)_k,$$

and say that

$$\text{sum of lengths of chords} = \sum_{k=1}^{n} \sqrt{[f'(w_k)]^2 + [g'(v_k)]^2}\,(\Delta t)_k. \tag{4}$$

If for each chord we could take $v_k = w_k$, then we could abbreviate by writing

$$\psi(t) = \sqrt{[f'(t)]^2 + [g'(t)]^2},$$

$$\text{length of }k\text{th chord} = \psi(w_k)(\Delta t)_k, \qquad t_{k-1} < w_k < t_k,$$

$$\text{length of arc} = \int_{t=a}^{b} \psi(t)\,dt = \int_{t=a}^{b} \sqrt{[f'(t)]^2 + [g'(t)]^2}\,dt. \tag{5}$$

Actually, however, we cannot assume that $v_k = w_k$. But since $g'(t)$ is continuous by hypothesis, we can at least be sure that $g'(v_k)$ and $g'(w_k)$ do not differ by much, and it may well be that as n grows beyond all bounds, the largest $(\Delta t)_k$ approaching zero,

$$\sum_{k=1}^{n} \sqrt{[f'(w_k)]^2 + [g'(v_k)]^2}\,(\Delta t)_k \qquad \text{and} \qquad \sum_{k=1}^{n} \sqrt{[f'(w_k)]^2 + [g'(w_k)]^2}\,(\Delta t)_k$$

approach the same limit. In Sec. 8.8 we shall discuss limits of sums that are not quite of the form necessary to define a definite integral directly. Here we shall assume that the sum given in Eq. (4) approaches the definite integral indicated by Eq. (5).

● **Remark 1**

If there is a vertical tangent at a point, dy/dx is infinite, and the integrand of the integral of Theorem 1 is not finite there. Similarly, if there is a horizontal tangent, there is difficulty with the integral of Theorem 2. But if $dx/dt = 0$ or $dy/dt = 0$, as might well happen at such points for a curve described parametrically, the integrand of the integral of Theorem 3 remains finite.

Example 4. Find the length of one arch of the cycloid. See Fig. 8.41. Parametric equations for the cycloid are $x = f(\phi) = a(\phi - \sin \phi)$, $y = g(\phi) = a(1 - \cos \phi)$, one arch of the cycloid corresponding to the ϕ interval $0 \le \phi \le 2\pi$. Let us break this interval into n parts. Then, as in Theorem 3,

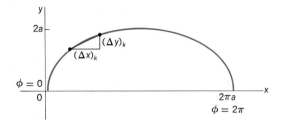

Fig. 8.41

$$\text{length of } k\text{th chord} = \sqrt{(\Delta x)_k{}^2 + (\Delta y)_k{}^2}$$

$$= \sqrt{[(\Delta x)_k/(\Delta \phi)_k]^2 + [(\Delta y)_k/(\Delta \phi)_k]^2}\,(\Delta \phi)_k$$

$$= \sqrt{[f'(w_k)]^2 + [g'(v_k)]^2}\,(\Delta \phi)_k,$$

and we assume that

$$\text{length of arc} = \int_{\phi=0}^{2\pi} \sqrt{[f'(\phi)]^2 + [g'(\phi)]^2}\, d\phi$$

$$= \int_{\phi=0}^{2\pi} \sqrt{(dx/d\phi)^2 + (dy/d\phi)^2}\, d\phi. \tag{6}$$

But $\dfrac{dx}{d\phi} = a(1 - \cos \phi)$ and $\dfrac{dy}{d\phi} = a \sin \phi$

so that $\left(\dfrac{dx}{d\phi}\right)^2 + \left(\dfrac{dy}{d\phi}\right)^2 = a^2[1 - 2 \cos \phi + \cos^2 \phi + \sin^2 \phi]$

$$= 2a^2(1 - \cos \phi) = 4a^2 \sin^2 \frac{\phi}{2}.$$

Hence Eq. (6) becomes

$$\text{length of arc} = 2a \int_{\phi=0}^{2\pi} \sin \frac{\phi}{2}\, d\phi = 4a \int_{\phi=0}^{2\pi} \sin \frac{\phi}{2} \frac{1}{2}\, d\phi$$

$$= -4a \cos \frac{\phi}{2} \Big|_{\phi=0}^{2\pi} = -4a[(-1) - (1)] = 8a.$$

Observe that $\sqrt{(dx/d\phi)^2 + (dy/d\phi)^2}$ must be nonnegative. We took

$$\sqrt{4a^2 \sin^2 (\phi/2)} = 2a \sin (\phi/2),$$

because $\sin (\phi/2) \geq 0$ for $0 \leq \phi \leq 2\pi$. If we had been concerned with the interval $2\pi \leq \phi \leq 4\pi$, we would have had to write

$$\sqrt{4a^2 \sin^2 (\phi/2)} = -2a \sin (\phi/2).$$

Example 5.   Find the length of the arc described by $x = f(t) = t^3$, $y = g(t) = t^2$, $-1 \leq t \leq 2$. See Fig.

Fig. 8.42

8.42. As we did before, we reason that

$$\text{length of typical chord} = \sqrt{(\Delta x)_k{}^2 + (\Delta y)_k{}^2}$$
$$= \sqrt{[(\Delta x)_k/(\Delta t)_k]^2 + [(\Delta y)_k/(\Delta t)_k]^2}\ (\Delta t)_k$$
$$= \sqrt{[f'(w_k)]^2 + [g'(v_k)]^2}\ (\Delta t)_k,$$

and we assume that

$$\text{length of arc} = \int_{t=-1}^{2} \sqrt{(dx/dt)^2 + (dy/dt)^2}\ dt. \tag{7}$$

In detail, $dx/dt = 3t^2$, $dy/dt = 2t$, and

$$\sqrt{(dx/dt)^2 + (dy/dt)^2} = \sqrt{9t^4 + 4t^2} = \begin{cases} t\sqrt{9t^2 + 4}, & t \geq 0, \\ -t\sqrt{9t^2 + 4}, & t \leq 0. \end{cases}$$

We must consider the negative t's and positive t's separately. Hence from Eq. (7) we get

$$\text{length of arc} = \int_{t=-1}^{0} \sqrt{(dx/dt)^2 + (dy/dt)^2}\ dt + \int_{t=0}^{2} \sqrt{(dx/dt)^2 + (dy/dt)^2}\ dt$$

$$= -\int_{t=-1}^{0} t\sqrt{9t^2 + 4}\ dt + \int_{t=0}^{2} t\sqrt{9t^2 + 4}\ dt$$

$$= -\frac{1}{18} \int_{-1}^{0} (9t^2 + 4)^{1/2}\ 18t\ dt + \frac{1}{18} \int_{0}^{2} (9t^2 + 4)^{1/2}\ 18t\ dt$$

$$= -\frac{1}{18}\frac{2}{3} (9t^2 + 4)^{3/2} \Big|_{-1}^{0} + \frac{1}{18}\frac{2}{3} (9t^2 + 4)^{3/2} \Big|_{0}^{2}$$

$$= -\tfrac{1}{27} [(4)^{3/2} - (13)^{3/2}] + \tfrac{1}{27}[(40)^{3/2} - (4)^{3/2}]$$

$$= \tfrac{1}{27} [40^{3/2} + 13^{3/2} - 16]$$

$$\approx 10.51.$$

∥

A natural parameter to use for any curve is its arc length. Choose a point on the curve as a point from which to measure lengths and call it A. Designate one direction on the curve as the positive direction. If point P is reached by traveling g units from A along the curve in the positive direction, we associate the arc-length parameter number $s = g$ with P. If we travel g units from A along the curve in the negative direction, we associate the arc-length parameter number $s = -g$ with P.

■ **THEOREM 4**

The arc length differential.

HYPOTHESIS: Curve C is described by

Case (a) $y = \phi(x)$, $\phi'(x)$ continuous,

Case (b) $x = \psi(y)$, $\psi'(y)$ continuous,

Case (c) $x = f(t)$, $y = g(t)$, $f'(t)$ and $g'(t)$ continuous.

CONCLUSION: $ds^2 = dx^2 + dy^2$.

PROOF: Case (c). Let the point from which arc length is measured be the point for which $t = a$ and let the direction of increasing s be the direction of increasing t. For each t a point on the curve is determined and then the s for this point follows from

$$s = \int_{t=a}^{t} \sqrt{(dx/dt)^2 + (dy/dt)^2} \, dt.$$

Observe that this integral definition for s makes s an increasing function of t, as it should. For, the integrand is positive, and if we increase t, the upper boundary, we increase the number of positive terms in the sums which are used in forming the integral for s, thus making s larger. If $F(t)$ has the property

$$\frac{dF}{dt} = \sqrt{\left(\frac{dx}{dt}\right)^2 + \left(\frac{dy}{dt}\right)^2},$$

then

$$s = F(t) - F(a).$$

But now

$$\frac{ds}{dt} = \frac{dF}{dt} - 0 = \sqrt{\left(\frac{dx}{dt}\right)^2 + \left(\frac{dy}{dt}\right)^2},$$

$$ds = \frac{ds}{dt} \, dt = \sqrt{\left(\frac{dx}{dt}\right)^2 + \left(\frac{dy}{dt}\right)^2} \, dt, \tag{8}$$

so that

$$ds^2 = \left(\frac{dx}{dt}\right)^2 dt^2 + \left(\frac{dy}{dt}\right)^2 dt^2 = dx^2 + dy^2.$$

The reader is asked to supply the proof for Case (a) in Exercise 2 below.

● **Remark 2**

Let a particle's motion be described by the parametric equations $x = f(t)$, $y = g(t)$. The vector

$$\mathbf{R} = \overrightarrow{OP} = x\mathbf{i} + y\mathbf{j}$$

is called the position vector because its terminal point describes the position of the particle. Consider next the vector

$$\frac{d\mathbf{R}}{dt} = \frac{dx}{dt}\mathbf{i} + \frac{dy}{dt}\mathbf{j}.$$

According to Eq. (8), the magnitude of this vector is

$$\sqrt{\left(\frac{dx}{dt}\right)^2 + \left(\frac{dy}{dt}\right)^2} = \frac{ds}{dt},$$

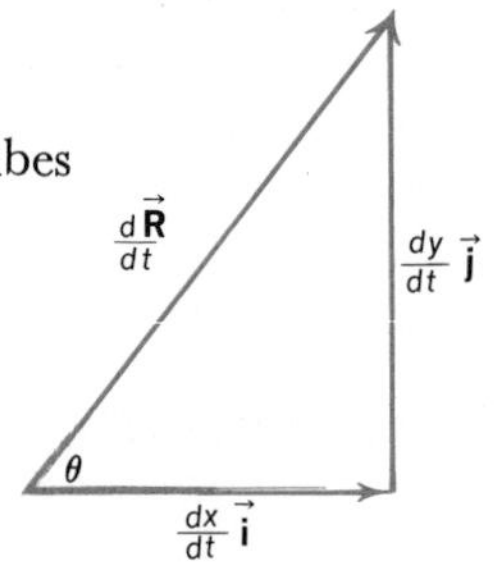

Fig. 8.43

or, physically, the speed of the particle in its path. From Fig. 8.43 we see that the tangent of the angle θ that $d\vec{R}/dt$ makes with the $\vec{i}$ direction is

$$\frac{dy}{dt} \div \frac{dx}{dt} = \frac{dy}{dx}.$$

Therefore $d\vec{R}/dt$ has the same direction as the tangent line to the path. Because the magnitude of $d\vec{R}/dt$ is the speed of the particle and the direction of $d\vec{R}/dt$ is that of the path, it is natural to call $d\vec{R}/dt$ the velocity vector:

$$\vec{v} = \frac{d\vec{R}}{dt} = \frac{dx}{dt}\vec{i} + \frac{dy}{dt}\vec{j}.$$

EXERCISES 8.6

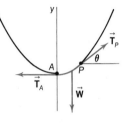

Fig. 8.44

1. Find the lengths of the arcs described.
   (a) $y = (x^2/2) - \frac{1}{4}\log x,\ 1 \le x \le 2$.
   (b) $y^2 = x^3,\ (0, 0)$ to $(1, 1)$.
   (c) $y = \log \cos x,\ 0 \le x \le \pi/3$.
   (d) $y = \cosh x,\ 0 \le x \le a$ (the catenary).
   (e) $y = e^x,\ 0 \le x \le 2$.
   (f) $y^2 = x,\ (0, 0)$ to $(1, 1)$.
   (g) $4y^4 - 12xy + 3 = 0$ from $(\frac{13}{24}, \frac{1}{2})$ to $(\frac{7}{12}, 1)$.
   (h) $x = a \cos \theta,\ y = a \sin \theta,\ 0 \le \theta \le 2\pi$ (the circle).
   (i) $x = a \cos^3 \theta,\ y = a \sin^3 \theta,\ 0 \le \theta \le 2\pi$ (the hypocycloid of four cusps).
   (j) $x = a(\cos \theta + \theta \sin \theta),\ y = a(\sin \theta - \theta \cos \theta),\ 0 \le \theta \le 2\pi$ (the involute of the circle).
   (k) $x = a(\cos \theta + \theta \sin \theta),\ y = a(\sin \theta - \theta \cos \theta),\ -\pi/4 \le \theta \le \pi/2$.
   (l) $x = \frac{1}{4} t^4,\ y = \frac{1}{5} t^5,\ -2 \le t \le 1$.
   (m) $x = t - a \tanh (t/a),\ y = a \operatorname{sech} (t/a),\ -a \le t \le 2a$.

2. (a) Explain how the proof for Case (a) of Theorem 4 can be made to depend on the proof for Case (c).
   (b) Write out a direct proof for Case (a) of Theorem 4.

3. A particle moves on a parabolic path with focus at the origin according to the equations $x = t^2 - 1,\ y = 2t$, where t is the time. Find its velocity vector at any time and in particular at the instant it passes through the vertex of its path.

4. The motion of a particle on the circumference of a wheel of radius a rolling on level ground is described by the formulas $x = bt - a \sin (b/a)t,\ y = a[1 - \cos (b/a)t]$, where t is the time. Find the velocity vector at any time and in particular at the instant the particle is highest. Find the relationship between the particle's speed and height.

5. Show that the particle whose motion is given by the equations $x = \sinh^{-1} t = \log (t + \sqrt{t^2 + 1}),\ y = \sqrt{t^2 + 1}$ moves on the catenary $y = \cosh x$ with constant speed.

6. Find parametric equations to describe the motion of a particle that moves along $y = \frac{2}{3} x^{3/2}$ with constant speed 1, starting at $(0, 0)$ when $t = 0$.

7. A uniform cable that hangs freely under its own weight takes the shape of a catenary:

$$y = a \cosh \frac{x}{a} + C \quad \text{or} \quad y = \frac{a}{2}(e^{x/a} + e^{-x/a}) + C.$$

Fill in the details for the following demonstration of this fact.

Step (a). In Fig. 8.44, let A be the lowest point of the cable, and draw the y axis through A. The cable will hang symmetrically with respect to the y axis, and the tangent at A is horizontal.

Step (b). Let $P(x, y)$ be any point on the cable, and let the tension at P be called $\vec{\mathbf{T}}_p$, of magnitude T_p.

Step (c). The portion of the cable AP is in equilibrium, and we shall analyze the forces acting on it. We have

$$\vec{\mathbf{T}}_A = -T_A \vec{\mathbf{i}},$$

$$\vec{\mathbf{T}}_p = T_p(\cos \theta \vec{\mathbf{i}} + \sin \theta \vec{\mathbf{j}}),$$

and
$$\vec{\mathbf{W}} = -ks\vec{\mathbf{j}} = \text{weight of cable } AP.$$

In our last statement we have assumed constant weight density k for the cable. Note that T_A can be regarded as fixed if we vary P.

Step (d). Since the forces listed in Step (c) are in equilibrium, we have

$$T_p \cos \theta = T_A \qquad \text{and} \qquad T_p \sin \theta = ks,$$

and then, dividing,

$$\tan \theta = \frac{k}{T_A} s \quad \text{or} \quad \frac{dy}{dx} = \frac{k}{T_A} s = \frac{1}{a} s,$$

where we have written a for T_A/k.

Step (e). Since a statement for s requires an integral, we prefer to differentiate:

$$a \frac{d^2y}{dx^2} = \frac{ds}{dx} = \sqrt{1 + \left(\frac{dy}{dx}\right)^2}.$$

Step (f). Now write

$$p = \frac{dy}{dx}; \quad \text{and} \quad a \frac{dp}{dx} = \sqrt{1 + p^2} \quad \text{or} \quad \frac{1}{\sqrt{1 + p^2}} \frac{dp}{dx} = \frac{1}{a},$$

$$\log (p + \sqrt{1 + p^2}) = \frac{1}{a} x + C_1.$$

Step (g). $C_1 = 0$ because $p = dy/dx = 0$ at A. Hence

$$\log (p + \sqrt{1 + p^2}) = \frac{1}{a} x,$$

$$p = \frac{dy}{dx} = \sinh \frac{x}{a}.$$

Step (h).
$$y = a \cosh \frac{x}{a} + C_2.$$

Step (i). If the x axis is drawn a units below A, C_2 will be 0.

8.7 Curvature

l

When considering differentials as tangent-line increments, we observe that sometimes, as in Fig. 8.45(a), a tangent line approximates a curve well for a relatively long distance, sometimes, as in Fig. 8.45(b), for only a relatively short

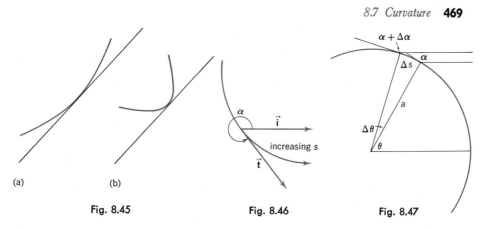

(a)   (b)

Fig. 8.45   **Fig. 8.46**   **Fig. 8.47**

distance. To describe the rate at which a curve turns away from its tangent line, we define the curvature.

■ DEFINITION 1

The curvature. Let α be the inclination angle of the tangent line, and let s be the arc-length parameter. Then $|d\alpha/ds|$ shall be called the curvature.*

Example 1. For a straight line, the inclination angle of the tangent line is constant. The curvature is therefore 0.

Example 2. For a circle of radius a, Fig. 8.47, we have $\alpha = \theta + \pi/2$ and $\alpha + \Delta\alpha = \theta + \Delta\theta + \pi/2$, so that $\Delta\alpha = \Delta\theta$. But $\Delta s = a\Delta\theta$, so that $\Delta\alpha/\Delta s = 1/a$. It then follows that the curvature is $K = 1/a$. Note that K does not depend on θ; in other words, the curvature does not vary with movement along the circle. Our result also says that K varies inversely as the radius; the larger the circle, the smaller the curvature.

■ THEOREM 1

A formula for the curvature.

HYPOTHESIS: $y = f(x)$, $dy/dx = f'(x)$, $d^2y/dx^2 = f''(x)$ are defined for domain D.

CONCLUSION: For x of D the curvature at the point (x, y) of the curve with equation $y = f(x)$ is

$$K = \frac{|d^2y/dx^2|}{[1 + (dy/dx)^2]^{3/2}}. \tag{1}$$

PROOF: We start with the fact that $\tan \alpha = dy/dx$, so that

$$\sec^2 \alpha \, \frac{d\alpha}{dx} = \frac{d^2y}{dx^2}$$

---

* Strictly speaking, the definition of the inclination angle requires $0 \le \alpha < \pi$. To avoid discontinuities in α, we shall take a slightly different definition here. Let the direction of increasing s on the curve determine the sense of the unit vector $\vec{t}$ chosen as tangent vector. The angle α shall be the angle through which one must rotate to go from $\vec{i}$ to $\vec{t}$. Tan α is the same for both definitions. See Fig. 8.46.

and

$$\frac{d\alpha}{dx} = \frac{1}{\sec^2 \alpha} \frac{d^2y}{dx^2} = \frac{1}{1 + \tan^2 \alpha} \frac{d^2y}{dx^2} = \frac{1}{1 + (dy/dx)^2} \frac{d^2y}{dx^2}.$$

Then, since

$$\left| \frac{ds}{dx} \right| = \sqrt{1 + \left(\frac{dy}{dx} \right)^2},$$

we can write

$$K = \left| \frac{d\alpha}{ds} \right| = \left| \frac{(d\alpha/dx) \, dx}{(ds/dx) \, dx} \right| = \frac{|d^2y/dx^2|}{1 + (dy/dx)^2} \div \sqrt{1 + (dy/dx)^2} = \frac{|d^2y/dx^2|}{[1 + (dy/dx)^2]^{3/2}}.$$

Example 3.   For the parabola $x^2 = 2py$, we have

$$\frac{dy}{dx} = \frac{1}{2p} \, 2x = \frac{x}{p} \quad \text{and} \quad \frac{d^2y}{dx^2} = \frac{1}{p}.$$

Thus

$$K = \frac{1/p}{[1 + x^2/p^2]^{3/2}} = \frac{1/p}{(1/p^3)[p^2 + x^2]^{3/2}} = \frac{p^2}{[p^2 + x^2]^{3/2}}.$$

In particular, at the vertex $(0, 0)$, we have maximum curvature, $K = 1/p$, for there $p^2 + x^2$ is a minimum.

Example 4.   For the cycloid, $x = a(\phi - \sin \phi)$, $y = a(1 - \cos \phi)$, we found in Example 8.5-2 that

$$\frac{dy}{dx} = \frac{\sin \phi}{1 - \cos \phi} \quad \text{and} \quad \frac{d^2y}{dx^2} = -\frac{1}{a} \frac{1}{(1 - \cos \phi)^2}, \quad 0 < \phi < 2\pi.$$

Here we can say that

$$K = \frac{(1/a)[1/(1 - \cos \phi)^2]}{\{1 + [\sin \phi/(1 - \cos \phi)]^2\}^{3/2}} = \frac{1}{a} \frac{1/(1 - \cos \phi)^2}{[(1 - \cos \phi)^2 + \sin^2 \phi]^{3/2}/(1 - \cos \phi)^3}$$

$$= \frac{1}{a} \frac{1 - \cos \phi}{[2 - 2 \cos \phi]^{3/2}} = \frac{1}{a \sqrt{8} \sqrt{1 - \cos \phi}} = \frac{1}{4a \sin (\phi/2)}, \quad 0 < \phi < 2\pi.$$

The curvature is a minimum at $\phi = \pi$, which corresponds to the highest point on the path, but is not defined at the cusps, the points for which $\phi = 0$ and 2π.

Curvature formulas that use the derivatives dx/dy and d^2x/dy^2 for a curve described by an equation of the form $x = f(y)$, and the derivatives dx/dt, d^2x/dt^2, dy/dt, and d^2y/dt^2 for a curve described in terms of a parameter t, are derived in Exercises 8.7-1 and 8.7-2. They should be consulted when the formula of Theorem 1 cannot be used, for instance when one wants K at a point where dy/dx is not finite.

$$\|$$

● **Remark 1**

Curvature as an invariant. If the same curve is studied by two different observers who refer it to different coordinate systems, they will use different equations to describe the curve, and they will report different values for dy/dx and d^2y/dx^2. The quantities dy/dx and d^2y/dx^2 are not "invariants." But the arc length s and the curvature K are invariants. In Fig. 8.48 we see that $\Delta\alpha$, the change in inclination with movement from P to Q, equals the angle between the tangent lines at P and Q. But the magnitude of an angle does not depend on which direction the observer agrees to call his x axis. Two different observers using the same units would report the same number for $\Delta\alpha$, no matter which coordinate systems they used. They

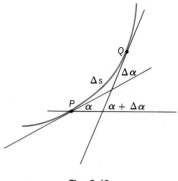

Fig. 8.48

would also report the same number for Δs, and hence compute the same numbers for $\Delta\alpha/\Delta s$ and K.

Example 5. Consider the hyperbola $-x^2 + y^2 = 1$, sketched in Fig. 8.49(a). If we write

$$y = \sqrt{x^2 + 1}, \qquad \frac{dy}{dx} = \frac{x}{\sqrt{x^2 + 1}}, \qquad \frac{d^2y}{dx^2} = \frac{1}{(x^2 + 1)^{3/2}},$$

we find that at $A(0, 1)$,

$$\frac{dy}{dx} = 0, \qquad \frac{d^2y}{dx^2} = 1, \qquad \text{and} \qquad K = \frac{1}{[1 + 0]^{3/2}} = 1.$$

But if we refer the very same hyperbola to new axes that make an angle of $45°$ with the old, as in Fig. 8.49(b), we find that the equation is now $xy = \frac{1}{2}$ and that the point A has coordinates $(1/\sqrt{2}, 1/\sqrt{2})$. From $y = \frac{1}{2}(1/x)$ we find that

$$\frac{dy}{dx} = -\frac{1}{2}\frac{1}{x^2} \qquad \text{and} \qquad \frac{d^2y}{dx^2} = \frac{1}{x^3},$$

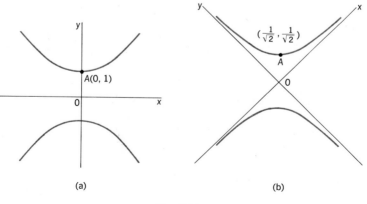

(a)

(b)

Fig. 8.49

so that at A we now have

$$\frac{dy}{dx} = -1 \qquad \text{and} \qquad \frac{d^2y}{dx^2} = 2\sqrt{2}.$$

These are not the same numbers we computed at the same point before; dy/dx and d^2y/dx^2 are not invariant. But for K at A we have

$$K = \frac{2\sqrt{2}}{[1 + (-1)^2]^{3/2}} = \frac{2\sqrt{2}}{2^{3/2}} = 1.$$

We do have the same curvature number as before.

III

Remark 2

Having decided that the arc length and the curvature are invariants for plane curves, we might well ask whether it is necessary to search for other invariants. The answer is "no!"; the arc length and curvature determine the curve and the other invariants. A fundamental theorem of differential geometry says that if $f(s)$ is any continuous and nonnegative function defined on a stated s domain, there is a plane curve for which s is the arc length and $K = f(s)$ is the curvature. Furthermore there is only one such plane curve in the sense that, if C_1 and C_2 are two curves that have the same curvature as a function of the arc length (for suitable choice of base point in measuring s and suitable direction of increasing s), then either C_1 and C_2 are congruent or they can be subdivided into parts that are congruent. To summarize, when the curvatures as functions of the arc length are the same, the curves are congruent (in the sense stated) and all other invariants are then the same, also.

Example 6. We discuss here the fundamental theorem described in Remark 2. Let $f(s)$ be continuous and nonnegative for $a \leq s \leq b$. We wish to make plausible the statement that there is one and only one curve, in the sense described above, which has s as its arc length and $f(s)$ as its curvature.

If we are to have $K = |d\alpha/ds| = f(s)$ we have essentially only two choices:

$$\frac{d\alpha}{ds} = f(s) \qquad \text{or} \qquad \frac{d\alpha}{ds} = -f(s). \tag{2a}$$

Consider the first choice; $\alpha(s)$ must be such that

$$\alpha(s) = \int_a^s f(s)\,ds + C_1, \tag{2b}$$

the continuity of f guaranteeing the existence of the integral. Because $(dx/ds)^2 + (dy/ds)^2 = 1$ if s is to be the arc length and $\tan \alpha = dy/dx$ if α is to be the inclination, we have no choice next but to write

$$\frac{dx}{ds} = \cos \alpha, \qquad \frac{dy}{ds} = \sin \alpha.$$

(The solution $dx/ds = -\cos \alpha$, $dy/ds = -\sin \alpha$ is also possible but is equivalent to the choice we did make, because replacing α by $\alpha + \pi$ will convert one choice to the other, and this means that one curve can be obtained from the other by rotation through 180°.) If we consider α determined as a differentiable function of s by Eq. (2b), the last equations require that x and y be such that

$$
\begin{aligned}
x(s) &= \int_a^s (\cos \alpha) \, ds + C_2, \\
y(s) &= \int_a^s (\sin \alpha) \, ds + C_3.
\end{aligned}
\tag{3}
$$

These are equations that determine x and y as functions of s and can be considered as a parametric description of the curve. Different choices for the constant C_1 in Eq. (2b) correspond to rotations; different choices for the constants C_2 and C_3 in Eqs. (3) correspond to translations; taking the second choice in Eqs. (2a) instead of the first would replace α by $-\alpha$, leave the x statement in Eqs. (3) unchanged, and change the statement for y in such a way as to lead to a curve that is symmetric to the first with respect to a horizontal line.

It remains to show that s is indeed the arc length for the curve described parametrically by Eqs. (3) and (2b), that α serves as its inclination, and that $d\alpha/ds = f(s)$. From Eqs. (3) and (2b) we have

$$
\frac{dx}{ds} = \cos \alpha, \qquad \frac{dy}{ds} = \sin \alpha, \qquad \frac{d\alpha}{ds} = f.
\tag{4}
$$

The first two of these equations enable us to say that $dy/dx = \tan \alpha$; α can serve as inclination angle. We also conclude that $(dx/ds)^2 + (dy/ds)^2 = \cos^2 \alpha + \sin^2 \alpha = 1$. Theorem 8.6-3 then enables us to say that

$$
\text{length of arc} = \int_a^s \sqrt{(dx/ds)^2 + (dy/ds)^2} \, ds = s - a;
$$

s can serve as arc length for the curve described by Eqs. (3) if we choose the base point for measuring arcs suitably. Finally, the third of Eqs. (4) tells us that $d\alpha/ds = f$ for this curve, as required.

In Exercise 8.7-19 the reader can carry out the details of this argument in the special case $K = \text{const}$.

IV

If we take the point Q on curve Γ near point P, the secant line PQ is determined. The limiting position approached by PQ as Q approaches P is the tangent line at P. See Fig. 8.50(a). Now, as in Fig. 8.50(b), take points Q and S on curve Γ near P, thus determining the circle PQS; for three points determine a circle. The limiting position approached by circle PQS as Q and S approach P is called the osculating circle or circle of curvature. It can be shown that this circle is tangent to the curve at P and has the same curvature as the curve there. Its radius and center are called the radius of curvature and the center of curvature. If we write R for the radius of this circle of curvature and K for the curvature common to the curve at P and to the circle of curvature, then $R = 1/K$, because, as in Example 2, the curvature and radius are reciprocal for a circle.

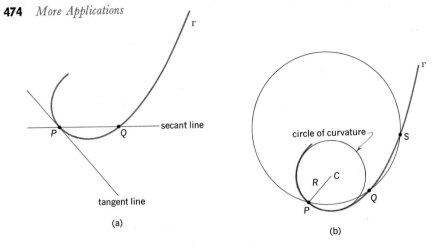

secant line

tangent line

(a)

circle of curvature

(b)

Fig. 8.50

■ DEFINITION 2

The radius of curvature. Let the curvature of a curve at a point be K. Then $R = 1/K$ is called the radius of curvature at that point.

The drawing of the circle of curvature can be described in two steps. Refer to Fig. 8.50(b). First draw at the point P the half-ray that points to the concave side of the curve and is perpendicular to the tangent, because any circle through P with center on this half-ray will be tangent to the curve. Then select for the center of curvature point, C, that point on the half-ray whose distance from P is R.

Example 7. Consider again the parabola $x^2 = 2py$ discussed in Example 3; see Fig. 8.51. At $(0, 0)$ the tangent line is horizontal and the curvature is $1/p$. A circle tangent to the parabola at $(0, 0)$, and having the same curvature there, would have to have its center on the y axis and radius p. Hence $C(0, p)$ is the center of the circle of curvature. Observe that $F(0, p/2)$, the focus point, is precisely the point midway between the vertex and the center of curvature. This fact is used in working with certain lenses and mirrors.

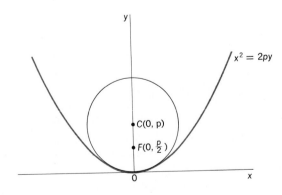

Fig. 8.51

EXERCISES 8.7

1. Prove the following theorem:

Theorem 2. A curvature formula.
Hypothesis: $x = f(y)$, $dx/dy = f'(y)$, $d^2x/dy^2 = f''(y)$ are defined for domain D.
Conclusion: For y of D the curvature at the point (x, y) of the curve with equation $x = f(y)$ is

$$K = \frac{|d^2x/dy^2|}{[1 + (dx/dy)^2]^{3/2}} \qquad (5)$$

Suggestion: Note that $\cot \alpha = dx/dy$.

2. Prove the following theorem:

Theorem 3. A curvature formula.
Hypothesis: $x = f(t)$, $dx/dt = f'(t)$, $d^2x/dt^2 = f''(t)$, $y = g(t)$, $dy/dt = g'(t)$, $d^2y/dt^2 = g''(t)$ are defined for domain D.
Conclusion: For t of D the curvature at the point $(x(t), y(t))$ of the curve with parametric equations $x = f(t)$, $y = g(t)$ is

$$K = \left| \frac{(dx/dt)(d^2y/dt^2) - (dy/dt)(d^2x/dt^2)}{[(dx/dt)^2 + (dy/dt)^2]^{3/2}} \right| \qquad (6)$$

Suggestion: Note that $\tan \alpha = (dy/dt)/(dx/dt)$.*

3. Sketch $y = \sin x$, $0 \le x \le \pi$.
(a) Find the curvature at any point and in particular at $(\pi/2, 1)$.
(b) Draw the circle of curvature at $(\pi/2, 1)$.
(c) Can you show that K is a maximum at $(\pi/2, 1)$ without consulting dK/dx?

4. Sketch the catenary

$$y = a \cosh \frac{x}{a} = \frac{a}{2} (e^{x/a} + e^{-x/a}).$$

(a) Show that $K = a/y^2$.
(b) Draw the circle of curvature at $(0, a)$.
(c) Can you show that K is a maximum at $(0, a)$ without consulting dK/dx?

5. (a) Show that the curvature of $y = \log x$ at $(x, \log x)$ is $x/(x^2 + 1)^{3/2}$.
(b) Show that the maximum curvature is $2/(3\sqrt{3})$, achieved at $(\sqrt{1/2}, -1/2 \log 2)$.
(c) Why is the curve $y = e^x$ congruent to $y = \log x$?
(d) Show that the curvature of $y = e^x$ at $(\log y, y)$ is $y/(y^2 + 1)^{3/2}$.
(e) Without further computation, what must the maximum curvature of $y = e^x$ be and where is it achieved?

6. (a) Find the curvature of the ellipse $x = a \cos \theta$, $y = b \sin \theta$.
(b) Can you show that K is a maximum at the major vertices and a minimum at the minor vertices without consulting $dK/d\theta$?†

---

* *Better suggestion:* Note that $\sin \alpha (dx/dt) = \cos \alpha (dy/dt)$, which is valid even if $\alpha = \pi/2$.
† For curves in general, a point at which the curvature has an extreme value is called a vertex. The ellipse has four. The ellipse is a special case of an "oval"; an oval is a closed curve whose parametric equations $x = f(t)$, $y = g(t)$ are twice differentiable and whose centers of curvature are always reached by traveling toward the inside of the closed curve. The "four-vertex" theorem of differential geometry says that every oval has at least four vertices.

7. (a) Find the curvature at any point of the branch of the hyperbola described by $x = a \cosh u$, $y = b \sinh u$.

  (b) Can you show that the curvature is a maximum at the vertex without consulting dK/du?

8. (a) Show that the curvature of the hypocycloid of four cusps, $x = a \cos^3 \theta$, $y = a \sin^3 \theta$, $0 \leq \theta \leq 2\pi$, is given by $K = 2/(3a |\sin 2\theta|)$, $\theta \neq 0$, $\pi/2$, π, $3\pi/2$, and 2π.

  (b) Draw the hypocycloid for $0 \leq \theta \leq \pi/2$ and draw the circle of curvature at the point for which $\theta = \pi/4$.

9. (a) Show that the curvature of the involute of a circle, $x = a(\cos \theta + \theta \sin \theta)$, $y = a(\sin \theta - \theta \cos \theta)$ is given by $K = 1/(a|\theta|)$.

  (b) Sketch this involute for $0 \leq \theta \leq \pi$ and draw the circle of curvature at the point for which $\theta = \pi/2$.

10. Find the curvature of the parabola $y^2 = 2px$ at $(0, 0)$.

11. Find the curvature of $4y^4 - 12xy + 3 = 0$ at $(\tfrac{7}{12}, 1)$.

12. Find the curvature at any point of $x^{1/2} + y^{1/2} = a^{1/2}$.

13. Find the curvature of $e^{x+y} = e^x + e^y$ at $(\log 2, \log 2)$.

14. Find the curvature of $\sin (x + y) + \sin x = 1$ at $(\pi/2, \pi/2)$.

15. By approximately how much will the inclination of the tangent change with movement of a distance .02 along the curve $y = 1/x$ from $(1, 1)$?

16. Approximately how far along the curve $y = \cos x$ must one move from $(\pi/3, 1/2)$ if the inclination of the tangent is to change by .001 radian?

17. (a) Show that $C: y = x^2$ has curvature $2/(5 \sqrt{5})$ at $A(1, 1)$.

  (b) Show that, if the same curve is referred to new axes parallel to the original ones and with origin at $(-2, -1)$, its equation becomes $y' - 1 = (x' - 2)^2$, and that the new coordinates for A are $(3, 2)$. Compute in this coordinate system and show that the curvature of C at A is still $2/(5 \sqrt{5})$.

  (c) Show that, if C is referred to new axes obtained from the original axes by rotating through $45°$, its equation becomes $(x' - y')^2 = \sqrt{2} (x' + y')$ and that the new coordinates for A are $(\sqrt{2}, 0)$. Compute in this coordinate system and show that the curvature of C at A is still $2/(5 \sqrt{5})$.

18. Let α be the inclination of the tangent line. Is $d\alpha/dx$ invariant with respect to rotations? Explain.

19. Carry through the discussion of Example 6 in the case where $K = 1/a$, a constant, arriving at parametric equations of a circle in terms of its arc length. This is an illustration of the fact that the curvature, as a function of the arc length, determines the curve.

20. From any point $P(x, y)$ of the catenary of Exercise 4, extend the line perpendicular to the tangent until it reaches the x axis at N. Show that PN equals the radius of curvature at P.

21. Here we continue the work of Example 3 on the parabola. At any point P draw the normal line, the line perpendicular to the tangent. Show that the radius of curvature at P is twice the length of the segment of the normal which lies between P and the directrix.

8.8 More on Limits of Sums and Definite Integrals

In studying area, work, and arc-length problems, we have adopted a certain summation technique. We take an interval $a \leq x \leq b$ and subdivide it into n parts by using subdivision points $x_0 = a < x_1 < x_2 < \cdots < x_{n-1} < x_n = b$. We have a quantity Q in mind and for each subinterval we state that

$$k\text{th element of } Q = (\Delta Q)_k = f(w_k)(\Delta x)_k, \qquad k = 1, 2, \cdots, n, \tag{1}$$

where $(\Delta x)_k = x_k - x_{k-1}$ is the width of the kth subinterval, $f(x)$ is a continuous function for $a \leq x \leq b$, and w_k is a point of the kth subinterval. Then we say that

$$Q = \lim_{n \to \infty} \sum_{k=1}^{n} f(w_k)(\Delta x)_k = \int_{x=a}^{b} f(x)\, dx, \tag{2}$$

it being understood that the largest $(\Delta x)_k$ approaches 0 as n grows beyond all bounds.

It has already happened once, in our study of arc lengths for curves defined parametrically, and it will happen frequently in other applications, that we must consider sums almost like the sum in Eq. (2), but not quite the same. Can the limits of these sums also be represented by definite integrals?

■ THEOREM 1

HYPOTHESIS: (a) $f(x)$ is continuous for the interval $a \leq x \leq b$.

(b) Whenever this interval is partitioned, we have for each subinterval

$$(\Delta Q)_k = f(w_k)(\Delta x)_k + C_k(\Delta x)_k,$$

where $x_{k-1} \leq w_k \leq x_k$.

(c) For any positive number ϵ, no matter how small, it is possible to specify another positive number δ with the following property: for every partition of $a \leq x \leq b$ in which the largest $(\Delta x)_k$ is less than δ we have $|C_k| < \epsilon$, $k = 1, 2, \cdots, n$.

CONCLUSION:

$$\lim_{n \to \infty} \sum_{k=1}^{n} (\Delta Q)_k = \int_{a}^{b} f(x)\, dx,$$

it being understood that the largest $(\Delta x)_k$ approaches 0 as n grows beyond all bounds.*

DISCUSSION: Hypothesis (b) says that the elements we wish to sum are like those we can already handle, but each element has, in addition, a term that might be called a correction, $C_k(\Delta x)_k$. Hypothesis (c) and the conclusion say that if the corrections are small enough, they can be ignored. To be more precise, we know that $\lim_{n \to \infty} \sum_{k=1}^{n} f(w_k)(\Delta x)_k = \int_a^b f(x)\, dx$, and we expect to show that $\lim_{n \to \infty} \sum_{k=1}^{n} C_k(\Delta x)_k = 0$, the largest $(\Delta x)_k$ approaching 0 as both limits are taken.

Note that it is not enough to require of the corrections merely that they approach 0 as the subintervals grow smaller. Suppose that we first have 10 subintervals with correction .1 each and thus total correction 1; then 100 subintervals with correction .01 each and total correction 1; then 1000 subintervals with correction .001 each; and so on. The corrections for the individual subintervals would ap-

---

* This theorem and other theorems that have the same goal in mind are sometimes called theorems of Duhamel or theorems of Bliss.

proach 0, but we could not claim that $\lim_{n \to \infty} \sum_{k=1}^{n} C_k(\Delta x)_k = 0$. The corrections must approach 0 faster than the subinterval size does, and this is why we have Hypothesis (c).

PROOF: Hypothesis (c) says that if any $\epsilon > 0$ is specified, no matter how small, we find that $|C_k| < \epsilon$ for all k for every partition in which the largest $(\Delta x)_k$ is small enough. But then

$$\sum_{k=1}^{n} |C_k|(\Delta x)_k = |C_1|(\Delta x)_1 + |C_2|(\Delta x)_2 + \cdots + |C_n|(\Delta x)_n$$

$$< \epsilon(\Delta x)_1 + \epsilon(\Delta x)_2 + \cdots + \epsilon(\Delta x)_n$$

$$= \epsilon[(\Delta x)_1 + (\Delta x)_2 + \cdots + (\Delta x)_n] = \epsilon(b - a).$$

Since $b - a$ is finite and ϵ could have been chosen as small as desired, $\epsilon(b - a)$ can be made as small as desired, and this means that

$$\lim_{n \to \infty} \sum_{k=1}^{n} |C_k|(\Delta x)_k = 0,$$

it being understood that the largest $(\Delta x)_k$ approaches 0 as n grows beyond all bounds. But if the sum of the absolute values of the corrections approaches 0, then

$$\lim_{n \to \infty} \sum_{k=1}^{n} C_k(\Delta x)_k = 0$$

also. Theorem 1 is demonstrated.

In Theorem 2 we illustrate Theorem 1 by considering a specific case that will arise frequently.

■ THEOREM 2

HYPOTHESIS: (a) $h(x)$, $g(x)$ are continuous for $a \leq x \leq b$.
(b) x_k, $k = 0, 1, \cdots, n$, are chosen so that $x_0 = a < x_1 < x_2 < \cdots < x_n = b$.
(c) v_k and w_k are chosen in each subinterval: $x_{k-1} \leq w_k$, $v_k \leq x_k$.

CONCLUSION: $\lim_{n \to \infty} \sum_{k=1}^{n} h(w_k)g(v_k)(\Delta x)_k = \int_{x=a}^{b} h(x)g(x)\, dx,$

it being assumed here that the largest of the $(\Delta x)_k$'s approaches 0 as n grows beyond all bounds.

PROOF: If we write $f(x) = h(x)g(x)$, we know that when the largest $(\Delta x)_k$ approaches 0,

$$\lim_{n \to \infty} \sum_{k=1}^{n} h(w_k)g(w_k)(\Delta x)_k = \lim_{n \to \infty} \sum_{k=1}^{n} f(w_k)(\Delta x)_k$$

$$= \int_{x=a}^{b} f(x)\, dx = \int_{x=a}^{b} h(x)g(x)\, dx,$$

but we must consider elements of the form $h(w_k)g(v_k)(\Delta x)_k$ rather than $h(w_k)$ $g(w_k)(\Delta x)_k$. However, we can say that

$$h(w_k)g(v_k)(\Delta x)_k = h(w_k)g(w_k)(\Delta x)_k + h(w_k)[g(v_k) - g(w_k)](\Delta x)_k,$$

so that we have a situation like that of Hypothesis (b) of Theorem 1, with

$$C_k = h(w_k)[g(v_k) - g(w_k)]. \tag{3}$$

By Hypothesis (a) of this theorem, $h(x)$ is continuous. According to the boundedness theorem for continuous functions,* there exists a number M such that

$$|h(w_k)| < M \qquad \text{for all } k. \tag{4}$$

Next, $g(x)$ is also continuous, and thus uniformly continuous for the closed interval $a \le x \le b$.† This means that if $\epsilon/M > 0$ is specified, no matter how small, a number δ can be found such that for any points z_1 and z_2 of the interval within δ of each other we shall have $|g(z_1) - g(z_2)| < \epsilon/M$. In a partition where all the $(\Delta x)_k$'s are smaller than δ, we shall have

$$|g(v_k) - g(w_k)| < \epsilon/M \text{ for all } k \tag{5}$$

because v_k and w_k are points of the same subinterval and therefore within δ of each other. But now it follows from Eqs. (3), (4), and (5) that when all the $(\Delta x)_k$'s are less than δ,

$$|C_k| < \epsilon \qquad \text{for all } k. \tag{6}$$

Thus Hypothesis (c) of Theorem 1 holds, and we can take the conclusion of Theorem 1. Theorem 2 is demonstrated.

We conclude this section by setting up an integral for the length of an arc described by parametric equations, a matter not completely discussed in the proof of Theorem 8.6-3.

■ THEOREM 3

HYPOTHESIS: (a) $f'(t)$ and $g'(t)$ are continuous for $a \le t \le b$.
(b) t_k, $k = 0, 1, 2, \cdots, n$, are chosen so that $t_0 = a < t_1 < t_2 < \cdots < t_n = b$.
(c) v_k and w_k are chosen in each subinterval: $t_{k-1} \le v_k$, $w_k \le t_k$.

CONCLUSION: $\displaystyle \lim_{n \to \infty} \sum_{k=1}^{n} \sqrt{[f'(w_k)]^2 + [g'(v_k)]^2}\,(\Delta t)_k$

$$= \int_{t=a}^{b} \sqrt{[f'(t)]^2 + [g'(t)]^2}\,dt,$$

assuming that the largest of the $(\Delta t)_k$'s approaches 0 as n grows beyond all bounds.

PROOF: We know that

$$\lim_{n \to \infty} \sum_{k=1}^{n} \sqrt{[f'(w_k)]^2 + [g'(w_k)]^2}\,(\Delta t)_k = \int_{t=a}^{b} \sqrt{[f'(t)]^2 + [g'(t)]^2}\,dt,$$

---

* Theorem 7.4-1.
† Theorem 7.4-4.

it being assumed that the largest $(\Delta t)_k$ approaches 0 in the limit process, but we must deal with elements of the form

$$\sqrt{[f'(w_k)]^2 + [g'(v_k)]^2} \; (\Delta t)_k.$$

Step (a): It is a numerical fact* that, if $A \geq 0$ and $B \geq 0$, then

$$|\sqrt{A} - \sqrt{B}| \leq \sqrt{|A - B|}. \tag{12}$$

Step (b): Now let

$$A = [f'(w_k)]^2 + [g'(v_k)]^2 \text{ and } B = [f'(w_k)]^2 + [g'(w_k)]^2.$$

Then Eq. (12) says that

$$|\sqrt{[f'(w_k)]^2 + [g'(v_k)]^2} - \sqrt{[f'(w_k)]^2 + [g'(w_k)]^2}| \leq \sqrt{|[g'(v_k)]^2 - [g'(w_k)]^2|},$$

or in the format of Hypothesis (b) of Theorem 1,

$$\sqrt{[f'(w_k)]^2 + [g'(v_k)]^2} \; (\Delta t)_k = \sqrt{[f'(w_k)]^2 + [g'(w_k)]^2} \; (\Delta t)_k + C_k(\Delta t)_k, \tag{13}$$

where

$$|C_k| \leq \sqrt{|[g'(v_k)]^2 - [g'(w_k)]^2|}. \tag{14}$$

Step (c): Since $g'(t)$ is continuous for $a \leq t \leq b$, so is $[g'(t)]^2$, and, further, $[g'(t)]^2$ is uniformly continuous for $a \leq t \leq b$ because it is continuous there. This means that for any positive number that might be specified, say ϵ^2, we can find a second positive number δ such that we shall have $|[g'(z_1)]^2 - [g'(z_2)]^2| < \epsilon^2$ for any numbers z_1 and z_2 of $a \leq t \leq b$ within δ of each other. In a partition where all the $(\Delta t)_k$'s are smaller than δ we shall have

$$|[g'(v_k)]^2 - [g'(w_k)]^2| < \epsilon^2 \qquad \text{for all } k,$$

---

* To prove this, we start by demonstrating that, if $A \geq B \geq 0$, then

$$\sqrt{A} - \sqrt{B} \leq \sqrt{A - B}. \tag{7}$$

If the inequality

$$A - 2\sqrt{A}\sqrt{B} + B \leq A - B, \tag{8}$$

obtained by squaring both members of Eq. (7), is valid, then Eq. (7) is valid, for both members of Eq. (7) are positive. But Inequality (8) is equivalent to

$$-2\sqrt{A}\sqrt{B} \leq -2B, \tag{9}$$

obtained by subtracting $(A + B)$ from both members of Eq. (8), and Eq. (9) is finally equivalent to

$$\sqrt{A} \geq \sqrt{B}, \tag{10}$$

obtained by dividing both members of Eq. (9) by $-2\sqrt{B}$. However, Eq. (10) is valid by hypothesis, and thus Eq. (7) is valid also. Of course if $B \geq A \geq 0$, then

$$\sqrt{B} - \sqrt{A} \leq \sqrt{B - A}. \tag{11}$$

Inequalities (7) and (11) together say that for $A \geq 0, B \geq 0$,

$$|\sqrt{A} - \sqrt{B}| \leq \sqrt{|A - B|}. \tag{12}$$

because v_k and w_k will be within the same subinterval and thus within δ of each other.

Step (d): To summarize, for every partition in which all $(\Delta t)_k$'s are smaller than δ, Eq. (14) says that

$$|C_k| < \epsilon \qquad \text{for all } k.$$

Thus Hypothesis (c) of Theorem 1 holds and we can conclude from Eq. (13) that

$$\lim_{n \to \infty} \sum_{k=1}^{n} \sqrt{[f'(w_k)]^2 + [g'(v_k)]^2}\,(\Delta t)_k = \lim_{n \to \infty} \sum_{k=1}^{n} \sqrt{[f'(w_k)]^2 + [g'(w_k)]^2}\,(\Delta t)_k$$

$$= \int_{t=a}^{b} \sqrt{[f'(t)]^2 + [g'(t)]^2}\,dt,$$

it being understood that the largest $(\Delta t)_k$ approaches 0 as n grows beyond all bounds.

8.9 Hydrostatic Force

To illustrate our summation-of-elements technique once again, we consider hydrostatic force. A cubic foot of water weighs 62.5 lb. If we take water to be incompressible, so that its density can be assumed constant, then a column of water of depth x ft and cross-section area 1 sq ft will weigh $62.5x$ lb. The force pressing against the one-square-foot area $ABCD$ in Fig. 8.52 is $62.5x$ lb, or, in other words, at the depth x ft below the surface, the hydrostatic pressure is $62.5x$ lb per sq ft; the greater the depth x, the greater the pressure. Further, at any point in a fluid at rest, the pressure is the same in all directions, a principle that seems plausible because any small portion of a fluid at rest is itself in equilibrium; the forces acting on it must balance each other.

Let water press against a vertical wall whose width w at depth x is given by $w = f(x)$. Let the wall be c ft deep and let us subdivide the interval $0 \le x \le c$ into n parts as usual by choosing subdivision depth numbers $0 = x_0 < x_1 < x_2 < \cdots < x_n = c$, thus subdividing the wall into n horizontal elements; see Fig. 8.53. There is an x_k^* of the kth subinterval and a corresponding $w_k^* = f(x_k^*)$ such that

$$\text{area of } k\text{th element} = w_k^*(\Delta x)_k = f(x_k^*)(\Delta x)_k \text{ sq ft.}$$

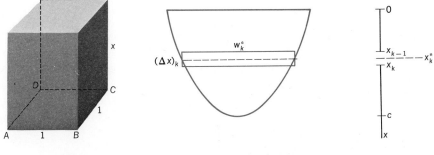

Fig. 8.52   Fig. 8.53

The pressure is not the same at all points of the kth element. If we assumed that the pressure at depth x_{k-1} was the pressure for the whole kth element, we would underestimate the force pressing on that element; if we assumed that the pressure at depth x_k was the pressure for the whole kth element, we would overestimate. There is an intermediate $\bar{x}_k$ of the kth element which we can use as a representative depth in computing the force pressing on the kth element. The pressure at depth $\bar{x}_k$ is $62.5\,\bar{x}_k$ lb per sq ft and

$$\text{force pressing on } k\text{th element} = [62.5\,\bar{x}_k \text{ lb per sq ft}][f(x_k^*)(\Delta x)_k \text{ sq ft}]$$

$$= 62.5\,\bar{x}_k f(x_k^*)(\Delta x)_k \text{ lb.}$$

It is reasonable now to define the force against the wall as the limit of the sum of the forces against the various elements:

$$\text{force} = \lim_{n \to \infty} \sum_{k=1}^{n} 62.5 \bar{x}_k f(x_k^*)(\Delta x)_k,$$

assuming that the largest of the $(\Delta x)_k$'s approaches 0 as n grows beyond all bounds.

According to Theorem 8.8-2, the limit of such a sum is still a definite integral;

$$\text{force} = \int_{x=0}^{c} 62.5x\, f(x)\, dx.$$

Example 1. A canal lock, rectangular in shape, is 30 ft wide. With what force does the water press against it when the water is 20 ft deep? See Fig. 8.54. We reason as follows:

area of kth element $= 30(\Delta x)_k,$

representative depth for kth element $= \bar{x}_k, \qquad x_{k-1} < \bar{x}_k < x_k,$

representative pressure for kth element $= 62.5\bar{x}_k,$

force on kth element $= (62.5\bar{x}_k)30(\Delta x)_k,$

$$\text{force} = \int_{x=0}^{20} 30(62.5)x\, dx,$$

$$\text{force} = 30(62.5)\left.\frac{x^2}{2}\right|_{x=0}^{20} = 30(62.5)\left(\frac{400}{2}\right)$$

$$= 375{,}000 \text{ lb} = 187.5 \text{ tons.}$$

Example 2. A plate in the form of an isosceles right triangle stands vertically in the water as in Fig. 8.55. Its two equal legs are 2 ft long, and the top of the triangle is 1 ft below the surface. Find the force pressing against one face of the plate. (The plate might serve as a rudder.)

We start by dividing the plate into n horizontal elements. Let y be the distance below the top of the plate and w the width at the distance y. Let $y_k^*, y_{k-1} < y_k^* < y_k,$ and the corresponding w_k^* be chosen so that

$$\text{area of } k\text{th element} = w_k^*(\Delta y)_k.$$

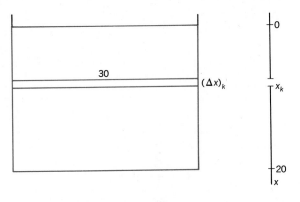

Fig. 8.54

Let $\bar{y}_k$, $y_{k-1} < \bar{y}_k < y_k$ be chosen as a representative distance for the kth element such that

$$\text{representative depth for } k\text{th element} = \bar{y}_k + 1,$$

$$\text{representative pressure for } k\text{th element} = 62.5(\bar{y}_k + 1),$$

$$\text{force against } k\text{th element} = 62.5(\bar{y}_k + 1)w_k^*(\Delta y)_k,$$

$$\text{force} = \int_{y=0}^{2} 62.5(y + 1)w \, dy.$$

But because the triangle is isosceles we have $w = y$. Hence

$$\text{force} = 62.5 \int_{y=0}^{2} (y + 1)y \, dy = 62.5 \int_{y=0}^{2} (y^2 + y) \, dy$$

$$= 62.5 \left(\frac{y^3}{3} + \frac{y^2}{2}\right)\Big|_0^2 = 62.5 \left(\frac{8}{3} + 2\right) \approx 291.7 \text{ lb.}$$

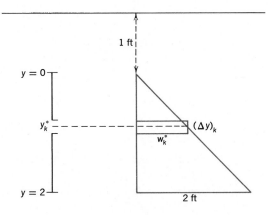

Fig. 8.55

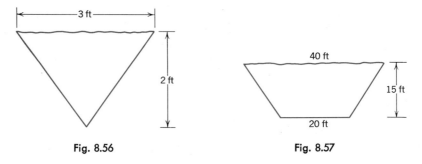

Fig. 8.56   Fig. 8.57

EXERCISES 8.9

1. Given a trough whose cross section is the isosceles triangle shown in Fig. 8.56. When the trough is full of water, with what force does the water press against an end?

2. With what force does the water press against the trapezoidal dam sketched in Fig. 8.57 when the dam is full?

3. A cylindrical drum stands in vertical position and is half filled with an oil that weighs 50 lb per cu ft. The radius of the drum is $1\frac{1}{2}$ ft, the height is 4 ft. With what force does the oil press against the lateral wall?

4. (a) The cylindrical drum of Exercise 3 lies in a horizontal position. With what force does the oil press against one of the circular ends of the drum?
   (b) What is the force if the drum is full of oil?

5. A rectangular gate in a dam has width 10 ft and height 8 ft. What force presses against the gate when the water level is 20 ft above the top of the gate?

6. Assume that the gate of Exercise 5 cannot withstand a force greater than 100 tons. How high above the top of the gate would the water level have to be to achieve this force?

7. If a horizontal line were drawn across the gate of Exercise 5, 4 ft below the top of the gate, the force pressing against the portion of the gate below the line would be greater than the force pressing against the portion of the gate above the line, because the pressures increase with depth. Where should a horizontal line be drawn if the forces on the two portions of the gate are to be equal?

8. An oil of weight 50 lb per cu ft lies above some water in a container with the rectangular cross section indicated in Fig. 8.58. What is the force against this cross section?

9. A cylindrical container of radius a and height h is filled with a gas whose density decreases with increasing height. If the weight density at height y is given by be^{-cy}, where b and c are constants, find the weight of the gas in the container. (*Suggestion:* Subdivide the interval $0 \leq y \leq h$ and consider the weight of an element of volume thus formed.)

8.10 Work

We have already considered the problem of defining and computing the work done when a particle moves in a straight line under the action of a force of either constant or variable strength.* Here we shall consider the work done by a force when a particle moves in a curved path.

Let a particle move along arc C, defined by parametric equations $x = f(t)$, $y = g(t)$, $a \leq t \leq b$, such that $f'(t)$ and $g'(t)$ exist and are continuous for $a \leq t \leq b$.

---

* Sec. 2.8, Example 3.6-6.

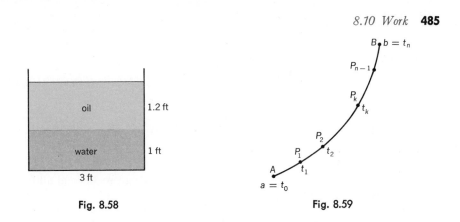

Fig. 8.58	Fig. 8.59

Subdivide the arc by selecting the points that correspond to the parameter values $a = t_0 < t_1 < t_2 < \cdots < t_{n-1} < t_n = b$, as in Fig. 8.59. If, as is customary in vector analysis, we write $\vec{R}$ for the position vector, $\vec{R} = \overrightarrow{OP} = x\vec{i} + y\vec{j}$, then the position vectors for the points $t = t_{k-1}$ and $t = t_k$ are $\vec{R}_{k-1} = x_{k-1}\vec{i} + y_{k-1}\vec{j}$ and $\vec{R}_k = x_k\vec{i} + y_k\vec{j}$, and the chord joining these points is given by $(\overrightarrow{\Delta R})_k = \vec{R}_k - \vec{R}_{k-1}$; see Fig. 8.60.

We shall imagine first that the particle travels along the inscribed chords. Let the force that causes the particle to move have the direction and magnitude given by $\vec{F}(t)$ at the point corresponding to parameter number t. Then we can say that

work done by $\vec{F}$ in moving particle along

$$\text{kth chord} \approx \vec{F}(t_{k-1}) \cdot (\overrightarrow{\Delta R})_k: \tag{1}$$

this statement says that the work done is the product of the displacement by the component of the force in the direction of the displacement, a statement made earlier in Definition 3.6-2. We have only an approximate statement in Eq. (1) because $\vec{F}$ could well vary with movement along the chord and we have taken $\vec{F}$ as it is at one end of the chord.

If we write $(\overrightarrow{\Delta R})_k = (\Delta x)_k\vec{i} + (\Delta y)_k\vec{j}$, as suggested by Fig. 8.60, and $\vec{F} = F_x\vec{i} + F_y\vec{j}$, then Eq. (1) becomes

work done in moving along kth chord $\approx F_x(t_{k-1})(\Delta x)_k + F_y(t_{k-1})(\Delta y)_k. \tag{2}$

Because $f'(t)$ and $g'(t)$ are continuous for $a \leq t \leq b$, the Theorem of Mean Value permits us to say that there are numbers t_k^* and $\bar{t}_k$, $t_{k-1} < t_k^*$, $\bar{t}_k < t_k$, such that

$$(\Delta x)_k = f(t_k) - f(t_{k-1}) = f'(t_k^*)(t_k - t_{k-1})$$

$$= f'(t_k^*)(\Delta t)_k$$

$$(\Delta y)_k = g(t_k) - g(t_{k-1}) = g'(\bar{t}_k)(t_k - t_{k-1})$$

$$= g'(\bar{t}_k)(\Delta t)_k.$$

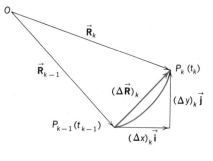

Fig. 8.60

Equation (2) can then be rewritten

work done in moving along kth chord $\approx F_x(t_{k-1})f'(t_k^*)(\Delta t)_k + F_y(t_{k-1})g'(\bar{t}_k)(\Delta t)_k,$

and we can continue with

work done for n chords $\approx \sum_{k=1}^{n} [F_x(t_{k-1})f'(t_k^*)(\Delta t)_k + F_y(t_{k-1})g'(\bar{t}_k)(\Delta t)_k].$

It is now natural to suggest for our definition of the work done in moving along the arc itself the limit of this sum as the number of chords grows beyond all bounds, the largest of the $(\Delta t)_k$'s approaching 0:

$$\text{work done} = \lim_{n \to \infty} \sum_{k=1}^{n} [F_x(t_{k-1}) f'(t_k^*)(\Delta t)_k + F_y(t_{k-1}) g'(\bar{t}_k)(\Delta t)_k]$$

$$\text{work done} = \int_{t=a}^{b} \left[F_x \frac{dx}{dt} dt + F_y \frac{dy}{dt} dt \right]. \tag{3}$$

Instead of Eq. (3) we sometimes write for abbreviation's sake

$$\text{work done} = \int_{t=a}^{b} [F_x \, dx + F_y \, dy] \tag{3a}$$

or

$$\text{work done} = \int_{t=a}^{b} \vec{F} \cdot d\vec{R}.$$

■ DEFINITION 1

Work. Let an arc be described by $x = f(t)$, $y = g(t)$, $a \le t \le b$, such that $f'(t)$ and $g'(t)$ exist and are continuous for $a \le t \le b$. Let a particle move along the arc under the influence of force $\vec{F} = F_x \vec{i} + F_y \vec{j}$. Then the work done is

$$\int_{t=a}^{b} \left[F_x \frac{dx}{dt} dt + F_y \frac{dy}{dt} dt \right],$$

sometimes indicated briefly by

$$\int_{t=a}^{b} (F_x \, dx + F_y \, dy) \qquad \text{or} \qquad \int_{t=a}^{b} \vec{F} \cdot d\vec{R}.$$

In our examples we shall deal with the "inverse square" force that occurs so frequently in nature.

Example 1. A particle is attracted toward the origin with a force inversely proportional to the square of its distance from the origin. Find the work done in moving this particle along the line $x = 3$ from $(3, 0)$ to $(3, 4)$.

First we shall describe the force in vector language. As we see in Fig. 8.61, $\vec{F}$ has the direction of the vector $-x\vec{i} - y\vec{j}$. A unit vector in the proper direction is then $(-x\vec{i} - y\vec{j})/\sqrt{x^2 + y^2}$. If we take into account $\vec{F}$'s magnitude, we can say that

$$\vec{F} = \frac{c}{(\sqrt{x^2 + y^2})^2} \frac{-x\vec{i} - y\vec{j}}{\sqrt{x^2 + y^2}} = -\frac{c}{(x^2 + y^2)^{3/2}} (x\vec{i} + y\vec{j}),$$

where c is a constant of proportionality.

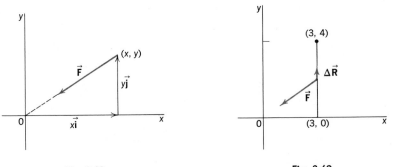

Fig. 8.61   Fig. 8.62

We have indicated the path along which the particle travels in Fig. 8.62. If we subdivide the path, we can say that

work done on element of path $\approx \vec{F}(t_{k-1}) \cdot (\overrightarrow{\Delta R})_k$

$$\approx -\frac{c}{(x^2 + y^2)^{3/2}} (x\vec{i} + y\vec{j}) \cdot (\Delta x\vec{i} + \Delta y\vec{j})^*$$

$$\approx -\frac{c}{(x^2 + y^2)^{3/2}} (x\,\Delta x + y\,\Delta y).$$

But for this particular path x is always 3 and $(\Delta x)_k = 0$ for all k. Hence

work done on element of path $\approx -\dfrac{c}{(9 + y^2)^{3/2}} y\,\Delta y,$

$$\text{work done} = -c \int_{y=0}^{4} \frac{y}{(9 + y^2)^{3/2}}\, dy$$

$$= -\frac{c}{2} \int_{0}^{4} (9 + y^2)^{-3/2}\, (2y)\, dy = \frac{c}{\sqrt{9 + y^2}}\Big|_{y=0}^{4}$$

$$= c(\tfrac{1}{5} - \tfrac{1}{3}) = -\tfrac{2}{15} c.$$

Example 2.   A particle is attracted toward the origin by the inverse square force of Example 1. It moves from $(3, 4)$ to $(-1, 0)$ along the parabola $x = t^2 - 1,\ y = 2t$, which has its focus at the origin. See Fig. 8.63. How much work was done by the force?

As in Example 1 we know that

$$\vec{F} = -\frac{c}{(x^2 + y^2)^{3/2}} (x\vec{i} + y\vec{j})$$

and that

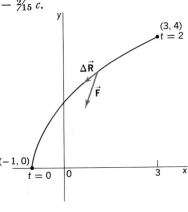

Fig. 8.63

---

* We dropped subscripts for the sake of convenience.

$$\text{work done on element of path} \approx -\frac{c}{(x^2 + y^2)^{3/2}} (x\,\Delta x + y\,\Delta y),*$$

so that we can write

$$\text{work done} = -c \int_{t=2}^{0} \frac{x\,dx + y\,dy}{(x^2 + y^2)^{3/2}} = -c \int_{t=2}^{0} \frac{x(dx/dt) + y(dy/dt)}{(x^2 + y^2)^{3/2}}\,dt.$$

But for this path we have $x = t^2 - 1$, $dx/dt = 2t$, $y = 2t$, and $dy/dt = 2$, so that

$$\text{work done} = -c \int_{t=2}^{0} \frac{(t^2 - 1)(2t) + 2t(2)}{[(t^2 - 1)^2 + 4t^2]^{3/2}}\,dt$$

$$= -c \int_{t=2}^{0} \frac{2t(t^2 + 1)}{(t^2 + 1)^3}\,dt$$

$$= -c \int_{t=2}^{0} \frac{2t}{(t^2 + 1)^2}\,dt$$

$$= c\,\frac{1}{t^2 + 1}\Big|_{t=2}^{0} = c\left[1 - \frac{1}{5}\right] = \frac{4}{5}\,c.$$

EXERCISES 8.10

1. How much work does the force $\vec{F} = (x^2 + y^2)\vec{i} + 2xy\vec{j}$ do in moving a particle from $(0, 0)$ to $(2, 2)$
   (a) along a straight-line path?
   (b) along the parabola $y^2 = 2x$?

2. How much work does the force $\vec{F} = x\vec{i} - y\vec{j}$ do if it moves a particle from $(a, 0)$ to $(0, a)$
   (a) along the first-quadrant part of $x = a \cos \theta$, $y = a \sin \theta$?
   (b) along the straight lines $x = a$ and $y = a$?

3. How much work is done by the force $\vec{F} = y\vec{i} + x^2\vec{j}$ in moving a particle from $(-1, 0)$ to $(7, 4)$
   (a) along the path $y = \frac{1}{16}(x + 1)^2$?
   (b) along the path $x = t^3 - 1$, $y = t^2$?

4. A current of magnitude c flowing in a long wire perpendicular to the x, y plane at the origin will produce at $P(x, y)$ a magnetic force of magnitude $2c/\sqrt{x^2 + y^2}$ and with direction in the x, y plane perpendicular to OP, as indicated in Fig. 8.64. In vector language,

$$\vec{F} = \frac{2c}{\sqrt{x^2 + y^2}}\,\frac{-y\vec{i} + x\vec{j}}{\sqrt{x^2 + y^2}} = 2c\,\frac{-y\vec{i} + x\vec{j}}{x^2 + y^2}.$$

   How much work is done by $\vec{F}$ in moving a particle in the counterclockwise direction once around
   (a) the circle $x = a \cos \theta$, $y = a \sin \theta$?
   (b) the square bounded by $x = \pm 1$, $y = \pm 1$?
   (c) the square bounded by $x = 1$, $x = 3$, $y = \pm 1$?

5. The ellipse $x = 1 + 2 \cos t$, $y = \sqrt{3} \sin t$ has a focus at the origin. How much work is done in moving a particle along the ellipse from $t = t_1$ to $t = t_2$ by an inverse square force directed toward the focus at the origin?

6. The same as Exercise 5 for the hyperbolic arc $x = -2 + \cosh t$, $y = \sqrt{3} \sinh t$, which also has a focus at the origin.

*We dropped subscripts for the sake of convenience.

7. (a) How much work is done by the force $\vec{F} = -(1/x)\vec{i}$ in moving a particle from $(1, 0)$ to $(3, 4)$ via the straight-line path?

(b) Show that the same amount of work would have been done if the particle had been moved via any other path with suitably differentiable equations that did not cross or touch the y axis in going from $(1, 0)$ to $(3, 4)$.

8. Let a rod of length $2a$ be placed on the x axis with its center at the origin. Let this rod carry a positive electric charge, uniformly distributed with charge density c. Coulomb's law says that two positively charged bodies will repel each other with a force that varies directly as the product of the charges and inversely as the square of the distance between them. If a unit positively charged body is placed at the point $(b, 0)$, $b > a$,* what force of repulsion will it experience? *Suggestion:* Consider the rod subdivided into elements. Show that the force of repulsion due to an element of length Δx at x is

$$\overrightarrow{\Delta F} \approx \frac{\alpha c\, \Delta x}{(b - x)^2}\vec{i}, \qquad \alpha \text{ a constant of proportionality.}$$

9. Repeat Exercise 8 placing the unit positive charge at $(0, b)$ instead of $(b, 0)$.

Suggestion: Explain why the x component of $\overrightarrow{\Delta F}$ can be ignored. Show that

$$(\overrightarrow{\Delta F})_y \approx \frac{\alpha c b\, \Delta x}{(b^2 + x^2)^{3/2}}.$$

8.11   First Moments. Center of Gravity

I

The effectiveness of a force in causing a rotation depends not only on the magnitude of the force but also on the point at which it is applied and the direction in which it acts. Consider, as in Fig. 8.65, a circular disk free to rotate about an axis AA' perpendicular to the disk and through its center C. Force $\vec{F}_1$, applied at point

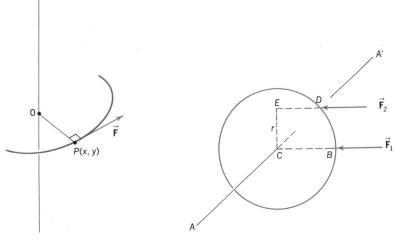

Fig. 8.64   Fig. 8.65

---

* It is assumed that the uniformly distributed charge on the rod is not distorted by the presence of the test charge.

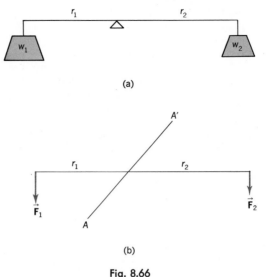

Fig. 8.66

B in such a way that its line of action passes through C, will cause no rotation about axis AA' at all. But force $\vec{F}_2$, of the same magnitude as $\vec{F}_1$ and parallel to it, *will* cause a rotation about axis AA'. The line of action of force $\vec{F}_2$, DE in Fig. 8.65, does not intersect the axis of rotation AA', but passes a distance $r = CE$ from it. The physicist states his ideas in the following language.

■ DEFINITION 1

Moment arm.   The moment arm for a force with respect to an axis perpendicular to it is the perpendicular distance between the axis and the line of action of the force.

■ DEFINITION 2

First moment or torque about an axis.   Let force $\vec{F}$, of magnitude f, have moment arm r with respect to an axis perpendicular to it. Its first moment or torque about that axis is $\pm fr$, the sign to be chosen according to the sense of the rotation caused by $\vec{F}$.

In Fig. 8.65, force $\vec{F}_1$ has moment arm zero with respect to the axis AA' and therefore moment zero; force $\vec{F}_2$ has moment arm r and therefore moment $r\|\vec{F}_2\|$. The two weights in Fig. 8.66 will balance if $M_1 = w_1 r_1$ and $M_2 = w_2 r_2$ are equal, for then $w_1 r_1$ or $\|\vec{F}_1\| r_1$, the moment of $\vec{F}_1$ for a counterclockwise rotation about axis AA', will be balanced by the moment of $\vec{F}_2$ for a clockwise rotation. Consider next a plate lying in a horizontal position on the x, y plane and free to rotate about the y axis, as in Fig. 8.67. Let the plate be bounded by the y axis, $x = a$, $y = f_1(x)$ and $y = f_2(x)$ for $0 \le x \le a$, with $f_1(x) \ge f_2(x)$. Let the plate's weight density be given by the continuous function $\rho(x)$, $0 \le x \le a$. This means

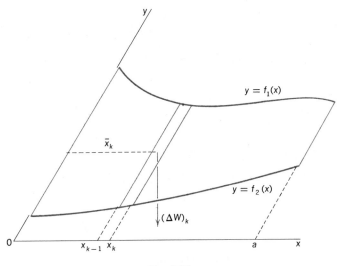

Fig. 8.67

the following: weigh a square of side s which includes the point (x, y), form the ratio of the weight to the area of the square, and repeat with s approaching 0; then the limit approached by the ratio is $\rho(x)$. Observe that we have a rather special plate here because the weight density, $\rho(x)$, varies with motion along the plate in the x direction but not with motion in the y direction.

We can divide the plate into n elements parallel to the y axis, the axis about which the rotation is to take place, by choosing $0 = x_0 < x_1 < x_2 < \cdots < x_n = a$ and drawing $x = x_1, x = x_2, \cdots$. There is a number $x_k^*, x_{k-1} \leq x_k^* \leq x_k$, of the kth element such that

$$(\Delta A)_k = \text{area of } k\text{th element} = [f_1(x_k^*) - f_2(x_k^*)](\Delta x)_k.$$

The continuous weight density function $\rho(x)$ will assume a maximum value M_k and a minimum value m_k for the kth element. If we were to assume that the weight density was M_k everywhere in the kth element and take the weight of the element to be $[M_k$ units of weight per sq cm]$\cdot[(\Delta A)_k$ sq cm], we would have too large an estimate for the weight of the element. Similarly, if we were to assume that the weight density was m_k everywhere in the kth element, we would have too small an estimate for the weight of the element. There is an $\bar{x}_k, x_{k-1} \leq \bar{x}_k \leq x_k$, such that

$$(\Delta W)_k = \text{weight of } k\text{th element} = \rho(\bar{x}_k)(\Delta A)_k.$$

But the fact that the kth element has weight $(\Delta W)_k$ means that the element is attracted toward the earth with a force of this magnitude, and this force has a moment about the y axis. If we were to assume that the moment arm for a rotation of the kth element about the y axis was x_{k-1} and to compute the moment as $(\Delta W)_k$ x_{k-1}, we would have an underestimate for the moment because while many molecules of the kth element are at a distance x_{k-1} from the y axis, this is the minimum possible distance for that element. Similarly, if we were to assume that the moment arm was x_k, we would have an overestimate. There is an $\bar{\bar{x}}_k$, $x_{k-1} < \bar{\bar{x}}_k < x_k$, such that

$$(\Delta M)_k = \text{moment of } k\text{th element} = (\Delta W)_k \bar{\bar{x}}_k,$$

$$(\Delta M)_k = \rho(\bar{x}_k)[f_1(x_k^*) - f_2(x_k^*)] \bar{\bar{x}}_k(\Delta x)_k.$$

We could say next that

$$\text{moment of plate} = \sum_{k=1}^{n} \rho(\bar{x}_k)[f_1(x_k^*) - f_2(x_k^*)]\bar{\bar{x}}_k(\Delta x)_k,$$

and it seems natural to compute this moment by taking a limit as n grows beyond all bounds, the largest $(\Delta x)_k$ approaching 0, thus forming an integral:

$$\text{moment of plate} = \int_{x=0}^{a} \rho(x)[f_1(x) - f_2(x)]x\, dx.$$

Since the numbers x_k^*, $\bar{x}_k$, and $\bar{\bar{x}}_k$ were not necessarily equal, it was necessary to appeal to an extension of Theorem 8.8-2 at the last step.

Example 1.   We are given a homogeneous rectangular plate with weight density $\rho = \text{const}$ and dimensions a and b, $a > b$. Find the moment about an axis through one of the shorter ends.

Let us choose a coordinate system as indicated in Fig. 8.68 and subdivide the plate into n elements by choosing subdivision points $x_0 = 0 < x_1 < x_2 < \cdots < x_n = a$. We can say that

$$\text{area of } k\text{th element} = b(\Delta x)_k,$$

$$\text{weight of } k\text{th element} = \rho b(\Delta x)_k.$$

The kth element is described by $x_{k-1} \leq x \leq x_k$. If we take its moment arm to be x_{k-1}, we get too small a moment. If we take its moment arm to be x_k, we get too large a moment. There exists an $\bar{\bar{x}}_k$, $x_{k-1} < \bar{\bar{x}}_k < x_k$, such that

$$\text{moment for } k\text{th element} = \rho b \bar{\bar{x}}_k(\Delta x)_k,$$

and

$$\text{moment for plate} = \rho b \int_{x=0}^{a} x\, dx = \rho b \left. \frac{x^2}{2} \right|_{x=0}^{a} = \tfrac{1}{2}\rho b a^2.$$

Example 2.   Consider again a rectangular plate of dimensions a and b, $a > b$, and again choose axes as in Fig. 8.68. But this time let the density ρ increase as one moves from one of the shorter ends toward the other according to the formula $\rho = \alpha + \beta x$, where α and β are positive constants. Find the moment about the y axis.

We use the same subdivision into elements as in Example 1. We can say again that

$$\text{area of } k\text{th element} = b(\Delta x)_k,$$

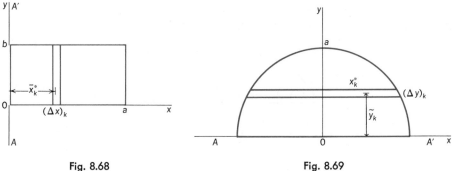

Fig. 8.68   Fig. 8.69

but since the density for the kth element is greater than $\rho(x_{k-1})$ and less than $\rho(x_k)$, we say this time that

$$\text{weight of } k\text{th element} = b\rho(\bar{x}_k)(\Delta x)_k, \tag{1}$$

where $\bar{x}_k$ is some x of the kth subinterval. Again the moment arm for the element must be greater than x_{k-1} and less than x_k; we shall say that it is $\bar{\bar{x}}_k$, where $x_{k-1} < \bar{\bar{x}}_k < x_k$. Thus

$$\text{moment for } k\text{th element} = b\rho(\bar{x}_k)\bar{\bar{x}}_k(\Delta x)_k,$$

and

$$\text{moment for plate} = \lim_{n \to \infty} \sum_{k=1}^{n} b\rho(\bar{x}_k)\bar{\bar{x}}_k(\Delta x)_k,$$

it being understood that all $(\Delta x)_k$'s approach 0 as n grows beyond all bounds. Now $\bar{\bar{x}}_k$ and $\bar{x}_k$ may or may not be equal, but Theorem 8.8-2 points out that such a limit of a sum is given by a definite integral. We have

$$\text{moment for plate} = \int_{x=0}^{a} b\rho x \, dx.$$

$$= b \int_{x=0}^{a} (\alpha + \beta x)x \, dx = b\left[\alpha \frac{x^2}{2} + \beta \frac{x^3}{3} \right]_{x=0}^{a}$$

$$= \tfrac{1}{6} ba^2[3\alpha + 2a\beta].$$

Example 3. We are given a homogeneous semicircular plate of radius a and density ρ. Find its moment about the diameter that bounds it.

Let us choose coordinate axes as in Fig. 8.69, so that the semicircular boundary is part of $x^2 + y^2 = a^2$. We are to find a moment about the x axis. Divide the plate into elements by subdividing the interval $0 \le y \le a$ into n parts. We can say that there is a y_k^*, $y_{k-1} < y_k^* < y_k$, such that

$$\text{area of } k\text{th element} = 2x_k^*(\Delta y)_k.$$

Since the plate is homogeneous and the density function is constant, we can say that

$$\text{weight of element} = 2\rho x_k^*(\Delta y)_k.$$

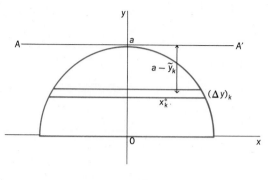

Fig. 8.70

There is a moment arm number $\bar{y}_k$, $y_{k-1} < \bar{y}_k < y_k$, such that

$$\text{moment for element} = 2\rho x_k^* \bar{y}_k (\Delta y)_k.$$

Hence

$$\text{moment for plate} = 2\rho \int_{y=0}^{a} xy \, dy = 2\rho \int_{y=0}^{a} \sqrt{a^2 - y^2} \, y \, dy$$

$$= -\rho \int_{y=0}^{a} (a^2 - y^2)^{1/2}(-2y) \, dy = -\rho \tfrac{2}{3} (a^2 - y^2)^{3/2} \Big|_{y=0}^{a}$$

$$= -\tfrac{2}{3} \rho [0 - a^3] = \tfrac{2}{3} \rho a^3.$$

Example 4.   Consider again the plate of Example 3. Find its moment about the tangent line parallel to the diameter that bounds it.

The coordinate axes are chosen in Fig. 8.70 as they were in Fig. 8.69, and the plate is divided into elements as it was in Example 3. As before, we can say that there is a y_k^* such that

$$\text{area of } k\text{th element} = 2x_k^* (\Delta y)_k,$$

$$\text{weight of element} = 2\rho x_k^* (\Delta y)_k.$$

For the moment this time we can say that there exists a $\bar{y}_k$, $y_{k-1} < \bar{y}_k < y_k$ such that the

$$\text{moment for element} = 2\rho x_k^* (a - \bar{y}_k)(\Delta y)_k,$$

and

$$\text{moment for plate} = 2\rho \int_{y=0}^{a} x(a - y) dy$$

$$= 2\rho \int_{y=0}^{a} \sqrt{a^2 - y^2} \, (a - y) \, dy$$

$$= 2\rho a \int_{y=0}^{a} \sqrt{a^2 - y^2} \, dy - 2\rho \int_{y=0}^{a} \sqrt{a^2 - y^2} \, y \, dy.$$

The second of these integrals can be evaluated as in Example 3. The first can be evaluated by using the trigonometric substitution $y = a \sin \theta$ or by noticing that $\int_0^a \sqrt{a^2 - y^2}\, dy$ also represents the area of a quarter-circle of radius a and must be $\pi a^2/4$. We conclude that

$$\text{moment for plate} = 2\rho a \frac{\pi a^2}{4} - \frac{2}{3} \rho a^3 = \frac{1}{6} \rho a^3 (3\pi - 4).$$

∥

The physicist refers frequently to a "center of gravity" point, a point at which the entire weight of the plate can be considered as concentrated without changing its moment about any axis. If a horizonal plate were supported at its center of gravity point, it would be in equilibrium because, imagining the entire weight concentrated at the point of support, the moment arm for this weight for any axis through the point of support would be 0 and the moment for any such axis would be 0.

Example 5. Find the center of gravity of the rectangular plate described in Example 2 and Fig. 8.68.

Let the center of gravity point have the coordinates $C(\bar{x}, \bar{y})$. Since the weight density of the plate does not vary as one moves in the y direction, it is intuitively clear that $\bar{y} = b/2$. From Eq. (1) of Example 2 we can say that

$$\text{weight of plate} = b \int_{x=0}^{a} \rho\, dx$$

$$= b \int_{x=0}^{a} (\alpha + \beta x)\, dx = b \left(\alpha a + \frac{\beta a^2}{2} \right) = \frac{1}{2} ba\, (2\alpha + \beta a).$$

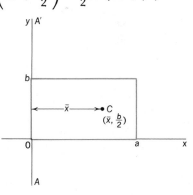

Now if the entire weight of the plate were considered concentrated at $C(\bar{x}, b/2)$, its moment about the y axis would be

$$M_y = (\text{weight})(\text{moment arm})$$

$$= \tfrac{1}{2}\, ba(2\alpha + \beta a)\bar{x};$$

see Fig. 8.71. However, we computed M_y in Example 2. There

$$M_y = \tfrac{1}{6}\, ba^2(3\alpha + 2\beta a).$$

Comparing the two results, we find that

Fig. 8.71

$$\frac{1}{2} ba(2\alpha + \beta a)\bar{x} = \frac{1}{6} ba^2(3\alpha + 2\beta a) \qquad \text{or} \qquad \bar{x} = \frac{1}{3}\, a\, \frac{3\alpha + 2\beta a}{2\alpha + \beta a}.$$

The center of gravity is the point $C(\tfrac{1}{3} a[3\alpha + 2\beta a]/[2\alpha + \beta a], b/2)$. As a common-sense check, note that when $\beta = 0$ the density is constant, and then C has the coordinates $(a/2, b/2)$, which would be expected for a homogeneous plate.

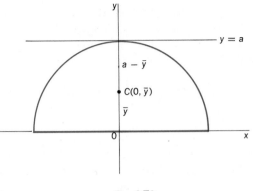

Fig. 8.72

Example 6.   Find the center of gravity of the semicircular plate of constant weight density considered in Examples 3 and 4.

Let the center of gravity be the point $C(\bar{x}, \bar{y})$. Because of the plate's symmetry with respect to the y axis, it is intuitively clear that $\bar{x} = 0$. To determine $\bar{y}$, we observe that the weight of the plate is $(\pi/2)\,a^2\rho$. Hence if the entire weight were considered concentrated at $C(0, \bar{y})$, the moment for the x axis would be

$$M_x = \frac{\pi}{2}\,a^2\rho\bar{y}.$$

See Fig. 8.72. But in Example 3 we pointed out that

$$M_x = \tfrac{2}{3}\,\rho a^3.$$

Hence, by comparison,

$$\frac{\pi}{2}\,a^2\rho\bar{y} = \frac{2}{3}\,\rho a^3 \qquad \text{or} \qquad \bar{y} = \frac{4}{3\pi}\,a \approx .42a.$$

It is interesting to compute $\bar{y}$ a second way. With all the weight considered concentrated at $C(0, \bar{y})$, the moment about the line $y = a$ would be

$$M_{y=a} = (\tfrac{1}{2}\,\pi a^2\rho)(a - \bar{y}).$$

But we found in Example 4 that

$$M_{y=a} = \tfrac{1}{6}\,\rho a^3(3\pi - 4).$$

Comparing results, we have

$$\tfrac{1}{2}\,\pi a^2\rho(a - \bar{y}) = \tfrac{1}{6}\,\rho a^3(3\pi - 4),$$

$$a - \bar{y} = \frac{1}{3\pi}\,a(3\pi - 4),$$

$$\bar{y} = a - \frac{a}{3\pi}\,(3\pi - 4) = \frac{4}{3\pi}\,a.$$

EXERCISES 8.11

Appropriate physical units for distances and weights are assumed in each exercise.

1. A rectangular plate is bounded by the lines $x = 0$, $x = 6$, $y = 0$, and $y = 2$. Its weight density is given by the formula $\rho = 1 + .1y$.
   (a) Find its moment about the x axis.
   (b) Find its moment about the line $y = 2$.
   (c) Find its moment about the line $y = 1$.
   (d) Locate its center of gravity.

2. A homogeneous right-triangular plate has vertices $(0, 0)$, $(a, 0)$, $(0, c)$.
   (a) Find its moment about the x axis.
   (b) Show that its center of gravity has y coordinate $c/3$.
   (c) Explain why the moment about the x axis and the y coordinate of the center of gravity would have been the same for any other triangle with the same base and equal altitude; that is, with vertices $(0, 0)$, $(a, 0)$, (b, c).
   (d) Result (c) says that for any homogeneous triangular plate the center of gravity lies on lines parallel to the sides and $\frac{1}{3}$ of the way from the sides to the opposite vertices. Show that this means that the center of gravity must be the intersection of the medians.

3. Consider the homogeneous plate bounded by the y axis and that half of the ellipse

$$\frac{x^2}{a^2} + \frac{y^2}{b^2} = 1$$

   which lies to the right of the y axis.
   (a) Find its moment about the y axis.
   (b) Locate its center of gravity.

4. Consider the homogeneous plate bounded by the x axis and that portion of the parabola $y = 9 - x^2$ which lies above the x axis.
   (a) Find its moment about the x axis.
   (b) Find its moment about the line $y = 9$.
   (c) Locate its center of gravity.

5. A semicircular plate is bounded by the y axis and $x = \sqrt{a^2 - y^2}$. Its density is given by $\rho = 1 + \alpha x$.
   (a) Find its moment about the y axis.
   (b) For which choice of the constant α will the center of gravity be the point $(a/2, 0)$?

6. A homogeneous plate is bounded by one arch of the sine curve, $y = \sin x$, and the x axis.
   (a) Find its moment about the x axis. (*Suggestion:* Use vertical elements. Compute the moment of an element by assuming its entire weight concentrated at its center of gravity; the center of gravity of a rectangle is its geometric center.)
   (b) Locate its center of gravity.

7. A homogeneous circular sector plate is bounded by $x = \sqrt{a^2 - y^2}$ and

$$y = \pm(\tan \alpha)x, \qquad 0 < \alpha < \pi/2.$$

   (a) Find its moment about the y axis.
   (b) Locate its center of gravity.

8. Let the moment of a homogeneous plate about the y axis be M_y. Show that the absolute value of the moment of the same plate about the parallel line $x = a$ is $|aW - M_y|$, where W is the weight of the plate. Note that the result holds even if the density is a function of x.

9. Consider a homogeneous plate. The x coordinate of the center of gravity of the plate is often located by comparing two computations for the moment about the y axis, one computation with the weight considered distributed through the plate and one with the weight considered concentrated at the center of gravity. Show that the same result may be obtained by comparing moments about any line $x = a$ instead.

8.12 Moment of Inertia

If the motion of a rigid body is a translation, its constituent particles all have the same velocity vectors. If a rigid body rotates, on the other hand, the constituent particles have different velocities, and the problem of describing the body's motion would be expected to be more difficult. However, we can define new rotational quantities that make it possible to study rotations by using formulas analogous to those already used for motions in general. There is thus achieved a remarkable economy of thought and effort.

First, in describing rotations of particles, we talk of the angle θ through which a particle rotates about the axis of rotation, the angular velocity $\omega = d\theta/dt$, and the angular acceleration $\alpha = d\omega/dt$. When r is the radius of the circle in which a particle rotates, these rotational quantities are related to the corresponding quantities s, $v = ds/dt$, and $a = dv/dt$ used in the general case by the formulas $s = r\theta$, $v = r\omega$ or $ds/dt = r\,d\theta/dt$, and $a = r\alpha$ or $dv/dt = r\,d\omega/dt$.

Second, we say, in general, that a force causes a motion; we say that a moment (or torque) causes a rotation.

Third, corresponding to the mass, in rotations we speak of the moment of inertia.

■ DEFINITION 1

Moment of inertia of a particle. The moment of inertia of a particle of mass m traveling in a circle of radius r is mr^2.

This definition is the only one possible for the physicist if he intends to develop formulas for rotations analogous to those he used for translations. This may be illustrated by a very important case. A particle of mass m moving with velocity v has kinetic energy given by the formula K.E. $= \frac{1}{2}mv^2$. If the particle rotates in a circle of radius r, however, then $v = r\omega$, K.E. $= \frac{1}{2}mr^2\omega^2$, and if $I = mr^2$, then K.E. $= \frac{1}{2}I\omega^2$.

To illustrate again, consider the statement $F = ma$. It says that the mass measures a body's tendency to resist a change in velocity, for a larger m would require a larger F to achieve the same a, and a is the rate of change of velocity. For a rotation about an axis A, the corresponding statement is $M = I\alpha$, where M is the moment about A that causes the rotation, I is the moment of inertia of the body about A, and α is the angular acceleration of the ensuing rotation about A. This formula says that the moment of inertia measures a body's tendency to resist a change in angular velocity, for a larger I would require a larger M to achieve the same angular acceleration α.

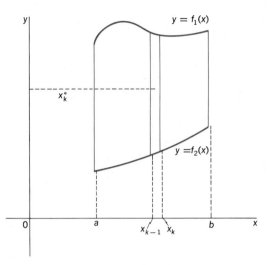

Fig. 8.73

In this section we are primarily concerned with the problem of computing the moment of inertia of a plate with respect to a given axis of rotation as a limit of a sum of the moments of inertia of its elements. Consider then a plate in the x, y plane and rotation about the y axis. Let the plate be bounded by the lines $x = a$, $x = b$ and the curves $y = f_1(x)$, $y = f_2(x)$, $a \leq x \leq b$, with $f_1(x) \geq f_2(x)$ for $a \leq x \leq b$; see Fig. 8.73. Let the mass density be given by the continuous function $\mu(x)$, $a \leq x \leq b$. This means the following: take the mass of a square of side s which includes the point (x, y), form the ratio of the mass to the area of square, and repeat with s approaching 0; then the limit approached by the ratio is $\mu(x)$. Observe that this is a rather special plate because $\mu(x)$ varies with motion along the plate in the x direction, but not with motion in the y direction.

Now subdivide the plate into n elements parallel to the axis of rotation, the y axis, by choosing $a = x_0 < x_1 < x_2 < \cdots < x_n = b$ and drawing $x = x_1$, $x = x_2$, $\cdots$. There is an $\bar{\bar{x}}_k$ of the kth subregion, $x_{k-1} \leq \bar{\bar{x}}_k \leq x_k$, such that

$$(\Delta A)_k = \text{area of } k\text{th subregion} = [f_1(\bar{\bar{x}}_k) - f_2(\bar{\bar{x}}_k)](\Delta x)_k.$$

Since $\mu(x)$ is a continuous function for $a \leq x \leq b$, μ attains a maximum value J_k and a minimum value j_k for $x_{k-1} \leq x \leq x_k$, and the mass of the kth subregion must lie between $J_k(\Delta A)_k$ and $j_k(\Delta A)_k$. There is a number $\bar{x}_k$, $x_{k-1} \leq \bar{x}_k \leq x_k$, such that

$$(\Delta m)_k = \text{mass of } k\text{th subregion} = \mu(\bar{x}_k)(\Delta A)_k.$$

Finally, since the particles of the kth subregion will rotate in circles whose radii vary from x_{k-1} to x_k, the moment of inertia for the kth subregion must lie between $(\Delta m)_k (x_{k-1})^2$ and $(\Delta m)_k (x_k)^2$. There is a number x_k^*, $x_{k-1} < x_k^* < x_k$, such that

$$(\Delta I)_k = \text{moment of inertia of } k\text{th subregion}$$

$$= (\Delta m)_k (x_k^*)^2$$

$$= \mu(\bar{x}_k)[f_1(\bar{\bar{x}}_k) - f_2(\bar{\bar{x}}_k)](x_k^*)^2 (\Delta x)_k,$$

$$I_y = \text{moment of inertia of plate for rotation about } y \text{ axis}$$

$$= \sum_{k=1}^{n} \mu(\bar{x}_k)[f_1(\bar{\bar{x}}_k) - f_2(\bar{\bar{x}}_k)](x_k^*)^2 (\Delta x)_k.$$

It is natural to try to evaluate this sum by taking a limit as n grows beyond all bounds, the largest $(\Delta x)_k$ approaching 0, thus forming an integral:

$$I_y = \int_a^b \mu(x)[f_1(x) - f_2(x)]x^2 \, dx.$$

Since $\bar{x}_k$, $\bar{\bar{x}}_k$, and x_k^* are not necessarily the same number, a refinement of Theorem 8.8-2 must be used in justifying the integral for I_y.

Example 1.   A homogeneous rectangular plate has constant mass density μ and dimensions a and b. Find its moment of inertia with respect to an axis parallel to, and midway between, the sides of length a.

Choose coordinate axes as indicated in Fig. 8.74. Divide the interval $-b/2 \le x \le b/2$ into n parts by choosing subdivision points. Then we can say that

$$(\Delta A)_k = \text{area of } k\text{th element} = a(\Delta x)_k,$$

and that

$$(\Delta m)_k = \text{mass of } k\text{th element} = a\mu(\Delta x)_k.$$

The radii of the circles in which the particles of the kth element travel, if they rotate about the y axis, vary from x_{k-1} to x_k. The moment of inertia for this element must fall between $(\Delta m)_k (x_{k-1})^2$ and $(\Delta m)_k (x_k)^2$, and there exists an x_k^*, $x_{k-1} < x_k^* < x_k$, such that

$$(\Delta I)_k = \text{moment of inertia for } k\text{th element} = (\Delta m)_k (x_k^*)^2 = a\mu(x_k^*)^2 (\Delta x)_k,$$

$$I_y = \text{moment of inertia for plate about } y \text{ axis}$$

$$= \int_{x=-b/2}^{b/2} a\mu x^2 \, dx = \frac{a\mu}{3} x^3 \Big|_{x=-b/2}^{b/2} = \frac{a\mu}{3}\left(\frac{b^3}{8} + \frac{b^3}{8}\right) = \frac{1}{12} a\mu b^3. \tag{1}$$

Two elements symmetrically situated with respect to the axis of rotation have the same moment of inertia. In Eq. (1) we could have written the integral

$$2 \int_{x=0}^{b/2} a\mu x^2 \, dx.$$

Example 2.   A semicircular plate of radius a is to rotate about the diameter that bounds it. The mass density μ varies directly as the distance from this diameter. Find the moment of inertia.

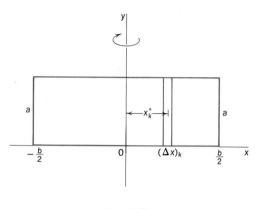

Fig. 8.74

Let the center of the circle be placed at the origin of coordinates and let the diameter which is to serve as the axis of rotation lie along the x axis, as in Fig. 8.75. Divide the plate into n elements by subdividing the interval $0 \leq y \leq a$ into n parts. For the kth element we know that there is a $\bar{y}_k$ and a corresponding $\bar{x}_k$ such that

$$\text{area of } k\text{th element} = (\Delta A)_k = 2\bar{x}_k(\Delta y)_k.$$

Next, the mass density function is $\mu = cy$, where c is a constant of proportionality. The mass of the kth element is greater than $cy_{k-1}(\Delta A)_k$ and less than $cy_k(\Delta A)_k$. There exists a $\bar{\bar{y}}_k, y_{k-1} < \bar{\bar{y}}_k < y_k$, such that

$$(\Delta m)_k = \text{mass of } k\text{th element} = 2c\bar{x}_k\bar{\bar{y}}_k(\Delta y)_k.$$

The radii of the circles in which the particles of the kth element travel if they rotate about the x axis vary from y_{k-1} to y_k. The moment of inertia for the kth element must lie between $(\Delta m)_k(y_{k-1})^2$ and $(\Delta m)_k(y_k)^2$. There exists a $y_k^*, y_{k-1} < y_k^* < y_k$, such that

$$(\Delta I)_k = (\Delta m)_k(y_k^*)^2 = 2c\bar{x}_k\bar{\bar{y}}_k(\Delta y)_k(y_k^*)^2.$$

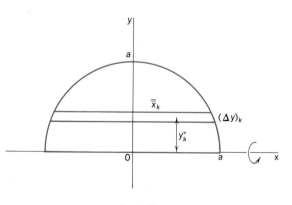

Fig. 8.75

Now we say that

$$I_x = \text{moment of inertia of plate}$$

$$= 2c \int_{y=0}^{a} xy^3 \, dy = 2c \int_{y=0}^{a} y^3 \sqrt{a^2 - y^2} \, dy.$$

To evaluate this integral, we could use the trigonometric substitution $y = a \sin \theta$ or the algebraic substitution $\sqrt{a^2 - y^2} = u$. The latter leads to

$$I_x = 2c \int_{y=0}^{a} y^2 \sqrt{a^2 - y^2} \, y \, dy = 2c \int_{u=a}^{0} (a^2 - u^2) u(-u \, du)$$

$$= -2c \int_{a}^{0} (a^2 u^2 - u^4) \, du = -2c \left[a^2 \frac{u^3}{3} - \frac{u^5}{5} \right] \Big|_{u=a}^{0} = \frac{4ca^5}{15}.$$

Example 3. A homogeneous circular plate of radius a and mass density μ is to rotate about an axis perpendicular to the plate and through its center. Find its moment of inertia.

In Fig. 8.76 we indicate that the plate is to be considered as consisting of a set of n concentric circular rings described by subdividing a radius interval $0 \le r \le a$; we choose numbers $r_0 = 0 < r_1 < r_2 < \cdots < r_{n-1} < r_n = a$. Since the area of a circular ring can be found by subtracting the area of the smaller circle from that of the larger, we can say that

$$(\Delta A)_k = \text{area of } k\text{th ring element} = \pi r_k^2 - \pi r_{k-1}^2$$

$$= \pi (r_k + r_{k-1})(r_k - r_{k-1}) = 2\pi \bar{r}_k (\Delta r)_k.$$

Here we have written $(\Delta r)_k = r_k - r_{k-1}$ and $\bar{r}_k = \frac{1}{2}(r_k + r_{k-1})$, so that $\bar{r}_k$ is the "average radius" for the element. It follows next that

$$(\Delta m)_k = \text{mass of } k\text{th ring element} = 2\pi \mu \bar{r}_k (\Delta r)_k.$$

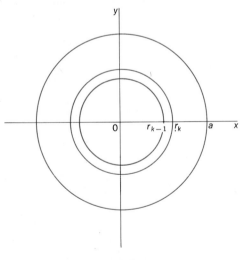

Fig. 8.76

Now, if the various particles of the ring element were to rotate about an axis through O perpendicular to the xy plane, the radii of the circles in which they would travel would vary from r_{k-1} to r_k. Hence the moment of inertia for this element would be greater than $(\Delta m)_k(r_{k-1})^2$, but less than $(\Delta m)_k(r_k)^2$. There exists an r_k^*, $r_{k-1} < r_k^* < r_k$, such that

$$(\Delta I)_k = \text{moment of inertia of } k\text{th ring element} = 2\pi\mu\bar{r}_k(\Delta r)_k(r_k^*)^2.$$

Then we say that

$I = $ moment of inertia of plate

$$= 2\pi\mu \int_{r=0}^{a} r^3 \, dr = 2\pi\mu \frac{a^4}{4} = \frac{1}{2}\pi\mu a^4 = \frac{1}{2}(\pi\mu a^2)a^2 = \frac{1}{2}(\text{mass})(\text{radius})^2.$$

EXERCISES 8.12

Appropriate units are assumed in each of the following exercises. Exercises 1, 2, and 3 deal with rods rather than plates, and the student can reason with elements that are subintervals on a line rather than with subregions as in the text examples.

1. Consider a homogeneous rod of length a and mass density μ. Find its moment of inertia about an axis perpendicular to the rod and through its midpoint.

2. Consider a rod of length 2 and mass density $1 + .01x^2$, where x is the distance from the center of the rod. Find its moment of inertia about an axis perpendicular to the rod and (a) through its center, (b) through one end.

3. A rod of length a is to be made of two metals, the first half of a metal A of mass density α, the other half of a metal of mass density β. The rod is to rotate about an axis perpendicular to the rod and through the end point made of metal A. What should the ratio of the densities be if the two halves of the rod are to have equal moments of inertia?

4. A homogeneous plate has mass density μ and the shape of a right triangle with legs of lengths a and b. Find the moment of inertia about an axis along the leg of length b.

5. A homogeneous triangular plate has mass density μ, base and altitude of lengths b and a, respectively. Find the moment of inertia about an axis along the base.

6. A circular plate of radius a has mass density $\mu = 1 + br$, where r is the distance from the center and b is a constant. Find its moment of inertia about an axis through its center and perpendicular to its plane.

7. A circular plate of radius a has constant mass density μ. Find its moment of inertia about an axis tangent to the plate.

8. A homogeneous plate of mass density μ has the shape of a segment of a circle of radius a. The central angle for the segment is 2α, $\alpha < \pi/2$. Find the moment of inertia about the axis of symmetry of the segment. See Fig. 8.77, where the segment is labeled ABC.

9. A homogeneous plate of mass density μ has the shape of an ellipse. Find its moment of inertia about its major axis.

10. A plate is bounded by the parabola $x^2 = y$ and the line $y = 1$. The mass

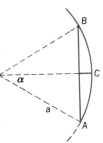

Fig. 8.77

density decreases as the distance from $y = 1$ increases according to the formula $\mu = 1 - .1(1 - y) = .9 + .1y$. Find the moment of inertia about the line $y = 1$.

11. A homogeneous plate of mass density μ is bounded by the x axis and $y = \sin x$ for $0 \leq x \leq \pi$. Find its moment of inertia about the line $x = \pi/2$.

12. The *radius of gyration* is the distance from the axis of rotation to a point at which the entire mass of a body can be considered concentrated for the purpose of computing the moment of inertia. Find the radius of gyration for the plate and axis described in (a) Example 1; (b) Example 2; and (c) Example 3.

13. Consider a plate with constant mass density μ placed so that its center of gravity lies on the y axis. Let $I_{x=0}$ be its moment of inertia about the y axis and let $I_{x=a}$ be its moment of enertia about the line $x = a$. Show that

$$I_{x=a} = I_{x=0} + ma^2,$$

where m is the mass of the plate.*

8.13 Improper Integrals

The symbol $\int_a^b f(x) \, dx$ is defined as the limit of a certain sum. First the interval $a \leq x \leq b$ is divided into n subintervals; then for $k = 1, \cdots, n$ we select x_k^*, an x of the kth subinterval, and form the product $f(x_k^*)(\Delta x)_k$; finally, we take

$$\lim_{n \to \infty} \sum_{k=1}^{n} f(x_k^*)(\Delta x)_k,$$

it being understood that the lengths of all subintervals approach 0 as n grows beyond all bounds. The symbol

$$\int_0^\infty f(x) \, dx$$

has no meaning according to this definition because the interval $0 \leq x \leq \infty$ cannot be subdivided into n parts such that the lengths of all subintervals are finite; at least one term of the form $f(x_k^*)(\Delta x)_k$ cannot be formed. Neither does the symbol

$$\int_{x=0}^{a} \frac{a}{\sqrt{a^2 - x^2}} \, dx \tag{1}$$

have meaning according to this definition, because

$$f(x) = \frac{a}{\sqrt{a^2 - x^2}}$$

grows beyond all bounds as x approaches a and the term $f(x_n^*)(\Delta x)_n$ of our sum $\sum_{k=1}^{n} f(x_k^*)(\Delta x)_k$ will give us difficulty when we let n grow beyond all bounds. And yet there are occasions when it would seem natural to write an integral expression like (1).

Example 1. In Example 8.6-2 we computed the circumference of the circle $x^2 + y^2 = a^2$ by setting up the integral

$$\int_0^{a/\sqrt{2}} \frac{a}{\sqrt{a^2 - x^2}} \, dx$$

---

* See Exercises 12.7-13 and 12.7-14.

for $\frac{1}{8}$ of the circumference. If we had tried to deal with the first-quadrant portion of the arc, we would have been led to the expression

$$\int_0^a \frac{a}{\sqrt{a^2 - x^2}}\, dx.$$

What shall we define such an integral expression to be? One suggestion is this: We can find the length of the circular arc $y = \sqrt{a^2 - x^2}$, $0 \le x \le b$, for any number $b < a$; this arc length is

$$\int_0^b \sqrt{1 + (dy/dx)^2}\, dx = \int_0^b \frac{a}{\sqrt{a^2 - x^2}}\, dx$$

$$= a \sin^{-1}\frac{x}{a}\Big|_0^b = a \sin^{-1}\frac{b}{a}.$$

Repeat this computation for the arc $0 \le x \le b_1$, where $b < b_1 < a$, then for an arc $0 \le x \le b_2$, where $b_1 < b_2 < a$, and so on. In other words, we can consider arcs that approach a quarter-circle as closely as desired and see if a limit is being approached. We find that

$$\lim_{b \to a^-} \int_0^b \frac{a}{\sqrt{a^2 - x^2}}\, dx = \lim_{b \to a^-} a \sin^{-1}\frac{b}{a} = a\frac{\pi}{2}.$$

Of course this result would lead us to the correct circumference of a full circle of radius a, namely $2\pi a$.

■ CONVENTION 1

The expression $\int_a^b f(x)\, dx$ shall be called an improper integral if one (or both) boundaries is infinite or if $f(x)$ is not defined at every point of the interval $a \le x \le b$.

■ DEFINITION 1

If $f(x)$ is defined for $a \le x < b$ but $f(b)$ is not defined, then $\int_a^b f(x)\, dx$ will mean $\lim_{c \to b^-} \int_a^c f(x)\, dx$.

■ DEFINITION 2

If $f(x)$ is defined for $a < x \le b$ but $f(a)$ is not defined, then $\int_a^b f(x)\, dx$ will mean $\lim_{c \to a^+} \int_c^b f(x)\, dx$.

■ DEFINITION 3

If we have $a < c < b$ and if $f(x)$ is defined for all x of $a \le x \le b$ except for $x = c$, then $\int_a^b f(x)\, dx$ will mean $\int_a^c f(x)\, dx + \int_c^b f(x)\, dx$.

■ DEFINITION 4

If $f(x)$ is defined for $x \ge a$, then $\int_a^\infty f(x)dx$ will mean $\lim_{L \to \infty} \int_a^L f(x)\, dx$.

■ DEFINITION 5

If $f(x)$ is defined for $x \le b$, then $\int_{-\infty}^b f(x)\, dx$ will mean $\lim_{L \to \infty} \int_{-L}^b f(x)\, dx$.

■ DEFINITION 6

If $f(x)$ is defined for all real x, then $\int_{-\infty}^{\infty} f(x)\, dx$ will mean $\int_{-\infty}^{0} f(x)\, dx$ $+ \int_{0}^{\infty} f(x)\, dx$.

■ CONVENTION 2

If the limit of proper integrals called for in the definition of an improper integral exists, the improper integral is said to be convergent; otherwise it is divergent.

Example 2. The integral $\int_{-1}^{1} 1/x^2\, dx$ is improper because $1/x^2$ is not defined at $x = 0$. We can say that

$$\int_{-1}^{1} \frac{1}{x^2}\, dx = \int_{-1}^{0} \frac{1}{x^2}\, dx + \int_{0}^{1} \frac{1}{x^2}\, dx,$$

and then that

$$\int_{0}^{1} \frac{1}{x^2}\, dx = \lim_{a \to 0^+} \int_{a}^{1} \frac{1}{x^2}\, dx = \lim_{a \to 0^+} \left(-\frac{1}{x} \right) \Big|_{a}^{1} = \lim_{a \to 0^+} \left(\frac{1}{a} - 1 \right) = \infty.$$

The improper integral $\int_{0}^{1} 1/x^2\, dx$ is divergent and, therefore, so is $\int_{-1}^{1} 1/x^2\, dx$.

Example 3. The integral $\displaystyle\int_{-1}^{1} \frac{dx}{\sqrt[3]{x^2}}$ is also improper, because its integrand is not defined at $x = 0$. Again we say that

$$\int_{-1}^{1} \frac{1}{\sqrt[3]{x^2}}\, dx = \int_{-1}^{0} \frac{1}{\sqrt[3]{x^2}}\, dx + \int_{0}^{1} \frac{1}{\sqrt[3]{x^2}}\, dx.$$

But this time

$$\int_{0}^{1} \frac{1}{\sqrt[3]{x^2}}\, dx = \lim_{a \to 0^+} \int_{a}^{1} \frac{1}{\sqrt[3]{x^2}}\, dx = \lim_{a \to 0^+} 3x^{1/3} \Big|_{x=a}^{1}$$

$$= \lim_{a \to 0^+} 3(1 - a^{1/3}) = 3$$

and

$$\int_{-1}^{0} \frac{1}{\sqrt[3]{x^2}}\, dx = \lim_{b \to 0^-} \int_{-1}^{b} \frac{1}{\sqrt[3]{x^2}}\, dx = \lim_{b \to 0^-} 3x^{1/3} \Big|_{-1}^{b}$$

$$= \lim_{b \to 0^-} 3(b^{1/3} + 1) = 3.$$

Hence $\displaystyle\int_{-1}^{1} \frac{1}{\sqrt[3]{x^2}}\, dx$ is a convergent improper integral. Its value is 6.

Example 4. Here is an example of some importance to a physicist. Consider an indefinitely long wire along the y axis carrying a uniform charge of Q coulombs per cm. With what force is an oppositely signed unit charge at $A(a, 0)$, $a > 0$, attracted toward the wire?

First let us consider the wire as consisting of two halves, the first the portion above the x axis, the second the portion below. Observe that $\vec{F}_1$, the attractive force on the charge at A due to the first half of the wire, will have an upward component and a horizontal component. By symmetry, $\mathbf{\bar{F}}_2$, the attractive force due to the second half of the wire, will have a downward component that just balances the upward component of $\mathbf{\bar{F}}_1$, and a horizontal component that duplicates that of $\mathbf{\bar{F}}_1$. Hence we shall restrict our attention to the horizontal component of $\mathbf{\bar{F}}_1$.

Subdivide the interval $0 \le y$ by choosing subdivision points $y_0 = 0 < y_1 < y_2 < y_3 < \cdots$. As in Fig. 8.78, for a typical subinterval or element we shall have

charge on element $= Q \, \Delta y$

$$\text{attractive force of element on unit charge at } A \approx \frac{cQ \, \Delta y}{r^2} \qquad (2)$$

$$\text{horizontal component of attractive force of element} \approx \frac{cQ \, \Delta y}{r^2} \cos \phi$$

$$\approx \frac{cQa \, \Delta y}{r^3}$$

$$\approx cQa \, \frac{1}{(a^2 + y^2)^{3/2}} \, \Delta y. \qquad (3)$$

Here, to arrive at Eq. (2) we used Coulomb's law, which says that the force of attraction or repulsion between two electrostatic charges is directly proportional to the product of the charges and inversely proportional to the square of the distance between them.* In both Eqs. (2) and (3) we approximated by assuming that the force of attraction had the direction and magnitude it would have had if all the charge in the element of wire were concentrated at its lower boundary (maximum estimate). It is natural to take for the attractive force of the whole wire the statement

$$\frac{1}{2} \text{ force} = cQa \int_{y=0}^{\infty} \frac{1}{(a^2 + y^2)^{3/2}} \, dy.$$

But now we compute

$$\text{force} = 2cQa \int_{0}^{\infty} \frac{1}{(a^2 + y^2)^{3/2}} \, dy$$

$$= 2cQa \lim_{L \to \infty} \int_{0}^{L} \frac{1}{(a^2 + y^2)^{3/2}} \, dy$$

$$= 2cQa \lim_{L \to \infty} \frac{1}{a^2} \frac{L}{\sqrt{a^2 + L^2}}$$

$$= \frac{2cQ}{a} \lim_{L \to \infty} \frac{1}{\sqrt{a^2/L^2 + 1}}$$

$$= \frac{2cQ}{a}.$$

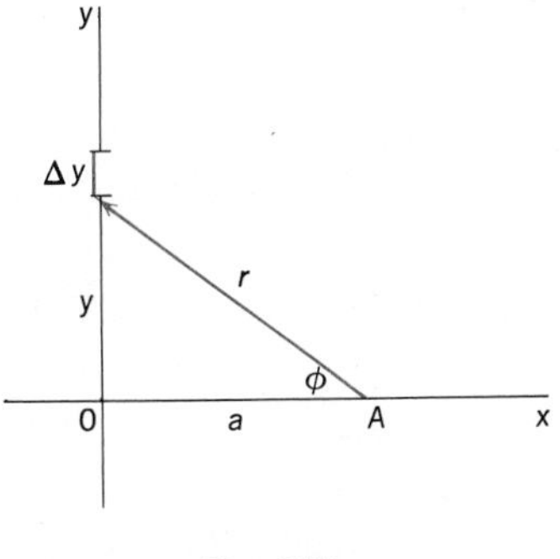

Fig. 8.78

The formal integration called for above can be accomplished by using the substitution $y = a \tan \theta$ or by using a table of integrals.

---
* c is the constant of proportionality.

EXERCISES 8.13

1. Decide whether each of the following integrals is proper or improper. If improper and convergent, find the value. If improper and divergent, say so.

(a) $\displaystyle\int_0^1 \frac{1}{\sqrt{x}}\, dx.$

(g) $\displaystyle\int_{-\infty}^{\infty} \frac{1}{1+x^2}\, dx.$

(l) $\displaystyle\int_2^{\infty} \frac{1}{(x-1)^2}\, dx.$

(b) $\displaystyle\int_0^{\infty} e^{-x}\, dx.$

(h) $\displaystyle\int_0^a \frac{x}{\sqrt{a^2-x^2}}\, dx.$

(m) $\displaystyle\int_0^2 \frac{1}{(x-1)^2}\, dx.$

(c) $\displaystyle\int_0^2 \frac{1}{\sqrt{x^3}}\, dx.$

(i) $\displaystyle\int_0^a \frac{1}{x\sqrt{a^2-x^2}}\, dx.$

(n) $\displaystyle\int_1^{\infty} \log x\, dx.$

(d) $\displaystyle\int_0^1 \tan x\, dx.$

(j) $\displaystyle\int_0^1 \sqrt{x(1-x)}\, dx.$

(o) $\displaystyle\int_0^{\infty} e^{-x}\cos x\, dx.$

(e) $\displaystyle\int_0^1 \cot^2 x\, dx.$

(k) $\displaystyle\int_0^{\infty} \cos x\, dx.$

(p) $\displaystyle\int_0^3 \frac{4}{x^2-2x-3}\, dx.$

(f) $\displaystyle\int_0^1 \cot x\, dx.$

(q) $\displaystyle\int_{-\pi/2}^{\pi/2} \tan x\, dx.$

2. (a) $\displaystyle\int_1^{\infty} \frac{1}{x^a}\, dx$ is convergent for which a?

(b) $\displaystyle\int_0^1 \frac{1}{x^a}\, dx$ is improper but convergent for which a?

3. (a) Show that $\displaystyle\int_2^{\infty} \frac{1}{x^7}\, dx$ is convergent and find its value.

(b) Describe a region with x axis as one boundary whose area is given by $\displaystyle\int_2^{L} \frac{1}{x^7}\, dx.$

(c) Same as (b) for $\displaystyle\int_2^{L} \frac{1}{1+x^7}\, dx.$

(d) Show that $\displaystyle\int_2^{\infty} \frac{1}{1+x^7}\, dx$ is convergent. State an upper bound for its value.

4. (a) Show that $\displaystyle\int_1^{\infty} e^{-x}\, dx$ is convergent and find its value.

(b) Describe a region with x axis as one boundary whose area is given by $\displaystyle\int_1^{L} e^{-x}\, dx.$

(c) Repeat (b) for $\displaystyle\int_1^{L} e^{-x^2}\, dx.$

(d) Show that $\displaystyle\int_1^{\infty} e^{-x^2}\, dx$ is convergent. State an upper bound for its value.

Polar Coordinates

The rectangular or Cartesian coordinate system sets up a certain correspondence between the points of the plane and pairs of numbers called coordinates. But the points of the plane can be set into correspondence with pairs of numbers in more than one way. In this chapter we shall consider a second correspondence, the polar coordinate system.

9.1 The Polar Coordinate System

Select a point in the plane and call it the *pole*. Draw the family of circles with center at the pole, and let these circles be described according to their radii: the circle of radius 1 shall be called $r = 1$, the circle of radius $a \geq 0$ shall be called $r = a$. Next, draw the family of straight lines through the pole and select the horizontal one, calling it the *initial line*. A line of the family which is reached by rotation through an angle α from the initial line is described by $\theta = \alpha$. See Fig. 9.1. Note that the same line may have several different descriptions; $\theta = \alpha$, $\theta = \alpha + \pi$, $\theta = \alpha + 2\pi$ all describe the same line through the pole.

Now a point other than the pole may be described by citing the circle and line on which it lies. Since a line $\theta = \alpha$ and a circle $r = a$ intersect in two points, as in Fig. 9.2, it is necessary to distinguish between the two possibilities.

■ DEFINITION 1

The initial line shall be horizontal. The positive half of the initial line is the half that lies to the right of the pole.

509

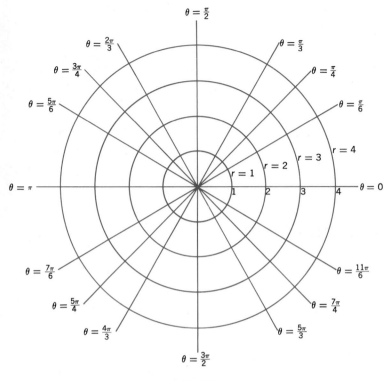

Fig. 9.1

■ DEFINITION 2

If we write $\theta = \alpha$ to describe a line, we take the positive half of that line to be the half assumed by the positive half of the initial line after rotation through the angle α.

■ DEFINITION 3

Polar coordinates. If a point P lies on the circle $r = a > 0$ and on the positive portion of $\theta = \alpha$, then the coordinates (a, α) shall be assigned to it; if it lies on $r = a > 0$ and on the negative portion of $\theta = \alpha$, then the coordinates $(-a, \alpha)$ shall be assigned to it. To the pole itself shall be assigned the coordinates $(0, \theta)$, θ arbitrary.

Example 1. In Fig. 9.2, if we describe the line P_1P_2 as the line $\theta = \alpha$, then P_1 has coordinates (a, α) and P_2 has coordinates $(-a, \alpha)$. But we can also call this line the line $\theta = \alpha + \pi$. Then the coordinates of P_1 would be $(-a, \alpha + \pi)$ and those of P_2 would be $(a, \alpha + \pi)$.

Example 2. Point A of Fig. 9.3 can be described by the coordinates $(2, 0)$, but it can also be described by the coordinates $(2, 2\pi)$, $(-2, \pi)$. Descriptions for point B are $(3, \pi/4)$, $(-3, 5\pi/4)$, $(3, 9\pi/4)$. Descriptions for point C are $(1.5, 5\pi/3)$, $(-1.5, 2\pi/3)$, $(1.5, -\pi/3)$. Descriptions for point D are $(1, 3\pi/2)$, $(-1, \pi/2)$, $(1, -\pi/2)$.

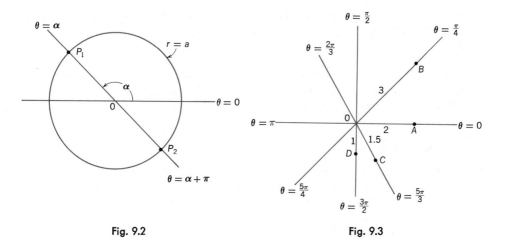

Fig. 9.2   Fig. 9.3

● **Remark 1**

The correspondence between points and coordinate pairs set up by Definition 3, unlike the Cartesian coordinate correspondence, is not "one-to-one" but "one-to-many." To each pair of coordinates there corresponds one point, but to one point there correspond many pairs of coordinates. First, if (r, θ) describes a point, $(-r, \theta + \pi)$ describes the same point. Second, if (r, θ) describes a point, $(r, \theta + 2k\pi)$, k any positive or negative integer, describes the same point. Finally, we have already pointed out that to the pole there correspond the pairs of coordinates $(0, \theta)$, where θ can be arbitrary.

● **Remark 2**

We have described the polar coordinate correspondence by using two families of orthogonal curves, the circles with centers at the pole and the lines through the pole. Rectangular coordinates could have been defined in terms of two families of straight lines. If a point P lies on $x = a$ of one family and $y = b$ of the other, then P's coordinates are (a, b). See Fig. 9.4.

In general, when two families of curves are given with the property that through each point there goes one member of each family,

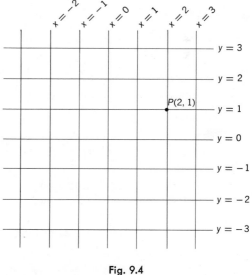

Fig. 9.4

we can set up a coordinate system. We set up two parameters to describe the two families of curves, and then the coordinates of a point are the parameter numbers of the two curves on which it lies. The Cartesian and polar coordinates are the two most frequently used systems, but others are also used in more advanced work. The families of confocal ellipses and hyperbolas on which "elliptic coordinates" are based were described in Example 3.20-4.

In Definition 3.7-1 we stated the relationship between a curve and the corresponding Cartesian equation. For polar coordinates this statement must be modified to take into account the fact that a point may be described in more than one way.

■ DEFINITION 4

The curve-equation relationship.   A curve and polar equation correspond if (a) for each point on the curve there is some pair of coordinates that satisfies the equation, and if (b) whenever a pair of coordinates satisfies the equation, the corresponding point lies on the curve.

Example 3.   The point $A(\frac{1}{2}, \pi/3)$ lies on the curve with equation $r = \sin \frac{1}{2}\theta$ because the coordinates $r = \frac{1}{2}$ and $\theta = \pi/3$ satisfy that equation. The coordinates $r = -\frac{1}{2}$ and $\theta = \pi/3$ do not satisfy the equation, and yet the point $B(-\frac{1}{2}, \pi/3)$ lies on the curve, because other coordinates for B, namely $r = -\frac{1}{2}$ and $\theta = 7\pi/3$, do satisfy the equation. Finally, the point $E(\sqrt{3}/2, \pi/4)$ does not lie on the curve, because the coordinates $r = \sqrt{3}/2$ and $\theta = \pi/4$ do not satisfy the equation, and neither do the alternate coordinates $r = \sqrt{3}/2$ and $\theta = \pi/4 + 2k\pi$, or $r = -\sqrt{3}/2$ and $\theta = 5\pi/4 + 2k\pi$, k any integer.

If a point is described both by rectangular coordinates and by polar coordinates, there is a simple relationship between the two descriptions.

■ THEOREM 1

The relationship between rectangular and polar coordinates.

HYPOTHESIS: (a) The origin and x axis of a rectangular coordinate system coincide with the pole and initial line of a polar coordinate system.

(b) A point P has coordinates (x, y) in one system and (r, θ) in the other.

CONCLUSION:

$$x = r \cos \theta \qquad \text{and} \qquad y = r \sin \theta. \tag{1}$$

$$r^2 = x^2 + y^2 \qquad \text{and} \qquad \tan \theta = y/x.^* \tag{2}$$

PROOF: See Fig. 9.5. Equations (1) follow immediately from the very definition of the sine and cosine functions, and Eqs. (2) follow from Eqs. (1).

EXERCISES 9.1

1. Plot the following points on a polar coordinate diagram. For each point write down two other sets of polar coordinates, one with the same r and one with an r of opposite sign.

---

* $\tan \theta = y/x$ only if $x \neq 0$. We have $\cos \theta = x/\sqrt{x^2 + y^2}$ and $\sin \theta = y/\sqrt{x^2 + y^2}$ for all (x, y) other than $(0, 0)$.

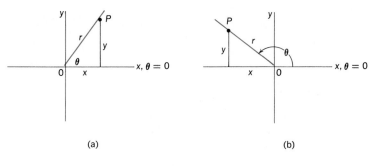

Fig. 9.5

(a) (4, 0).   (c) (3, 5π/4).   (e) (1, −π/4).
(b) (2, 2π/3).   (d) (−2, 3π/4).   (f) (−3, −5π/6).

2. Which of the following points lie on the curve with equation $r = \sin \theta$? (a) (0, 0), (b) (½, π/6), (c) (−½, π/6), (d) ($\sqrt{2}/2$, 3π/4), (e) ($\sqrt{2}/2$, −3π/4), (f) (−$\sqrt{2}/2$, −3π/4).

3. Which of the following points lie on the curve with equation $r = \cos \tfrac{1}{2}\theta$? (a) (½, 2π/3), (b) ($\sqrt{2}/2$, π/2), (c) (½, −2π/3), (d) (−½, 2π/3), (e) (−$\sqrt{2}/2$, π/2), (f) (1, 2π), (g) (0, π), (h) (0, 2π).

4. Find Cartesian coordinates for each of the points listed in Exercise 1.

5. Find polar coordinates for the points with the following Cartesian coordinates: (a) (2, 0), (b) (−2, 2), (c) (0, −3), (d) (1, $\sqrt{3}$), (e) (−1, −$\sqrt{3}$), (f) (−$\sqrt{3}$, −1), (g) (1, −1), (h) ($\sqrt{3}$, −1).

6. As a check on the conclusions of Theorem 1, show that when (r_1, θ_1) in polar coordinates correspond to (x_1, y_1) in Cartesian coordinates according to Eqs. (1), then $(−r_1, \theta_1 + \pi)$ and $(r_1, \theta_1 + 2\pi)$ also correspond to (x_1, y_1).

7. Show that the distance between the points (r_1, θ_1) and (r_2, θ_2) is

$$\sqrt{r_1{}^2 + r_2{}^2 - 2r_1r_2 \cos (\theta_2 - \theta_1)}.$$

9.2 Curve Sketching in Polar Coordinates

To sketch a curve whose equation is given in polar coordinates, a table of values can always be drawn up and a point-by-point plot made, but it is usually more efficient first to analyze the equation for symmetry and for tangents through the pole.

Because a point may be described in many ways in polar coordinates, there are alternate criteria for the same symmetry. We shall not draw up an exhaustive list of symmetry tests, but shall emphasize instead in our examples the reasoning that enables us to deduce these symmetries. The trigonometric facts listed here for the sake of easy reference will be used frequently.

(a) $\cos (-\phi) = \cos \phi$, $\sin (-\phi) = -\sin \phi$.

(b) $\cos (\pi - \phi) = -\cos \phi$, $\sin (\pi - \phi) = \sin \phi$.

(c) $\cos b\phi$ and $\sin b\phi$ are periodic with period $2\pi/b$.

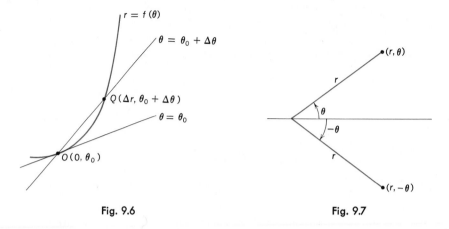

Fig. 9.6   Fig. 9.7

■ THEOREM 1

Tangents at the pole.

HYPOTHESIS: There is a positive number α such that (a) $f(\theta)$ is defined and continuous for $\theta_0 - \alpha \le \theta \le \theta_0 + \alpha$.

(b) $f(\theta_0) = 0$ but $f(\theta) \ne 0$ for any other θ of $\theta_0 - \alpha \le \theta \le \theta_0 + \alpha$.

CONCLUSION: $\theta = \theta_0$ is a line tangent at the pole to the curve with equation $r = f(\theta)$, $\theta_0 - \alpha \le \theta \le \theta_0 + \alpha$.

PROOF: See Fig. 9.6. The pole lies on the curve $r = f(\theta)$, because $0 = f(\theta_0)$ by Hypothesis (b). For $\Delta\theta$ such that $0 < \Delta\theta \le \alpha$, we have $f(\theta_0 + \Delta\theta) \ne 0$ by Hypothesis (b); hence for each such $\Delta\theta$ there is a point $Q(0 + \Delta r, \theta_0 + \Delta\theta)$, $\Delta r = f(\theta_0 + \Delta\theta) \ne 0$, on the curve that is distinct from the pole. The secant line OQ can then be drawn and it has the equation $\theta = \theta_0 + \Delta\theta$, because any line through the pole has an equation of the form $\theta = $ const. When $\Delta\theta \to 0$, $\Delta r \to 0$ also, because r is continuous at θ_0 by Hypothesis (a). Thus, when $\Delta\theta \to 0$, Q approaches O along the curve, and the secant line, $\theta = \theta_0 + \Delta\theta$, approaches $\theta = \theta_0$, which must be the tangent line by the very definition of tangent line as the limiting position of secant lines.

Example 1.   Discuss and sketch $r = a \cos\theta$, $a > 0$. Find the Cartesian equation for the same curve.

Symmetry: Because $\cos(-\theta) = \cos\theta$, the coordinates $(r, -\theta)$ satisfy this equation whenever (r, θ) do. But, as we see in Fig. 9.7, points with these coordinates are symmetrically situated with respect to the initial line; the curve has initial line symmetry.

Tangent at the pole: $r = 0$ when $\theta = \pi/2$; according to Theorem 1 the line $\theta = \pi/2$ is a tangent at the pole.

Finally, we draw up the accompanying table of values (Table 9.1) and plot the corresponding points, together with those symmetrically situated with respect to the initial line; see Fig. 9.8. For θ entries of the interval $90° < \theta \le 180°$, we find r

TABLE 9.1

θ	0°	15°	30°	45°	60°	75°	90°
θ	0	$\pi/12$	$\pi/6$	$\pi/4$	$\pi/3$	$5\pi/12$	$\pi/2$
r	a	$.97a$	$.87a$	$.71a$	$.5a$	$.26a$	0

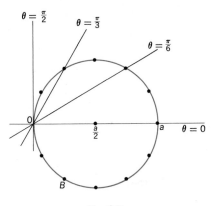

Fig. 9.8

negative and are referred to points already plotted. Thus for $\theta = 2\pi/3 = 120°$ we find $r = -\frac{1}{2}a$ and are referred to the point $B(\frac{1}{2}a, -\pi/3)$, already plotted.

One might guess from Fig. 9.8 that the curve is a circle of radius $a/2$, through the pole, and with center on the initial line. This is indeed the case. To obtain the corresponding rectangular coordinate equation, we use the formulas of Theorem 9.1-1 and write:

$$r = a \cos \theta \qquad \text{or} \qquad r^2 = ar \cos \theta,$$

$$x^2 + y^2 = ax \qquad \text{or} \qquad \left(x - \frac{a}{2}\right)^2 + y^2 = \frac{a^2}{4}.$$

Example 2. Discuss and sketch the lemniscate, $r^2 = a^2 \cos 2\theta$, $a > 0$. Find its Cartesian equation.

Symmetry: We observe first that $(-r, \theta)$ will satisfy the equation whenever (r, θ) does. As Fig. 9.9 indicates, points with these coordinates are symmetrically situated with respect to the pole; the curve has polar symmetry.

Second, because $\cos 2(-\theta) = \cos 2\theta$, the point $(r, -\theta)$ will lie on the curve whenever (r, θ) does. Figure 9.7 indicates that in this case we have initial line symmetry.

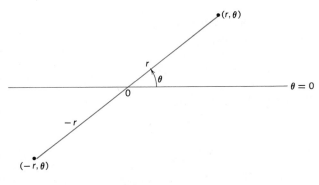

Fig. 9.9

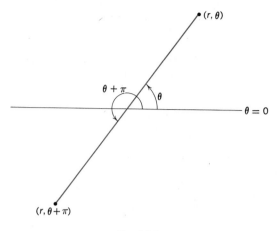

Fig. 9.10

Third, because the function $\cos 2\theta$ has period π, we can say that the point $(r, \theta + \pi)$ lies on the curve whenever (r, θ) does, for $\cos 2(\theta + \pi) = \cos (2\theta + 2\pi) = \cos 2\theta$. But Fig. 9.10 indicates that these points are symmetrically situated with respect to the pole; here is a second test for polar symmetry.

Tangents at the pole: $r = 0$ when $\cos 2\theta = 0$, $2\theta = \pi/2$ or $3\pi/2$, $\theta = \pi/4$ or $3\pi/4$.

Table of values: Because of our symmetry knowledge, we need investigate r only for $0 \leq \theta \leq \pi/2$. The points corresponding to the entries in Table 9.2, and

TABLE 9.2

θ	0°	15°	22½°	30°	45°
θ	0	$\pi/12$	$\pi/8$	$\pi/6$	$\pi/4$
r	a	$.93a$	$.84a$	$.71a$	0

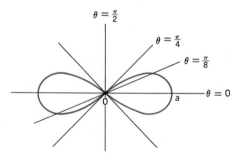

Fig. 9.11

those symmetrically situated with respect to the initial line and the pole, are plotted in Fig. 9.11, and the graph is sketched. For $\pi/4 < \theta \leq \pi/2$, we find $r^2 < 0$, r not real.

To get the Cartesian equation, we can write

$$r^2 = a^2 \cos 2\theta = a^2(\cos^2 \theta - \sin^2 \theta) = a^2 \left(\frac{x^2}{r^2} - \frac{y^2}{r^2} \right),$$

$$r^4 = a^2(x^2 - y^2), \quad \text{and} \quad (x^2 + y^2)^2 = a^2(x^2 - y^2).$$

Example 3a. $r = a(1 - \sin \theta), a > 0.$

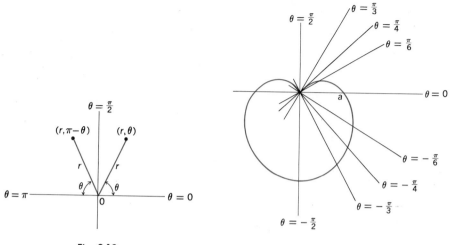

Fig. 9.12   Fig. 9.13

Symmetry: The point $(r, \pi - \theta)$ lies on the curve whenever (r, θ) does, for we have $\sin(\pi - \theta) = \sin \theta$. As we see in Fig. 9.12, these points are symmetrically situated with respect to the line $\theta = \pi/2$; the curve has symmetry with respect to this line.

Tangents at the pole: $r = 0$ when $\sin \theta = 1$, $\theta = \pi/2$.

Table of values: We take advantage of our symmetry knowledge and work only with the interval $-\pi/2 \le \theta \le \pi/2$. The points given in Table 9.3 are plotted and the graph is sketched in Fig. 9.13.

TABLE 9.3

θ	0	$\pi/6$	$\pi/4$	$\pi/3$	$\pi/2$	$-\pi/6$	$-\pi/4$	$-\pi/3$	$-\pi/2$
r	a	$.5a$	$.29a$	$.13a$	0	$1.5a$	$1.71a$	$1.87a$	$2a$

To find an equation satisfied by the Cartesian coordinates of the points on this curve, we can write

$$r = a(1 - \sin \theta), \qquad r = a\left(1 - \frac{y}{r}\right),$$

$$r^2 = a(r - y), \qquad r^2 + ay = ar,$$

$$(r^2 + ay)^2 = a^2 r^2 \qquad \text{and} \qquad (x^2 + y^2 + ay)^2 = a^2(x^2 + y^2).$$

Example 3b. $r = a(2 - \sin \theta)$, $a > 0$.

Symmetry: With respect to the line $\theta = \pi/2$, as in Example 3a.

Tangents at the pole: r is never 0, because $\sin \theta$ is never 2.

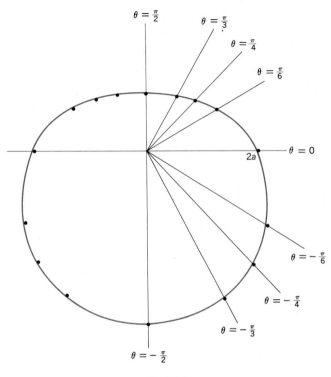

$\theta = \frac{\pi}{2}$

$\theta = \frac{\pi}{3}$

$\theta = \frac{\pi}{4}$

$\theta = \frac{\pi}{6}$

$\theta = 0$

$2a$

$\theta = -\frac{\pi}{6}$

$\theta = -\frac{\pi}{4}$

$\theta = -\frac{\pi}{3}$

$\theta = -\frac{\pi}{2}$

Fig. 9.14

Table of values: The points in Table 9.4 are plotted and the graph is sketched in Fig. 9.14.

Table 9.4

θ	0	$\pi/6$	$\pi/4$	$\pi/3$	$\pi/2$	$-\pi/6$	$-\pi/4$	$-\pi/3$	$-\pi/2$
r	$2a$	$1.5a$	$1.29a$	$1.13a$	$1a$	$2.5a$	$2.71a$	$2.87a$	$3a$

An equation satisfied by the Cartesian coordinates of the points on this curve is

$$(x^2 + y^2 + ay)^2 = 4a^2(x^2 + y^2).$$

Example 3c. $r = a(1 - 2\sin\theta)$, $a > 0$.

Symmetry: With respect to the line $\theta = \pi/2$ as in Example 3a.

Tangents at the pole: $r = 0$ when $\sin\theta = \frac{1}{2}$, $\theta = \pi/6$ or $5\pi/6$.

Table of values: The points in Table 9.5 are plotted and the graph is sketched

Table 9.5

θ	0	$\pi/6$	$\pi/4$	$\pi/3$	$\pi/2$	$-\pi/6$	$-\pi/4$	$-\pi/3$	$-\pi/2$
r	a	0	$-.41a$	$-.73a$	$-1a$	$2a$	$2.41a$	$2.73a$	$3a$

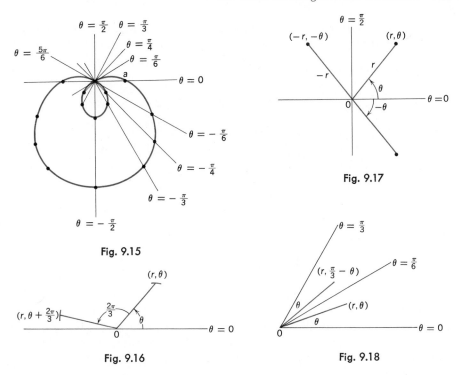

Fig. 9.15

Fig. 9.16

Fig. 9.17

Fig. 9.18

in Fig. 9.15. An equation satisfied by the Cartesian coordinates of the points on this curve is

$$(x^2 + y^2 + 2ay)^2 = a^2(x^2 + y^2).$$

Curves with equations of the form $r = a - b \sin \theta$ or $r = a - b \cos \theta$ are called limaçons. In the special case where $a = b$, as in Example 3a, the curve is called a cardioid.

Example 4. $r = a \sin 3\theta, \ a > 0.$

Symmetry: First, observe that the function $\sin 3\theta$ has a period $2\pi/3$ so that the point $(r, \theta + 2\pi/3)$ lies on the curve when (r, θ) does. Whatever configuration appears for the interval $0 \le \theta \le 2\pi/3$ is repeated for the interval $2\pi/3 \le \theta \le 4\pi/3$ and again for the interval $4\pi/3 \le \theta \le 2\pi$; the curve is carried into itself by a rotation through angle $2\pi/3$. See Fig. 9.16.

Next, observe that the point $(-r, -\theta)$ lies on the curve whenever (r, θ) does, for the equation $-r = a \sin 3(-\theta)$ soon reduces to $r = a \sin 3\theta$. As Fig. 9.17 indicates, the graph is symmetric with respect to the line $\theta = \pi/2$.

Finally, we can take advantage of the identity $\sin (\pi - 3\theta) = \sin 3\theta$. The point $(r, \pi/3 - \theta)$ lies on the curve whenever (r, θ) does, because the equation $r = a \sin 3(\pi/3 - \theta)$ reduces to $r = a \sin 3\theta$. Figure 9.18 indicates that we have symmetry with respect to the line $\theta = \pi/6$.

Tangents at the pole: $r = 0$ when $\sin 3\theta = 0$, $3\theta = 0, \pi$, or 2π; $\theta = 0, \pi/3$, or $2\pi/3$.

Table of values: Little table computation is necessary, because there is so much symmetry information. Those points given in Table 9.6 are plotted and the

TABLE 9.6

θ	0°	10°	15°	20°	30°	75°	90°
r	0	.5a	.71a	.87a	a	−.71a	−1a

graph is sketched in Fig. 9.19. This curve is often called a rose of three petals.
To get the Cartesian equation, we can write

$$r = a \sin 3\theta = a \sin (2\theta + \theta) = a (\sin 2\theta \cos \theta + \cos 2\theta \sin \theta),$$
$$r = a[2 \sin \theta \cos \theta \cos \theta + (2 \cos^2 \theta - 1) \sin \theta]$$
$$r = a \sin \theta (4 \cos^2 \theta - 1),$$
$$r = a \frac{y}{r} \left(\frac{4x^2}{r^2} - 1 \right), \qquad r^4 = ay(4x^2 - r^2),$$
$$(x^2 + y^2)^2 = ay(3x^2 - y^2).$$

Example 5. $r = e^{a\theta}$, $a > 0$. Here we cannot predict symmetry; neither does the graph ever pass through the origin. But if we start at the point $(1, 0)$ the equation tells us that r increases as θ increases and that r decreases, approaching 0, as θ decreases. The curve is called a logarithmic spiral.

Table of values: For the special choice $a = .2$ we have Table 9.7 and Fig. 9.20.

TABLE 9.7

θ	0	$\pi/4$	$\pi/2$	π	$3\pi/2$	2π	$-\pi/4$	$-\pi/2$	$-\pi$	$-3\pi/2$	-2π
r	1	$e^{(\pi/4)a}$	$e^{(\pi/2)a}$	$e^{\pi a}$	$e^{(3\pi/2)a}$	$e^{2\pi a}$	$e^{(-\pi/4)a}$	$e^{(-\pi/2)a}$	$e^{-\pi a}$	$e^{(-3\pi/2)a}$	$e^{-2\pi a}$
r	1	1.17	1.37	1.87	2.57	3.51	.85	.73	.53	.39	.28

The Cartesian equation for this curve is unwieldy.

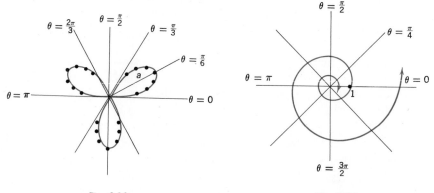

Fig. 9.19   Fig. 9.20

EXERCISES 9.2

1. Discuss and sketch the curves with equations.

(a) $r = -4 \cos \theta$.

(b) $r = 2 \sin \theta$.

(c) $r = -2 \sin \theta$.

(d) $r = \dfrac{4}{\cos \theta}$.

(e) $r = -2 \csc \theta$.

(f) $r = \dfrac{2}{1 + \cos \theta}$.

(g) $r = \dfrac{6}{2 - \sin \theta}$.

(h) $r = \dfrac{6}{1 - 2 \cos \theta}$.

(i) $r^2 = a^2 \sin 2\theta$, $a > 0$.

(j) $r = a \cos 2\theta$, $a > 0$.

(k) $r = a \cos 3\theta$, $a > 0$.

(l) $r = a \cos 4\theta$, $a > 0$.

(m) $r = a(1 + \cos \theta)$, $a > 0$.

(n) $r = a(2 + \cos \theta)$, $a > 0$.

(o) $r = a(1 + 2 \cos \theta)$, $a > 0$.

(p) $r = a \sin \tfrac{1}{2} \theta$, $a > 0$.

(q) $r = 1 + \sin 2\theta$.

(r) $r = 1 - 2 \sin 2\theta$.

(s) $r^2 = \sin \theta$.

(t) $r^2 = 1 + \sin^2 \theta$.

(u) $r = \sec \theta + 2$ (conchoid). Can you prove that the line $r \cos \theta = 1$ is an asymptote?

(v) $r = a\theta$, $a > 0$.

(w) $r = a \dfrac{1}{\theta}$, $a > 0$. Can you prove that the line $r \sin \theta = a$ is an asymptote?

2. Find the Cartesian equation for each curve of Exercise 1.

3. Change to polar coordinates and sketch

(a) $(x^2 + y^2)^3 = 4a^2x^2y^2$.

(b) $(x^2 + y^2)(x^2 + y^2 - 1)^2 = y^2$.

(c) $x(x^2 + y^2) = 2ay^2$.

4. Complete the following sentence: When the combination _____ occurs prominently in a Cartesian equation, a change to polar coordinates might well simplify the analysis.

5. Which two of the following equations describe the same curve? Explain.

(a) $r = 1 - \sin \theta$.

(b) $r = -1 - \sin \theta$.

(c) $r = 1 + \sin \theta$.

6. Which of the following equations describe the same curve? Explain.

(a) $r = \sin \tfrac{1}{2} \theta$.

(b) $r = -\sin \tfrac{1}{2} \theta$.

(c) $r = -\cos \tfrac{1}{2} \theta$.

7. Prove the following theorem.

Theorem 2. Rotations in polar coordinates.

Hypothesis: Point P has coordinates (r, θ) in one polar coordinate system and coordinates (r', θ') in a second system that has the same pole as the first, but an initial line that makes an angle α with the initial line of the first system. See Fig. 9.21.

Conclusion: $r' = r$,

$\theta' = \theta - \alpha$.

8. What is the equation of the circle C' obtained by rotating $C: r = a \cos \theta$ about the pole (a) through the angle $\pi/2$? (b) through the angle π? (c) through the angle $\pi/3$?

9. In Example 3a we squared both members of an equation when working out the Cartesian equation $(x^2 + y^2 + ay)^2 = a^2(x^2 + y^2)$, alleged to be equivalent to the polar equation $r = a(1 - \sin \theta)$. Are there points that lie on the locus of the former but not on the locus of the latter?

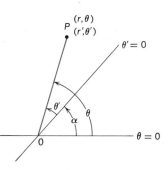

Fig. 9.21

9.3 Intersections of Curves in Polar Coordinates

If one particular set of polar coordinates for a point P satisfies two different polar coordinate equations, then P lies on both curves and is a point of intersection of the two curves. Conversely, however, if P lies on two curves, it might be that one particular set of coordinates for P satisfies both equations, but it might also happen that a first set of coordinates for P satisfies one equation while a second set satisfies the other equation. In the latter case, the simultaneous solution of the given equations will not give us the point of intersection. A reasonable working procedure is this:

(a) Solve the equations simultaneously. Any point thus located is a point of intersection.

(b) Sketch both curves on the same set of axes.

(c) If the diagram indicates that the pole lies on both curves, check each equation separately for this fact.

(d) If the diagram indicates that there is a point on both curves not located in Steps (a) and (c), rewrite one equation by replacing r and θ by $-r$ and $\theta + \pi$, and then solve simultaneously again. If the question is still not settled, rewrite one equation by replacing r and θ by r and $\theta + 2\pi$ and solve simultaneously again.

(e) Continue the work of Step (d) if necessary; rewrite equations either by replacing r and θ by $-r$ and $\theta + (2k + 1)\pi$, k an integer, or by replacing r and θ by r and $\theta + 2k\pi$, k an integer.

Example 1. Find the points of intersection of $r^2 = 2a^2 \cos 2\theta$ and $r = a$, $a > 0$. To solve simultaneously we write

$$r^2 = a^2 = 2a^2 \cos 2\theta \qquad \text{and} \qquad \cos 2\theta = \tfrac{1}{2},$$

$$2\theta = \frac{\pi}{3}, \quad \frac{5\pi}{3}, \quad \frac{7\pi}{3}, \qquad \text{or} \qquad \frac{11\pi}{3},$$

$$\theta = \frac{\pi}{6}, \quad \frac{5\pi}{6}, \quad \frac{7\pi}{6}, \qquad \text{or} \qquad \frac{11\pi}{6}.$$

The four points $(a, \pi/6)$, $(a, 5\pi/6)$, $(a, 7\pi/6)$, and $(a, 11\pi/6)$ are points of intersection. The equation $r^2 = 2a^2 \cos 2\theta$ represents a lemniscate, very much like

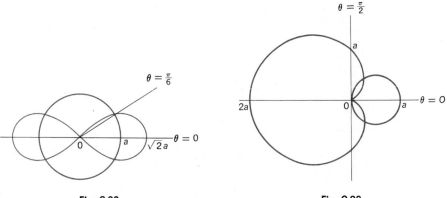

Fig. 9.22   Fig. 9.23

the one sketched in Example 9.2-2. The equation $r = a$ represents a circle of radius a with center at the origin. It is clear from Fig. 9.22 that there are no points of intersection other than the four already described.

Example 2. Find the points of intersection of $r = a \cos \theta$ and $r = a(1 - \cos \theta)$, $a > 0$. To solve simultaneously we write $r = a \cos \theta = a(1 - \cos \theta)$, $2 \cos \theta = 1$, $\cos \theta = \frac{1}{2}$, $\theta = \pi/3$ or $5\pi/3$; the points $(\frac{1}{2}a, \pi/3)$ and $(\frac{1}{2}a, 5\pi/3)$ are points of intersection.

The equation $r = a(1 - \cos \theta)$ represents a cardioid, congruent to the cardioid sketched in Example 9.2-3a. The equation $r = a \cos \theta$ represents a circle of radius $a/2$, center at $(a/2, 0)$, as we saw in Example 9.2-1. From Fig. 9.23 it would appear that we have not only the points of intersection already located but also the pole as a point of intersection. The pole lies on $r = a \cos \theta$, because the coordinates $(0, \pi/2)$ satisfy the equation; the pole lies on $r = a(1 - \cos \theta)$, because the coordinates $(0, 0)$ satisfy that equation. No single pair of coordinates for the pole satisfies both equations, and so we did not find the pole as a point of intersection when we solved simultaneously.

Example 3. Find the points of intersection of $r = 1 + \sin \theta$ and $r^2 = \frac{1}{2} \sin \theta$. To solve simultaneously we write $r^2 = (1 + \sin \theta)^2 = \frac{1}{2} \sin \theta$, and then $2 \sin^2 \theta + 3 \sin \theta + 2 = 0$. But this quadratic equation has a negative discriminant; when we solve for $\sin \theta$ we get nonreal solutions. So far we have no points of intersection.

The graph for $r = 1 + \sin \theta$ is again a cardioid, similar to the cardioid of Example 9.2-3a. The graph for $r^2 = \frac{1}{2} \sin \theta$ has symmetry (a) with respect to the pole because $(-r, \theta)$ satisfies the equation if (r, θ) does, and (b) with respect to the line $\theta = \pi/2$, because $(r, \pi - \theta)$ satisfies the equation if (r, θ) does. The line $\theta = 0$ is a tangent at the pole. When these curves are sketched, as in Fig. 9.24, it appears that there are points of intersection.

Let us replace the equation $r = 1 + \sin \theta$ for the cardioid by an equivalent

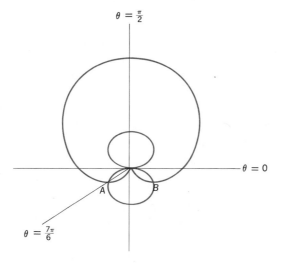

Fig. 9.24

equation and try again. This can be done by observing that (r, θ) and $(-r, \theta + \pi)$ describe the same point, and by replacing r by $-r$ and θ by $\theta + \pi$. The equation $r = 1 + \sin \theta$ is replaced by $-r = 1 + \sin (\theta + \pi)$, which is $-r = 1 - \sin \theta$ or $r = \sin \theta - 1$. Now if we solve $r = \sin \theta - 1$ and $r^2 = \frac{1}{2} \sin \theta$ simultaneously, we get

$$(\sin \theta - 1)^2 = \frac{1}{2} \sin \theta \qquad \text{or} \qquad 2 \sin^2 \theta - 5 \sin \theta + 2 = 0,$$

$$(2 \sin \theta - 1)(\sin \theta - 2) = 0,$$

$$\sin \theta = \frac{1}{2} \qquad \text{and} \qquad \theta = \frac{\pi}{6} \text{ or } \frac{5\pi}{6}.$$

The points $A(-\frac{1}{2}, \pi/6)$ and $B(-\frac{1}{2}, 5\pi/6)$ are points of intersection. Note that point A lies on the cardioid $r = 1 + \sin \theta$ (as originally described), because the coordinates $(+\frac{1}{2}, 7\pi/6)$ satisfy that equation, and on the curve $r^2 = \frac{1}{2} \sin \theta$ because the coordinates $(-\frac{1}{2}, \pi/6)$ satisfy that equation.

The pole lies on both curves because the coordinates $(0, 3\pi/2)$ satisfy $r = 1 + \sin \theta$ while $(0, 0)$ satisfy $r^2 = \frac{1}{2} \sin \theta$.

EXERCISES 9.3

Find the points of intersection.

1. $r = a, r = 2a \sin \theta$.

2. $r = -a \cos \theta, r = a \sin 2\theta$.

3. $r = \sin \theta, r = \dfrac{2}{1 - \sin \theta}$.

4. $r = 2 \sin^2 \theta, r = 1 - \sin \theta$.

5. $r = \cos \theta - 1, r = 1$.

6. $r = 2 + \sin \theta, r = 2(\sin \theta - 1)$.

9.4 Loci in Polar Coordinates. The Conic Sections

Polar coordinates are often useful in problems where one point has a special role to play; that point is made the pole of a polar coordinate system. If at every point of its path a particle is attracted toward a fixed point F with a force inversely proportional to the square of the distance from F, the analysis of the particle's motion can be started by choosing F as the pole of a polar coordinate system. It is then found that the particle travels in a conic section path with focus at F. The polar coordinate description of the conic section family is treated in the following theorem.

■ THEOREM 1

The conic sections in polar coordinates.

HYPOTHESIS: (a) The pole is a focus of a conic section of eccentricity e.

(b) The corresponding directrix is p units distant from the focus, and has the equation $r \cos \theta = -p$.

CONCLUSION: The equation of the conic section is

$$r = \frac{ep}{1 - e \cos \theta}. \tag{1a}$$

PROOF: Let $P(r, \theta)$ be any point on the conic section. According to the focus-directrix definition for the conic sections, Definition 3.15-1, we have

$$\frac{PF}{PN} = e \quad \text{or} \quad PF = ePN;$$

see Fig. 9.25. But

$$PF = r \quad \text{and} \quad PN = PQ + QN = r\cos\theta + p.$$

Hence we have

$$r = e(r\cos\theta + p),$$

or, solving for r, Eq. (1a).

Conversely, if the coordinates of $P(r, \theta)$ are such that Eq. (1a) is satisfied we can say that

$$\frac{PF}{PN} = \frac{r}{r\cos\theta + p} = \frac{ep/(1 - e\cos\theta)}{[ep\cos\theta/(1 - e\cos\theta)] + p} = \frac{ep/(1 - e\cos\theta)}{p/(1 - e\cos\theta)} = e,$$

so that P lies on the conic section.

● **Remark 1**

If the directrix had been chosen p units distant from the focus but in one of the positions $r\cos\theta = p$, $r\sin\theta = p$, or $r\sin\theta = -p$, then the equation of the conic section would have been

$$r = \frac{ep}{1 + e\cos\theta}, \quad (1b)$$

$$r = \frac{ep}{1 + e\sin\theta}, \quad (1c)$$

$$\text{or} \quad r = \frac{ep}{1 - e\sin\theta}. \quad (1d)$$

The reader is asked to demonstrate one of these facts in Exercise 9.4-3 below.

Example 1. Discuss and sketch

$$r = \frac{6}{1 - \cos\theta}.$$

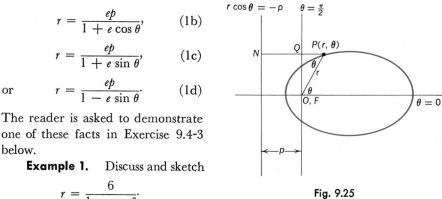

Fig. 9.25

We recognize the equation as that of a conic section with a focus at the pole. By comparison with Formula (1a) we deduce first that $e = 1$ and then that $p = 6$, so that we are dealing with a parabola whose directrix is 6 units from its focus. Because the point $(r, -\theta)$ lies on the parabola if (r, θ) does, the curve is symmetric with respect to the initial line. From these facts and the entries of Table 9.8,

TABLE 9.8

θ	0	$\pi/2$	π	$3\pi/2$
r	∞	6	3	6

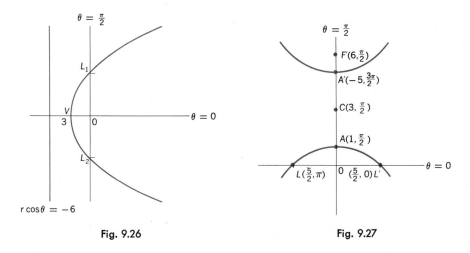

r cos θ = −6

Fig. 9.26   **Fig. 9.27**

the curve is sketched; see Fig. 9.26. In Cartesian coordinates the equation of the directrix is $x = -6$; in polar coordinates it is $r \cos \theta = -6$. The vertex is the point $(3, \pi)$. The latus rectum L_1L_2, a perpendicular segment through the focus, is of length 12.

Example 2.   Discuss and sketch

$$r = \frac{5}{2 + 3 \sin \theta}.$$

If we divide the numerator and denominator by 2, getting

$$r = \frac{5/2}{1 + 3/2 \sin \theta},$$

we recognize our equation as that of a conic section with a focus at the pole. By comparison with the formulas for such conics we see first that $e = \frac{3}{2}$ and then that $ep = \frac{5}{2}$, $p = \frac{5}{3}$. The conic is an hyperbola whose directrix is $\frac{5}{3}$ units from the focus. The graph is symmetric with respect to the line $\theta = \pi/2$ because the coordinates $(r, \pi - \theta)$ satisfy the equation whenever coordinates (r, θ) do. Some easily determined entries are given in Table 9.9. From these few points and the knowledge

TABLE 9.9

θ	0	$\pi/2$	π	$3\pi/2$
r	$\frac{5}{2}$	1	$\frac{5}{2}$	-5

that the two wings of the hyperbola are symmetric, we can sketch the graph roughly but quickly. See Fig. 9.27. The center falls midway between the vertices, at $(3, \pi/2)$; the second focus, F', must be placed at $(6, \pi/2)$, as far above A' as the first focus is below A. A latus rectum segment, LL', is of length 5. Since $p = \frac{5}{3}$, the directrix corresponding to the focus at the pole will have the Cartesian equation $y = \frac{5}{3}$ and the polar equation $r \sin \theta = \frac{5}{3}$.

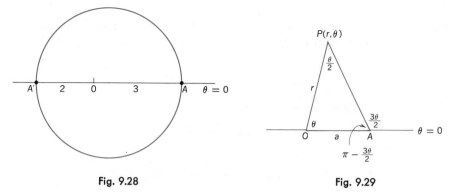

Fig. 9.28   **Fig. 9.29**

Example 3.   A particle travels an elliptic path with perihelion and ab-helion distances 2 and 3. Find a polar equation for the ellipse.

The perihelion and abhelion points are the major vertices of the ellipse, for these are the points closest to and farthest from one focus.[*] Let us take a polar coordinate system with pole at one focus and initial line along the major axis; refer, to Fig. 9.28. We can say that the ellipse passes through the points $A(3, 0)$ and $A'(2, \pi)$ and that it must have an equation of the form

$$r = \frac{ep}{1 \pm e \cos \theta},$$

because the graph has initial line symmetry. We choose the negative sign because r must be larger for $\theta = 0$ than for $\theta = \pi$. When we try to make sure that the coordinates for A and A' satisfy

$$r = \frac{ep}{1 - e \cos \theta},$$

we get $\qquad\qquad 3 = \dfrac{ep}{1 - e} \qquad$ and $\qquad 2 = \dfrac{ep}{1 + e}.$

To solve, we write

$$ep = 3(1 - e) = 2(1 + e),$$

$$e = \tfrac{1}{5}, \qquad ep = \tfrac{12}{5}, \qquad p = 12.$$

The ellipse has the equation

$$r = \frac{12/5}{1 - 1/5 \cos \theta} = \frac{12}{5 - \cos \theta}.$$

If we had used $r = ep/(1 + e \cos \theta)$ instead of $r = ep/(1 - e \cos \theta)$, we would have computed $e = -\tfrac{1}{5}$, and this would have suggested the other choice of sign.

Example 4.   *A trisectrix.* Find the locus of the vertex P of a triangle OPA whose side OA is of length a and for which angle P is $\tfrac{1}{2}$ of angle O. Consider Fig. 9.29. We have chosen the vertex O as the pole of a polar coordinate system

[*] See Exercise 3.15-6.

and placed the initial line along OA. Since the sum of the angles of a triangle is π, angle A must be $\pi - 3\theta/2$, and then the sine law of trigonometry says that

$$\frac{r}{\sin(\pi - 3\theta/2)} = \frac{a}{\sin \theta/2}.$$

We can rewrite this equation as follows:

$$r = a \frac{\sin 3\theta/2}{\sin \theta/2} = \frac{a(3 \sin \theta/2 - 4 \sin^3 \theta/2)}{\sin \theta/2}$$

$$= a\,(3 - 4 \sin^2 \theta/2) = a(3 - 2[1 - \cos \theta])$$

$$r = a(1 + 2 \cos \theta). \tag{2}$$

In this simplification we used the identities $\sin 3\alpha = 3 \sin \alpha - 4 \sin^3 \alpha$ and $2 \sin^2 \alpha = 1 - \cos 2\alpha$.

Equation (2) tells us that the locus of P is a limaçon, very much like the one sketched in Example 9.2-3c. The limaçon has initial line symmetry and the lines $\theta = 2\pi/3$, $\theta = 4\pi/3$ as tangents at the pole; see Fig. 9.30.

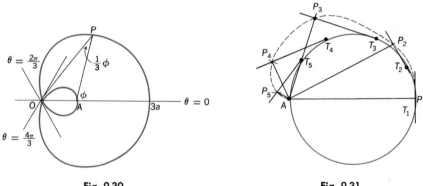

Fig. 9.30   Fig. 9.31

Figure 9.29 explains how we can trisect an angle with the help of this graph, for angle P is ⅓ the exterior angle at A. To trisect an angle ϕ, $0 < \phi < \pi$, place its vertex at A in Fig. 9.30 and the initial side along the initial line. Let its terminal side intersect the limaçon at P.* Draw OP. Angle APO will be ⅓ϕ.

Example 5.   *A pedal curve.* Consider a curve C and a fixed point A. At each point of C draw the tangent line, and select on that tangent line the point P that is the foot of the perpendicular drawn from A. The locus of these foot points or pedal points P is called the pedal curve for C with respect to A. We shall illustrate by finding the pedal curve for a circle with respect to a point on the circle.

First, we shall experiment roughly as in Fig. 9.31. At various points T of the circle we draw tangents, and then on each tangent we select P, the foot of the perpendicular drawn from A. These foot points seem to lie on a cardioid.

---

* If the terminal side intersects the limacon twice, take the point that is farther from A.

To study the problem analytically, let us place the pole of a polar coordinate system at A and the initial line through A and the center of the circle, as in Fig. 9.32. For a point T on the circle, draw the radius CT and the tangent line, and on the tangent line select P, the foot of the perpendicular drawn from O. We know that OP and CT are parallel, because they are both perpendicular to the line tangent at T. If the radius of the circle is a, then we see from the figure that

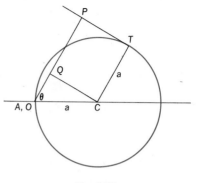

Fig. 9.32

$$r = OP = OQ + QP = a\cos\theta + a = a(1 + \cos\theta).$$

The locus of foot points is indeed a cardioid.

EXERCISES 9.4

1. Sketch each of the following conic sections with focus at the pole. Find the eccentricity, the equation of the directrix that corresponds to the focus at the pole, and the length of the latus rectum.

(a) $r = \dfrac{4}{1 + \cos\theta}$.

(b) $r = \dfrac{4}{1 - \frac{1}{3}\sin\theta}$.

(c) $r = \dfrac{4}{1 - 3\cos\theta}$.

(d) $r = \dfrac{6}{2 + \cos\theta}$.

(e) $r = \dfrac{5}{2 + 2\sin\theta}$.

(f) $r = \dfrac{7}{3 - 4\sin\theta}$.

2. Find the equation of each of the conic sections with focus at the pole described below:

(a) parabola with vertex at $(2, \pi/2)$.
(b) hyperbola with eccentricity $\frac{4}{3}$ and $r\cos\theta = 6$ as directrix nearest pole.
(c) ellipse with vertex at $(2, \pi)$, eccentricity $\frac{1}{2}$.
(d) center at $(4, \pi/2)$, vertex at $(2, \pi/2)$.
(e) passing through $(8, \pi/2)$, $(8, 3\pi/2)$, and $(16, \pi/3)$.
(f) directrix corresponding to the focus at the pole at $r\sin\theta = -4$, and latus rectum of length 2.

3. In Remark 1 it is stated that $r = ep/(1 + e\sin\theta)$ is the equation of the conic section of eccentricity e with focus at the pole and corresponding directrix $r\sin\theta = p$. Prove this.

4. A line is drawn through a focus of a conic. Show that the sum of the reciprocals of the lengths of the focal radii is a constant.

5. Given O, the pole of a polar coordinate system, and $A(a, 0)$. Find the locus of points P at which the segment OA subtends a right angle.

6. Find the locus of the midpoints of the chords drawn from a fixed point on a circle.

7. *A construction for the conchoid.* Through each point Q of the line $r\cos\theta = a$ draw a line through the pole O. Select on OQ the points P that lie b units from Q. What is the equation of the curve on which the points P must lie?

8. *A construction for the limaçon.* Through each point Q of the circle $r = a\cos\theta$ draw a line through the pole. On OQ select the points P that lie b units from Q. What is the equation of the curve on which the points P must lie?

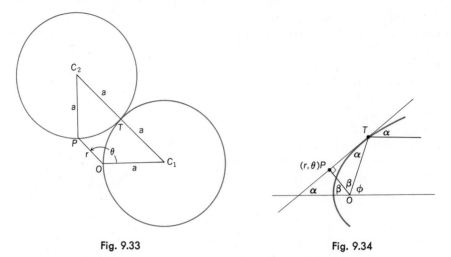

Fig. 9.33   Fig. 9.34

9. *A trisectrix.* Given O, the pole of a polar coordinate system, and $A(a, 0)$. Find the locus of points P such that angle P of triangle OAP is twice angle O. Explain how this curve can be used to trisect angles.

10. Line segment AB is of length a and moves with A always on the line $\theta = 0$, B always on the line $\theta = \pi/2$. Let P be the foot of the perpendicular drawn from O to AB. Find the locus of P.

11. Let A and B be the points at which a tangent to $r = a$ meets the lines $\theta = 0$ and $\theta = \pi/2$. Let P be the midpoint of AB. Find the locus of P.

12. A fixed wheel of radius a stands in the position $r = 2a \cos \theta$. A second wheel of the same radius rolls on the first wheel without slipping or sliding. Show that the path traveled by a specific point P on the circumference of the second wheel is a cardioid. (In Fig. 9.33, P started its motion at the pole, in contact with the fixed circle; therefore

$$\overset{\frown}{TP} = \overset{\frown}{OT}.)$$

This curve is an epicycloid; see Ex. 8.4-10.

13. Find the pedal curve for a circle of radius a with respect to a point A that is b units from the center of the circle. Let the point A be the pole of a polar coordinate system and let the center of the circle lie on the initial line, to the right of A.

14. Show that the pedal curve for a parabola with respect to its focus is the straight line through its vertex which is perpendicular to its axis of symmetry.

Step (a). Choose polar coordinates so that the parabola has the equation

$$r = \frac{p}{1 - \cos \theta}.$$

Thus, in Fig. 9.34,

$$OT = \frac{p}{1 - \cos \phi}.$$

Step (b). Let $P(r, \theta)$ be the foot of the perpendicular drawn from the focus to the tangent at T. Use the fact that a tangent at T makes equal angles with the focal radius through T and the axis of symmetry of the parabola to justify the labeling of the angles in Fig. 9.34.

Step (c). From $r = OT \cos \beta$ and $\theta = \beta + \phi$ show that $r \cos \theta = -p/2$.

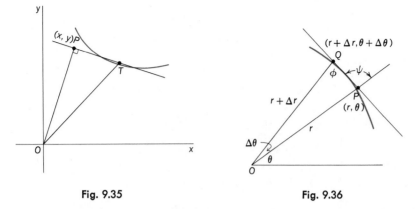

Fig. 9.35   Fig. 9.36

15. In a more general problem, if we want the pedal curve for a given curve with respect to a given point we can choose *rectangular* coordinate axes with the origin at the given point. Let the given curve then have rectangular parametric equations $x = f(t)$, $y = g(t)$. Let $P(x, y)$ be the foot of the perpendicular drawn from the origin to the tangent to the given curve at T. Then, in Fig. 9.35, where

$$\overrightarrow{OP} = \overrightarrow{OT} + \overrightarrow{TP} \quad \text{and} \quad \overrightarrow{OT} = f(t)\mathbf{i} + g(t)\mathbf{j},$$

show that

$$\overrightarrow{TP} = -\frac{ff' + gg'}{f'^2 + g'^2}\,(f'\mathbf{i} + g'\mathbf{j})$$

so that parametric equations for the pedal curve are

$$x = \frac{g'(fg' - gf')}{f'^2 + g'^2} \quad \text{and} \quad y = \frac{f'(f'g - fg')}{f'^2 + g'^2}.$$

9.5 Tangents to Polar Curves

Let curve C be described in polar coordinates by the equation $r = f(\theta)$ for θ in domain $D, f'(\theta)$ existing for θ of D. Let $P(r, \theta)$ be a point on C other than the pole, the coordinate numbers r and θ such that $r = f(\theta)$. By definition, the tangent line at P is the line obtained by taking a second point Q on the curve, drawing the secant line PQ, and taking the limiting position of PQ as Q approaches P.

Let the coordinates of Q be $(r + \Delta r, \theta + \Delta\theta)$, $\Delta\theta \neq 0$, and $r + \Delta r \neq 0$. The points O, P, and Q then determine a triangle, as in Fig. 9.36, and if we apply the sine law of trigonometry to triangle OPQ, we can say that

$$\frac{r}{\sin\phi} = \frac{r + \Delta r}{\sin(\pi - \psi)}. \tag{1}$$

Since $\psi = \phi + \Delta\theta$ or $\phi = \psi - \Delta\theta$, Eq. (1) can be restated in the following ways:

$$\frac{r}{\sin\phi} = \frac{r + \Delta r}{\sin\psi},$$

$$r\sin\psi = (r + \Delta r)\sin\phi = (r + \Delta r)\sin(\psi - \Delta\theta)$$
$$= (r + \Delta r)(\sin\psi\cos\Delta\theta - \cos\psi\sin\Delta\theta),$$

or
$$r \sin \psi (1 - \cos \Delta\theta) = -r \cos \psi \sin \Delta\theta$$
$$+ \Delta r(\sin \psi \cos \Delta\theta - \cos \psi \sin \Delta\theta).$$

Dividing by $\Delta\theta$, we get

$$r \sin \psi \frac{1 - \cos \Delta\theta}{\Delta\theta} = -r \cos \psi \frac{\sin \Delta\theta}{\Delta\theta} + \frac{\Delta r}{\Delta\theta} (\sin \psi \cos \Delta\theta - \cos \psi \sin \Delta\theta). \quad (2)$$

As point Q approaches P, $\Delta\theta$ approaches 0. Recalling that

$$\lim_{\Delta\theta \to 0} \frac{\sin \Delta\theta}{\Delta\theta} = 1 \quad \text{and} \quad \lim_{\Delta\theta \to 0} \frac{1 - \cos \Delta\theta}{\Delta\theta} = 0,*$$

we deduce from Eq. (2) that for the tangent line at P

$$0 = -r \cos \psi + \frac{dr}{d\theta} \sin \psi \quad (3)$$

or, if $dr/d\theta \neq 0$,
$$\tan \psi = \frac{r}{dr/d\theta}. \quad (4)$$

If $dr/d\theta = 0$ we deduce from Eq. (3) that $\cos \psi = 0$ or $\psi = \pi/2$, because P is not the pole and $r \neq 0$. We have proved the following theorem.

■ THEOREM 1

Tangent lines to polar curves.

HYPOTHESIS: (a) Curve C is described by $r = f(\theta)$ for θ of domain D, with $f'(\theta)$ existing for θ of D.

(b) $P(r, \theta)$, $r \neq 0$, lies on C, and the numbers r and θ are such that $r = f(\theta)$.

(c) the angle between the radial vector $\overrightarrow{OP}$ and the tangent vector at P in the direction of increasing θ has measure ψ.

CONCLUSION: If $dr/d\theta = 0$ at P, then $\psi = \pi/2$. If $dr/d\theta \neq 0$ at P, then $\tan \psi = r/(dr/d\theta)$.

● Remark 1

In most polar coordinate work it is easier to find an angle between the tangent line and the radius vector than it is to find the inclination angle for the tangent

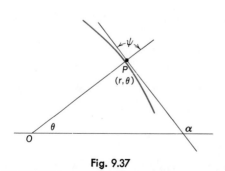

Fig. 9.37

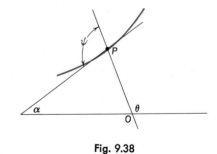

Fig. 9.38

* See Lemmas 4.2-1 and 4.2-2.

line, but once ψ is known, α, the inclination angle for the tangent line, can be determined. In Fig. 9.37 we have $\alpha = \theta + \psi$. In Fig. 9.38 we have $\theta = \alpha + (\pi - \psi)$ or $\alpha = \theta + \psi - \pi$. In any case, $\tan \alpha = \tan (\theta + \psi)$.

● **Remark 2**

The proof of Theorem 1 does not apply when $P(r, \theta)$ is the pole, $r = 0$, because there is no triangle OPQ in Fig. 9.36 when O and P coincide. But Theorem 9.2-1 discusses the case of the tangent line at the pole.

Example 1. What angle does the tangent to $r = a(1 - \cos \theta)$ at $A(a, \pi/2)$ make with the radial line, $\theta = \pi/2$? What is the inclination angle of this tangent line?

Since $dr/d\theta = a \sin \theta$, we have

$$\tan \psi = \frac{r}{dr/d\theta} = \frac{a(1 - \cos \theta)}{a \sin \theta} = 1$$

at A; hence $\psi = \pi/4$. From Fig. 9.39 we see that

$$\alpha = \frac{\pi}{2} + \psi = \frac{\pi}{2} + \frac{\pi}{4} = \frac{3\pi}{4}.$$

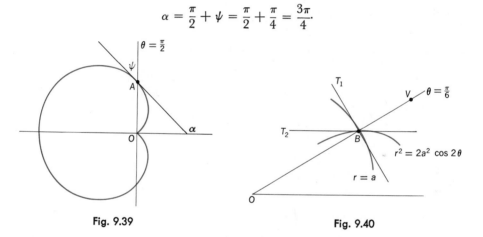

Fig. 9.39   Fig. 9.40

Example 2. In Example 9.3-1 we saw that $B(a, \pi/6)$ is a point of intersection of $r = a$ and $r^2 = 2a^2 \cos 2\theta$. At what angle do these curves intersect at B?

In Fig. 9.40 the pertinent part of Fig. 9.22 is reproduced. Since $r = a$ is a circle with its center at the pole, we know that the angle from the radius line to the tangent must be a right angle; $\sphericalangle VBT_1 = \pi/2$. For the lemniscate $r^2 = 2a^2 \cos 2\theta$ we have

$$2r \frac{dr}{d\theta} = -4a^2 \sin 2\theta,$$

and, at $B(a, \pi/6)$,

$$2a \frac{dr}{d\theta} = -4a^2 \frac{\sqrt{3}}{2} \quad \text{or} \quad \frac{dr}{d\theta} = -a \sqrt{3}.$$

Thus, by Theorem 1,

$$\tan VBT_2 = \frac{r}{dr/d\theta} = \frac{a}{-a\sqrt{3}} = -\frac{1}{\sqrt{3}} \quad \text{and} \quad \sphericalangle VBT_2 = \frac{5\pi}{6}.$$

An angle between the tangents is

$$\measuredangle T_1 B T_2 = \measuredangle V B T_2 - \measuredangle V B T_1 = \frac{5\pi}{6} - \frac{\pi}{2} = \frac{\pi}{3}.$$

EXERCISES 9.5

1. What angle does the tangent line make with the radial line at the points indicated on the following curves?

(a) $r = a, \left(a, \dfrac{\pi}{2}\right)$.

(f) $r = \dfrac{a}{\cos \theta}, \left(2a, \dfrac{\pi}{3}\right)$.

(b) $r = a \sin \theta, \left(\dfrac{a}{2}, \dfrac{5\pi}{6}\right)$.

(g) $r^2 = a^2 \sin 2\theta, \left(\dfrac{a}{\sqrt{2}}, \dfrac{5\pi}{12}\right)$.

(c) $r = a \sin 2\theta, \left(\dfrac{\sqrt{3}}{2} a, \dfrac{\pi}{6}\right)$.

(h) $r = a(2 + \cos \theta), \left(\dfrac{3}{2} a, \dfrac{4\pi}{3}\right)$.

(d) $r = \dfrac{6}{1 - \cos \theta}, \left(4, \dfrac{2\pi}{3}\right)$.

(i) $r = a\theta, \left(\dfrac{5\pi}{2} a, \dfrac{5\pi}{2}\right)$.

(e) $r = \dfrac{6}{2 + \sin \theta}, \left(4, -\dfrac{\pi}{6}\right)$.

2. What is the inclination angle for each tangent line of Exercise 1?
3. The logarithmic spiral, $r = be^{a\theta}$, is sometimes called the equiangular spiral. Prove that it cuts the radial lines at a constant angle. Prove that a curve must be a logarithmic spiral if it cuts the radial lines at a constant angle.
4. Prove the following theorem.
   Hypothesis: (a) For $\beta \leq \theta \leq \gamma$, the curve $r = f(\theta)$ is closest to, or farthest from, the pole when $\theta = \theta_0$, $\beta < \theta_0 < \gamma$.
   (b) $f'(\theta_0)$ exists.
   (c) $r_0 = f(\theta_0) \neq 0$.
   Conclusion: The curve cuts the radial line orthogonally at (r_0, θ_0).
5. Find the angle of intersection of the given curves at the point indicated.*

(a) $r = a, r = 2a \sin \theta; \left(a, \dfrac{\pi}{6}\right)$.

(b) $r = -a \cos \theta, r = a \sin 2\theta; \left(\dfrac{\sqrt{3}}{2} a, \dfrac{7\pi}{6}\right)$.

(c) $r = -a \cos \theta, r = a \sin 2\theta;$ pole.

(d) $r = 2 \sin^2 \theta, r = 1 - \sin \theta; \left(2, \dfrac{3\pi}{2}\right)$.

(e) $r = \cos \theta - 1, r = 1; \left(1, \dfrac{\pi}{2}\right)$.

(f) $r = 2 + \sin \theta, r = 2(\sin \theta - 1); (2, 0)$.

6. Show that the distance from the pole to the line tangent to $r = f(\theta)$ at (r, θ) is given by $r^2/\sqrt{r^2 + (dr/d\theta)^2}$.
7. Prove Theorem 3.10-2, on the reflection property for the parabola, by working with a polar description of the parabola, perhaps $r = p/(1 - \cos \theta)$.

---

* These intersections were studied earlier in Exercises 9.3-1, 9.3-2, 9.3-4, 9.3-5, and 9.3-6.

8. Show that at any point of the lemniscate arc $r^2 = a^2 \cos 2\theta$, $0 \leq \theta \leq \pi/4$, the angle between the radial direction and the outward pointed normal is 2θ.

9. At any point (r, θ) of a polar curve the angle between the radial direction and the tangent vector in the direction of increasing θ is $\frac{1}{2} \theta$. Show that the curve is a cardioid.

10. Here is an outline of a second proof for Theorem 1. Fill in the details.

   Step (a). Refer the curve $r = f(\theta)$ to rectangular coordinates by writing $x = r \cos \theta$, $y = r \sin \theta$. Here we have parametric equations for x and y in terms of θ, for r is considered a function of θ.

   Step (b). Compute $dx = (dx/d\theta) \, d\theta$, dy, and $dy/dx = \tan \alpha$.

   Step (c). From Remark 1, $\tan \psi = \tan (\alpha - \theta)$. Compute $\tan \psi$.

9.6 Areas in Polar Coordinates

We know that the area of a circle of radius r is πr^2 and that the area of a circular sector of central angle ϕ would be the $\phi/2\pi$ part of the area of a whole circle, or $\frac{1}{2}r^2\phi$; see Fig. 9.41. To select a definition for the area of a region bounded by curves that have polar coordinate descriptions, we divide the region into elements that are like circular sectors and add up the areas of these elements.

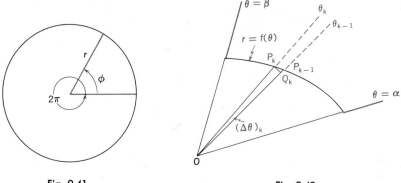

Fig. 9.41   Fig. 9.42

   In detail, let $f(\theta)$ be continuous for $\alpha \leq \theta \leq \beta$ and consider the region R bounded by $r = f(\theta)$ for $\alpha \leq \theta \leq \beta$, $\theta = \alpha$ and $\theta = \beta$; see Fig. 9.42. If we subdivide the θ interval $\alpha \leq \theta \leq \beta$ by taking $\theta_0 = \alpha < \theta_1 < \theta_2 < \cdots < \theta_{n-1} < \theta_n = \beta$, we divide R to n subregions. The kth such subregion will be bounded by the radial lines $\theta = \theta_{k-1}$ and $\theta = \theta_k$ and by that portion of the curve $r = f(\theta)$ for which $\theta_{k-1} \leq \theta \leq \theta_k$. In Fig. 9.42, $OP_{k-1}P_k$ is the kth subregion.

   In the kth θ subinterval we can find a θ_k' for which r takes on a minimum value, r_k', for that subinterval.* If $(\Delta A)_k$ is the area of the kth subregion, we have

$$\tfrac{1}{2}(r_k')^2(\Delta\theta)_k \leq (\Delta A)_k;$$

in Fig. 9.42 the area of OP_kP_{k-1} is greater than that of OP_kQ_k. Similarly, there is a θ_k'' for which r takes on a maximum value, r_k'', and we have

$$\tfrac{1}{2}(r_k')^2(\Delta\theta)_k \leq (\Delta A)_k \leq \tfrac{1}{2}(r_k'')^2(\Delta\theta)_k. \tag{1}$$

---

* See Theorem 7.4-2, the Extreme Value Theorem for continuous functions.

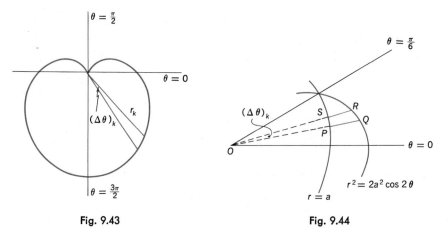

Fig. 9.43   **Fig. 9.44**

But then there must be a θ_k^*, somewhere between θ_k' and θ_k'', such that

$$(\Delta A)_k = \tfrac{1}{2}(r_k^*)^2(\Delta\theta)_k = \tfrac{1}{2}[f(\theta_k^*)]^2(\Delta\theta)_k.\dagger \qquad (2)$$

Now our path is a familiar one. We take as our definition of the area of the region the limit of the sum of the areas of the subregions as the number of subregions increases beyond all bounds, it being understood that the largest of the $(\Delta\theta)_k$'s approaches 0:

$$A = \lim_{n\to\infty} \sum_{k=1}^{n} (\Delta A)_k = \lim_{n\to\infty} \sum_{k=1}^{n} \tfrac{1}{2}(r_k^*)^2(\Delta\theta)_k = \tfrac{1}{2}\int_{\theta=\alpha}^{\beta} r^2\, d\theta. \qquad (3)$$

■ DEFINITION 1

Areas in polar coordinates. If $r = f(\theta)$ is continuous for $\alpha \le \theta \le \beta$, then the area of the region bounded by $\theta = \alpha$, $\theta = \beta$, and $r = f(\theta)$ for $\alpha \le \theta \le \beta$ shall be $\tfrac{1}{2}\int_{\theta=\alpha}^{\beta} r^2\, d\theta$.

Example 1. Find the area of the region included within the cardioid $r = a(1 - \sin\theta)$. For the subregion sketched in Fig. 9.43 we reason that there is a θ_k^* such that

$$(\Delta A)_k = \tfrac{1}{2}(r_k^*)^2(\Delta\theta)_k,$$

and then that $A = \dfrac{1}{2}\displaystyle\int_{\theta=0}^{2\pi} r^2\, d\theta = \dfrac{a^2}{2}\displaystyle\int_0^{2\pi} (1 - \sin\theta)^2\, d\theta.$

To evaluate this integral, we turn to the antidifferentiation point of view.

$$A = \frac{a^2}{2}\int_0^{2\pi} (1 - 2\sin\theta + \sin^2\theta)\, d\theta$$

$$= \frac{a^2}{2}\left[\theta + 2\cos\theta + \tfrac{1}{2}\int (1 - \cos 2\theta)\, d\theta\right]\Big|_{\theta=0}^{2\pi}$$

$$= \frac{a^2}{2}\left[\theta + 2\cos\theta + \frac{\theta}{2} - \frac{1}{4}\sin 2\theta\right]\Big|_0^{2\pi} = \frac{3}{2}a^2\pi.$$

$\dagger$ See Theorem 7.4-3, the Intermediate Value Theorem for continuous functions.

Example 2. Find the area of the region that lies outside the circle $r = a$, but inside the lemniscate $r^2 = 2a^2 \cos 2\theta$. These curves have already been considered in Example 9.3-1. Figure 9.44 reproduces an essential part of Fig. 9.22. The element of area we seek is the area of $PQRS$, and we can say that

$$(\Delta A)_k = (\text{area } OQR) - (\text{area } OPS),$$

$$(\Delta A)_k \approx \tfrac{1}{2} r_k^2 (\Delta\theta)_k - \tfrac{1}{2} a^2 (\Delta\theta)_k \;\dagger$$

$$(\Delta A)_k \approx \frac{1}{2}(2a^2 \cos 2\theta_k)(\Delta\theta)_k - \frac{1}{2} a^2(\Delta\theta)_k = \frac{a^2}{2}(2\cos 2\theta_k - 1)(\Delta\theta)_k,$$

$$\frac{1}{4} \text{ area} = \frac{a^2}{2} \int_{\theta=0}^{\pi/6} (2\cos 2\theta - 1)\,d\theta,$$

$$\text{area} = 2a^2 \int_{\theta=0}^{\pi/6} (2\cos 2\theta - 1)\,d\theta$$

$$= 2a^2\,[\sin 2\theta - \theta]\Big|_{\theta=0}^{\pi/6} = 2a^2\left[\left(\frac{\sqrt{3}}{2} - \frac{\pi}{6}\right) - (0)\right] \approx .685a^2.$$

Example 3. Find the area of the region common to $r = a \cos \theta$ and $r = a(1 - \cos \theta)$. These curves were considered in Example 9.3-2, and Fig. 9.45 reproduces an essential part of Fig. 9.23. This time we get elements of two different kinds when we subdivide our region; those elements for which $0 \le \theta \le \pi/3$ are bounded by the cardioid $r = a(1 - \cos\theta)$; those elements for $\pi/3 \le \theta \le \pi/2$ are bounded by the circle $r = a \cos\theta$. Hence $\tfrac{1}{2}$ the area we seek will be found as a sum of the areas of the regions OCB and OBD.

For the region OCB we can say that

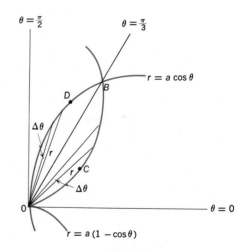

Fig. 9.45

$$(\Delta A)_k \approx \tfrac{1}{2} r_k^2 (\Delta\theta)_k,$$

$$\text{area } OCB = \tfrac{1}{2} \int_{\theta=0}^{\pi/3} r^2\,d\theta$$

$$= \frac{a^2}{2} \int_{\theta=0}^{\pi/3} (1 - \cos\theta)^2\,d\theta.$$

---

† We could have asserted the existence of θ_k^* such that

$$(\Delta A)_k = \tfrac{1}{2} r_k^{*2}(\Delta\theta)_k - \tfrac{1}{2} a^2(\Delta\theta)_k,$$

thus making the exposition resemble that of Example 1 more closely.

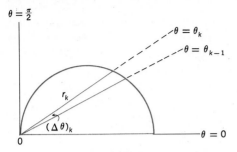

Fig. 9.46

For the region OBD we can say that

$$(\Delta A)_k \approx \tfrac{1}{2}\, r_k^2 (\Delta \theta)_k,$$

$$\text{area } OBD = \tfrac{1}{2} \int_{\theta = \pi/3}^{\pi/2} r^2\, d\theta$$

$$= \frac{a^2}{2} \int_{\pi/3}^{\pi/2} \cos^2 \theta\, d\theta.$$

For the area we seek we have, accordingly,

$$\frac{1}{2}\,\text{area} = \frac{a^2}{2} \int_0^{\pi/3} (1 - \cos \theta)^2\, d\theta + \frac{a^2}{2} \int_{\pi/3}^{\pi/2} \cos^2 \theta\, d\theta$$

$$\text{area} = a^2 \int_0^{\pi/3} (1 - 2\cos \theta + \cos^2 \theta)\, d\theta + a^2 \int_{\pi/3}^{\pi/2} \cos^2 \theta\, d\theta$$

$$= a^2 [\theta - 2\sin \theta + \tfrac{1}{2}\theta + \tfrac{1}{4}\sin 2\theta]_0^{\pi/3} + a^2 [\tfrac{1}{2}\theta + \tfrac{1}{4}\sin 2\theta]_{\pi/3}^{\pi/2}$$

$$= a^2 \left[\frac{\pi}{2} - \sqrt{3} + \frac{\sqrt{3}}{8} \right] + a^2 \left[\frac{\pi}{4} - \frac{\pi}{6} - \frac{\sqrt{3}}{8} \right]$$

$$= a^2 \left[\frac{7\pi}{12} - \sqrt{3} \right] \approx 0.10a^2.$$

Example 4.   Find the weight of that half of the circular plate bounded by $r = a \cos \theta$ for $0 \leq \theta \leq \pi/2$ and $\theta = 0$ if the weight density ρ is given by the formula $\rho = c(2 - \theta)$ for $0 \leq \theta \leq \pi/2$, c a constant.

In Fig. 9.46 we have drawn the plate and indicated an element. First, there exists a θ_k^* of the kth θ subinterval and a corresponding r_k^* such that

$$(\Delta A)_k = \text{area of element} = \tfrac{1}{2}(r_k^*)^2 (\Delta \theta)_k.$$

Next, the density is not uniform throughout the element, being greatest at the boundary $\theta = \theta_{k-1}$, and least at the boundary $\theta = \theta_k$, but since ρ is continuous we can say that there is a θ_k^{**} such that

$$(\Delta W)_k = \text{weight of element} = \rho_k^{**}(\Delta A)_k = c(2 - \theta_k^{**})\tfrac{1}{2}(r_k^*)^2 (\Delta \theta)_k. \tag{4}$$

We would then say that

$$\text{weight of plate} = \lim_{n \to \infty} \sum_{k=1}^n (\Delta W)_k = \lim_{n \to \infty} \sum_{k=1}^n \frac{c}{2}(2 - \theta_k^{**})(r_k^*)^2 (\Delta \theta)_k, \tag{5}$$

it being understood that the largest of the $(\Delta \theta)_k$'s approaches 0.

Because θ_k^* and θ_k^{**} will not be equal in general, we have in Eq. (5) a limit of a sum of the type considered in Theorem 8.8-2. The conclusion of that theorem assures us that such a limit of a sum is a definite integral, so that we can conclude the setting up of this problem by writing

$$\text{weight of plate} = \frac{a^2 c}{2} \int_{\theta=0}^{\pi/2} (2 - \theta) \cos^2 \theta\, d\theta.$$

To evaluate this integral we write

$$\text{weight of plate} = \frac{a^2 c}{4} \int_0^{\pi/2} (2 - \theta)(1 + \cos 2\theta)\, d\theta$$

$$= \frac{a^2 c}{4} \left[\int_0^{\pi/2} (2 - \theta)\, d\theta + 2 \int_0^{\pi/2} \cos 2\theta\, d\theta - \int_0^{\pi/2} \theta \cos 2\theta\, d\theta \right]$$

$$= \frac{a^2 c}{4} \left[2\theta - \frac{\theta^2}{2} + \sin 2\theta - \frac{1}{2} \theta \sin 2\theta - \frac{1}{4} \cos 2\theta \right]_0^{\pi/2}.$$

In the last step it was necessary to integrate by parts and only the end result is shown. Finally, we have

$$\text{weight of plate} = \frac{a^2 c}{4} \left[\left(\pi - \frac{\pi^2}{8} + \frac{1}{4} \right) - \left(-\frac{1}{4} \right) \right] \approx 0.60 a^2 c.$$

EXERCISES 9.6

1. Find the area of the region bounded by $r = a \sin \theta$. Use integration.

2. Find the area of the region bounded by one loop of the lemniscate $r^2 = a^2 \cos 2\theta$.

3. Find the area of the region bounded by $r = a(2 + \cos \theta)$.

4. Find the area of the region within $r = a(1 - 2 \sin \theta)$.

5. Find the area of the region bounded by one petal of $r = a \cos 2\theta$.

6. Find the area of the region bounded by one petal of $r = a \cos n\theta$.

7. Find the area of the region bounded by the parabola $r = p/(1 - \cos \theta)$ and its latus rectum.

8. Find the area of the region bounded by that portion of the spiral $r = a\theta$ for which $0 \le \theta \le 2\pi$ and that portion of $\theta = 0$ for which $0 \le r \le 2\pi a$.

9. Find the area of the region inside $r = 2a \sin \theta$ but outside $r = a$.

10. Find the area of the region inside the circle $r = a \cos \theta$ but outside $r = a \sin 2\theta$.

11. Find the area of the region inside $r = 2 \sin^2 \theta$ and outside $r = 1 - \sin \theta$.

12. Find the area of the region common to $r = a$ and $r^2 = 2a^2 \cos 2\theta$.

13. Find the area of the region common to $r = 1 + \sin \theta$ and the lower loop of $r^2 = \frac{1}{2} \sin \theta$.*

14. Find the area of the region bounded by the four arcs (i) that portion of $r = e^{a\theta}$ for which $0 \le \theta \le 2\pi$, (ii) that portion of $\theta = 0$ for which $e^{2\pi a} < r < e^{4\pi a}$, (iii) that portion of $r e^{a\theta}$ for which $2\pi \le \theta \le 4\pi$, and (iv) that portion of $\theta = 0$ for which $1 \le r \le e^{2\pi a}$.

15. Use integration in polar coordinates to show that the area of the region bounded by $x = 0$, $y = 0$, $x = a$, and $y = b$ is ab.

16. A plate is bounded by the lemniscate $r^2 = a^2 \cos 2\theta$. Its weight density is symmetric with respect to the lines $\theta = 0$ and $\theta = \pi/2$ and is a function of θ alone, $\rho = g(\theta)$. Set up an integral for the weight of the plate.

17. A circular plate is bounded by $r = a$. Its weight density is a function of the distance from the center only; $\rho = g(r)$. Set up an integral for the weight of the plate.

---

* See Example 9.3-3.

18. Write out a second explanation for Definition 1 based on the observation that the area of triangle OPQ of Fig. 9.36 is

$$\frac{1}{2}\,(r)(r+\Delta r)\sin \Delta\theta = \frac{1}{2}\,r(r+\Delta r)\,\frac{\sin \Delta\theta}{\Delta\theta}\,\Delta\theta.$$

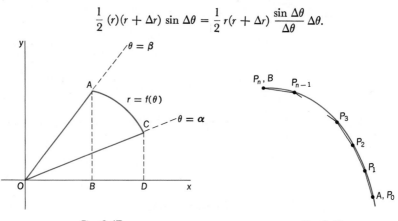

Fig. 9.47   Fig. 9.48

19. Consider the region bounded by $r = f(\theta)$ for $\alpha \le \theta \le \beta$ and the lines $\theta = \alpha,\ \theta = \beta$; see Fig. 9.47. We know that the area of OCA is $\frac{1}{2}\int_{\theta=\alpha}^{\beta} f^2(\theta)\,d\theta$ if the area is defined according to Definition 1 of this section.

To describe AC in Cartesian coordinates, we take the parametric equations

$$x = r\cos\theta = f(\theta)\cos\theta \qquad \text{and} \qquad y = r\sin\theta = f(\theta)\sin\theta$$

with parameter θ. If we define area as we did when studying Cartesian coordinates, the area of OCA would be

$$A_{OCA} = A_{OBA} + A_{BDCA} - A_{ODC},$$

$$A_{OCA} = \frac{1}{2}f^2(\beta)\cos\beta\sin\beta + \int_{x=f(\beta)\cos\beta}^{f(\alpha)\cos\alpha} y_{AC}\,dx - \frac{1}{2}f^2(\alpha)\cos\alpha\sin\alpha,$$

$$A_{OCA} = \frac{1}{2}f^2(\beta)\cos\beta\sin\beta + \int_{\theta=\beta}^{\alpha} f(\theta)\sin\theta[-f(\theta)\sin\theta + f'(\theta)\cos\theta]\,d\theta$$

$$- \frac{1}{2}f^2(\alpha)\cos\alpha\sin\alpha. \tag{6}$$

Show that Eq. (6) reduces to

$$A_{OCA} = \frac{1}{2}\int_{\theta=\alpha}^{\beta} f^2(\theta)\,d\theta.$$

9.7   Arc Length in Polar Coordinates. Curvature

The length of a curve has been defined as the limit of a sum of inscribed chords.* One of the inscribed chords of Fig. 9.48 is shown in greater detail in Fig.

---

* Definition 8.6-1

9.49. The cosine law of trigonometry says that

$$(\text{chord})^2 = r^2 + (r + \Delta r)^2 - 2r(r + \Delta r) \cos \Delta\theta,$$

$$= (2r^2 + 2r\,\Delta r)(1 - \cos \Delta\theta) + \Delta r^2,$$

or, as the result of multiplying and dividing by $(\Delta\theta)^2$,

$$(\text{chord})^2 = \left[(2r^2 + 2r\,\Delta r) \frac{1 - \cos \Delta\theta}{(\Delta\theta)^2} + \left(\frac{\Delta r}{\Delta\theta}\right)^2 \right] (\Delta\theta)^2. \tag{1}$$

Now if we assume that $r = f(\theta)$ is differentiable (and thus also continuous), we can be sure that

$$\lim_{\Delta\theta \to 0} \frac{\Delta r}{\Delta\theta} = \frac{dr}{d\theta} \quad \text{and} \quad \lim_{\Delta\theta \to 0} \Delta r = 0.$$

Moreover,

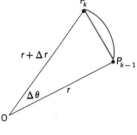

Fig. 9.49

$$\lim_{\Delta\theta \to 0} \frac{1 - \cos \Delta\theta}{(\Delta\theta)^2} = \lim_{\Delta\theta \to 0} \frac{1 - \cos \Delta\theta}{(\Delta\theta)^2} \frac{1 + \cos \Delta\theta}{1 + \cos \Delta\theta}$$

$$= \lim_{\Delta\theta \to 0} \left(\frac{\sin \Delta\theta}{\Delta\theta}\right)^2 \frac{1}{1 + \cos \Delta\theta}$$

$$= (1)^2 \tfrac{1}{2} = \tfrac{1}{2}.$$

Thus the expression in the square bracket of Eq. (1) approaches $r^2 + (dr/d\theta)^2$ as $\Delta\theta$ approaches 0 and we can say that

$$\text{chord} = [\sqrt{r^2 + (dr/d\theta)^2} + c]\,\Delta\theta, \tag{2}$$

where c approaches 0 as $\Delta\theta$ approaches 0.

We have here the essentials of an argument that says that the hypotheses of Theorem 8.8-1 are satisfied. That theorem tells us that, when we take a limit of a sum of elements like those described in Eq. (2), the correction terms c may be ignored. We have the following theorem.

■ THEOREM 1

Length of a curve in polar coordinates.

HYPOTHESIS: $f'(\theta)$ is continuous for $\alpha \le \theta \le \beta$.

CONCLUSION: The length of the arc $r = f(\theta)$, $\alpha \le \theta \le \beta$, is

$$\int_{\theta=\alpha}^{\beta} \sqrt{r^2 + (dr/d\theta)^2}\, d\theta. \tag{3}$$

■ THEOREM 2

The arc length differential in polar coordinates.

HYPOTHESIS: An arc is described in polar coordinates by $r = f(\theta)$, $\alpha \le \theta \le \beta$, with $f'(\theta)$ continuous for $\alpha \le \theta \le \beta$.

CONCLUSION: $\qquad ds^2 = dr^2 + r^2\,d\theta^2 \qquad$ for this arc. $\tag{4}$

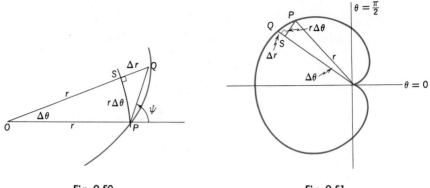

Fig. 9.50   Fig. 9.51

PROOF: Let the point A from which the arc length is measured be the point for which $\theta = \alpha$, and let the direction of increasing θ be the direction of increasing s. Then with each point of the curve we associate a θ, and the distance from A to this point, as measured along the curve, is given by

$$s = \int_{\alpha}^{\theta} \sqrt{r^2 + \left(\frac{dr}{d\theta}\right)^2}\, d\theta.$$

If $F(\theta)$ is a function with the property

$$\frac{dF}{d\theta} = \sqrt{r^2 + \left(\frac{dr}{d\theta}\right)^2},$$

then

$$s = F(\theta) - F(\alpha),$$

and

$$\frac{ds}{d\theta} = \frac{dF}{d\theta} = \sqrt{r^2 + \left(\frac{dr}{d\theta}\right)^2}.$$

Finally,

$$ds = \frac{ds}{d\theta}\, d\theta = \sqrt{r^2 + \left(\frac{dr}{d\theta}\right)^2}\, d\theta,$$

so that

$$ds^2 = \left[r^2 + \left(\frac{dr}{d\theta}\right)^2\right] d\theta^2 = \left(\frac{dr}{d\theta}\, d\theta\right)^2 + r^2\, d\theta^2 = dr^2 + r^2\, d\theta^2. \qquad (4)$$

● **Remark 1**

A mnemonic device.   Consider the points $P(r, \theta)$ and $Q(r + \Delta r, \theta + \Delta\theta)$ on the curve with polar equation $r = f(\theta)$. Draw a circular arc of radius r, center O, intersecting OQ at S. Then, if in Fig. 9.50 we consider PSQ as a right triangle with right angle at S, we can say that

$$(\text{chord } PQ)^2 \approx \Delta r^2 + (r\, \Delta\theta)^2,$$

and that

$$\tan \psi \approx \frac{r\, \Delta\theta}{\Delta r} = \frac{r}{\Delta r/\Delta\theta}. \qquad (6)$$

We do not have proofs of Theorems 2 and 9.5-1 here, but we do have a simple diagram to help us remember the statements of these theorems.

Example 1.   Find the length of the cardioid $r = a(1 - \cos \theta)$. See Fig. 9.51. We can write that

$$(\text{chord } PQ)^2 \approx \Delta r^2 + (r \, \Delta\theta)^2,$$

$$\text{chord } PQ \approx \sqrt{r^2 + (\Delta r/\Delta\theta)^2} \, \Delta\theta, \tag{7}$$

$$\text{length of curve} = \int_{\theta=0}^{2\pi} \sqrt{r^2 + (dr/d\theta)^2} \, d\theta. \tag{8}$$

We compute

$$r^2 + \left(\frac{dr}{d\theta}\right)^2 = a^2(1 - \cos \theta)^2 + a^2(\sin \theta)^2$$

$$= a^2(2 - 2\cos \theta) = 2a^2(1 - \cos \theta) = 4a^2 \sin^2 \frac{\theta}{2}.$$

Thus,

$$\text{length of curve} = 2a \int_{\theta=0}^{2\pi} \sin \frac{\theta}{2} \, d\theta = 4a\left(-\cos \frac{\theta}{2}\right)\Big|_{\theta=0}^{2\pi}$$

$$= 4a[1 - (-1)] = 8a.$$

Note that the positive value must be taken when working with $\sqrt{r^2 + (dr/d\theta)^2}$. We took $2a \sin (\theta/2)$ rather than $-2a \sin (\theta/2)$ for $\sqrt{r^2 + (dr/d\theta)^2}$, because $\sin (\theta/2) \geq 0$ for $0 \leq \theta \leq 2\pi$.

||

We can work out a curvature formula for a curve described in polar coordinates by referring to our curvature formula for a curve described in Cartesian coordinates.

If the polar coordinate description for a curve is $r = f(\theta)$, for $\alpha \leq \theta \leq \beta$, then the same curve is described by the parametric Cartesian equations

$$\begin{cases} x = r \cos \theta = f(\theta) \cos \theta \\ y = r \sin \theta = f(\theta) \sin \theta, \end{cases} \quad \alpha \leq \theta \leq \beta.$$

Assuming that $f'(\theta)$ and $f''(\theta)$ exist for $\alpha \leq \theta \leq \beta$, we can compute

$$\frac{dx}{d\theta} = f'(\theta) \cos \theta - f(\theta) \sin \theta$$

$$\frac{dy}{d\theta} = f'(\theta) \sin \theta + f(\theta) \cos \theta$$

$$\frac{d^2x}{d\theta^2} = f''(\theta) \cos \theta - 2f'(\theta) \sin \theta - f(\theta) \cos \theta$$

$$\frac{d^2y}{d\theta^2} = f''(\theta) \sin \theta + 2f'(\theta) \cos \theta - f(\theta) \sin \theta,$$

$$\left(\frac{dx}{d\theta}\right)^2 + \left(\frac{dy}{d\theta}\right)^2 = (f')^2 + f^2$$

$$\left(\frac{dx}{d\theta}\right)\left(\frac{d^2y}{d\theta^2}\right) = f'f'' \sin\theta \cos\theta - ff'' \sin^2\theta + 2(f')^2 \cos^2\theta$$

$$- 3ff' \sin\theta \cos\theta + f^2 \sin^2\theta$$

$$\left(\frac{dy}{d\theta}\right)\left(\frac{d^2x}{d\theta^2}\right) = f'f'' \sin\theta \cos\theta + ff'' \cos^2\theta - 2(f')^2 \sin^2\theta$$

$$- 3ff' \sin\theta \cos\theta - f^2 \cos^2\theta,$$

and then from Eq. 8.7-6 for the curvature when a curve is described by parametric Cartesian equations,

$$K = \frac{|(dx/d\theta)(d^2y/d\theta^2) - (dy/d\theta)(d^2x/d\theta^2)|}{[(dx/d\theta)^2 + (dy/d\theta)^2]^{3/2}}$$

$$K = \frac{|-ff'' + 2(f')^2 + f^2|}{[(f')^2 + f^2]^{3/2}}.$$

We have proved the following theorem.

■ THEOREM 3

A curvature formula in polar coordinates.

HYPOTHESIS: $f(\theta)$, $f'(\theta)$, $f''(\theta)$ exist for $\alpha \le \theta \le \beta$, and for no θ_0 of $\alpha \le \theta \le \beta$ do we have $f(\theta_0) = f'(\theta_0) = 0$.

CONCLUSION: The curvature at a point of $r = f(\theta)$, $\alpha \le \theta \le \beta$ is

$$K = \frac{|r^2 + 2(dr/d\theta)^2 - r(d^2r/d\theta^2)|}{[(dr/d\theta)^2 + r^2]^{3/2}}. \tag{9}$$

In most cases a reader would refer to the statement of this theorem rather than memorize it. A derivation of Eq. (9) that does not refer to Cartesian coordinates is described in Exercise 4.

Example 2.   Let us study the curvature of the cardioid $r = a(1 - \cos\theta)$. We have

$$\frac{dr}{d\theta} = a\sin\theta \qquad \text{and} \qquad \frac{d^2r}{d\theta^2} = a\cos\theta$$

so that

$$K = \frac{|r^2 + 2(dr/d\theta)^2 - r(d^2r/d\theta^2)|}{[(dr/d\theta)^2 + r^2]^{3/2}}$$

$$= \frac{|a^2(1 - \cos\theta)^2 + 2a^2\sin^2\theta - a^2(1 - \cos\theta)\cos\theta|}{[a^2\sin^2\theta + a^2(1 - \cos\theta)^2]^{3/2}}$$

$$K = \frac{1}{a}\frac{3(1 - \cos\theta)}{[2(1 - \cos\theta)]^{3/2}} = \frac{1}{a}\frac{3}{2\sqrt{2}}\frac{1}{\sqrt{1 - \cos\theta}} = \frac{3}{4a}\frac{1}{\sin(\theta/2)}, \tag{10}$$

it being assumed that we shall consider only $0 \le \theta \le 2\pi$. In Eq. (10) we have a statement for the curvature at any point. In particular, the curvature is a minimum when $\sin(\theta/2) = 1$, and thus when $\theta/2 = \pi/2$, $\theta = \pi$. See Fig. 9.51. The curvature is not defined at the cusp $(0, 0)$. At that point we have $r = dr/d\theta = 0$ and the hypothesis of Theorem 3 is not satisfied.

EXERCISES 9.7

1. Find by integration the arc lengths indicated.
 (a) The circumference of the circle $r = a$.
 (b) The circumference of the circle $r = a \sin \theta$.

 (c) $r = 3 \sec \theta, 0 \le \theta \le \dfrac{\pi}{4}$.

 (f) $r = e^{a\theta}, 0 \le \theta \le 2\pi$.

 (d) $r = \dfrac{p}{1 - \cos \theta}, \beta \le \theta \le \pi$.

 (g) $r = a \sin^3 \dfrac{\theta}{3}, 0 \le \theta \le \beta$.

 (e) $r = a\theta, 0 \le \theta \le 2\pi$.

 (h) $r = \tan^2 \theta \sec \theta, -\dfrac{\pi}{4} \le \theta \le \dfrac{\pi}{3}$.

2. Derive Eq. (4) by studying the curve $r = f(\theta)$ in parametric Cartesian form, $x = r \cos \theta = f(\theta) \cos \theta$ and $y = r \sin \theta = f(\theta) \sin \theta$, with θ as parameter, and rewriting the statement $ds^2 = dx^2 + dy^2$.

3. Find a formula for the curvature of each of the following curves and demonstrate the additional statements made, if any.
 (a) The circle $r = a$.
 (c) $r = 3 \sec \theta$.
 (b) The circle $r = a \sin \theta$.
 (d) $r = a(2 - \cos \theta)$. The curvature is a minimum at $(a, 0)$ and a maximum at $\left(\dfrac{3}{2} a, \dfrac{\pi}{3}\right)$.

 (e) $r = e^{a\theta}$. R, the radius of curvature, and r are always proportional. R is also a linear function of s.

 (f) Parabola $r = \dfrac{p}{1 - \cos \theta} = \dfrac{p}{2} \csc^2 \dfrac{\theta}{2}$. The curvature is a maximum at the vertex.

 (g) Lemniscate $r^2 = a^2 \cos 2\theta$. The curvature is a maximum at $(a, 0)$ and a minimum at the pole.

 (h) $r = a \sin 2\theta$.

4. Derive Eq. (9) by working directly with the curvature definition $K = |d\alpha/ds|$. When $r \ne 0$ and $dr/d\theta \ne 0$ we can determine ψ from Eq. (9.5-4),

$$\psi = \tan^{-1} (r/r'),$$

and then, since $\alpha = \theta + \psi$ or $\alpha = \theta + \psi - \pi$, we compute

$$K = \left| \dfrac{d\theta}{ds} + \dfrac{d\psi}{ds} \right|.$$

Show that

$$\dfrac{d\psi}{d\theta} = \dfrac{(r')^2 - rr''}{(r')^2 + r^2}$$

$$\dfrac{d\theta}{ds} = \dfrac{1}{\sqrt{(r')^2 + r^2}}$$

$$\dfrac{d\psi}{ds} = \dfrac{(r')^2 - rr''}{[(r')^2 + r^2]^{3/2}}$$

and compute K. [When $r \ne 0$ and $dr/d\theta = 0$ we can work with Eq. (9.5-3) instead of (9.5-4). When $r = f(\theta_0) = 0$ and $dr/d\theta = f'(\theta_0) \ne 0$, we compute $\Delta \alpha$ at $\theta = \theta_0$ directly, then $d\alpha/d\theta = \lim_{\Delta\theta \to 0} \Delta\alpha/\Delta\theta$, then $d\alpha/ds$. The $\lim_{\Delta\theta \to 0} \Delta\alpha/\Delta\theta$ computation is not easy; Theorem 13.10-3, to be studied later, would be helpful here.]

Solid Analytic Geometry

The first nine chapters of this textbook dealt primarily with two-dimensional analytic geometry and functions of one variable. In this chapter we shall study some three-dimensional analytic geometry, and then, in later chapters, functions of two or more variables.

10.1 Three-Dimensional Cartesian Coordinates

With the help of three mutually perpendicular axes we can set up a one-to-one correspondence between the points of space and trios of numbers. In illustrating this correspondence with diagrams on paper or on a blackboard, however, it is necessary to create the illusion that three perpendicular directions have been portrayed. We select a point, O, to serve as the origin and through it draw two perpendicular lines, which we shall call the y and z axes; see Fig. 10.1. Of course, we cannot draw a third line through O perpendicular to the y and z axes, but we do draw a third line through O which makes an angle of roughly $135°$ with the y axis line, and we *make believe* that this line, called the x axis, is perpendicular to the y and z axes.

In space, three such mutually perpendicular axes do exist. Thus, imagine that the reader sits in a room whose floor, ceiling, and walls are rectangular, with all intersections at right angles, and imagine that he faces one particular wall, called the front wall. For the positive y axis he can choose the line that is the intersection of the floor and the front wall. For the positive z axis he can choose the line that is the intersection of the front wall and the left side wall. For the positive x axis he can choose the line that is the intersection of the floor and the left side wall.

On the y and z axes we mark off scales with equal unit distances, but on the x axis we mark off a unit distance that is only about $\frac{7}{10}$ as long physically as the unit distances on the other two axes. We treat the x axis in a different way, because this "foreshortening" helps us to create the illusion that we have figures in space when in reality the drawing is two-dimensional. In Fig. 10.2(a), for instance, we have marked off a unit distance on the x axis which is physically equal to the unit distances on the other axes, and have portrayed a "circle" in the xy plane with radius

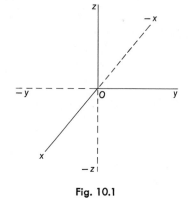

Fig. 10.1

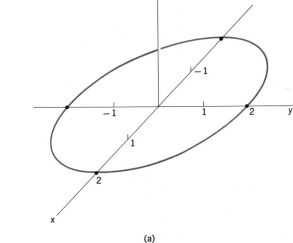

(a)

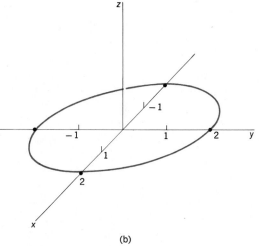

(b)

Fig. 10.2

2 and center at the origin, passing through the points marked 2 or −2 on the *x* and *y* axes. In Fig. 10.2(b), however, we have marked off a unit distance on the *x* axis which is $\frac{7}{10}$ as long as the unit distance on the *y* axis, and then we have again portrayed a circle of radius 2 in the *xy* plane, center at the origin. The curve drawn in Fig. 10.2(b) seems to portray the circle better than the curve drawn in Fig. 10.2(a).

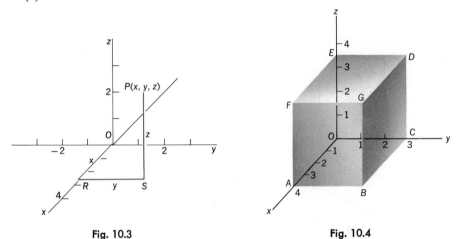

Fig. 10.3   Fig. 10.4

Once scales have been selected on the three axes, a one-to-one correspondence between points in space and trios of coordinate numbers can be set up. If we are given a set of coordinates (x, y, z), we can locate the corresponding point *P* by moving from the origin to the point *R* with coordinate *x* on the *x* axis, thence a distance *y* in the *y*-axis direction to *S*, and from *S* a distance *z* in the *z*-axis direction to *P*. Conversely, given a point *P* we drop a perpendicular from *P* to *S* in the *xy* plane. In the *xy* plane we draw a line through *S* perpendicular to the *x* axis at *R*. The coordinates assigned to *P* are then $x = OR, y = RS$, and $z = SP$, the coordinates being positive or negative according as the directed distances *OR*, *RS*, and *SP* are in the respective positive or negative axis directions. See Fig. 10.3.

Example 1. Let us describe the vertices, sides, and edges of the rectangular parallelepiped or box of Fig. 10.4. Vertex *A* is +4 units from the origin in the *x* direction; its coordinates are $(4, 0, 0)$. The coordinates of *B* are $(4, 3, 0)$ because *B* is 3 units from *A* in the positive *y* direction. The coordinates of *G* are $(4, 3, 3.5)$ because *G* is 3.5 units from *B* in the positive *z* direction. The coordinates of *D* and *F* are $(0, 3, 3.5)$ and $(4, 0, 3.5)$, respectively.

Side *OABC* lies in the *xy* plane. The *z* coordinate of every point in this plane is 0 and the *z* coordinate of no other point is 0. Hence the equation $z = 0$ is an analytic description for the *xy* plane. The side *DEFG* lies in a plane parallel to the *xy* plane and 3.5 units above it. A point lies in this plane if and only if its *z* coordinate is 3.5; the analytic description for this plane is $z = 3.5$. Similarly, side *OAFE* lies in the *xz* plane, whose analytic description is $y = 0$; side *BCDG* lies in the plane $y = 3$. Finally, side $OCDE$ lies in the yz plane with analytic description $x = 0$; side $ABGF$ lies in the plane $x = 4$.

Edge OA lies on the x axis. A point lies on this line if and only if its y and z coordinates both vanish; hence the x axis can be described analytically by the two statements $y = 0$ and $z = 0$. From another point of view, we ought to expect these two equations to describe the x axis, for the x axis is determined as the intersection of the two planes with equations $y = 0$ and $z = 0$. The edge BC lies in the planes $z = 0$ and $y = 3$; these two equations describe the line on which BC lies. Similarly, the edge FG is part of the line described by the two equations $x = 4$, $z = 3.5$.

Example 2. Sketch the ellipse whose coordinates satisfy the equations

$$\frac{x^2}{9} + \frac{y^2}{4} = 1 \quad \text{and} \quad z = 2.$$

The second of these equations tells us that the ellipse lies in the plane parallel to the xy plane and 2 units above it. The first equation then tells us that the center of the ellipse is the point $C(0, 0, 2)$, that the major vertices are the points $A(3, 0, 2)$, $A'(-3, 0, 2)$ and that the minor vertices are the points $B(0, 2, 2)$, $B'(0, -2, 2)$. The ellipse is sketched in Fig. 10.5. In drawing guide lines for the sketching, one can take advantage of the fact that the tangents at the vertices A and A' are parallel to the y axis, and that those at B and B' are parallel to the x axis.*

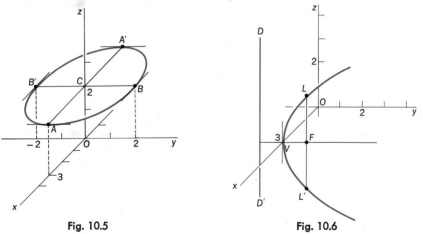

Fig. 10.5   **Fig. 10.6**

Example 3. Sketch the parabola whose equations are $x = 3$ and $z^2 = 4y$. The first of these equations tells us that the parabola lies in a plane parallel to the yz plane and 3 units in front of it. From the second equation we then state that the vertex is the point $V(3, 0, 0)$ and that the distance from the focus to the directrix is $p = 2$, so that the focus is the point $F(3, 1, 0)$ and the directrix DD' has equations $x = 3$, $y = -1$. The parabola is sketched in Fig. 10.6. The latus

---

* The reader with no previous experience in drawing is advised to fix directions and measure distances parallel to the coordinate directions with care. Also, whenever one curve or line passes over another in a diagram, he should emphasize that curve or line which is to appear to the reader to pass in front.

rectum points $L(3, 1, 2)$ and $L'(3, 1, -2)$, equidistant from the focus and directrix, are useful in the sketching, and so is the tangent line at the vertex, known to have the z axis direction.

Example 4. Sketch the hyperbola whose equations are

$$y = -2 \quad \text{and} \quad \frac{z^2}{1} - \frac{x^2}{1} = 1.$$

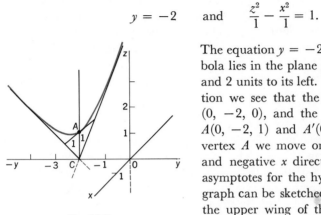

Fig. 10.7

The equation $y = -2$ tells us that the hyperbola lies in the plane parallel to the xz plane and 2 units to its left. From the second equation we see that the center C is the point $(0, -2, 0)$, and the vertices are the points $A(0, -2, 1)$ and $A'(0, -2, -1)$. From the vertex A we move one unit in the positive and negative x directions to determine the asymptotes for the hyperbola, and then the graph can be sketched. See Fig. 10.7, where the upper wing of the hyperbola is drawn. Once more the tangents at the vertices can serve as guide lines.

Example 5. In Figs. 10.8(a) and (b) we see that

(a) the points $P(a, b, c)$ and $Q(-a, b, c)$ are symmetrically situated with respect to the yz plane;

(b) $P(a, b, c)$ and $R(a, -b, c)$ are symmetrically situated with respect to the xz plane;

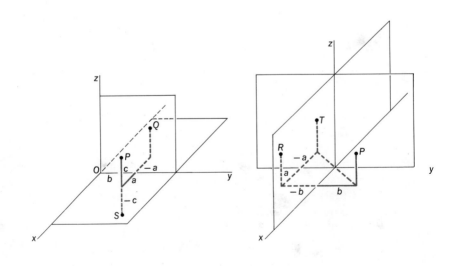

(a)

(b)

Fig. 10.8

(c) $P(a, b, c)$ and $S(a, b, -c)$ are symmetrically situated with respect to the xy plane;

(d) $P(a, b, c)$ and $T(-a, -b, c)$ are symmetrically situated with respect to the z axis.

It is also true that

(e) $P(a, b, c)$ and $U(-a, b, -c)$ are symmetrically situated with respect to the y axis;

(f) $P(a, b, c)$ and $V(a, -b, -c)$ are symmetrically situated with respect to the x axis;

(g) $P(a, b, c)$ and $W(-a, -b, -c)$ are symmetrically situated with respect to the origin.

We cannot pretend that this section and the next two discuss the theory of perspective in drawing. At best, these sections present a set of working instructions sufficient to enable a student without previous training in drawing to sketch and analyze the drawings he needs for his work in this course.

EXERCISES 10.1

1. Sketch the triangles with the following vertices and answer the questions asked.
 (a) $O(0, 0, 0)$, $Q(3, 0, 0)$, $R(3, 3, 0)$. Find the length of the hypotenuse.
 (b) $S(0, 2, 0)$, $T(4, 2, 0)$, $U(0, 2, 3)$. Find the length of the hypotenuse.
 (c) $V(4, -2, 0)$, $W(4, 2, 0)$, $K(0, 0, 5)$. Find the lengths of the equal sides.
 (d) $L(2, 0, 0)$, $M(0, -2, 0)$, $N(0, 0, 2)$. Find the lengths of the sides.

2. Sketch the rectangular parallelepipeds (boxes) with the following vertices. Write down the equations of the sides and edges that pass through the last-named vertex.
 (a) $(0, 0, 0)$, $(0, 5, 0)$, $(-5, 5, 0)$, $(-5, 0, 0)$, $(0, 0, 4)$, $(0, 5, 4)$, $(-5, 5, 4)$, $(-5, 0, 4)$.
 (b) $(2, -3, 3)$, $(2, 3, 3)$, $(-2, 3, 3)$, $(-2, -3, 3)$, $(2, -3, 1)$, $(2, 3, 1)$, $(-2, 3, 1)$, $(-2, -3, 1)$.

3. Sketch the pyramid whose base vertices are $(2, 5, 0)$, $(2, -5, 0)$, $(-2, -5, 0)$, and $(-2, 5, 0)$ and whose fifth vertex is $(0, 0, 3)$. The volume of a pyramid is $\frac{1}{3}$(base area)(altitude); find the volume.

4. Sketch the rectangular parallelepipeds bounded by the following planes.
 (a) $x = 0$, $x = 3$, $y = 0$, $y = 7$, $z = 0$, $z = 4$.
 (b) $x = -4$, $x = +4$, $y = 0$, $y = 3$, $z = -1$, $z = +3$.
 Find the coordinates of the vertices.

5. Sketch the straight lines whose equations are given. Sketch also portions of the planes parallel to the coordinate planes of which these lines are the intersections.
 (a) $x = 2$, $z = 0$.   (c) $x = -4$, $y = 5$.
 (b) $y = 0$, $z = 3$.   (d) $x = 1$, $z = 5$.

6. Sketch the following lines in one diagram: (a) $x = 1$, $y = 0$; (b) $x = 0$, $y = 2$; (c) $z = 0$, $2x + y = 2$; (d) $z = 4$, $2x + y = 2$. Find the coordinates of the vertices of the rectangle determined by these lines.

7. Sketch the following curves. If there are centers or vertices, list their coordinates.

(a) $\dfrac{x^2}{9} + \dfrac{z^2}{1} = 1$, $y = 0$.   (d) $x^2 + z^2 = 4$, $y = 5$.   (g) $\dfrac{y^2}{16} - \dfrac{x^2}{4} = 1$, $z = 5$.

(b) $x^2 = y + 1$, $z = 0$.   (e) $\dfrac{x^2}{4} + \dfrac{y^2}{16} = 1$, $z = 4$.   (h) $z = \log y$, $x = 5$.

(c) $\dfrac{y^2}{1} - \dfrac{z^2}{2} = 1$, $x = 0$.   (f) $y^2 = z$, $x = -1$.   (i) $z = \dfrac{2}{1 + x^2}$, $y = -2$.

8. List the coordinates of the points symmetric to $(2, 5, 3)$
   (a) with respect to the coordinate planes;
   (b) with respect to the coordinate axes;
   (c) with respect to the origin.
9. List the coordinates of the feet of the perpendiculars drawn from the point $P(a, b, c)$
   (a) to the coordinate planes;
   (b) to the coordinate axes.

10.2   On Surface Sketching

The points whose coordinates satisfy an equation in three variables usually constitute a surface. To sketch the surface from its equation, the following procedure is often useful. First, from the equation of the surface, find the equations of the curves in which the surface intersects the coordinate planes, and sketch these curves. These curves are often called the *traces* or the *principal sections*. Second, from the equation of the surface again, decide what the sections of the surface by planes parallel to the coordinate planes are, and sketch as many of these sections as are necessary to make the diagram clear for the purpose at hand. Closed curves are usually easier to sketch, and we therefore seek out elliptic sections where possible and sketch them first. Symmetry considerations should also be kept in mind, for a suitable fraction of a symmetric diagram will often suffice to enable a student to analyze the whole diagram.

Example 1.   Discuss and sketch the ellipsoid

$$\frac{x^2}{4} + \frac{y^2}{16} + \frac{z^2}{9} = 1.$$

Symmetry: We observe that the surface is symmetric with respect to the xy plane, for if a point with coordinates (x, y, z) lies on the surface, so does the point with coordinates $(x, y, -z)$. These points are symmetrically situated with respect to the xy plane. Similarly, the surface is also symmetric with respect to the other coordinate planes. We shall sketch that portion of the surface for which $z \geq 0$.

Traces: The intersection with the xy plane, or the "xy trace" is obtained by setting $z = 0$. We can say that the

xy trace is the ellipse: $z = 0$ and $\dfrac{x^2}{4} + \dfrac{y^2}{16} = 1$,

yz trace is the ellipse: $x = 0$ and $\dfrac{y^2}{16} + \dfrac{z^2}{9} = 1$,

xz trace is the ellipse: $y = 0$ and $\dfrac{x^2}{4} + \dfrac{z^2}{9} = 1$.

These traces are sketched in Fig. 10.9(a). For some purposes the surface is already sketched sufficiently clearly.

Sections: A plane parallel to the xy plane has an equation of the form $z = $ const. Its intersection with the surface would be an ellipse with equations

$$z = c \quad \text{and} \quad \frac{x^2}{4} + \frac{y^2}{16} = 1 - \frac{c^2}{9}.$$

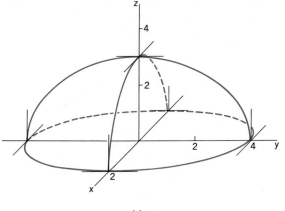

(a)

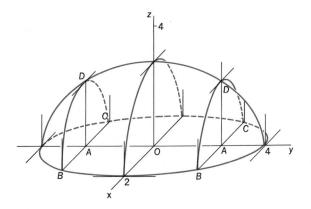

(b)

Fig. 10.9

To abbreviate, we might say that we have ellipses for the sections

$$z = c, \qquad -3 \leq c \leq 3.$$

Similarly, we also have ellipses for the sections

$$x = c, \qquad -2 \leq c \leq 2,$$
$$y = c, \qquad -4 \leq c \leq 4.$$

These sections are about equally easy to draw. In Fig. 10.9(b) we have continued Fig. 10.9(a) by adding two sections parallel to the xz plane. Each section drawing was started by selecting a point A on the y axis. From A a line was drawn parallel to the x axis, intersecting the xy trace at B and C. A second line through A, parallel to the z axis, intersected the yz trace at D. Knowing that B, C, and D were three vertices of an ellipse, and using tangents at the vertices parallel to the axes as guide lines, the elliptic sections were drawn.

Example 2.   Discuss and sketch the elliptic paraboloid

$$\frac{x^2}{4} + \frac{y^2}{9} = \frac{z}{4}.$$

Symmetry: Since the points $(x, -y, z)$ and $(-x, y, z)$ lie on the surface whenever the point (x, y, z) does, the surface is symmetric with respect to the xz and yz planes.

Traces: $z = 0$ and $\dfrac{x^2}{4} + \dfrac{y^2}{9} = 0,$ the one point $(0, 0, 0)$,

$y = 0$ and $x^2 = z,$ parabola,

$x = 0$ and $y^2 = \tfrac{9}{4}z,$ parabola.

Sections: $z = c > 0,$ ellipse,

$x = c,$ parabola,

$y = c,$ parabola.

The traces are drawn first, as in Fig. 10.10(a), a few simple table values sufficing for each parabola. Since ellipses are usually easier to draw than parabolas, the elliptic sections

$$z = c > 0, \qquad \frac{x^2}{4} + \frac{y^2}{9} = \frac{c}{4}$$

$$z = c > 0, \qquad \frac{x^2}{c} + \frac{y^2}{9c/4} = 1,$$

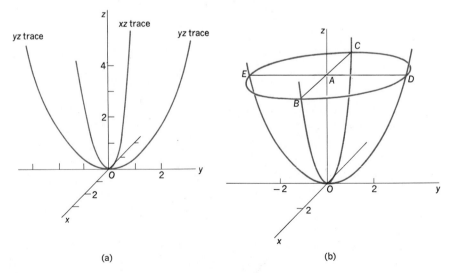

(a)   (b)

Fig. 10.10

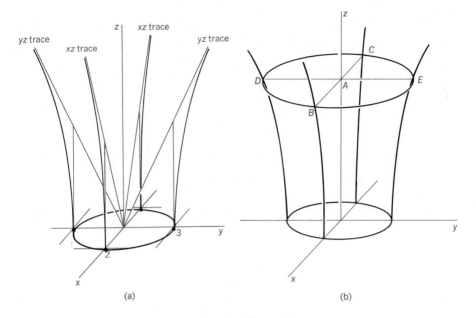

Fig. 10.11 (a) and (b)

with semimajor axes $\frac{3}{2}\sqrt{c}$ and semiminor axes $\sqrt{c}$, are considered in greater detail. For larger c, thus for higher planes $z = c$, we have larger ellipses. Point A was selected on the z axis, and then lines were drawn parallel to the x and y axes, meeting the xz and yz traces at B, C and D, E. An ellipse was then sketched with B, C, D, E as vertices. See Fig. 10.10(b).

Example 3. Discuss and sketch the hyperboloid of one sheet,

$$\frac{x^2}{4} + \frac{y^2}{9} - \frac{z^2}{36} = 1.$$

Symmetry. The surface is symmetric with respect to all three coordinate planes. We shall sketch that portion of the surface for which $z \geq 0$.

Traces: $z = 0$ and $\dfrac{x^2}{4} + \dfrac{y^2}{9} = 1,$ ellipse,

   $y = 0$ and $\dfrac{x^2}{4} - \dfrac{z^2}{36} = 1,$ hyperbola,

   $x = 0$ and $\dfrac{y^2}{9} - \dfrac{z^2}{36} = 1,$ hyperbola.

Sections: $z = c,$ ellipse,

   $y = c,$ hyperbola,

   $x = c,$ hyperbola.

The traces are drawn first, as in Fig. 10.11(a). For the ellipse the four vertices and the tangents at these points are helpful. For the hyperbolas the asymptotes are useful guide lines.

Of the various sections possible, the elliptic sections, parallel to the xy plane, are easiest to draw. In detail, the elliptic sections have equations

$$z = c, \qquad \frac{x^2}{4} + \frac{y^2}{9} = 1 + \frac{c^2}{36}$$

$$z = c, \qquad \frac{x^2}{4 + (c^2/9)} + \frac{y^2}{9 + (c^2/4)} = 1,$$

with semimajor axes $\sqrt{9 + c^2/4}$ and semiminor axes $\sqrt{4 + c^2/9}$; when $|c|$ is larger, the plane $z = c$ will be further from the xy plane and the ellipse will be larger. In Fig. 10.11(b) a point A was selected on the z axis, and then lines were drawn through A parallel to the x and y axes, meeting the xz and yz traces at B, C and D, E. An ellipse was then drawn with B, C, D, and E as vertices.

Example 4.   Discuss and sketch the hyperboloid of two sheets,

$$\frac{x^2}{4} - \frac{y^2}{2} - \frac{z^2}{4} = 1.$$

Symmetry: The surface is symmetric with respect to all three coordinate planes. We shall sketch that portion of the surface for which $z \geq 0$.

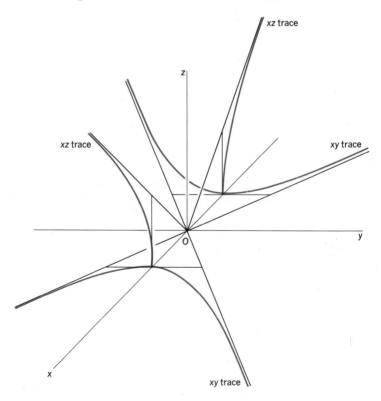

Fig. 10.12 (a)

Traces:

$z = 0$	and	$\dfrac{x^2}{4} - \dfrac{y^2}{2} = 1,$	hyperbola with transverse vertices $(\pm 2, 0, 0),$
$y = 0$	and	$\dfrac{x^2}{4} - \dfrac{z^2}{4} = 1,$	hyperbola with transverse vertices $(\pm 2, 0, 0),$
$x = 0$	and	$-\dfrac{y^2}{2} - \dfrac{z^2}{4} = 1,$	no real locus.

Sections:

$z = c,$		hyperbola,
$y = c,$		hyperbola,
$x = c,$	$\lvert c \rvert > 2,$	ellipse.

In Fig. 10.12(a) the hyperbolic traces are drawn in the xy and xz planes with the help of their asymptotes as guide lines. In Fig. 10.12(b) elliptic sections, parallel to the yz plane, have been added to the sketch. The points A were selected on the x axis, and then lines were drawn through A parallel to the y and z axes, meeting the xy and xz traces at B, C, and D. These points were the vertices of the elliptic sections. The elliptic sections grow larger as the section plane $x = c \geq 2$ is brought forward in the x direction, because the equations of these sections, in greater detail, are

$$x = c, \qquad \frac{y^2}{2} + \frac{z^2}{4} = \frac{c^2}{4} - 1$$

$$x = c, \qquad \frac{y^2}{(c^2 - 4)/2} + \frac{z^2}{c^2 - 4} = 1,$$

and the semimajor and semiminor axes are $\sqrt{c^2 - 4}$ and $\sqrt{(c^2 - 4)/2}$.

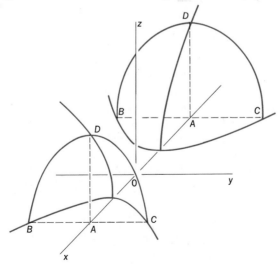

Fig. 10.12 (b)

Example 5. The surfaces sketched in the first four examples of this section all have second-degree equations and are called *quadric surfaces*. Many students find that the hyperbolic paraboloid or "saddle surface" is the most difficult of the quadric surfaces to sketch. Let us consider the surface with equation

$$-\frac{x^2}{1}+\frac{y^2}{3} = z.$$

Symmetry: The surface is symmetric with respect to the yz and xz planes because the points with coordinates $(-x, y, z)$ and $(x, -y, z)$ lie on the surface whenever the point (x, y, z) does. We shall sketch that portion of the surface for which $x \geq 0$.

Traces:

$z = 0$ and $-\dfrac{x^2}{1}+\dfrac{y^2}{3} = 0$ or $y^2 = 3x^2$ or $y = \pm \sqrt{3}\, x$, 2 straight lines,

$y = 0$ and $x^2 = -z$, a parabola through $(0, 0, 0)$, $(1, 0, -1)$, $(2, 0, -4)$,

$x = 0$ and $y^2 = 3z$, a parabola through $(0, 0, 0)$, $(0, 3, 3)$, $(0, -3, 3)$.

Sections:

$z = \text{const} > 0,$ hyperbola with transverse axis in y direction,

$z = \text{const} < 0,$ hyperbola with transverse axis in x direction,

$y = \text{const},$ parabola,

$x = \text{const},$ parabola.

We begin by sketching the traces in Fig. 10.13(a). In Fig. 10.13(b) several hyperbolic sections are added to these traces. In the plane $z = 3$, for instance, we have the hyperbolic section

$$-\frac{x^2}{3}+\frac{y^2}{9} = 1$$

with vertices at $(0, \pm 3, 3)$. In the plane $z = 5$ we have the hyperbolic section

$$-\frac{x^2}{5}+\frac{y^2}{15} = 1$$

with vertices at $(0, \pm\sqrt{15}, 5)$. In the plane $z = -3$, we have the hyperbolic section

$$\frac{x^2}{3}-\frac{y^2}{9} = 1$$

with vertices at $(\pm\sqrt{3}, 0, -3)$.

Example 6. The base of a solid is a circle of radius 4. Every section perpendicular to one diameter is an isosceles triangle of altitude 8. Sketch the solid.

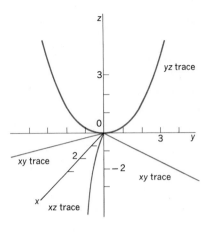

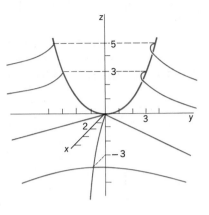

(a)

(b)

Fig. 10.13

We can start by drawing a circle of radius 4 in the xy plane with the center at the origin. Let the diameter perpendicular to the isosceles triangle sections lie along the y axis. Then the xz trace will be an isosceles triangle of base 8, altitude 8; the section by the plane $y = 2$ will be an isosceles triangle of base $2\sqrt{12}$, altitude 8;* the section by the plane $y = 4$ will be the "isosceles triangle" of base 0, altitude 8. See Fig. 10.14. Each section was drawn by starting at a point on the y axis and drawing parallels to the x and z axes to locate the vertices of the isosceles triangle section.

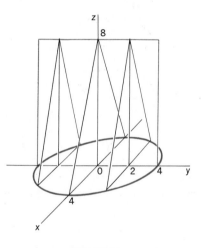

Fig. 10.14

In the examples we have given we have sketched the traces for a surface in the coordinate planes first and then sketched other sections that seemed suitable. Some students prefer to sketch sections first and then the traces. To illustrate this procedure, let us return to Example 3.

Example 3A. We shall sketch again the hyperboloid of one sheet

$$\frac{x^2}{4} + \frac{y^2}{9} - \frac{z^2}{36} = 1$$

sketched in Example 3 above. The discussion of symmetry, traces, and sections

---

* The points $(\pm\sqrt{12}, 2)$ lie on the circle $x^2 + y^2 = 16$.

given in Example 3 indicates that the easiest sections to sketch will be the elliptic sections

$$z = c, \qquad \frac{x^2}{4 + (c^2/9)} + \frac{y^2}{9 + (c^2/4)} = 1.$$

Let us start, as in Fig. 10.11(c), by sketching the sections

$$z = 0, \qquad \frac{x^2}{4} + \frac{y^2}{9} = 1,$$

$$z = 2, \qquad \frac{x^2}{40/9} + \frac{y^2}{10} = 1,$$

$$z = 4, \qquad \frac{x^2}{52/9} + \frac{y^2}{13} = 1.$$

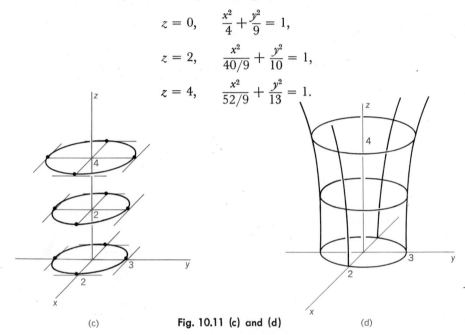

(c)   **Fig. 10.11 (c) and (d)**   (d)

Then we sketch the xz and yz traces as in Fig. 10.11(d), knowing in advance that the hyperbolas are to pass through the vertices of the ellipses drawn as sections.

EXERCISES 10.2

1. Discuss and sketch the following surfaces. Take advantage of the symmetry to sketch only part of a surface if you can visualize the whole surface from that part.

    (a) $x^2 + y^2 + z^2 = 25$ (sphere).

    (d) $\dfrac{x^2}{25} + \dfrac{y^2}{4} + \dfrac{z^2}{1} = 1$ (ellipsoid).

    (b) $\dfrac{x^2}{4} + \dfrac{y^2}{4} + \dfrac{z^2}{16} = 1$ (prolate spheroid).

    (e) $\dfrac{x^2}{16} + \dfrac{z^2}{4} = \dfrac{y}{4}$ (elliptic paraboloid).

    (c) $\dfrac{x^2}{9} + \dfrac{y^2}{9} + \dfrac{z^2}{4} = 1$ (oblate spheroid).

    (f) $\dfrac{x^2}{4} + \dfrac{y^2}{9} = \dfrac{4 - z}{4}$ (elliptic paraboloid).

    (g) $\dfrac{x^2}{16} + \dfrac{z^2}{9} - \dfrac{y^2}{49} = 1$ (hyperboloid of one sheet).

    (h) $\dfrac{y^2}{9} + \dfrac{z^2}{4} - \dfrac{x^2}{25} = 1$ (hyperboloid of one sheet).

    (i) $-\dfrac{x^2}{4} + \dfrac{y^2}{16} - \dfrac{z^2}{9} = 1$ (hyperboloid of two sheets).

(j) $-\dfrac{x^2}{1} - \dfrac{y^2}{9} + \dfrac{z^2}{4} = 1$ (hyperboloid of two sheets).

(k) $-\dfrac{x^2}{4} + \dfrac{y^2}{16} = z$ (hyperbolic paraboloid).

(l) $x^2 + z^2 = \frac{1}{4} y^2$ (right circular cone).

2. The base of a solid is a rectangle of dimensions 4 by 2. Each section perpendicular to the sides of length 4 is a semicircle. Sketch the solid.

3. The base of a solid is the half of the ellipse $x^2/4 + y^2/16 = 1$ in the xy plane for which $y \geq 0$. Each section perpendicular to the y axis is a square. Sketch the solid.

4. The base of a solid is a quarter-circle of radius 4. Each section perpendicular to one radial boundary is an isosceles right triangle with the hypotenuse in the base plane. Sketch the solid.

5. We shall show in Sec. 10.6 that first-degree equations represent planes. A portion of a plane can frequently be sketched well enough for the purpose at hand by locating the points at which the plane intercepts the coordinate axes and then joining these points in pairs by straight lines. Sketch such portions of
   (a) $2x + 3y + 4z = 12$.
   (b) $5x - 2y + 2z = 10$.
   (c) $z - x - y = 4$.

6. Use traces and sections to sketch a portion of the plane $x + y + z = 0$.

10.3 On Cylinders, Cones, and Surfaces of Revolution

■ DEFINITION 1

Cylinders. Given a curve C. Let a line L move along C, always parallel to itself. The surface generated by the line L is called a cylinder; the straight lines on the surface are called its elements.

Example 1. If we start with the circle C of radius a in the xy plane with center at the origin, and move a line L which is parallel to the z axis around C, we sweep out a right circular cylinder, part of which is pictured in Fig. 10.15. The curve C can be considered a right section of the cylinder, because it lies in a plane

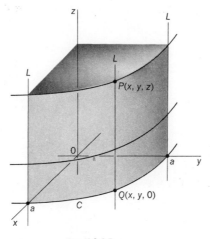

Fig. 10.15

that makes a right angle with each of the generating elements. Every other right section will also be a circle of radius a; two such sections are drawn in Fig. 10.15.

Each point on this cylinder lies on one line element and also on one of the circular sections perpendicular to the z axis. If it lies on C itself, its coordinates satisfy the equations $x^2 + y^2 = a^2$ and $z = 0$. If it lies on the circle in the plane $z = b$, its coordinates satisfy the equations $x^2 + y^2 = a^2$ and $z = b$. An equation satisfied by the coordinates of every point on the cylinder, and by no other point, is $x^2 + y^2 = a^2$. This is the equation of the cylinder.

The elements of the cylinder of Example 1 are parallel to the z axis. Corresponding to this fact, the equation of the cylinder is an equation in the variables x and y alone; the letter z is missing. This is an illustration of the following theorem.

■ THEOREM 1

On the equation of a cylinder parallel to a coordinate axis.

HYPOTHESIS: Surface S is a cylinder (a) whose elements are parallel to the z axis;

(b) whose xy trace is a curve C with equations $f(x, y) = 0$ and $z = 0$.

CONCLUSION: The equation of S is

$$f(x, y) = 0. \tag{1}$$

PROOF: Refer to Fig. 10.15 again. Let $P(x, y, z)$ be a point of S. Through P on S we can draw a line element parallel to the z axis, and this line element intersects C at $Q(x, y, 0)$. Since one of the equations of C is $f(x, y) = 0$, the coordinates of Q satisfy Eq. (1); since P and Q have the same x and y coordinates, and since (1) is concerned only with x and y coordinates, the coordinates of P also satisfy Eq. (1).

Conversely, if the coordinates of $P(x, y, z)$ satisfy Eq. (1), then the coordinates of $Q(x, y, 0)$ satisfy $f(x, y) = 0$ and $z = 0$ so that Q lies on curve C. Since $P(x, y, z)$ lies on the line through $Q(x, y, 0)$ parallel to the z axis, P lies on S.

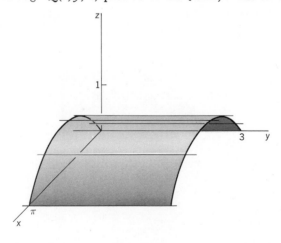

Fig. 10.16

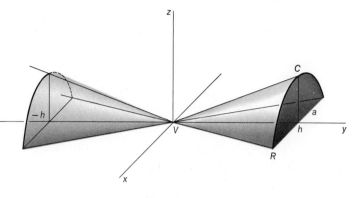

Fig. 10.17

Example 2.   Discuss the surface $z = \sin x$ and sketch that portion of it for which $0 \le x \le \pi$. The variable y does not appear in the equation of the surface. Hence the surface is a cylinder whose line elements are parallel to the y axis and whose xz trace is the curve $z = \sin x$, $y = 0$. In Fig. 10.16 the xz trace was drawn first. Then several line elements parallel to the y axis were drawn, and, finally, a second section in a plane perpendicular to the elements was drawn at $y = 3$.

■ DEFINITION 2

Cones.   Given a curve C and a point V not on C. Let a line L move along C, always passing through V. The surface generated by L is called a cone; the straight lines on the surface are called its elements, and the point V through which all the line elements pass is called the vertex.

Example 3.   Start with the circle C of radius a in the plane $y = h$, center on the y axis, and vertex $V(0, 0, 0)$ at the origin. The straight lines joining the points of C to V determine a right circular cone. The portion of the cone for which $z \ge 0$ appears in Fig. 10.17. A second circular section in the plane $y = -h$ was also sketched.

Example 4.   Sketch the parabolic cone generated by the lines that join $V(0, 0, 5)$ to the points of C with equations $x^2 = 4(4 - y)$, $z = 0$. In Fig. 10.18 the parabola C was sketched, using the points $(0, 4, 0)$ and $(\pm 4, 0, 0)$, and then some generating lines through V were drawn. The upper nappe of the cone, formed by continuing the generating lines upward through V, is not shown in Fig. 10.18.

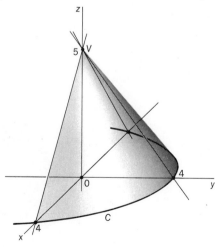

Fig. 10.18

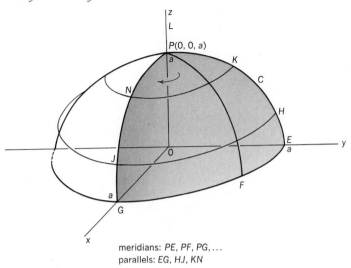

meridians: *PE, PF, PG,* ...
parallels: *EG, HJ, KN*

Fig. 10.19

■ **DEFINITION 3**

Surface of revolution. The surface generated by a plane curve C when it is rotated about a line L in its plane is called a surface of revolution. The curve C is called the profile curve; L is called the axis of revolution or the axis of symmetry; the sections in planes perpendicular to L are circles and are called parallels; the sections in planes through L are congruent to the profile curve and are called meridians.

Example 5.   The sphere is a surface of revolution. Take as profile curve C the circle $y^2 + z^2 = a^2$, $x = 0$, and as axis L the z axis. The circles in the planes $z = c$ are the parallels, and the great circles through the points $(0, 0, a)$ and $(0, 0, -a)$ are the meridians. See Fig. 10.19 where the eighth of the sphere for which $z \geq 0$, $x \geq 0$, and $y \geq 0$ is shown.

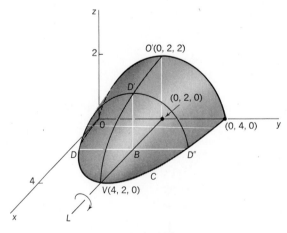

Fig. 10.20

Example 6. Given the parabola C with equation $(y - 2)^2 = 4 - x$ in the xy plane. Let that portion of C for which $0 \leq x \leq 4$ be rotated about the line $y = 2$. Sketch the surface of revolution generated.

The profile curve C and the axis L in the xy plane are sketched first; we know that C is a parabola through the points $(4, 2, 0)$, $(0, 0, 0)$, and $(0, 4, 0)$. Second, after rotation through $90°$ we reach the meridian curve $VD'O'$ in the plane $y = 2$. This meridian parabola must have vertex $V(4, 2, 0)$ as C did, and must pass through a point $O'(0, 2, 2)$, 2 units above $(0, 2, 0)$, because C passed through $O(0, 0, 0)$, 2 units to the left of $(0, 2, 0)$. Finally, a circular section perpendicular to the axis L was drawn. Point B was selected on the axis L, radial lines were drawn from B in the y and z axis directions to locate points D, D', D'' on the circle, and then the circle was drawn. In Fig. 10.20 the half of the surface for which $z \geq 0$ appears.

■ **THEOREM 2**

On the equation of a surface of revolution with a coordinate axis as axis of symmetry.

HYPOTHESIS: A surface of revolution S has (a) the y axis as axis of symmetry or revolution.

(b) the curve described by the equations $x = f(y)$ and $z = 0$ as profile curve.

CONCLUSION: The equation of S is

$$x^2 + z^2 = [f(y)]^2 \tag{2}$$

PROOF: See Fig. 10.21. Let $P(x_1, y_1, z_1)$ be any point of S. Then P must lie on a circle in the plane $y = y_1$ with center at $(0, y_1, 0)$, and this circle can be described by equations of the form

$$x^2 + z^2 = (\text{radius})^2, \qquad y = y_1.$$

But the radius of this circle is given to us by the equation of the profile curve; radius $= |f(y_1)|$ or $(\text{radius})^2 = [f(y_1)]^2$. The circle can be described by the equations

$$x^2 + z^2 = [f(y_1)]^2, \qquad y = y_1,$$

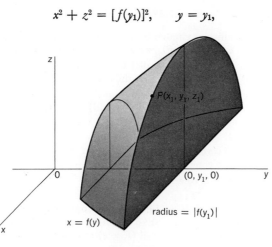

Fig. 10.21

and P's coordinates satisfy these equations. In particular, for the coordinates of P we have

$$x_1^2 + z_1^2 = [f(y_1)]^2.$$

This shows that the coordinates of a point on S satisfy Eq. (2).

Conversely, let the coordinates of $P(x_1, y_1, z_1)$ satisfy Eq. (2); thus

$$x_1^2 + z_1^2 = [f(y_1)]^2.$$

From this it follows that the coordinates of P also satisfy

$$x^2 + z^2 = [f(y_1)]^2 \quad \text{and} \quad y = y_1.$$

Hence P lies on a circle in the plane $y = y_1$ with center at $(0, y_1, 0)$ and radius equal to $|f(y_1)|$; P must lie on S.

Example 7.   The cone discussed in Example 3 can be considered a surface of revolution, because the cone is swept out when the element line VR of Fig. 10.17 is rotated about the y axis. The element line VR passes through the points $(0, 0, 0)$ and $(a, h, 0)$, so that its equations are $x = (a/h)y$ and $z = 0$. Theorem 2 says that the equation of this cone is

$$x^2 + z^2 = \frac{a^2}{h^2}y^2.$$

Example 8.   The sphere of Example 5 can be obtained by rotating the semi-circle with equations $y = \sqrt{a^2 - z^2}$ and $x = 0$ about the z axis. If we rewrite Theorem 2, replacing y by z, x by y, and z by x, then we can say that the equation of the sphere is

$$y^2 + x^2 = (\sqrt{a^2 - z^2})^2 \quad \text{or} \quad x^2 + y^2 + z^2 = a^2.$$

In Exercise 10.3-18 we shall consider the equation of a surface of revolution about the y axis when the profile curve is described by equations of the form $\phi(x, y) = 0$, $z = 0$.

EXERCISES 10.3

1. The elements of an elliptic cylinder are parallel to the z axis. The xy trace is an ellipse with vertices at $(\pm a, 0, 0)$ and $(0, \pm b, 0)$. Sketch the cylinder and find its equation.

2. The elements of a cylinder are parallel to the x axis. The yz trace is a circle with center at $(0, 0, a)$ and radius a. Sketch the cylinder and find its equation.

3. Discuss and sketch the surfaces with equations
   (a) $x + y = 4$;
   (b) $z - 4x = 4$;
   (c) $x^2 = 6y$;
   (d) $xz = 4$;
   (e) $z = 2e^{-v^2}$.

4. An elliptic cone has vertex at $V(0, 5, 0)$ and the ellipse $(x^2/9) + (z^2/4) = 1$, $y = 0$ as xz trace. Sketch the cone.

5. A cone has vertex at $(0, 2, 8)$ and the circle $x^2 + y^2 = 4$, $z = 0$ as xy trace. Sketch the cone.

6. *Definition 4. Homogeneous function.* Let region R contain the points (tx, ty, tz), $t > 0$, whenever it contains (x, y, z). We shall say that $f(x, y, z)$ is homogeneous of degree k in R if $f(tx, ty, tz) = t^k f(x, y, z)$ for all (x, y, z) of R and all $t > 0$.

(a) Show that $f(x, y, z) = x^2 + xy + z^2$ is homogeneous of degree 2 in all of space.

(b) Show that there is no three-dimensional region for which $f(x, y, z) = x^2 + y + z^2$ is homogeneous.

(c) Show that $f(x, y, z) = 1/(x + y + 2z)$ is homogeneous of degree -1 in the region $R: x + y + 2z \neq 0$.

(d) Show that $f(x, y, z) = x \sin z/x + y \cos 2z/y$ is homogeneous of degree 1 in the region $R: xy \neq 0$.

(e) Show that $f(x, y, z) = \sqrt{x + y + 2z}$ is homogeneous of degree $\frac{1}{2}$ in the region $R: x + y + 2z \geq 0$.

7. Fill in the details and complete the proof of Theorem 3.

Theorem 3. On the equation of a cone with vertex at the origin.

Hypothesis: A cone with vertex at the origin is generated by the lines joining the origin to the points of the curve in the plane $y = 1$ with equations $y = 1$ and $f(x, z) = 0$.

Conclusion: An equation satisfied by all points on the cone except for the vertex $(0, 0, 0)$ is

$$f\left(\frac{x}{y}, \frac{z}{y}\right) = 0.$$

Proof: Part of the proof is as follows. If the point $P(x_P, y_P, z_P)$, not the origin, is a point of the cone, every point on the line joining P to the vertex O lies on the cone. Now if Q is the point on the line twice as far from O as P is and in the same direction, then the coordinates of Q are $(2x_P, 2y_P, 2z_P)$. In general, the point with coordinates $(\alpha x_P, \alpha y_P, \alpha z_P)$, α any number, lies on the line joining O to P and therefore on the cone.

We cannot have $y_P = 0$ because, by hypothesis, the vertex is the only point of the plane $y = 0$ that lies on the cone. Hence, if we choose $\alpha = 1/y_P$ we find that the point $R(x_P/y_P, 1, z_P/y_P)$ lies on the cone. But R certainly lies in the plane $y = 1$ and must be a point on the curve with equation $f(x, z) = 0$ in the plane $y = 1$; $f(x_R, z_R) = 0$ or $f(x_P/y_P, z_P/y_P) = 0$. We have shown that, if P lies on the cone, its coordinates satisfy $f(x/y, z/y) = 0$.

It remains to show that, if the coordinates of a point $P(x_P, y_P, z_P)$, $y_P \neq 0$, satisfy $f(x_P/y_P, z_P/y_P) = 0$, that point lies on the cone. Show this.

8. Use Theorem 3 to find the equation of the circular cone discussed in Example 3.

9. An elliptic cone has vertex at the origin and the section

$$z = 1 \qquad \text{and} \qquad \frac{x^2}{1/9} + \frac{y^2}{4/9} = 1.$$

Find its equation. Sketch the cone.

10. Let $f(u, v)$ be defined for all ordered number pairs u, v of a domain D of number pairs. Show that, if the coordinates of $P(x_P, y_P, z_P)$ have the property that the number pair $x_P/y_P, z_P/y_P$ lies in D, then the coordinates of $Q(tx_P, ty_P, tz_P)$, $t > 0$, are also such that the number pair $x_Q/y_Q, z_Q/y_Q$ lies in D. Show that there is a region R for which $\phi(x, y, z) = f(x/y, z/y)$ is homogeneous of degree 0. This result, together with Theorem 3 and obvious extensions of Theorem 3, shows that a very wide class of cones with vertices at the origin, perhaps all, have homogeneous equations.

11. As a natural sequel to the observation made at the end of Exercise 10, we ask whether cones with vertices at the origin are the only surfaces that can have homogeneous equations. Fill in the details of the following proof for Theorem 4.

Theorem 4. On surfaces with homogeneous equations.

Hypothesis: (a) Surface S has equation $f(x, y, z) = 0$.

(b) R is a three-dimensional region that contains the points (tx, ty, tz), $t > 0$, whenever it contains the point (x, y, z).

(c) f is homogeneous in R.

Conclusion: That portion of S that lies in R is a cone (or part of a cone) with vertex at the origin.

Proof: Step (a). For any (x, y, z) of R there is a number k such that $f(tx, ty, tz) = t^k f(x, y, z)$, $t > 0$.

Step (b). If $P_1(x_1, y_1, z_1)$ lies on S and in R, so does (tx_1, ty_1, tz_1) for all $t > 0$. Through every point P_1 of S in R the line joining P_1 to O can be drawn, and at least the infinite portion of OP_1 which lies on the P_1 side of O will lie on S.

Step (c). Let the intersection of the sphere with the center at the origin and radius 1 with that portion of S which lies in R be called curve C. This curve can be used in Definition 2 to show that the part of S in R is a cone with vertex at the origin.

12. The following equations are homogeneous for suitable regions, and each surface is a cone with the vertex at the origin. Discuss and sketch

(a) $16y^2 + 16z^2 = x^2$.   (b) $\dfrac{x^2}{y} = y - z$.

13. (a) Sketch the surface of revolution swept out when the line $x = 3$, $z = 0$ is rotated about the y axis. (b) Find the equation of this surface.

14. That portion of the parabola $z = 0$ and $(x - 2)^2 = 4 - y$ for which $y \geq 0$ is rotated about the x axis.

(a) Sketch the surface of revolution thus generated.

(b) Find its equation.

15. That portion of the straight line $z = 0$ and $5y - 2x = 0$ for which $0 \leq x \leq 5$ is rotated about the line $z = 0$, $y = 2$. Sketch the surface of revolution thus formed.

16. That portion of the circle $x = 0$ and $y^2 + z^2 = 1$ for which $z \geq 0$ is rotated about the line $x = 0$, $y = 3$. Sketch the surface of revolution thus formed (torus).

17. The tractrix, described by parametric equations

$$x = t - a \tanh \frac{t}{a} \quad \text{and} \quad y = a \operatorname{sech} \frac{t}{a},$$

is rotated about the x axis. Sketch the surface of revolution thus formed. (This surface is of interest in differential geometry, because it is a surface of "constant negative curvature.")

18. Theorem 2 tells us how to get the equation of a surface of revolution about the y axis when the profile curve is described by equations of the form $x = f(y)$, $z = 0$. But what if the profile curve is described by equations of the form $\phi(x, y) = 0$, $z = 0$? Complete the proof indicated for the following theorem, Theorem 5.

Theorem 5. On the equation of a surface of revolution with a coordinate axis as axis of symmetry.

Hypothesis: (a) A surface of revolution S has the y axis as axis of symmetry, and the curve described by the equations $\phi(x, y) = 0$, $z = 0$ as profile curve.

(b) There is one and only one function f such that the substitution of $x = f(y)$, $a \leq y \leq b$ reduces $\phi(x, y) = 0$ to an identity in y for $a \leq y \leq b$, and

Case (1)	$f(y) \geq 0$	for $a \leq y \leq b$.
Case (2)	$f(y) \leq 0$	for $a \leq y \leq b$.

Conclusion: The equation of the portion of S for which $a \leq y \leq b$ is

$$\text{Case (1)} \qquad \phi(\sqrt{x^2 + z^2}, y) = 0.$$

$$\text{Case (2)} \qquad \phi(-\sqrt{x^2 + z^2}, y) = 0.$$

Proof: Theorem 2 enables us to say that S has the equation $x^2 + z^2 = [f(y)]^2$ or $f(y) = \pm\sqrt{x^2 + z^2}$, $a \leq y \leq b$, the positive sign to be taken in Case (1), the negative in Case (2). But Hypothesis (b) says that

$$\phi(f(y), y) = 0, \qquad a \leq y \leq b.$$

Now if $P(x, y, z)$ is a point of S, then $\cdots\cdot$.

Conversely, if $P(x, y, z)$ is such that $\phi(\pm\sqrt{x^2 + z^2}, y) = 0$ for $a \leq y \leq b$, then $\cdots\cdot$.

19. Illustrate Theorem 5 in the case $\phi(x, y) = x + y$. For Case (1) take $x = f(y) = -y$ for $y \leq 0$. For Case (2) take $x = f(y) = -y$ for $y \geq 0$.

10.4 Distance between Two Points. Vectors. The Scalar Product

We have gained a certain familiarity with three-dimensional diagrams in the first sections of this chapter. We turn now to the algebraic analysis of three-dimensional diagrams.

■ THEOREM 1

The distance between two points.

HYPOTHESIS: We are given points $P_1(x_1, y_1, z_1)$ and $P_2(x_2, y_2, z_2)$.

CONCLUSION: $P_1P_2 = \sqrt{(x_2 - x_1)^2 + (y_2 - y_1)^2 + (z_2 - z_1)^2}$.

PROOF: Consider Fig. 10.22. The Pythagorean Theorem applied to $\triangle P_1RP_2$ tells us that

$$\overline{P_1P_2^2} = \overline{P_1R^2} + \overline{RP_2^2}.$$

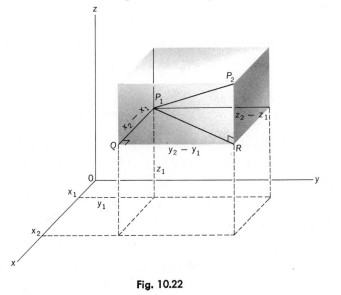

Fig. 10.22

But $\Delta P_1 QR$ is also a right triangle, so that

$$\overline{P_1 R^2} = \overline{P_1 Q^2} + \overline{QR^2},$$

$$\overline{P_1 P_2^2} = \overline{P_1 Q^2} + \overline{QR^2} + \overline{RP_2^2}. \tag{1}$$

Since $P_1 Q$, QR, and RP_2 are displacements in the coordinate directions, they have numerical values $P_1 Q = x_2 - x_1$, $QR = y_2 - y_1$, and $RP_2 = z_2 - z_1$. Our proof is concluded when we observe from Eq. (1) that

$$\overline{P_1 P_2^2} = (x_2 - x_1)^2 + (y_2 - y_1)^2 + (z_2 - z_1)^2.$$

In Chapter 3 we found it convenient to use vector analysis as a tool for plane geometry. It is an even more valuable tool in the algebraic analysis of three-dimensional diagrams. In this section we shall generalize to three dimensions the vector analysis we have already studied for two dimensions. In the next section we shall introduce a new product of vectors.

The definitions of scalar and vector given in Sec. 3.4 and the conventions for writing vectors adopted there apply without change in our new work. So does the definition of the product of a vector by a scalar and the definition of the sum of two vectors. For the sake of emphasis and easy reference we repeat the latter.

■ DEFINITION 1

The addition af vectors. To get $\vec{a} + \vec{b}$, first move $\vec{b}$ parallel to itself so that its initial point coincides with terminal point of $\vec{a}$ and then take for $\vec{a} + \vec{b}$ the vector whose initial point is the initial point of $\vec{a}$ and whose terminal point is the terminal point of $\vec{b}$.

As before, the addition of vectors is commutative and associative:

$$\vec{a} + \vec{b} = \vec{b} + \vec{a}$$

$$(\vec{a} + \vec{b}) + \vec{c} = \vec{a} + (\vec{b} + \vec{c});$$

and there is the following distributive law for the multiplication of vectors by scalars,

$$c(\vec{a} + \vec{b}) = c\vec{a} + c\vec{b}.$$

The proofs given in Sec. 3.4 apply without essential change; indeed, two vectors determine a plane, and two of these statements are really plane geometry statements.

In Sec. 3.5 we defined unit vectors $\vec{i}$ and $\vec{j}$ in the x- and y-axis directions. Now we define unit vectors $\vec{i}$, $\vec{j}$, and $\vec{k}$ in the x-, y-, and z-axis directions. These vectors form a "basis" for our vector analysis. Other vectors are written as combinations of these.

■ THEOREM 2

The vector joining two points.

HYPOTHESIS: $P_1(x_1, y_1, z_1)$ and $P_2(x_2, y_2, z_2)$ have the coordinates indicated.

CONCLUSION: $\overrightarrow{P_1P_2} = (x_2 - x_1)\mathbf{i} + (y_2 - y_1)\mathbf{j} + (z_2 - z_1)\mathbf{k}.$

PROOF: From Fig. 10.22 we see directly that

$$\overrightarrow{P_1P_2} = \overrightarrow{P_1Q} + \overrightarrow{QR} + \overrightarrow{RP_2}, \tag{2}$$

because $\overrightarrow{P_1Q}$, $\overrightarrow{QR}$, and $\overrightarrow{RP_2}$ are joined, initial point to terminal point, as required by Definition 1 for the sum of vectors. But the direction of $\overrightarrow{P_1Q}$ is that of the x axis and its directed magnitude is $x_2 - x_1$; hence $\overrightarrow{P_1Q} = (x_2 - x_1)\mathbf{i}$. Similarly $\overrightarrow{QR} = (y_2 - y_1)\mathbf{j}$ and $\overrightarrow{RP_2} = (z_2 - z_1)\mathbf{k}$. Thus Eq. (2) can be rewritten as in the conclusion of Theorem 2.

● **Remark 1**

To repeat what was pointed out in Remarks 3.5-1 and 3.5-2, this theorem shows how any vector can be written as a sum of $\mathbf{i}$, $\mathbf{j}$, and $\mathbf{k}$ components when initial and terminal points are known for it. Simply subtract the coordinates of the initial point from those of the terminal point to get the components.

If $\overrightarrow{OP_1}$ and $\overrightarrow{OP_2}$ are called the position vectors for P_1 and P_2, then from

$$\overrightarrow{P_1P_2} = \overrightarrow{P_1O} + \overrightarrow{OP_2} = -\overrightarrow{OP_1} + \overrightarrow{OP_2} = \overrightarrow{OP_2} - \overrightarrow{OP_1}$$

we read that any vector may be written as the difference between the position vectors for its terminal and initial points. (See Fig. 3.27.)

For the sum of two vectors written in terms of $\mathbf{i}$, $\mathbf{j}$, and $\mathbf{k}$ we have the following analogue of Theorem 3.5-3.

■ **THEOREM 3**

On the addition of vectors.

HYPOTHESIS: $\vec{v}_1 = a_1\mathbf{i} + b_1\mathbf{j} + c_1\mathbf{k}$ and $\vec{v}_2 = a_2\mathbf{i} + b_2\mathbf{j} + c_2\mathbf{k}.$

CONCLUSION: $\vec{v}_1 + \vec{v}_2 = (a_1 + a_2)\mathbf{i} + (b_1 + b_2)\mathbf{j} + (c_1 + c_2)\mathbf{k}.$

In words, vectors in $\mathbf{i}$, $\mathbf{j}$, $\mathbf{k}$ form are added by adding components.

For the length of a vector in $\mathbf{i}$, $\mathbf{j}$, $\mathbf{k}$ form we rewrite Theorem 1 on the distance between two points. Theorem 4 is the analogue of Theorem 3.5-5.

■ **THEOREM 4**

On the length of a vector.

HYPOTHESIS: $\vec{v} = a\mathbf{i} + b\mathbf{j} + c\mathbf{k}.$

CONCLUSION: $\|\vec{v}\|^2 = a^2 + b^2 + c^2.$

Finally, the scalar product of two vectors arose naturally when one tried to find the angle between two vectors in Sec. 3.6. It arises in exactly the same way here. Let $\vec{v}_1 = a_1\vec{i} + b_1\vec{j} + c_1\vec{k}$ and $\vec{v}_2 = a_2\vec{i} + b_2\vec{j} + c_2\vec{k}$ be given, and let one of these be moved so that they have a common initial point; see Fig. 10.23. Again the angle θ can be determined by using the cosine law of trigonometry. We have

$$\|\overrightarrow{RQ}\|^2 = \|\overrightarrow{PR}\|^2 + \|\overrightarrow{PQ}\|^2 - 2\|\overrightarrow{PR}\|\,\|\overrightarrow{PQ}\|\cos\theta,$$

$$\cos\theta = \frac{\|\overrightarrow{PR}\|^2 + \|\overrightarrow{PQ}\|^2 - \|\overrightarrow{RQ}\|^2}{2\|\overrightarrow{PR}\|\|\overrightarrow{PQ}\|} = \frac{\|\vec{v}_1\|^2 + \|\vec{v}_2\|^2 - \|\vec{v}_2 - \vec{v}_1\|^2}{2\|\vec{v}_1\|\|\vec{v}_2\|}.$$

But here Theorems 3 and 4 say that

$$\cos\theta = \frac{a_1{}^2 + b_1{}^2 + c_1{}^2 + a_2{}^2 + b_2{}^2 + c_2{}^2 - (a_2 - a_1)^2 - (b_2 - b_1)^2 - (c_2 - c_1)^2}{2\|\vec{v}_1\|\|\vec{v}_2\|}$$

$$= \frac{a_1a_2 + b_1b_2 + c_1c_2}{\|\vec{v}_1\|\|\vec{v}_2\|}.$$

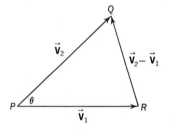

Q

$\vec{v}_2$

$\vec{v}_2 - \vec{v}_1$

P θ

$\vec{v}_1$

R

Fig. 10.23

Again, the product

$$\|\vec{v}_1\|\|\vec{v}_2\|\cos\theta = a_1a_2 + b_1b_2 + c_1c_2 \qquad (3)$$

has a prominent role to play; we repeat the definition of scalar product given in Sec. 3.6.

■ DEFINITION 2

The scalar product of two vectors. The scalar product of $\vec{v}_1$ and $\vec{v}_2$, written $\vec{v}_1\cdot\vec{v}_2$, is the product of their lengths and the cosine of the angle between them. In symbols,

$$\vec{v}_1\cdot\vec{v}_2 = \|\vec{v}_1\|\|\vec{v}_2\|\cos\theta.$$

The scalar product still has the commutative property from its very definition,

$$\vec{A}\cdot\vec{B} = \vec{B}\cdot\vec{A}, \qquad\qquad (4)$$

and it still obeys a distributive law.

■ THEOREM 5

The distributive law for the scalar product.

HYPOTHESIS: $\vec{v}_1, \vec{v}_2, \vec{v}_3$ are vectors.

CONCLUSION: $(\vec{v}_1 + \vec{v}_2)\cdot\vec{v}_3 = (\vec{v}_1\cdot\vec{v}_3) + (\vec{v}_2\cdot\vec{v}_3).$

PROOF: We can give essentially the same proof we gave for Theorem 3.6-6. There we pointed out that

$$\vec{v}_1\cdot\frac{\vec{v}_3}{\|\vec{v}_3\|}, \qquad \vec{v}_2\cdot\frac{\vec{v}_3}{\|\vec{v}_3\|}, \qquad \text{and} \qquad (\vec{v}_1 + \vec{v}_2)\cdot\frac{\vec{v}_3}{\|\vec{v}_3\|}$$

can all be interpreted as projections. It would be instructive, however, to consider a second proof based on Eq. (3). That equation says that, if we write

$$\vec{v}_1 = a_1\vec{i} + b_1\vec{j} + c_1\vec{k},$$

$$\vec{v}_2 = a_2\vec{i} + b_2\vec{j} + c_2\vec{k},$$

$$\vec{v}_3 = a_3\vec{i} + b_3\vec{j} + c_3\vec{k},$$

then

$$\vec{v}_1 \cdot \vec{v}_3 = a_1a_3 + b_1b_3 + c_1c_3, \qquad \vec{v}_2 \cdot \vec{v}_3 = a_2a_3 + b_2b_3 + c_2c_3,$$

$$(\vec{v}_1 + \vec{v}_2) \cdot \vec{v}_3 = (a_1 + a_2)a_3 + (b_1 + b_2)b_3 + (c_1 + c_2)c_3.$$

But then

$$(\vec{v}_1 + \vec{v}_2) \cdot \vec{v}_3 = a_1a_3 + a_2a_3 + b_1b_3 + b_2b_3 + c_1c_3 + c_2c_3$$

$$= (a_1a_3 + b_1b_3 + c_1c_3) + (a_2a_3 + b_2b_3 + c_2c_3)$$

$$= (\vec{v}_1 \cdot \vec{v}_3) + (\vec{v}_2 \cdot \vec{v}_3).$$

In computing scalar products in two dimensions, we used the multiplication table for the unit vectors:

$$\vec{i} \cdot \vec{i} = \vec{j} \cdot \vec{j} = 1 \qquad \text{and} \qquad \vec{i} \cdot \vec{j} = 0.$$

Now we use an enlarged multiplication table:

$$\vec{i} \cdot \vec{i} = \vec{j} \cdot \vec{j} = \vec{k} \cdot \vec{k} = 1 \qquad \text{and} \qquad \vec{i} \cdot \vec{j} = \vec{i} \cdot \vec{k} = \vec{j} \cdot \vec{k} = 0.$$

For example, we can compute

$$\vec{k} \cdot \vec{k} = \|\vec{k}\|\|\vec{k}\| \cos 0° = 1(1)(1) = 1,$$

$$\vec{i} \cdot \vec{k} = \|\vec{i}\|\|\vec{k}\|(\cos 90°) = (1)(1)(0) = 0.$$

We still use the scalar product for the same applications as before. Theorems 3.6-1, 3.6-2, and 3.6-4 are restated for easy reference.

■ **THEOREM 6**

The length of a vector.

HYPOTHESIS: $\vec{v}$ is a vector.

CONCLUSION: $\|\vec{v}\|^2 = \vec{v} \cdot \vec{v}.$

■ **THEOREM 7**

The angle between two vectors.

HYPOTHESIS: θ is an angle between $\vec{v}_1$ and $\vec{v}_2$.

CONCLUSION: $$\cos \theta = \frac{\vec{v}_1 \cdot \vec{v}_2}{\|\vec{v}_1\|\|\vec{v}_2\|}.$$

■ THEOREM 8

The projection of $\vec{A}$ on $\vec{B}$'s direction.

HYPOTHESIS: $\vec{A}$ and $\vec{B}$ are vectors.

CONCLUSION: The (directed length of the) projection of $\vec{A}$ on $\vec{B}$'s direction is

$$\vec{A} \cdot \frac{\vec{B}}{\|\vec{B}\|}.$$

Example 1. Find the point that divides the segment joining $W(3, 1, 9)$ to $Q(5, -2, 4)$ in the ratio $3 : 2$. Let $P(x, y, z)$ be the point we seek. Then, as Fig. 10.24 suggests, $\overrightarrow{WP} = \frac{3}{5} \overrightarrow{WQ}$. In $\mathbf{i}, \mathbf{j}, \mathbf{k}$ form we have

$$(x - 3)\mathbf{i} + (y - 1)\mathbf{j} + (z - 9)\mathbf{k} = \tfrac{3}{5}(2\mathbf{i} - 3\mathbf{j} - 5\mathbf{k}).$$

If we take the scalar product of both members with $\mathbf{i}$, we have $x - 3 = \frac{6}{5}$, or $x = {}^{21}\!/_5$. Similarly, if we take scalar products with $\mathbf{j}$ and then with $\mathbf{k}$, we find that $y - 1 = -\frac{9}{5}$, or $y = -\frac{4}{5}$, and that $z - 9 = -3$, or $z = 6$. The point we seek is $P({}^{21}\!/_5, -\frac{4}{5}, 6)$.

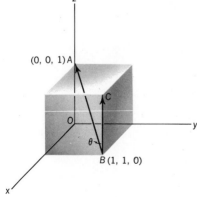

Fig. 10.24

Fig. 10.25

Example 2. *The midpoint formula.* Let $P(x, y, z)$ be the midpoint of P_1 (x_1, y_1, z_1) and $P_2(x_2, y_2, z_2)$. See Fig. 10.25. Then $\overrightarrow{P_1P} = \frac{1}{2} \overrightarrow{P_1P_2}$, or, in $\mathbf{i}, \mathbf{j}, \mathbf{k}$ form,

$$(x - x_1)\mathbf{i} + (y - y_1)\mathbf{j} + (z - z_1)\mathbf{k} = \tfrac{1}{2}[(x_2 - x_1)\mathbf{i} + (y_2 - y_1)\mathbf{j} + (z_2 - z_1)\mathbf{k}].$$

Since equal vectors have equal $\mathbf{i}, \mathbf{j}, \mathbf{k}$ components, we have

$$x - x_1 = \tfrac{1}{2}(x_2 - x_1), \qquad y - y_1 = \tfrac{1}{2}(y_2 - y_1), \qquad z - z_1 = \tfrac{1}{2}(z_2 - z_1),$$
$$x = \tfrac{1}{2}(x_1 + x_2), \qquad y = \tfrac{1}{2}(y_1 + y_2),$$
$$z = \tfrac{1}{2}(z_1 + z_2).$$

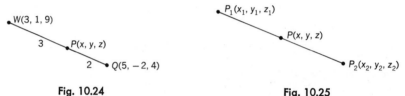

Fig. 10.26

Example 3. Find the cosine of the angle between an edge of a cube and a diagonal. Let the cube have edges of length 1 and be placed as in Fig. 10.26. We shall find the angle between edge BC and diagonal BA. Since

$$\overrightarrow{BC} = 1\mathbf{k} \qquad \text{and}$$
$$\overrightarrow{BA} = -1\mathbf{i} - 1\mathbf{j} + 1\mathbf{k},$$

we can say that

$$\|\overrightarrow{BC}\| = 1 \qquad \text{and} \qquad \|\overrightarrow{BA}\|^2 = (-\mathbf{i} - \mathbf{j} + \mathbf{k}) \cdot (-\mathbf{i} - \mathbf{j} + \mathbf{k}) = 3, \text{ and then that}$$

$$\overrightarrow{BA} \cdot \overrightarrow{BC} = \|\overrightarrow{BA}\| \|\overrightarrow{BC}\| \cos \theta$$
$$(-\vec{i} - \vec{j} + \vec{k}) \cdot \vec{k} = \sqrt{3} \,(1) \cos \theta,$$
$$1 = \sqrt{3} \,(1) \cos \theta,$$
$$\cos \theta = \frac{1}{\sqrt{3}}.$$

Example 4. We are given $\vec{A} = -2\vec{i} + 3\vec{j} + 7\vec{k}$ and $\vec{B} = 2\vec{j} + \vec{k}$. Find the directed length of the projection of $\vec{A}$ on $\vec{B}$'s direction and also the vector description of that projection. We seek $\|\overrightarrow{QP}\|$ and $\overrightarrow{QP}$ in Fig. 10.27(a).

$$\|\overrightarrow{QP}\| = \|\vec{A}\| \cos \theta = \vec{A} \cdot \frac{\vec{B}}{\|\vec{B}\|}$$
$$= (-2\vec{i} + 3\vec{j} + 7\vec{k}) \cdot \frac{2\vec{j} + \vec{k}}{\sqrt{(2\vec{j} + \vec{k}) \cdot (2\vec{j} + \vec{k})}} = \frac{6 + 7}{\sqrt{4 + 1}} = \frac{13}{\sqrt{5}}.$$

A unit vector in the direction of $\overrightarrow{QP}$ is

$$\frac{\vec{B}}{\|\vec{B}\|} = \frac{1}{\sqrt{5}} (2\vec{j} + \vec{k}).$$

Since $\overrightarrow{QP}$ has length $13/\sqrt{5}$ we can say that

$$\overrightarrow{QP} = \frac{13}{\sqrt{5}} \frac{2\vec{j} + \vec{k}}{\sqrt{5}} = \frac{13}{5} (2\vec{j} + \vec{k}).$$

Example 5. Consider again the vectors $\vec{A}$ and $\vec{B}$ that appear in Example 4. Find the length of the projection of $\vec{A}$ on a plane perpendicular to $\vec{B}$ and also the vector description of that projection. In this example we seek $\|\overrightarrow{RQ}\|$ and $\overrightarrow{RQ}$. In Fig. 10.27(b),

$$\overrightarrow{RQ} + \overrightarrow{QP} = \overrightarrow{RP},$$
$$\overrightarrow{RQ} = \overrightarrow{RP} - \overrightarrow{QP}$$
$$= (-2\vec{i} + 3\vec{j} + 7\vec{k}) - \tfrac{13}{5}(2\vec{j} + \vec{k})$$
$$= -2\vec{i} - \tfrac{11}{5}\vec{j} + \tfrac{22}{5}\vec{k}.$$

Next we have

$$\|\overrightarrow{RQ}\|^2 = \overrightarrow{RQ} \cdot \overrightarrow{RQ} = 4 + \tfrac{121}{25} + \tfrac{484}{25} = \tfrac{705}{25},$$
$$\|\overrightarrow{RQ}\| = \tfrac{1}{5}\sqrt{705}.$$

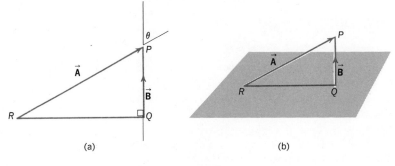

(a)   (b)

Fig. 10.27

■ THEOREM 9

The equation of a sphere.

HYPOTHESIS: A sphere has its center at $C(h, k, m)$ and radius a.

CONCLUSION: The sphere's equation is

$$(x - h)^2 + (y - k)^2 + (z - m)^2 = a^2.$$

PROOF: $P(x, y, z)$ lies on the sphere if and only if $PC = a$, and thus if and only if

$$\sqrt{(x - h)^2 + (y - k)^2 + (z - m)^2} = a,$$
$$(x - h)^2 + (y - k)^2 + (z - m)^2 = a^2.$$

EXERCISES 10.4

1. Find the point $\frac{2}{5}$ of the way from $A(-2, 0, 4)$ to $B(3, 6, 14)$.

2. Find the point that divides the line segment joining $C(6, 2, -1)$ to $D(3, 5, 8)$ in the ratio $2 : 5$.

3. Find the point $\frac{3}{4}$ of the way from $E(2, 2, 4)$ to $F(6, -8, -8)$: (a) by using the midpoint formula twice and (b) directly.

4. Show in two ways that $\triangle PQR$ is a right triangle.
   (a) $P(2, 1, 5)$, $Q(-4, 8, 11)$, $R(11, 7, 7)$.
   (b) $P(4, -1, 9)$, $Q(1, 2, 3)$, $R(3, 6, 4)$.

5. Decide whether the best name for $JKLM$ is "parallelogram," "rectangle," "rhombus," or "square." Explain.
   (a) $J(0, 0, 0)$, $K(4, 8, -4)$, $L(6, 11, 4)$, $M(2, 3, 8)$.
   (b) $J(-3, -2, 2)$, $K(0, 2, 0)$, $L(5, 0, 0)$, $M(2, -4, 2)$.
   (c) $J(0, -10, 15)$, $K(15, -10, -5)$, $L(3, 10, -14)$, $M(-12, 10, 6)$.

6. We are given $A(0, \sqrt{10}, 0)$, $B(\sqrt{10}, 0, 0)$, $C(0, -3, 1)$, $D(-\sqrt{10}, 0, 0)$. Show that $\|\overrightarrow{AB}\| = \|\overrightarrow{BC}\| = \|\overrightarrow{CD}\| = \|\overrightarrow{DA}\|$. Show that $\sphericalangle DAB = \sphericalangle BCD = 90°$. Is $ABCD$ a square?

7. (a) Find angle U of triangle $S(2, 1, 4)$, $T(3, -1, 2)$, $U(0, 0, 2)$.
   (b) Find angle Q of triangle $P(-3, 4, 1)$, $Q(2, 1, 3)$, $R(0, 4, -2)$.

8. The angles a vector makes with the x, y, and z directions are frequently called its *direction angles* and named α, β, and γ, respectively; $\cos \alpha$, $\cos \beta$, and $\cos \gamma$ are called the *direction cosines*. For vector $\vec{v} = a\vec{i} + b\vec{j} + c\vec{k}$ show that

   (a) $\cos \alpha = \dfrac{a}{\sqrt{a^2 + b^2 + c^2}}$, $\cos \beta = \dfrac{b}{\sqrt{a^2 + b^2 + c^2}}$, $\cos \gamma = \dfrac{c}{\sqrt{a^2 + b^2 + c^2}}$.

   (b) $\cos^2 \alpha + \cos^2 \beta + \cos^2 \gamma = 1$.

9. Let $\vec{u}$ be a unit vector with direction angles α, β, γ. Show that $\vec{u} = (\cos \alpha)\vec{i} + (\cos \beta)\vec{j} + (\cos \gamma)\vec{k}$

10. The diagonals of two faces of a cube intersect at a vertex. Find the angle between these diagonals.

11. We are given $\vec{v}_1 = 2\vec{i} - 3\vec{j}$ and $\vec{v}_2 = \vec{i} - 2\vec{j} + 3\vec{k}$.
    (a) Find the length of the projection of $\vec{v}_1$ on $\vec{v}_2$'s direction.
    (b) Find the vector description of that projection.

(c) Find the vector description of the projection of $\vec{v}_1$ on a plane perpendicular to $\vec{v}_2$.

(d) Find the length of the projection of $\vec{v}_1$ on a plane perpendicular to $\vec{v}_2$.

12. The same as Exercise 11 for $\vec{v}_1 = 2\vec{i} + \vec{j} - 2\vec{k}$ and $\vec{v}_2 = \vec{j} + 2\vec{k}$.

13. Prove Theorem 3.

14. Prove Theorem 4.

15. The end points of a diameter of a sphere are $(2, 1, 4)$, $(-4, 3, 8)$. Find its equation.

16. Find the equations of the spheres of radius a tangent to the xy plane at $(b, c, 0)$.

17. Find the equation of the locus of points equidistant from the plane $y = -p/2$ and the point $(0, p/2, 0)$.

18. Find the equation of the locus of points the sum of whose distances from the fixed points $(0, -c, 0)$ and $(0, c, 0)$ is $2a$, $a > c$.

10.5 The Vector Product

A new product, called the vector product, will help us to find the direction perpendicular to a plane. First we shall define this product, then we shall describe its formal algebraic properties so that we can compute it reasonably quickly, and finally we shall apply it.

Two nonparallel vectors $\vec{A}$ and $\vec{B}$ with common initial point O determine a plane E through point O, as in Fig. 10.28. We want to define a new vector whose direction shall be perpendicular to the plane of $\vec{A}$ and $\vec{B}$. There are two possible choices for such a direction, one the negative of the other. We have already chosen a right-handed system of coordinate axes for our three-dimensional diagrams, and we shall take for our definition the choice determined by

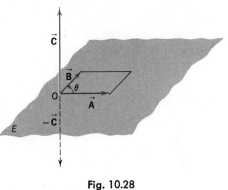

Fig. 10.28

the right-hand rule. If the four fingers of the *right* hand extend from $\vec{A}$ to $\vec{B}$, in the direction of θ in the diagram, the thumb of the *right* hand will extend in $\vec{C}$'s direction.

Not only do vectors $\vec{A}$ and $\vec{B}$ determine plane E, but, in greater detail, they determine a parallelogram in plane E. We take the area of that parallelogram for the magnitude of the vector we are defining.

■ DEFINITION 1

The vector product. The vector product of $\vec{A}$ and $\vec{B}$, written $\vec{A} \times \vec{B}$, is the vector (a) whose direction is perpendicular to the plane of $\vec{A}$ and $\vec{B}$ and whose sense is such that $\vec{A}$, $\vec{B}$, and $\vec{A} \times \vec{B}$ in that order form a "right-handed" system of vectors; and (b) whose magnitude is the area of the parallelogram determined by $\vec{A}$ and $\vec{B}$.

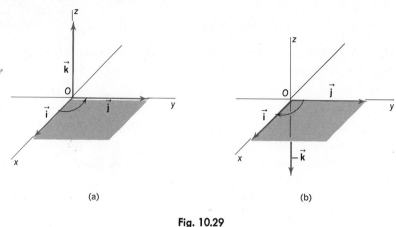

(a) (b)

Fig. 10.29

● **Remark 1**

We extend Definition 1 to cover the case $\vec{A} \times \vec{A}$ by taking $\vec{A} \times \vec{A} = \vec{0}$. It seems reasonable to say that the area of the "parallelogram" determined by $\vec{A}$ and $\vec{A}$ is 0.

Example 1. Consider Fig. 10.29(a). The right-hand rule says that the direction of $\vec{i} \times \vec{j}$ is that of $\vec{k}$. The area of the square determined by $\vec{i}$ and $\vec{j}$ is 1. Since $\vec{k}$ itself has magnitude 1, we have

$$\vec{i} \times \vec{j} = \vec{k}. \tag{1a}$$

On the other hand, we see in Fig. 10.29(b) that the direction of $\vec{j} \times \vec{i}$, determined by the right-hand rule, is that of $-\vec{k}$. The area of the square determined by $\vec{j}$ and $\vec{i}$ is 1. Since $-\vec{k}$ itself has magnitude 1, we have

$$\vec{j} \times \vec{i} = -\vec{k}. \tag{1b}$$

Similarly, we can compute

$$\vec{j} \times \vec{k} = \vec{i} \quad \text{and} \quad \vec{k} \times \vec{j} = -\vec{i}, \tag{2}$$

$$\vec{k} \times \vec{i} = \vec{j} \quad \text{and} \quad \vec{i} \times \vec{k} = -\vec{j}. \tag{3}$$

Following Remark 1, we take

$$\vec{i} \times \vec{i} = \vec{j} \times \vec{j} = \vec{k} \times \vec{k} = \vec{0}. \tag{4}$$

The fact that $\vec{i} \times \vec{j}$ and $\vec{j} \times \vec{i}$ are of equal magnitude but oppositely directed is just one illustration of a more general fact.

■ **THEOREM 1**

The anticommutative property for the vector product.

HYPOTHESIS: $\vec{A}$ and $\vec{B}$ are vectors.

CONCLUSION: $\vec{A} \times \vec{B} = -\vec{B} \times \vec{A}.$

PROOF: The magnitudes of $\vec{A} \times \vec{B}$ and $\vec{B} \times \vec{A}$ are the same; each magnitude is the area of the parallelogram determined by $\vec{A}$ and $\vec{B}$. Vectors $\vec{A} \times \vec{B}$ and $\vec{B} \times \vec{A}$ are also both perpendicular to the plane of $\vec{A}$ and $\vec{B}$, but the right-hand rule says that they are oppositely directed. For, if the four fingers of the right hand extend from $\vec{A}$ to $\vec{B}$, the thumb points in one direction; but the thumb points in the opposite direction when the four fingers of the right hand extend from $\vec{B}$ to $\vec{A}$. See Fig. 10.30.

■ THEOREM 2

Scalar multipliers for the vector product.

HYPOTHESIS: $\vec{A}$ and $\vec{B}$ are vectors; c is a scalar.

CONCLUSION: $(c\vec{A}) \times \vec{B} = c(\vec{A} \times \vec{B})$.

PROOF: The proof is left to the reader in Exercise 10.5-9.

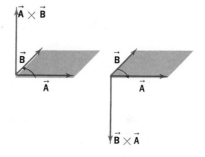

■ THEOREM 3

The distributive law for the vector product.

Fig. 10.30

HYPOTHESIS: $\vec{A}$, $\vec{B}$, and $\vec{C}$ are vectors.

CONCLUSION: $(\vec{A} + \vec{B}) \times \vec{C} = (\vec{A} \times \vec{C}) + (\vec{B} \times \vec{C})$.

PROOF: See Exercises 10.5-10 and 10.5-11.

● Remark 2

The conclusion of Theorem 3 can also be written

$$\vec{C} \times (\vec{A} + \vec{B}) = (\vec{C} \times \vec{A}) + (\vec{C} \times \vec{B}),$$

for Theorems 1 and 3 together say that

$$\vec{C} \times (\vec{A} + \vec{B}) = -(\vec{A} + \vec{B}) \times \vec{C} = -(\vec{A} \times \vec{C}) - (\vec{B} \times \vec{C})$$
$$= (\vec{C} \times \vec{A}) + (\vec{C} \times \vec{B}).$$

The computation of $\vec{A} \times \vec{B}$ when $\vec{A}$ and $\vec{B}$ are given in $\vec{i}, \vec{j}, \vec{k}$ form depends on Eqs. (1), (2), (3), and (4), and Theorems 2 and 3.

Example 2. If $\vec{A} = 3\vec{i} + 2\vec{j} - \vec{k}$ and $\vec{B} = 5\vec{i} - 3\vec{j} + 2\vec{k}$, then

$$\vec{A} \times \vec{B} = (3\vec{i} + 2\vec{j} - \vec{k}) \times (5\vec{i} - 3\vec{j} + 2\vec{k})$$

$$= 15\vec{i} \times \vec{i} - 9\vec{i} \times \vec{j} + 6\vec{i} \times \vec{k} + 10\vec{j} \times \vec{i} - 6\vec{j} \times \vec{j} + 4\vec{j} \times \vec{k}$$
$$- 5\vec{k} \times \vec{i} + 3\vec{k} \times \vec{j} - 2\vec{k} \times \vec{k}$$

$$= 15(\vec{0}) - 9\vec{k} - 6\vec{j} - 10\vec{k} - 6(\vec{0}) + 4\vec{i} - 5\vec{j} - 3\vec{i} - 2(\vec{0})$$

$$= 1\vec{i} - 11\vec{j} - 19\vec{k}.$$

Example 3. In more general form, if $\vec{A} = a_1\vec{i} + a_2\vec{j} + a_3\vec{k}$ and $\vec{B} = b_1\vec{i} + b_2\vec{j} + b_3\vec{k}$, then

$$\vec{A} \times \vec{B} = (a_1\vec{i} + a_2\vec{j} + a_3\vec{k}) \times (b_1\vec{i} + b_2\vec{j} + b_3\vec{k})$$

$$= a_1b_1\vec{i} \times \vec{i} + a_1b_2\vec{i} \times \vec{j} + a_1b_3\vec{i} \times \vec{k}$$

$$+ a_2b_1\vec{j} \times \vec{i} + a_2b_2\vec{j} \times \vec{j} + a_2b_3\vec{j} \times \vec{k}$$

$$+ a_3b_1\vec{k} \times \vec{i} + a_3b_2\vec{k} \times \vec{j} + a_3b_3\vec{k} \times \vec{k}$$

$$= \vec{0} + a_1b_2\vec{k} - a_1b_3\vec{j} - a_2b_1\vec{k} + \vec{0} + a_2b_3\vec{i} + a_3b_1\vec{j} - a_3b_2\vec{i} + \vec{0}$$

$$\vec{A} \times \vec{B} = (a_2b_3 - a_3b_2)\vec{i} + (a_3b_1 - a_1b_3)\vec{j} + (a_1b_2 - a_2b_1)\vec{k}. \tag{5}$$

Those who are familiar with the determinant notation often prefer to write Eq. (5) in the form

$$\vec{A} \times \vec{B} = \begin{vmatrix} \vec{i} & \vec{j} & \vec{k} \\ a_1 & a_2 & a_3 \\ b_1 & b_2 & b_3 \end{vmatrix}. \tag{6}$$

Example 4a. Find a vector perpendicular to the plane determined by vectors $\vec{A} = 3\vec{i} + 4\vec{j}$ and $\vec{B} = \vec{i} + 2\vec{j} - 3\vec{k}$. The product $\vec{A} \times \vec{B}$ is a vector perpendicular to the plane determined by $\vec{A}$ and $\vec{B}$. To compute $\vec{A} \times \vec{B}$, we have

$$\vec{A} \times \vec{B} = (3\vec{i} + 4\vec{j}) \times (\vec{i} + 2\vec{j} - 3\vec{k}) = \vec{0} + 6\vec{k} + 9\vec{j} - 4\vec{k} + \vec{0} - 12\vec{i}$$

$$= -12\vec{i} + 9\vec{j} + 2\vec{k}.$$

Example 4b. Find the area of the parallelogram determined by $\vec{A}$ and $\vec{B}$. By the very definition of the vector product, the area of the parallelogram determined by $\vec{A}$ and $\vec{B}$ is given by $\|\vec{A} \times \vec{B}\|$. We have

$$\|\vec{A} \times \vec{B}\|^2 = \|-12\vec{i} + 9\vec{j} + 2\vec{k}\|^2$$

$$= (-12\vec{i} + 9\vec{j} + 2\vec{k}) \cdot (-12\vec{i} + 9\vec{j} + 2\vec{k})$$

$$= 144 + 81 + 4 = 229.$$

The area of the parallelogram is $\sqrt{229}$.

Example 5. Find the area of the triangle in the xy plane with vertices $P_1(x_1, y_1)$, $P_2(x_2, y_2)$, and $P_3(x_3, y_3)$; see Fig. 10.31. The area of $\triangle P_1P_2P_3$ is $\frac{1}{2}$ the area of the parallelogram $P_1P_2QP_3$. Hence

$$\text{area of } \triangle P_1P_2P_3 = \frac{1}{2}\|\overrightarrow{P_1P_2} \times \overrightarrow{P_1P_3}\|$$

$$= \frac{1}{2}\|[(x_2 - x_1)\vec{i} + (y_2 - y_1)\vec{j}] \times [(x_3 - x_1)\vec{i} + (y_3 - y_1)\vec{j}]\|$$

$$= \frac{1}{2}\|\vec{0} + (x_2 - x_1)(y_3 - y_1)\vec{k} - (y_2 - y_1)(x_3 - x_1)\vec{k} + \vec{0}\|$$

$$= \frac{1}{2}\|(x_2y_3 - x_2y_1 - x_1y_3 + x_1y_1 - y_2x_3 + y_2x_1 + y_1x_3 - y_1x_1)\vec{k}\|$$

$$= \frac{1}{2}|(x_2y_3 - x_3y_2 + x_3y_1 - x_1y_3 + x_1y_2 - x_2y_1)|.$$

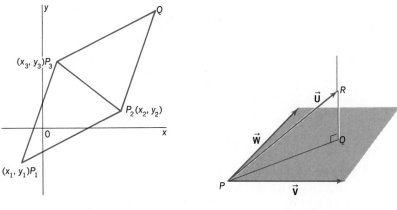

Fig. 10.31   Fig. 10.32

Those who are familiar with determinant notation will recognize that this formula can be written in the form

$$\text{area of } \triangle P_1 P_2 P_3 = \tfrac{1}{2}|1(x_2 y_3 - x_3 y_2) + 1(x_3 y_1 - x_1 y_3) + 1(x_1 y_2 - x_2 y_1)|$$

$$= \tfrac{1}{2} \text{ absolute value of } \begin{vmatrix} 1 & x_1 & y_1 \\ 1 & x_2 & y_2 \\ 1 & x_3 & y_3 \end{vmatrix}.$$

Example 6. We are given vectors $\vec{u} = 2\vec{k}$, $\vec{v} = 3\vec{j} - 2\vec{k}$, and $\vec{w} = -\vec{i} + 3\vec{j}$. Find the length of the projection of $\vec{u}$ on a line perpendicular to the plane of $\vec{v}$ and $\vec{w}$, and find the length of the projection of $\vec{u}$ on the plane of $\vec{v}$ and $\vec{w}$. Consider the symbolic diagram, Fig. 10.32. There the line QR is perpendicular to the plane determined by $\vec{v}$ and $\vec{w}$, and we seek the lengths QR and PQ.

First we point out that $\vec{v} \times \vec{w}$ can be taken as a vector along the line QR, and that a unit vector along this line is $\vec{v} \times \vec{w}/\|\vec{v} \times \vec{w}\|$. Except perhaps for sign, the length of the projection of $\vec{u}$ on a line perpendicular to the plane of $\vec{v}$ and $\vec{w}$ is then $\vec{u} \cdot \vec{v} \times \vec{w}/\|\vec{v} \times \vec{w}\|$. We compute as follows:

$$\vec{v} \times \vec{w} = (3\vec{j} - 2\vec{k}) \times (-\vec{i} + 3\vec{j}) = 3\vec{k} + \vec{0} + 2\vec{j} + 6\vec{i} = 6\vec{i} + 2\vec{j} + 3\vec{k},$$

$$\|\vec{v} \times \vec{w}\|^2 = (6\vec{i} + 2\vec{j} + 3\vec{k}) \cdot (6\vec{i} + 2\vec{j} + 3\vec{k}) = 36 + 4 + 9 = 49,$$

$$\frac{\vec{v} \times \vec{w}}{\|\vec{v} \times \vec{w}\|} = \frac{1}{7}(6\vec{i} + 2\vec{j} + 3\vec{k}),$$

$$\vec{u} \cdot \frac{\vec{v} \times \vec{w}}{\|\vec{v} \times \vec{w}\|} = 2\vec{k} \cdot \frac{1}{7}(6\vec{i} + 2\vec{j} + 3\vec{k}) = \frac{6}{7} = QR.$$

Second, to get PQ, the length of the projection of $\vec{u}$ on the plane of $\vec{v}$ and $\vec{w}$, we shall use the Pythagorean Theorem. We can see at a glance that $PR = \|\vec{u}\| = \|2\vec{k}\| = 2$, so that

$$PQ = \sqrt{PR^2 - QR^2} = \sqrt{4 - \frac{36}{49}} = \frac{\sqrt{160}}{7}.$$

EXERCISES 10.5

1. Compute the following vector products.
   (a) $3\vec{j} \times (2\vec{i} - \vec{j} + 3\vec{k})$.
   (b) $(3\vec{i} - 5\vec{j} + \vec{k}) \times (2\vec{k})$.
   (c) $(2\vec{i} + 3\vec{j}) \times 5(3\vec{i} - 2\vec{k})$.
   (d) $(\vec{i} + 4\vec{k}) \times (2\vec{i} - 1\vec{j} + 3\vec{k})$.
   (e) $2(2\vec{i} + 7\vec{j} - 2\vec{k}) \times (3\vec{i} - 6\vec{j} + 4\vec{k})$.
   (f) $\frac{1}{3}(5\vec{i} + 3\vec{j} - 2\vec{k}) \times 2(\vec{i} + \vec{j} - 2\vec{k})$.

2. Assume that $\vec{R}$ and $\vec{S}$ have common initial point. Find a unit vector perpendicular to the plane of
   (a) $\vec{R} = \vec{i} + 4\vec{k}$ and $\vec{S} = 2\vec{i} - 1\vec{j} + 3\vec{k}$.
   (b) $\vec{R} = 2(2\vec{i} + 7\vec{j} - 2\vec{k})$ and $\vec{S} = 3\vec{i} - 6\vec{j} + 4\vec{k}$.
   (c) $\vec{R} = \vec{i} + \vec{j}$ and $\vec{S} = \vec{i} - \vec{j} - \vec{k}$.

3. Compute the area of the parallelogram
   (a) determined by $\vec{R} = \vec{i} + 4\vec{k}$ and $\vec{S} = 2\vec{i} - 1\vec{j} + 3\vec{k}$, assuming that $\vec{R}$ and $\vec{S}$ have a common initial point.
   (b) with vertices $T(1, 1, 1)$, $U(2, 5, -2)$, $V(4, 3, 0)$, $W(3, -1, 3)$.

4. Compute the area of the triangle with vertices
   (a) $O(0, 0, 0)$, $Q(0, 2, 4)$, $R(0, 3, 0)$;
   (b) $P(2, 1, 5)$, $Q(4, 0, 2)$, $R(-1, 0, -1)$;
   (c) $P_1(x_1, y_1, z_1)$, $P_2(x_2, y_2, z_2)$, $P_3(x_3, y_3, z_3)$.*

5. We are given vectors $\vec{F} = 2\vec{i} + 3\vec{j}$, $\vec{G} = \vec{k}$, $\vec{H} = \vec{i} + \vec{j} + \vec{k}$. Find
   (a) the length of the projection of $\vec{F}$ on a line perpendicular to the plane of $\vec{G}$ and $\vec{H}$;
   (b) the vector description of this projection.
   (c) the vector description of the projection of $\vec{F}$ on the plane of $\vec{G}$ and $\vec{H}$.
   (d) the length of the projection of $\vec{F}$ on the plane of $\vec{G}$ and $\vec{H}$.

6. Repeat Exercise 5 for the vectors $\vec{F} = 3\vec{i} - 4\vec{j} + 2\vec{k}$, $\vec{G} = \vec{i} + 2\vec{j} + 3\vec{k}$, $\vec{H} = \vec{i} - \vec{j}$.

7. As a check on Formulas (5) and (6) of Example 3, verify that $\vec{A} \times \vec{B}$ is perpendicular to $\vec{A}$ and to $\vec{B}$ by showing that $(\vec{A} \times \vec{B}) \cdot \vec{A} = 0$ and that $(\vec{A} \times \vec{B}) \cdot \vec{B} = 0$.

8. Show that the following statement is equivalent to Definition 1:
   Definition 1A. The vector product. The vector product of $\vec{A}$ and $\vec{B}$, written $\vec{A} \times \vec{B}$, is the vector (a) whose direction is perpendicular to the plane of $\vec{A}$ and $\vec{B}$ and whose sense is such that $\vec{A}$, $\vec{B}$, and $\vec{A} \times \vec{B}$ in that order form a "right-handed" system of vectors; and (b) whose magnitude is $\|\vec{A}\| \, \|\vec{B}\| \, |\sin \theta|$, where θ is the angle between $\vec{A}$ and $\vec{B}$.

9. Prove Theorem 2. Remember that c may be negative as well as positive.

   In Exercises 10 and 11 below we outline a proof for Theorem 3. Fill in the details.

10. *Lemma. A geometric construction for the vector product.*
    Hypothesis: $\vec{C}$ is a unit vector.
    Conclusion: $\vec{V} \times \vec{C}$ can be constructed in two steps: (a) form $\vec{V}_1$, the projection of $\vec{V}$ on the plane perpendicular to $\vec{C}$; (b) rotate $\vec{V}_1$ about $\vec{C}$ as axis through the angle $-\pi/2$.†
    Proof: See Fig. 10.33(a). We must verify that this construction leads to the correct direction and magnitude for $\vec{V} \times \vec{C}$. Is the direction supplied for $\vec{V} \times \vec{C}$ correct? What is the magnitude of $\vec{V}_1$?‡ Is the magnitude supplied for $\vec{V} \times \vec{C}$ correct?

---

* This exercise leads to a useful formula, but can be quite lengthy.

† In describing a rotation about an axis described by $\vec{C}$, we use the right-hand rule. If the thumb of the right hand extends in the direction of $\vec{C}$, the four fingers extend in the positive direction of rotation.

‡ See Exercise 8.

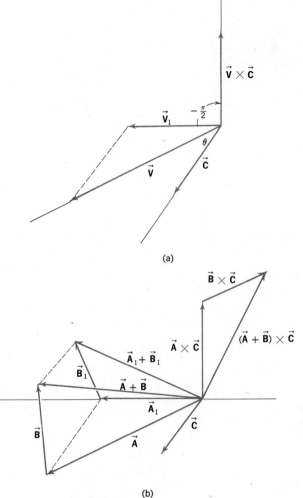

(a)

(b)

Fig. 10.33

11. Proof of Theorem 3. See Fig. 10.33(b).

Step (a). It suffices to demonstrate the conclusion of this theorem when $\vec{C}$ is a unit vector, for if $\vec{C}$ were not a unit vector, we could divide both sides by $\|\vec{C}\|$.

Step (b). The vectors $\vec{A}$, $\vec{B}$, and $\vec{A} + \vec{B}$ are the sides of a triangle.

Step (c). When this triangle is projected onto the plane perpendicular to $\vec{C}$ and then rotated about $\vec{C}$ through an angle $-\pi/2$, a new triangle is formed.

Step (d). But the sides of this new triangle are $\vec{A} \times \vec{C}$, $\vec{B} \times \vec{C}$, and $(\vec{A} + \vec{B}) \times \vec{C}$, and from the new triangle $(\vec{A} + \vec{B}) \times \vec{C} = \vec{A} \times \vec{C} + \vec{B} \times \vec{C}$.

In plane geometry nonparallel lines intersect. In solid geometry, however, we may have nonparallel lines that do not intersect. In the following exercises we shall find perpen-

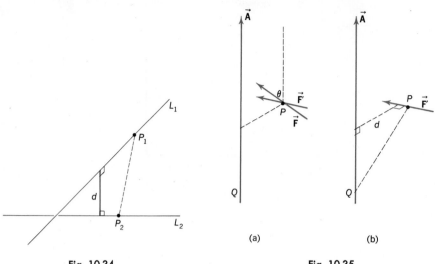

Fig. 10.34   Fig. 10.35

dicular distances between nonparallel lines. If the perpendicular distance d between L_1 and L_2 is 0, L_1 and L_2 intersect; if $d \neq 0$, L_1 and L_2 are "skew."

12. Let L_1 pass through P_1 and have the direction of $\vec{v}_1$; let L_2 pass through P_2 and have the direction of $\vec{v}_2$, $\vec{v}_2 \nparallel \vec{v}_1$; see Fig. 10.34. Show that the direction perpendicular to both L_1 and L_2 is that of $\vec{v}_1 \times \vec{v}_2$ and that d, the perpendicular distance between L_1 and L_2, is

$$d = \left| \overrightarrow{P_1P_2} \cdot \frac{\vec{v}_1 \times \vec{v}_2}{\|\vec{v}_1 \times \vec{v}_2\|} \right|.$$

13. Show that L_1 through $P_1(1, 2, 3)$, in the direction of $\vec{v}_1 = 2\vec{i} + \vec{j} - \vec{k}$, and L_2 through $P_2(5, 0, 1)$, in the direction of $\vec{v}_2 = \vec{j}$, intersect.

14. Find the perpendicular distance between L_1 through $P_1(2, 1, 3)$ and $Q_1(3, 5, -1)$ and L_2 through $P_2(5, -2, 7)$ and $Q_2(3, 0, 0)$.

15. Force $\vec{F} = 2\vec{i} + 3\vec{j} - 5\vec{k}$, acting at point $(1, 2, 5)$, has component $\vec{F}'$ perpendicular to the x axis. What is the moment arm for $\vec{F}'$ about the x axis?

16. Let force $\vec{F}$ be applied at point P, and let an axis with the direction of unit vector $\vec{A}$ pass through Q; see Fig. 10.35. Show that
(a) if $\vec{F}'$ is the component of $\vec{F}$ perpendicular to $\vec{A}$, then

$$\vec{F} = \vec{F}' + (\vec{F} \cdot \vec{A})\vec{A}, \qquad \vec{F} \times \vec{A} = \vec{F}' \times \vec{A}, \qquad \|\vec{F}'\| = \|\vec{F}\| \, |\sin \theta|,$$

where θ is the angle between $\vec{F}$ and $\vec{A}$.
(b) the moment arm for $\vec{F}'$ about the axis is

$$d = \left| \overrightarrow{QP} \cdot \frac{\vec{F}' \times \vec{A}}{\|\vec{F}' \times \vec{A}\|} \right|.$$

(c) the moment of $\vec{F}'$ about the axis is $\|\vec{F}'\| \, d = |\overrightarrow{QP} \cdot (\vec{F} \times \vec{A})|$.
(d) $\vec{F}$ and $\vec{F}'$ have the same moment about the axis. The moment of $\vec{F}$ is also $|\overrightarrow{QP} \cdot (\vec{F} \times \vec{A})|$.

17. Let a particle rotate with angular speed ω about an axis through point O in the direction of unit vector $\vec{A}$. Let the velocity vector at the instant the particle is at point P be called $\vec{v}$. Show that $\vec{v} = \omega \vec{A} \times \overrightarrow{OP}$. (See Fig. 10.36. Remember that $\vec{v}$ must be tangent to the circular path in which P travels and that $\|\vec{v}\| = (\text{radius}) \, \omega$.)

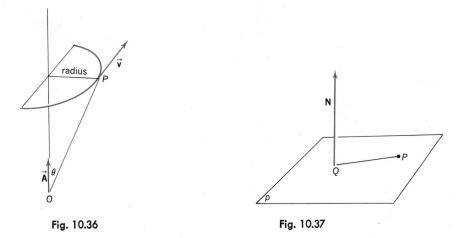

Fig. 10.36   **Fig. 10.37**

18. In Exercise 3.4-8 we showed that the medians of a triangle were such that a new triangle could be constructed with sides equal and parallel to these medians. Show that the area of this new triangle would be $\frac{3}{4}$ of the area of the original triangle.

10.6 Planes and Lines

I

A plane can be described geometrically by citing a point Q through which the plane passes and a normal direction $\bar{\mathbf{N}}$ perpendicular to the plane. A point P then lies in the plane if and only if the line joining P to Q is perpendicular to $\bar{\mathbf{N}}$.

■ THEOREM 1

On the equation of a plane.

HYPOTHESIS: (a) Plane p passes through point $Q(x_0, y_0, z_0)$.
(b) Vector $\bar{\mathbf{N}} = A\mathbf{i} + B\mathbf{j} + C\mathbf{k}$ is normal to p.

CONCLUSION: The equation of plane p is

$$A(x - x_0) + B(y - y_0) + C(z - z_0) = 0. \tag{1}$$

PROOF: As in Fig. 10.37, take the normal vector $\bar{\mathbf{N}}$ at Q. Let $P(x, y, z)$ be any other point of p. Since the vector $\overrightarrow{\mathbf{QP}}$ is perpendicular to $\bar{\mathbf{N}}$ no matter what the choice of P, we can say that

$$\bar{\mathbf{N}} \cdot \overrightarrow{\mathbf{QP}} = 0, \tag{2}$$

$$(A\mathbf{i} + B\mathbf{j} + C\mathbf{k}) \cdot [(x - x_0)\mathbf{i} + (y - y_0)\mathbf{j} + (z - z_0)\mathbf{k}] = 0, \tag{3}$$

$$A(x - x_0) + B(y - y_0) + C(z - z_0) = 0. \tag{1}$$

Here, then, is an equation satisfied by the coordinates of any point $P(x, y, z)$ of plane p other than $Q(x_0, y_0, z_0)$. But Eq. (1) is satisfied by the coordinates of Q also, as direct substitution shows, and thus Eq. (1) is an equation satisfied by all the points of p.

Conversely, if the coordinates of $P(x, y, z)$ satisfy Eq. (1), then either $x = x_0, y = y_0$, and $z = z_0$, so that P is Q and lies in plane p, or else Eq. (1) is equivalent to Eq. (2), $\vec{\mathbf{N}} \cdot \overrightarrow{\mathbf{QP}} = 0$, in which case $\overrightarrow{\mathbf{QP}} \perp \vec{\mathbf{N}}$ and P again lies in the plane p.

● **Remark 1**

The equation of the plane p can be rewritten by multiplying out and transposing terms not containing the variables:

$$Ax + By + Cz = Ax_0 + By_0 + Cz_0$$

$$Ax + By + Cz = D, \tag{4}$$

where D is the constant $Ax_0 + By_0 + Cz_0$. This is the form we shall use for the plane equation for the most part.

Theorem 1 says that a plane has a first-degree equation and that the coefficients of x, y, and z in that equation are the components of a vector normal to the plane. We can also say that every first-degree equation represents a plane, for if Eq. (4) is presented, we need only point out that it is the plane through the point $(0, 0, D/C)^*$ with normal vector $A\vec{\mathbf{i}} + B\vec{\mathbf{j}} + C\vec{\mathbf{k}}$ which is described by this equation.

Example 1. According to Theorem 1, the plane with normal vector $\vec{\mathbf{k}} = 0\vec{\mathbf{i}} + 0\vec{\mathbf{j}} + 1\vec{\mathbf{k}}$ and passing through $Q(x_0, y_0, z_0)$ has an equation of the form $0x + 0y + z = D$. Since the coordinates of Q satisfy the equation, we have $z_0 = D$ and the equation of the plane is $z = z_0$. All this agrees, of course, with our earlier work. See Fig. 10.38.

Example 2. Find the equation of the plane p through $Q(1, 5, -2)$ with normal vector $\vec{\mathbf{N}} = \vec{\mathbf{i}} + 2\vec{\mathbf{j}} - 3\vec{\mathbf{k}}$. Theorem 1 says that the equation of p must be of the form

$$x + 2y - 3z = D.$$

Since the coordinates of $Q(1, 5, -2)$ must satisfy the equation, we have

$$1 + 2(5) - 3(-2) = D, \quad \text{or} \quad D = 17.$$

Hence the equation of p is

$$x + 2y - 3z = 17.$$

Example 3. Find the equation of the plane p determined by $P(1, 4, 3)$, $Q(3, 5, -1)$, and $R(2, 4, 0)$. We can write down an equation of the form of Eq. (4) for p, and then the equations which say that the coordinates of P, Q, R must satisfy the equation of plane p. These equations are

$$P: \quad 1A + 4B + 3C = D,$$

$$Q: \quad 3A + 5B - 1C = D,$$

$$R: \quad 2A + 4B \qquad = D.$$

---

*If $C = 0$, we can take the point $(0, D/B, 0)$ or the point $(D/A, 0, 0)$. At least one of A, B, C must be nonvanishing.

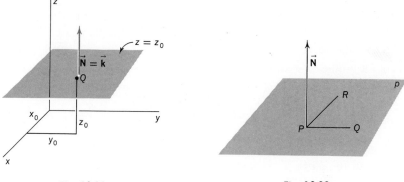

Fig. 10.38   Fig. 10.39

The problem can be completed by solving these equations, but we prefer, in this example, to reason geometrically. Let $\vec{N}$ be a vector normal to the plane p. As we see in Fig. 10.39, $\vec{N}$ is to be a vector perpendicular to $\overrightarrow{PQ}$ and to $\overrightarrow{PR}$. But $\overrightarrow{PQ} \times \overrightarrow{PR}$ is such a vector, and we therefore choose

$$\vec{N} = \overrightarrow{PQ} \times \overrightarrow{PR} = (2\mathbf{i} + 1\mathbf{j} - 4\mathbf{k}) \times (1\mathbf{i} - 3\mathbf{k})$$
$$= 6\mathbf{j} - \mathbf{k} - 3\mathbf{i} - 4\mathbf{j} = -3\mathbf{i} + 2\mathbf{j} - \mathbf{k}.$$

Hence, according to Theorem 1, p has an equation of the form

$$-3x + 2y - 1z = D.$$

Since the coordinates of $P(1, 4, 3)$ satisfy this equation, we have

$$-3(1) + 2(4) - 1(3) = D, \quad \text{or} \quad D = 2,$$

and our final answer is

$$p: \quad -3x + 2y - 1z = 2.$$

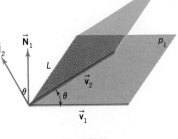

Fig. 10.40

Example 4. Find the cosine of the angle between planes p_1: $3x - 2y + z = 6$ and p_2: $x - 2z = 8$. See Fig. 10.40. The angle θ we seek could be determined directly by finding the vectors $\vec{v}_1$ and $\vec{v}_2$ in p_1 and p_2 that are perpendicular to the line of intersection, L, and then finding the angle between $\vec{v}_1$ and $\vec{v}_2$. But it is easier to reason instead that the vectors $\vec{v}_1$, $\vec{v}_2$, $\vec{N}_1$, and $\vec{N}_2$ all lie in the plane perpendicular to L and that the angle between $\vec{N}_1$ and $\vec{N}_2$ is also equal to θ.

According to Theorem 1, a vector $\vec{N}_1$ perpendicular to p_1 is $3\mathbf{i} - 2\mathbf{j} + \mathbf{k}$ and a vector $\vec{N}_2$ perpendicular to p_2 is $\mathbf{i} - 2\mathbf{k}$. To get the angle between these vectors, we say that

$$\vec{N}_1 \cdot \vec{N}_2 = \|\vec{N}_1\| \|\vec{N}_2\| \cos \theta,$$
$$3 - 0 - 2 = \sqrt{9 + 4 + 1} \sqrt{1 + 4} \cos \theta,$$
$$\cos \theta = \frac{1}{\sqrt{70}}.$$

Example 5. Find the distance from the point $R(2, 1, 5)$ to the plane p: $3x - 2y + 4z = 16$. By inspection of p's equation we see that the point $S(0, 0, 4)$ lies in p. Then in Fig. 10.41 we reason that the distance we seek, $d = \|\overrightarrow{TR}\|$, is the projection of $\overrightarrow{SR}$ on the direction perpendicular to p. Theorem 1 says that a vector perpendicular to p is $\vec{N} = 3\vec{i} - 2\vec{j} + 4\vec{k}$, so that we can say that

$$d = \overrightarrow{SR} \cdot \frac{\vec{N}}{\|\vec{N}\|} = (2\vec{i} + 1\vec{j} + 1\vec{k}) \cdot \frac{3\vec{i} - 2\vec{j} + 4\vec{k}}{\sqrt{9 + 4 + 16}} = \frac{6 - 2 + 4}{\sqrt{29}} = \frac{8}{\sqrt{29}}.$$

In Exercise 7 at the end of this section the reader can show that the distance from $R(x_1, y_1, z_1)$ to the plane p: $Ax + By + Cz - D = 0$ is given by

$$\frac{Ax_1 + By_1 + Cz_1 - D}{\sqrt{A^2 + B^2 + C^2}}.$$

||

A straight line can be considered as the intersection of any two planes through it, and is therefore described by two equations of the first degree.

■ THEOREM 2

The symmetric form equations for a straight line.

HYPOTHESIS: (a) Line L passes through $P_1(x_1, y_1, z_1)$.
(b) Line L has the direction of $\vec{v} = a\vec{i} + b\vec{j} + c\vec{k}$.

CONCLUSION: Equations for line L can be written in the form

$$\frac{x - x_1}{a} = \frac{y - y_1}{b} = \frac{z - z_1}{c}. \tag{5}$$

PROOF: Let $P(x, y, z)$ be any point on L other than P_1. Vector $\overrightarrow{P_1P}$ must be parallel to $\vec{v}$. Hence there exists a constant t such that $\overrightarrow{P_1P} = t\vec{v}$, or such that

$$(x - x_1)\vec{i} + (y - y_1)\vec{j} + (z - z_1)\vec{k} = t(a\vec{i} + b\vec{j} + c\vec{k}).$$

But equal vectors have equal components; hence

$$x - x_1 = ta, \qquad y - y_1 = tb, \qquad z - z_1 = tc,$$

or

$$\frac{x - x_1}{a} = \frac{y - y_1}{b} = \frac{z - z_1}{c} = t,$$

so that the Eqs. (5) hold for any point P on the line other than P_1. Upon inspection, we see that the coordinates of $P_1(x_1, y_1, z_1)$ also satisfy the Eqs. (5), which therefore hold for all points on L.

Conversely, P_1 is one of the points whose coordinates satisfy the Eqs. (5). If $P(x, y, z)$ is any other point whose coordinates satisfy Eqs. (5), we can say that the vectors $\overrightarrow{P_1P}$ and $\vec{v}$ are parallel because Eqs. (5) say that their $\vec{i}$, $\vec{j}$, and $\vec{k}$ components are proportional. Hence P lies on L.

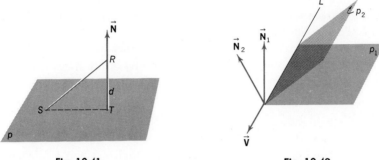

Fig. 10.41   Fig. 10.42

Example 6. Find equations for the line L through $P_1(1, 3, 5)$ and P_2 $(-2, 4, -1)$. Line L has the direction of $\overrightarrow{P_1P_2} = -3\mathbf{i} + 1\mathbf{j} - 6\mathbf{k}$. Hence according to Theorem 2, its equations can be written in the form

$$\frac{x-1}{-3} = \frac{y-3}{1} = \frac{z-5}{-6}.$$

We can use the coordinates of P_2 as well as those of P_1. Line L is also described by

$$\frac{x+2}{-3} = \frac{y-4}{1} = \frac{z+1}{-6}.$$

Example 7. Find the angle between the lines

$$L_1: \quad \frac{x-2}{1} = \frac{y-3}{1} = \frac{z+1}{2},$$

$$L_2: \quad \frac{x-2}{2} = \frac{y-3}{-1} = \frac{z+1}{3}.$$

In the first place, we observe that L_1 and L_2 both pass through $(2, 3, -1)$. Then, according to Theorem 2, $\vec{v}_1 = \mathbf{i} + \mathbf{j} + 2\mathbf{k}$ and $\vec{v}_2 = 2\mathbf{i} - 1\mathbf{j} + 3\mathbf{k}$ have the directions of these lines, so that the angle we seek is the angle between $\vec{v}_1$ and $\vec{v}_2$. We write

$$\vec{v}_1 \cdot \vec{v}_2 = \|\vec{v}_1\| \|\vec{v}_2\| \cos \theta,$$

$$2 - 1 + 6 = \sqrt{1 + 1 + 4}\sqrt{4 + 1 + 9} \cos \theta,$$

$$\cos \theta = \frac{7}{\sqrt{84}} = \sqrt{\frac{7}{12}}, \quad \text{or} \quad \theta = \cos^{-1}\sqrt{\frac{7}{12}}.$$

Example 8. Let line L be the intersection of planes p_1: $2x - 3y + z = 5$ and p_2: $x + y - z = 3$. These equations describe L, for a point lies on L if and only if it lies in both planes, and therefore if and only if its coordinates satisfy both equations, but we prefer the symmetric form description of L, because we can then read off L's direction at a glance.

First Solution: Let $\vec{v}$ be a vector in L's direction. Since L lies in p_1, $\vec{v} \perp \vec{N}_1$, and since L lies in p_2, $\vec{v} \perp \vec{N}_2$; see Fig. 10.42. Thus, for $\vec{v}$ we can take $\vec{N}_1 \times \vec{N}_2$. We have

$$\vec{v} = \vec{N}_1 \times \vec{N}_2 = (2\mathbf{i} - 3\mathbf{j} + 1\mathbf{k}) \times (1\mathbf{i} + 1\mathbf{j} - 1\mathbf{k})$$
$$= 2\mathbf{k} + 2\mathbf{j} + 3\mathbf{k} + 3\mathbf{i} + 1\mathbf{j} - 1\mathbf{i} = 2\mathbf{i} + 3\mathbf{j} + 5\mathbf{k}.$$

To write down the equations of L in symmetric form, we still need any one point on L. To get such a point, we can substitute $x = 0$ in the equations for p_1 and p_2 and solve for the corresponding y and z. We find that $(0, -4, -7)$ is a point on both p_1 and p_2 and therefore a point on L. Equations of L are

$$\frac{x - 0}{2} = \frac{y + 4}{3} = \frac{z + 7}{5}.$$

Second Solution: We could write the equations of L quickly if we knew two points on L. We found one such point, $R(0, -4, -7)$, by substituting 0 for x in the equations for p_1 and p_2 and solving for the corresponding y and z. We can find a second point on L by substituting 1 for x in the equations for p_1 and p_2 and solving for y and z. We get the equations $-3y + z = 3$ and $y - z = 2$, whose solution is $y = -\frac{5}{2}$ and $z = -\frac{9}{2}$, so that another point on L is $S(1, -\frac{5}{2}, -\frac{9}{2})$. Thus $\overrightarrow{RS} = \mathbf{i} + \frac{3}{2}\mathbf{j} + \frac{5}{2}\mathbf{k}$ is a vector in L's direction, and the equations for L can be written

$$\frac{x - 0}{1} = \frac{y + 4}{3/2} = \frac{z + 7}{5/2}.$$

These equations are equivalent to those we obtained above.

● **Remark 2**

If one of the components of $\vec{\mathbf{v}}$ is 0, then one of the members of the symmetric-form equations for a line L in $\vec{\mathbf{v}}$'s direction will have 0 as its denominator. In such a case, the symmetric-form description of L is to be interpreted as a statement about proportional trios of numbers.

EXERCISES 10.6

1. Find the equation of the plane through the following points.
   (a) $(2, 1, 0)$, $(0, 1, 5)$, $(-3, 2, 2)$.   (c) $(2, 0, 4)$, $(-3, 1, 1)$, $(1, -1, 2)$.
   (b) $(-1, 2, 5)$, $(3, 1, 3)$, $(0, 0, 0)$.

2. Find the cosine of the angle between the following planes.
   (a) $y - 3z = 4$, $2x + y - 5z = 7$.
   (b) $3x + y - z = -1$, $x - 2y + 3z = 0$.
   (c) $x + y - 2z = 4$, $x = 0$.

3. Which pairs of the following planes are parallel? perpendicular?
   p_a: $2x + 3y - z = 5$. p_c: $4x + 6y - 2z = 11$.
   p_b: $3x - 2y - z = 4$. p_d: $x - 2y - 4z = 0$.

4. (a) Find the equation of the plane parallel to $2x + 3y - z = 7$ and passing through $(0, 0, 1)$.
   (b) Find the equation of the plane parallel to $3x - y + z = 11$ and passing through $(2, 2, -1)$.

5. Find the equation of the plane perpendicular to p_1 and p_2 and passing through Q.
   (a) p_1: $x + 2z = 7$; p_2: $x - y - z = 5$; $Q(0, 0, 0)$.
   (b) p_1: $3x - y - z = 5$; p_2: $x = 0$; $Q(2, 1, -1)$.

6. Find the distance from p_1 to Q.
   (a) p_1: $2x - y - z = 10$; $Q(1, 2, 3)$.
   (b) p_1: $3x + y - 5z = -1$; $Q(-1, 2, -3)$.
   (c) p_1: $y = 2$; $Q(0, 0, 4)$.

7. (a) Show that the distance from $R(x_1, y_1, z_1)$ to plane p: $Ax + By + Cz - D = 0$ is given by

$$d = \frac{Ax_1 + By_1 + Cz_1 - D}{\sqrt{A^2 + B^2 + C^2}}.$$

(b) Show that if $C > 0$ and R lies above p, then $d > 0$; but that, if R lies below p, then $d < 0$.*

8. Find equations in symmetric form for the line L through P_1 and P_2.
   (a) $P_1(1, 0, 5)$, $P_2(2, -1, 3)$.   (b) $P_1(2, -1, 6)$, $P_2(-1, -1, 0)$.

9. Find the angle between L_1 and L_2.

   (a) L_1: $\dfrac{x}{2} = \dfrac{y}{3} = \dfrac{z}{1}$; L_2: the y axis.

   (b) L_1: $\dfrac{x-1}{3} = \dfrac{y-2}{0} = \dfrac{z+1}{1}$; L_2: $\dfrac{x-1}{5} = \dfrac{y-2}{1} = \dfrac{z+1}{-3}$.

10. Which of $P(4, 4, 5)$, $Q(6, 8, -1)$, $R(-1, -6, 0)$ lie on L: $\dfrac{x-2}{1} = \dfrac{y}{2} = \dfrac{z-3}{1}$?

11. Which pairs of the following lines are parallel? perpendicular?

   L_a: $\dfrac{x}{2} = \dfrac{y}{3} = \dfrac{z}{-1}$. L_c: $\dfrac{x-2}{-3} = \dfrac{y-3}{4} = \dfrac{z+1}{6}$.

   L_b: $\dfrac{x}{3} = \dfrac{y}{-4} = \dfrac{z}{-6}$. L_d: $\dfrac{x-2}{5} = \dfrac{y-3}{-2} = \dfrac{z+1}{4}$.

12. Find the equation of plane p perpendicular to L and passing through Q.

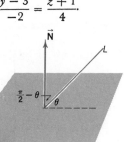

   (a) L: $\dfrac{x-1}{2} = \dfrac{y-2}{1} = \dfrac{z+3}{-5}$; $Q(1, 2, -3)$.

   (b) L: $\dfrac{x+1}{1} = \dfrac{y-2}{0} = \dfrac{z}{2}$; $Q(0, 1, 0)$.

13. Find equations in symmetric form of the line of intersection of p_1 and p_2.
   (a) p_1: $x + y + z = 2$; p_2: $-x + 2y + z = 4$.   **Fig. 10.43**
   (b) p_1: $3x - y - z = 5$; p_2: $x + y + 2z = -1$.

14. Find the angle between line L and plane p. See Fig. 10.43.

   (a) p: $2x + y - z = 7$; L: $\dfrac{x}{2} = \dfrac{y}{1} = \dfrac{z}{3}$.

   (b) p: $3x - y - z = -1$; L: $\dfrac{x-1}{3} = \dfrac{y+2}{1} = \dfrac{z-5}{0}$.

15. Find the equation of the plane p in which L_1 and L_2 lie.

   (a) L_1: $\dfrac{x-2}{3} = \dfrac{y-1}{1} = \dfrac{z}{2}$; L_2: $\dfrac{x-2}{-1} = \dfrac{y-1}{1} = \dfrac{z}{1}$.

   (b) L_1: $\dfrac{x+1}{0} = \dfrac{y-1}{1} = \dfrac{z+1}{1}$; L_2: $\dfrac{x+1}{3} = \dfrac{y-1}{-1} = \dfrac{z+1}{-2}$.

---

* *Suggestion:* If $R(x_1, y_1, z_1)$ lies above p, then a point of p directly below R is $(x_1, y_1, [D - Ax_1 - By_1]/C)$ and $z_1 > (D - Ax_1 - By_1)/C$.

16. Find the equation of the plane p in which L and Q lie.

(a) L: $\dfrac{x-3}{2} = \dfrac{y+1}{1} = \dfrac{z}{-2}$; $Q(5, 0, 4)$.

(b) L: $\dfrac{x+2}{-1} = \dfrac{y-5}{2} = \dfrac{z-4}{-4}$; $Q(1, 1, -3)$.

17. Does the line L lie in the plane $2x - 5y - z = 10$? Explain.

(a) L: $\dfrac{x-5}{2} = \dfrac{y}{-5} = \dfrac{z}{-1}$.

(c) L: $\dfrac{x}{3} = \dfrac{y}{1} = \dfrac{z}{1}$.

(b) L: $\dfrac{x-5}{3} = \dfrac{y}{1} = \dfrac{z}{1}$.

18. Find the point of intersection of line L and plane p.

(a) p: $2x + y - z = 7$, L: $\dfrac{x}{2} = \dfrac{y}{1} = \dfrac{z}{3}$.

(b) p: xy plane, L: $\dfrac{x+1}{3} = \dfrac{y-1}{-1} = \dfrac{z+1}{-2}$.

(c) p: $x + 2y - 2z = 3$, L: line of intersection of $x - 3y + 4z = -3$, $2x + 5y - 3z = 5$.

19. Find the distance from point P to line L.

(a) $P(1, 0, 2)$, L: $\dfrac{x+1}{2} = \dfrac{y-1}{2} = \dfrac{z}{3}$.

(b) $P(3, -1, -1)$, L: $\dfrac{x-1}{0} = \dfrac{y+2}{1} = \dfrac{z-3}{2}$.

20. Demonstrate this theorem:
Hypothesis: (a) Plane p_1 has the equation $A_1x + B_1y + C_1z - D_1 = 0$.
(b) Plane p_2 has the equation $A_2x + B_2y + C_2z - D_2 = 0$.
(c) m and n are constants, not both 0.
Conclusion:
$$m(A_1x + B_1y + C_1z - D_1) + n(A_2x + B_2y + C_2z - D_2) = 0$$
is the equation of a plane through the intersection of p_1 and p_2 if they intersect, and parallel to them if they are parallel.

21. Demonstrate this theorem:
Hypothesis: (a) Plane p_1 has the equation $A_1x + B_1y + C_1z - D_1 = 0$.
(b) Plane p_2 has the equation $A_2x + B_2y + C_2z - D_2 = 0$.
(c) Plane p goes through the intersection of p_1 and p_2 if they intersect and is parallel to p_1 and p_2 if they are parallel.
Conclusion: There exist constants m and n such that the equation of p can be written in the form
$$m(A_1x + B_1y + C_1z - D_1) + n(A_2x + B_2y + C_2z - D_2) = 0.$$

22. Find the equation of the plane through the intersection of $3x + 2y - z = 5$ and $2x - y + z = 4$ and passing through $(2, 1, 0)$.

23. Find the equation of the plane through the intersection of $2x - y - 5z = 4$ and $3x + y - z = 0$ and parallel to $12x - y - 17z = 4$.

10.7 Curves in Space

I

A curve in space can be described analytically by stating the equations of two surfaces of which it is the intersection, but for many purposes it is more convenient to describe a curve by parametric equations for the coordinates x, y, and z.

Example 1. Consider the straight line L with equations in symmetric form

$$\frac{x-1}{1} = \frac{y+2}{-1} = \frac{z-3}{2}. \tag{1}$$

If we set each of the three fractions equal to 0, we find the point $(1, -2, 3)$ of L. If we set each of the three fractions equal to 1, we find the point $(2, -3, 5)$ of L. But we can set each of the three fractions equal to any number u and get a point of L. If we do this, we compute

$$x = u + 1, \qquad y = -u - 2, \qquad z = 2u + 3. \tag{2}$$

For different choices of the parameter u, Eqs. (2) give us different points of L. The reader may demonstrate in Exercise 12 that Eqs. (2) give us all the points of L.

In general, the line L with equations

$$\frac{x - x_1}{a} = \frac{y - y_1}{b} = \frac{z - z_1}{c}$$

can also be described by the parametric equations

$$x = au + x_1, \qquad y = bu + y_1, \qquad z = cu + z_1.$$

Example 2. *The circular helix.* Consider the arc described by the parametric equations

$$x = 2\cos u, \qquad y = 2\sin u, \qquad z = \tfrac{1}{4} u, \qquad 0 \le u \le 3\pi. \tag{3}$$

We can draw up a table of values and plot the corresponding points. See Table 10.1 and Fig. 10.44.

TABLE 10.1

u	0	$\pi/4$	$\pi/2$	$3\pi/4$	π	$3\pi/2$	2π	$5\pi/2$	3π
x	2	$\sqrt{2}$	0	$-\sqrt{2}$	-2	0	2	0	-2
y	0	$\sqrt{2}$	2	$\sqrt{2}$	0	-2	0	2	0
z	0	$\pi/16$	$\pi/8$	$3\pi/16$	$\pi/4$	$3\pi/8$	$\pi/2$	$5\pi/8$	$3\pi/4$

The helix lies on the circular cylinder $x^2 + y^2 = 4$, because for each u of $0 \le u \le 3\pi$ the x and y coordinates furnished by Eqs. (3) satisfy $x^2 + y^2 = 4$. The points whose coordinates are given in the table were plotted on the cylinder, and then

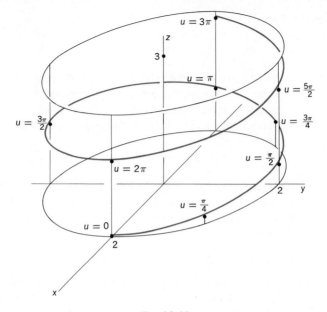

Fig. 10.44

joined, taking 3.14 as an approximate value for π and labeling each point with its parameter value.

To measure the length of arc, we take the definition used in our plane geometry.*

■ DEFINITION 1

The length of an arc. The length of an arc shall be the limit of the sum of the lengths of the inscribed chords as the number of these chords grows beyond all bounds, the length of the longest of these chords approaching 0.

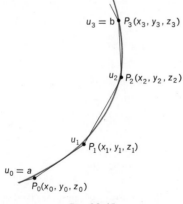

Fig. 10.45

We can rewrite this definition in integral form, as we did in Theorem 8.6-3.

■ THEOREM 1

On the length of an arc.

HYPOTHESIS: $f'(u)$, $g'(u)$, and $h'(u)$ are continuous for $a \leq u \leq b$.

CONCLUSION: The length of the arc de-

* Definition 8.6-1.

scribed by $x = f(u), y = g(u)$, and $z = h(u)$ for $a \leq u \leq b$ is given by

$$\int_{u=a}^{b} \sqrt{\left(\frac{dx}{du}\right)^2 + \left(\frac{dy}{du}\right)^2 + \left(\frac{dz}{du}\right)^2}\, du.$$

PROOF: We subdivide the arc whose length we want by choosing as subdivision points the points corresponding to the parameter values $u_0 = a < u_1 < u_2 < \cdots < u_n = b$; see Fig. 10.45, where $n = 3$. Then

$$\text{length of } k\text{th inscribed chord} = \sqrt{(\Delta x)_k^2 + (\Delta y)_k^2 + (\Delta z)_k^2}. \qquad (4)$$

But $x = f(u)$ is differentiable for $a \leq u \leq b$. Hence the Theorem of Mean Value applies, and we can say that there exists a v_k, $u_{k-1} < v_k < u_k$, such that

$$(\Delta x)_k = x_k - x_{k-1} = f(u_k) - f(u_{k-1}) = f'(v_k)(u_k - u_{k-1}) = f'(v_k)(\Delta u)_k.$$

Similarly, there exist v_k' and v_k'', $u_{k-1} < v_k'$, $v_k'' < u_k$, such that

$$(\Delta y)_k = g'(v_k')(\Delta u)_k \qquad \text{and} \qquad (\Delta z)_k = h'(v_k'')(\Delta u)_k.$$

Hence, returning to Eq. (4), we can say that

$$\text{length of } k\text{th inscribed chord} = \sqrt{[f'(v_k)]^2 + [g'(v_k')]^2 + [h'(v_k'')]^2}\,(\Delta u)_k,$$

$$\text{sum of lengths of inscribed chords} = \sum_{k=1}^{n} \sqrt{[f'(v_k)]^2 + [g'(v_k')]^2 + [h'(v_k'')]^2}\,(\Delta u)_k. \qquad (5)$$

If v_k, v_k', and v_k'' were equal, we could write the limit of this sum as an integral immediately. Instead, we must appeal to Theorem 8.8-1 and use an argument patterned after that of Theorem 8.8-3 in order to be sure that we can ignore the fact that v_k, v_k', and v_k'' are not equal in general. If this is done, we conclude from Eq. (5) that

$$\text{arc length} = \int_{u=a}^{b} \sqrt{[f'(u)]^2 + [g'(u)]^2 + [h'(u)]^2}\, du$$

$$= \int_{u=a}^{b} \sqrt{\left(\frac{dx}{du}\right)^2 + \left(\frac{dy}{du}\right)^2 + \left(\frac{dz}{du}\right)^2}\, du. \qquad (6)$$

Example 3. Let us find the length of the helix considered in Example 2 from the point for which $u = 0$ to the point for which $u = 2\pi$. As in Theorem 1, we choose subdivision points $0 = u_0 < u_1 < u_2 < u_3 < \cdots < u_n = 2\pi$, and then we can say that

$$\text{length of } k\text{th chord} = \sqrt{(\Delta x)_k^2 + (\Delta y)_k^2 + (\Delta z)_k^2}$$

$$= \sqrt{\left(\frac{\Delta x}{\Delta u}\right)_k^2 + \left(\frac{\Delta y}{\Delta u}\right)_k^2 + \left(\frac{\Delta z}{\Delta u}\right)_k^2}\,(\Delta u)_k,$$

$$\text{arc length} = \int_{u=0}^{2\pi} \sqrt{\left(\frac{dx}{du}\right)^2 + \left(\frac{dy}{du}\right)^2 + \left(\frac{dz}{du}\right)^2}\, du.$$

In this case

$$\frac{dx}{du} = -2 \sin u, \qquad \frac{dy}{du} = 2 \cos u, \qquad \text{and} \qquad \frac{dz}{du} = \frac{1}{4}$$

so that

$$\text{arc length} = \int_{u=0}^{2\pi} \sqrt{4 \sin^2 u + 4 \cos^2 u + \tfrac{1}{16}} \; du$$

$$= \sqrt{\frac{65}{16}} \int_0^{2\pi} du = \frac{\sqrt{65}}{2} \pi.$$

● **Remark 1**

As a finer point, we shall add to the hypothesis of Theorem 1 the restriction that there shall be no subinterval of $a \le u \le b$ for which all three of $f'(u)$, $g'(u)$, $h'(u)$ vanish identically. According to Theorem 7.5-3A, if there were such a subinterval, we would have $f(u)$, $g(u)$, $h(u)$ all constant on that subinterval, say $f(u) = f(u_1)$, $g(u) = g(u_1)$, $h(u) = h(u_1)$, and then all the u numbers of that subinterval would be associated with the one point $(f(u_1), g(u_1), h(u_1))$ of the curve. We prefer to have a one-to-one correspondence between the points of the curve and the parameter numbers.

II

In the theory of space curves it is convenient to use the arc length itself as a parameter. Select one point, A, on the curve as the base point and select one direction on the curve as the positive direction. Then for any point P on the curve we compute L, the length of arc from A to P, and assign to P the parameter value $s = +L$ if P is reached by traveling from A in the positive direction and the parameter value $s = -L$ if P is reached by traveling from A in the negative direction.

Let a curve be described in terms of the parameter u by the equations $x = f(u)$, $y = g(u)$, $z = h(u)$ for u of $a \le u \le b$, with the functions f, g, h all differentiable for u of this interval and satisfying the further restriction described in Remark 1. If the point A corresponding to parameter number $u = a$ is chosen as base point, and if the direction of increasing s is chosen to be the direction of increasing u, then Theorem 1 says that the arc length s is the function of u given by the equation

$$s = \int_a^u \sqrt{\left(\frac{dx}{du}\right)^2 + \left(\frac{dy}{du}\right)^2 + \left(\frac{dz}{du}\right)^2} \; du, \tag{7}$$

for all u of $a \le u \le b$. Let $0 \le s \le d = s(b)$ be the range set of s numbers corresponding to the u numbers $a \le u \le b$. From Theorem 7.7-2, it will follow that

$$\frac{ds}{du} = \sqrt{\left(\frac{dx}{du}\right)^2 + \left(\frac{dy}{du}\right)^2 + \left(\frac{dz}{du}\right)^2}, \tag{8}$$

for each u of $a \le u \le b$, and in differential form that

$$ds^2 = \left(\frac{ds}{du} du\right)^2 = \left[\left(\frac{dx}{du}\right)^2 + \left(\frac{dy}{du}\right)^2 + \left(\frac{dz}{du}\right)^2\right] du^2$$

$$ds^2 = \left(\frac{dx}{du} du\right)^2 + \left(\frac{dy}{du} du\right)^2 + \left(\frac{dz}{du} du\right)^2$$

$$ds^2 = dx^2 + dy^2 + dz^2.* \tag{9}$$

---

* Compare Theorem 8.6-4.

There is a one-to-one correspondence between the numbers of $a \le u \le b$ and those of $0 \le s \le d$. This follows intuitively from the method of assignment of the parameter numbers s, but also, from Eq. (8), which says that ds/du is never negative and, further, that there is no subinterval on which ds/du is identically 0. A refinement of Theorem 7.5-4 would enable us to say that s is an increasing function of u and that two different numbers u of $a \le u \le b$ cannot correspond to the same number s of $0 \le s \le d$. Hence if we write Eq. (7) in the form

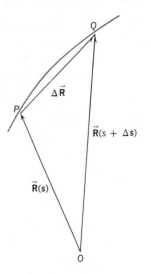

$$s = \phi(u), \qquad a \le u \le b,$$

we can say that there is an inverse function

$$u = \phi^{-1}(s), \qquad 0 \le s \le d.$$

The curve C can then be described in terms of its arc length s as parameter. For if a number s of $0 \le s \le d$ is specified, a number u of $a \le u \le b$ is then determined and the point $(f(u), g(u), h(u))$ of the curve is assigned. Conversely, with each point of the curve we associate a number u of $a \le u \le b$ through the original parametric equation system for the curve and we associate an s number of $0 \le s \le d$ with this number u through Eq. (7). In detail, the parametric description for C in terms of s would be

$$x = f(\phi^{-1}(s)), \qquad y = g(\phi^{-1}(s)), \qquad z = h(\phi^{-1}(s)), \qquad 0 \le s \le d.$$

Let a curve C be described, then, in terms of its arc length as the parameter. Let $P(s)$ be any point on this curve and consider the "position vector"

$$\vec{R}(s) = \overrightarrow{OP} = x\mathbf{i} + y\mathbf{j} + z\mathbf{k}.$$

Let $Q(s + \Delta s)$, $\Delta s \ne 0$, be a nearby point on C and form the new position vector

$$\vec{R}(s + \Delta s) = \overrightarrow{OQ} = (x + \Delta x)\mathbf{i} + (y + \Delta y)\mathbf{j} + (z + \Delta z)\mathbf{k}.$$

See Fig. 10.46. Then,

$$\overrightarrow{\Delta R} = \vec{R}(s + \Delta s) - \vec{R}(s) = \overrightarrow{PQ} = \Delta x\,\mathbf{i} + \Delta y\,\mathbf{j} + \Delta z\,\mathbf{k}, \tag{10}$$

and

$$\frac{\overrightarrow{\Delta R}}{\Delta s} = \frac{\Delta x}{\Delta s}\mathbf{i} + \frac{\Delta y}{\Delta s}\mathbf{j} + \frac{\Delta z}{\Delta s}\mathbf{k}.$$

If we give to $\lim_{\Delta s \to 0} (\overrightarrow{\Delta R}/\Delta s)$ the name $d\vec{R}/ds$, we arrive at

$$\frac{d\vec{R}}{ds} = \frac{dx}{ds}\mathbf{i} + \frac{dy}{ds}\mathbf{j} + \frac{dz}{ds}\mathbf{k}.$$

But what is the geometric meaning of $d\vec{R}/ds$?

In Eq. (10) we pointed out that $\overrightarrow{\Delta R}$ is the vector $\overrightarrow{PQ}$. If we multiply $\overrightarrow{\Delta R}$ by $1/\Delta s$, we get a new vector with the same direction but with a new magnitude; $\overrightarrow{\Delta R}/\Delta s$ is therefore a vector in the direction of the secant line PQ and with magnitude equal to the ratio of the length of the chord PQ to the length of the arc PQ. If now point Q approaches point P, the position of the secant line PQ approaches that of the tangent line at P and the ratio of $\|\overrightarrow{PQ}\|/\widehat{PQ}$ approaches unity.* Therefore $d\vec{R}/ds$ is a unit vector in the tangent direction at P. We have demonstrated the following theorem.

■ THEOREM 2

The unit tangent vector.

HYPOTHESIS: Curve C is described by the equation $\vec{R} = \overrightarrow{OP} = x\vec{i} + y\vec{j} + z\vec{k}$, where x, y, and z are differentiable functions of the arc length parameter s for s of a certain interval.

CONCLUSION: For any s of that interval, $\vec{t} = d\vec{R}/ds$ is a unit vector in the tangent direction.

Example 4. Let us consider further the helix of Examples 2 and 3. We have

$$\vec{R} = x\vec{i} + y\vec{j} + z\vec{k} = 2 \cos u\vec{i} + 2 \sin u\vec{j} + \tfrac{1}{4} u\vec{k},$$

$$\frac{ds}{du} = \sqrt{\left(\frac{dx}{du}\right)^2 + \left(\frac{dy}{du}\right)^2 + \left(\frac{dz}{du}\right)^2} = \sqrt{4 \sin^2 u + 4 \cos^2 u + \tfrac{1}{16}} = \frac{\sqrt{65}}{4},$$

so that $du/ds = 4/\sqrt{65}$. Next we form

$$\frac{d\vec{R}}{du} = -2 \sin u\vec{i} + 2 \cos u\vec{j} + \frac{1}{4}\vec{k}$$

and then

$$\vec{t} = \frac{d\vec{R}}{ds} = \frac{d\vec{R}}{du}\frac{du}{ds} = \frac{4}{\sqrt{65}}\left(-2 \sin u\vec{i} + 2 \cos u\vec{j} + \frac{1}{4}\vec{k}\right).$$

---

* Since arc length is defined as a limit of a sum of inscribed chords, it seems natural to expect that $\lim_{Q \to P} (\|\overrightarrow{PQ}\|/\widehat{PQ}) = 1$. Observe that

$$\frac{\|\overrightarrow{PQ}\|^2}{\widehat{PQ}^2} = \frac{\Delta x^2 + \Delta y^2 + \Delta z^2}{\Delta s^2} = \left(\frac{\Delta x}{\Delta s}\right)^2 + \left(\frac{\Delta y}{\Delta s}\right)^2 + \left(\frac{\Delta z}{\Delta s}\right)^2,$$

$$\lim_{\Delta s \to 0} \frac{\|\overrightarrow{PQ}\|^2}{\widehat{PQ}^2} = \left(\frac{dx}{ds}\right)^2 + \left(\frac{dy}{ds}\right)^2 + \left(\frac{dz}{ds}\right)^2,$$

and that by Eq. (8)

$$\frac{dx}{ds} = \frac{dx/du}{ds/du} = \frac{dx/du}{\sqrt{(dx/du)^2 + (dy/du)^2 + (dz/du)^2}},$$

$$\frac{dy}{ds} = \frac{dy/du}{\sqrt{(dx/du)^2 + (dy/du)^2 + (dz/du)^2}},$$

$$\frac{dz}{ds} = \frac{dz/du}{\sqrt{(dx/du)^2 + (dy/du)^2 + (dz/du)^2}},$$

so that

$$\lim_{\Delta s \to 0} \frac{\|\overrightarrow{PQ}\|^2}{\widehat{PQ}^2} = \frac{(dx/du)^2 + (dy/du)^2 + (dz/du)^2}{(dx/du)^2 + (dy/du)^2 + (dz/du)^2} = 1.$$

We have here an expression for the unit tangent vector at any point of the helix. At the point $u = 0$, for instance,

$$\mathbf{\vec{t}} = \frac{4}{\sqrt{65}}\left(2\mathbf{\vec{j}} + \frac{1}{4}\mathbf{\vec{k}}\right)$$

has no $\mathbf{\vec{i}}$ component. This seems reasonable when we locate the point for which $u = 0$ in Fig. 10.44. The reader can also check the fact that $\mathbf{\vec{t}} \cdot \mathbf{\vec{t}} = 1$; $\mathbf{\vec{t}}$ is a unit vector as Theorem 2 predicts.

The next theorem is a corollary of Theorem 2.

■ THEOREM 3

On tangent vectors to curves.

HYPOTHESIS: Curve C is described by the equation $\mathbf{\vec{R}} = x\mathbf{\vec{i}} + y\mathbf{\vec{j}} + z\mathbf{\vec{k}}$, where x, y, and z are differentiable functions of a parameter u for u of $a \leq u \leq b$.

CONCLUSION: For any u of $a \leq u \leq b$ such that dx/du, dy/du, dz/du are not all 0, $d\mathbf{\vec{R}}/du$ is a vector in the tangent direction.

PROOF: From Eq. (8) we see that ds/du will not vanish at a point where dx/du, dy/du, dz/du do not all vanish. Then we can form $du/ds = 1/(ds/du)$ and write

$$\mathbf{\vec{t}} = \frac{d\mathbf{\vec{R}}}{ds} = \frac{d\mathbf{\vec{R}}}{du}\frac{du}{ds},$$

which says that the vectors $d\mathbf{\vec{R}}/ds$ and $d\mathbf{\vec{R}}/du$ are parallel, since it says that one is a scalar multiple of the other.

● Remark 2

We found it convenient to introduce the vectors $d\mathbf{\vec{R}}/ds$ and $d\mathbf{\vec{R}}/du$. These are special instances of a more general process of differentiating vector functions of scalar variables.

■ DEFINITION 2

Let $\mathbf{\vec{V}} = f(u)\mathbf{\vec{i}} + g(u)\mathbf{\vec{j}} + h(u)\mathbf{\vec{k}}$ for u of domain D. Let $f'(u)$, $g'(u)$, $h'(u)$ be defined for u of D. Then for each u of D,

$$\frac{d\mathbf{\vec{V}}}{du} = f'(u)\mathbf{\vec{i}} + g'(u)\mathbf{\vec{j}} + h'(u)\mathbf{\vec{k}}.$$

The reader can show in Exercise 10.7-13 that many of the results of the calculus of scalar functions are valid for derivatives of vector functions also. Thus

$$\frac{d(\mathbf{\vec{v}} + \mathbf{\vec{w}})}{du} = \frac{d\mathbf{\vec{v}}}{du} + \frac{d\mathbf{\vec{w}}}{du}$$

$$\frac{d(\phi(u)\mathbf{\vec{v}})}{du} = \phi(u)\frac{d\mathbf{\vec{v}}}{du} + \phi'(u)\mathbf{\vec{v}}$$

$$\frac{d(\vec{v} \cdot \vec{w})}{du} = \vec{v} \cdot \frac{d\vec{w}}{du} + \frac{d\vec{v}}{du} \cdot \vec{w}$$

$$\frac{d(\vec{v} \times \vec{w})}{du} = \vec{v} \times \frac{d\vec{w}}{du} + \frac{d\vec{v}}{du} \times \vec{w}.$$

III

When the curve is described in terms of its arc length as the parameter we have considered $\vec{R}(s)$ and $d\vec{R}/ds = \vec{t}(s)$. It seems natural to form $d\vec{t}/ds$ next and to inquire about its properties. Because $\vec{t}$ is a unit vector, we know that $\vec{t} \cdot \vec{t} = 1$, and if we differentiate with respect to s we compute

$$\vec{t} \cdot \frac{d\vec{t}}{ds} + \frac{d\vec{t}}{ds} \cdot \vec{t} = 0, \qquad 2\vec{t} \cdot \frac{d\vec{t}}{ds} = 0, \qquad \vec{t} \cdot \frac{d\vec{t}}{ds} = 0.$$

The last equation says that either $d\vec{t}/ds = \vec{0}$ or the vectors $d\vec{t}/ds$ and $\vec{t}$ are perpendicular. If we choose a unit vector in the direction of $d\vec{t}/ds$ and call it $\vec{n}$, we can write

$$\frac{d\vec{t}}{ds} = K\vec{n}. \tag{11}$$

■ DEFINITION 2

The principal normal vector. The unit vector in the direction of $d\vec{t}/ds$ is the principal normal vector, $\vec{n}$.

■ DEFINITION 3

The curvature. The magnitude of $d\vec{t}/ds$ is the curvature of the curve, K.

Example 5.   We continue our discussion of the helix of Examples 2, 3, 4. We already know that

$$\vec{t} = \frac{4}{\sqrt{65}} (-2 \sin u \vec{i} + 2 \cos u \vec{j} + \tfrac{1}{4} \vec{k})$$

and that $du/ds = 4/\sqrt{65}$. Hence

$$\frac{d\vec{t}}{du} = \frac{4}{\sqrt{65}} (-2 \cos u \vec{i} - 2 \sin u \vec{j}) = +\frac{8}{\sqrt{65}} (-\cos u \vec{i} - \sin u \vec{j})$$

and

$$K\vec{n} = \frac{d\vec{t}}{ds} = \frac{d\vec{t}}{du} \frac{du}{ds} = \frac{32}{65} (-\cos u \vec{i} - \sin u \vec{j}).$$

Since $-\cos u \vec{i} - \sin u \vec{j}$ is a unit vector, we have

$$\vec{n} = -\cos u \vec{i} - \sin u \vec{j} \qquad \text{and} \qquad K = \tfrac{32}{65}.$$

Observe that

$$\vec{n} \cdot \vec{t} = \frac{4}{\sqrt{65}} (2 \sin u \cos u - 2 \sin u \cos u) = 0;$$

$\vec{n}$ and $\vec{t}$ are perpendicular, as expected.

We first defined curvature for plane curves in Chapter 8. Of course, we want to be sure that that definition and the one given here agree when both are applied to a plane curve; this question is investigated in Exercise 10.7-9.

● **Remark 3**

We shall not carry our investigation of curves in space further, although many interesting questions remain. When studying plane curves we mentioned the fact that a plane curve was determined, except for its location in the plane, when its curvature was given as a function of its arc length. Is a curve in space determined completely by its curvature as a function of arc length, or must other invariants also be studied in order to complete the theory? In differential geometry we learn that there is a second essential invariant, called the *torsion*, and that a curve in space is determined by its curvature and torsion as functions of arc length. For a plane curve the torsion is always 0.

● **Remark 4**

The portion of the theory of space curves that we have developed is of considerable importance in mechanics. Let the path of a particle be given by parametric equations for x, y and z in terms of the time t, and let $\vec{R} = x\vec{i} + y\vec{j} + z\vec{k}$. Then

$$\frac{d\vec{R}}{dt} = \frac{d\vec{R}}{ds}\frac{ds}{dt} = \frac{ds}{dt}\vec{t}.$$

The vector $d\vec{R}/dt$ has the tangential direction and the magnitude ds/dt, the rate of change of the distance moved along the curve. Hence $d\vec{R}/dt$ is the velocity vector, $\vec{v}$. Using a product rule, then a chain rule, and, finally, Eq. (11), we obtain

$$\frac{d\vec{v}}{dt} = \frac{d^2\vec{R}}{dt^2} = \frac{d^2s}{dt^2}\vec{t} + \frac{ds}{dt}\frac{d\vec{t}}{dt} = \frac{d^2s}{dt^2}\vec{t} + \frac{ds}{dt}\left(\frac{d\vec{t}}{ds}\frac{ds}{dt}\right),$$

$$\vec{A} = \frac{d\vec{v}}{dt} = \frac{d^2s}{dt^2}\vec{t} + \left(\frac{ds}{dt}\right)^2 K\vec{n}. \tag{12}$$

If we accept $d\vec{v}/dt$ as the acceleration vector, Eq. (12) can be interpreted as a statement for the acceleration vector in terms of its tangential and normal components. The normal component is in the direction of the principal normal vector and its magnitude is Kv^2. For the special case of a particle traveling in a circular path of radius a, we have $K = 1/a$, and the normal component magnitude is v^2/a.

EXERCISES 10.7

1. Consider the circular helix: $x = \cos u$, $y = \sin u$, $z = \frac{1}{3}u$.
   (a) Show that the helix lies on the cylinder $x^2 + y^2 = 1$ and sketch that portion of it for which $0 \le u \le 2\pi$.
   At each point, find
   (b) the unit tangent vector,   (d) the principal normal vector.
   (c) the curvature,   (e) Find the length of the arc $0 \le u \le 2\pi$.
2. Consider the twisted cubic: $x = u$, $y = u^2$, $z = u^3$.
   (a) Show that the curve lies on the cylinder $y = x^2$ and sketch that portion of it for which $0 \le u \le 2$.
   (b) Find a tangent vector at each point.
   (c) Find the equations of the tangent line at $u = 1$.

3. Consider the curve $x = u$, $y = 2u$, $z = \frac{2}{3} u^{3/2}$. At each point, find
   (a) the unit tangent vector,
   (c) the principal normal vector.
   (b) the curvature,
   (d) Find the length of the arc $0 \leq u \leq 4$.
   (e) This curve is a plane curve. In which plane does it lie?

4. Consider the curve $x = u - \frac{1}{3} u^3$, $y = u^2$, $z = u + \frac{1}{3} u^3$. At each point, find
   (a) the unit tangent vector,
   (c) the principal normal vector.
   (b) the curvature,
   (d) Find the length of the arc $0 \leq u \leq 1$.

5. Consider the curve $x = a \sin u$, $y = a \cos u$, $z = a \log \cos u$. At each point, find
   (a) the unit tangent vector,
   (c) the principal normal vector.
   (b) the curvature,
   (d) Find the length of the arc $0 \leq u \leq \pi/3$.

6. Consider the curve $x = 2u + \dfrac{\sqrt{8}}{3} u^{3/2}$, $y = u - \dfrac{\sqrt{32}}{3} u^{3/2}$, $z = \dfrac{u^2}{2} - 2u$.

   At the point for which $u = 1$, find
   (a) the unit tangent vector,
   (c) the principal normal vector.
   (b) the curvature,
   (d) Find the length of the arc $1 \leq u \leq 2$.

7. Show that the unit tangent vector to the helix $x = a \cos u$, $y = a \sin u$, $z = bu$ always makes the same angle with the z axis direction. (For this reason we sometimes say that the helix rises at a constant rate as it travels around the cylinder.)

8. Show that at each point P of the helix $x = a \cos u$, $y = a \sin u$, $z = bu$ the principal normal vector has the direction of the line drawn perpendicular to the z axis from P.

9. The plane curve $y = f(x)$ can be described as a curve in space by the parametric equations $x = u$, $y = f(u)$, $z = 0$. Show that

   (a) $\dfrac{du}{ds} = \dfrac{1}{\sqrt{1 + f'^2}}$,

   (c) $\dfrac{d\mathbf{t}}{ds} = \dfrac{f''}{(1 + [f']^2)^{3/2}} \dfrac{-f'\,\mathbf{i} + \mathbf{j}}{\sqrt{1 + [f']^2}}$,

   (b) $\mathbf{t} = \dfrac{1}{\sqrt{1 + f'^2}}(\mathbf{i} + f'\mathbf{j})$,

   (d) $K = \left\| \dfrac{d\mathbf{t}}{ds} \right\| = \dfrac{|f''|}{(1 + [f']^2)^{3/2}}$.

10. Show that the acceleration of a particle moving with constant speed is always in the principal normal direction, and conversely.

11. Show that the magnitude of the acceleration of a particle moving in a curved path is given by $\sqrt{\left(\dfrac{d^2s}{dt^2}\right)^2 + K^2 \left(\dfrac{ds}{dt}\right)^4}$.

12. Consider Example 1. Let $P_0(x_0, y_0, z_0)$ be a point of L. For which choice of the parameter u will Eqs. (2) give us P_0?

13. Let $\vec{v} = f_1(u)\mathbf{i} + f_2(u)\mathbf{j} + f_3(u)\mathbf{k}$ and let $\vec{w} = g_1(u)\mathbf{i} + g_2(u)\mathbf{j} + g_3(u)\mathbf{k}$. Show that

   (a) $\dfrac{d}{du}(\vec{v} + \vec{w}) = \dfrac{d\vec{v}}{du} + \dfrac{d\vec{w}}{du}$.

   (b) $\dfrac{d}{du}(\phi(u)\vec{v}) = \phi(u)\dfrac{d\vec{v}}{du} + \phi'(u)\vec{v}$.

   (c) $\dfrac{d}{du}(\vec{v} \cdot \vec{w}) = \vec{v} \cdot \dfrac{d\vec{w}}{du} + \dfrac{d\vec{v}}{du} \cdot \vec{w}$.

   (d) $\dfrac{d}{du}(\vec{v} \times \vec{w}) = \vec{v} \times \dfrac{d\vec{w}}{du} + \dfrac{d\vec{v}}{du} \times \vec{w}$.

14. In the proof of Theorem 1, carry out in detail the proof of the fact that from Eq. (5) we may conclude Eq. (6). *Suggestion:* Modify the work of Theorem 8.8-3.

Partial Differentiation

11.1 Definition of Partial Derivative. Geometric Interpretation

There are many cases in which we wish to assign a number z to each ordered pair of numbers x, y selected from a domain set of ordered number pairs. When considering some gas in a cylinder, for instance, the physicist can assign a pressure number P to each suitable pair of volume and temperature numbers V, T.

■ DEFINITION 1

Function of two variables. Domain. Range. Given a set of ordered number pairs, called the *domain D*, and instructions for associating a number z with each number pair x, y of D. The set of all numbers z associated with number pairs x, y of D is called the *range R*. The correspondence between D and R is called a *function*.

■ NOTATION CONVENTION 1

Let x, y be an ordered number pair in the domain of function f. Then $f(x, y)$ shall be the number associated with x, y by f.

● Remark 1

The coordinates of a point in the Cartesian plane (x, y) constitute a very familiar ordered pair. We shall often use the phrase "point with coordinates (x, y)" or "point (x, y)" instead of "ordered pair x, y" where it seems natural to do so.

Example 1. If we write

$$z = c\sqrt{1 - \frac{x^2}{a^2} - \frac{y^2}{b^2}}, \qquad \frac{x^2}{a^2} + \frac{y^2}{b^2} \le 1,$$

603

we have furnished instructions for associating a number z with each point (x, y) of the domain D of points inside or on the ellipse $x^2/a^2 + y^2/b^2 = 1$. With the point $(0, 0)$ of D we associate the number $z = c$; with the point $(a, 0)$ of D we associate the number $z = 0$. A drawing of the upper half of the ellipsoid $x^2/a^2 + y^2/b^2 + z^2/c^2 = 1$ is actually a geometric description of this function.

It happens in this example that the instructions are given in one formula, but of course this need not always be the case. It is necessary only that instructions be furnished for each point of the domain D. There is no specification as to how the instructions shall be furnished.

● **Remark 2**

We have similar definitions for functions of three or more variables. If for every instant t of a certain time interval we describe the temperature T at every point (x, y, z) of a certain region of space, we have assigned a T number to each ordered quadruple x, y, z, t of a certain domain of suitable quadruples. We might write $T = f(x, y, z, t)$.

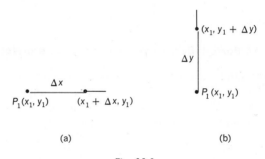

(a)   (b)

Fig. 11.1

Consider now a function of two variables, $u = f(x, y)$, at a point $P_1(x_1, y_1)$ of its domain. We can move from P_1 in many directions, thus causing different changes in u in general. We shall consider in this section those changes in u arising with movement from P_1 in the x direction, with y fixed, as in Fig. 11.1(a) or from P_1 in the y direction, with x fixed, as in Fig. 11.1(b). In these special cases, where we allow only one variable to change at a time, we are really discussing functions of one variable, and the work we have already done on rates of change can be applied.

■ **DEFINITION 2**

The partial derivatives.   We are given $u = f(x, y)$ defined over a domain D in the xy plane. At $P_1(x_1, y_1)$ of D let y be held fixed at $y = y_1$ and consider $u = f(x, y_1)$ as a function of x alone. If the derivative of this function with respect to x exists at $x = x_1$, we call it the partial derivative of u with respect to x and write $(\partial u/\partial x)_{P_1}$ or $f_1(x_1, y_1)$ for this number. Similarly, considering $f(x_1, y)$ as a function of y alone, if the derivative of this function with respect to y exists at $y = y_1$, we call it the partial derivative of u with respect to y and write $(\partial u/\partial y)_{P_1}$ or $f_2(x_1, y_1)$ for this number.

By going back to the definition of the derivative of a function of one variable, we can rewrite these definitions more concisely.

■ **DEFINITION 2A**

The partial derivatives. Let $u = f(x, y)$ be defined over a domain D in the xy plane. At $P_1(x_1, y_1)$ of D we write

$$\left(\frac{\partial u}{\partial x}\right)_{P_1} = f_1(x_1, y_1) = \lim_{\Delta x \to 0} \frac{f(x_1 + \Delta x, y_1) - f(x_1, y_1)}{\Delta x},$$

$$\left(\frac{\partial u}{\partial y}\right)_{P_1} = f_2(x_1, y_1) = \lim_{\Delta y \to 0} \frac{f(x_1, y_1 + \Delta y) - f(x_1, y_1)}{\Delta y},$$

if these limits exist.

Example 2. Consider $u = f(x, y) = xy^2 + x^3 y^3$. To find $\partial u/\partial x = f_1(x, y)$, we treat y as if it were a constant and differentiate with respect to x. We can write

$$\frac{\partial u}{\partial x} = y^2(1) + y^3(3x^2) = y^2 + 3x^2 y^3.$$

Similarly, to find $\partial u/\partial y = f_2(x, y)$, we treat x as if it were a constant and differentiate with respect to y. We can write

$$\frac{\partial u}{\partial y} = f_2(x, y) = x(2y) + x^3(3y^2) = 2xy + 3x^3 y^2.$$

Example 3. Consider again the function

$$z = f(x, y) = c\sqrt{1 - \frac{x^2}{a^2} - \frac{y^2}{b^2}}$$

defined over the domain D of points inside and on the ellipse $x^2/a^2 + y^2/b^2 = 1$. If we hold y fixed and let x alone vary, our differentiation rules tell us that

$$f_1(x, y) = \frac{\partial z}{\partial x} = c\frac{1}{2}\left(1 - \frac{x^2}{a^2} - \frac{y^2}{b^2}\right)^{-1/2}\left(-\frac{1}{a^2}2x\right)$$

$$= -\frac{cx}{a^2\sqrt{1 - x^2/a^2 - y^2/b^2}} = -\frac{c^2}{a^2}\frac{x}{z}, \qquad z \neq 0.$$

In particular, $f_1(0, 0) = 0$ and

$$\left(\frac{\partial z}{\partial x}\right)_{(a/2, b/2)} = -\frac{c(a/2)}{a^2\sqrt{1 - 1/4 - 1/4}} = -\frac{c}{a\sqrt{2}}.$$

On the other hand, if we hold x fixed and let y alone vary, we have

$$f_2(x, y) = \frac{\partial z}{\partial y} = c\frac{1}{2}\left(1 - \frac{x^2}{a^2} - \frac{y^2}{b^2}\right)^{-1/2}\left(-\frac{1}{b^2}2y\right)$$

$$= -\frac{cy}{b^2\sqrt{1 - x^2/a^2 - y^2/b^2}} = -\frac{c^2}{b^2}\frac{y}{z}, \qquad z \neq 0.$$

We can also work implicitly. Consider z to be a function of x and y that satisfies

$$\frac{x^2}{a^2} + \frac{y^2}{b^2} + \frac{z^2}{c^2} = 1$$

identically for (x, y) of the domain D mentioned above. If we differentiate both members of this identity in x and y with respect to x, regarding y as a constant, we have

$$\frac{1}{a^2} 2x + 0 + \frac{1}{c^2} 2z \frac{\partial z}{\partial x} = 0, \quad \text{or} \quad \frac{\partial z}{\partial x} = -\frac{c^2}{a^2} \frac{x}{z}, \quad z \neq 0.$$

Similarly, if we differentiate with respect to y, regarding x as a constant, we have

$$0 + \frac{1}{b^2} 2y + \frac{1}{c^2} 2z \frac{\partial z}{\partial y} = 0, \quad \text{or} \quad \frac{\partial z}{\partial y} = -\frac{c^2}{b^2} \frac{y}{z}, \quad z \neq 0.$$

Example 4.   Let coordinate axes be chosen so that a rectangular membrane of dimensions a and b is described as in Fig. 11.2. Under certain conditions the membrane will vibrate in such a way that u, the vertical displacement from equilibrium at the point (x, y) at time t, is given by

$$u(x, y, t) = \cos \omega t \sin \frac{\pi x}{a} \sin \frac{\pi y}{b}.$$

Observe that the membrane is fixed along its edges, for $u = 0$ for all t when $x = 0$, when $x = a$, when $y = 0$, or when $y = b$. The displacement is greatest at $(a/2, b/2)$; there we have $u = \cos \omega t(1)(1) = \cos \omega t$.

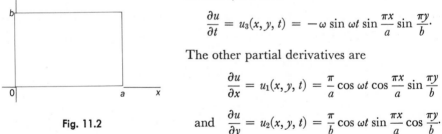

To get the velocity of the particle at (x, y) at time t, we take

$$\frac{\partial u}{\partial t} = u_3(x, y, t) = -\omega \sin \omega t \sin \frac{\pi x}{a} \sin \frac{\pi y}{b}.$$

The other partial derivatives are

$$\frac{\partial u}{\partial x} = u_1(x, y, t) = \frac{\pi}{a} \cos \omega t \cos \frac{\pi x}{a} \sin \frac{\pi y}{b}$$

Fig. 11.2

and $\quad \dfrac{\partial u}{\partial y} = u_2(x, y, t) = \dfrac{\pi}{b} \cos \omega t \sin \dfrac{\pi x}{a} \cos \dfrac{\pi y}{b}.$

For $u = f(x, y)$ defined over a domain D the partial derivatives $\partial u/\partial x$ and $\partial u/\partial y$ at x, y of D can be given a simple geometric interpretation. Let $u = f(x,y)$ represent a surface S sketched on x, y, and u axes, and let $P_1(x_1, y_1, u_1)$ be a point on S. The section of S by the plane $y = y_1$ is a curve C through P_1 that satisfies the equation $u = f(x, y_1)$; see Fig. 11.3(a). With movement from P_1 along C, y stays fixed at y_1; x alone varies. The slope of C at P_1 is $(\partial u/\partial x)_{P_1} = f_1(x_1, y_1)$; this partial derivative is the rate of change of height with respect to the horizontal displacement for C. Similarly, $(\partial u/\partial y)_{P_1} = f_2(x_1, y_1)$ is the slope at P_1 of the section of S by the plane $x = x_1$; see Fig. 11.3(b).

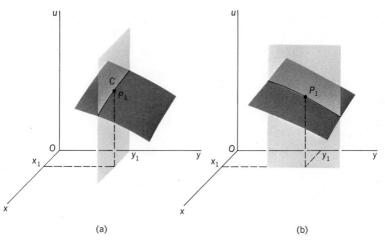

Fig. 11.3

Example 5.   Consider again

$$z = c\sqrt{1 - \frac{x^2}{a^2} - \frac{y^2}{b^2}}, \qquad \frac{x^2}{a^2} + \frac{y^2}{b^2} \le 1,$$

for which $\dfrac{\partial z}{\partial x} = -\dfrac{c^2}{a^2}\dfrac{x}{z}$ and $\dfrac{\partial z}{\partial y} = -\dfrac{c^2}{b^2}\dfrac{y}{z},$ $z \ne 0.$

We hold y fixed while forming $\partial z/\partial x$; $\partial z/\partial x$ gives us the slopes of sections by planes $y = \text{const}$. In Fig. 11.4(a) we have sketched the portion of $z = f(x, y)$ for which $x \ge 0$ and $y \ge 0$ and we have also sketched the section by the plane $y = b/2$. The slope of this curve at $P_1(a/2, b/2, c/\sqrt{2})$ is

$$\left(\frac{\partial z}{\partial x}\right)_{P_1} = -\frac{c}{\sqrt{2}\,a}.$$

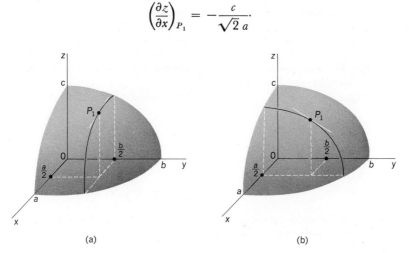

(a)   (b)

Fig. 11.4

We hold x fixed while forming $\partial z/\partial y$; $\partial z/\partial y$ gives us the slopes of sections by planes $x =$ const. In Fig. 11.4(b) we have sketched the section by the plane $x = a/2$. The slope of this curve at $P_1(a/2,\ b/2,\ c/\sqrt{2})$ is

$$\left(\frac{\partial z}{\partial y}\right)_{P_1} = -\frac{c}{\sqrt{2}\,b}.$$

EXERCISES 11.1

1. $u = f(x, y) = (x + 2y)^3$. Find $\dfrac{\partial u}{\partial x}, \dfrac{\partial u}{\partial y}, f_1(1, 0), f_2(a, b)$.

2. $v = f(x, y) = \dfrac{x + y}{x - y}, x \neq y$. Find $\dfrac{\partial v}{\partial x}, \dfrac{\partial v}{\partial y}, f_1(3, 4)$, points (x, y) for which $f_2(x, y) = 0$.

3. $u = e^{2z}\sqrt{x^2 + y^2}$. Find $\dfrac{\partial u}{\partial x}, \dfrac{\partial u}{\partial y}, \dfrac{\partial u}{\partial z}$.

4. $L = f(r, \theta) = \sinh 2r \cos \theta$. Find $\dfrac{\partial L}{\partial r}, \dfrac{\partial L}{\partial \theta}, f_1(0, 0), f_2\left(1, \dfrac{\pi}{2}\right)$.

5. $T = \phi(x, y, z) = \log(x^2 + y^2 + z^2)$, $(x, y, z) \neq (0, 0, 0)$. Find $\dfrac{\partial T}{\partial x}, \dfrac{\partial T}{\partial y}, \dfrac{\partial T}{\partial z}$, $\phi_3(2, 1, -1)$.

6. $x = f(u, v) = e^{-(u^2+v^2)}$. Find $f_1(u, v), f_2(u, v)$, point (u, v) for which $f_1(u, v) = f_2(u, v) = 0$.

7. $u = \sin \dfrac{2\pi}{a} x \sin \dfrac{2\pi}{b} y\, e^{-.1t} \cos \pi t$. Find $\dfrac{\partial u}{\partial x}, \dfrac{\partial u}{\partial y}, \dfrac{\partial u}{\partial t}$, and the points of the region $0 \leq x \leq a, 0 \leq y \leq b$ for which $u = 0$ for all t.

8. $z = f(x, y) = \tan^{-1}\dfrac{y}{x}, x \neq 0$. Find $\dfrac{\partial z}{\partial x}, \dfrac{\partial z}{\partial y}, f_1(1, 0), f_2(3, 2)$.

9. $u = \cos(x + ct) + \cos(x - ct)$, c a constant. Find $\partial u/\partial x, \partial u/\partial t$.

10. Consider z defined implicitly as a function of x and y by the equation $(2x + y + z)^2 + xyz = 17$. Find $\partial z/\partial x$ and $\partial z/\partial y$ and evaluate for $x = 1, y = 1, z = 1$.

11. (a) Consider z defined implicitly as a function of x and y by the equation $(x^2 - y - 2z)^2 + xy^2z^2 = 9$. Find $\partial z/\partial x$ and $\partial z/\partial y$ and evaluate for $x = 1, y = 0, z = 2$.

(b) Consider x defined implicitly as a function of y and z. Find $\partial x/\partial y$ and $\partial x/\partial z$ and evaluate for $x = 1, y = 0, z = 2$.

12. Show that $u = 3x + \frac{1}{3} y$ is a solution of the partial differential equation

$$x\left(\frac{\partial u}{\partial x}\right)^2 - u\frac{\partial u}{\partial x} + y = 0.$$

13. Show that $z = 7x - \dfrac{y^3}{x^2}, x \neq 0$, is a solution of the partial differential equation

$$x\frac{\partial z}{\partial x} + y\frac{\partial z}{\partial y} = z.$$

14. Show that the function z defined implicitly by $x^2 + y^2 + z^2 = x + y + z$ is a solution of the partial differential equation

$$(y - z)\frac{\partial z}{\partial x} + (z - x)\frac{\partial z}{\partial y} = x - y.$$

15. Find the slope at $(4, 1, 17)$ of the section of $z = x^2 + y^2$ by the plane $x = 4$.

16. Find the slope at $\left(\dfrac{\pi}{2}, \dfrac{\pi}{4}, \dfrac{\sqrt{2}}{2}\right)$ of the section of $z = \sin(x - y)$ by the plane $y = \pi/4$.

17. Find the slope at $(1, 1, 1)$ of the section of $x^3 + x^2 y + y^2 z + z^3 = 4$ by the plane $y = 1$.

18. Consider $u = f(x, y) = \begin{cases} x^2, & x \geq 0 \\ 0, & x < 0 \end{cases}$. Find $f_1(0, 0)$ and $f_2(0, 0)$, if they exist.

19. Find the approximate change in $u = x^3 + xy^2$
   (a) if one moves from $(2, 1)$ to $(2.1, 1)$;
   (b) if one moves from $(2, 1)$ to $(2, 1.1)$.

20. Find the approximate change in the volume of a cylinder if the height is fixed at 20 cm, while the radius of the base changes from 10 cm to 9.97 cm.

21. Consider that portion of the section of $z = x^2 + y^2$ by the plane $y = 1$ which is bounded by the points $A(0, 1, 1)$ and $B(2, 1, 5)$. Find a point on this arc at which the tangent line is parallel to the chord AB.

22. Consider that portion of the section of $z = x^2/y^2$ by the plane $x = 2$ which is bounded by $A(2, 2, 1)$ and $B(2, 3, \frac{4}{9})$. Find a point on this arc at which the tangent line is parallel to the chord AB.

11.2   The Total Differential

I

In the preceding section we considered special changes in $u = f(x, y)$ corresponding to changes in x alone or to changes in y alone. In this section we shall consider more general changes in u arising when both x and y change. We shall start by explaining what we mean by the statements

$$\lim_{(x,y) \to (a,b)} f(x, y) = L$$

and $\qquad\qquad\qquad f(x, y)$ is continuous at (a, b),

and then we shall show how to express general changes in u in terms of the special changes that arise when only one variable changes at a time.

The equation $\lim_{(x,y) \to (a,b)} f(x, y) = L$ attempts to convey some information about the values of $f(x, y)$ near the point (a, b). We may or may not know the value of $f(x, y)$ at (a, b), but we do mean that when (x, y) is "close" to (a, b), $f(x, y)$ is close to L and the "closer" (x, y) is to (a, b), the closer $f(x, y)$ is to L. Of course we must make precise the meaning of the word *close* and this we shall do as we did in Sec. 7.1. To say that $f(x, y)$ comes "closer and closer" to L or "approaches" L is equivalent to saying that $|f(x, y) - L|$ approaches 0, and this in turn means that $|f(x, y) - L|$ shall become, and remain, less than any challenge number that may be specified, no matter how small. Thus, if by a neighborhood of (a, b) we mean the interior of a circle with center at (a, b) and positive radius δ, we state our definition as follows:

■ **DEFINITION 1**

$$\lim_{(x,y)\to(a,b)} f(x, y) = L$$

if for every positive challenge number ϵ, no matter how small, there is a neighborhood N of (a, b) such that $|f(x, y) - L| < \epsilon$ for every (x, y) of N except perhaps for (a, b) itself.

● **Remark 1**

Note that in this definition of $\lim_{(x,y)\to(a,b)} f(x, y) = L$ the number $f(a, b)$ may or may not exist, and that if it does exist, we may or may not have $f(a, b) = L$. Note also that the size of the neighborhood N, that is, the radius δ of the circle, will depend on the size of the challenge number ϵ. A sterner challenge will be met by the points of a smaller circle.

● **Remark 2**

If $\lim_{(x,y)\to(a,b)} f(x, y) = L$, then we have $|f(x, y) - L| < \epsilon$ for all points of a neighborhood of (a, b) other than (a, b). There are many point sequences within the neighborhood that approach (a, b). If $f(x, y)$ is evaluated along these sequences, then, in each case, the difference between $f(x, y)$ and L will become, and remain, less than ϵ. If we get different limits when considering the function values assigned by $g(x, y)$ along two different point sequences that approach (a, b), then $\lim_{(x,y)\to(a,b)} g(x, y)$ does not exist.

Example 1. Consider $f(x, y) = xy^2$. We know that $f(1, 2) = 4$, and it is natural to ask whether $\lim_{(x,y)\to(1,2)} f(x, y) = 4$. If the answer is to be "yes," then when an $\epsilon > 0$ is specified, no matter how small, we must furnish a neighborhood of $(1, 2)$ for all of whose points, except perhaps $(1, 2)$ itself, we shall have

$$|xy^2 - 4| < \epsilon.$$

In order to see which neighborhood of $(1, 2)$ to specify, we study $xy^2 - 4$. We have

$$xy^2 - 4 = xy^2 - y^2 + y^2 - 4 = y^2(x - 1) + (y + 2)(y - 2),$$

$$|xy^2 - 4| \le |y|^2|x - 1| + |y + 2|\,|y - 2|.^*$$

Now the neighborhood can be specified. Let N_1 be the neighborhood of $(1, 2)$ of radius 1; see Fig. 11.5. For any point (x, y) of N_1 we can say that $1 < y < 3$, and adding 2 to each member, that $3 < y + 2 < 5$, so that $|y| < 3$, $|y + 2| < 5$ and

$$|xy^2 - 4| < 9|x - 1| + 5|y - 2|.$$

This suggests that we choose N_2 to be the neighborhood of $(1, 2)$ of radius $\epsilon/14$. For any point of N_2 we shall have

$$|x - 1| < \frac{\epsilon}{14}, \qquad |y - 2| < \frac{\epsilon}{14}.$$

---

* The absolute value of a sum of two terms is less than or equal to the sum of the absolute values of the terms: $|A + B| \le |A| + |B|$. The absolute value of a product is the product of the absolute values: $|AB| = |A|\,|B|$.

Hence, if N is the smaller of N_1 and N_2, for any point of N we shall have

$$|xy^2 - 4| < 9|x - 1| + 5|y - 2| < 9\frac{\epsilon}{14} + 5\frac{\epsilon}{14} = \epsilon.$$

This shows that $\lim_{(x,y)\to(1,2)} f(x, y) = 4$.

Example 2. Consider

$$f(x, y) = \frac{x^2}{x^2 + y^2}.$$

The function $f(x, y)$ is not defined at $(0, 0)$, but does $\lim_{(x,y)\to(0,0)} f(x, y)$ exist?

If we let (x, y) approach $(0, 0)$ via the x axis, $y = 0$, we must consider

$$\lim_{x\to 0} f(x, 0) = \lim_{x\to 0} \frac{x^2}{x^2 + 0} = \lim_{x\to 0} 1 = 1.$$

But if we let (x, y) approach $(0, 0)$ via the line $y = x$, we must consider

$$\lim_{x\to 0} f(x, x) = \lim_{x\to 0} \frac{x^2}{x^2 + x^2} = \lim_{x\to 0} \frac{1}{2} = \frac{1}{2}.$$

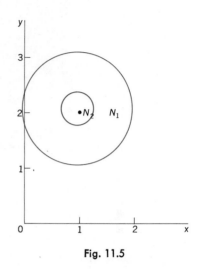

Fig. 11.5

The $\lim_{(x,y)\to(0,0)} f(x, y)$ does not exist, because the number approached by $f(x, y)$ as (x, y) approaches $(0, 0)$ depends on the path used.

The definition of continuity is now stated in terms of our definition of limit, just as it was when we considered functions of one variable.

■ DEFINITION 2

Continuity. The function $f(x, y)$ is continuous at (a, b) if, first, $f(a, b)$ exists and, second, if $\lim_{(x,y)\to(a,b)} f(x, y) = f(a, b)$.

This definition requires that at all points near (a, b) f shall assign values that are close to the value it assigns at (a, b).

Example 3. Our work with $f(x, y) = xy^2$ in Example 1 shows that $f(x, y) = xy^2$ is continuous at $(1, 2)$, because $f(1, 2) = 4$ and $\lim_{(x,y)\to(1,2)} f(x, y) = 4$. But our work with $f(x, y) = x^2/(x^2 + y^2)$ in Example 2 shows that even if we were to complete the definition of $f(x, y) = x^2/(x^2 + y^2)$ by choosing a value for f at $(0, 0)$ we could not specify this value in such a way as to make $f(x, y)$ continuous at $(0, 0)$. The number $\lim_{(x,y)\to(0,0)} f(x, y)$ does not exist, and the question of whether it equals $f(0, 0)$ does not arise.

||

Let $u = f(x, y)$ for (x, y) of domain D, let us choose Δx and Δy such that the rectangle with vertices (x, y), $(x, y + \Delta y)$, $(x + \Delta x, y)$, $(x + \Delta x, y + \Delta y)$ lies en-

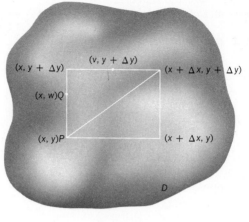

Fig. 11.6

tirely in D, as in Fig. 11.6, and let us inquire about the increment in u in a case where x and y both change. We can write

$$\Delta u = f(x + \Delta x, y + \Delta y) - f(x, y). \tag{1}$$

Since we know more about the special cases where one variable changes at a time, we rewrite Eq. (1) in the form

$$\Delta u = [f(x + \Delta x, y + \Delta y) - f(x, y + \Delta y)] + [f(x, y + \Delta y) - f(x, y)] \tag{2}$$

by adding and subtracting the number $f(x, y + \Delta y)$. Consider now the second bracket, where we ask for $f(x, y + \Delta y) - f(x, y)$, the increase in f if we keep x fixed but change y to $y + \Delta y$. If f is such that f_2 exists in D, then the Theorem of Mean Value tells us that there exists a point (x, w), w between y and $y + \Delta y$, such that

$$f(x, y + \Delta y) - f(x, y) = f_2(x, w)\Delta y.$$

Similarly, if f_1 exists in D, there exists a point $(v, y + \Delta y)$, v between x and $x + \Delta x$, such that

$$f(x + \Delta x, y + \Delta y) - f(x, y + \Delta y) = f_1(v, y + \Delta y)\Delta x.$$

Then $$\Delta u = f_1(v, y + \Delta y)\Delta x + f_2(x, w)\,\Delta y. \tag{3}$$

If in addition to requiring that f_1 and f_2 shall exist in D we require that they shall be continuous, then the difference between the values of f_2 at $P(x, y)$ and at $Q(x, w)$ can be made as small as desired by bringing Q close enough to P. We can say that

$$f_2(x, w) = f_2(x, y) + \epsilon_2,$$

where ϵ_2 approaches 0 as Δy approaches 0. Similarly, we can say that

$$f_1(v, y + \Delta y) = f_1(x, y) + \epsilon_1,$$

where ϵ_1 approaches 0 as Δx and Δy approach 0. Thus we arrive at

$$\Delta u = f_1(x, y)\,\Delta x + f_2(x, y)\,\Delta y + \epsilon_1\,\Delta x + \epsilon_2\,\Delta y, \tag{4}$$

where ϵ_1 and ϵ_2 approach 0 as Δx and Δy approach 0. To recapitulate, we have proved the following theorem.

■ THEOREM 1

The total increment.

HYPOTHESIS: (a) $u = f(x, y)$ is defined for domain D in the xy plane.

(b) $\dfrac{\partial u}{\partial x} = f_1(x, y)$ and $\dfrac{\partial u}{\partial y} = f_2(x, y)$ are continuous for D.

CONCLUSION: For each (x, y) of D and for each Δx and Δy such that the rectangle with vertices (x, y) $(x + \Delta x, y)$, $(x, y + \Delta y)$, $(x + \Delta x, y + \Delta y)$ lies entirely in D, there are numbers ϵ_1 and ϵ_2 such that

$$\Delta u = f(x + \Delta x, y + \Delta y) - f(x, y)$$
$$= f_1(x, y)\, \Delta x + f_2(x, y)\, \Delta y + \epsilon_1\, \Delta x + \epsilon_2\, \Delta y, \tag{4}$$

and, further, ϵ_1 and ϵ_2 approach 0 as Δx and Δy approach 0.

We can rewrite Eq. (4) in the slightly different form

$$\Delta u = f(x + \Delta x, y + \Delta y) - f(x,y) = \frac{\partial u}{\partial x}\, \Delta x + \frac{\partial u}{\partial y}\, \Delta y + \epsilon_1\, \Delta x + \epsilon_2\, \Delta y. \tag{5}$$

III

When dealing with a function of one variable, we found it convenient to introduce differentials and we do so again. In Sec. 8.3, in the case $u = f(x)$, we defined dx to be Δx, and du to be $du/dx\, \Delta x$. There we found in Eq. 8.3-(1) that

$$\Delta u = du + \epsilon\, \Delta x,$$

where ϵ approaches 0 as Δx approaches 0. Equations (4) and (5) here suggest

■ DEFINITION 3

Differentials. Let $u = f(x, y)$ for (x, y) of domain D, with $\partial u/\partial x = f_1(x, y)$, $\partial u/\partial y = f_2(x, y)$ continuous for D. To each (x, y) of D and to each dx and dy, not both 0, such that the rectangle with vertices (x, y), $(x, y + dy)$, $(x + dx, y)$, $(x + dx, y + dy)$ lies entirely in D we assign

$$du = f_1(x,y)\, dx + f_2(x,y)\, dy = \frac{\partial u}{\partial x}\, dx + \frac{\partial u}{\partial y}\, dy.$$

Equations (4) and (5) then read

$$\Delta u = du + \epsilon_1\, \Delta x + \epsilon_2\, \Delta y, \tag{6}$$

where ϵ_1 and ϵ_2 approach 0 as Δx and Δy approach 0. We have defined the total differential du in such a way that it approximates the total increment Δu. The correction terms are $\epsilon_1\, \Delta x$ and $\epsilon_2\, \Delta y$. These terms are smaller, in general, than the terms

$(\partial u / \partial x) \, \Delta x$ and $(\partial u / \partial y) \, \Delta y$, for both factors in $\epsilon_1 \, \Delta x$ and $\epsilon_2 \, \Delta y$ must approach 0 as Δx and Δy approach 0, whereas only one of the factors of $(\partial u / \partial x) \, \Delta x$ or $(\partial u / \partial y) \, \Delta y$ must do so.

Example 4. Consider $u = xy^2$. Suppose that x is stated to be 1 when it really is 1.02 and that y is stated to be 2 when it really is 1.97. Approximately what change is there in the computed value for u because of the change from $(1, 2)$ to $(1.02, 1.97)$?

We are given $x = 1$, $\Delta x = .02$, $y = 2$, $\Delta y = -.03$ and asked for an approximate value for Δu. If we take du as an approximation for Δu, we can write

$$\Delta u \approx du = \frac{\partial u}{\partial x} \, \Delta x + \frac{\partial u}{\partial y} \, \Delta y = y^2 \, \Delta x + 2xy \, \Delta y = 4(.02) + 4(-.03) = -.04.$$

To get Δu exactly, we would compute

$$\Delta u = (1.02)(1.97)^2 - 1(2)^2 = 3.958518 - 4.000000 = -.041482.$$

Example 5. If the pressure of a gas is given in terms of the volume and temperature by the formula $P = RT/V$, where R is a constant, and if there is a 1-percent error in reporting T and an error of .5 percent in reporting V, find approximately the greatest error made in computing P from the formula.

We are given $\Delta T = \pm .01T$ and $\Delta V = \pm .005V$ and asked for an approximate value for ΔP. If we approximate to ΔP by taking dP, we can write

$$\Delta P \approx dP = \frac{\partial P}{\partial T} \, \Delta T + \frac{\partial P}{\partial V} \, \Delta V = \frac{R}{V} \, \Delta T - \frac{RT}{V^2} \, \Delta V$$

$$= \frac{R}{V} \, (\pm .01T) - \frac{RT}{V^2} \, (\pm .005V) = (\pm .01P) - (\pm .005P).$$

If the signs for ΔT and ΔV are opposed, we will have

$$\Delta P \approx \pm .015P.$$

The error for P in the worst case is approximately 1.5 percent.

We conclude this section by pointing out that our work can be generalized directly if u is a function of three variables, according to the following theorem.

■ THEOREM 1A

The total increment.

HYPOTHESIS: (a) $u = f(x, y, z)$ is defined for domain D in space.

(b) $\dfrac{\partial u}{\partial x}, \dfrac{\partial u}{\partial y}$, and $\dfrac{\partial u}{\partial z}$ are continuous for D.

CONCLUSION: For each (x, y, z) of D and for each Δx, Δy, and Δz such that the rectangular parallelepiped with vertices (x, y, z) $(x + \Delta x, y, z)$, $(x, y + \Delta y, z)$,

$\cdots$, $(x + \Delta x, y + \Delta y, z + \Delta z)$ lies entirely in D, there are numbers ϵ_1, ϵ_2, and ϵ_3 such that

$$\Delta u = f(x + \Delta x, y + \Delta y, z + \Delta z) - f(x, y, z) = f_1(x, y, z) \, \Delta x + f_2(x, y, z) \, \Delta y$$
$$+ f_3(x, y, z) \, \Delta z + \epsilon_1 \, \Delta x + \epsilon_2 \, \Delta y + \epsilon_3 \, \Delta z$$
$$= \frac{\partial u}{\partial x} \, \Delta x + \frac{\partial u}{\partial y} \, \Delta y + \frac{\partial u}{\partial z} \, \Delta z + \epsilon_1 \, \Delta x + \epsilon_2 \, \Delta y + \epsilon_3 \, \Delta z,$$

and, further, ϵ_1, ϵ_2, and ϵ_3 approach 0 as Δx, Δy, and Δz approach 0.

■ **DEFINITION 3A**

Differentials. Let $u = f(x, y, z)$ for (x,y,z) of domain D, with $f_1(x,y,z)$, $f_2(x, y, z), f_3(x, y, z)$ continuous for D. To each (x, y, z) of D and to each dx, dy, and dz, not all 0, such that the rectangular parallelepiped with vertices $(x, y, z), (x + dx, y, z)$, $(x, y + dy, z), \cdots, (x + dx, y + dy, z + dz)$ lies entirely in D, we assign

$$du = f_1(x, y, z) \, dx + f_2(x, y, z) \, dy + f_3(x, y, z) \, dz = \frac{\partial u}{\partial x} \, dx + \frac{\partial u}{\partial y} \, dy + \frac{\partial u}{\partial z} \, dz.$$

EXERCISES 11.2

1. Find the total differential in each of the following cases:
   (a) $u = \sqrt{x + 2y}$.
   (b) $L = e^{-x} \cos(x - ct)$.

   (c) $v = \dfrac{2xy}{\sqrt{x^2 + y^2}}$.

   (d) $u = x^2 \log \sqrt{x^2 + y^2}$.
   (e) $u = x^2 + y^2 + z^2 + xy^2 z^3$.

   (f) $T = (\log r)(\cosh \theta)(\cos \phi)$.

2. If $u = \sqrt{x + 2y}$ and x changes from 3 to 2.98 while y changes from .5 to .51, find an approximate value for the change in u.

3. If $u = x^2 + y^2 + z^2 + xy^2 z^3$ and x changes from 2 to 2.01, y changes from 1 to 1.02, and z changes from -1 to -0.99, find an approximate value for the change in u.

4. A rectangular plate expands in such a way that its base changes from 10 to 10.03 while its height changes from 8 to 8.02. Find an approximate value for the change in its area.

5. The lateral surface area of a cone is computed from the formula $S = \pi r \sqrt{r^2 + h^2}$, where r is the radius of the base and h is the height. If r is reported as 6 with an accuracy of 1 percent and h as 8 with an accuracy of .25 percent, with approximately what accuracy will S be reported?

6. The moment of inertia of a homogeneous cylinder of mass M and radius r rotating about its own axis is $\frac{1}{2} Mr^2$. If M is taken to be 10 when it really is 10.003 and r is taken to be 4.0 when it really is 4.08, approximately what error will be made in computing the moment of inertia?

7. The volume of a rectangular parallelepiped is given by the formula $V = xyz$. If this solid is compressed from above so that z is decreased by 2 percent while x and y each increase by .75 percent, approximately what percentage change will there be in V? Approximately what percentage change will there be in the density?

8. A formula for the area of a triangle is $K = \frac{1}{2} ab \sin C$. Approximately what error is made in computing K if a is taken to be 9 instead of 9.1, b is taken to be 4 instead of 4.08, and C is taken to be $30°$ instead of $30° 30'$?

9. If a particle is displaced a distance D against a force of magnitude F, and θ is the angle between the force and the displacement, then the work done is $W = FD \cos \theta$. If F is reported as $8 \pm .1$, D as $6 \pm .02$, and θ as $60° \pm 1°$, what can be said for W?

10. We are given a cylindrical shell of length L, inner radius a, and outer radius b. If K is the thermal conductivity and θ the temperature difference between the inner and outer surfaces, then the heat current through the shell is given by

$$H = 2\pi K \frac{L\theta}{\log b - \log a}.$$

If b is $2 \pm .01$, a is $1 \pm .05$, $L = 10 \pm .01$, and $\theta = 30 \pm .1$, what can be said for H?

11. If a circular ring of radius R carries charge q, then the electric intensity at a point a distance r from the center of the ring, on a line perpendicular to the ring, is given by

$$E = k \frac{qr}{(r^2 + R^2)^{3/2}},$$

where k is a constant of proportionality in the statement of Coulomb's Law. If R is taken to be 8 when it really is 8.001, q is taken to be 4 when it really is 3.98, and r is taken to be 6 when it really is 6.1, by approximately how much is the computed value for E in error?

12. Prove that $\displaystyle\lim_{(x,y)\to(0,0)} x^2 y = 0$. Is $x^2 y$ continuous at $(0, 0)$?

13. Prove that $\displaystyle\lim_{(x,y)\to(1,2)} \frac{y}{x} = 2$. *Suggestion:* Rewrite $\dfrac{y}{x} - 2$ as $\dfrac{y - 2 - 2(x - 1)}{x}$.

14. Consider $f(x, y) = \begin{cases} \dfrac{x^3}{x^2 + y^2}, & (x, y) \neq (0,0), \\ 0, & (x, y) = (0,0). \end{cases}$

Prove that $\displaystyle\lim_{(x,y)\to(0,0)} f(x, y) = 0$ and thus that f is continuous at $(0, 0)$.

Suggestion A: Note that $f = 0$ for $x = 0$ and that

$$|f| = \frac{1}{1 + y^2/x^2} |x| \leq |x| \qquad \text{for } x \neq 0.$$

Suggestion B: Change to polar coordinates.

15. Consider $f(x, y) = \begin{cases} y/x, & x \neq 0, \\ 0, & x = 0. \end{cases}$

(a) Is f continuous at $(0, 1)$? Explain.

(b) Show that f approaches 0 as (x, y) approaches $(0, 0)$ along the y axis. Show that f approaches 0 as (x, y) approaches $(0, 0)$ along the x axis. Is f continuous at $(0, 0)$? Explain.

16. Consider $f(x, y) = \begin{cases} \dfrac{x^3 + y^2}{x^2 - y}, & y \neq x^2, \\ 1, & y = x^2. \end{cases}$

(a) Show that $f(x, y)$ approaches 0 if (x, y) approaches $(0, 0)$ via any straight line.

(b) Show that $f(x, y)$ approaches 1 if (x, y) approaches $(0, 0)$ via $y = x^2$. Despite the result of part (a), $\displaystyle\lim_{(x,y)\to(0,0)} f(x, y)$ does not exist.

17. Consider $f(x, y) = \begin{cases} \dfrac{x^3 + y^2}{x^2 - y}, & y \neq x^2, \\ 0, & y = x^2. \end{cases}$

(a) Show, as in Exercise 16, that $f(x, y) \to 0$ if $(x, y) \to (0, 0)$ via any straight line.

(b) Show that $f(x, y) \to 0$ if $(x, y) \to (0, 0)$ via $y = x^2$.

(c) Despite these results, show that $\lim\limits_{(x,y) \to (0,0)} f(x, y)$ does not exist.

18. Prove the following theorem.

Theorem 2. Differentials of sums, products and quotients.

Hypothesis: $u = f(x, y)$ and $v = g(x, y)$ are defined for a domain D with $\partial u/\partial x$, $\partial u/\partial y$, $\partial v/\partial x$, $\partial v/\partial y$ all continuous in D.

Conclusion: (a) $d(u + v) = du + dv$ for (x, y) of D and suitable dx, dy.

(b) $d(uv) = u\,dv + v\,du$ for (x, y) of D and suitable dx, dy.

(c) $d\left(\dfrac{u}{v}\right) = \dfrac{v\,du - u\,dv}{v^2}$ for (x, y) of D such that $v \neq 0$ and for suitable dx, dy.

11.3 Directional Derivatives. Gradients

Let u be defined as a function of x, y, and z in a domain that includes point P. At what rate does u change if we move from point P in a specified direction? In the x axis direction, the rate of change for u is $\partial u/\partial x$, and corresponding statements can be made for other coordinate directions. But what can be said about the rate of change of u if we move in a direction that is not a coordinate direction?

■ DEFINITION 1

The directional derivative. Let $u = f(x, y, z)$ be defined for domain D. Let P be a point of D, let L be a line through P, let Q be a point of L at a distance Δs from P, $\Delta s \neq 0$, such that the line segment PQ lies in D, and let Δu be $f(x_Q, y_Q, z_Q) - f(x_P, y_P, z_P)$. Then $\lim_{\Delta s \to 0} (\Delta u/\Delta s)$ is the derivative of u at P in the direction of L, and is denoted by du/ds.

■ THEOREM 1

HYPOTHESIS: $u = f(x, y, z)$ is defined for domain D with $\partial u/\partial x$, $\partial u/\partial y$, $\partial u/\partial z$ continuous for D.

CONCLUSION: At a point P in D the derivative of u in the direction of the vector $\vec{v} = a\vec{i} + b\vec{j} + c\vec{k}$ is given by

$$\frac{du}{ds} = \frac{a(\partial u/\partial x) + b(\partial u/\partial y) + c(\partial u/\partial z)}{\sqrt{a^2 + b^2 + c^2}}.$$

PROOF: Consider a displacement $\Delta x\vec{i} + \Delta y\vec{j} + \Delta z\vec{k}$ from point P in the direction of vector $\vec{v}$. Because this displacement is in $\vec{v}$'s direction, it is a multiple of $\vec{v}$; there is a constant $q \neq 0$ such that $\Delta x\vec{i} + \Delta y\vec{j} + \Delta z\vec{k} = q\vec{v} = q(a\vec{i} + b\vec{j} + c\vec{k})$, or such that $\Delta x = qa$, $\Delta y = qb$, $\Delta z = qc$. The magnitude of the displacement is

$$\Delta s = \sqrt{\Delta x^2 + \Delta y^2 + \Delta z^2} = q\sqrt{a^2 + b^2 + c^2}.$$

The theorem on total increments, Theorem 11.2-1a, tells us that there exist numbers ϵ_1, ϵ_2, ϵ_3, which approach 0 as Δs approaches 0, such that

$$\Delta u = \frac{\partial u}{\partial x} \Delta x + \frac{\partial u}{\partial y} \Delta y + \frac{\partial u}{\partial z} \Delta z + \epsilon_1 \Delta x + \epsilon_2 \Delta y + \epsilon_3 \Delta z.$$

Then we have

$$\frac{\Delta u}{\Delta s} = \frac{\partial u}{\partial x} \frac{\Delta x}{\Delta s} + \frac{\partial u}{\partial y} \frac{\Delta y}{\Delta s} + \frac{\partial u}{\partial z} \frac{\Delta z}{\Delta s} + \epsilon_1 \frac{\Delta x}{\Delta s} + \epsilon_2 \frac{\Delta y}{\Delta s} + \epsilon_3 \frac{\Delta z}{\Delta s}$$

or

$$\frac{\Delta u}{\Delta s} = \frac{1}{\sqrt{a^2 + b^2 + c^2}} \left(a \frac{\partial u}{\partial x} + b \frac{\partial u}{\partial y} + c \frac{\partial u}{\partial z} + a\epsilon_1 + b\epsilon_2 + c\epsilon_3 \right).$$

But then

$$\frac{du}{ds} = \lim_{\Delta s \to 0} \frac{\Delta u}{\Delta s} = \frac{a(\partial u/\partial x) + b(\partial u/\partial y) + c(\partial u/\partial z)}{\sqrt{a^2 + b^2 + c^2}}.$$

Example 1. Consider $u = xyz$. Find du/ds at $P(1, 1, 3)$ in the direction of the origin. At $P(1, 1, 3)$ we have

$$\frac{\partial u}{\partial x} = yz = 3, \qquad \frac{\partial u}{\partial y} = xz = 3, \qquad \frac{\partial u}{\partial z} = xy = 1,$$

and we are to find du/ds for the direction of $\overrightarrow{PO} = -\mathbf{i} - \mathbf{j} - 3\mathbf{k}$. But Theorem 1 tells us that the required rate of change is

$$\frac{du}{ds} = \frac{-1(3) - 1(3) - 3(1)}{\sqrt{1 + 1 + 9}} = -\frac{9}{\sqrt{11}}.$$

The conclusion of Theorem 1 will be easier for us to understand and to apply if we observe that its right member suggests the scalar product of two vectors,

$$\frac{\partial u}{\partial x} \mathbf{i} + \frac{\partial u}{\partial y} \mathbf{j} + \frac{\partial u}{\partial z} \mathbf{k} \qquad \text{and} \qquad \frac{a\mathbf{i} + b\mathbf{j} + c\mathbf{k}}{\sqrt{a^2 + b^2 + c^2}}.$$

■ DEFINITION 2

The gradient of a scalar u. Let $u = f(x, y, z)$ be defined in a domain D and let $\partial u/\partial x$, $\partial u/\partial y$, $\partial u/\partial z$ exist in D. Then by the gradient of u, written grad u or ∇u, we mean the vector

$$\text{grad } u = \frac{\partial u}{\partial x} \mathbf{i} + \frac{\partial u}{\partial y} \mathbf{j} + \frac{\partial u}{\partial z} \mathbf{k}.$$

Since the vector $\dfrac{a\mathbf{i} + b\mathbf{j} + c\mathbf{k}}{\sqrt{a^2 + b^2 + c^2}}$ is a vector of unit length and since

$$(\text{grad } u) \cdot \frac{a\mathbf{i} + b\mathbf{j} + c\mathbf{k}}{\sqrt{a^2 + b^2 + c^2}} = \frac{a(\partial u/\partial x) + b(\partial u/\partial y) + c(\partial u/\partial z)}{\sqrt{a^2 + b^2 + c^2}},$$

we can restate Theorem 1 as follows.

■ THEOREM 2

The directional derivative.

HYPOTHESIS: $u = f(x, y, z)$ is defined for domain D with $\partial u/\partial x$, $\partial u/\partial y$, $\partial u/\partial z$ continuous there.

CONCLUSION: At a point P in D, the directional derivative of u for the direction of vector $\vec{v}$ is obtained by taking the scalar product of grad u by the unit vector in the direction of $\vec{v}$;

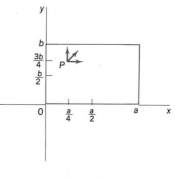

Fig. 11.7

$$\frac{du}{ds} = \text{grad } u \cdot \frac{\vec{v}}{\|\vec{v}\|}.$$

Example 2. Let us return to the function $u = xyz$ discussed in Example 1. In the language of gradients, we have

$$\text{grad } u = \frac{\partial u}{\partial x}\vec{i} + \frac{\partial u}{\partial y}\vec{j} + \frac{\partial u}{\partial z}\vec{k} = yz\vec{i} + xz\vec{j} + xy\vec{k}$$

$$= 3\vec{i} + 3\vec{j} + 1\vec{k} \qquad \text{at } P(1,1,3).$$

But we asked for du/ds at P in the direction of the origin. A unit vector in this direction is $(-\vec{i} - \vec{j} - 3\vec{k})/\sqrt{11}$. Hence

$$\frac{du}{ds} = (3\vec{i} + 3\vec{j} + \vec{k}) \cdot \frac{1}{\sqrt{11}} (-\vec{i} - \vec{j} - 3\vec{k}) = \frac{1}{\sqrt{11}} (-3 - 3 - 3) = \frac{-9}{\sqrt{11}}.$$

Example 3. At the instant $t = 0$, the position of the rectangular membrane of Example 11.1-4 is given by

$$u = \sin \frac{\pi}{a} x \sin \frac{\pi}{b} y.$$

What are the rates of change of u if one moves from the point $P(a/4, 3b/4)$ in the x axis direction, in the y axis direction, or in the direction of inclination $45°$? See Fig. 11.7.

The rates of change of u at P in the x- and y-axis directions are

$$\frac{\partial u}{\partial x} = \frac{\pi}{a} \cos \frac{\pi}{a} x \sin \frac{\pi}{b} y = \frac{\pi}{a} \cos \frac{\pi}{4} \sin \frac{3\pi}{4} = \frac{\pi}{2a},$$

$$\frac{\partial u}{\partial y} = \frac{\pi}{b} \sin \frac{\pi}{a} x \cos \frac{\pi}{b} y = \frac{\pi}{b} \sin \frac{\pi}{4} \cos \frac{3\pi}{4} = -\frac{\pi}{2b}.$$

If we compute

$$\text{grad } u = \frac{\partial u}{\partial x}\vec{i} + \frac{\partial u}{\partial y}\vec{j} + 0\,\vec{k}$$

$$= \frac{\pi}{2a}\vec{i} - \frac{\pi}{2b}\vec{j},$$

and observe that $(\mathbf{i} + \mathbf{j})/\sqrt{2}$ is a unit vector in the direction of inclination $45°$, then Theorem 2 tells us that the directional derivative in that direction is

$$\frac{du}{ds} = \operatorname{grad} u \cdot \frac{\mathbf{i} + \mathbf{j}}{\sqrt{2}} = \left(\frac{\pi}{2a}\mathbf{i} - \frac{\pi}{2b}\mathbf{j}\right) \cdot \frac{\mathbf{i} + \mathbf{j}}{\sqrt{2}} = \frac{\pi}{2\sqrt{2}}\left(\frac{1}{a} - \frac{1}{b}\right).$$

Comparison of the various directional derivatives of $u = f(x, y, z)$ at a particular point P leads to the questions: "In what direction or directions does u change most rapidly?" and "In what direction or directions, if any, does u change not at all?" To answer these questions, observe that Theorem 2 says that the derivative of u in a particular direction is obtained by taking the projection of grad u on that direction, for Theorem 2 directs us to take the scalar product of grad u and a unit vector in the desired direction, and this is how we find projections. Thus, if the angle between the specified direction and grad u is θ, then

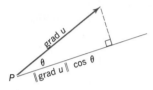

Fig. 11.8

$$\left(\frac{du}{ds}\right)_P = \|\operatorname{grad} u\|_P \cos\theta;$$

see Fig. 11.8. But the maximum value for $\cos\theta$ is 1, achieved when $\theta = 0$. Hence the directional derivative is greatest in the direction of the gradient itself, and the magnitude of that greatest directional derivative is the magnitude of the gradient vector.

On the other hand, $\cos\theta = 0$ for $\theta = \pi/2$. The directions of no change for u are the directions perpendicular to grad u. We have, then, Theorems 3 and 4 as corollaries of Theorem 2.

■ THEOREM 3

The gradient.

HYPOTHESIS: $u = f(x, y, z)$ is defined for domain D with $\partial u/\partial x$, $\partial u/\partial y$, $\partial u/\partial z$ continuous for D.

CONCLUSION: At a point P of D at which grad $u \neq \vec{0}$ the direction of grad u is the direction of greatest rate of change for u and the magnitude of grad u is the magnitude of that greatest rate of change.

■ THEOREM 4

Directions of no change.

HYPOTHESIS: $u = f(x, y, z)$ is defined for domain D with $\partial u/\partial x$, $\partial u/\partial y$, $\partial u/\partial z$ continuous for D.

CONCLUSION: At a point P of D at which grad $u \neq \vec{0}$, the directions of zero rate of change for u are those perpendicular to grad u.

Example 4. Consider again the function $u = xyz$. At $P(1, 1, 3)$ we have

$$\operatorname{grad} u = yz\mathbf{i} + xz\mathbf{j} + xy\mathbf{k} = 3\mathbf{i} + 3\mathbf{j} + \mathbf{k}.$$

Theorem 3 says that the direction of greatest change for u at P is that of grad u itself and that the magnitude of that greatest rate of change is $\sqrt{19}$. Theorem 4 says that, if one leaves P in a direction perpendicular to grad $u = 3\vec{i} + 3\vec{j} + \vec{k}$, then $du/ds = 0$. These directions of no change all lie in the plane $3x + 3y + z = 9$ which passes through $P(1, 1, 3)$ and has grad $u = 3\vec{i} + 3\vec{j} + \vec{k}$ as its normal.

Example 5. Consider again the function

$$u = \sin \frac{\pi}{a} x \sin \frac{\pi}{b} y$$

discussed in Example 3. At $P(a/4, 3b/4)$ we have

$$\text{grad } u = \frac{\pi}{2a}\vec{i} - \frac{\pi}{2b}\vec{j}.$$

Theorem 3 says that at P the direction of greatest rate of change for u is that of grad u itself and that this greatest rate of change is $(\pi/2)\sqrt{1/a^2 + 1/b^2}$. Theorem 4 says that the direction of zero rate of change for u at P is that of $\vec{v} = k\vec{i} + n\vec{j}$ where $(\text{grad } u) \cdot \vec{v} = 0$. To determine k and n we write

$$\left(\frac{\pi}{2a}\vec{i} - \frac{\pi}{2b}\vec{j} \right) \cdot (k\vec{i} + n\vec{j}) = 0,$$

$$\frac{\pi}{2}\left[\frac{k}{a} - \frac{n}{b} \right] = 0, \quad \text{or} \quad \frac{k}{a} = \frac{n}{b}.$$

One solution for k and n is $k = a$, $n = b$. The direction of no change is that of $a\vec{i} + b\vec{j}$.

● **Remark 1**

The fact that the directions of greatest change and no change are perpendicular is used frequently in applications. We mention just a few. If one uses a temperature distribution to study a heat-flow problem, T is given as a function of position. The "isothermal curves," curves of constant temperature, have at each point the direction of zero rate of change for T; at a given point, the "heat flow vector" is in the direction of the greatest rate of change of T, perpendicular to the isothermal curve through that point. If u is the "electrostatic potential," described as a function of position, the "equipotential curves" are those that have at each point the direction of zero rate of change of u; at a given point the "field intensity vector" is $-\text{grad } u$ and is perpendicular to the equipotential curve through that point. Finally, on a topographical map, elevation z is described as a function of position and the "level curves" are the curves for which z is constant; at a given point the direction of steepest descent is perpendicular to the level curve through that point. Figure 11.9 is a topographical map of part of a hill whose elevation is more than 150 ft but less than 160 ft. At P the elevation is 130 ft and the direction of steepest descent is indicated.

We conclude with an application of the ideas of this section to a geometry problem we have already discussed.

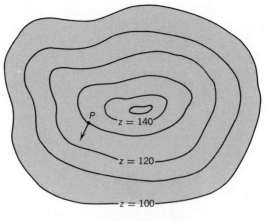

Fig. 11.9

Example 6. The ellipse $x^2/a^2 + y^2/b^2 = 1$ has foci $F_1(c, 0)$ and $F_2(-c, 0)$; see Fig. 11.10. Let $P(x, y)$ be any point and consider

$$u = F_1P + F_2P = \sqrt{(x-c)^2 + y^2} + \sqrt{(x+c)^2 + y^2}.$$

We know that $u = 2a$ for all points on the ellipse; if P is on the ellipse and if one moves from P in the direction of the ellipse, u stays fixed at $2a$. Thus, if $\vec{t}$ is the unit tangent vector, we must have

$$\left(\frac{du}{ds}\right)_P = (\text{grad } u) \cdot \vec{t} = 0. \tag{1}$$

But we compute that

$$\text{grad } u = \frac{\partial u}{\partial x}\vec{i} + \frac{\partial u}{\partial y}\vec{j} = \left(\frac{x-c}{\sqrt{(x-c)^2 + y^2}} + \frac{x+c}{\sqrt{(x+c)^2 + y^2}}\right)\vec{i}$$

$$+ \left(\frac{y}{\sqrt{(x-c)^2 + y^2}} + \frac{y}{\sqrt{(x+c)^2 + y^2}}\right)\vec{j}$$

$$= \frac{(x-c)\vec{i} + y\vec{j}}{\sqrt{(x-c)^2 + y^2}} + \frac{(x+c)\vec{i} + y\vec{j}}{\sqrt{(x+c)^2 + y^2}} = \vec{u}_1 + \vec{u}_2.$$

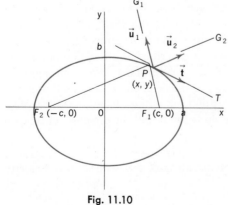

Fig. 11.10

Since the magnitude of $(x-c)\vec{i} + y\vec{j}$ is precisely $\sqrt{(x-c)^2 + y^2}$ and since the coordinates of P and F_1 are (x, y) and $(c, 0)$, we see that

$$\vec{u}_1 = \frac{(x-c)\vec{i} + y\vec{j}}{\sqrt{(x-c)^2 + y^2}}$$

is a unit vector in the direction of $\overrightarrow{F_1P}$; similarly

$$\vec{u}_2 = \frac{(x+c)\vec{i} + y\vec{j}}{\sqrt{(x+c)^2 + y^2}}$$

is a unit vector in the direction of $\overrightarrow{F_2P}$.

But now Eq. (1) says that

$$(\vec{u}_1 + \vec{u}_2) \cdot \vec{t} = 0, \qquad \text{or} \qquad \vec{u}_1 \cdot \vec{t} = -\vec{u}_2 \cdot \vec{t}.$$

Since $\vec{u}_1$, $\vec{u}_2$, and $\vec{t}$ are all unit vectors, this means that

$$\cos TPG_1 = -\cos TPG_2 \qquad \text{and} \qquad \angle TPG_2 = 180° - \angle TPG_1 = \angle TPF_1.$$

In other words, the focal radii make equal angles with the tangent.

EXERCISES 11.3

1. (a) $u = (x + 2y)^3$; grad $u = ?$
   (b) $T = \log(x^2 + y^2 + z^2)$, $(x, y, z) \neq (0, 0, 0)$; grad $T = ?$
   (c) $(2x + y + v)^2 + xyv = 17$; grad $v = ?$
   (d) $u = \tan^{-1}(y/x)$, $x \neq 0$; grad $u = ?$

2. At what rate does $u = 2xy - y/x$ change if one leaves the point $(1, 2)$ in the direction of the vector $2\vec{i} - 3\vec{j}$?

3. At what rate does $v = ye^{-x}(x^2 + y^2 + z^2 + 1)$ change if one leaves the point $(0, 0, 0)$ in the direction of the point $(2, 1, 2)$?

4. At what rate does $L = \sinh(x + y)\cosh z$ change if one leaves the point $(1, 0, 1)$ in the direction of the point $(-1, 2, 0)$?

5. Let v be given as a function of x and y implicitly by the equation $(2x + y + v)^2 + xyv = 17$. Suppose that when $x = 1$ and $y = 1$ we have $v = 1$. At what rate will v change at $(1, 1)$ if we now change x and y in such a way that $\Delta y : \Delta x = 1 : 2$?

6. Consider $u = x^2 + y^2$ at (a, b).
   (a) Find the direction of greatest rate of change of u at (a, b) and the magnitude of this greatest rate of change. Find the direction of no change at (a, b).
   (b) On one diagram draw the curves for which $u = 1, 4, 9, 16$. What is the geometric interpretation for your answers of Part (a)?

7. Consider $u = \tan^{-1}(y/x)$ at (a, b), $a \neq 0$.
   (a) Find the direction of greatest rate of change of u at (a, b) and the magnitude of this greatest rate of change. Find the direction of no change at (a, b).
   (b) On one diagram draw the curves for which $u = 0, \pi/6, \pi/4, \pi/3$. What is the geometric interpretation for your answers of Part (a)?

8. The temperature distribution for the semicircular plate $x^2 + y^2 \leq 1$, $y \geq 0$ is given by the formula $T = 3x^2y - y^3 + 273$ under certain special conditions. Find T at $A(0, \frac{1}{2})$, dT/ds at A for the y axis direction, dT/ds at A for the direction of $\vec{i} - 2\vec{j}$, the direction of greatest rate of change at A, the magnitude of that greatest rate of change, and the direction of the "isothermal" through A (the direction of zero rate of change at A).

9. Repeat Exercise 8 for the temperature distribution $T = 4x^3y - 4xy^3 + 273$ and the point $A(\frac{1}{2}, \frac{1}{2})$.

10. Consider the vibrating rectangular membrane at $t = 0$ discussed in Examples 3 and 5. What are the rates of change of u if one leaves $Q(a/3, b/4)$ in the coordinate directions? toward the origin? In which direction must one move from Q to get the greatest rate of change? rate of change $= 0$?

11. Consider again the rectangular membrane discussed in Examples 3 and 5. Suppose that $a > b$ and that one moves along the line $x = a/3$ from $y = 0$ to $y = b$. As one moves from point to point on this line, the vector grad u changes both its direction and its magnitude. At which points on the line will $\|\text{grad } u\|$ be a maximum? A minimum?

12. Prove that the tangent at a point of the parabola $y^2 = 2px$ makes equal angles with the focal radius and the horizontal direction by considering

$$u = \sqrt{(x - p/2)^2 + y^2} - (x + p/2).$$

13. Prove that the tangent at a point of the hyperbola $x^2/a^2 - y^2/b^2 = 1$ makes equal angles with the focal radii by considering $u = \sqrt{(x - c)^2 + y^2} - \sqrt{(x + c)^2 + y^2}$, where $c^2 = a^2 + b^2$.

11.4   Normals to Surfaces. Tangent Planes

Our work on gradients enables us to describe the tangent plane at a point of a surface. Let a surface S be described by an equation of the form $F(x, y, z) = 0$ and let P be a point of S. Thus, at P we have $F = 0$, and if we move from P along any curve C on S we shall find that F remains 0, because each point of C is a point of S and $F = 0$ at every point of S by definition. In other words, the various curves of S through P furnish the directions of zero rate of change of F at P. If one moves from P off the surface S, then F will change from 0 to some number other than 0. But when $\partial F/\partial x$, $\partial F/\partial y$, and $\partial F/\partial z$ are all continuous at P and not all 0 there, grad F can be computed at P and Theorem 11.3-4 assures us that $(\text{grad } F)_P$ will be perpendicular to all the directions of zero rate of change at P. We restate this result after defining what we mean by a direction normal to a surface.

■ DEFINITION 1

The direction normal to a surface at a point.   Consider all curves through point P on surface S. If there exists a unique direction perpendicular to all these curves, it is called the direction normal to S at P. See Fig. 11.11(a).

■ THEOREM 1

On the normal to a surface.

HYPOTHESIS: (a) Surface S is described by the equation $F(x, y, z) = 0$. (b) At P on S, $\partial F/\partial x$, $\partial F/\partial y$, and $\partial F/\partial z$ are all continuous and not all 0.

CONCLUSION: The normal to the surface at P has the direction of $(\text{grad } F)_P$.

By the tangent plane to the surface S at P we mean the plane that has the same normal direction as S at P; see Fig. 11.11(b). We shall point out in Example 11.5-4 below that the tangent plane is also the plane of the tangents to the curves of S through P.

■ DEFINITION 2

The plane tangent to a surface at a point. The plane tangent to a surface at a point is the plane which has the same normal direction as the surface at that point.

Theorem 1 above and Theorem 10.6-1, on the equation of a plane, enable us to write the equation of a tangent plane to a surface.

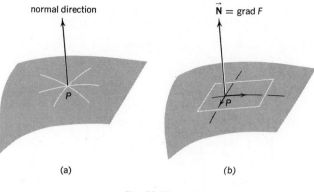

normal direction

$\vec{N} = \text{grad } F$

(a)

(b)

Fig. 11.11

■ THEOREM 2

On the tangent plane to a surface.

HYPOTHESIS: (a) Surface S is described by the equation $F(x, y, z) = 0$.

(b) At $P_1 (x_1, y_1, z_1,)$ on S, $\dfrac{\partial F}{\partial x}, \dfrac{\partial F}{\partial y}, \dfrac{\partial F}{\partial z}$ are all continuous and not all 0.

CONCLUSION: The tangent plane to S at P_1 has the equation

$$\left(\frac{\partial F}{\partial x}\right)_{P_1} (x - x_1) + \left(\frac{\partial F}{\partial y}\right)_{P_1} (y - y_1) + \left(\frac{\partial F}{\partial z}\right)_{P_1} (z - z_1) = 0.$$

Example 1. We know that the vector $A\vec{i} + B\vec{j} + C\vec{k}$ is normal to the plane $Ax + By + Cz = D$. Let us check Theorem 1 in this simple case. If we write the equation of the plane in the form

$$F(x, y, z) = Ax + By + Cz - D = 0,$$

we find that, as was expected, at each point,

$$\text{grad } F = \frac{\partial F}{\partial x}\vec{i} + \frac{\partial F}{\partial y}\vec{j} + \frac{\partial F}{\partial z}\vec{k} = A\vec{i} + B\vec{j} + C\vec{k}.$$

Example 2. The equation

$$\frac{x^2}{a^2} + \frac{y^2}{b^2} + \frac{z^2}{c^2} = 1$$

for the ellipsoid can be rewritten in the form

$$F(x, y, z) = \frac{1}{a^2} x^2 + \frac{1}{b^2} y^2 + \frac{1}{c^2} z^2 - 1 = 0.$$

We have

$$\text{grad } F = \frac{2}{a^2} x\vec{i} + \frac{2}{b^2} y\vec{j} + \frac{2}{c^2} z\vec{k}.$$

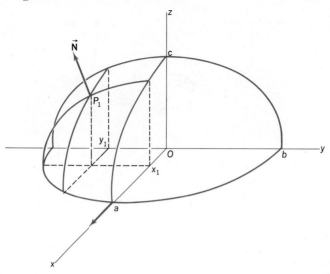

Fig. 11.12

Thus, the normal at $A(a, 0, 0)$ has the direction of $(\text{grad } F)_A = (2/a)\mathbf{i}$, or that of $\mathbf{i}$. See Fig. 11.12. The equation of the tangent plane at this point is $x = a$.

At any point $P_1(x_1, y_1, z_1)$ the normal has the direction of

$$(\text{grad } F)_{P_1} = 2\left[\frac{1}{a^2}x_1\mathbf{i} + \frac{1}{b^2}y_1\mathbf{j} + \frac{1}{c^2}z_1\mathbf{i}\right].$$

Thus the tangent plane at P_1 has an equation of the form

$$2\left[\frac{x_1}{a^2}x + \frac{y_1}{b^2}y + \frac{z_1}{c^2}z\right] = D. \tag{1}$$

Now, we must have

$$2\left[\frac{x_1^2}{a^2} + \frac{y_1^2}{b^2} + \frac{z_1^2}{c^2}\right] = D$$

because $P_1(x_1, y_1, z_1)$ is a point of the tangent plane and Eq. (1) must be satisfied when we substitute x_1 for x, y_1 for y, z_1 for z. Since P_1 is also a point of the ellipsoid and its coordinates must satisfy the ellipsoid equation as well, we read $D = 2$ from the last equation. Finally, from Eq. (1), the equation of the tangent plane is

$$\frac{x_1}{a^2}x + \frac{y_1}{b^2}y + \frac{z_1}{c^2}z = 1.$$

Frequently the equation of a surface is presented in the form $z = f(x, y)$. We need only rewrite the equation in the form

$$F(x, y, z) = f(x, y) - z = 0$$

and proceed as before.

Example 3. The elliptic paraboloid

$$z = x^2 + \tfrac{4}{9} y^2$$

was sketched in Example 10.2-2. If we rewrite the equation in the form

$$F(x, y, z) = x^2 + \tfrac{4}{9} y^2 - z = 0$$

we have

$$\text{grad } F = 2x\vec{i} + \tfrac{8}{9} y\vec{j} - 1\vec{k}.$$

Thus at $O(0, 0, 0)$ we can take for $\vec{N}$ the vector $(\text{grad } F)_0 = -\vec{k}$ and the tangent plane there is $z = 0$. At the point $P_1(x_1, y_1, z_1)$ we can take for the normal to the surface the vector

$$(\text{grad } F)_{P_1} = 2x_1\vec{i} + \tfrac{8}{9} y_1\vec{j} - 1\vec{k},$$

and the equation of the tangent plane is of the form

$$2x_1x + \tfrac{8}{9} y_1y - 1z = D. \quad (2)$$

Since the tangent plane passes through $P_1(x_1, y_1, z_1)$, we must have

$$2x_1^2 + \tfrac{8}{9} y_1^2 - z_1 = D;$$

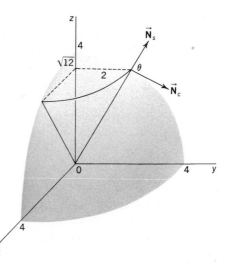

Fig. 11.13

but since the coordinates of P_1 also satisfy the paraboloid equation, we have

$$D = 2(x_1^2 + \tfrac{4}{9} y_1^2) - z_1 = 2z_1 - z_1 = z_1.$$

From Eq. (2), the equation of the tangent plane at P_1 is now

$$2x_1x + \tfrac{8}{9} y_1y - z = z_1.$$

Example 4. We know that the sphere $x^2 + y^2 + z^2 = 16$ and the cone $3(x^2 + y^2) = z^2$ intersect orthogonally, because the straight lines through the vertex of the cone are radii of the sphere and radii of a sphere are always perpendicular to the sphere, but let us illustrate Theorem 1 in checking this result.

The portions of these surfaces for which $x \geq 0, y \geq 0, z \geq 0$ are sketched in Fig. 11.13. By working with the equations simultaneously we find that $\tfrac{1}{3} z^2 + z^2 = 16$, $z^2 = 12$, $x^2 + y^2 = 4$. Thus the surfaces intersect along the circle $x^2 + y^2 = 4$ in the plane $z = \sqrt{12}$.

For the sphere let us write

$$F = x^2 + y^2 + z^2 - 16 = 0$$

so that

$$\text{grad } F = 2(x\vec{i} + y\vec{j} + z\vec{k}).$$

(The normal to the sphere is in the radial direction, as we expect.) For the cone we can write

$$G(x, y, z) = 3x^2 + 3y^2 - z^2 = 0,$$

so that

$$\text{grad } G = 2(3x\vec{\mathbf{i}} + 3y\vec{\mathbf{j}} - z\vec{\mathbf{k}}).$$

The angle between the normals to the surfaces is then given by

$$\cos \theta = \frac{(x\vec{\mathbf{i}} + y\vec{\mathbf{j}} + z\vec{\mathbf{k}}) \cdot (3x\vec{\mathbf{i}} + 3y\vec{\mathbf{j}} - z\vec{\mathbf{k}})}{\|x\vec{\mathbf{i}} + y\vec{\mathbf{j}} + z\vec{\mathbf{k}}\|\|3x\vec{\mathbf{i}} + 3y\vec{\mathbf{j}} - z\vec{\mathbf{k}}\|}$$

$$= \frac{3x^2 + 3y^2 - z^2}{\sqrt{x^2 + y^2 + z^2}\sqrt{9x^2 + 9y^2 + z^2}}.$$

But because the intersection takes place at a point for which $x^2 + y^2 = 4$ and $z^2 = 12$, we have $\cos \theta = 0$, $\theta = \pi/2$.

II

Surfaces are often described parametrically and, indeed, many differential geometry texts proceed almost entirely on that basis, because the parametric discussion makes it easier to use the vector analysis tool. Let a surface S be presented to us in the form

$$x = f(u, v), \qquad y = g(u, v), \qquad z = h(u, v), \tag{3}$$

or in the equivalent vector form

$$\vec{\mathbf{R}} = \overrightarrow{\mathbf{OP}} = x\vec{\mathbf{i}} + y\vec{\mathbf{j}} + z\vec{\mathbf{k}}, \tag{4}$$

and let it be required to find the normal vector at the point P_0 determined by the parametric numbers $u = u_0$ and $v = v_0$. Observe that, in general, Eqs. (3) will be such that one can solve in two of these equations, say the first two, for u and v in terms of x and y

$$u = \phi(x, y), \qquad v = \tau(x, y),$$

and then substitute in the third equation to get an equation in a form we have already considered:

$$z = h(\phi(x, y), \tau(x, y)).$$

To illustrate, if surface S has the parametric equations

$$x = u + v, \qquad y = u - v, \qquad z = u^2 + v^2,$$

we can solve in the first two equations for u and v,

$$u = \tfrac{1}{2}(x + y), \qquad v = \tfrac{1}{2}(x - y),$$

and substitute in the third equation to get

$$z = \tfrac{1}{4}(x^2 + 2xy + y^2) + \tfrac{1}{4}(x^2 - 2xy + y^2)$$

$$z = \tfrac{1}{2}(x^2 + y^2).$$

But the algebraic details may be formidable in other cases, and we shall return to the parametric equation discussion.

If we hold v fixed at v_0 but let u vary, then Eqs. (3) become

$$x = f(u, v_0), \qquad y = g(u, v_0), \qquad z = h(u, v_0)$$

and these equations constitute parametric equations for a curve on S through P_0, the parameter being u. The tangent vector to this curve will be parallel to $\partial \vec{R}/\partial u$, according to Theorem 10.7-3. We have used the partial derivative symbol, because only the variable u was allowed to vary.

Similarly if we hold u fixed at u_0 but let v vary, then Eqs. (3) or (4) are parametric equations of a second curve on S through P_0 with parameter v. The tangent vector to this curve will be parallel to $\partial \vec{R}/\partial v$. Since the normal vector at P_0 must be perpendicular to the tangent vectors to all curves on S through P_0, and to these tangent vectors in particular, we can say that $\vec{N}$ at P_0 is parallel to $(\partial \vec{R}/\partial u)_{P_0} \times (\partial \vec{R}/\partial v)_{P_0}$. See Fig. 11.14 and Example 11.5-4.

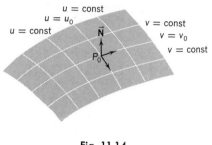

Fig. 11.14

Example 5. The sphere $x^2 + y^2 + z^2 = a^2$ can be described by the parametric equations

$$\left. \begin{aligned} x &= a \sin \phi \cos \theta \\ y &= a \sin \phi \sin \theta \\ z &= a \cos \phi \end{aligned} \right\}, \qquad -\pi < \theta \leq \pi, \qquad 0 \leq \phi \leq \pi.$$

Figure 11.15(a) explains these equations. When parameters θ and ϕ are specified, we can locate the corresponding point $P(\theta, \phi)$ in two steps. First we select half of a

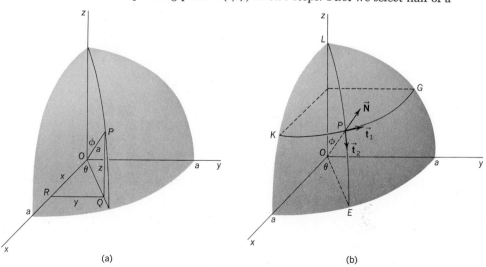

(a)   (b)

Fig. 11.15

great circle on the sphere by taking the half-plane through the z axis which makes an angle θ with the half of the xz plane for which $x \geq 0$. Then on this half of a great circle we select the point P by drawing the radial line that makes angle ϕ with the positive z axis. For the coordinate z we have

$$z = QP = OP \cos \phi = a \cos \phi.$$

Then, also

$$OQ = OP \sin \phi = a \sin \phi,$$
$$x = OR = OQ \cos \theta = a \sin \phi \cos \theta,$$
$$y = RQ = OQ \sin \theta = a \sin \phi \sin \theta.$$

The angles θ and ϕ are called the angles of longitude and colatitude in geography.

Now, at $P(\theta, \phi)$, if we hold θ fixed and let ϕ vary, we get the great circle through P, circle LPE in Fig. 11.15(b). The parameter curve obtained by holding ϕ fixed and letting θ vary is the "small" circle KPG. The normal vector at P must be perpendicular to the tangents to both parameter curves at P. We have

$$\vec{R} = x\vec{i} + y\vec{j} + z\vec{k},$$
$$= a(\sin \phi \cos \theta \, \vec{i} + \sin \phi \sin \theta \, \vec{j} + \cos \phi \, \vec{k}),$$

$$\vec{t}_1 \parallel \frac{\partial \vec{R}}{\partial \theta} = a(- \sin \phi \sin \theta \, \vec{i} + \sin \phi \cos \theta \, \vec{j})$$

$$= a \sin \phi \, (- \sin \theta \, \vec{i} + \cos \theta \, \vec{j}),$$

$$\vec{t}_2 \parallel \frac{\partial \vec{R}}{\partial \phi} = a(\cos \phi \cos \theta \, \vec{i} + \cos \phi \sin \theta \, \vec{j} - \sin \phi \, \vec{k}),$$

and

$$\vec{N} \parallel \frac{\partial \vec{R}}{\partial \phi} \times \frac{\partial \vec{R}}{\partial \theta} \parallel (\cos \phi \cos \theta \, \vec{i} + \cos \phi \sin \theta \, \vec{j} - \sin \phi \, \vec{k})$$

$$\times (- \sin \theta \, \vec{i} + \cos \theta \, \vec{j})$$

$$= \cos \theta \sin \phi \, \vec{i} + \sin \theta \sin \phi \, \vec{j} + (\cos \phi \cos^2 \theta + \cos \phi \sin^2 \theta)\vec{k}$$

$$= \cos \theta \sin \phi \, \vec{i} + \sin \theta \sin \phi \, \vec{j} + \cos \phi \, \vec{k} = \frac{1}{a} \vec{R}.$$

Note that the normal vector at P is in the radial direction, as expected.

III

In Definition 11.2-3 we defined the differential of a function of two variables,

$$du = \frac{\partial u}{\partial x} \, dx + \frac{\partial u}{\partial y} \, dy,$$

in such a way that it would be the principal part of the increment Δu when x and y were increased by dx and dy. Now we point out that du is also the increment achieved by the tangent plane to the surface $u = f(x, y)$. This is a direct extension of our result for a function of one variable. There

$$du = \frac{du}{dx} dx$$

was the increment achieved by the tangent line to the curve $u = f(x)$.

Consider, then, the relationship $u = f(x, y)$ as a description of a surface in the three-dimensional Cartesian space x, y, u. If we write the equation of the surface in the form

$$F(x, y, u) = f(x, y) - u = 0,$$

we know that the normal to the surface at a particular point has the direction of

$$\text{grad } F = \frac{\partial F}{\partial x}\mathbf{i} + \frac{\partial F}{\partial y}\mathbf{j} + \frac{\partial F}{\partial u}\mathbf{k} = \frac{\partial f}{\partial x}\mathbf{i} + \frac{\partial f}{\partial y}\mathbf{j} - 1\mathbf{k}$$

$$= \frac{\partial u}{\partial x}\mathbf{i} + \frac{\partial u}{\partial y}\mathbf{j} - 1\mathbf{k}.$$

Thus the tangent plane to the surface at $P_1(x_1, y_1, u_1)$ has the equation

$$\left(\frac{\partial u}{\partial x}\right)_1 (x - x_1) + \left(\frac{\partial u}{\partial y}\right)_1 (y - y_1) - 1(u - u_1) = 0,$$

or

$$u - u_1 = \left(\frac{\partial u}{\partial x}\right)_1 (x - x_1) + \left(\frac{\partial u}{\partial y}\right)_1 (y - y_1).$$

For any point $T(x, y, u)$ in the tangent plane, Eq. (5) says directly that the increment $(\Delta u)_{tan} = u - u_1$ caused by increments $\Delta x = x - x_1$ and $\Delta y = y - y_1$ is given by

$$(\Delta u)_{tan} = \left(\frac{\partial u}{\partial x}\right)_1 \Delta x + \left(\frac{\partial u}{\partial y}\right)_1 \Delta y.$$

Since, by definition, at P_1 we also have

$$du = \left(\frac{\partial u}{\partial x}\right)_1 \Delta x + \left(\frac{\partial u}{\partial y}\right)_1 \Delta y,$$

we can say that

$$du = (\Delta u)_{tan}.$$

See Fig. 11.16.

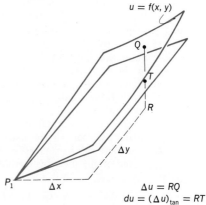

Fig. 11.16

$u = f(x, y)$

$\Delta u = RQ$
$du = (\Delta u)_{tan} = RT$

EXERCISES 11.4

1. Consider the elliptic paraboloid, $\dfrac{x^2}{4} + \dfrac{y^2}{9} = \dfrac{4 - z}{4}$, of Exercise 10.2-1(f).

(a) Find the equations of the tangent planes at $(0, 0, 4)$ and at $(2, 0, 0)$.

(b) Is there at any point a tangent plane parallel to the z axis? Explain.

2. Consider the hyperboloid of one sheet, $\dfrac{x^2}{4} + \dfrac{y^2}{9} - \dfrac{z^2}{36} = 1$, of Example 10.2-3.

(a) Find the equation of the tangent plane at $(2, 3, 6)$.

(b) At each point this surface lies on both sides of its tangent plane. What is the intersection of the tangent plane at $(0, 3, 0)$ with the surface?

3. Consider the hyperboloid of two sheets, $\dfrac{x^2}{4} - \dfrac{y^2}{2} - \dfrac{z^2}{4} = 1$, of Example 10.2-4.

(a) Find the tangent plane at $(-6, 2, \sqrt{24})$.

(b) Find the points at which the tangent planes are parallel to $2x + y + z = 0$.

4. Consider the hyperbolic paraboloid, $z = -x^2 + \tfrac{1}{3} y^2$, of Example 10.2-5.

(a) Find the tangent plane at the origin.

(b) Find the tangent plane at any point (x_1, y_1, z_1).

5. Consider the cylinder $x^2 + y^2 = a^2$.

(a) Find the tangent plane at the point $(\tfrac{3}{5}a, \tfrac{4}{5}a, 2a)$.

(b) Show that at any point the tangent plane touches the cylinder all along the straight-line generator through that point.

6. Consider the cylinder $xz = 4$. Find the tangent planes at $(1, 0, 4)$ and $(-2, 2, -2)$.

7. Consider the cone, $x^2 + z^2 = \dfrac{a^2}{h^2} y^2$, of Example 10.3-3.

(a) Find the tangent plane at $(a/\sqrt{2}, h, a/\sqrt{2})$.

(b) Show that at any point the tangent plane touches the cone all along the straight-line generator through that point.

8. (a) Find the equation of the tangent plane to $x^2/y = y - z$ at $(1, 1, 0)$.

(b) This surface is a cone with vertex at the origin; see Exercise 10.3-12(b). Show that the direction of the normal to the surface does not vary as one moves along the straight-line generator joining $(1, 1, 0)$ to the origin.

9. Consider the surface with parametric equations
$$x = 2 \cosh u \cos v, \qquad y = 3 \cosh u \sin v, \qquad z = 6 \sinh u.$$

(a) Show that the parametric curves for which u is constant and v varies are ellipses in planes parallel to the xy plane.

(b) Show that the parametric curves for which v is constant and u varies lie in planes through the z axis. *Suggestion:* Eliminate the parameter u between the equations for x and y.

(c) Find a vector normal to the surface at the point for which $u = 1$, $v = \pi/3$ by taking a vector perpendicular to the parametric curves at that point.

(d) Eliminate the parameters u and v and thus show that this surface is the hyperboloid of one sheet of Exercise 2.

10. The equations
$$\left. \begin{array}{l} x = (3 + \cos \phi) \cos \theta \\ y = (3 + \cos \phi) \sin \theta \\ z = \sin \phi \end{array} \right\}, \qquad 0 \le \theta < 2\pi, \qquad -\pi < \phi \le \pi \qquad (6)$$

describe a surface called the torus, part of which is sketched in Fig. 11.17. This surface is obtained by revolving the circle $(y - 3)^2 + z^2 = 1$ about the z axis.

(a) Show that the parametric curves for which ϕ is constant and θ varies are circles in planes parallel to the xy plane.

(b) Show that the parametric curves for which θ is constant and ϕ varies lie in planes through the z axis. *Suggestion:* Eliminate ϕ between the equations for x and y.*

---

* You can show that these curves are circles if you write $r = \sqrt{x^2 + y^2} = 3 + \cos \phi$, $z = \sin \phi$, $(r - 3)^2 + z^2 = 1$. These circles are the meridians.

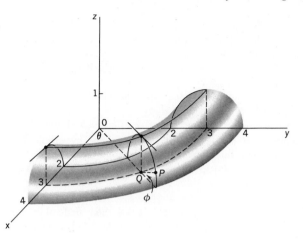

Fig. 11.17

(c) Find a vector normal to this surface at the point for which $\theta = \pi/4$, $\phi = 2\pi/3$.

(d) It appears from Fig. 11.17 that, first at a point for which $-\pi/2 < \phi < \pi/2$, the surface lies entirely on one side of its tangent plane; second, at a point for which $\pi/2 < |\phi| \leq \pi$, the surface lies on both sides of its tangent plane; and, third, at a point for which $\phi = \pm\pi/2$, the surface lies on one side of its tangent plane except for one curve that the surface and tangent plane have in common. Prove the third statement.

(e) Derive Eqs. (6). *Suggestion:* Show that

$$\overrightarrow{OQ} = 3(\cos\theta\vec{i} + \sin\theta\vec{j})$$

and that

$$\overrightarrow{QP} = 1\cos\phi(\cos\theta\vec{i} + \sin\theta\vec{j}) + 1\sin\phi\vec{k}.$$

11. The surface with parametric equations $x = r\cos\theta$, $y = r\sin\theta$, $z = a\theta$, $(r \geq 0)$ is called the right helicoid. See Fig. 11.18.

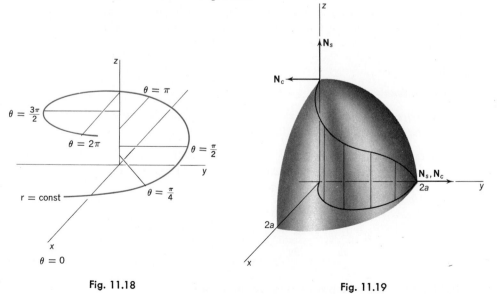

Fig. 11.18   **Fig. 11.19**

(a) Show that the parametric curves for which θ is constant and r varies are straight lines through the z axis parallel to the xy plane.

(b) Show that the parametric curves for which r is constant and θ varies are helices.

(c) Find a normal vector at the point for which $r = r_1$, $\theta = \theta_1$; at the point for which $r = a/2$, $\theta = \pi/4$.

12. Where do the cone $x^2 + y^2 = \frac{1}{2} z^2$ and the cylinder $x^2 + y^2 = 4$ intersect? At what angle do they intersect?

13. At what angle do the sphere $x^2 + y^2 + z^2 = 16$ and the plane $y = 2$ intersect?

14. The ellipsoid $y^2/16 + x^2/12 + z^2/12 = 1$ and the hyperboloid $y^2/3 - x^2 - z^2 = 1$ have the same foci. Show that they intersect orthogonally.

15. Show that the sphere $x^2 + y^2 + z^2 = 18$ and the cone $x^2 + z^2 = (y - 6)^2$ are tangent along their intersection.

16. Show that the sphere $x^2 + y^2 + z^2 = 4a^2$ and the cylinder $x^2 + (y - a)^2 = a^2$ do not intersect at a constant angle, but that their angle of intersection at a point of intersection (x_1, y_1, z_1) is given by $\cos \theta = y_1/2a$. See Fig. 11.19.

11.5 Chain Rules for Partial Derivatives

I

In Sec. 1.7 we pointed out that, if $x = g(t)$ with domain S_t and range S_x and that if $u = f(x)$ with domain including S_x, then we could form the composite function $u = \phi(t) = f(g(t))$ with domain S_t and that if, further, $g'(t)$ existed for t of S_t and $f'(x)$ existed for x of S_x, then the derivative of the composite function could be found by the chain rule: For each t_1 of S_t we can write $x_1 = g(t_1)$ and then

$$\phi'(t_1) = f'(x_1)g'(t_1),$$

or, with less precision,

$$\left(\frac{du}{dt}\right)_{t_1} = \left(\frac{du}{dx}\right)_{x_1} \left(\frac{dx}{dt}\right)_{t_1}.$$

Here we shall consider the chain rules that arise when we deal with functions of several variables. Theorem 11.2-1 serves as a unifying idea for all this work; we restate it here for easy reference.

■ THEOREM 1

The total increment.

HYPOTHESIS: (a) $u = f(x, y)$ is defined for domain D in the xy plane.

(b) $\partial u/\partial x$ and $\partial u/\partial y$ are continuous for D.

CONCLUSION: For each (x, y) of D and for each Δx and Δy such that the rectangle with vertices (x, y), $(x + \Delta x, \Delta y)$, $(x, y + \Delta y)$, $(x + \Delta x, y + \Delta y)$ lies entirely in D, there are numbers ϵ_1 and ϵ_2 such that

$$\Delta u = f(x + \Delta x, y + \Delta y) - f(x, y)$$

$$= f_1(x, y) \, \Delta x + f_2(x, y) \, \Delta y + \epsilon_1 \, \Delta x + \epsilon_2 \, \Delta y$$

$$= \frac{\partial u}{\partial x} \Delta x + \frac{\partial u}{\partial y} \Delta y + \epsilon_1 \, \Delta x + \epsilon_2 \, \Delta y, \tag{1}$$

and, further, ϵ_1 and ϵ_2 approach 0 as Δx and Δy approach 0.

Example 1.   Suppose that u is a function of the position of a particle in the plane and that the position of the particle changes with time. At what rate does u change with time?

To describe the position of the particle we have $x = g(t)$ and $y = h(t)$ for t of a t domain S_t and to describe u we have $u = f(x, y)$ for points (x, y) of a domain D of the x, y plane, it being understood that the point (x, y) assigned to each number t of S_t by the g and h functions lies in D. Then we can form the composite function

$$u = \phi(t) = f(g(t), h(t))$$

and inquire about $\phi'(t)$, which we can indicate somewhat more loosely by du/dt. Assuming that g' and h' are continuous for t of S_t and that f_1 and f_2 are continuous for (x, y) of D, we start with a number t of S_t, take $\Delta t \neq 0$ such that the interval bounded by t and $t + \Delta t$ lies in S_t and the rectangle with vertices $(x, y),(x + \Delta x, y)$, $(x, y + \Delta y)$, $(x + \Delta x, y + \Delta y)$ lies entirely in D, and write Eq. (1). When we divide by Δt we have

$$\frac{\Delta u}{\Delta t} = \frac{\partial u}{\partial x}\frac{\Delta x}{\Delta t} + \frac{\partial u}{\partial y}\frac{\Delta y}{\Delta t} + \epsilon_1 \frac{\Delta x}{\Delta t} + \epsilon_2 \frac{\Delta y}{\Delta t}. \tag{2}$$

Next we let Δt approach 0. Then $\Delta x/\Delta t$ and $\Delta y/\Delta t$ will approach dx/dt and dy/dt, and

$$\Delta x = \frac{\Delta x}{\Delta t} \Delta t \quad\text{and}\quad \Delta y = \frac{\Delta y}{\Delta t} \Delta t$$

will both approach 0. But ϵ_1 and ϵ_2 approach 0 when Δx and Δy do. Hence from Eq. (2) we conclude that

$$\frac{du}{dt} = \frac{\partial u}{\partial x}\frac{dx}{dt} + \frac{\partial u}{\partial y}\frac{dy}{dt},$$

or, writing with greater precision, that

$$\phi'(t) = f_1(g(t), h(t))\, g'(t) + f_2(g(t), h(t))h'(t).$$

Example 2.   Suppose that at first u is defined as a function of x and y, $u = f(x, y)$, but that we decide to change to polar coordinates via the equations $x = r\cos\theta, y = r\sin\theta$ so that we can write u also as a composite function of r and θ: $u = g(r, \theta) = f(r\cos\theta, r\sin\theta)$. It is reasonable to ask for $\partial u/\partial r$ or $g_1(r, \theta)$ and $\partial u/\partial\theta$ or $g_2(r, \theta)$.

To be more precise, let f be defined for domain D of the x, y plane and let the domain D' of (r, θ) ordered number pairs be such that for every (r, θ) of D' the equations $x = r\cos\theta, y = r\sin\theta$ assign an (x, y) of D. Assuming that $f_1(x, y)$ and $f_2(x, y)$ are continuous in D, we start with an (r, θ) of D', take $\Delta r \neq 0$ such that the line segment joining (r, θ) to $(r + \Delta r, \theta)$ is in D' and the rectangle with the corresponding vertices (x, y), $(x + \Delta x, y)$, $(x, y + \Delta y)$, $(x + \Delta x, y + \Delta y)$ lies entirely in D, and then we use Theorem 1, the theorem on the total increment. We write

$$\Delta u = \frac{\partial u}{\partial x}\Delta x + \frac{\partial u}{\partial y}\Delta y + \epsilon_1 \Delta x + \epsilon_2 \Delta y,$$

$$\frac{\Delta u}{\Delta r} = \frac{\partial u}{\partial x}\frac{\Delta x}{\Delta r} + \frac{\partial u}{\partial y}\frac{\Delta y}{\Delta r} + \epsilon_1 \frac{\Delta x}{\Delta r} + \epsilon_2 \frac{\Delta y}{\Delta r}. \tag{3a}$$

Now if we let Δr approach 0, we know that $\Delta x/\Delta r$ and $\Delta y/\Delta r$ will approach $\partial x/\partial r$ and $\partial y/\partial r$. Moreover, if θ is held fixed, $\Delta x = \Delta r \cos \theta$ and $\Delta y = \Delta r \sin \theta$ approach 0 when Δr does, and ϵ_1 and ϵ_2 approach 0 with Δx and Δy. From Eq. (3a) we deduce

$$\frac{\partial u}{\partial r} = \frac{\partial u}{\partial x}\frac{\partial x}{\partial r} + \frac{\partial u}{\partial y}\frac{\partial y}{\partial r}. \tag{4}$$

If we had taken $\Delta\theta \neq 0$ such that the arc joining (r, θ) to $(r, \theta + \Delta\theta)$ was in D' and had worked in similar fashion, we would have had

$$\frac{\Delta u}{\Delta\theta} = \frac{\partial u}{\partial x}\frac{\Delta x}{\Delta\theta} + \frac{\partial u}{\partial y}\frac{\Delta y}{\Delta\theta} + \epsilon_1\frac{\Delta x}{\Delta\theta} + \epsilon_2\frac{\Delta y}{\Delta\theta}, \tag{3b}$$

and

$$\frac{\partial u}{\partial\theta} = \frac{\partial u}{\partial x}\frac{\partial x}{\partial\theta} + \frac{\partial u}{\partial y}\frac{\partial y}{\partial\theta}. \tag{5}$$

Since

$$\frac{\partial x}{\partial r} = \cos\theta, \qquad \frac{\partial y}{\partial r} = \sin\theta, \qquad \frac{\partial x}{\partial\theta} = -r\sin\theta, \qquad \frac{\partial y}{\partial\theta} = r\cos\theta$$

when $x = r\cos\theta$ and $y = r\sin\theta$, Eqs. (4) and (5) become

$$\frac{\partial u}{\partial r} = \frac{\partial u}{\partial x}\cos\theta + \frac{\partial u}{\partial y}\sin\theta, \tag{6}$$

$$\frac{\partial u}{\partial\theta} = -\frac{\partial u}{\partial x}r\sin\theta + \frac{\partial u}{\partial y}r\cos\theta. \tag{7}$$

With greater precision, Eq. (6) could be written in the form

$$\frac{\partial u}{\partial r} = g_1(r, \theta) = f_1(r\cos\theta, \sin\theta)\cos\theta + f_2(r\cos\theta, r\sin\theta)\sin\theta.$$

Example 3. If $u = f(x, y, z)$ we can form grad u. Suppose that $v = \phi(u)$. What can be said about grad v?

In detail, let $f(x, y, z)$ have domain D and the range set S_u, with f_1, f_2, f_3 continuous for D. Let the domain for $\phi(u)$ include S_u, with ϕ' continuous for S_u. Then for any (x, y, z) of D we can form the composite function

$$v = \tau(x, y, z) = \phi(f(x, y, z)),$$

and we shall compute $\partial v/\partial x = \partial\tau/\partial x$, $\partial v/\partial y$, $\partial v/\partial z$ so that grad v can be computed.

Take $\Delta x \neq 0$ such that the line segment joining (x, y, z) to $(x + \Delta x, y, z)$ lies entirely in D and form $u = f(x, y, z)$, $u + \Delta u = f(x + \Delta x, y, z)$, both in S_u, then $v = \phi(u)$ and $v + \Delta v = \phi(u + \Delta u)$. Because $\phi'(u)$ is continuous in S_u, we can write

$$\Delta v = \frac{dv}{du}\Delta u + \epsilon_1\Delta u,$$

where ϵ_1 approaches 0 as Δu does. If we divide by Δx we get

$$\frac{\Delta v}{\Delta x} = \frac{dv}{du}\frac{\Delta u}{\Delta x} + \epsilon_1\frac{\Delta u}{\Delta x},$$

where we know that $\Delta u/\Delta x$ approaches $\partial u/\partial x$ when Δx approaches 0, y and z held fixed. Further, when y and z are held fixed, we can write

$$\Delta u = \frac{\partial u}{\partial x}\,\Delta x + \epsilon_2\,\Delta x,$$

where ϵ_2 approaches 0 when Δx does. Now we know that Δu and, with it, the ϵ_1 of the previous equation approach 0 when Δx does, so that

$$\frac{\partial v}{\partial x} = \frac{dv}{du}\frac{\partial u}{\partial x}.$$

Similarly, we also have

$$\frac{\partial v}{\partial y} = \frac{dv}{du}\frac{\partial u}{\partial y} \qquad \text{and} \qquad \frac{\partial v}{\partial z} = \frac{dv}{du}\frac{\partial u}{\partial z}.$$

Finally, we can say that

$$\operatorname{grad} v = \frac{\partial v}{\partial x}\,\mathbf{i} + \frac{\partial v}{\partial y}\,\mathbf{j} + \frac{\partial v}{\partial z}\,\mathbf{k} = \frac{dv}{du}\left(\frac{\partial u}{\partial x}\,\mathbf{i} + \frac{\partial u}{\partial y}\,\mathbf{j} + \frac{\partial u}{\partial z}\,\mathbf{k}\right),$$

or

$$\operatorname{grad}\phi(u) = \phi'(u)\operatorname{grad} u. \tag{8}$$

With greater precision, Eq. (8) is a vector identity valid for all (x, y, z) of D:

$$\operatorname{grad}\phi(f(x, y, z)) = \phi'(f(x, y, z))\operatorname{grad} f(x, y, z).$$

If, in particular $u = f(x, y, z) = x^2 + y^2 + z^2$ with domain D consisting of all of space except for the point $(0, 0, 0)$, then the range set S_u consists of the set of numbers $u > 0$. If, also, $v = \phi(u) = \sqrt{u}$ with domain $S_u : u > 0$, we have $\phi'(u) = \frac{1}{2}(1/\sqrt{u})$ and Eq. (8) says that

$$\operatorname{grad}\sqrt{x^2 + y^2 + z^2} = \frac{1}{2}\frac{1}{\sqrt{x^2 + y^2 + z^2}}\operatorname{grad}(x^2 + y^2 + z^2).$$

Example 4. Let C with parametric equations

$$x = f(u), \qquad y = g(u), \qquad z = h(u), \qquad a \le u \le b, \tag{9}$$

be an arbitrary curve on surface S with equation

$$F(x, y, z) = 0. \tag{10}$$

Since every point of C lies on the surface S, the x, y, and z furnished by Eqs. (9) satisfy Eq. (10);

$$F(f(u), g(u), h(u)) = 0 \qquad \text{for} \qquad a \le u \le b.$$

Here we have an identity in u, and we can differentiate with respect to u;

$$\frac{dF}{du} = 0 \qquad \text{for} \qquad a \le u \le b. \tag{11}$$

For any u of $a \le u \le b$ we choose $\Delta u \ne 0$ such that $a \le u + \Delta u \le b$ and form $\Delta x = f(u + \Delta u) - f(u)$, $\Delta y = g(u + \Delta u) - g(u)$, $\Delta z = h(u + \Delta u) - h(u)$.

Assuming that $F(x, y, z)$ has continuous partial derivatives in a region that includes all the points of curve C, we can write

$$\Delta F = \frac{\partial F}{\partial x} \Delta x + \frac{\partial F}{\partial y} \Delta y + \frac{\partial F}{\partial z} \Delta z + \epsilon_1 \Delta x + \epsilon_2 \Delta y + \epsilon_3 \Delta z,$$

where ϵ_1, ϵ_2, and ϵ_3 approach 0 as Δx, Δy, and Δz do. Then we write

$$\frac{\Delta F}{\Delta u} = \frac{\partial F}{\partial x} \frac{\Delta x}{\Delta u} + \frac{\partial F}{\partial y} \frac{\Delta y}{\Delta u} + \frac{\partial F}{\partial z} \frac{\Delta z}{\Delta u} + \epsilon_1 \frac{\Delta x}{\Delta u} + \epsilon_2 \frac{\Delta y}{\Delta u} + \epsilon_3 \frac{\Delta z}{\Delta u},$$

and reason as in Example 1 to get

$$\frac{dF}{du} = \frac{\partial F}{\partial x} \frac{dx}{du} + \frac{\partial F}{\partial y} \frac{dy}{du} + \frac{\partial F}{\partial x} \frac{dz}{du},$$

it being assumed that dx/du, dy/du, dz/du exist for $a \le u \le b$. Thus Eq. (11) becomes

$$\frac{\partial F}{\partial x} \frac{dx}{du} + \frac{\partial F}{\partial y} \frac{dy}{du} + \frac{\partial F}{\partial z} \frac{dz}{du} = 0. \tag{12}$$

From $\vec{R} = x\vec{i} + y\vec{j} + z\vec{k}$ we get

$$\frac{d\vec{R}}{du} = \frac{dx}{du} \vec{i} + \frac{dy}{du} \vec{j} + \frac{dz}{du} \vec{k},$$

so that Eq. (12) can be rewritten

$$\text{grad } F \cdot \frac{d\vec{R}}{du} = 0. \tag{12a}$$

Since $d\vec{R}/du$ is in the direction of the tangent to C, Eq. (12a) says that at a given point of S all tangents to curves on S through that point lie perpendicular to one direction, the direction of grad F. This direction we have already called the surface normal.

Example 5.   We shall show that any expression of the form $u = f(xy)$ is a solution of the partial differential equation

$$x \frac{\partial u}{\partial x} - y \frac{\partial u}{\partial y} = 0, \tag{13}$$

provided that f is a differentiable function. For instance, it is alleged that, if we choose $f(w) = e^{-w}$, then $u = f(xy) = e^{-xy}$ will be a solution. Let us write

$$u = f(xy) = f(w), \qquad w = xy.$$

Then, as in Example 3, we reason that

$$\Delta u = \frac{df}{dw} \Delta w + \epsilon_1 \Delta w,$$

and that if $\Delta x \ne 0$,

$$\frac{\Delta u}{\Delta x} = \frac{df}{dw} \frac{\Delta w}{\Delta x} + \epsilon_1 \frac{\Delta w}{\Delta x}.$$

Then

$$\frac{\partial u}{\partial x} = \frac{df}{dw}\frac{\partial w}{\partial x} = \frac{df}{dw}y.$$

Similarly, we write

$$\frac{\partial u}{\partial y} = \frac{df}{dw}\frac{\partial w}{\partial y} = \frac{df}{dw}x.$$

Now we have

$$x\frac{\partial u}{\partial x} - y\frac{\partial u}{\partial y} = xy\frac{df}{dw} - yx\frac{df}{dw} = 0.$$

Example 6. If z is defined implicitly as a differentiable function of x and y by an equation of the form

$$F(x, y, z) = 0, \tag{14}$$

we can find $\partial z/\partial x$ and $\partial z/\partial y$ by implicit differentiation. But we can also proceed as follows.

Suppose that F_1, F_2, F_3 are continuous for a domain D so that for a point (x, y, z) of D and suitable Δx, Δy, Δz we can write

$$\Delta F = \frac{\partial F}{\partial x}\Delta x + \frac{\partial F}{\partial y}\Delta y + \frac{\partial F}{\partial z}\Delta z + \epsilon_1\Delta x + \epsilon_2\Delta y + \epsilon_3\Delta z, \tag{15a}$$

where ϵ_1, ϵ_2, and ϵ_3 will approach 0 when Δx, Δy, Δz approach 0. Now, when we say that z is defined as a function of x and y by $F(x, y, z) = 0$, we mean that to the number pair x, y a number z is assigned such that $F(x, y, z) = 0$ and that to the number pair $x + \Delta x$, $y + \Delta y$ a number $z + \Delta z$ is assigned such that $F(x + \Delta x, y + \Delta y, z + \Delta z) = 0$. Hence we have $\Delta F = F(x + \Delta x, y + \Delta y, z + \Delta z) - F(x, y, z) = 0 - 0 = 0$ and Eq. (15a) becomes

$$0 = \frac{\partial F}{\partial x}\Delta x + \frac{\partial F}{\partial y}\Delta y + \frac{\partial F}{\partial z}\Delta z + \epsilon_1\Delta x + \epsilon_2\Delta y + \epsilon_3\Delta z.$$

If, further, $\partial F/\partial z \neq 0$ at (x, y, z), we can write

$$\Delta z = -\frac{1}{\partial F/\partial z}\left(\frac{\partial F}{\partial x}\Delta x + \frac{\partial F}{\partial y}\Delta y + \epsilon_1\Delta x + \epsilon_2\Delta y + \epsilon_3\Delta z\right).$$

Take $\Delta y = 0$, so that y is held fixed, but $\Delta x \neq 0$ and write next

$$\frac{\Delta z}{\Delta x} = -\frac{1}{\partial F/\partial z}\left[\frac{\partial F}{\partial x} + \epsilon_1 + \epsilon_3\frac{\Delta z}{\Delta x}\right]. \tag{15b}$$

Now if Δx approaches 0, Δz will approach 0 also, because we are assuming that z is defined implicitly as a differentiable function of x and y and hence also as a continuous function, and because we already have $\Delta y = 0$. Under these conditions the ϵ's, originally stated to approach 0 when Δx, Δy, and Δz do, would approach 0 when Δx does. Hence we learn from Eq. (15b) that

$$\frac{\partial z}{\partial x} = -\frac{\partial F/\partial x}{\partial F/\partial z}. \tag{16a}$$

Similarly, we can derive

$$\frac{\partial z}{\partial y} = -\frac{\partial F/\partial y}{\partial F/\partial z}. \tag{16b}$$

Example 7. Let $w = \phi(x, y, z)$ be defined for points on the surface S with parametric equations $x = f(u, v)$, $y = g(u, v)$, $z = h(u, v)$. For instance, we might wish to discuss $w = k/(x^2 + y^2 + z^2)$ in a problem concerned with an inverse square force and distances from points on S to a charge at the origin. We can also consider w to be a composite function of u and v,

$$w = \tau(u,v) = \phi(f(u,v), g(u,v), h(u,v)),$$

and we could ask for $\partial w/\partial u$ or τ_1 and $\partial w/\partial v$ or τ_2.

Assuming that ϕ, f, g, and h have continuous partial derivatives in the proper domains, we can write

$$\Delta w = \frac{\partial w}{\partial x} \Delta x + \frac{\partial w}{\partial y} \Delta y + \frac{\partial w}{\partial z} \Delta z + \epsilon_1 \Delta x + \epsilon_2 \Delta y + \epsilon_3 \Delta z, \tag{17}$$

where by $\partial w/\partial x$, $\partial w/\partial y$, $\partial w/\partial z$ we mean ϕ_1, ϕ_2, ϕ_3, and we can also write

$$\Delta x = \frac{\partial x}{\partial u} \Delta u + \frac{\partial x}{\partial v} \Delta v + \epsilon_4 \Delta u + \epsilon_5 \Delta v, \tag{18}$$

$$\Delta y = \frac{\partial y}{\partial u} \Delta u + \frac{\partial y}{\partial v} \Delta v + \epsilon_6 \Delta u + \epsilon_7 \Delta v, \tag{19}$$

$$\Delta z = \frac{\partial z}{\partial u} \Delta u + \frac{\partial z}{\partial v} \Delta v + \epsilon_8 \Delta u + \epsilon_9 \Delta v. \tag{20}$$

Substituting from Eqs. (18), (19), and (20) into Eq. (17), we get

$$\Delta w = \left(\frac{\partial w}{\partial x}\frac{\partial x}{\partial u} + \frac{\partial w}{\partial y}\frac{\partial y}{\partial u} + \frac{\partial w}{\partial z}\frac{\partial z}{\partial u}\right) \Delta u + \left(\frac{\partial w}{\partial x}\frac{\partial x}{\partial v} + \frac{\partial w}{\partial y}\frac{\partial y}{\partial v} + \frac{\partial w}{\partial z}\frac{\partial z}{\partial v}\right) \Delta v$$

$$+ \text{ terms containing } \epsilon\text{'s.} \tag{21}$$

If we hold v fixed, writing $\Delta v = 0$, then divide by $\Delta u \neq 0$ and let Δu approach 0, we can write

$$\frac{\Delta w}{\Delta u} = \frac{\partial w}{\partial x}\frac{\partial x}{\partial u} + \frac{\partial w}{\partial y}\frac{\partial y}{\partial u} + \frac{\partial w}{\partial z}\frac{\partial z}{\partial u} + \text{ terms containing } \epsilon\text{'s,}$$

$$\frac{\partial w}{\partial u} = \frac{\partial w}{\partial x}\frac{\partial x}{\partial u} + \frac{\partial w}{\partial y}\frac{\partial y}{\partial u} + \frac{\partial w}{\partial z}\frac{\partial z}{\partial u}.$$

Similarly, from Eq. (21) we can also derive

$$\frac{\partial w}{\partial v} = \frac{\partial w}{\partial x}\frac{\partial x}{\partial v} + \frac{\partial w}{\partial y}\frac{\partial y}{\partial v} + \frac{\partial w}{\partial z}\frac{\partial z}{\partial v}.$$

▌▌

We have considered many special composite functions and their derivatives in the examples of this section. We can state a theorem of some generality that includes them all.

■ **THEOREM 2**

The Chain Rule.

HYPOTHESIS: (a) $u = f(x_1, x_2, \cdots, x_n)$ for ordered n-tuples $(x_1, x_2, \cdots, x_n)$ selected from a domain set D of ordered n-tuples.

(b) $\partial f/\partial x_k$, $k = 1, 2, \cdots, n$, are continuous for all n-tuples $(x_1, x_2, \cdots, x_n)$ of D.

(c) $x_k = \phi_k(t_1, t_2, \cdots, t_\sigma)$, $k = 1, 2, \cdots, n$, for ordered σ-tuples $(t_1, t_2, \cdots, t_\sigma)$ selected from a domain set D' of ordered σ-tuples.

(d) For each σ-tuple $(t_1, t_2, \cdots, t_\sigma)$ of D' the corresponding $(x_1, x_2, \cdots, x_n)$ n-tuple lies in D.

(e) $\partial \phi_k/\partial t_\gamma$, $\gamma = 1, 2, \cdots, \sigma$ and $k = 1, 2, \cdots, n$ exist for all σ-tuples $(t_1, t_2, \cdots, t_\sigma)$ of D'.

CONCLUSION: For each σ-tuple $(t_1, t_2, \cdots, t_\sigma)$ of D' the composite function $u = g(t_1, t_2, \cdots, t_\sigma) = f(\phi_1(t_1, \cdots, t_\sigma), \phi_2(t_1, \cdots, t_\sigma), \cdots, \phi_n(t_1, \cdots, t_\sigma))$ can be formed by replacing the x's in $u = f(x_1, x_2, \cdots, x_n)$ by t's according to the equations of Hypothesis (c), and

$$\frac{\partial u}{\partial t_\gamma} = \frac{\partial g}{\partial t_\gamma} = \frac{\partial u}{\partial x_1}\frac{\partial x_1}{\partial t_\gamma} + \frac{\partial u}{\partial x_2}\frac{\partial x_2}{\partial t_\gamma} + \cdots + \frac{\partial u}{\partial x_n}\frac{\partial x_n}{\partial t_\gamma}, \gamma = 1, 2, \cdots, \sigma.$$

PROOF: We shall demonstrate the formula for $\partial u/\partial t_1$.

Step (a): At a σ-tuple $(t_1, t_2, \cdots, t_\sigma)$ of D' let us choose $\Delta t_2 = \Delta t_3 = \cdots = \Delta t_\sigma$ $= 0$, but $\Delta t_1 \neq 0$, and let us form $\Delta x_k = \phi_k(t_1 + \Delta t_1, t_2, \cdots, t_\sigma) - \phi_k(t_1, t_2, \cdots, t_\sigma)$ for each $k = 1, 2, \cdots, n$ at the n-tuple $(x_1, x_2, \cdots, x_n)$ associated with $(t_1, t_2, \cdots, t_\sigma)$ by the equations of Hypothesis (c).

Step (b): Hypotheses (a) and (b) enable us to write

$$\Delta u = \sum_{k=1}^{n}\left[\frac{\partial u}{\partial x_k}\Delta x_k + \epsilon_k \Delta x_k\right],$$

where by $\partial u/\partial x_k$ we mean $\partial f/\partial x_k$ and where the ϵ_k's approach 0 when the Δx_k's approach 0.

Step (c): Divide by Δt_1 to get

$$\frac{\Delta u}{\Delta t_1} = \sum_{k=1}^{n}\left[\frac{\partial u}{\partial x_k}\frac{\Delta x_k}{\Delta t_1} + \epsilon_k \frac{\Delta x_k}{\Delta t_1}\right].$$

Step (d): Observe that Δx_k must approach 0 if Δt_1 approaches 0, because ϕ_k must be a continuous function of $t_1, t_2, \cdots, t_\sigma$ (since its partial derivatives exist according to Hypothesis (e)) and because we already have $\Delta t_2 = \cdots = \Delta t_\sigma = 0$. Hence the ϵ_k's, which approach 0 when the Δx_k's approach 0, also approach 0 when Δt_1 approaches 0.

Step (e): Now we conclude from Step (c) that

$$\frac{\partial u}{\partial t_1} = \sum_{k=1}^{n}\frac{\partial u}{\partial x_k}\frac{\partial x_k}{\partial t_1} = \frac{\partial u}{\partial x_1}\frac{\partial x_1}{\partial t_1} + \frac{\partial u}{\partial x_2}\frac{\partial x_2}{\partial t_1} + \cdots + \frac{\partial u}{\partial x_n}\frac{\partial x_n}{\partial t_1}.$$

If we repeat our work for t_1 with $t_2, t_3, \cdots, t_\sigma$ we derive the remaining formulas of the conclusion of this theorem.

Step (f): It is understood in an equation like that of Step (e) that $\partial u/\partial t_1$ means $\partial g/\partial t_1$ while $\partial u/\partial x_k$ means $\partial f/\partial x_k$ and that $\partial u/\partial x_k$ is to be evaluated at the n-tuple $(x_1, x_2, \cdots, x_n)$ corresponding to the σ-tuple $(t_1, t_2, \cdots, t_\sigma)$ with which we started.

EXERCISES 11.5

1. Let $v = xy + yz + zx$ and let $x = t, y = t^2, z = t^3$. Find dv/dt
   (a) by using a chain rule, and
   (b) by substituting for x, y, and z and thus writing v directly as a function of t.

2. $u = \dfrac{1}{(x^2 + y^2 + z^2)^2}$ is a function of the position of a particle in space. Let the particle move along the helix $x = \cos \pi t, y = \sin \pi t, z = t$ for the time interval $0 \le t \le 2$, so that u can also be considered a composite function of t. Find du/dt at $t = 1$.

3. Let $u = \dfrac{xy}{x^2 + y^2}$ where $x = r \cos \theta$ and $y = r \sin \theta$. Find $\partial u/\partial r$ and $\partial u/\partial \theta$
   (a) by using the chain rules of Eqs. (6) and (7), and
   (b) by substituting for x and y and thus writing u directly as a function of r and θ.

4. Repeat Exercise 3 for $u = x + x^2 + 2y^2$.

5. Let $u = f(x, y)$ with $\partial u/\partial x$ and $\partial u/\partial y$ continuous. Suppose that we translate coordinates according to the formulas $x = x' + a, y = y' + b$ and consider u as a composite function of the new coordinates x' and y'. Find $\partial u/\partial x'$ and $\partial u/\partial y'$ in terms of $\partial u/\partial x$ and $\partial u/\partial y$.

6. Let $u = f(x, y)$ with $\partial u/\partial x$ and $\partial u/\partial y$ continuous. Suppose that we rotate coordinates according to the formulas $x = x' \cos \alpha - y' \sin \alpha, y = x' \sin \alpha + y' \cos \alpha$ and consider u as a composite function of the new coordinates x' and y'. Find $\partial u/\partial x'$ and $\partial u/\partial y'$ in terms of $\partial u/\partial x$ and $\partial u/\partial y$.

7. Let $u = f(x, y)$ with $\partial u/\partial x$ and $\partial u/\partial y$ continuous. Suppose that we change to parabolic coordinates by using the equations $x = \tfrac{1}{2} (v^2 - w^2)$ and $y = vw$, and consider u as a composite function of the new coordinates v and w. Find $\partial u/\partial v$ and $\partial u/\partial w$ in terms of $\partial u/\partial x$ and $\partial u/\partial y$.

8. Let $u = f(x, y)$ with $\partial u/\partial x$ and $\partial u/\partial y$ continuous. Suppose that we change to elliptic coordinates by using the equations $x = \cosh v \cos w$ and $y = \sinh v \sin w$, and consider u as a composite function of the coordinates v and w. Find $\partial u/\partial v$ and $\partial u/\partial w$ in terms of $\partial u/\partial x$ and $\partial u/\partial y$.

9. Let $r = (x^2 + y^2 + z^2)^{1/2}$.
   (a) Find grad r.
   (b) Find grad r^n, where n is a constant.
   (c) For which n will grad r^n be a vector with radial direction and magnitude inversely proportional to the square of the distance from the origin?

10. Let $\theta = \tan^{-1} \dfrac{y}{x}, x \ne 0$.

    (a) Find grad θ.
    (b) Find grad $f(\theta)$ in general and grad $\sin \tfrac{1}{2}\theta$ in particular.

11. (a) Show that the curve $C: x = \cos^2 u, y = \cos u \sin u, z = \sin u$ lies on the sphere
        $S: x^2 + y^2 + z^2 = 1$.
    (b) Find a vector tangent to C at the point $u = u_0$.
    (c) Find $\vec{\mathbf{N}}$, a vector normal to S at this point.
    (d) Show that these vectors are perpendicular.

12. The same as Exercise 11 for the curve C: $x = u \cos u, y = u \sin u, z = 4u^2$ and the surface S: $4(x^2 + y^2) = z$.

13. Let $u = f(x, y, z)$ with $\partial u/\partial x$, $\partial u/\partial y$, $\partial u/\partial z$ continuous. Suppose that we change to "cylindrical coordinates" by using the equations $x = r \cos \theta, y = r \sin \theta, z = z$ and consider u to be a composite function of the new coordinates r, θ, and z. Find $\partial u/\partial r$, $\partial u/\partial \theta$, and $\partial u/\partial z$ in terms of $\partial u/\partial x$, $\partial u/\partial y$, and $\partial u/\partial z$.

14. Let $u = f(x, y, z)$ as in Exercise 13. Suppose that we change to "spherical coordinates" by using the equations $x = \rho \sin \phi \cos \theta, y = \rho \sin \phi \sin \theta, z = \rho \cos \phi$ and consider u to be a composite function of the new coordinates ρ, ϕ, θ. Find $\partial u/\partial \rho$, $\partial u/\partial \phi$, and $\partial u/\partial \theta$ in terms of $\partial u/\partial x$, $\partial u/\partial y$, and $\partial u/\partial z$.

15. Show that $u = xf(y/x)$, where f can be any differentiable function, will satisfy the partial differential equation $x \dfrac{\partial u}{\partial x} + y \dfrac{\partial u}{\partial y} = u$.

16. Show that $u = xy f\left(\dfrac{x+y}{xy}\right)$, where f can be any differentiable function, will satisfy the partial differential equation $x^2 (\partial u/\partial x) - y^2 (\partial u/\partial y) = (x - y)u$.

17. In Exercise 11.1-10, z was defined implicitly as a function of x and y and $\partial z/\partial x$ and $\partial z/\partial y$ were computed. Compute $\partial z/\partial x$ and $\partial z/\partial y$ again by using Eqs. (16a) and (16b).

18. In Exercise 11.1-11(a) z was defined implicitly as a function of x and y and $\partial z/\partial x$ and $\partial z/\partial y$ were computed. Compute $\partial z/\partial x$ and $\partial z/\partial y$ again by using Eqs. (16a) and (16b).

19. Find the partial derivatives called for in Exercise 11.1-11(b) by using formulas analogous to Eqs. (16a) and (16b).

20. Let $u = 1/[(x - x_0)^2 + (y - y_0)^2 + (z - z_0)^2]$ and let z be given implicitly as a function of x and y, $z = \phi(x, y)$, by $\dfrac{x^2}{a^2} + \dfrac{y^2}{b^2} + \dfrac{z^2}{c^2} = 1$ so that we can consider u to be a function of x and y alone, $u = \eta(x, y)$, by considering z to have been replaced by $\phi(x, y)$ in the original statement for u. Find $\partial \eta/\partial x$, $\partial \eta/\partial y$.

11.6 Higher Order Partial Derivatives

I

When given a function which has partial derivatives we often find that these partial derivative functions can themselves be differentiated further. In order to be able to refer to these higher order derivatives quickly we adopt the following system of notation.

■ NOTATION CONVENTION 1

On higher order partial derivatives. Let $u = f(x, y)$ and its partial derivatives be defined over domain D. Then for (x, y) of D

$$\frac{\partial^2 u}{\partial x^2} \text{ or } f_{11} \text{ means } \frac{\partial}{\partial x}\left(\frac{\partial u}{\partial x}\right), \qquad \frac{\partial^2 u}{\partial x \, \partial y} \text{ or } f_{21} \text{ means } \frac{\partial}{\partial x}\left(\frac{\partial u}{\partial y}\right),$$

$$\frac{\partial^2 u}{\partial y \, \partial x} \text{ or } f_{12} \text{ means } \frac{\partial}{\partial y}\left(\frac{\partial u}{\partial x}\right), \qquad \frac{\partial^2 u}{\partial y^2} \text{ or } f_{22} \text{ means } \frac{\partial}{\partial y}\left(\frac{\partial u}{\partial y}\right),$$

$$\frac{\partial^3 u}{\partial x^3} \text{ or } f_{111} \text{ means } \frac{\partial}{\partial x}\left(\frac{\partial^2 u}{\partial x^2}\right), \qquad \frac{\partial^3 u}{\partial x \, \partial y \, \partial x} \text{ or } f_{121} \text{ means } \frac{\partial}{\partial x}\left(\frac{\partial^2 u}{\partial y \, \partial x}\right),$$

$$\frac{\partial^3 u}{\partial x^2 \, \partial y} \text{ or } f_{211} \text{ means } \frac{\partial}{\partial x}\left(\frac{\partial^2 u}{\partial x \, \partial y}\right), \qquad \frac{\partial^3 u}{\partial x \, \partial y^2} \text{ or } f_{221} \text{ means } \frac{\partial}{\partial x}\left(\frac{\partial^2 u}{\partial y^2}\right),$$

and so on.

Example 1.   For $u = f(x, y) = x^2 y + y^3 + x^3 y^2$ we have, for all (x, y),

$$\frac{\partial u}{\partial x} = f_1 = 2xy + 3x^2 y^2, \qquad \frac{\partial^2 u}{\partial x^2} = f_{11} = 2y + 6xy^2, \qquad \frac{\partial^3 u}{\partial x^3} = f_{111} = 6y^2,$$

$$\frac{\partial u}{\partial y} = f_2 = x^2 + 3y^2 + 2x^3 y, \qquad \frac{\partial^2 u}{\partial y \, \partial x} = f_{12} = \frac{\partial}{\partial y}\left(\frac{\partial u}{\partial x}\right) \qquad \frac{\partial^3 u}{\partial x^2 \, \partial y} = f_{211} = \frac{\partial}{\partial x}\left(\frac{\partial^2 u}{\partial x \, \partial y}\right)$$

$$= 2x + 6x^2 y, \qquad\qquad = 2 + 12xy,$$

$$\frac{\partial^2 u}{\partial x \, \partial y} = f_{21} = \frac{\partial}{\partial x}\left(\frac{\partial u}{\partial y}\right) \qquad \frac{\partial^3 u}{\partial x \, \partial y^2} = f_{221} = \frac{\partial}{\partial x}\left(\frac{\partial^2 u}{\partial y^2}\right)$$

$$= 2x + 6x^2 y, \qquad\qquad = 6x^2,$$

$$\frac{\partial^2 u}{\partial y^2} = f_{22} = 6y + 2x^3, \qquad \frac{\partial^4 u}{\partial x^4} = f_{1111} = 0,$$

and so on.

Example 2.   For $v = f(x, y, z) = x^2 yz - xz^2$ we have, for all (x, y, z),

$$\frac{\partial v}{\partial x} = f_1 = 2xyz - z^2, \qquad \frac{\partial^2 v}{\partial y \, \partial x} = f_{12} = \frac{\partial}{\partial y}\left(\frac{\partial v}{\partial x}\right) = 2xz,$$

$$\frac{\partial v}{\partial y} = f_2 = x^2 z, \qquad \frac{\partial^2 v}{\partial x \, \partial y} = f_{21} = \frac{\partial}{\partial x}\left(\frac{\partial v}{\partial y}\right) = 2xz,$$

$$\frac{\partial v}{\partial z} = f_3 = x^2 y - 2xz, \qquad \frac{\partial^2 v}{\partial x \, \partial z} = f_{31} = \frac{\partial}{\partial x}\left(\frac{\partial v}{\partial z}\right) = 2xy - 2z,$$

$$\frac{\partial^2 v}{\partial z \, \partial x} = f_{13} = \frac{\partial}{\partial z}\left(\frac{\partial v}{\partial x}\right) = 2xy - 2z,$$

$$\frac{\partial^3 v}{\partial z \, \partial y \, \partial x} = f_{123} = \frac{\partial}{\partial z}\left(\frac{\partial^2 v}{\partial y \, \partial x}\right) = 2x,$$

$$\frac{\partial^3 v}{\partial y \, \partial x \, \partial z} = f_{312} = \frac{\partial}{\partial y}\left(\frac{\partial^2 v}{\partial x \, \partial z}\right) = 2x.$$

Example 3. $u = r^n \sin n\theta$ is a solution of the Laplace equation in polar coordinates,

$$r^2 \frac{\partial^2 u}{\partial r^2} + r \frac{\partial u}{\partial r} + \frac{\partial^2 u}{\partial \theta^2} = 0,$$

for we have

$$\frac{\partial u}{\partial r} = nr^{n-1} \sin n\theta, \qquad \frac{\partial^2 u}{\partial r^2} = n(n-1)r^{n-2} \sin n\theta,$$

$$\frac{\partial u}{\partial \theta} = r^n n \cos n\theta, \qquad \frac{\partial^2 u}{\partial \theta^2} = -r^n n^2 \sin n\theta,$$

so that

$$r^2 \frac{\partial^2 u}{\partial r^2} + r \frac{\partial u}{\partial r} + \frac{\partial^2 u}{\partial \theta^2} = n(n-1)r^n \sin n\theta + nr^n \sin n\theta - r^n n^2 \sin n\theta$$

$$= r^n \sin n\theta [n^2 - n + n - n^2] = 0.$$

Example 4. Let z be defined implicitly as a function of x and y for (x, y) of domain $D: x^2/a^2 + y^2/b^2 \le 1$ by the equation

$$\frac{x^2}{a^2} + \frac{y^2}{b^2} + \frac{z^2}{c^2} = 1.$$

By differentiating both members with respect to x and y as in Example 11.1-3, we get

$$\frac{1}{a^2} 2x + \frac{1}{c^2} 2z \frac{\partial z}{\partial x} = 0 \quad \text{or} \quad \frac{\partial z}{\partial x} = -\frac{c^2}{a^2} \frac{x}{z}, \quad z \ne 0,$$

and

$$\frac{1}{b^2} 2y + \frac{1}{c^2} 2z \frac{\partial z}{\partial y} = 0 \quad \text{or} \quad \frac{\partial z}{\partial y} = -\frac{c^2}{b^2} \frac{y}{z}, \quad z \ne 0.$$

We can also compute higher order derivatives for (x, y) of D such that $z \ne 0$:

$$\frac{\partial^2 z}{\partial x^2} = \frac{\partial}{\partial x}\left(\frac{\partial z}{\partial x}\right) = -\frac{c^2}{a^2} \frac{z(1) - x(\partial z/\partial x)}{z^2} = -\frac{c^2}{a^2} \frac{z - x[-c^2 x/a^2 z]}{z^2}$$

$$= -\frac{c^2}{a^2} \frac{a^2 z^2 + c^2 x^2}{a^2 z^3} = -\frac{c^2(a^2 z^2 + c^2 x^2)}{a^4 z^3},$$

$$\frac{\partial^2 z}{\partial y \, \partial x} = \frac{\partial}{\partial y}\left(\frac{\partial z}{\partial x}\right) = -\frac{c^2 x}{a^2}\left(\frac{-1}{z^2}\right)\frac{\partial z}{\partial y} = -\frac{c^4 xy}{a^2 b^2 z^3},$$

$$\frac{\partial^2 z}{\partial x \, \partial y} = \frac{\partial}{\partial x}\left(\frac{\partial z}{\partial y}\right) = -\frac{c^2 y}{b^2}\left(-\frac{1}{z^2}\right)\frac{\partial z}{\partial x} = -\frac{c^4 yx}{a^2 b^2 z^3},$$

$$\frac{\partial^2 z}{\partial y^2} = \frac{\partial}{\partial y}\left(\frac{\partial z}{\partial y}\right) = -\frac{c^2}{b^2} \frac{z(1) - y(\partial z/\partial y)}{z^2} = -\frac{c^2}{b^2} \frac{z - y[-c^2 y/b^2 z]}{z^2}$$

$$= -\frac{c^2(b^2 z^2 + c^2 y^2)}{b^4 z^3}.$$

∥

The formal differentiation work we have done in these examples suggests that often

$$\frac{\partial^2 u}{\partial x \, \partial y} = \frac{\partial^2 u}{\partial y \, \partial x}.$$

This is indeed the case under suitable hypotheses. In Exercise 11.6-24, however, we shall exhibit a function for which this equality of mixed partial derivatives does not hold.

■ THEOREM 1

On the equality of mixed partial derivatives.

HYPOTHESIS: (a) $u = f(x, y)$ is defined in a neighborhood of point $P(x, y)$ and so are $\partial u/\partial x$, $\partial u/\partial y$, $\partial^2 u/\partial x\ \partial y$.

(b) $\partial^2 u/\partial x\ \partial y$ is continuous at P.

CONCLUSION: $\dfrac{\partial^2 u}{\partial y\ \partial x}$ exists at P and $\dfrac{\partial^2 u}{\partial x\ \partial y} = \dfrac{\partial^2 u}{\partial y\ \partial x}$ at P.

The proof of this theorem is fairly long. We leave it to advanced calculus texts.

● Remark 1

From Theorem 1 follows the equality of other mixed partial derivatives, provided the necessary derivatives exist and are continuous. Thus, for instance, from $f_{12}(x, y) = f_{21}(x, y)$ it follows upon differentiation with respect to x that $f_{121}(x, y) = f_{211}(x, y)$. If we write $\partial u/\partial x = g$, then from $\partial^2 g/\partial x\ \partial y = \partial^2 g/\partial y\ \partial x$ we can conclude that

$$\frac{\partial^3 u}{\partial x\ \partial y\ \partial x} = \frac{\partial^3 u}{\partial y\ \partial x\ \partial x} \qquad \text{or} \qquad f_{121} = f_{112}.$$

Here three partial derivatives with the same combination of subscripts are equal:

$$f_{112} = f_{121} = f_{211}.$$

Similar theorems hold for functions of more than two variables.[*]

III

We can usually find higher order partial derivatives for composite functions by repeated applications of the chain rule, as in the following examples.

Example 5.   We shall show that any function of the form

$$u = f(x - ct) + g(x + ct)$$

is a solution of the "one-dimensional wave equation"

$$\frac{\partial^2 u}{\partial t^2} = c^2 \frac{\partial^2 u}{\partial x^2},$$

provided that f and g are twice differentiable. It is alleged for instance, that

$$u = \sin (x - ct) + \cos (x + ct)$$

and

$$u = e^{x - ct}(x - ct)^2 + \log (x + ct)$$

are solutions of this partial differential equation.

---

[*] See Exercise 11.6-15.

Write $x - ct = w$ and consider first the $f(x - ct) = f(w)$ term of u. From the total increment statement

$$\Delta f = \frac{df}{dw} \Delta w + \epsilon_1 \Delta w$$

we soon get the chain rule statements

$$\frac{\partial f(x - ct)}{\partial t} = \frac{df}{dw} \frac{\partial w}{\partial t} = \frac{df}{dw} (-c) = -cf'(w) = -cf'(x - ct) \tag{1}$$

$$\frac{\partial f(x - ct)}{\partial x} = \frac{df}{dw} \frac{\partial w}{\partial x} = \frac{df}{dw} (1) = f'(w) = f'(x - ct). \tag{2}$$

We wish to compute

$$\frac{\partial^2}{\partial t^2} f(x - ct) = \frac{\partial}{\partial t}\left(\frac{\partial f(x - ct)}{\partial t}\right)$$

next. Equation (1) says that $\partial f(x - ct)/\partial t$ is itself a function of $x - ct$, and so we are asking now for a derivative with respect to t of a function of $x - ct$. But Eq. (1) explains just how to find such a derivative. Rewrite Eq. (1) in the form

$$\frac{\partial \phi(x - ct)}{\partial t} = -c\phi'(x - ct) \tag{1a}$$

and take ϕ to be $-cf'$. We find, by using Eqs. (1) and (1a), that

$$\frac{\partial^2}{\partial t^2} f(x - ct) = \frac{\partial}{\partial t}\left(\frac{\partial f(x - ct)}{\partial t}\right) = \frac{\partial}{\partial t} (-cf'(x - ct))$$

$$= \frac{\partial}{\partial t} \phi(x - ct) = -c\phi'(x - ct)$$

$$= -c[-cf''(x - ct)] = c^2 f''(x - ct). \tag{3}$$

Similarly we can rewrite Eq. (2) in the form

$$\frac{\partial \tau(x - ct)}{\partial x} = \tau'(x - ct) \tag{2a}$$

and take τ to be f'. Then we find, using Eqs. (2) and (2a), that

$$\frac{\partial^2}{\partial x^2} f(x - ct) = \frac{\partial}{\partial x}\left(\frac{\partial f(x - ct)}{\partial x}\right) = \frac{\partial}{\partial x} (f'(x - ct))$$

$$= \frac{\partial \tau(x - ct)}{\partial x} = \tau'(x - ct) = f''(x - ct). \tag{4}$$

We can discuss the $g(x + ct)$ term of u by writing $v = x + ct$ and reasoning in a similar manner. We write

$$\Delta g = \frac{dg}{dv} \Delta v + \epsilon_2 \Delta v$$

$$\frac{\partial g(x + ct)}{\partial t} = \frac{dg}{dv} \frac{\partial v}{\partial t} = \frac{dg}{dv} (c) = cg'(v) = cg'(x + ct) \tag{5}$$

$$\frac{\partial g(x + ct)}{\partial x} = \frac{dg}{dv} \frac{\partial v}{\partial x} = \frac{dg}{dv} (1) = g'(v) = g'(x + ct). \tag{6}$$

Equation (5) says that $\partial g(x + ct)/\partial t$ is itself a function of $x + ct$. If we rewrite Eq. (5) in the form

$$\frac{\partial \eta(x + ct)}{\partial t} = c\eta'(x + ct)$$

and take η to be cg' we can write

$$\frac{\partial^2 g(x + ct)}{\partial t^2} = \frac{\partial}{\partial t}\left(\frac{\partial g(x + ct)}{\partial t}\right) = \frac{\partial}{\partial t}\left(cg'(x + ct)\right)$$

$$= \frac{\partial}{\partial t}\left(\eta(x + ct)\right) = c\eta'(x + ct)$$

$$= c\left[cg''(x + ct)\right] = c^2 g''(x + ct). \tag{7}$$

In an entirely analogous fashion we learn that

$$\frac{\partial^2 g(x + ct)}{\partial x^2} = g''(x + ct) \tag{8}$$

by applying Eq. (6) twice.

To summarize for the original function u with which we started, we now have from Eqs. (3) and (7):

$$\frac{\partial^2 u}{\partial t^2} = c^2 f''(x - ct) + c^2 g''(x + ct)$$

and from Eqs. (4) and (8):

$$\frac{\partial^2 u}{\partial x^2} = f''(x - ct) + g''(x + ct),$$

so that, indeed, as required,

$$\frac{\partial^2 u}{\partial t^2} = c^2 \frac{\partial^2 u}{\partial x^2}.$$

Example 6.   Suppose that $u = f(x, y)$ for (x, y) of domain D and that $x = g(r, s), y = h(r, s)$ for (r, s) of domain D', with the ranges of g and h such that each (r, s) pair of D' corresponds to an (x, y) pair that lies in D. Suppose further that whatever partial derivatives of these functions are required below exist and are continuous. Then we can form the composite function

$$u = \phi(r, s) = f(g(r, s), h(r, s)) \text{ for } (r, s) \text{ of } D$$

and we can ask for various partial derivatives like $\partial u/\partial r = \partial \phi/\partial r$, $\partial u/\partial s = \partial \phi/\partial s$, $\partial^2 u/\partial r^2 = \partial^2 \phi/\partial r^2$, $\partial^2 u/\partial s\, \partial r = \partial^2 \phi/\partial s\, \partial r$, and so forth.

Let us start by writing the total increment statement

$$\Delta u = \frac{\partial u}{\partial x}\Delta x + \frac{\partial u}{\partial y}\Delta y + \epsilon_1 \Delta x + \epsilon_2 \Delta y,$$

where by $\partial u/\partial x$ and $\partial u/\partial y$ we mean $f_1(x, y)$ and $f_2(x, y)$, and by deducing the chain rules

$$\frac{\partial u}{\partial r} = \frac{\partial u}{\partial x}\frac{\partial x}{\partial r} + \frac{\partial u}{\partial y}\frac{\partial y}{\partial r}, \tag{9}$$

$$\frac{\partial u}{\partial s} = \frac{\partial u}{\partial x}\frac{\partial x}{\partial s} + \frac{\partial u}{\partial y}\frac{\partial y}{\partial s}. \tag{10}$$

Observe that with more precise use of the composite-function language Eq. (9) can be rewritten as

$$\frac{\partial}{\partial r}f(g(r,s), h(r,s)) = f_1(g(r,s), h(r,s))\frac{\partial x}{\partial r} + f_2(g(r,s)\, h(r,s))\frac{\partial y}{\partial r}. \tag{9a}$$

If we differentiate with respect to r in Eq. (9), using the product rule, we are led to

$$\frac{\partial^2 u}{\partial r^2} = \frac{\partial}{\partial r}\left(\frac{\partial u}{\partial r}\right) = \left[\frac{\partial}{\partial r}\left(\frac{\partial u}{\partial x}\right)\right]\frac{\partial x}{\partial r} + \frac{\partial u}{\partial x}\frac{\partial^2 x}{\partial r^2} + \left[\frac{\partial}{\partial r}\left(\frac{\partial u}{\partial y}\right)\right]\frac{\partial y}{\partial r} + \frac{\partial u}{\partial y}\frac{\partial^2 y}{\partial r^2}, \tag{11}$$

where, with more precise use of composite-function language,

$$\frac{\partial}{\partial r}\left(\frac{\partial u}{\partial x}\right) = \frac{\partial}{\partial r}[f_1(x,y)] = \frac{\partial}{\partial r}[f_1(g(r,s),h(r,s))]$$

$$\frac{\partial}{\partial r}\left(\frac{\partial u}{\partial y}\right) = \frac{\partial}{\partial r}[f_2(x,y)] = \frac{\partial}{\partial r}[f_2(g(r,s),h(r,s))].$$

But Eq. (9a), with f replaced by f_1 or f_2, or Eq. (9) with u replaced by $\partial u/\partial x$ or $\partial u/\partial y$, tells us exactly how to write these expressions out. We can write

$$\frac{\partial}{\partial r}[f_1(g(r,s),h(r,s))] = f_{11}(g(r,s),h(r,s))\frac{\partial x}{\partial r} + f_{12}(g(r,s),h(r,s))\frac{\partial y}{\partial r}$$

or

$$\frac{\partial}{\partial r}\left[\frac{\partial u}{\partial x}\right] = \frac{\partial^2 u}{\partial x^2}\frac{\partial x}{\partial r} + \frac{\partial^2 u}{\partial y\partial x}\frac{\partial y}{\partial r},$$

and similarly

$$\frac{\partial}{\partial r}\left[\frac{\partial u}{\partial y}\right] = \frac{\partial^2 u}{\partial x\,\partial y}\frac{\partial x}{\partial r} + \frac{\partial^2 u}{\partial y^2}\frac{\partial y}{\partial r}.$$

Then Eq. (11) becomes

$$\frac{\partial^2 u}{\partial r^2} = \left[\frac{\partial^2 u}{\partial x^2}\frac{\partial x}{\partial r} + \frac{\partial^2 u}{\partial y\,\partial x}\frac{\partial y}{\partial r}\right]\frac{\partial x}{\partial r} + \frac{\partial u}{\partial x}\frac{\partial^2 x}{\partial r^2} + \left[\frac{\partial^2 u}{\partial x\,\partial y}\frac{\partial x}{\partial r} + \frac{\partial^2 u}{\partial y^2}\frac{\partial y}{\partial r}\right]\frac{\partial y}{\partial r} + \frac{\partial u}{\partial y}\frac{\partial^2 y}{\partial r^2},$$

$$\frac{\partial^2 u}{\partial r^2} = \frac{\partial^2 u}{\partial x^2}\left(\frac{\partial x}{\partial r}\right)^2 + 2\frac{\partial^2 u}{\partial y\,\partial x}\frac{\partial x}{\partial r}\frac{\partial y}{\partial r} + \frac{\partial^2 u}{\partial y^2}\left(\frac{\partial y}{\partial r}\right)^2 + \frac{\partial u}{\partial x}\frac{\partial^2 x}{\partial r^2} + \frac{\partial u}{\partial y}\frac{\partial^2 y}{\partial r^2}. \tag{12}$$

In a similar fashion we compute

$$\frac{\partial^2 u}{\partial s\, \partial r} = \frac{\partial}{\partial s}\left(\frac{\partial u}{\partial r}\right) = \left[\frac{\partial}{\partial s}\left(\frac{\partial u}{\partial x}\right)\right]\frac{\partial x}{\partial r} + \frac{\partial u}{\partial x}\frac{\partial^2 x}{\partial s\, \partial r} + \left[\frac{\partial}{\partial s}\left(\frac{\partial u}{\partial y}\right)\right]\frac{\partial y}{\partial r} + \frac{\partial u}{\partial y}\frac{\partial^2 y}{\partial s\, \partial r}$$

$$= \left[\frac{\partial^2 u}{\partial x^2}\frac{\partial x}{\partial s} + \frac{\partial^2 u}{\partial y\, \partial x}\frac{\partial y}{\partial s}\right]\frac{\partial x}{\partial r} + \frac{\partial u}{\partial x}\frac{\partial^2 x}{\partial s\, \partial r}$$

$$+ \left[\frac{\partial^2 u}{\partial x\, \partial y}\frac{\partial x}{\partial s} + \frac{\partial^2 u}{\partial y^2}\frac{\partial y}{\partial s}\right]\frac{\partial y}{\partial r} + \frac{\partial u}{\partial y}\frac{\partial^2 y}{\partial s\, \partial r},$$

$$\frac{\partial^2 u}{\partial s\, \partial r} = \frac{\partial^2 u}{\partial x^2}\frac{\partial x}{\partial s}\frac{\partial x}{\partial r} + \frac{\partial^2 u}{\partial y\, \partial x}\frac{\partial y}{\partial s}\frac{\partial x}{\partial r} + \frac{\partial^2 u}{\partial x\, \partial y}\frac{\partial x}{\partial s}\frac{\partial y}{\partial r} + \frac{\partial^2 u}{\partial y^2}\frac{\partial y}{\partial s}\frac{\partial y}{\partial r}$$

$$+ \frac{\partial u}{\partial x}\frac{\partial^2 x}{\partial s\, \partial r} + \frac{\partial u}{\partial y}\frac{\partial^2 y}{\partial s\, \partial r}. \tag{13}$$

For the sake of reference we list also

$$\frac{\partial^2 u}{\partial r\, \partial s} = \frac{\partial^2 u}{\partial x^2}\frac{\partial x}{\partial r}\frac{\partial x}{\partial s} + \frac{\partial^2 u}{\partial y\, \partial x}\frac{\partial y}{\partial r}\frac{\partial x}{\partial s} + \frac{\partial^2 u}{\partial x\, \partial y}\frac{\partial x}{\partial r}\frac{\partial y}{\partial s} + \frac{\partial^2 u}{\partial y^2}\frac{\partial y}{\partial r}\frac{\partial y}{\partial s}$$

$$+ \frac{\partial u}{\partial x}\frac{\partial^2 x}{\partial r\, \partial s} + \frac{\partial u}{\partial y}\frac{\partial^2 y}{\partial r\, \partial s}, \tag{14}$$

$$\frac{\partial^2 u}{\partial s^2} = \frac{\partial^2 u}{\partial x^2}\left(\frac{\partial x}{\partial s}\right)^2 + 2\frac{\partial^2 u}{\partial y\, \partial x}\frac{\partial y}{\partial s}\frac{\partial x}{\partial s} + \frac{\partial^2 u}{\partial y^2}\left(\frac{\partial y}{\partial s}\right)^2 + \frac{\partial u}{\partial x}\frac{\partial^2 x}{\partial s^2} + \frac{\partial u}{\partial y}\frac{\partial^2 y}{\partial s^2}. \tag{15}$$

It is to be emphasized that each of Eqs. (9), (10), (12), (13), (14), and (15) is an identity that holds for the (r, s) pairs of D'. The derivatives of u with respect to r and s that occur mean derivatives of the composite function $\phi(r, s) = f(g(r, s), h(r, s))$ with respect to r and s. The derivatives of u with respect to x and y mean derivatives of $f(x, y)$ with respect to x and y, with x and y then replaced by $g(r, s)$ and $h(r, s)$.

IV

We conclude this section with a sketchy discussion of the criteria for maximum and minimum values. We shall allow geometric examples to guide us.

It is plausible to say that if the surface $z = f(x, y)$ has a tangent plane at a maximum or minimum point P_0, not on the boundary of the domain of definition, that tangent plane is parallel to the xy plane. Furthermore, at $P_0(x_0, y_0)$ the surface must lie entirely above the tangent plane, or entirely below, as in Fig. 11.20. If the surface does lie entirely below the tangent plane at P_0, so that we have a maximum point, then the section of the surface by the plane $x = x_0$ or by $y = y_0$ or by any other plane through P_0 will be a curve with a maximum point at P_0. In analytic language we have the following theorem.

■ **THEOREM 2**

On maximum and minimum values.

HYPOTHESIS: (a) $z = f(x, y)$ is defined for a domain D in the xy plane containing $P_0(x_0, y_0)$, as are the first and second partial derivatives of f.

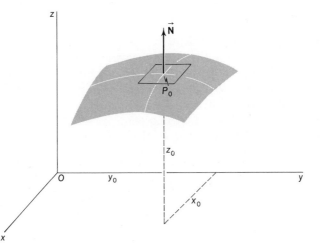

Fig. 11.20

(b) At P_0, $\dfrac{\partial f}{\partial x} = \dfrac{\partial f}{\partial y} = 0.$

(c) At P_0, $\dfrac{\partial^2 f}{\partial x^2}\dfrac{\partial^2 f}{\partial y^2} - \left(\dfrac{\partial^2 f}{\partial x\,\partial y}\right)^2 > 0.$

(d) At P_0, either (1) $\dfrac{\partial^2 f}{\partial x^2} < 0$, or (2) $\dfrac{\partial^2 f}{\partial x^2} > 0.$

CONCLUSION: (1) z has a relative maximum at P_0 or (2) z has a relative minimum at P_0.

PLAUSIBILITY ARGUMENT: If the equation $z = f(x, y)$ is rewritten in the form $F(x, y, z) = f(x, y) - z = 0$, we see that the normal to the surface S with this equation has the direction of

$$\operatorname{grad} F = \frac{\partial F}{\partial x}\,\mathbf{i} + \frac{\partial F}{\partial y}\,\mathbf{j} + \frac{\partial F}{\partial z}\,\mathbf{k} = \frac{\partial f}{\partial x}\,\mathbf{i} + \frac{\partial f}{\partial y}\,\mathbf{j} - 1\mathbf{k}.$$

Hypothesis (b) therefore says that, at P_0, $\operatorname{grad} F = -\mathbf{k}$; that is, the tangent plane is horizontal.

Hypothesis (c) is taken over from differential geometry. It is a sufficient condition that at P_0 the surface S shall lie entirely on one side of its tangent plane.*

Hypothesis (d1) says that one of the curves on S, namely the curve in the section $y = $ const, has a maximum point at P_0, rather than a minimum. It would do just as well to choose any other curve on S through P_0 and say that it has a maximum point at P_0.

---

* If $(\partial^2 z/\partial x^2)(\partial^2 z/\partial y^2) - [(\partial^2 z/\partial x \partial y)]^2 < 0$, then the surface lies on both sides of its tangent plane and we cannot have a maximum or minimum point even if the tangent plane is parallel to the xy plane.

● **Remark 2**

Theorem 2 provides a sufficient, but not necessary, condition that P_0 shall be a maximum point for z. Not all maximum points satisfy the requirements of the hypothesis of Theorem 2. To mention just two other possibilities, a maximum point might occur at a place where the surface $z = f(x, y)$ has no tangent plane at all, as at the top of a pyramid; and a maximum point might also occur at a boundary point of domain D where a tangent plane could be defined, but where it was not necessarily parallel to the xy plane. Nevertheless, Theorem 2 is of considerable value in locating relative maxima and minima.

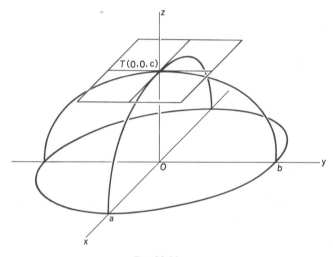

Fig. 11.21

Example 7. For the ellipsoid

$$\frac{x^2}{a^2} + \frac{y^2}{b^2} + \frac{z^2}{c^2} = 1$$

we know that the maximum and minimum values for z occur at $(0, 0, c)$ and $(0, 0, -c)$, but let us see what Theorem 2 says. See Fig. 11.21.

First, we saw in Example 4 that

$$\frac{\partial z}{\partial x} = -\frac{c^2}{a^2}\frac{x}{z}, \qquad \frac{\partial z}{\partial y} = -\frac{c^2}{b^2}\frac{y}{z}, \qquad \frac{\partial^2 z}{\partial x^2} = -\frac{c^2(a^2 z^2 + c^2 x^2)}{a^4 z^3},$$

$$\frac{\partial^2 z}{\partial x\, \partial y} = -\frac{c^4 xy}{a^2 b^2 z^3}, \qquad \frac{\partial^2 z}{\partial y^2} = -\frac{c^2(b^2 z^2 + c^2 y^2)}{b^4 z^3}.$$

Now Theorem 2 suggests that we look first for those points for which $\partial z/\partial x = \partial z/\partial y = 0$. But $\partial z/\partial x = 0$ requires that $x = 0$ and $\partial z/\partial y = 0$ requires that $y = 0$. The only points on the surface for which $x = y = 0$ are $T(0, 0, c)$ and $B(0, 0, -c)$.

Next, we must make sure that the surface lies entirely on one side of the tangent plane at these points. At $T(0, 0, c)$ we have

$$\frac{\partial^2 z}{\partial x^2}\frac{\partial^2 z}{\partial y^2} - \left(\frac{\partial^2 z}{\partial x \, \partial y}\right)^2 = \left(-\frac{c^4 a^2}{a^4 c^3}\right)\left(-\frac{c^4 b^2}{b^4 c^3}\right) - (0)^2 = \frac{c^2}{a^2 b^2} > 0,$$

as required by Hypothesis (c), and at $B(0, 0, -c)$ we have

$$\frac{\partial^2 z}{\partial x^2}\frac{\partial^2 z}{\partial y^2} - \left(\frac{\partial^2 z}{\partial x \, \partial y}\right)^2 = \left(\frac{c^4 a^2}{a^4 c^3}\right)\left(\frac{c^4 b^2}{b^4 c^3}\right) - (0)^2 = \frac{c^2}{a^2 b^2} > 0,$$

so that Hypothesis (c) is satisfied again.

Finally, at $T(0, 0, c)$ we have

$$\frac{\partial^2 z}{\partial x^2} = -\frac{c}{a^2} < 0$$

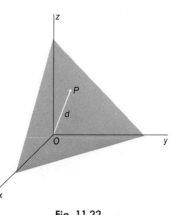

Fig. 11.22

while at $B(0, 0, -c)$ we have

$$\frac{\partial^2 z}{\partial x^2} = \frac{c}{a^2} > 0,$$

so that z assumes a maximum value at T and a minimum value at B.

Example 8. Which point of the plane $Ax + By + Cz = D$, $D \neq 0$, is nearest the origin? One can use a geometric argument to show that the point is to be located by taking the intersection of the plane with the normal to the plane that passes through the origin, but let us see what Theorem 2 says.

Let $P(x, y, z)$ be a point of the plane and let $d = OP$; see Fig. 11.22. We have

$$d^2 = (x - 0)^2 + (y - 0)^2 + (z - 0)^2,$$

but since the coordinates of P satisfy the equation of the plane, we can write

$$d^2 = x^2 + y^2 + \frac{1}{C^2}(D - Ax - By)^2.*$$

It will suffice to find the point P for which d^2 is a minimum because d and d^2 attain their minimum values at the same place. We have

$$\frac{\partial d^2}{\partial x} = 2x + \frac{2}{C^2}(D - Ax - By)(-A) = \frac{2}{C^2}[(C^2 + A^2)x + ABy - AD],$$

$$\frac{\partial d^2}{\partial y} = 2y + \frac{2}{C^2}(D - Ax - By)(-B) = \frac{2}{C^2}[ABx + (C^2 + B^2)y - BD],$$

and by solving two equations in the two unknowns x and y we soon find that $\partial d^2/\partial x = \partial d^2/\partial y = 0$ only if

$$x = \frac{AD}{A^2 + B^2 + C^2} \qquad \text{and} \qquad y = \frac{BD}{A^2 + B^2 + C^2}.$$

* If $C \neq 0$. Not all of A, B, C can vanish. If $C = 0$ but $A \neq 0$, solve the plane equation for x and treat d^2 as a function of y and z.

From the equation of the plane itself we then find

$$z = \frac{CD}{A^2 + B^2 + C^2}.$$

Thus the point we seek seems to be the point

$$P_0\left(\frac{AD}{A^2 + B^2 + C^2}, \frac{BD}{A^2 + B^2 + C^2}, \frac{CD}{A^2 + B^2 + C^2}\right).$$

To be sure, note that

$$\frac{\partial^2 d^2}{\partial x^2} = \frac{2}{C^2}(C^2 + A^2), \qquad \frac{\partial^2 d^2}{\partial y^2} = \frac{2}{C^2}(C^2 + B^2), \qquad \frac{\partial^2 d^2}{\partial x\,\partial y} = \frac{2AB}{C^2}$$

so that

$$\left(\frac{\partial^2 d^2}{\partial x^2}\right)\left(\frac{\partial^2 d^2}{\partial y^2}\right) - \left(\frac{\partial^2 d^2}{\partial x\,\partial y}\right)^2 = 4\,\frac{(C^2 + A^2)(C^2 + B^2) - A^2 B^2}{C^4}$$

$$= 4\,\frac{C^2 + A^2 + B^2}{C^2} > 0$$

and $\partial^2 d^2/\partial x^2 > 0$. Now the hypothesis of Theorem 2 is known to apply, and we can draw Conclusion (2): P_0 is the point at which d and d^2 attain a minimum.

Observe that

$$\overrightarrow{OP_0} = \frac{D}{A^2 + B^2 + C^2}(A\vec{i} + B\vec{j} + C\vec{k})$$

and that the normal vector to the plane is $A\vec{i} + B\vec{j} + C\vec{k}$, so that P_0 is indeed the point we were expecting.

EXERCISES 11.6

1. The following functions have already been considered in Exercises 11.1. Find the higher order derivatives asked for.

(a) $u = (x + 2y)^3$. Find $\dfrac{\partial^2 u}{\partial x^2}, \dfrac{\partial^2 u}{\partial x\,\partial y}, \dfrac{\partial^2 u}{\partial y\,\partial x}, \dfrac{\partial^3 u}{\partial x^3}$.

(b) $f(x, y) = \dfrac{x + y}{x - y}$, $x \neq y$. Find $f_{12}(x, y), f_{21}(x, y), f_{22}(x, y), f_{22}(3, 4)$.

(c) $L = \sinh 2r \cos \theta$. Find $\dfrac{\partial^2 L}{\partial r^2}, \dfrac{\partial^2 L}{\partial \theta^2}, \dfrac{\partial^2 L}{\partial r\,\partial \theta}, \dfrac{\partial^2 L}{\partial \theta\,\partial r}$.

(d) $\phi(x, y, z) = \log (x^2 + y^2 + z^2)$, $(x, y, z) \neq (0, 0, 0)$. Find $\phi_{13}, \phi_{31}, \phi_{312}, \phi_{123}$.

(e) $x = e^{-(u^2 + v^2)}$. Find $\dfrac{\partial^2 x}{\partial u^2}, \dfrac{\partial^2 x}{\partial v\,\partial u}, \dfrac{\partial^2 x}{\partial u\,\partial v}, \dfrac{\partial^2 x}{\partial v^2}$.

(f) $f(x, y) = \tan^{-1}\dfrac{y}{x}$, $x \neq 0$. Find $f_{11}, f_{21}, f_{12}, f_{22}$.

(g) $u = \cos (x + ct) + \cos (x - ct)$, c a constant. Find $\dfrac{\partial^2 u}{\partial x^2}, \dfrac{\partial^2 u}{\partial t^2}$.

2. Show that $u = \sin x \sinh y$ satisfies the Laplace equation $\dfrac{\partial^2 u}{\partial x^2} + \dfrac{\partial^2 u}{\partial y^2} = 0$. Can you write down other solutions?

3. Show that $u = f(x, t) = \sin \dfrac{n\pi x}{L} e^{(-n^2 \pi^2 \alpha^2 / L^2)t}$ satisfies the one-dimensional heat-flow equation $\dfrac{\partial u}{\partial t} = \alpha^2 \dfrac{\partial^2 u}{\partial x^2}$. Observe that for n an integer, $f(0, t) = f(L, t) = 0$.

4. Show that $u = \sin \dfrac{\pi}{a} x \sin \dfrac{\pi}{b} y \cos \omega t$, with $\omega^2 = \dfrac{\pi^2}{k^2}\left(\dfrac{1}{a^2} + \dfrac{1}{b^2}\right)$, discussed in Example 11.1-4, satisfies the partial differential equation

$$\frac{\partial^2 u}{\partial x^2} + \frac{\partial^2 u}{\partial y^2} = k^2 \frac{\partial^2 u}{\partial t^2}.$$

5. Show that $u = \sin ax \sin by\, e^{-.1t} \cos \pi t$, with $a^2 + b^2 = \dfrac{.01 + \pi^2}{k^2}$, satisfies the partial differential equation

$$\frac{\partial^2 u}{\partial t^2} + .2 \frac{\partial u}{\partial t} = k^2 \left(\frac{\partial^2 u}{\partial x^2} + \frac{\partial^2 u}{\partial y^2}\right).$$

6. Let z be defined implicitly as a function of x and y by the equation

(a) $\dfrac{x^2}{4} + \dfrac{y^2}{1} - \dfrac{z^2}{9} = 1$; find $\dfrac{\partial^2 z}{\partial x^2}, \dfrac{\partial^2 z}{\partial y\, \partial x}$.

(b) $x^{2/3} + y^{2/3} + z^{2/3} = a^{2/3}$; find $\dfrac{\partial^2 z}{\partial x\, \partial y}, \dfrac{\partial^2 z}{\partial y\, \partial x}$.

(c) $x + z + (y + z)^2 = 6$; find $\dfrac{\partial^2 z}{\partial x\, \partial y}, \dfrac{\partial^2 z}{\partial y\, \partial x}$.

7. Let $u = f(x, y)$, translate coordinates according to the formulas $x = x' + a$, $y = y' + b$, and consider u to be a composite function of x' and y'. Find $\dfrac{\partial^2 u}{\partial x'^2}, \dfrac{\partial^2 u}{\partial x'\, \partial y'}$, and $\dfrac{\partial^2 u}{\partial y'^2}$ in terms of $\dfrac{\partial^2 u}{\partial x^2}, \dfrac{\partial^2 u}{\partial x\, \partial y}$, and $\dfrac{\partial^2 u}{\partial y^2}$.

8. Let $u = f(x, y)$, rotate coordinates according to the formulas $x = x' \cos \alpha - y' \sin \alpha$, $y = x' \sin \alpha + y' \cos \alpha$, and consider u to be a composite function of x', y'. Find $\dfrac{\partial^2 u}{\partial x'^2}, \dfrac{\partial^2 u}{\partial x'\, \partial y'}, \dfrac{\partial^2 u}{\partial y'^2}$ in terms of $\dfrac{\partial^2 u}{\partial x^2}, \dfrac{\partial^2 u}{\partial x\, \partial y}, \dfrac{\partial^2 u}{\partial y^2}$. Show that

$$\frac{\partial^2 u}{\partial x^2} + \frac{\partial^2 u}{\partial y^2} = \frac{\partial^2 u}{\partial x'^2} + \frac{\partial^2 u}{\partial y'^2}.$$

9. Let $u = f(x, y)$, change to polar coordinates by the formulas $x = r \cos \theta$, $y = r \sin \theta$, and consider u to be a composite function of r, θ. Find $\partial^2 u / \partial r^2$ and $\partial^2 u / \partial \theta^2$ in terms of partials with respect to x and y and show that

$$\frac{\partial^2 u}{\partial x^2} + \frac{\partial^2 u}{\partial y^2} = \frac{\partial^2 u}{\partial r^2} + \frac{1}{r}\frac{\partial u}{\partial r} + \frac{1}{r^2}\frac{\partial^2 u}{\partial \theta^2}.$$

10. Let $u = f(x, y)$, change to parabolic coordinates by the formulas $x = \frac{1}{2}(v^2 - w^2)$, $y = vw$, and consider u to be a composite function of v, w. Find $\partial^2 u/\partial v^2$ and $\partial^2 u/\partial w^2$ in terms of partials with respect to x and y and show that

$$\frac{\partial^2 u}{\partial x^2} + \frac{\partial^2 u}{\partial y^2} = \frac{1}{v^2 + w^2}\left(\frac{\partial^2 u}{\partial v^2} + \frac{\partial^2 u}{\partial w^2}\right).$$

11. Let $u = f(x, y)$, change to elliptic coordinates by the formulas $x = \cosh v \cos w$, $y = \sinh v \sin w$, and consider u to be a composite function of v, w. Find $\partial^2 u/\partial v^2$ and $\partial^2 u/\partial w^2$ in terms of partials with respect to x and y and show that

$$\frac{\partial^2 u}{\partial x^2} + \frac{\partial^2 u}{\partial y^2} = \frac{1}{\sinh^2 v \cos^2 w + \cosh^2 v \sin^2 w}\left(\frac{\partial^2 u}{\partial v^2} + \frac{\partial^2 u}{\partial w^2}\right).$$

12. The partial differential equation for a vibrating string is $a^2\dfrac{\partial^2 u}{\partial x^2} = \dfrac{\partial^2 u}{\partial t^2}.$ Show that if $f(x)$ satisfies $\dfrac{d^2 f}{dx^2} + \dfrac{k^2}{a^2}f = 0$ and if $g(t)$ satisfies $\dfrac{d^2 g}{dt^2} + k^2 g = 0$, where k is a constant, then $u = f(x)g(t)$ is a solution of the partial differential equation.

13. The one-dimensional, heat-flow partial differential equation is $\alpha^2\dfrac{\partial^2 u}{\partial x^2} = \dfrac{\partial u}{\partial t}.$ Let $f(x)$ satisfy $\dfrac{d^2 f}{dx^2} + \dfrac{k^2}{\alpha^2}f = 0$, and let $g(t)$ satisfy $\dfrac{dg}{dt} + k^2 g = 0$, where k is a constant. Show that $u = f(x)g(t)$ satisfies the partial differential equation.

14. The partial differential equation for a vibrating circular membrane is

$$a^2\left(\frac{\partial^2 u}{\partial r^2} + \frac{1}{r}\frac{\partial u}{\partial r} + \frac{1}{r^2}\frac{\partial^2 u}{\partial \theta^2}\right) = \frac{\partial^2 u}{\partial t^2}.$$

Let $f(t)$ satisfy

$$\frac{d^2 f}{dt^2} + k^2 a^2 f = 0;$$

let $g(\theta)$ satisfy

$$\frac{d^2 g}{d\theta^2} + n^2 g = 0;$$

and let $h(r)$ satisfy

$$r^2\frac{d^2 h}{dr^2} + r\frac{dh}{dr} + (k^2 r^2 - n^2)h = 0,$$

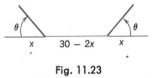

Fig. 11.23

k and n constants. Show that $u = h(r)g(\theta)f(t)$ satisfies the partial differential equation.

15. Let $u = f(x, y, z)$. Assume that the required partial derivatives exist and are continuous, and show that $f_{123} = f_{132} = f_{213} = f_{312} = f_{231} = f_{321}$.

16. Use Theorem 2 to locate the highest point on the surface $x^2 + y^2 = 4 - z$.

17. Show that the plane tangent to $x^2 + z^2 - y^2 = 1$ at $A(0, 0, 1)$ is horizontal, but that A is not a relative maximum point.

18. Which rectangular box of volume 8 will have minimum surface area?

19. An aquarium of volume 18,000 cu in. is to be constructed in the form of a rectangular box. The base costs 3 cents per square inch; the front face costs 2 cents per square inch; the side and back faces cost 1 cent per square inch; there is no top. For which dimensions will the cost be least?

20. We have a sheet of metal of width 30 in. which is to be folded to form a chute, as in Fig. 11.23. What length x should be folded at each side, and through what angle θ, if the chute is to have maximum carrying capacity?

21. Show that the triangle of given perimeter and maximum area is equilateral. *Suggestion:* Heron's formula for the area of a triangle is $K = \sqrt{s(s-a)(s-b)(s-c)}$ where $2s = a + b + c$.

22. Let the sphere of unit radius be described parametrically by the equations $x = \sin\phi\cos\theta$, $y = \sin\phi\sin\theta$, $z = \cos\phi$, with $-\pi < \theta \leq \pi$, $0 \leq \phi \leq \pi$; see Example 11.4-5. Use Theorem 2 to locate the points on the sphere that are closest to, and farthest from, $P_0(0, \frac{1}{2}, 0)$.

23. In Example 8 for a plane and again in Exercise 22 for a sphere, where we were given a point P_0 and were required to locate a point P on a surface that was at a minimum or maximum distance from P_0, we took a point P such that $\overrightarrow{PP_0}$ was normal to the surface at P. Now consider a surface S, $z = f(x, y)$, and point $P_0(x_0, y_0, z_0)$. Form $d^2 = (x - x_0)^2 + (y - y_0)^2 + (z - z_0)^2$ and show that a point P of S for which $\dfrac{\partial d^2}{\partial x} = \dfrac{\partial d^2}{\partial y} = 0$ is such that $\overrightarrow{PP_0}$ is normal to the surface at P.

24. Here we shall exhibit a function for which $f_{12} \neq f_{21}$. Consider

$$f(x, y) = \begin{cases} xy\,\dfrac{x^2 - y^2}{x^2 + y^2} & \text{except at } (0, 0) \\ 0 & \text{at } (0, 0) \end{cases}$$

Show that

(a) $f_1(x, y) = \dfrac{y(x^4 + 4x^2y^2 - y^4)}{(x^2 + y^2)^2}$ and $f_1(0, y) = -y$ except at $(0, 0)$.

(b) $f_1(0, 0) = \lim\limits_{\Delta x \to 0} \dfrac{f(\Delta x, 0) - f(0, 0)}{\Delta x} = 0$.

(c) $f_{12}(0, 0) = \left[\dfrac{\partial}{\partial y} f_1(x, y)\right]_{(0,0)} = \lim\limits_{\Delta y \to 0} \dfrac{f_1(0, \Delta y) - f_1(0, 0)}{\Delta y} = -1$.

(d) $f_2(x, y) = \dfrac{x(x^4 - 4x^2y^2 - y^4)}{(x^2 + y^2)^2}$ and $f_2(x, 0) = x$ except at $(0, 0)$.

(e) $f_2(0, 0) = \lim\limits_{\Delta y \to 0} \dfrac{f(0, \Delta y) - f(0, 0)}{\Delta y} = 0$.

(f) $f_{21}(0, 0) = \left[\dfrac{\partial}{\partial x} f_2(x, y)\right]_{(0,0)} = \lim\limits_{\Delta x \to 0} \dfrac{f_2(\Delta x, 0) - f_2(0, 0)}{\Delta x} = +1$.

(g) We have now shown that $f_{12}(0, 0) \neq f_{21}(0, 0)$. Which hypothesis of Theorem 1 was not satisfied?

11.7 The Statement of the Implicit Function Theorem

In Sec. 1.9 we said that, when we were given an equation

$$F(x, y) = 0, \tag{1}$$

we could often assert the existence of a function f such that

$$y = f(x) \tag{2}$$

reduced Eq. (1) to an identity in x. Considering that y in Eq. (1), then, stood for this function of x, we differentiated Identity (1) with respect to x and went on to compute dy/dx, calling the process "implicit differentiation."

We also have, in Example 11.5-6, a second way of computing dy/dx when we assume that Eq. (1) defines y as a differentiable function of x. To repeat that argument, suppose that F_1 and F_2 are continuous for a domain D. Then, for a point (x, y) of D and for suitable Δx and Δy we have

$$\Delta F = \frac{\partial F}{\partial x} \Delta x + \frac{\partial F}{\partial y} \Delta y + \epsilon_1 \Delta x + \epsilon_2 \Delta y,$$

where ϵ_1, ϵ_2 approach 0 when Δx, Δy do. But, when we say that y is defined as a function of x by $F(x, y) = 0$, we mean that to the number x a number y is assigned such that $F(x, y) = 0$ and that to the number $x + \Delta x$ a number $y + \Delta y$ is assigned such that $F(x + \Delta x, y + \Delta y) = 0$. Hence we have $\Delta F = F(x + \Delta x, y + \Delta y) - F(x, y) = 0 - 0 = 0$ and

$$0 = \frac{\partial F}{\partial x} \Delta x + \frac{\partial F}{\partial y} \Delta y + \epsilon_1 \Delta x + \epsilon_2 \Delta y.$$

If $\partial F / \partial y \neq 0$ at (x, y) we can say that

$$\Delta y = -\frac{1}{\partial F / \partial y} \left(\frac{\partial F}{\partial x} \Delta x + \epsilon_1 \Delta x + \epsilon_2 \Delta y \right)$$

and that for $\Delta x \neq 0$

$$\frac{\Delta y}{\Delta x} = -\frac{1}{\partial F / \partial y} \left(\frac{\partial F}{\partial x} + \epsilon_1 + \epsilon_2 \frac{\Delta y}{\Delta x} \right).$$

Now if Δx approaches 0, Δy will approach 0 also, because we are assuming that y is defined implicitly as a differentiable function of x and hence also as a continuous function. Under these conditions, ϵ_1 and ϵ_2, originally stated to approach 0 when Δx and Δy did, would approach 0 when Δx does. Then, from our last equation, in the limit,

$$\frac{dy}{dx} = -\frac{\partial F / \partial x}{\partial F / \partial y}. \tag{3}$$

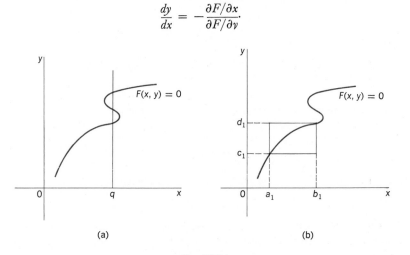

(a)   (b)

Fig. 11.24

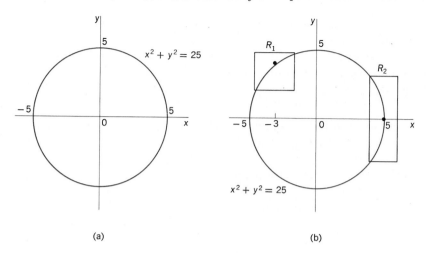

Fig. 11.25

Now let us explain in geometric terms what the Implicit Function Theorem says. To each pair (x, y) that satisfies $F(x, y) = 0$, there corresponds a point on a graph. The totality of such pairs usually corresponds to a curve; see Fig. 11.24(a). For instance, if we consider $F(x, y) = x^2 + y^2 - 25$, the curve is a circle with center at the origin, radius 5; see Fig. 11.25(a). We would like to describe the same curve by using an explicit statement of the form of Eq. (2).

It is clear at the outset that we cannot expect always to describe the *entire* curve with one explicit function. For the circle, for instance, we describe the upper half by $y = +\sqrt{25 - x^2}$ and the lower half by $y = -\sqrt{25 - x^2}$. In Fig. 11.24(a), there are three possible values for y when $x = q$; one explicit description for the whole curve is impossible. Which value of y would we choose for $x = q$?

What we can expect to do is to describe a suitable *portion* of the curve with one function. For instance, in Fig. 11.24(b) we might expect to describe the portion of the curve enclosed in the rectangle by means of an explicit statement, because to each x between a_1 and b_1 that portion of the curve does assign one y, which lies between c_1 and d_1. Similarly, for the portion of the circle enclosed within the rectangle R_1 of Fig. 11.25(b) we would expect to find an explicit statement; it is, in fact, $y = +\sqrt{25 - x^2}$. But we could not expect to find an explicit statement for the portion of the circle enclosed within the rectangle R_2 of Fig. 11.25(b). For each $x < 5$ of R_2, the circle assigns two values of y; for each $x > 5$, the circle assigns no y at all.

We may state the theorem as follows.

■ THEOREM 1

The Implicit Function Theorem.

HYPOTHESIS: (a) $F(x, y)$ is defined for domain D of the xy plane.
(b) F_1 and F_2 are continuous for (x, y) of D.
(c) For (x_0, y_0) of D we have $F(x_0, y_0) = 0$, $F_2(x_0, y_0) \neq 0$.

CONCLUSION: There will be an x interval, call it N_1, which includes x_0 and a y interval, call it N_2, such that

(a) for every x of N_1 there is a unique y in N_2 for which $F(x, y) = 0$. We can express this association of y with x by writing $y = f(x)$, x in N_1.

(b) $f'(x) = \dfrac{dy}{dx} = -\dfrac{\partial F/\partial x}{\partial F/\partial y}$ for x of N_1.

DISCUSSION AND ILLUSTRATION: In Hypothesis(a) we state where the $F(x, y)$ we are talking about is defined. In the case $F(x, y) = x^2 + y^2 - 25$, for instance, F exists for all x and y.

In Hypothesis (b) we impose a restriction on the functions F we shall consider. For $F(x, y) = x^2 + y^2 - 25$, we have $\partial F/\partial x = 2x$ and $\partial F/\partial y = 2y$, and both of these partial derivatives are everywhere continuous.

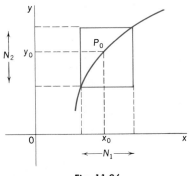

Fig. 11.26

In Hypothesis (c) we explain for which portions of the curve representing $F(x, y) = 0$ we can expect explicit representations. Let $P_0(x_0, y_0)$ be a point on the curve with $(\partial F/\partial y)_{(x_0, y_0)} \neq 0$. Then, as in Fig. 11.26, the neighborhoods N_1 and N_2 mentioned in the conclusion of the theorem determine a rectangle enclosing (x_0, y_0) and the portion of the curve in this rectangle has an explicit representation. Equation (3) says that the requirement $(\partial F/\partial y)_{(x_0, y_0)} \neq 0$ is tantamount to asking that the tangent at (x_0, y_0) be not vertical. For our illustrative case, $F(x, y) = x^2 + y^2 - 25$, we have $\partial F/\partial y = 2y$. For a point like $x_0 = -3, y_0 = 4$, we can draw a rectangle and get an explicit statement, $y = +\sqrt{25 - x^2}$; see Fig. 11.25(b). At this point, $\partial F/\partial y = 8$. However, at point $x_0 = 5$, $y_0 = 0$, we have $\partial F/\partial y = 0$. There we cannot specify a rectangle and an explicit function $y = f(x)$ that describes the portion of the curve within the rectangle.

EXERCISES 11.7

1. The Implicit Function Theorem states conditions on $F(x, y)$ *sufficient* to ensure the existence of an explicit function $y = f(x)$ which reduces $F(x, y) = 0$ to an identity in x, but these conditions are not *necessary* conditions. If the hypotheses of the theorem are satisfied, the explicit function exists; if the hypotheses are not satisfied, the theorem says nothing—the explicit function may or may not exist. For $F = x^2 + y^2 - 25$, the hypotheses were not satisfied at $(5, 0)$; an explicit solution for $F = 0$ for the neighborhood of this point could not be found. Consider now the graph of $\overline{F}(x, y) = y^3 - x = 0$. Show that the hypotheses of Theorem 1 are not satisfied for $\overline{F}$ at $(0, 0)$. Nevertheless, the portion of the curve $y^3 - x = 0$ within any rectangular neighborhood of $(0, 0)$ can be described by an explicit statement of the form $y = f(x)$. Find $f(x)$.

2. Let $v = f(u)$ be defined for an interval. What conditions on $f(u)$ for this interval are sufficient, according to Theorem 1, to assure the existence of an explicit function $u = \phi(v)$ which will reduce $F(v, u) = v - f(u) = 0$ to an identity in v? Compare your result with the conditions imposed on $f(u)$ in Definition 1 and Theorem 1 of Sec. 4.4, where we dealt with inverse functions.

Applications of Integral Calculus in Three Space. Multiple Integrals

12.1 Review

Let us review quickly the basic integration facts before we apply them to three-dimensional situations. First, we found that limits of sums of the form

$$\lim_{n \to \infty} \sum_{k=1}^{n} f(x_k^*)(\Delta x)_k$$

arose frequently. Here it was understood that an interval $a \leq x \leq b$ was subdivided into n parts by subdivision points $a = x_0 < x_1 < x_2 < \cdots < x_n = b$, that $(\Delta x)_k = x_k - x_{k-1}$ was the length of the kth subinterval, that x_k^* was a number of the kth subinterval, and that the length of the longest subinterval approached 0 as n grew beyond all bounds. A function f was called integrable if this limit existed and was independent of the choice of x_k's and x_k^*'s. For an integrable function f we agreed on the integral notation

$$\int_a^b f(x)\, dx = \lim_{n \to \infty} \sum_{k=1}^{n} f(x_k^*)(\Delta x)_k,$$

and we pointed out that, if a function f was continuous for an interval, it was integrable for that interval.

Second, we dealt with the problem of evaluating these definite integrals. The Fundamental Theorem of the Integral Calculus said essentially that, if there

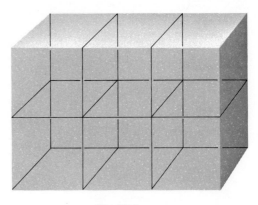

Fig. 12.1

existed an antiderivative function for f, namely, a new function F such that $dF/dx = f$, then we could evaluate the definite integral by saying that

$$\int_a^b f(x)\,dx = F(b) - F(a).$$

Third, we extended our work to limits of sums not quite of the form $\lim_{n\to\infty} \sum_{k=1}^n f(x_k^*)(\Delta x)_k$. For instance, we pointed out in Sec. 8.8 that if we dealt with $\lim_{n\to\infty} \sum_{k=1}^n f(x_k^*)g(\bar{x}_k)(\Delta x)_k$, where f and g were both continuous functions and x_k^* and $\bar{x}_k$ were both points of the kth subinterval but not necessarily the same point, we could still say that

$$\lim_{n\to\infty} \sum_{k=1}^n f(x_k^*)g(\bar{x}_k)(\Delta x)_k = \int_a^b f(x)g(x)\,dx,$$

it being assumed as usual that the length of the longest subinterval approached 0 as n grew beyond all bounds.

Now let us turn to some basic volume definitions. We agree, because of our experience, that any definition of volume ought to be consistent with the following assumptions:

(a) The volume number assigned to a solid shall be nonnegative.

(b) The volume numbers assigned to congruent solids shall be equal.

(c) The volume number assigned to a solid formed by uniting two nonoverlapping solids shall be the sum of the volume numbers assigned to those solids.

■ DEFINITION 1

The volume of a rectangular parallelepiped shall be the product of the area of the base by the height.

The motivation for this definition also follows from our experience. For instance, in Fig. 12.1 we observe that the area of the base is 3 square units and that the solid contains 2 layers of 3 cubic units each or $(3)(2)$ cubic units. In Fig. 12.2 we see that $ABCDEF$ and $A'B'C'D'E'F'$ are congruent solids and that therefore the

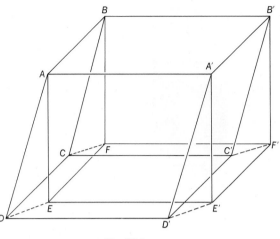

Fig. 12.2

volume of $ABCDD'C'B'A'$, which is a parallelpiped with rectangular base, should be the same as that of $ABFEE'F'B'A'$, which is a rectangular parallelepiped with the same height and with base of the same area. We choose the following definition for a parallelepiped with rectangular base in order to be consistent with Definition 1 and Assumptions (a), (b), and (c) made above.

■ DEFINITION 2

The volume of a parallelepiped with rectangular base shall be the product of the area of the base by the height.

When considering a right cylindrical solid with base area A and height h we can reason as follows. As in Fig. 12.3(a), let the base be subdivided into parallel area elements by choosing numbers $a = x_0 < x_1 < x_2 < \cdots < x_n = b$ and drawing the various lines $x = x_k$, and let $w(x)$ be the width of the base for an x of $a \le x \le b$, $w(x)$ a continuous function for $a \le x \le b$. Then if $w(x'_k)$ and $w(x''_k)$ are the mini-

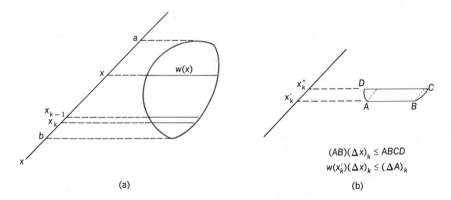

$$(AB)(\Delta x)_k \le ABCD$$
$$w(x'_k)(\Delta x)_k \le (\Delta A)_k$$

(a)   (b)

Fig. 12.3 (a) and (b)

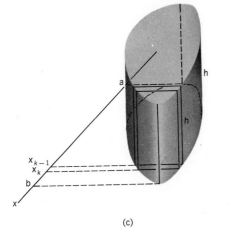

(c)

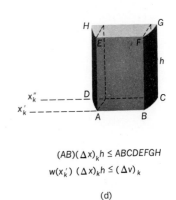

$(AB)(\Delta x)_k h \le ABCDEFGH$

$w(x_k')\,(\Delta x)_k h \le (\Delta v)_k$

(d)

Fig. 12.3 (c) and (d)

mum and maximum values of $w(x)$ for the kth subinterval, $x_{k-1} \le x \le x_k$, we can say that

$$w(x_k')(\Delta x)_k \le (\Delta A)_k \le w(x_k'')(\Delta x)_k;$$

see Fig. 12.3(b) where the rectangle with dimension $w(x_k')$ is drawn. It follows from the Intermediate Value Theorem for continuous functions that there is a number x_k^*, $x_{k-1} \le x_k^* \le x_k$, such that

$$(\Delta A)_k = w(x_k^*)(\Delta x)_k,$$

and we can write

$$A = \int_a^b w(x)\,dx.$$

Now consider the right cylindrical solid subdivided into parallel volume elements as in Fig. 12.3(c). Definition 1 allows us to form the volume numbers for two rectangular parallelepipeds, which are in turn surely smaller and larger in volume than $(\Delta V)_k$; in Fig. 12.3(d) we have drawn a rectangular parallelepiped that is surely smaller than $(\Delta V)_k$. Hence we can say that

$$w(x_k')(\Delta x)_k h \le (\Delta V)_k \le w(x_k'')(\Delta x)_k h,$$

and then that there is an x_k^{**}, $x_{k-1} \le x_k^{**} \le x_k$, such that

$$(\Delta V)_k = w(x_k^{**})(\Delta x)_k h$$

$$V = h \int_a^b w(x)\,dx$$

$$V = hA$$

■ **DEFINITION 3**

The volume of a right cylindrical solid shall be the product of the area of the base by the height.

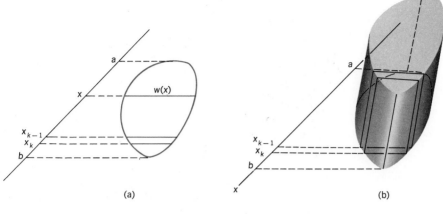

Fig. 12.4

Finally, by reasoning with parallelepipeds that have rectangular bases instead of with rectangular parallelepipeds, and using Definition 2 instead of Definition 1, we are led to a definition for cylindrical solids that are not necessarily right cylindrical solids. See Figs. 12.4(a) and (b).

■ DEFINITION 4

The volume of a cylindrical solid shall be the product of the area of the base by the height.

12.2 Volume by Summation of Parallel Disk Elements

There are solids that can be described as having been swept out by sections of specified shape moving perpendicular to a specified line. To illustrate, in Fig. 12.5 there appears $\frac{1}{4}$ of a cone which can be described as having been swept out by a circular section moving perpendicular to the x axis from $x = 0$ to $x = h$. As the

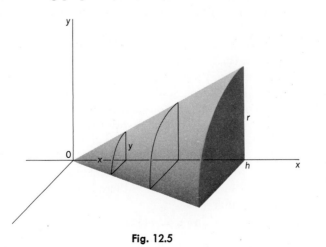

Fig. 12.5

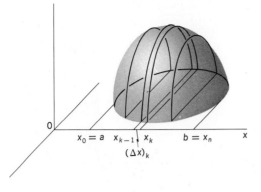

$x_0 = a$ x_{k-1} x_k $b = x_n$ x
$(\Delta x)_k$

Fig. 12.6

section moves, its radius and area increase in a specific way. Thus, if y is the radius at position x, we have $y = (r/h)x$.

To analyze a general case, choose the x axis to be the line perpendicular to the moving sections; let the moving section have area A at position x, $A = A(x)$ being a continuous function; and let the moving section move from $x = a$ to $x = b$. First we subdivide the interval $a \leq x \leq b$ by choosing subdivision points $x_0 = a < x_1 < x_2 < \cdots < x_n = b$, and cut the solid into n parallel slices by drawing sections perpendicular to the x axis at these points; see Fig. 12.6.

Consider next the kth of these slices or volume elements. Since we are assuming that the cross-section area A is a continuous function, A will assume maximum and minimum values for the kth subinterval, call them $A(x_k'')$ and $A(x_k')$, and we can say that the kth element is included within a cylinder of area $A(x_k'')$ and height $(\Delta x)_k$ but that the kth volume element includes a cylinder of area $A(x_k')$ and height $(\Delta x)_k$.* Thus

$$A(x_k')(\Delta x)_k \leq (\Delta V)_k \leq A(x_k'')(\Delta x)_k,$$

and there is an x_k^*, $x_{k-1} \leq x_k^* \leq x_k$, such that

$$(\Delta V)_k = A(x_k^*)(\Delta x)_k.$$

Then we define the volume of the solid by taking

$$V = \lim_{n \to \infty} \sum_{k=1}^{n} A(x_k^*)(\Delta x)_k = \int_a^b A(x)\, dx,$$

it being understood that the largest $(\Delta x)_k$ approaches 0 as n grows beyond all bounds.

Example 1. Let us find the volume of a right circular cone of height h and base radius r. As in Figs. 12.7(a) and (b), let us divide the interval $0 \leq x \leq h$ into n parts by choosing subdivision points $x_0 = 0 < x_1 < x_2 < \cdots < x_n = h$. At each subdivision point we take a section of the cone perpendicular to its axis, the x axis, thus cutting the cone up into parallel circular disks.

The line OA, $y = (r/h)x$, associates a y with each x. Figure 12.7(b) points out that the volume of the kth slice, $(\Delta V)_k$, is greater than $\pi y_{k-1}^2 (\Delta x)_k$, the volume of a circular cylinder of radius y_{k-1} and thickness $(\Delta x)_k$. Similarly, $(\Delta V)_k$ is less than $\pi y_k^2 (\Delta x)_k$, and, since $y^2 = (r/h)^2 x^2$ is a continuous function, the Intermediate Value Theorem for continuous functions says that there is an intermediate x of this kth subinterval, say x_k^*, such that

$$(\Delta V)_k = \pi (y_k^*)^2 (\Delta x)_k.$$

---

* To be more precise, the element may be included within a set of cylinders of area $A(x_k'')$ whose heights have sum $(\Delta x)_k$.

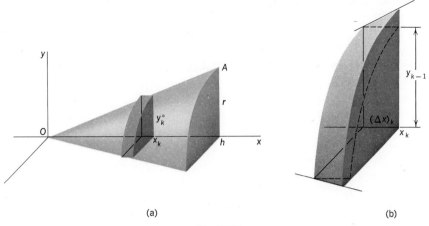

(a)   (b)

Fig. 12.7

Then we can define our volume as

$$V = \lim_{n \to \infty} \sum_{k=1}^{n} (\Delta V)_k = \lim_{n \to \infty} \sum_{k=1}^{n} \pi(y_k^*)^2 (\Delta x)_k$$

$$= \int_{x=0}^{h} \pi y^2 \, dx = \int_{x=0}^{h} \pi \frac{r^2}{h^2} x^2 \, dx,$$

it being understood that the largest $(\Delta x)_k$ approaches 0 as n grows beyond all bounds.

To compute V is now a relatively easy matter. We have

$$V = \pi \frac{r^2}{h^2} \frac{x^3}{3} \Big|_0^h = \frac{\pi r^2}{3h^2} (h^3 - 0) = \frac{1}{3} \pi r^2 h.$$

Example 2. Consider the cycloid $x = a(\theta - \sin \theta)$, $y = a(1 - \cos \theta)$. Let us find the volume obtained by revolving about the x axis the region bounded by one arch of the cycloid and the x axis.

One arch of the cycloid is determined by the parameter interval $0 \le \theta \le 2\pi$. Let us divide this interval into n parts by choosing subdivision θ values $\theta_0 = 0 < \theta_1 < \theta_2 < \cdots < \theta_n = 2\pi$; to each θ_k there will correspond an x_k and y_k. If, as in Fig. 12.8, we draw sections perpendicular to the x axis at each x_k, we can consider the solid to be a sum of parallel circular disks. For the kth element there will be a maximum y and a minimum y. If we substitute these y's in $\pi y^2 (\Delta x)_k$, we get estimates that are too large and too small for $(\Delta V)_k$. There is an intermediate θ, call it θ_k^*, for which

$$(\Delta V)_k = \pi (y_k^*)^2 (\Delta x)_k.$$

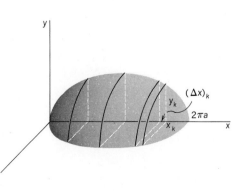

Fig. 12.8

Then we say that

$$V = \lim_{n \to \infty} \sum_{k=1}^{n} (\Delta V)_k = \lim_{n \to \infty} \sum_{k=1}^{n} \pi (y_k^*)^2 (\Delta x)_k = \int_{x=0}^{2\pi a} \pi y^2 \, dx,$$

it being understood that all $(\Delta \theta)_k$'s and all $(\Delta x)_k$'s approach 0 as n grows beyond all bounds.

To evaluate this integral, we observe that $y = a(1 - \cos \theta)$ and that $dx/d\theta = a(1 - \cos \theta)$, so that we can write

$$V = \int_{\theta=0}^{2\pi} \pi a^3 (1 - \cos \theta)^3 \, d\theta$$

$$= \pi a^3 \left[\int_0^{2\pi} 1 \, d\theta - 3 \int_{\theta=0}^{2\pi} \cos \theta \, d\theta + 3 \int_0^{2\pi} \cos^2 \theta \, d\theta - \int_0^{2\pi} \cos^3 \theta \, d\theta \right].$$

Here the first integral is elementary; the second and fourth have value 0 because $\cos \theta$ and $\cos^3 \theta$ assume positive values for two of the θ quadrants over which we sum, but equal negative values for the other two; for the third integral we use an identity.

$$V = \pi a^3 \left[\theta \Big|_0^{2\pi} - 0 + \frac{3}{2} \int_0^{2\pi} (1 + \cos 2\theta) \, d\theta - 0 \right]$$

$$= \pi a^3 [2\pi + 3\pi] = 5\pi^2 a^3.$$

Example 3. Find the volume swept out when the region bounded by the parabola $y = 1 - x^2$ and the lines $y = 1$, $x = 1$ is rotated about the line $x = 1$.

The region to be rotated is sketched in Fig. 12.9(a), a portion of the solid swept out in Fig. 12.9(b). Subdivide the interval $0 \le y \le 1$ by choosing subdivision points $y_0 = 0 < y_1 < y_2 < \cdots < y_n = 1$. At each y_k take a section of the solid by a

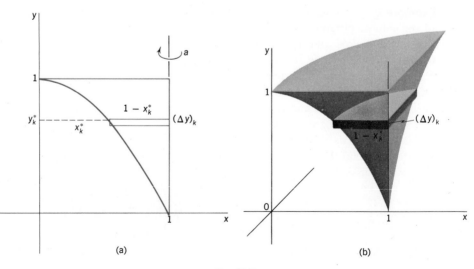

(a)   (b)

Fig. 12.9

plane perpendicular to the y axis, thus dividing the solid into n parallel slices. The kth volume element can be considered as approximately a circular disk of radius $1 - x_k$ and thickness $(\Delta y)_k$. In fact, a y_k^* of the kth subinterval can be found such that

$$(\Delta V)_k = \pi(1 - x_k^*)^2(\Delta y)_k,$$

and then we take

$$V = \int_{y=0}^{1} \pi(1 - x)^2 \, dy.$$

Since $x = \sqrt{1 - y}$, we have

$$V = \pi \int_{y=0}^{1} (1 - 2\sqrt{1 - y} + 1 - y) \, dy = \pi \int_{y=0}^{1} (2 - 2\sqrt{1 - y} - y) \, dy$$

$$= \pi \left[2y + \frac{4}{3}(1 - y)^{3/2} - \frac{y^2}{2} \right]_0^1 = \pi \left[\left(2 + 0 - \frac{1}{2} \right) - \left(0 + \frac{4}{3} - 0 \right) \right] = \frac{\pi}{6}.$$

Example 4.   A wedge is cut out of a right circular cylinder of radius a by a plane perpendicular to the axis of the cylinder and a second plane that intersects the first at an angle α along a diameter of the circular section. Find the volume of this wedge.

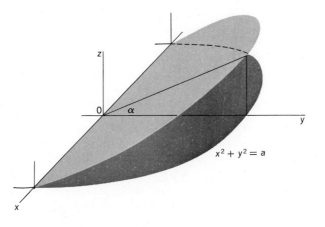

Fig. 12.10 (a)

Consider Fig. 12.10(a). The wedge we want to study is symmetric with respect to the yz plane and we shall reason with the half of the wedge for which $x \geq 0$, as in Fig. 12.10(b). Subdivide the interval $0 \leq x \leq a$ by choosing subdivision points $x_0 = 0 < x_1 < x_2 < \cdots < x_n = a$, and draw planes perpendicular to the x axis at these points, thus dividing the wedge into n parallel triangular slices. As an underestimate for the volume of the element sketched, we can take $\frac{1}{2}y_k z_k (\Delta x)_k$. As an overestimate, we can take $\frac{1}{2}y_{k-1}z_{k-1}(\Delta x)_k$. Indeed, we can choose an x_k^* of the kth subinterval such that

$$(\Delta V)_k = \frac{1}{2}y_k^* z_k^* (\Delta x)_k.$$

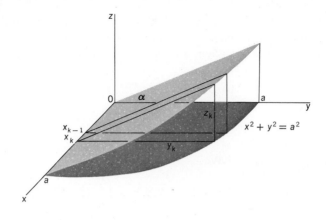

Fig. 12.10 (b)

Because the planes intersect at an angle α, we can say that tan $\alpha = z_k^*/y_k^*$,

$$(\Delta V)_k = \tfrac{1}{2}(\tan \alpha)(y_k^*)^2(\Delta x)_k,$$

and because the base of the wedge is described by $x^2 + y^2 = a^2$, we have

$$(\Delta V)_k = \tfrac{1}{2}(\tan \alpha)(a^2 - x_k^{*2})(\Delta x)_k.$$

We conclude by writing

$$\tfrac{1}{2} V = \int_{x=0}^{a} \tfrac{1}{2} \tan \alpha \, (a^2 - x^2) \, dx$$

$$V = \tan \alpha \, [a^2 x - \tfrac{1}{3} x^3]_0^a = \tfrac{2}{3} a^3 \tan \alpha.$$

Example 5.   Let us find the moment of inertia of a sphere of radius a and constant mass density μ for a rotation about a diameter of the sphere.

Choose the y axis to be the axis of rotation as in Fig. 12.11 where part of the sphere is drawn. The interval $-a \le y \le a$ is divided into n parts by subdivision points $y_0 = -a < y_1 < y_2 < \cdots < y_n = a$, and planes are drawn at these points, perpendicular to the y axis. The sphere is thus divided into n parallel circular disks. For the kth element we can say that there is a y_k^* such that

$$(\Delta V)_k = \pi(x_k^*)^2(\Delta y)_k,$$

$$(\Delta m)_k = \mu(\Delta V)_k = \mu\pi(x_k^*)^2(\Delta y)_k = \text{mass of } k\text{th element}.$$

But we showed in Example 8.12-3 that the moment of inertia of a circular plate of constant density for an axis perpendicular to the plate and through its center was $\tfrac{1}{2}$ (mass of plate)(radius of plate)^2. The moment of inertia of the kth element shown in Fig. 12.11 will be less than that of a plate of radius x_{k-1} and greater than that of a plate of radius x_k. Hence there is a y_k^{**} of the kth subinterval and a corresponding x_k^{**} such that

$$(\Delta I)_k = \tfrac{1}{2}(\Delta m)_k(x_k^{**})^2 = \tfrac{1}{2}\mu\pi(x_k^*)^2(x_k^{**})^2(\Delta y)_k.$$

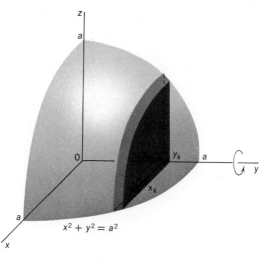

Fig. 12.11

Then our integration technique leads us to

$$I = \int_{y=-a}^{a} \tfrac{1}{2}\, \mu\pi x^4 \, dy.$$

Since each y and the corresponding x satisfy $x^2 + y^2 = a^2$,

$$I = \tfrac{1}{2}\, \mu\pi \int_{y=-a}^{a} (a^2 - y^2)^2 \, dy = \tfrac{1}{2}\, \mu\pi \int_{-a}^{a} (a^4 - 2a^2y^2 + y^4) \, dy$$

$$= \tfrac{1}{2}\, \mu\pi [a^4 y - \tfrac{2}{3}\, a^2 y^3 + \tfrac{1}{5}\, y^5]_{-a}^{a} = \tfrac{8}{15}\, \mu\pi a^5.$$

Again, since our integrand is unchanged by the substitution of $-y$ for y, we might have summed from $y = 0$ to $y = a$ to get $\tfrac{1}{2} I$ and then doubled. This corresponds to the fact that the moment of inertia for the hemisphere to the left of the xz plane is the same as that for the hemisphere to the right of the xz plane.

Example 6. Consider the solid of constant weight density ρ bounded by the elliptic paraboloid $x^2/a^2 + z^2/b^2 = y$ and the plane $y = h$. We shall compute its moment about the x axis and locate its center of gravity point.

The solid is symmetric with respect to the x and z axes and only the quarter for which $x \geq 0$ and $z \geq 0$ is drawn in Fig. 12.12. Divide the interval $0 \leq y \leq h$ into n parts by choosing subdivision points $y_0 = 0 < y_1 < y_2 < \cdots < y_n = h$ and divide the solid into n parallel elliptic slices by drawing planes perpendicular to the y axis at these points. The kth element has volume less than that of the elliptic cylinder with semimajor and semiminor axes x_k and z_k and thickness $(\Delta y)_k$ and volume greater than that of the elliptic cylinder with dimensions x_{k-1} and z_{k-1};

$$\pi x_{k-1} z_{k-1} (\Delta y)_k \leq (\Delta V)_k \leq \pi x_k z_k (\Delta y)_k.$$

There is a number y_k^*, $y_{k-1} \leq y_k^* \leq y_k$, and corresponding x_k^*, z_k^* such that

$$(\Delta V)_k = \pi x_k^* z_k^* (\Delta y)_k,$$

$$(\Delta w)_k = \rho \pi x_k^* z_k^* (\Delta y)_k = \text{weight of } k\text{th element.} \tag{1}$$

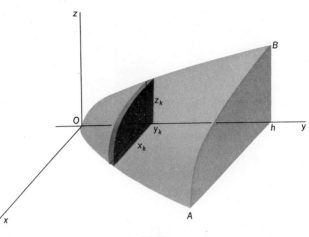

Fig. 12.12

If we consider the entire weight of this element to be concentrated at its center of gravity point $(0, y_k^{**}, 0)$, where $y_{k-1} < y_k^{**} < y_k$, we can write

$$(\Delta M)_k = y_k^{**}(\Delta w)_k = \rho \pi x_k^* z_k^* y_k^{**}(\Delta y)_k = x \text{ axis moment for } k\text{th element},$$

$$M_x = \int_{y=0}^{h} \rho \pi x z y \, dy = x \text{ axis moment for solid.}$$

But the equation of the xy trace, curve OA of Fig. 12.12, is $x^2/a^2 = y$, so that $x = a\sqrt{y}$. Similarly, the equation of OB, the yz trace, is $z^2/b^2 = y$, so that $z = b\sqrt{y}$. Hence

$$M_x = \int_{y=0}^{h} \rho \pi a b y^2 \, dy = \tfrac{1}{3} \rho \pi a b h^3. \tag{2}$$

On the other hand, if the weight of the entire body had been considered as concentrated at the center of gravity point of the solid, $(0, \bar{y}, 0)$, we could have written

$$M_x = (W)\bar{y}, \tag{3}$$

where W is the weight of the entire solid. But from Eq. (1),

$$W = \int_{y=0}^{h} \rho \pi x z \, dy = \int_{y=0}^{h} \rho \pi a b y \, dy = \tfrac{1}{2} \rho \pi a b h^2, \tag{4}$$

so that Eq. (3) becomes

$$M_x = \tfrac{1}{2} \rho \pi a b h^2 \bar{y}. \tag{5}$$

Thus, from Eqs. (2) and (5), $\bar{y} = \tfrac{2}{3}h$ and the center of gravity is the point $(0, \tfrac{2}{3}h, 0)$. Since a and b do not enter into our statement for $\bar{y}$, we can conclude that all elliptic paraboloid caps of the same depth have the same center of gravity, even though their elliptic bases will have different eccentricities and sizes.

EXERCISES 12.2

1. Find the volume of the solid formed when the region bounded by the arc $y = 2 - \frac{1}{2}x^2$ for $0 \le x \le 2$ and the coordinate axes is revolved
(a) about the x axis,
(b) about the y axis.

2. Find the volume of the solid formed when the region bounded by the arc $y = \cos x$ for $0 \le x \le \pi/2$ and the coordinate axes is revolved (a) about the x axis, (b) about the y axis.

3. (a) Find the volume of a sphere of radius a.
(b) Find the volume of the smaller portion of this sphere cut off by a plane that passes at a distance h from the center.
(c) Locate the center of gravity of a hemisphere of radius a, assuming constant weight density ρ.

4. Find the volume of the ellipsoid $\dfrac{x^2}{a^2} + \dfrac{y^2}{b^2} + \dfrac{z^2}{c^2} = 1$. (Remember that the area of an ellipse with semimajor and semiminor axes u and v is πuv.)

5. (a) Find the volume enclosed by the paraboloid of revolution $x^2 + y^2 = 4(4 - z)$ and the xy plane.
(b) Reconsider Example 6. Show that the volume of the segment of an elliptic paraboloid cut off by a plane perpendicular to the planes of symmetry is $\frac{1}{2}$ the product of the height of the segment by the area of the base of the segment. Check your answer to Part (a) against this formula.

6. (a) Find the volume enclosed by the hyperboloid of one sheet, $\dfrac{x^2}{a^2} + \dfrac{y^2}{a^2} - \dfrac{z^2}{c^2} = 1$, and the planes $z = 0$ and $z = h$.
(b) Find the moment of inertia of this solid for a rotation about the z axis, assuming constant mass density μ.

7. Find the volume enclosed by the hyperboloid of two sheets, $\dfrac{y^2}{4} - \dfrac{x^2}{4} - \dfrac{z^2}{3} = 1$, and the plane $y = 4$.

8. (a) Find the volume swept out when the region bounded by the catenary $y = \frac{1}{2}(e^x + e^{-x}) = \cosh x$, $x = -a$, $x = +a$, and the x axis is rotated about the x axis.
(b) Find the volume swept out when the region bounded by the catenary $y = \frac{1}{2}(e^x + e^{-x}) = \cosh x$, $x = -a$, $x = +a$, and $y = \cosh a$ is rotated about $y = \cosh a$.

9. (a) Find the volume swept out when the first-quadrant region bounded by the hypocycloid $x^{2/3} + y^{2/3} = a^{2/3}$ and the coordinate axes is rotated about the y axis.
(b) Find the same volume but use the parametric equations of the hypocycloid: $x = a \cos^3 \theta$, $y = a \sin^3 \theta$.

10. Let a right circular cone have base radius r and height h, as in Example 1.
(a) Locate the center of gravity, assuming constant weight density.
(b) Find the moment of inertia for a rotation about its axis of symmetry, assuming constant mass density.

11. Find the volume swept out when the region bounded by the tractrix arc $x = t - a \tanh (t/a)$, $y = a \operatorname{sech} (t/a)$, $0 \le t \le 2a$, and the lines $x = 0$, $x = 2a - a \tanh 2$, and the x axis is rotated about the x axis.

12. Find the volume swept out when the region bounded by the cycloid $x = a(\theta - \sin \theta)$, $y = a(1 - \cos \theta)$, and the lines $x = 0$, $x = 2\pi a$, $y = 2a$ is rotated about $y = 2a$.

13. The region bounded by $y = e^{-x}$, $y = 1$, and $x = 1$ is rotated about $x = 1$.
(a) Find the volume swept out.
(b) Set up a definite integral for the moment of inertia of this solid for a rotation about $x = 1$, assuming constant mass density μ.

14. The region bounded by $y^2 = 9(4 - x)$, $y = 6$, $y = 0$, and $x = 6$ is rotated about $x = 6$. Find the volume swept out.

15. A loudspeaker horn is formed by a circle moving perpendicular to the x axis from $x = 2$ to $x = 20$. The circle's radius at position x is given by $r = .02x^2$. Find the volume enclosed.

16. A church steeple in the form of a pyramid is 30 ft high. Its cross sections are all squares, the base being a square of side 10 ft. Find the volume by integration.

17. For the right circular cone and again for a square pyramid we have the formula $V = \frac{1}{3}$(base area) (height). Let R be any region of the xy plane of area A. Form a cone by connecting the boundary points of R to vertex $(0, 0, h)$. Show that $V = \frac{1}{3}Ah$.*

18. The base of a solid is a quarter-circle of radius a. Each section perpendicular to one edge of the base is a semicircle. Find the volume.

19. A container has a circular base of radius 2. Each section perpendicular to one diameter is an isosceles triangle of altitude 6. Find the volume.

20. Find the volume common to the cylinders $x^2 + y^2 = a^2$ and $y^2 + z^2 = a^2$. *Suggestion:* Consider that eighth of the solid that lies in the first octant. Observe that each section perpendicular to the y axis is a square.

21. The side of a barrel has the shape of the surface formed by rotating the arc of $(y - 2)^2 = 20(\frac{3}{2} - x)$ from $y = 0$ to $y = 4$ about the y axis. The barrel is filled with a liquid of weight density ρ. Set up an integral for the work done in lifting the liquid out over the edge of the barrel.

12.3 Volume of Solid of Revolution by Concentric Shell Elements

The volumes of solids of revolution can be analyzed by a second method. Let a plane region R be rotated about a line L in the plane of R to form a solid of revolution. If region R is divided into rectangular elements parallel to L, then, upon rotation, these elements sweep out concentric cylindrical shells, and we can compute the volume of the solid by summation of these shells.

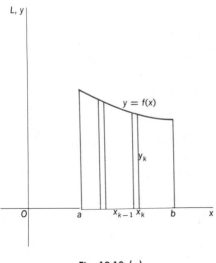

Fig. 12.13 (a)

To state this argument in the language of integration, choose the line L to be the y axis, as in Figs. 12.13(a) and (b), and let the region R be bounded by $y = f(x)$ for $a \leq x \leq b$, $x = a$, $x = b$, and the x axis. Divide the interval $a \leq x \leq b$ into n parts by choosing subdivision points $a = x_0 < x_1 < x_2 < \cdots < x_n = b$, and erect ordinates at these points. To each rectangular subregion of R there corresponds a cylindrical shell of the solid.

To get the volume of a cylindrical shell of height h, inner radius r, and thickness Δr (see Fig. 12.14), we subtract the volume of a cylinder of radius r from

* *Suggestion:* Let $A(z)$ be the area of the section of the cone at height z. Observe that $A(z)/A(0) = [(h - z)/h]^2$.

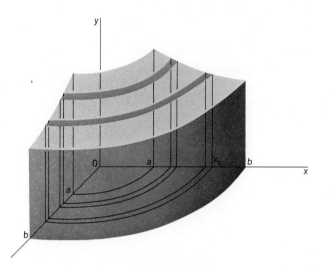

Fig. 12.13 (b)

that of one of radius $r + \Delta r$:

volume of cylindrical shell $= \pi(r + \Delta r)^2 h - \pi r^2 h$

$$= \pi(2r\,\Delta r + \Delta r^2)h = 2\pi\left(r + \frac{\Delta r}{2}\right)h\,\Delta r$$

$$= 2\pi(\text{average radius})(\text{height})(\text{thickness}).$$

Returning, then, to our solid of revolution, we shall let y_k'' and y_k' be the maximum and minimum values for $f(x)$ for $x_{k-1} \le x \le x_k$. The kth cylindrical shell

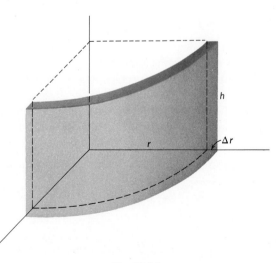

Fig. 12.14

element has a volume less than that of a shell of the same radius and thickness and constant height y_k'' and volume greater than that of a shell of constant height y_k';

$$2\pi(x_k^*)(y_k')(\Delta x)_k \leq (\Delta V)_k \leq 2\pi x_k^* y_k''(\Delta x)_k,$$

where x_k^* is the average radius of the shell element. We assume that $y = f(x)$ is continuous for $a \leq x \leq b$, and then the Intermediate Value Theorem for continuous functions permits us to say that there is an x_k^{**} and a corresponding y_k^{**} such that

$$(\Delta V)_k = 2\pi x_k^* y_k^{**}(\Delta x)_k.$$

Finally, we have

$$V = 2\pi \int_{x=a}^{b} xy \, dx.$$

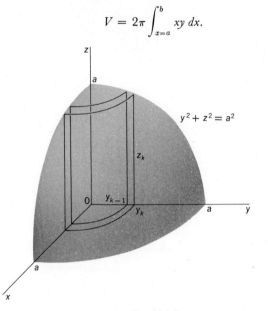

Fig. 12.15

Example 1. We shall use the shell method to compute the volume of a sphere of radius a and its moment of inertia about a diameter, assuming uniform mass density μ.

In Fig. 12.15, $\frac{1}{8}$ of a sphere of radius a is shown. The interval $0 \leq y \leq a$ is subdivided into n parts, and we say that there exist y_k^* and y_k^{**} of the kth subinterval such that

$$(\Delta V)_k = 2\pi \, (\text{average radius})(\text{height number})(\text{thickness})$$
$$= 2\pi y_k^* z_k^{**}(\Delta y)_k.$$

$$\tfrac{1}{2} V = \int_{y=0}^{a} 2\pi yz \, dy.$$

We wrote $\frac{1}{2} V$ here, because our analysis takes into account only the upper half of the sphere.

But the relationship between the y and z of our diagram is $y^2 + z^2 = a^2$. Hence

$$V = 4\pi \int_{y=0}^{a} yz \, dy = 4\pi \int_{y=0}^{a} y \sqrt{a^2 - y^2} \, dy = -2\pi \int_{0}^{a} (a^2 - y^2)^{1/2}(-2y) \, dy$$

$$= -\tfrac{4}{3}\pi(a^2 - y^2)^{3/2}\Big|_{y=0}^{a} = \tfrac{4}{3}\pi a^3.$$

The mass of the kth cylindrical shell element is

$$(\Delta m)_k = \mu(\Delta V)_k = 2\pi\mu y_k^* z_k^{**}(\Delta y)_k.$$

Each particle of the shell will rotate in a circle if the sphere rotates about the z axis, and the moment of inertia of each particle will be the product of its mass by the square of the radius of the circle in which it travels. Since the particles of the shell are all a distance from the z axis at least as great as y_{k-1} and at most as great as y_k, we can say that

$$(\Delta m)_k y_{k-1}^2 \le (\Delta I)_k \le (\Delta m)_k y_k^2.$$

The function y^2 is a continuous function of y so that there is a number y_k^{***}, $y_{k-1} \le y_k^{***} \le y_k$, such that

$$(\Delta I)_k = (\Delta m)_k (y_k^{***})^2 = 2\pi\mu y_k^* z_k^{**}(y_k^{***})^2(\Delta y)_k.$$

Then

$$\tfrac{1}{2} I = 2\pi\mu \int_{y=0}^{a} y^3 z \, dy = 2\pi\mu \int_{y=0}^{a} y^3 \sqrt{a^2 - y^2} \, dy.$$

To evaluate this integral, we can use either the trigonometric substitution $y = a \sin \theta$ or the algebraic substitution $w = \sqrt{a^2 - y^2}$. We obtain

$$\tfrac{1}{2} I = \tfrac{4}{15}\pi\mu a^5, \qquad \text{or} \qquad I = \tfrac{8}{15}\pi\mu a^5.$$

Example 2. The torus, or doughnut, is formed by rotating a circle about a nonintersecting line in its plane. In Fig. 12.16(a) the center of the circle is placed on the x axis, the equation being $(x - a)^2 + y^2 = b^2$, $a \ge b$, and the line about which the circle rotates is the y axis; only part of the solid is shown in Fig. 12.16(b).

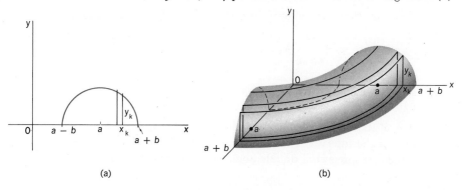

(a)   (b)

Fig. 12.16 (a) and (b)

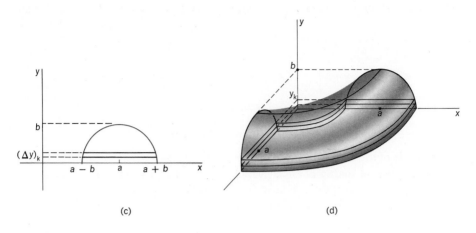

Fig. 12.16 (c) and (d)

Divide the x interval $a - b < x \leq a + b$ into n parts by choosing subdivision points $a - b = x_0 < x_1 < x_2 < \cdots < x_n = a + b$ and draw ordinate lines at each of these points. To each rectangular element of Fig. 12.16(a) there corresponds a cylindrical shell in Fig. 12.16(b). Then we choose intermediate x_k^* and x_k^{**}, $x_{k-1} \leq x_k^*, x_k^{**} \leq x_k$, such that

$$(\Delta V)_k = 2\pi \text{ (average radius) (height number) (thickness)}$$

$$(\Delta V)_k = 2\pi \, (x_k^*)(y_k^{**})(\Delta x)_k$$

$$\tfrac{1}{2} V = 2\pi \int_{x=a-b}^{a+b} xy \, dx.$$

From the equation of the circle in the xy plane we have $y^2 = b^2 - (x - a)^2$ so that

$$V = 4\pi \int_{x=a-b}^{a+b} \sqrt{b^2 - (x - a)^2} \, x \, dx.$$

Here we can use the trigonometric substitution $x - a = b \sin \theta$ and get

$$V = 4\pi \int_{\theta=-\pi/2}^{\pi/2} b \cos \theta \, (a + b \sin \theta) \, b \cos \theta \, d\theta$$

$$= 4\pi a b^2 \int_{-\pi/2}^{\pi/2} \cos^2 \theta \, d\theta + 4\pi b^3 \int_{-\pi/2}^{\pi/2} \cos^2 \theta \sin \theta \, d\theta.$$

The second of these integrals has the value 0 because the integrand has negative values for half the interval of integration and equal positive values for the other half. For the first integral, a double angle identity is used, and we have

$$V = 2\pi a b^2 \int_{-\pi/2}^{\pi/2} (1 + \cos 2\theta) d\theta = 2\pi^2 a b^2.$$

Example 3.   For the sake of comparing the methods, we shall find the volume of the same torus by taking parallel slices. In Fig. 12.16(c) we divide the y axis interval $0 \leq y \leq b$ into n parts and draw horizontal lines at the subdivision points. To each of the rectangular elements in Fig. 12.16(c) there corresponds a circular ring or "washer" element, perpendicular to the y axis, in Fig. 12.16(d). The thickness of this circular ring element is $(\Delta y)_k$; its cross-section area is the difference between the areas of two circles, one of radius $x^+ = a + \sqrt{b^2 - y^2}$ and the other of radius $x^- = a - \sqrt{b^2 - y^2}$, these values of x following from the circle equation $(x - a)^2 + y^2 = b^2$. There is a y_k^*, $y_{k-1} \leq y_k^* \leq y_k$, such that

$$(\Delta V)_k = \{\pi[a + \sqrt{b^2 - (y_k^*)^2}]^2 - \pi[a - \sqrt{b^2 - (y_k^*)^2}]^2\}\,(\Delta y)_k$$

$$(\Delta V)_k = \pi 4a \sqrt{b^2 - (y_k^*)^2}\,(\Delta y)_k,$$

$$\tfrac{1}{2} V = \int_{y=0}^{b} 4\pi a \sqrt{b^2 - y^2}\; dy.$$

To evaluate this integral we can use the substitution $y = b \sin \theta$ or else observe that $\int_0^b \sqrt{b^2 - y^2}\, dy$ represents the area of a quarter circle of radius b, as in Fig. 12.17,

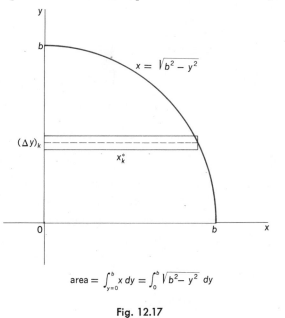

$$\text{area} = \int_{y=0}^{b} x\, dy = \int_0^b \sqrt{b^2 - y^2}\; dy$$

Fig. 12.17

and hence has the value $\tfrac{1}{4}\pi b^2$; then

$$V = 2(4\pi a)(\tfrac{1}{4}\pi b^2) = 2\pi^2 a b^2.$$

Example 4.   Consider that region bounded by the parabola $y = 2 - x^2$ and the lines $x = 0, y = 1$ which lies to the right of the y axis. Find the volume swept out when this region is rotated about $x = 1$.

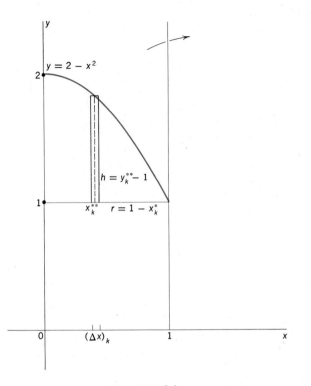

Fig. 12.18 (a)

In Fig. 12.18(a) the region to be rotated is sketched, and in Fig. 12.18(b) part of the solid swept out. The x interval $0 \le x \le 1$ is divided into n parts; corresponding to each subinterval, there is a rectangular element in the plane area rotated and a cylindrical shell in the volume swept out. For the kth element of volume there are x_k^* and x_k^{**}, $x_{k-1} \le x_k^*$, $x_k^{**} \le x_k$, such that

$$(\Delta V)_k = 2\pi \text{ (average radius) (height number) (thickness)}$$
$$(\Delta V)_k = 2\pi \, (1 - x_k^*)(y_k^{**} - 1)(\Delta x)_k,$$
$$V = \int_{x=0}^{1} 2\pi \, (1 - x)(y - 1) \, dx.$$

But we have $y = 2 - x^2$, so that

$$V = 2\pi \int_{x=0}^{1} (1 - x)(2 - x^2 - 1) \, dx = 2\pi \int_{0}^{1} (1 - x - x^2 + x^3) \, dx = \frac{5\pi}{6}.$$

EXERCISES 12.3

1. Use the shell method to find the volume of the right circular cone of base radius r and height h swept out when the triangle bounded by the coordinate axes and $y/h + x/r = 1$ is rotated about the y axis.

2. Find the volume of the solid swept out when the region bounded by $x = 2$, $x = 3$, the x axis, and $y = 4 - x$ is rotated about the y axis.

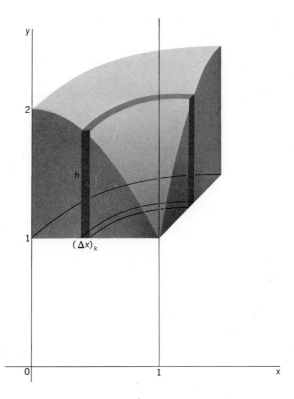

Fig. 12.18 (b)

3. Find the volume of the solid swept out when the region bounded by $y = \frac{1}{2} x$, the x axis, and the arc of $y = (x - 1)^2$ for which $\frac{1}{2} \leq x \leq 1$ is rotated about the x axis.

4. Find the volume of the solid swept out when the first-quadrant region bounded by $y = 1 + x^2$, $y = 2$, and $x = 0$ is rotated about (a) the y axis; (b) the x axis; (c) $y = 1$; (d) $x = 1$.

5. Find the volume of the solid swept out when the region bounded by $y = \sin x$ for $0 \leq x \leq \pi/2$, $y = 0$, and $x = \pi/2$ is rotated about (a) the y axis; (b) the x axis; (c) $x = \pi/2$; (d) $y = 1$.

6. Find the volume of the solid swept out when the region bounded by $y = 1/(1 + x^2)$, $x = 0$, $x = 1$, and $y = 0$ is rotated about (a) the y axis; (b) the x axis; (c) $x = 2$; (d) $y = 1$.

7. Find the volume of the solid formed by rotating the region bounded by $y = x^2$ and $y = \frac{1}{4} + \frac{3}{4} x^2$ about the y axis.

8. Find the volume of the solid formed by rotating the region bounded by $y = x^2$ and $y = x + 2$ about the x axis.

9. (a) Set up an integral for the volume of the solid swept out when the region bounded by the x axis and the arch of the cycloid $x = a(\theta - \sin \theta)$, $y = a(1 - \cos \theta)$, $0 \leq \theta \leq 2\pi$, is rotated about the y axis.
(b) Evaluate the integral.

10. Find the volume of the solid swept out when the region bounded by the catenary $y = \frac{1}{2}(e^x + e^{-x}) = \cosh x$ and $y = 2$ is rotated about the y axis. [Note that if $\cosh x = 2$, then $x = \pm \log (2 + \sqrt{3})$.]

11. Let the material of which the torus of Example 2 is composed be of constant mass density μ. Find the moment of inertia of the torus about the y axis.

12. A solid is formed by rotating about the y axis the region bounded by $y = 3x - x^2 - 2$ and the x axis. The solid has constant mass density μ. Find its moment of inertia for a rotation about its axis.

13. (a) Find the volume of the solid formed by rotating about the y axis the region bounded by $y = e^{-x^2}$, $y = 0$, $x = 0$, and $x = L$.
    (b) Explain what is meant by the volume of the solid formed by rotating about the y axis the first-quadrant region bounded by $y = e^{-x^2}$ and the coordinate axes. Find this volume.

14. Let $f(x)$ be continuous and decrease steadily for $0 \le x \le a$, with $f(0) = b > 0$ and $f(a) = 0$. Consider the solid formed by rotating about the x axis the first-quadrant region bounded by $y = f(x)$ and the coordinate axes. From the point of view of Sec. 12.2, the volume of this solid is given by $I_1 = \pi \int_{x=0}^{a} f^2(x)\ dx$. From the point of view of this section, the volume is given by $I_2 = 2\pi \int_{y=0}^{b} yx\ dy$. Show that I_2 can be reduced to I_1. (In I_2 use the substitution $y = f(x)$; then use integration by parts.) For the special solid here considered, we have shown that the definitions of volume used in Sec. 12.2 and in this section are consistent.

12.4   Surface Area of Surfaces of Revolution

The portion of a right circular cone cut off by two planes perpendicular to its axis is called a frustum; see $ACA\ DFD$ in Fig. 12.19. We shall derive a formula for the surface area of a frustum of a cone by geometric reasoning, and we shall make the computations of areas of other surfaces of revolution depend on this one.

We use the fact that a cone can be developed from a sector of a circle, as is done, for instance, in forming a conical filter from a circular piece of filter paper in a chemical laboratory. If the cone of Fig. 12.19 is cut along line ODA and rolled out, we get the circular sector of Fig. 12.20. Since circle DFD of Fig. 12.19 becomes circular arc $D'F'D'$ of Fig. 12.20, we have

$$2\pi r_1 = \alpha L_1,$$

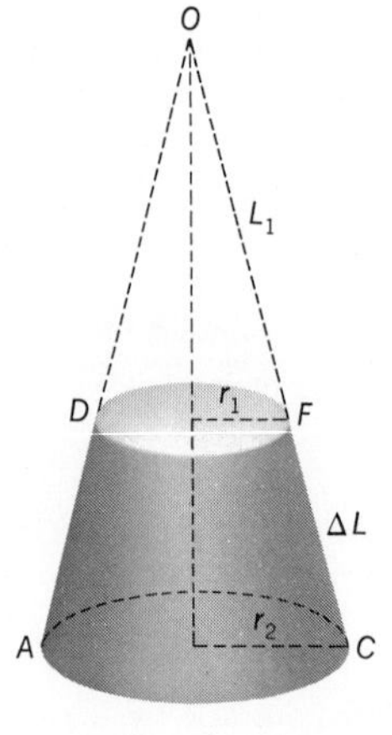

Fig. 12.19

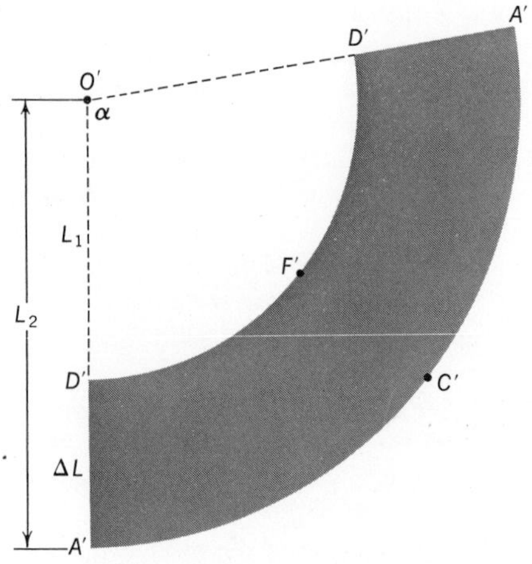

Fig. 12.20

and similarly, since circle ACA becomes circular arc $A'C'A'$,

$$2\pi r_2 = \alpha L_2.$$

The surface area of the frustum $ACA\,DFD$ of Fig. 12.19 becomes the area of the circular ring sector $A'C'A'\,D'F'D'$ of Fig. 12.20. We have

$$\text{area } A'C'A'D'F'D' = (\text{area } O'A'C'A'O') - (\text{area } O'D'F'D'O')$$

$$= \frac{\alpha}{2\pi}\,\pi(L_2)^2 - \frac{\alpha}{2\pi}\,\pi(L_1)^2*$$

$$= \frac{\alpha}{2}\,(L_2{}^2 - L_1{}^2) = \frac{\alpha}{2}\,(L_2 + L_1)(L_2 - L_1)$$

$$= \tfrac{1}{2}(\alpha L_2 + \alpha L_1)\,\Delta L = \tfrac{1}{2}\,(2\pi r_2 + 2\pi r_1)\,\Delta L$$

$$= 2\pi\left(\frac{r_1 + r_2}{2}\right)\Delta L.$$

We have proved the following theorem.

■ THEOREM 1

The surface area of a frustum of a cone.

HYPOTHESIS: A frustum of a cone has slant height ΔL and average radius $\bar{r}$.

CONCLUSION: The surface area of the frustum is $2\pi\bar{r}\Delta L$.

Now let plane arc C be rotated about a line λ in its plane to form a surface of revolution, as in Figs. 12.21(a) and (b). Let us choose partition points on arc C and join them by chords, as we do when we start to define the length of arc C. When C is rotated about line λ to form a surface of revolution, these chords sweep out frusta of cones. The following definition is then intuitively reasonable.

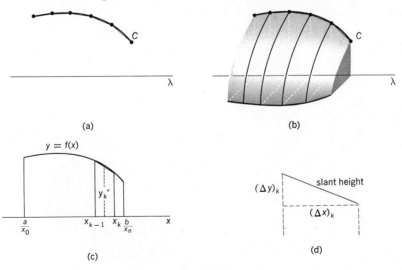

(a)

(b)

(c)

(d)

Fig. 12.21

---

* The area of a sector of central angle α is to the area of the whole circle as α is to 2π.

■ DEFINITION 1

The surface area of a surface of revolution. The surface area of a surface of revolution shall be the limit of the sum of the surface areas of the inscribed frusta as the number of these frusta grows beyond all bounds, the thicknesses of all the frusta approaching 0.

If the line λ is taken to be the x axis and arc C is described by the equation $y = f(x)$, $a \leq x \leq b$, with f' continuous for this interval, we can partition the interval $a \leq x \leq b$ as usual and then follow Figs. 12.21(c) and (d) to say that

$$(\Delta S)_k = \text{surface area of } k\text{th frustum} = 2\pi(\text{average radius})(\text{slant height})$$

$$= 2\pi y_k^* \sqrt{(\Delta x)_k^2 + (\Delta y)_k^2}$$

$$= 2\pi y_k^* \sqrt{1 + [(\Delta y)_k/(\Delta x)_k]^2}\ (\Delta x)_k.$$

Here $y_k^* = \tfrac{1}{2}(y_{k-1} + y_k)$, to be precise, and according to the Theorem of Mean Value, as we reasoned in Sec. 8.6, there exists an x_k^{**}, $x_{k-1} \leq x_k^{**} \leq x_k$, such that

$$(\Delta y)_k = f'(x_k^{**})(\Delta x)_k.$$

Hence, to continue the surface area computation, we have

$$(\Delta S)_k = 2\pi y_k^* \sqrt{1 + [f'(x_k^{**})]^2}\ (\Delta x)_k$$

$$S = \int_{x=a}^{b} 2\pi y \sqrt{1 + (dy/dx)^2}\ dx.$$

Example 1.   We shall find the surface area of a sphere. As in Fig. 12.22(a), take $\tfrac{1}{4}$ of the circle $x^2 + y^2 = a^2$, partition the x interval, $0 \leq x \leq a$, find the corresponding points on the circle, and draw the chords joining these points. When the circle is rotated about the x axis to form a sphere, as in Fig. 12.22(b), these chords sweep out frusta of cones. For the kth frustum we have, as above,

$$(\Delta S)_k = 2\pi\ (\text{average radius})(\text{slant height})$$

$$= 2\pi y_k^* \sqrt{1 + [f'(x_k^{**})]^2}\ (\Delta x)_k,$$

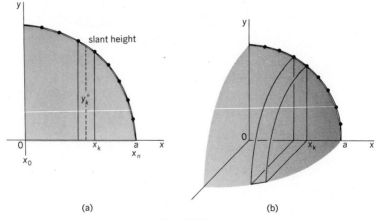

(a)   (b)

Fig. 12.22

and then, for the surface area,

$$\tfrac{1}{2} S = \int_{x=0}^{a} 2\pi y \sqrt{1 + (dy/dx)^2}\, dx.$$

But from $x^2 + y^2 = a^2$ we soon compute $dy/dx = -x/y$, so that

$$1 + \left(\frac{dy}{dx}\right)^2 = 1 + \frac{x^2}{y^2} = \frac{a^2}{y^2},$$

and thus

$$S = 4\pi \int_{x=0}^{a} a\, dx = 4\pi a^2.$$

Example 2. A parabolic reflector has the shape of a paraboloid of revolution. We shall compute the surface area swept out when the arc of $y = \sqrt{2px}$, $0 \leq x \leq h$, is rotated about the x axis.

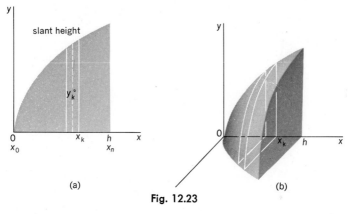

(a)   (b)

Fig. 12.23

Partition the x interval, $0 \leq x \leq h$, find the corresponding points on the parabola of Fig. 12.23(a), draw the chords that join these points, and form the inscribed frusta of Fig. 12.23(b) by rotation. We have, as before,

$$(\Delta S)_k = 2\pi \,(\text{average radius})\,(\text{slant height})$$
$$= 2\pi y_k^* \sqrt{1 + [f'(x_k^{**})^2]}\,(\Delta x)_k$$
$$S = 2\pi \int_{x=0}^{h} y \sqrt{1 + (dy/dx)^2}\, dx.$$

But

$$y = \sqrt{2p}\,\sqrt{x}, \quad \frac{dy}{dx} = \sqrt{p/2x},$$

$$y\sqrt{1 + (dy/dx)^2} = \sqrt{2px}\,\sqrt{1 + p/2x} = \sqrt{2px + p^2},$$

and hence

$$S = 2\pi \int_{0}^{h} \sqrt{2px + p^2}\, dx$$

$$= \frac{2\pi}{2p} \int_{0}^{h} [2px + p^2]^{1/2}(2p)\, dx = \frac{2\pi}{3p} [2px + p^2]^{3/2}\Big|_{0}^{h}$$

$$= \frac{2}{3}\frac{\pi}{p} \{(2ph + p^2)^{3/2} - p^3\} = \frac{2}{3}\pi\{\sqrt{p(2h + p)^3} - p^2\}.$$

Example 3. Let us rotate the hypocycloid of four cusps, $x = a \cos^3 \theta$, $y = a \sin^3 \theta$, about the y axis and find the surface area thus swept out.

This time we partition the θ interval, $0 \leq \theta \leq \pi/2$, find the corresponding points on the curve in Fig. 12.24(a) and draw the inscribed chords. In Fig. 12.24(b) the corresponding frusta elements are indicated. We can write

$$(\Delta S)_k = 2\pi(\text{average radius})\,(\text{slant height})$$
$$= 2\pi x_k^* \sqrt{(\Delta x)_k^2 + (\Delta y)_k^2}$$
$$= 2\pi x_k^* \sqrt{[(\Delta x)_k/(\Delta\theta)_k]^2 + [(\Delta y)_k/(\Delta\theta)_k]^2}\,(\Delta\theta)_k.$$

$$\tfrac{1}{2}S = \int_{\theta=0}^{\pi/2} 2\pi x \sqrt{(dx/d\theta)^2 + (dy/d\theta)^2}\, d\theta.$$

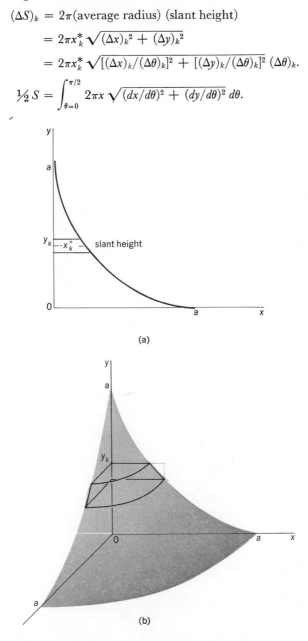

(a)

(b)

Fig. 12.24

But from $x = a \cos^3 \theta$, $y = a \sin^3 \theta$ we have

$$\left(\frac{dx}{d\theta}\right)^2 + \left(\frac{dy}{d\theta}\right)^2 = (-3a \cos^2 \theta \sin \theta)^2 + (3a \sin^2 \theta \cos \theta)^2$$

$$= 9a^2 \cos^2 \theta \sin^2 \theta.$$

Hence

$$\tfrac{1}{2} S = 2\pi \int_{\theta=0}^{\pi/2} a \cos^3 \theta \; 3a \cos \theta \sin \theta \; d\theta$$

$$= 6\pi a^2 \int_0^{\pi/2} \cos^4 \theta \sin \theta \; d\theta.$$

$$S = -12\pi a^2 \frac{\cos^5 \theta}{5} \Big|_0^{\pi/2} = \frac{12}{5} \pi a^2.$$

EXERCISES 12.4

1. Find the surface area swept out when the arc $y = \tfrac{1}{3} x^3 + (1/4x)$, $1 \leq x \leq 2$, is rotated (a) about $y = 0$; (b) about $x = 0$.

2. Let a torus be swept out by rotating the circle $x = b \cos \theta$, $y = b \sin \theta$ about the line $x = a$, $a > b > 0$. Find its surface area.

3. Find the surface area swept out when the arc $x = e^\theta \cos \theta$, $y = e^\theta \sin \theta$, $0 \leq \theta \leq \pi/2$, is rotated (a) about $y = 0$; (b) about $y = -1$.

4. Find the surface area swept out when the arc of the catenary $y = \cosh x$, $|x| \leq \log (2 + \sqrt{3})$ and $1 \leq y \leq 2$, is rotated (a) about $x = 0$; (b) about $y = 1$.

5. (a) Find the surface area swept out when the arc of the tractrix $x = t - a \tanh (t/a)$, $y = a \operatorname{sech} (t/a)$, $0 \leq t \leq 2a$, is rotated about $y = 0$.
   (b) The same for the arc $-a \leq t \leq 2a$. (This surface is a surface of "constant negative curvature.")

6. Find the surface area swept out when the cycloid arc, $x = a(\theta - \sin \theta)$, $y = a (1 - \cos \theta)$, $0 \leq \theta \leq 2\pi$, is rotated (a) about $y = 0$; (b) about $x = 0$.

7. Find the surface area swept out when the arc $y = x^3$, $0 \leq x \leq 1$, is rotated (a) about $y = 0$; (b) about $x = 0$.

8. Find the surface area swept out when the arc $y^2 = x^3$, $0 \leq y \leq 1$, is rotated (a) about $x = 0$; (b) about $x = -1$.

9. Find the surface area swept out when the loop of $9y^2 = x(3 - x)^2$ is rotated about the x axis.

10. Find the surface area swept out when either loop of $8y^2 = x^2 - x^4$ is rotated about the x axis.

11. Find the surface area swept out when the arc $y = \log x$, $1 \leq x \leq 2$, is rotated (a) about $x = 0$; (b) about $x = 1$.

12. (a) Find the surface area swept out when the arc $x = \tfrac{1}{4} t^4$, $y = \tfrac{1}{5} t^5$, $0 \leq t \leq 1$, is rotated about the y axis.
    (b) Set up the integrals for the surface area swept out when the arc $-2 \leq t \leq 1$ is rotated about the y axis.

13. The ellipse $(x^2/a^2) + (y^2/b^2) = 1$, $a > b$, is rotated about its shorter axis to form an oblate spheroid. Find its surface area.

14. To find the volume of a solid of revolution in Sec. 12.2, we took the volume of a cylindrical disk for the element of volume. In this section, why did we not take the surface area of a cylindrical disk for the surface-area element of a surface of revolution?

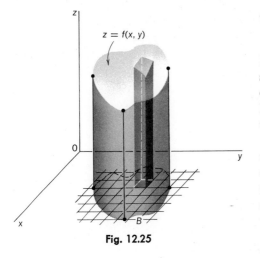

$z = f(x, y)$

Fig. 12.25

12.5 Volumes by Prisms. The Double Integral

In Sec. 12.2 we computed volumes of solids when we knew the areas of the cross sections perpendicular to a line. Here we present a different attack on the volume problem.

Let a solid have for its base the region R in the xy plane with boundary B; let its side walls be given by the cylinder through B which is parallel to the z axis; and let its roof be the surface with equation $z = f(x, y)$. Then, as in Fig. 12.25, we first divide the region R into rectangles by drawing a network of lines parallel to the x and y axes. Second, at each rectangle vertex we draw a line parallel to the z axis, thus dividing the solid into a finite number of prismlike elements, one volume element for each area element of the base.

Next, if we want an underestimate for our volume, we can take those rectangles of the base that lie entirely within B, assign to each one a height number equal to the *minimum* value of $z = f(x, y)$ for the x's and y's pertaining to that element, and take as an underestimate for that particular volume element the product of the base area by the height number. By summing these products, we get an underestimate for the volume of the solid.

On the other hand, if we want an overestimate for our volume, we can take those rectangles of the base that lie either entirely *or partly* within B, assign to each one a height number equal to the *maximum* value of $z = f(x, y)$ for the x's and y's pertaining to that element, and take as an overestimate for that particular volume element the product of the base area by the height number.

It is intuitively plausible to say that, if we repeat this process with finer and finer networks of rectangles in the xy plane, the difference between the overestimate and the underestimate will decrease, for the differences between the maximum and minimum heights of the prism elements will decrease and so will the sum of the areas of those base rectangles which are taken in the overestimate and neglected in the underestimate. Hence our intuition suggests the following theorem.

■ THEOREM 1

On volumes by summation of prisms.

HYPOTHESIS: (a) The base of a solid lies in the xy plane and has a "suitable" boundary B.

(b) The side of the solid is parallel to the z axis.

(c) The roof of the solid is the surface $z = f(x, y)$, f a continuous function for (x, y) in, or on, B.

(d) The base has been subdivided into n rectangles by a network of lines parallel to the x and y axes. Let δ be the maximum of the lengths of the diagonals of these rectangles, $(\Delta A)_k$ the area of the kth rectangle, and (x_k, y_k) a point of the kth rectangle.

CONCLUSION: $\lim\limits_{\substack{n \to \infty \\ \delta \to 0}} \sum\limits_{k=1}^{n} f(x_k, y_k)(\Delta A)_k$ exists.

■ DEFINITION 1

The volume of the solid described in the hypothesis of Theorem 1 is the limit number whose existence is asserted by the conclusion of that theorem.

● Remark 1

In Hypothesis (a), a "suitable" boundary would be one that meets the following criterion: Let s be the sum of the areas of those rectangles that lie partly but not entirely within B. Then B is a suitable boundary for the purposes of this theorem if $\lim_{\delta \to 0} s = 0$.

In all the problems with which we shall be concerned, the boundaries B consist of a finite number of curves that can be described by statements of the form $x = \phi(y)$ or $y = \psi(x)$, ϕ and ψ continuous functions. It can be shown that such boundaries B do meet the criterion we have set up for "suitable" boundaries.

● Remark 2

In Hypothesis (d), it does not matter whether or not we include among the n rectangles those that lie only partly within B.

SKETCH OF PROOF OF THEOREM 1: We shall enlarge somewhat on the plausibility argument that led us to the statement of this theorem, but we leave a complete argument to an advanced calculus course.

For a particular subdivision of the base into rectangles, let t be the value of $\Sigma f(x_k, y_k)(\Delta A)_k$ obtained by taking only those rectangles that lie entirely within the boundary B and the points (x_k, y_k) within these rectangles that lead to minimum values of $z = f(x, y)$ for the respective rectangles. Let T be the value of $\Sigma f(x_k, y_k)$ $(\Delta A)_k$ obtained by taking not only the rectangles used in defining t but also those that lie only partly within B, and by using the points (x_k, y_k) that lead to maximum values of z. The strategy for a proof would be to show that as δ approaches 0 the t's increase and the T's decrease, both approaching the same value. We shall not discuss this question fully here, but we shall outline a proof of the fact that the difference $T - t$ approaches 0.

The difference $T - t$ may be said to consist of two parts. The first part arises because for T we used maximum values for $z = f(x, y)$ in considering the rectangles that lie entirely within B while for t we used minimum values. For this part of $T - t$, we can reason as follows: First we show that if f is continuous, it is uniformly continuous. This means that if a challenge number is presented, no matter how small, we can always find a number δ such that two points within distance δ of each other have corresponding z's which differ by less than the challenge number, no matter where, within or on B, the two points are chosen. If A is the area included within boundary B and if a positive number ϵ is specified, we can take the number $\epsilon/2A$ to be a challenge number, and we can choose a positive number δ such that $z_{max} - z_{min} < \epsilon/2A$ for all rectangles of all partitions of the base where the maximum diagonal size is less than δ. For such a partition we could indicate by z_k'' and z_k' the maximum and minimum values of z for the kth rectangle and the first part of $T - t$ could be written

$$(z_1'' - z_1')(\Delta A)_1 + \cdots + (z_n'' - z_n')(\Delta A)_n < \frac{\epsilon}{2A}[(\Delta A)_1 + \cdots + (\Delta A)_n] < \frac{\epsilon}{2}.$$

The second part of $T - t$ arises because T uses some rectangles that t does not. But the boundary B is assumed to be such that the sum of the areas of these extra rectangles approaches 0 as δ does. After showing that a continuous function is bounded, we could say that it is possible to choose δ small enough to make the sum of the areas of these extra rectangles less than $\epsilon/2L$, where L is an upper bound for $z = f(x, y)$. But then the second part of $T - t$ would read

$$\sum_{\substack{\text{certain} \\ k\text{'s}}} f(x_k, y_k)(\Delta A)_k < \sum L(\Delta A)_k = L \sum (\Delta A)_k < L\frac{\epsilon}{2L} = \frac{\epsilon}{2}.$$

With this we would have shown that $T - t$ could be made less than ϵ by choosing δ small enough; in other words, $\lim_{\delta \to 0} (T - t) = 0$.

We could now conclude that if either the underestimates t or the overestimates T approach a limit, then both approach the same limit. But it remains to show that the underestimates t do approach a limit. The argument uses the simple idea that the underestimate increases if a network of lines is made finer by introducing new lines, but the details are not easy to arrange for a first course, and are not presented here.

Finally, if minimum and maximum values of f lead to the same limit, we will surely achieve the same limit with intermediate values of f, and therefore in Hypothesis (d) we were free to choose any point (x_k, y_k) of the kth rectangle we thought convenient. We were also free to include those rectangles that were only partly in B, or not to include them, as stated in Remark 2.

Example 1. Consider the solid whose base is the rectangle bounded by the lines $x = 0$, $x = 2$,

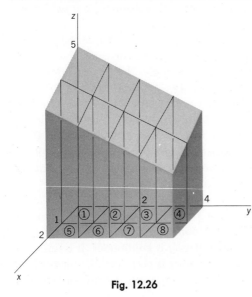

Fig. 12.26

$y = 0$, and $y = 4$ in the xy plane, whose sides are parallel to the z axis, and whose roof is the plane $z = f(x, y) = 5 - \frac{1}{2}(x + y)$.

Let us divide the base into 8 rectangles by drawing the lines $x = 1$, $y = 1$, $y = 2$, $y = 3$ in the xy plane, and let us order the rectangles as in Fig. 12.26. If as a representative height for each prism element we choose to evaluate z at the rectangle vertex farthest from the origin, we get an underestimate for the volume. The computations for this underestimate are to be found in the first part of Table 12.1;

TABLE 12.1

Rectangle	$(\Delta A)_k$	z_k min	$(\Delta V)_k$ min	z_k max	$(\Delta V)_k$ max
1	1	$f(1, 1) = 4$	4	$f(0, 0) = 5$	5
2	1	$f(1, 2) = 3.5$	3.5	$f(0, 1) = 4.5$	4.5
3	1	$f(1, 3) = 3$	3	$f(0, 2) = 4$	4
4	1	$f(1, 4) = 2.5$	2.5	$f(0, 3) = 3.5$	3.5
5	1	$f(2, 1) = 3.5$	3.5	$f(1, 0) = 4.5$	4.5
6	1	$f(2, 2) = 3$	3	$f(1, 1) = 4$	4
7	1	$f(2, 3) = 2.5$	2.5	$f(1, 2) = 3.5$	3.5
8	1	$f(2, 4) = 2$	2	$f(1, 3) = 3$	3
Sum			24		32

the underestimate is 24. On the other hand, if as a representative height for each prism element we choose z evaluated at the rectangle vertex closest to the origin, we get an overestimate for the volume. This overestimate is 32; the computations leading to this number are given in the second part of Table 12.1.

If we had divided the base into 32 rectangles by drawing the network of lines $x = \frac{1}{2}$, $x = 1$, $x = \frac{3}{2}$, $y = \frac{1}{2}$, $y = 1$, $y = \frac{3}{2}$, $y = 2$, $y = \frac{5}{2}$, $y = 3$, and $y = \frac{7}{2}$, and if we had again taken the minimum and maximum z's for our representative heights, we would have had 26 and 30 as underestimate and overestimate, respectively. The correct answer is 28, as we shall see in Example 12.6-1.

Example 2. Consider the solid that has as base the first quadrant quarter-circle of radius 4 with center at the origin, the planes $x = 0$ and $y = 0$ as sides, and the paraboloid $z = f(x, y) = 4 - \frac{1}{4}(x^2 + y^2)$ as roof.

This solid is sketched in Fig. 12.27. Let us divide the base into rectangles by drawing the lines $x = 1, 2, 3, 4$ and $y = 1, 2, 3, 4$ and let us number these rectangles as in the figure.

To get an underestimate for the volume, we can take those rectangles that lie entirely within the quarter-circle and take as representative height for each such volume element the minimum value of z, the value of z at the rectangle vertex farthest from the origin. This computation is shown in Table 12.2; this underestimate is 15.50.

TABLE 12.2

Rectangle	$(\Delta A)_k$	z_k min	$(\Delta V)_k$
1	1	$f(1, 1) = 3.50$	3.50
2	1	$f(1, 2) = 2.75$	2.75
3	1	$f(1, 3) = 1.50$	1.50
5	1	$f(2, 1) = 2.75$	2.75
6	1	$f(2, 2) = 2.00$	2.00
7	1	$f(2, 3) = 0.75$	0.75
9	1	$f(3, 1) = 1.50$	1.50
10	1	$f(3, 2) = 0.75$	0.75

15.50

To get an overestimate for the volume, we can take the rectangles we took before and in addition those that lie only partly within the quarter-circle. As representative height for each of these elements, we take the maximum value of z, the value of z at the rectangle vertex nearest the origin. This computation is shown

TABLE 12.3

Rectangle	$(\Delta A)_k$	z_k max	$(\Delta V)_k$
1	1	$f(0, 0) = 4.00$	4.00
2	1	$f(0, 1) = 3.75$	3.75
3	1	$f(0, 2) = 3.00$	3.00
4	1	$f(0, 3) = 1.75$	1.75
5	1	$f(1, 0) = 3.75$	3.75
6	1	$f(1, 1) = 3.50$	3.50
7	1	$f(1, 2) = 2.75$	2.75
8	1	$f(1, 3) = 1.50$	1.50
9	1	$f(2, 0) = 3.00$	3.00
10	1	$f(2, 1) = 2.75$	2.75
11	1	$f(2, 2) = 2.00$	2.00
12	1	$f(2, 3) = 0.75$	0.75
13	1	$f(3, 0) = 1.75$	1.75
14	1	$f(3, 1) = 1.50$	1.50
15	1	$f(3, 2) = 0.75$	0.75

36.50

in Table 12.3; the overestimate is 36.50. The volume is 8π, as we shall see in Exercise 12.6-8, but of course we would have to use a much finer network of rectangles in the xy plane to come very close to this answer.

We conclude this section with another definition.

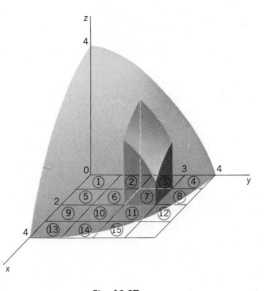

Fig. 12.27

■ **DEFINITION 2**

The double integral. Let region R of the xy plane have a boundary B that meets the requirement stated in Remark 1. Let R be divided into n rectangles by a network of lines parallel to the x and y axes, and let δ be the maximum of the lengths of the diagonals of these rectangles. Let these rectangles be labeled with integers $1, 2, \cdots ; n$, let $(\Delta A)_k$ be the area of the kth rectangle, and let (x_k, y_k) be a point of this kth rectangle. Let $f(x, y)$ be continuous in, and on, B. Then by $\iint\limits_{R} f(x, y)\ dA$,

we mean

$$\lim_{\substack{\delta \to 0 \\ n \to \infty}} \sum_{k=1}^{n} f(x_k, y_k)(\Delta A)_k.$$

We can now restate Definition 1.

■ **DEFINITION 1A**

The solid whose base is region R of the xy plane with suitable boundary, whose sides are parallel to the z axis, and whose roof is $z = f(x, y)$ has volume $\iint\limits_{R} f(x, y)\ dA$.

EXERCISES 12.5

1. A solid is bounded by the coordinate planes, the planes $x = 5$ and $y = 2$, and $z = \frac{1}{2} xy$. Divide the solid into elements by taking the planes $x = 1, 2, 3, 4$ and $y = 1$. Estimate the volume of the solid by taking as representative height for each element (a) the minimum height; (b) the maximum height; (c) the height at the center of the base of that element.

2. Repeat Exercise 1 for the solid whose base is the rectangle in the xy plane for which $0 \leq x \leq 4$ and $1 \leq y \leq 3$, whose side walls are parallel to the z axis, and whose roof is $z = x/y$. Divide the solid into elements by taking the planes $x = 1, 2, 3$ and $y = 2$.

3. Consider the tetrahedron determined by the coordinate planes and $2x + y + z = 6$. In the xy plane draw the network of lines $x = c$, $y = d$, c and d integers.
   (a) For each rectangle that lies entirely within the base of the solid, take the minimum height and thus form underestimates for the volumes of the elements and the volume of the solid.
   (b) For each rectangle that lies entirely or partly within the base of the tetrahedron, take the maximum height and thus form an overestimate for the volume of the solid.

4. Repeat Exercise 3 for the solid whose base lies in the first quadrant of the xy plane and is bounded by the x and y axes and $x^2 + y^2 = 16$, whose side walls are parallel to the z axis, and whose roof is the plane $z = 4 + \frac{1}{2}x - y$.

5. Repeat Exercise 3 for the solid whose base lies in the first quadrant of the xy plane and is bounded by $x = 0$, $y = 4$, and $x^2 = 4y$, whose side walls are parallel to the z axis, and whose roof is the plane $z = -\frac{1}{2}x + \frac{1}{2}y + 1$.

6. Consider the solid bounded by the xy plane, the cylinder $(y - 1)^2 + x^2 = 1$, and the paraboloid $z = 3 - \frac{1}{2}(x^2 + y^2)$. In the xy plane draw the network of lines $x = c/2$, $y = d/2$, c and d integers. For each element of volume thus determined, estimate $(\Delta A)_k$ and a representative z_k and thus estimate the volume of the solid. Observe that the solid is symmetric with respect to the yz plane.

12.6 Double Integrals and Iterated Single Integrals

In Sec. 12.5 we defined the volumes of certain solids as limits of sums of volumes of prismlike elements, and defined the double integral to be such a limit of a sum. Here we return to the point of view of Sec. 12.2 and try to find the same volumes. Then we compare results.

Consider again, then, a solid with base in the xy plane, side walls parallel to the z axis, and the surface $z = f(x, y)$ as its roof. Let f be a continuous function for whatever number pairs (x, y) are in question, and let the boundary of the base in the xy plane consist of the arcs with equations $x = \phi_1(y)$ and $x = \phi_2(y)$ for $a \leq y \leq b$ and perhaps portions of the lines $y = a$ and $y = b$; ϕ_1 and ϕ_2 are to be continuous for $a \leq y \leq b$. In Sec. 12.2 it was pointed out that, if we knew the areas of the sections of the solid by various planes $y = $ const, we could analyze the solid as a sum of slices perpendicular to the y axis; see Fig. 12.28. Let the area of the section by the plane for a particular y value be $A(y)$. Then for the volume of one slice element we would have

$$(\Delta V)_k = A(y_k^*)\,(\Delta y)_k$$

for a properly chosen number y_k^* of the kth element and

$$V = \int_{y=a}^{b} A(y)\,dy. \tag{1}$$

But how can we describe $A(y)$?

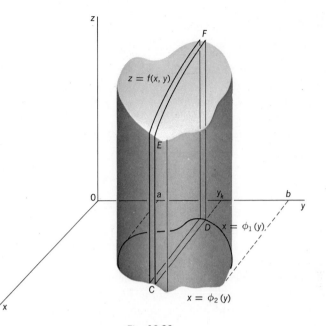

Fig. 12.28

In Fig. 12.29 we have redrawn section $DCEF$ of Fig. 12.28. The x for point D is $\phi_1(y)$; that for point C is $\phi_2(y)$. The area of the section $CDFE$ is then

$$A(y) = \int_{x=\phi_1(y)}^{\phi_2(y)} z \, dx = \int_{x=\phi_1(y)}^{\phi_2(y)} f(x, y) \, dx \tag{2}$$

because the area element is $z \, \Delta x$. Thus Eqs. (1) and (2) together tell us that

$$V = \int_{y=a}^{b} \left[\int_{x=\phi_1(y)}^{\phi_2(y)} f(x, y) \, dx \right] dy. \tag{3}$$

It is to be emphasized that all points of the plane of Fig. 12.29 have the same y coordinate. Therefore in working with the integral of Eq. (2), which is the inner integral of Eq. (3), *y is to be considered constant.*

In the last paragraph of Sec. 12.5 we pointed out that the volume of this solid could also be written $V = \iint_R f(x, y)$

dA. Comparing results, we have an intuitively plausible argument for the following theorem. The proof will be left for a more advanced course.

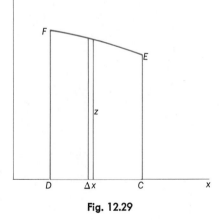

Fig. 12.29

■ THEOREM 1

Volumes as double integrals or as iterated single integrals.

HYPOTHESIS: A solid has (a) for base the region R in the xy plane bounded by the arcs $x = \phi_1(y)$ and $x = \phi_2(y)$ for $a \leq y \leq b$ and perhaps $y = a$ and $y = b$; ϕ_1 and ϕ_2 are continuous, with $\phi_1 \leq \phi_2$, for $a \leq y \leq b$.

(b) sides parallel to the z axis.

(c) for roof the surface $z = f(x, y)$, f continuous for (x, y) of R.

CONCLUSION:

$$V = \int\!\!\int_R f(x,y)\, dA = \int_{y=a}^{b} \left[\int_{x=\phi_1(y)}^{\phi_2(y)} f(x,y)\, dx \right] dy.$$

Example 1. We consider again the solid of Example 12.5-1; see Fig. 12.30. Its base is the rectangle R in the xy plane bounded by $x = 0$, $x = 2$, $y = 0$, and $y = 4$; its roof is $z = 5 - \frac{1}{2}(x + y)$.

If we were to divide the base into rectangles by a network of lines parallel to the x and y axes, as we did in Example 12.5-1, we could estimate the volume of one prism element as $z\, \Delta A$ and the volume could be described as

$$V = \int\!\!\int_R z\, dA.$$

In Example 12.5-1 we computed some of the sums whose limit would be V. Here we find V. We do this by turning to the iterated integral point of view.

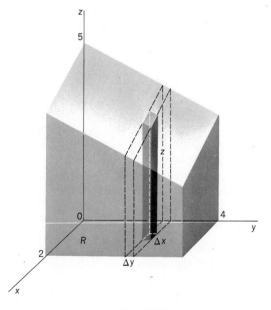

Fig. 12.30

For any y of $0 \le y \le 4$ the area of the corresponding section is

$$A(y) = \int_{x=0}^{2} z\, dx$$

because the element of area for this section is $z\, \Delta x$. A slice volume element for the solid is then $A(y)\, \Delta y$ and we have

$$V = \int_{y=0}^{4} A(y)\, dy = \int_{y=0}^{4} \left[\int_{x=0}^{2} z\, dx \right] dy = \int_{y=0}^{4} \left[\int_{x=0}^{2} \{5 - \tfrac{1}{2}(x+y)\}\, dx \right] dy$$

$$= \int_{y=0}^{4} [5x - \tfrac{1}{4}x^2 - \tfrac{1}{2}yx]_{x=0}^{2}\, dy = \int_{y=0}^{4} [(10 - 1 - y) - (0)]\, dy$$

$$= \left[9y - \frac{y^2}{2} \right]_{0}^{4} = (36 - 8) - (0) = 28.$$

Observe that in evaluating the $A(y)$ integral we treated y as if it were a constant, because we were finding an area in a plane with equation $y = \text{const.}$

In the iterated integration we have discussed so far, we have integrated first with respect to x and then with respect to y. But it is often convenient to analyze a solid by taking sections perpendicular to the x axis rather than the y axis. In such a case the alternate form of Theorem 1 would read as follows.

■ **THEOREM 1A**

HYPOTHESIS: A solid has (a) for base the region R of the xy plane bounded by the arcs $y = \psi_1(x)$ and $y = \psi_2(x)$ for $c \le x \le d$ and perhaps $x = c$ and $x = d$; ψ_1 and ψ_2 are continuous, with $\psi_1 \le \psi_2$, for $c \le x \le d$.
  (b) sides parallel to the z axis.
  (c) for roof the surface $z = f(x, y)$, f continuous for (x, y) of R.

CONCLUSION:

$$V = \int\int_R f(x,y)\, dA = \int_{x=c}^{d} \left[\int_{y=\psi_1(x)}^{\psi_2(x)} f(x,y)\, dy \right] dx.$$

Example 2. The tetrahedron bounded by the coordinate planes and $2x + y + z = 6$ has as its base in the xy plane the triangular region R bounded by the x and y axes and the line $2x + y = 6$ or $y = 6 - 2x$; see Fig. 12.31.

If we were to draw a network of lines in the xy plane parallel to the axes and then erect prism volume elements, we could write

$$\Delta V \approx z\Delta A,$$

$$V = \int\int_R z\, dA.$$

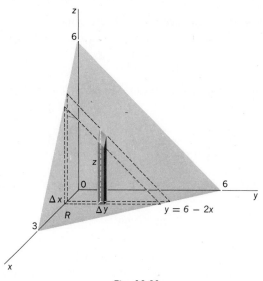

Fig. 12.31

To evaluate this integral as a limit of a sum, however, is difficult. Instead, let us consider sections perpendicular to the x axis. For any x of $0 \le x \le 3$ the area of the corresponding section is

$$A(x) = \int_{y=0}^{6-2x} z \, dy$$

because the element for this area is $z \, \Delta y$. A slice element perpendicular to the x axis has volume

$$\Delta V = A(x) \, \Delta x,$$

and then we write

$$V = \int_{x=0}^{3} A(x) \, dx = \int_{x=0}^{3} \left[\int_{y=0}^{6-2x} (6 - 2x - y) \, dy \right] dx$$

$$= \int_{x=0}^{3} \left[(6 - 2x)y - \frac{y^2}{2} \right]_{y=0}^{6-2x} dx$$

$$= \int_{x=0}^{3} \left[(6 - 2x)^2 - \frac{(6 - 2x)^2}{2} \right] dx$$

$$= \tfrac{1}{2} \int_{x=0}^{3} (6 - 2x)^2 \, dx = -\tfrac{1}{4} \int_{x=0}^{3} (6 - 2x)^2 (-2) \, dx$$

$$= -\frac{1}{4} \frac{(6 - 2x)^3}{3} \Big|_{x=0}^{3}$$

$$= -\tfrac{1}{12}[(0) - (6)^3] = 18.$$

Observe that in computing the $A(x)$ integral, the inner integral, we were careful to treat x as a constant, because we were computing an area in a plane $x = \text{const}$.

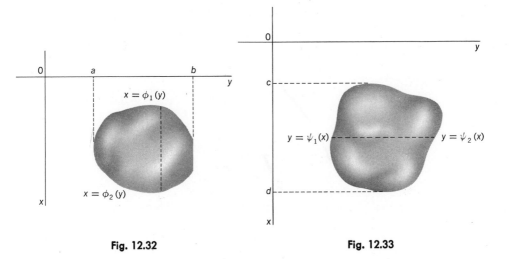

Fig. 12.32   **Fig. 12.33**

We have illustrated the conclusions of Theorems 1 and 1A. These statements say that a double integral representing a volume can be replaced by iterated single integrals. More precisely, if, as in Fig. 12.32, the region R of the xy plane over which the double integral $\iint\limits_{R} f(x, y)\, dA$ is taken can be visualized as swept out in two steps:

(a) moving a point in the x direction from the curve $x = \phi_1(y)$ to the curve $x = \phi_2(y)$ to form a line segment, and

(b) moving this line segment in the y direction from $y = a$ to $y = b$, then

$$\iint\limits_{R} f(x, y)\, dA = \int_{y=a}^{b} \left[\int_{x=\phi_1(y)}^{\phi_2(y)} f(x, y)\, dx \right] dy.$$

The two steps (a) and (b) in which region R is swept out determine the order in which the single integrals are taken and their boundaries. First, we move a point in the x direction from $x = \phi_1(y)$ to $x = \phi_2(y)$; we integrate with respect to x, taking as boundaries $x = \phi_1(y)$ and $x = \phi_2(y)$. As we move, y does not vary; as we integrate, y is held fixed. Second, we move a line segment in the y direction from $y = a$ to $y = b$; second, we integrate with respect to y, taking as boundaries $y = a$ and $y = b$.

On the other hand, if, as in Fig. 12.33, R can be visualized as swept out in two steps—moving a point in the y direction from $y = \psi_1(x)$ to $y = \psi_2(x)$ to form a line segment and moving this line segment in the x direction from $x = c$ to $x = d$—then

$$\iint\limits_{R} f(x, y)\, dA = \int_{x=c}^{d} \left[\int_{y=\psi_1(x)}^{\psi_2(x)} f(x, y)\, dy \right] dx.$$

Again the setting up of the single integrals is determined by the way region R is swept out. First we move a point in the y direction from $y = \psi_1(x)$ to $y = \psi_2(x)$ to form a line segment; first we integrate with respect to y, taking as boundaries

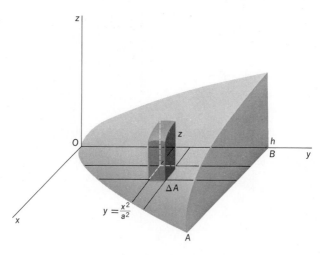

Fig. 12.34

$y = \psi_1(x)$ and $y = \psi_2(x)$. Second, we move the line segment in the x direction from $x = c$ to $x = d$; second, we integrate with respect to x, taking $x = c$ and $x = d$ as boundaries.

Example 3.   Let us reconsider the solid of Example 12.2-6. This solid is bounded by the elliptic paraboloid $x^2/a^2 + z^2/b^2 = y$ and the plane $y = h$. In Fig. 12.34 we indicate that $\frac{1}{4}$ of the solid can be considered to be a sum of prismlike elements of base $\Delta A = \Delta x \, \Delta y$ and height z. Hence

$$\tfrac{1}{4} V = \iint\limits_{\hat{O}AB} z \, dA.$$

In Fig. 12.35 we point out that region OAB can be swept out by (a) moving a point in the y direction from $y = x^2/a^2$ to $y = h$ to form a line segment and (b) moving this line segment in the x direction from $x = 0$ to $x = a\sqrt{h}$. Hence

$$\tfrac{1}{4} V = \int_{x=0}^{a\sqrt{h}} \left[\int_{y=x^2/a^2}^{h} z \, dy \right] dx,$$

$$V = 4 \int_{x=0}^{a\sqrt{h}} \left[\int_{y=x^2/a^2}^{h} \frac{b}{a} (a^2 y - x^2)^{1/2} \, dy \right] dx,$$

using the equation of the surface to write z in terms of x and y.

For the first, inner integration, we hold x fixed:

$$V = 4 \frac{b}{a} \frac{1}{a^2} \frac{2}{3} \int_{x=0}^{a\sqrt{h}} (a^2 y - x^2)^{3/2} \Big|_{y=x^2/a^2}^{h} dx$$

$$= \frac{8}{3} \frac{b}{a^3} \int_{x=0}^{a\sqrt{h}} (a^2 h - x^2)^{3/2} \, dx.$$

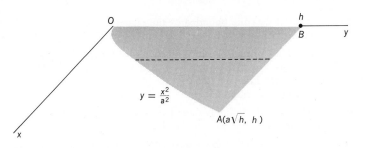

Fig. 12.35

This integral can be evaluated with the help of a table of integrals, or we can write $x = a\sqrt{h} \sin \theta$. Then

$$V = \frac{8}{3} \frac{b}{a^3} a^4 h^2 \int_{\theta=0}^{\pi/2} \cos^4 \theta \, d\theta = \frac{8}{3} bah^2 \frac{1}{4} \int_{\theta=0}^{\pi/2} (1 + \cos 2\theta)^2 \, d\theta$$

$$= \tfrac{2}{3} bah^2 \int_{\theta=0}^{\pi/2} (\tfrac{3}{2} + 2 \cos 2\theta + \tfrac{1}{2} \cos 4\theta) \, d\theta = \tfrac{1}{2} \pi abh^2.$$

This answer agrees with that of Example 12.2-6.

We conclude this section with an agreement on notation.

■ NOTATION CONVENTION 1

For the iterated integrals

$$\int_{x=a}^{b} \left[\int_{y=\psi_1(x)}^{\psi_2(x)} f(x, y) \, dy \right] dx$$

we shall write

$$\int_{x=a}^{b} \int_{y=\psi_1(x)}^{\psi_2(x)} f(x, y) \, dy \, dx;$$

for

$$\int_{y=a}^{b} \left[\int_{x=\phi_1(y)}^{\phi_2(y)} f(x, y) \, dx \right] dy$$

we shall write

$$\int_{y=a}^{b} \int_{x=\phi_1(y)}^{\phi_2(y)} f(x, y) \, dx \, dy.$$

In other words, we shall no longer use brackets to indicate the sequence of integrations; we agree to work from the inside out.

EXERCISES 12.6

1. Find the volume of the solid bounded by the coordinate planes, the planes $x = 5$ and $y = 2$, and the surface $z = \tfrac{1}{2} xy$. (See Exercise 12.5-1.)

2. Find the volume of the solid bounded by the planes $x = 0$, $x = 4$, $y = 1$, $y = 3$, and $z = 0$ and the surface $z = x/y$. (See Exercise 12.5-2.)

3. (a) Find the volume of the solid in the first octant bounded by the cylinder $x^2 = 4y$ and the planes $z = 0$, $x = 0$, $y = 4$, and $x - y + 2z = 2$. Integrate first with respect to x. (See Exercise 12.5-5.)
   (b) Integrate first with respect to y.

4. Find the volume of the solid bounded by the coordinate planes, and the planes $z = 2$, $y = 3$, and $4x - 3y + 2z = 12$. Use prism elements parallel to the x axis.

5. Consider the solid bounded by $y = 0$ and the paraboloid of revolution $x^2 + z^2 = 5(4 - y)$. A rectangular hole is bored out by cutting along the planes $x = +1$, $x = -1$, $z = 2$, and $z = -2$. Find the volume of the hole bored out. Use prism elements parallel to the y axis.

6. Find the volume of the solid bounded by the planes $x = 0$, $x = 4$, $z = 0$, $y = 6$, $2y - x = 2$, and $x - 2y + 4z = 0$.

7. Find the volume of the solid bounded by that part of the cylinder $x^2 + y^2 = 16$ for which $x \geq 0$ and $y \geq 0$, the coordinate planes, and $2y + 2z - x = 8$. (See Exercise 12.5-4.)

8. (a) Find the volume of the solid in the first octant bounded by $x^2 + y^2 = 4(4 - z)$ and the coordinate planes. Use prism elements parallel to the z axis. (See Example 12.5-2.)
   (b) Find the volume by using a single integration.

9. Find the volume of the solid bounded by the planes $x = 0$, $y = 0$, and $2x + 3z = 6$ and the surface $4z = (4 - x)y$.

10. Consider the solid bounded by the plane $x = 1$, the cylinder $(y^2/4) + (z^2/1) = 1$, and the paraboloid $(y^2/4) + (z^2/1) = x - 4$.
    (a) Set up an iterated integral for the volume.
    (b) Find the volume.

11. Find the volume enclosed within the surface $x^{2/3} + y^{2/3} + z^{2/3} = a^{2/3}$.

In each of the following exercises, (a) list the equations of the surfaces that bound a solid whose volume is described by the given integral; (b) describe the same volume with iterated integrals that use a different order of integration.

12. $\displaystyle\int_{y=1}^{4} \int_{x=2}^{4} (x + y)\, dx\, dy.$

15. $\displaystyle\int_{z=0}^{1} \int_{y=0}^{z} \sqrt{9 - y^2 - z^2}\, dy\, dz.$

13. $\displaystyle\int_{y=1}^{4} \int_{x=1}^{y} x^2\, dx\, dy.$

16. $\displaystyle\int_{x=0}^{1} \int_{z=0}^{2\sqrt{1-x^2}} 3\sqrt{1 - x^2 - z^2/4}\, dz\, dx.$

14. $\displaystyle\int_{x=0}^{2} \int_{y=x^2}^{6-x} (1 + x + y)\, dy\, dx.$

12.7 Other Applications for Double Integrals

In Sec. 12.5 we set up a double integral to describe a certain volume. In Sec. 12.6 we pointed out that such a double integral could be evaluated by considering in its place iterated single integrals that described the same volume. In this section we shall set up double integrals in applications other than volume applications, and here, too, we shall evaluate the double integrals by replacing them by iterated

single integrals. We justify this strategy by
pointing out that no matter what the source
of the double integral

$$\iint\limits_{R} f(x,\, y)\ dA,$$

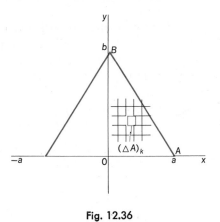

Fig. 12.36

there is a solid whose volume this integral
represents, namely, the solid whose base is
region R in the xy plane, whose sides are
parallel to the z axis, and whose roof is
given by $z = f(x,\, y)$, and that the volume
of that solid can be found by iterated single
integrals instead.

Example 1. A plate has the shape of an isosceles triangle of base $2a$ and
altitude b. Its weight density varies as the square of the distance from that altitude.
Find its weight.

Let us choose coordinate axes as in Fig. 12.36. For the weight density ρ we
can then write $\rho = kx^2$, where k is a constant, and for the side AB we have the
equation $y = -(b/a)\, x + b$. If we draw a network of lines parallel to the coordinate axes, we divide the plate into rectangular area elements, and for the
area of the kth element we write $(\Delta A)_k$. If the weight density ρ were constant, the
weight of the element would be simply $(\Delta w)_k = \rho(\Delta A)_k$. But ρ is not constant. If
we choose as a representative ρ the value ρ has along the left side of the element, we
get too small an estimate for $(\Delta w)_k$; if we choose the value ρ has along the right
side of the element, we get too large an estimate for $(\Delta w)_k$. There is a point of the
kth element, call it $(x_k^*,\, y_k^*)$ such that

$$(\Delta w)_k = \rho(x_k^*,\, y_k^*)\ (\Delta A)_k,$$

and then summing and passing to the limit we get

$$w = \lim_{n\to\infty} \sum_{k=1}^{n} (\Delta w)_k = \lim_{n\to\infty} \sum_{k=1}^{n} \rho(x_k^*, y_k^*)(\Delta A)_k = \iint\limits_{R} \rho\ dA,$$

$$w = \iint\limits_{R} kx^2\ dA, \tag{1}$$

it being understood that the largest $(\Delta A)_k$ approaches 0. Here R is the isosceles
triangle region of the xy plane.

The integral in Eq. (1) did not arise in a volume problem but there is a solid
whose volume is given by precisely that integral. This solid has the region R in
the xy plane as its base; its sides are parallel to the z axis; its roof is the surface
$z = kx^2$. If we were finding the volume of that solid, we would now turn to iterated
single integrals, and that is precisely what we shall do here.

We observe that the left and right halves of the plate have equal weights. Then, in Fig. 12.37 we indicate that the right half of region R can be swept out in the two steps: (a) forming a line segment by moving a point in the y direction from $y = 0$ to $y = -(b/a)x + b$, and (b) moving this line segment from $x = 0$ to $x = a$. Hence

$$w = \int\int_R kx^2\, dA = 2\int_{x=0}^{a}\int_{y=0}^{-(b/a)x+b} kx^2\, dy\, dx. \tag{2}$$

First we integrate with respect to y, holding x fixed. We get

$$w = 2\int_{x=0}^{a} kx^2 y\, \Big|_{y=0}^{-(b/a)x+b}\, dx = 2k\int_{x=0}^{a}\left(-\frac{b}{a}x^3 + bx^2\right) dx,$$

and then

$$w = 2k\left[-\frac{b}{a}\frac{x^4}{4} + b\frac{x^3}{3}\right]_{x=0}^{a} = \frac{1}{6}kba^3.$$

Example 2. Here we shall locate the center of gravity, $C(\bar{x}, \bar{y})$, of the triangular plate of Example 1. Because the left and right halves of the plate have equal weights, $\bar{x} = 0$. To get $\bar{y}$, we shall compute M_x, the moment about the x axis.

For the kth element of Fig. 12.36 we already know that

$$(\Delta w)_k = \rho(x_k^*, y_k^*)\, (\Delta A)_k.$$

The moment for any particle is the product of its weight by its distance from the axis about which the moment is being computed. If all the particles of the kth element were the same distance y from the x axis, the moment would be simply $(\Delta M)_k = y(\Delta w)_k$. But they are not all the same distance from the axis. If we were to assume that all the particles were at a distance from the x axis equal to the distance from the upper edge of the element, we would have too large an estimate for $(\Delta M)_k$; if we were to assume that all the particles were at a distance equal to the distance from the lower edge of the element, we would have too small an estimate. There is an interior point of the kth element, call it (x_k^{**}, y_k^{**}), such that

$$(\Delta M)_k = y_k^{**}(\Delta w)_k = y_k^{**}\rho(x_k^*, y_k^*)\, (\Delta A)_k.$$

Now we sum and pass to the limit, writing

$$M_x = \int\int_R y\rho\, dA = \int\int_R kyx^2 dA.*$$

To evaluate this double integral, we turn to iterated single integrals.

$$M_x = 2\int_{x=0}^{a}\int_{y=0}^{-(b/a)x+b} kyx^2\, dy\, dx = 2\int_{x=0}^{a} kx^2\frac{y^2}{2}\,\Big|_{y=0}^{-(b/a)x+b}\, dx$$

$$= k\int_{x=0}^{a} x^2\left(-\frac{b}{a}x + b\right)^2 dx = kb^2\int_{x=0}^{a}\left(\frac{x^4}{a^2} - \frac{2}{a}x^3 + x^2\right) dx = \frac{1}{30}ka^3b^2.$$

---

* We have used tacitly here a theorem for double integrals that is an extension of Theorem 8.8-2 for single integrals.

But if all the weight is considered concentrated at $C(0, \bar{y})$, we have

$$M_x = (\text{weight})\,\bar{y} = \tfrac{1}{6}\,ka^3b\bar{y}.$$

Hence $\tfrac{1}{6}\,ka^3b\bar{y} = \tfrac{1}{30}\,ka^3b^2$, $\bar{y} = \tfrac{1}{5}b$. The center of gravity is the point $(0, b/5)$.

Example 3. Here we shall compute the moment of inertia of the plate of Example 1 for a rotation about its axis of symmetry, the y axis.

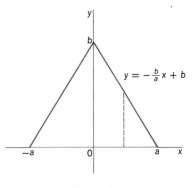

$$y = -\frac{b}{a}x + b$$

Fig. 12.37

Weight and mass are not the same physically, the weight being a force, but the relationship between them is weight $= (g)$ (mass). Hence for the mass of the kth element of Fig. 12.36 we have

$$(\Delta m)_k = \frac{(\Delta w)_k}{g} = \frac{1}{g}\,\rho(x_k^*, y_k^*)(\Delta A)_k.$$

Now the moment of inertia for a particle of mass m rotating in a circle of radius r is mr^2. In this case the particles of the kth element would not all rotate in circles of quite the same radius if the plate were rotated about the y axis, but we can use the maximum-, minimum-, and intermediate-value argument we have already used frequently and say that there is a point of the kth element, call it $(\bar{x}_k, \bar{y}_k)$, such that

$$(\Delta I)_k = (\Delta m)_k(\bar{x}_k)^2 = \frac{1}{g}\,\rho(x_k^*, y_k^*)(\bar{x}_k)^2(\Delta A)_k,$$

$$I = \int\!\!\int_R \frac{1}{g}\,\rho x^2\,dA = \int\!\!\int_R \frac{k}{g}\,x^4\,dA.$$

To evaluate this integral, we turn to iterated single integrals.

$$I = 2\int_{x=0}^{a}\int_{y=0}^{-(b/a)x+b} \frac{k}{g}\,x^4\,dy\,dx = 2\,\frac{k}{g}\int_{x=0}^{a} x^4\left(-\frac{b}{a}x + b\right)dx$$

$$= \frac{2k}{g}\left[-\frac{b}{a}\frac{x^6}{6} + b\,\frac{x^5}{5}\right]_0^a = \frac{kba^5}{15g}.$$

Example 4. A homogeneous circular plate of radius 2 is to rotate about an axis perpendicular to its plane, the axis piercing the plane at a point that is at a distance of one unit from the center. Find the moment of inertia.

Let us choose coordinate axes as indicated in Fig. 12.38. The equation of the circle is then $x^2 + y^2 = 4$, and the point at which the axis pierces the plane is $(1, 0)$. If the constant mass density is μ, we have

$$(\Delta m)_k = \mu(\Delta A)_k$$

for a typical element. Since the moment of inertia for a particle of mass m is mr^2, where by r we mean the radius of the circle in which the particle will rotate, and

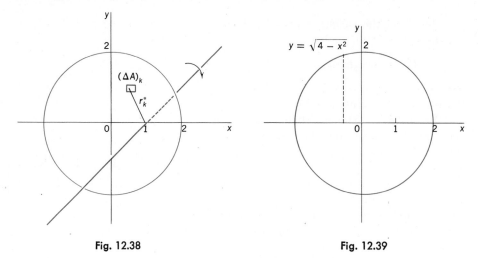

Fig. 12.38   **Fig. 12.39**

since the particles of the kth element are not all at the same distance from the axis about which they will rotate, we use a maximum-, minimum-, and intermediate-value argument to claim that there is a point of the kth element, call it (x_k^*, y_k^*), such that

$$(\Delta I)_k = (\Delta m)_k (r_k^*)^2 = \mu (\Delta A)_k [(x_k^* - 1)^2 + (y_k^* - 0)^2].$$

Then
$$I = \iint_R \mu [(x - 1)^2 + y^2]\, dA,$$

where R is the circular region of the xy plane bounded by $x^2 + y^2 = 4$.

To evaluate this integral, we turn to iterated single integrals. We observe first that the moment of inertia for the lower half of the plate will equal that for the upper half so that we need sum only over the upper half. Figure 12.39 indicates that we can sweep out the upper semicircle if we (a) form a line segment by moving a point in the y direction from $y = 0$ to $y = \sqrt{4 - x^2}$ and (b) move this line segment from $x = -2$ to $x = +2$. Hence

$$I = 2 \int_{x=-2}^{2} \int_{y=0}^{\sqrt{4-x^2}} \mu [(x - 1)^2 + y^2]\, dy\, dx.$$

Then
$$I = 2\mu \int_{x=-2}^{2} \left[(x - 1)^2 y + \tfrac{1}{3} y^3 \right]_{y=0}^{\sqrt{4-x^2}} dx$$

$$= 2\mu \int_{x=-2}^{2} [(x - 1)^2 + \tfrac{1}{3}(4 - x^2)] \sqrt{4 - x^2}\, dx$$

$$= 2\mu \int_{x=-2}^{2} (\tfrac{2}{3} x^2 - 2x + \tfrac{7}{3}) \sqrt{4 - x^2}\, dx$$

$$= \tfrac{4}{3}\mu \int_{-2}^{2} x^2 \sqrt{4 - x^2}\, dx + 2\mu \int_{-2}^{2} \sqrt{4 - x^2}\, (-2x)\, dx$$

$$+ \tfrac{14}{3}\mu \int_{x=-2}^{2} \sqrt{4 - x^2}\, dx. \qquad (3)$$

Of these integrals the second is of the form $\int u^{1/2} \, (du/dx) \, dx$ and is the easiest to evaluate. Its value is found to be 0, as could have been predicted, because its integrand is positive for $-2 \le x \le 0$ and negative with equal absolute values for $0 \le x \le 2$. For the third integral we can use tables of integrals, or we can substitute $x = 2 \sin \theta$, or, better, we can notice that the integral represents the area of a semicircle of radius 2. For the third term we can write

$$\frac{14\mu}{3} \frac{1}{2} \pi(2)^2 = \frac{28\mu}{3} \pi.$$

For the first integral we can use tables of integrals or the substitution mentioned above. We have

$$\int_{x=-2}^{2} x^2 \sqrt{4 - x^2} \, dx = \int_{\theta=-\pi/2}^{\pi/2} 4 \sin^2 \theta \, 2 \cos \theta \, 2 \cos \theta \, d\theta$$

$$= 16 \int_{-\pi/2}^{\pi/2} \sin^2 \theta \cos^2 \theta \, d\theta$$

$$= 4 \int_{-\pi/2}^{\pi/2} \sin^2 2\theta \, d\theta = 2 \int_{-\pi/2}^{\pi/2} (1 - \cos 4\theta) \, d\theta$$

$$= (2\theta - \tfrac{1}{2} \sin 4\theta) \Big|_{-\pi/2}^{\pi/2} = 2\pi.$$

To conclude then, we return to Eq. (3) and write

$$I = \frac{4}{3} \mu(2\pi) + 0 + \frac{28\mu}{3} \pi = \frac{36}{3} \mu\pi = 12\mu\pi.$$

EXERCISES 12.7

In each of the following exercises it is assumed that lengths and densities for plates are given in consistent units. If the mass density is μ, the weight density is $g\mu$.

1. Consider a rectangular plate bounded by $x = 0$, $x = a$, $y = 0$, and $y = b$. Let its mass density be $\mu = kxy$. Find (a) the mass; (b) I_x; and (c) the moment of inertia about the line $y = b/2$. (d) Locate the center of gravity.

2. Consider a rectangular plate bounded by $x = 0$, $x = a$, $y = 0$, and $y = b$. Let its mass density be $\mu = k(x^2 + y^2)$, thus proportional to the square of the distance from the origin. Find (a) the mass; (b) I_y; and (c) the moment of inertia about the line $x = a$. (d) Locate the center of gravity.

3. Consider the triangular plate with vertices $(0, 0)$, $(a, 0)$, and (a, b). Let its mass density be $\mu = kx$. Find (a) the mass; (b) I_x; and (c) I for the line $x = a$. (d) Locate the center of gravity, and (e) find the moment about the line $x = a$.

4. Consider the homogeneous plate of mass density μ bounded by $y = x^2$ and $y = x + 2$. Find I_0, the moment of inertia about the line perpendicular to the plane at $(0, 0)$.

5. A plate is bounded by $x^3 = y$, $y = 2 - x$, and the x axis. Its mass density is $\mu = kx$. Find its mass by double integration.

6. A plate is described as the smaller of the regions bounded by $x^2 + y^2 = 4$ and $x = 1$. Its mass density is $\mu = k |y/x|$. Find its mass.

7. A plate is bounded by $x^2 - y^2 = 1$ and $x = 2$. Its mass density is $\mu = 2 - |y|$. Find its mass by double integration.

8. An elliptic plate has semimajor axis 2 and semiminor axis 1. The mass density μ is 1 more than the square of the distance from the center of the plate. Find the mass of the plate.

9. A homogeneous plate in the shape of a crescent is bounded by $y^2 = 4x$ and $y^2 = 8(x - 2)$. Locate the center of gravity.

10. A homogeneous plate of mass density μ is bounded by $y = x^{3/2}$ and $y = x^{2/3}$. Find (a) its mass and (b) I_0, its moment of inertia about the axis through $(0, 0)$ perpendicular to the plane. (c) Locate its center of gravity.

11. A plate is bounded by the x axis, the y axis, $x = 2$, and $y = \cosh x$. Its weight density $\rho = 1 - .1y$. (a) Set up a double integral for the weight and (b) compute the weight. (c) Set up a double integral for M_y and (d) compute M_y.

12. A plate is bounded by $y^2 = 4x$ and $x = 1$. Its weight density is $\rho = 1 + \frac{1}{2}(x^2 + y^2)$. (a) Find its weight and (b) locate its center of gravity.

13. Reconsider Exercise 8.12-13. Show that the result quoted there is true even if $\mu = f(x, y)$.

14. Consider a plate with mass density $\mu = f(x, y)$ placed so that its center of gravity C lies at the origin. Let I_C be its moment of inertia about a line through C perpendicular to the plate. Let I_B be its moment of inertia about a line through B perpendicular to the plate. Show that $I_B = I_C + ma^2$, where m is the mass of the plate and a is the distance between C and B.

15. (a) Let a plate be placed so that its weight density is $\rho = f(x, y)$ and so that its moments about the x and y axes are both 0. Show that the moment of the plate about any other line through the origin is also 0.

(b) In Part II of Sec. 8.11 we assumed that there would exist a "center of gravity" point for a plate, a point such that the plate would have moment 0 about any line through that point. Complete the following sketch of an argument for the existence of such a point.

Step (1). In the set of lines parallel to a given direction we can find a line for which the moment of the given plate is greater than 0 and another for which the moment is less than 0. There will be an intermediate line for which the moment is 0. Choose the coordinate axes so that this line is the x axis.

Step (2). From the set of lines perpendicular to the first set select the line for which the moment is 0. Choose the coordinate axes so that this line is the y axis. .

Step (3). The existence of the center of gravity point now follows from Part (a) of this exercise.

12.8   Surface Area by Double Integration

In Sec. 12.4 we set up single integrals for surface areas of surfaces of revolution. Those surface areas were defined as limits of sums of areas of frusta of cones. Here we present a more general analysis of surface area, based on the fact that the area T of a plane region and the area P of its projection are related by

$$P = T \cos \theta,$$

where θ is the acute angle between the planes. See Fig. 12.40.

Let surface S project into region R of the xy plane in such a way that no two points of S project into the same point of R. See Fig. 12.41. In the xy plane draw a network of lines parallel to the x and y axes, thus dividing R into elements of area $(\Delta A)_k$, $k = 1, 2, \cdots, n$. Each such element $(\Delta A)_k$ in the xy plane is the projection of an element in the original surface, which we shall call $(\Delta S)_k$. Now $(\Delta S)_k$ is not planar, but if it is small we can say that it is approximately planar, and that

$$(\Delta A)_k \approx (\Delta S)_k \cos \theta_k \quad \text{or} \quad (\Delta S)_k \approx \frac{1}{\cos \theta_k} (\Delta A)_k,$$

where θ_k is the acute angle between $(\Delta A)_k$ and the planar approximation to $(\Delta S)_k$.

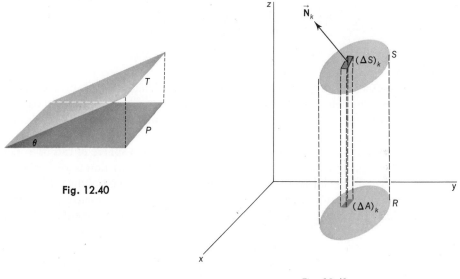

Fig. 12.40

Fig. 12.41

To determine the angle between two planes, we compute the angle between the normals to these planes. The unit vector $\vec{\mathbf{k}}^*$ is normal to $(\Delta A)_k$; if $\vec{\mathbf{N}}_k$ is the unit vector normal to S at a point P_k of $(\Delta S)_k$, then

$$\cos \theta_k \approx |\vec{\mathbf{N}}_k \cdot \vec{\mathbf{k}}|,$$

and
$$(\Delta S)_k \approx \frac{1}{|\vec{\mathbf{N}}_k \cdot \vec{\mathbf{k}}|} (\Delta A)_k. \tag{1}$$

To compute the vector $\vec{\mathbf{N}}$ used in Eq. (1), we recall that, if S has the equation $F(x, y, z) = 0$, then

$$\text{grad } F = \frac{\partial F}{\partial x}\mathbf{i} + \frac{\partial F}{\partial y}\mathbf{j} + \frac{\partial F}{\partial z}\mathbf{k}$$

is a vector normal to S,† and that $\text{grad } \vec{\mathbf{F}}/\|\text{grad } \vec{\mathbf{F}}\|$ can therefore serve as the unit vector $\vec{\mathbf{N}}$.

Finally, we sum these approximations to the elements $(\Delta S)_k$, and compute the limit of this sum as we refine the network of coordinate lines in the xy plane.

---

* Do not confuse the unit vector $\vec{\mathbf{k}}$ with the subscript label k, which can assume the values $1, 2, \cdots, n$.

† Theorem 11.4-1.

■ DEFINITION 1

Surface area. Let surface S be projected onto region R of the xy plane, no two points of S projecting onto the same point of R. Let R be subdivided into elements $(\Delta A)_k$, $k = 1, 2, \cdots, n$, by a network of coordinate lines, thus inducing a subdivision of S into elements $(\Delta S)_k$. Let $\bar{\mathbf{N}}_k$ be a unit vector normal to S at a point of $(\Delta S)_k$. Then for the surface area of S we take the number

$$\lim_{n \to \infty} \sum_{k=1}^{n} \frac{1}{|\bar{\mathbf{N}}_k \cdot \mathbf{k}|} (\Delta A)_k = \int\int_R \frac{1}{|\bar{\mathbf{N}} \cdot \mathbf{k}|} \, dA,$$

it being understood that the largest $(\Delta A)_k$ approaches 0.

In Exercise 12.8-14 the reader can show that this definition of surface area is consistent with the definition given in Sec. 12.4 for surfaces of revolution. Of course, this definition is more general, in that it applies not only to surfaces of revolution but to others.

Example 1.   We shall compute the surface area of a sphere of radius a. Let the origin be placed at the center of the sphere, so that its equation is $x^2 + y^2 + z^2 = a^2$. Observe, as in Fig. 12.42, that the projection of one octant of the sphere onto the xy plane is a quarter-circle R, and that if we subdivide the quarter-circle into elements $(\Delta A)_k$ and at the same time the sphere octant into elements $(\Delta S)_k$, we can say that

$$(\Delta A)_k \approx (\Delta S)_k \cos \theta_k,$$

$$(\Delta S)_k \approx \frac{1}{\cos \theta_k} (\Delta A)_k.$$

From the sphere equation, $F(x, y, z) = x^2 + y^2 + z^2 - a^2 = 0$, we compute

$$\operatorname{grad} F = \frac{\partial F}{\partial x} \mathbf{i} + \frac{\partial F}{\partial y} \mathbf{j} + \frac{\partial F}{\partial z} \mathbf{k} = 2x\mathbf{i} + 2y\mathbf{j} + 2z\mathbf{k}$$

and then take for our unit vector normal to the sphere

$$\bar{\mathbf{N}} = \frac{x\mathbf{i} + y\mathbf{j} + z\mathbf{k}}{\sqrt{x^2 + y^2 + z^2}} = \frac{1}{a} (x\mathbf{i} + y\mathbf{j} + z\mathbf{k}).$$

Thus
$$\cos \theta = \bar{\mathbf{N}} \cdot \mathbf{k} = \frac{z}{a},$$

and
$$(\Delta S)_k = \frac{a}{z_k} (\Delta A)_k,$$

$$\frac{1}{8} S = \int\int_R \frac{a}{z} \, dA = \int\int_R \frac{a}{\sqrt{a^2 - x^2 - y^2}} \, dA$$

$$= \int_{x=0}^{a} \int_{y=0}^{\sqrt{a^2-x^2}} \frac{a}{\sqrt{a^2 - x^2 - y^2}} \, dy \, dx.$$

Here, because
$$\int \frac{1}{\sqrt{b^2 - y^2}} \, dy = \sin^{-1} \frac{y}{b},$$

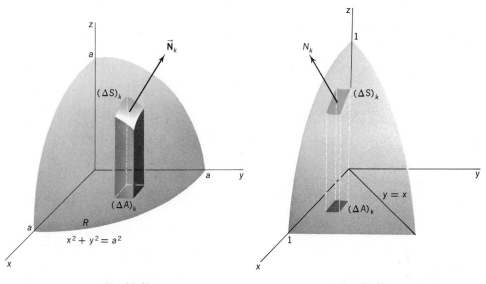

Fig. 12.42   Fig. 12.43

we substitute b for $\sqrt{a^2 - x^2}$ and write

$$S = 8a \int_{x=0}^{a} \sin^{-1} \frac{y}{\sqrt{a^2 - x^2}} \Big|_{y=0}^{\sqrt{a^2-x^2}} dx = 8a \int_{x=0}^{a} \frac{\pi}{2} dx = 4\pi a^2.$$

Example 2.   One of the portions of the parabolic cylinder $x^2 = 1 - z$ cut out by the planes $y = 0$, $z = 0$, and $y = x$ lies in the first octant. Find the surface of that portion.

The projection on the xy plane of the portion of the cylinder we want to study is the triangular region bounded by $y = 0$, $x = 1$, and $y = x$, as shown in Fig. 12.43. When we write the equation of the surface in the form $F = x^2 + z - 1 = 0$, we compute grad $F = 2x\vec{i} + 1\vec{k}$ and take as a unit normal to the surface

$$\vec{N} = \frac{2x\vec{i} + 1\vec{k}}{\sqrt{4x^2 + 1}},$$

so that

$$\vec{N} \cdot \vec{k} = \frac{1}{\sqrt{4x^2 + 1}}.$$

Hence

$$(\Delta A)_k \approx (\Delta S)_k \cos \theta_k,$$

$$(\Delta S)_k \approx \frac{1}{\cos \theta_k} (\Delta A)_k,$$

$$(\Delta S)_k \approx \frac{1}{|\vec{N}_k \cdot \vec{k}|} (\Delta A)_k = \sqrt{1 + 4x_k^2} \, (\Delta A)_k,$$

$$S = \iint_R \sqrt{1 + 4x^2}\, dA$$

$$= \int_{x=0}^{1} \int_{y=0}^{x} \sqrt{1 + 4x^2}\, dy\, dx$$

$$= \int_{x=0}^{1} \sqrt{1 + 4x^2}\, y\, \Big|_{y=0}^{x} dx$$

$$= \int_{x=0}^{1} \sqrt{1 + 4x^2}\, x\, dx = \tfrac{1}{8}\, \tfrac{2}{3}\, (1 + 4x^2)^{3/2}\, \Big|_{x=0}^{1} = \tfrac{1}{12}\, [5^{3/2} - 1].$$

Example 3. Consider that region of the plane $x + 2y = 8$ which lies within the paraboloid $x^2/4 + z^2 = 4y$. Find the area of that portion of this region for which $x \geq 0$.

The area ABC of Fig. 12.44 is half the area we want; the second half lies below the xy plane. Since this area lies in a plane that is perpendicular to the xy plane, we project onto the xz plane this time, the projection being $O\,A'C'$.

To get the equation of $A'C'$, we observe that corresponding points of AC and $A'C'$ have the same x and z coordinates but different y coordinates. Now the coordinates of a point on AC satisfy both the plane and paraboloid equations

$$x + 2y = 8 \qquad \text{and} \qquad \frac{x^2}{4} + z^2 = 4y. \tag{2}$$

These coordinates also satisfy any equation we can get from Eqs. (2), including the equation

$$\frac{x^2}{4} + z^2 = 2(8 - x), \tag{3}$$

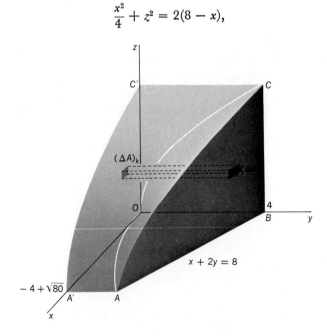

Fig. 12.44

which we get by eliminating y in Eqs. (2). But Eq. (3) is soon rewritten as

$$x^2 + 8x + 4z^2 = 64$$

or
$$(x + 4)^2 + 4z^2 = 80. \tag{4}$$

This equation is also satisfied by the coordinates of the points of $A'C'$, for the equation deals only with x and z coordinates and the points of $A'C'$ have the same x and z coordinates as those of AC; $A'C'$ is part of an ellipse.

To each element $(\Delta A)_k$ of $OA'C'$ corresponds an element $(\Delta S)_k$ of BAC, and

$$(\Delta S)_k = \frac{1}{\cos \theta_k} (\Delta A)_k.$$

This time we must say that $\cos \theta_k = |\vec{N}_k \cdot \vec{j}|$. But from the plane equation we find that

$$\vec{N} = \frac{\vec{i} + 2\vec{j}}{\sqrt{5}}, \qquad \vec{N} \cdot \vec{j} = \frac{2}{\sqrt{5}},$$

and thus that
$$(\Delta S)_k = \frac{\sqrt{5}}{2} (\Delta A)_k,$$

and
$$\frac{1}{2} S = \frac{\sqrt{5}}{2} \iint_{OA'C'} dA$$

$$= \frac{\sqrt{5}}{2} \int_{x=0}^{-4+\sqrt{80}} \int_{z=0}^{\sqrt{80-(x+4)^2}/2} 1 \, dz \, dx,$$

the boundaries of the iterated integrals having been selected after rewriting Eq. (4) in the form

$$z^2 = \tfrac{1}{4}[80 - (x + 4)^2].$$

When we continue the computation for S we have

$$S = \sqrt{5} \int_{x=0}^{-4+\sqrt{80}} \tfrac{1}{2}\sqrt{80 - (x + 4)^2} \, dx.$$

Substitute $x + 4 = \sqrt{80} \sin \theta$ and observe that $dx/d\theta = \sqrt{80} \cos \theta$.

$$S = \frac{\sqrt{5}}{2} 80 \int_{\theta=\sin^{-1}(1/\sqrt{5})}^{\pi/2} \cos^2 \theta \, d\theta = 20\sqrt{5} \int_{\sin^{-1}(1/\sqrt{5})}^{\pi/2} (1 + \cos 2\theta) d\theta$$

$$= 20\sqrt{5} \left[\theta + \tfrac{1}{2}\sin 2\theta\right]_{\theta=\sin^{-1}(1/\sqrt{5})}^{\pi/2} = 20\sqrt{5} \left[\theta + \sin\theta \cos\theta\right]_{\sin^{-1}(1/\sqrt{5})}^{\pi/2}$$

$$= 20\sqrt{5} \left[\frac{\pi}{2} - \sin^{-1}\frac{1}{\sqrt{5}} - \frac{2}{5}\right].*$$

---

* Observe that $\cos \sin^{-1} (1/\sqrt{5}) = 2/\sqrt{5}$ and $\sin^{-1} (1/\sqrt{5}) = \tan^{-1} \tfrac{1}{2} \approx .4637$, so that $S \approx 20\sqrt{5}[1.5708 - .4637 - .4000] = 14.142\sqrt{5} \approx 31.62$.

EXERCISES 12.8

1. Find the area of that portion of the plane $4x + 3y + 6z = 24$ whose projection in the xy plane is the triangle bounded by $x = 0$, $y = 0$, and $x + y = 3$.

2. One of the portions of the cylinder $x^2 + z^2 = a^2$ cut out by the planes $y = 0$ and $y = x$ lies in front of the yz plane. Find the surface area of that portion.

3. Find the surface area of that portion of the cylinder $x^2 + y^2 = a^2$ cut out by the cylinder

$$(y^2/a^2) + (z^2/b^2) = 1.$$

4. Find the area of that portion of the plane $x + y + z = 6$ cut out by the cylinder

$$(x^2/16) + (y^2/4) = 1.$$

5. A cone of base radius r and altitude h is formed by rotating the line segment

$$\frac{z}{h} + \frac{x}{r} = 1, \qquad 0 \le z \le h,$$

of the xz plane about the z axis. The equation of this cone is

$$x^2 + y^2 = \frac{r^2}{h^2}(h - z)^2, \qquad 0 \le z \le h.$$

Show that its surface area is $\pi r \sqrt{r^2 + h^2}$ by projecting elements onto the xy plane and summing.

6. (a) Show that the area cut off the upper nappe of the cone $x^2 + y^2 = (r^2/h^2)z^2$ by the cylinder $x^2 + (y - r/2)^2 = r^2/4$ is $\frac{1}{4}\pi r\sqrt{h^2 + r^2}$.
   (b) Show that the area cut off the upper nappe of this cone by a cylinder parallel to the z axis and of cross-section area K is $\dfrac{\sqrt{h^2 + r^2}}{r}\,K$.

7. One of the portions of the parabolic cylinder $y^2 = x$ cut off by the planes $z = 0$, $y = z$, and $x = 1$ lies in the first octant. Find the surface area of this portion of the parabolic cylinder.

8. Find the surface area of that portion of the sphere $x^2 + y^2 + z^2 = a^2$ included within the elliptic cylinder $4x^2 + y^2 = a^2$.

9. Find the surface area of that portion of the sphere $x^2 + y^2 + z^2 = a^2$ included within the cylinder $a^2x^2 = y^2(a^2 - y^2)$.

10. Find the surface area of that portion of the elliptic cylinder $2x^2 + z^2 = 2$ cut out by the cylinder $x^2 + y^2 = 1$.

11. Find the surface area of that portion of the cylinder $z = 1 - x^3$ cut out by the planes $y = 0$, $z = 0$, and $y = ax$, $a > 0$.

12. Find the area of that portion of the plane $2x + 5y - 10 = 0$ which lies within the ellipsoid

$$(x^2/25) + (y^2/16) + (z^2/4) = 1.$$

13. Find the area of that portion of the plane $y = x$ which lies within the hyperboloid

$$(x^2/16) + (y^2/9) - (z^2/36) = 1$$

and between the planes $z = 0$ and $z = 6$.

14. Let the arc $x = f(y)$, $a \le y \le b$, f and f' continuous for $a \le y \le b$, be rotated about the y axis to form a surface of revolution.

(a) Show that the definition of surface area for surfaces of revolution given in Sec. 12.4 leads to the definite integral $2\pi \int_{y=a}^{b} f\sqrt{1+f'^2}\ dy$ for the surface area of this surface.

(b) The equation of this surface of revolution is

$$x^2 + z^2 = [f(y)]^2, \qquad a \le y \le b.$$

Show that Definition 1 of this section leads to the multiple integral

$$4 \int_{y=a}^{b} \int_{x=0}^{f(y)} \frac{f\sqrt{1+f'^2}}{\sqrt{f^2 - x^2}}\ dx\ dy$$

for this surface area.

(c) Show that the results obtained in Parts (a) and (b) are equal in value. You will then have shown that the definition of this section is indeed a generalization of that of Sec. 12.4.

15. *Fluid flow across the surface S.* Let S be a surface, with unit normal vector $\vec{N}$, in a region in which a fluid is moving. Let the vector $\vec{F}(x, y, z)$ describe at each point (x, y, z) the velocity of the fluid at that point. Then, in Fig. 12.45, in a short time Δt, the particle of fluid at P will move approximately the distance $\|\vec{F}\|\ \Delta t$ to point Q, and the fluid passing through the element of surface ΔS in time Δt will fill the cylinderlike solid formed by drawing $\vec{F}\ \Delta t$ at each point of ΔS. Show that the volume of this solid is approximately $\vec{F} \cdot \vec{N}\ \Delta S\ \Delta t$. This suggests that the flow across S itself in time Δt is $(\int\int_S \vec{F} \cdot \vec{N}\ dS)\ \Delta t$, so that the flow rate across surface S is $\int\int_S \vec{F} \cdot \vec{N}\ dS$.

16. Let the surface S be the portion of the xz plane bounded by $x = 0$, $x = 1$, $z = 0$, $z = 1$. Let $\vec{F} = 2\vec{i} + 3\vec{j} + 1\vec{k}$. Let $\vec{N}$ be the unit vector normal to S which makes an acute angle with $\vec{F}$. Compute $\int\int_S \vec{F} \cdot \vec{N}\ dS$.

17. Repeat Exercise 16 for the case in which S is the half of the sphere $x^2 + y^2 + z^2 = a^2$ for which $z \ge 0$, and $\vec{F} = x\vec{i} + y\vec{j} + [z - (a/2)]\vec{k}$.

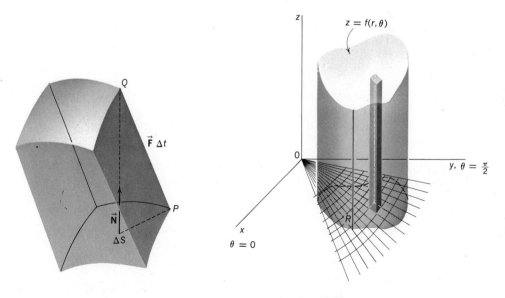

Fig. 12.45   **Fig. 12.46**

12.9 Double Integrals in Polar Coordinates

It is sometimes more convenient to describe the boundaries of a plane region by using polar coordinates than by using Cartesian coordinates. Let us discuss, then, the volume of a solid that has for its base a region R in the xy plane, for its roof a surface with equation $z = f(r, \theta)$, and side walls parallel to the z axis.

We draw a network of polar coordinate curves $r = $ const and $\theta = $ const in the base plane, thus dividing R into polar coordinate elements, as sketched in Fig. 12.46. Then at the vertices of the area elements we draw lines parallel to the z axis, thus dividing the solid into volume elements, one for each area element of the base.

Let $(\Delta A)_k$ be the area of the kth element of R. Since we assume $z = f(r, \theta)$ to be continuous for the number pairs (r, θ) in question, there will be points of the kth area element at which f assumes maximum and minimum values, M_k and m_k, for that element. We have adopted Definition 12.1-3, which says that the volume of any right cylindrical solid is the product of the area of the base by the height, and hence we can continue with the statement

$$m_k(\Delta A)_k \leq (\Delta V)_k \leq M_k(\Delta A)_k$$

and claim that there will be a point of the kth area element, call it (r_k^*, θ_k^*), such that

$$(\Delta V)_k = f(r_k^*, \theta_k^*)(\Delta A)_k.$$

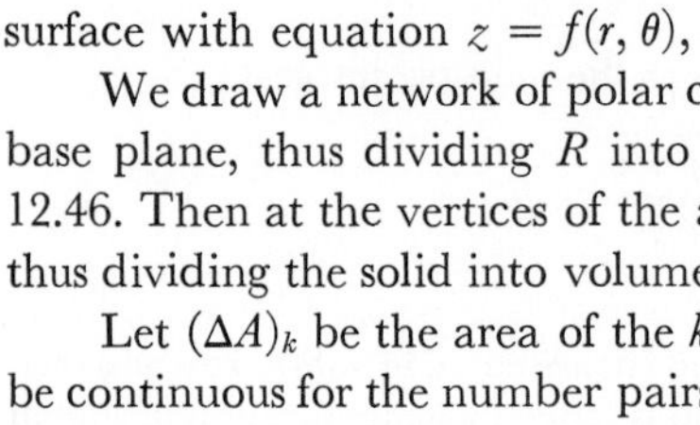

Fig. 12.47

As Fig. 12.47 indicates, for an area element ΔA we can write

$$\Delta A = (\text{area } OBC) - (\text{area } OAD)$$

$$= \tfrac{1}{2}(r + \Delta r)^2 \Delta \theta - \tfrac{1}{2}r^2 \,\Delta \theta^*$$

$$= \frac{1}{2}[2r\,\Delta r + \Delta r^2]\,\Delta \theta = \left[r + \frac{\Delta r}{2}\right]\Delta r\,\Delta \theta$$

$$= (\text{average radius})\,\Delta r\,\Delta \theta. \dagger$$

Hence

$$(\Delta V)_k = f(r_k^*, \theta_k^*)r_k^{**}(\Delta r)_k(\Delta \theta)_k,$$

where r_k^{**} is the average radius for the kth element, and

$$V = \lim_{n \to \infty} \sum_{k=1}^{n} (\Delta V)_k = \int\int_R f(r, \theta)r \, dr \, d\theta, \qquad (1)$$

it being understood that the largest $(\Delta r)_k$ and the largest $(\Delta \theta)_k$ both approach 0 as n grows beyond all bounds. The boundary of region R will usually consist of arcs with equations $r = g_1(\theta)$ and $r = g_2(\theta)$ for $\alpha \leq \theta \leq \beta$, $g_1(\theta) \leq g_2(\theta)$ for $\alpha \leq \theta \leq \beta$, and $\theta = \alpha$, $\theta = \beta$. Here r and θ are the usual polar coordinates.

Now consider a region R' which has for boundaries $x = g_1(y)$ and $x = g_2(y)$ for $\alpha \leq y \leq \beta$ and $y = \alpha$, $y = \beta$, x and y being the usual Cartesian coordinates. Even

---

* We have used the fact that a circle sector of central angle $\Delta \theta$ has for area the $\Delta \theta/2\pi$ part of a whole circle: $(\Delta \theta/2\pi)\,\pi(\text{rad})^2 = \tfrac{1}{2}\,\Delta \theta(\text{rad})^2$.

† Since we want ΔA to be positive, we must always be careful to choose the descriptions of the arcs of the polar curves we use so that $r \geq 0$.

through R and R' will not be congruent regions in general, or similarly shaped, or regions with the same area, nevertheless integrals

$$\iint\limits_{R} f(r, \theta) \, r \, dr \, d\theta \qquad \text{and} \qquad \iint\limits_{R'} f(x, y) \, x \, dx \, dy$$

are equal because the sums of which these integrals are the limits can be written so that they are equal term by term.* But, to evaluate $\iint\limits_{R'} f(x, y)x \, dx \, dy$, we use iterated single integrals:

$$\iint\limits_{R'} f(x, y)x \, dx \, dy = \int_{y=\alpha}^{\beta} \left[\int_{x=g_1(y)}^{g_2(y)} f(x, y)x \, dx \right] dy.$$

The iterated single integrals

$$\int_{\theta=\alpha}^{\beta} \left[\int_{r=g_1(\theta)}^{g_2(\theta)} f(r, \theta)r \, dr \right] d\theta$$

will have the same value, because in single integration the name of the variable used to "carry" the integration is not significant; what matters are the function appearing as the integrand and the boundaries of integration. Hence, to evaluate

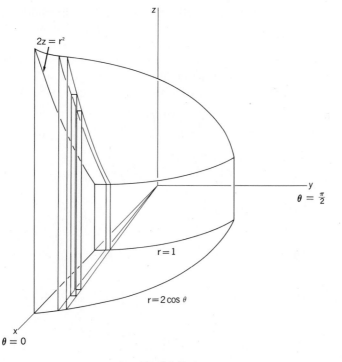

Fig. 12.48

---

double integrals in polar coordinates, we turn to iterated single integrals just as before:

$$V = \int\int_R f(r, \theta)r \, dr \, d\theta = \int_{\theta=\alpha}^{\beta} \left[\int_{r=g_1(\theta)}^{g_2(\theta)} f(r, \theta)r \, dr \right] d\theta.$$

Example 1.   Consider the solid whose base is the xy plane region R that lies outside the circle $r = 1$ and inside the circle $r = 2\cos\theta$, whose side walls are parallel to the z axis, and whose roof is the paraboloid $2z = x^2 + y^2$ or $2z = r^2$. One half of this solid is sketched in Fig. 12.48.

For the area element of the base we have

$$(\Delta A)_k = r_k^{**}(\Delta r)_k(\Delta\theta)_k,$$

where r_k^{**} is the average radius of the element. For the volume element we have

$$(\Delta V)_k = z_k^* r_k^{**}(\Delta r)_k(\Delta\theta)_k,$$

where z_k^* is the height at a properly selected point of the element. Then we write

$$V = \int\int_R zr \, dr \, d\theta = \int\int_R \tfrac{1}{2} r^2 r \, dr \, d\theta. \tag{2}$$

The region R itself, Fig. 12.49, tells us how to replace the multiple integral in Eq. (2) by iterated single integrals. Half of the region R is swept out if we first move a point in the r direction, with θ fixed, from $r = 1$ to $r = 2\cos\theta$, to form a radial line segment, and then rotate this line segment from $\theta = 0$ to $\theta = \pi/3$. Hence in the integration we perform the r summation first, from $r = 1$ to $r = 2\cos\theta$, keeping θ fixed; then we perform the θ summation from $\theta = 0$ to $\theta = \pi/3$. We write

$$\tfrac{1}{2}V = \tfrac{1}{2}\int_{\theta=0}^{\pi/3}\int_{r=1}^{2\cos\theta} r^3 \, dr \, d\theta,$$

$$V = \int_{\theta=0}^{\pi/3} \left[\frac{r^4}{4}\right]_{r=1}^{2\cos\theta} d\theta = \int_0^{\pi/3} \left(4\cos^4\theta - \frac{1}{4}\right) d\theta$$

$$= \int_0^{\pi/3} \left[(1 + \cos 2\theta)^2 - \frac{1}{4}\right] d\theta$$

$$= \int_0^{\pi/3} \left[1 + 2\cos 2\theta + \frac{1 + \cos 4\theta}{2} - \frac{1}{4}\right] d\theta$$

$$= \int_0^{\pi/3} [\tfrac{5}{4} + 2\cos 2\theta + \tfrac{1}{2}\cos 4\theta) \, d\theta = [\tfrac{5}{4}\theta + \sin 2\theta + \tfrac{1}{8}\sin 4\theta]_0^{\pi/3}$$

$$= \frac{5}{12}\pi + \frac{\sqrt{3}}{2} - \frac{1}{8}\frac{\sqrt{3}}{2} = \frac{5}{12}\pi + \frac{7}{16}\sqrt{3}.$$

Example 2.   Consider the circular plate of radius a bounded by $r = a$ whose mass density is given by $\mu = a^2/(a^2 + r^2)$. We shall find its mass and then its moment of inertia about the z axis. See Fig. 12.50. For a typical element we can say that there are points (r_k^*, θ_k^*), $(r_k^{**}, \theta_k^{**})$, $(\bar{r}_k, \bar{\theta}_k)$ of the element such that

$$(\Delta A)_k = r_k^*(\Delta r)_k(\Delta \theta)_k,$$

$$(\Delta m)_k = \frac{a^2}{a^2 + r_k^{**2}} r_k^*(\Delta r)_k(\Delta \theta)_k,$$

$$(\Delta I)_k = (\Delta m)_k \bar{r}_k^2 = \frac{a^2}{a^2 + r_k^{**2}} r_k^*(\Delta r)_k(\Delta \theta)_k \bar{r}_k^2.$$

Hence

$$m = \iint_R \frac{a^2}{a^2 + r^2} r \, dr \, d\theta = a^2 \int_{\theta=0}^{2\pi} \int_{r=0}^{a} \frac{r}{a^2 + r^2} \, dr \, d\theta$$

$$= \frac{a^2}{2} \int_{\theta=0}^{2\pi} \log (a^2 + r^2) \Big|_{r=0}^{a} \, d\theta = \frac{a^2}{2} \log 2 \int_{0}^{2\pi} 1 \, d\theta = \pi a^2 \log 2,$$

and

$$I = \iint_R \frac{a^2 r^3}{a^2 + r^2} \, dr \, d\theta = a^2 \int_{\theta=0}^{2\pi} \int_{r=0}^{a} \frac{r^3}{a^2 + r^2} \, dr \, d\theta$$

$$= a^2 \int_{\theta=0}^{2\pi} \int_{r=0}^{a} \left[r - \frac{a^2 r}{a^2 + r^2} \right] dr \, d\theta = a^2 \int_{\theta=0}^{2\pi} \left[\frac{a^2}{2} - \frac{a^2}{2} \log 2 \right] d\theta$$

$$= \pi a^4 (1 - \log 2).$$

Example 3. Find the surface area of that portion of the sphere $x^2 + y^2 + z^2 = a^2$ (or $r^2 + z^2 = a^2$) that lies within the cylinder $x^2 + [y - (a/2)]^2 = a^2/4$ (or $r = a \sin \theta$).

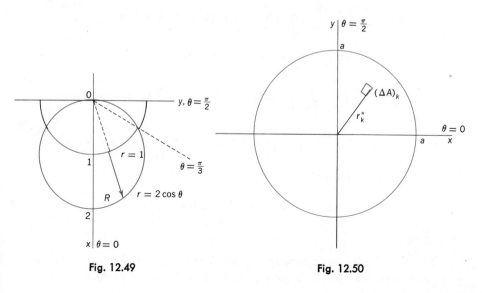

Fig. 12.49   Fig. 12.50

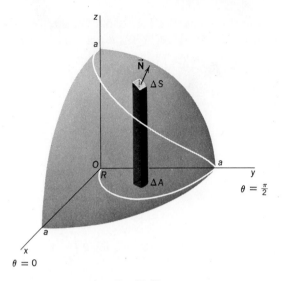

Fig. 12.51

In Fig. 12.51, $\frac{1}{4}$ of the surface described is drawn. For the element of surface area we can say that

$$\Delta A \approx \vec{\mathbf{N}} \cdot \vec{\mathbf{k}} \, \Delta S \qquad \text{or} \qquad \Delta S \approx \frac{1}{\vec{\mathbf{N}} \cdot \vec{\mathbf{k}}} \, \Delta A.$$

Here $\vec{\mathbf{N}}$ is the unit vector normal to the sphere. It has the direction of

$$\text{grad } (x^2 + y^2 + z^2 - a^2) = 2x\vec{\mathbf{i}} + 2y\vec{\mathbf{j}} + 2z\vec{\mathbf{k}},$$

so that

$$\vec{\mathbf{N}} = \frac{x\vec{\mathbf{i}} + y\vec{\mathbf{j}} + z\vec{\mathbf{k}}}{\sqrt{x^2 + y^2 + z^2}} = \frac{1}{a}(x\vec{\mathbf{i}} + y\vec{\mathbf{j}} + z\vec{\mathbf{k}}), \quad \vec{\mathbf{N}} \cdot \vec{\mathbf{k}} = \frac{z}{a} = \frac{\sqrt{a^2 - r^2}}{a},$$

$$\Delta S \approx \frac{a}{\sqrt{a^2 - r^2}} \, r \, \Delta r \, \Delta\theta,$$

$$\frac{1}{4} S = \iint\limits_{R} \frac{a}{\sqrt{a^2 - r^2}} r \, dr \, d\theta = a \int_{\theta=0}^{\pi/2} \int_{r=0}^{r=a\sin\theta} (a^2 - r^2)^{-1/2} r \, dr \, d\theta$$

$$= -\frac{a}{2} \int_{\theta=0}^{\pi/2} 2(a^2 - r^2)^{1/2} \Big|_{r=0}^{a\sin\theta} d\theta = -a^2 \int_{0}^{\pi/2} (\cos\theta - 1) \, d\theta$$

$$= -a^2 [\sin\theta - \theta]_0^{\pi/2},$$

$$S = -4a^2 \left(1 - \frac{\pi}{2}\right) = 2a^2(\pi - 2).$$

● **Remark 1**

The alert reader has probably noticed already that the factor r in the polar coordinate area element $r \, \Delta r \, \Delta\theta$ is often of considerable help in evaluating integrals.

EXERCISES 12.9

1. Find, by multiple integration, the area of the region bounded by $r = a \sin \theta$.

2. Find, by multiple integration, the area of a region bounded by a petal of $r = a \cos 2\theta$.

3. Find, by multiple integration, the area of the region outside $r = a$ and inside $r^2 = 2a^2 \cos 2\theta$.

4. The circular plate bounded by $r = a \cos \theta$ has mass density $\mu = 1 + kr^2/a^2$. Find its mass.

5. A plate bounded by the lemniscate $r^2 = \cos 2\theta$ has mass density $(1 + r^2)(\cos^2 \theta)$. Find its mass.

6. Consider a plate bounded by one petal of $r = a \cos 3\theta$. Find the mass if the mass density is 1 for $0 \le r \le a/2$ and 1.2 for $r > a/2$.

7. Two distinct planes through the z axis, one through the line $\theta = \alpha$ of the xy plane and the other through $\theta = \beta$, $0 \le \alpha < \beta < \pi$, divide the sphere $x^2 + y^2 + z^2 = a^2$ into 4 parts. Use multiple integration to find the volume of one of these parts.

8. Find the volume of the solid that lies to the right of the xz plane and is bounded by $z = 0, y = 0, x^2 + y^2 = a^2$, and $2z - y + 2x = 4a$.

9. Find the volume of the solid that lies within $x^2 + y^2 = ay$ (or $r = a \sin \theta$) and is bounded above and below by $x^2 + y^2 + z^2 = a^2$ (or $r^2 + z^2 = a^2$).

10. Find the volume of the solid bounded below by $z = 0$, on the sides by the cylinder $x^2 + y^2 = 2y$, and above by the lower nappe of the cone $x^2 + y^2 = (z - 4)^2$.

11. Consider the circular plate of radius a and uniform mass density μ bounded by $x^2 + y^2 = 2ax$ or $r = 2a \cos \theta$. Find its moment of inertia about (a) the z axis, (b) the x axis, (c) the y axis.

12. A plate of uniform mass density μ is bounded by one petal of $r = a \cos 3\theta$. Find its moment of inertia about the z axis.

13. Repeat Exercise 11 for a plate of uniform mass density μ bounded by the lemniscate $r^2 = a^2 \cos 2\theta$.

14. A homogeneous plate is bounded by that petal of $r = a \cos 2\theta$ which lies in the first and fourth quadrants. Locate its center of gravity.*

15. A homogeneous plate is bounded by the cardioid $r = a(1 + \cos \theta)$. Locate its center of gravity.

16. A homogeneous plate is bounded by that half of the lemniscate $r^2 = a^2 \cos 2\theta$ which lies in the first and fourth quadrants. Locate its center of gravity.

17. Find the surface area of the smaller portion of the sphere $x^2 + y^2 + z^2 = a^2$ cut off by the plane $z = h$, $0 < h < a$.

18. Find the surface area of that portion of the paraboloid $x^2 + y^2 = z$ which lies within the cylinder $x^2 + y^2 = a^2$.

19. Find the surface area of that portion of the paraboloid $x^2 + y^2 = z$ whose projection on the xy plane is the lemniscate $r^2 = \frac{1}{4} \cos 2\theta$.

20. Draw region R bounded by $r = 1, r = 2, \theta = \pi/6$ and $\theta = \pi/3$. Subdivide region R by drawing the circles $r = 1.2, 1.4, 1.6, 1.8$ and the rays $\theta = 4\pi/18, \theta = 5\pi/18$. On a second diagram draw region R' bounded by $x = 1, x = 2, y = \pi/6$, and $y = \pi/3$. Subdivide R' by drawing the lines $x = 1.2, 1.4, 1.6, 1.8$ and the lines $y = 4\pi/18$, $5\pi/18$. Show that R has 15 subregions, as does R', and that if these are ordered properly and that if $r_k, \theta_k, k = 1, \cdots, 15$ on the one hand and x_k, y_k on the other hand are chosen suitably, then

$$\sum_{k=1}^{15} f(r_k, \theta_k) r_k (\Delta r)_k (\Delta \theta)_k = \sum_{k=1}^{15} f(x_k, y_k) x_k (\Delta x)_k (\Delta y)_k.$$

* See Exercise 12.9-2.

12.10   Triple Integration

Suppose that we are interested in computing a quantity Q for a given solid. This solid can be divided into a finite number of Cartesian elements of volume by drawing planes parallel to the coordinate planes; see Fig. 12.52. Then, if there exists a continuous function f and a point (x_k^*, y_k^*, z_k^*) of the kth volume element such that the value of Q for this volume element is

$$(\Delta Q)_k = f(x_k^*, y_k^*, z_k^*)(\Delta V)_k,$$

we can take as the value of Q for the entire solid the expression

$$\lim_{n \to \infty} \sum_{k=1}^{n} (\Delta Q)_k = \lim_{n \to \infty} \sum_{k=1}^{n} f(x_k^*, y_k^*, z_k^*)(\Delta V)_k = \iiint_{\text{solid}} f(x, y, z)\, dV.$$

It is understood that the diagonals of all the elements of volume approach 0 as the number of elements of volume grows beyond all bounds.

To set up a triple integral for the volume of the solid, we can say that

$$(\Delta V)_k = 1(\Delta x)_k (\Delta y)_k (\Delta z)_k, \qquad \text{or} \qquad V = \iiint_{\text{solid}} 1\, dx\, dy\, dz.$$

If $\mu(x, y, z)$, the mass density, is given to us as a continuous function, we can reason that when μ_k' and μ_k'' are the minimum and maximum values of μ for the kth element of volume,

$$\mu_k'(\Delta V)_k \leq (\Delta m)_k \leq u_k''(\Delta V)_k.$$

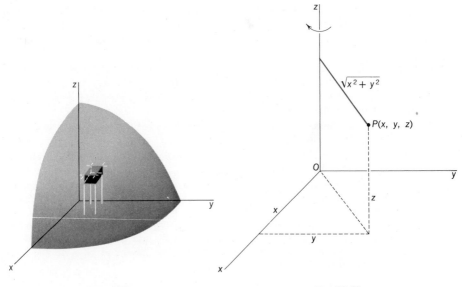

Fig. 12.52   Fig. 12.53

There is then a point (x_k^*, y_k^*, z_k^*) of this element for which μ has the proper intermediate value;

$$(\Delta m)_k = \mu(x_k^*, y_k^*, z_k^*)(\Delta V)_k.$$

For the mass of the entire solid we have

$$m = \iiint\limits_{\text{solid}} \mu \, dV = \iiint\limits_{\text{solid}} \mu \, dx \, dy \, dz.$$

If we were interested in the moment of inertia of this solid for a rotation about the z axis, we could point out that a particle at the point (x, y, z) would rotate in a circle of radius $\sqrt{x^2 + y^2}$, as in Fig. 12.53; and that if (x_k', y_k', z_k') and (x_k'', y_k'', z_k'') are the points of the kth volume element at minimum and maximum distance from the z axis, then

$$(x_k'^2 + y_k'^2)(\Delta m)_k \leq (\Delta I)_k \leq (x_k''^2 + y_k''^2)(\Delta m)_k.$$

There is a point $(\bar{x}_k, \bar{y}_k, \bar{z}_k)$ of the kth volume element such that

$$(\Delta I)_k = (\Delta m)_k[\bar{x}_k^2 + \bar{y}_k^2] = [\bar{x}_k^2 + \bar{y}_k^2]\mu(x_k^*, y_k^*, z_k^*)(\Delta V)_k,$$

$$I_z = \iiint\limits_{\text{solid}} (x^2 + y^2)\mu \, dV.$$

To compute the triple integrals we have set up, we turn to iterated single integrals as before.

Example 1. Let us compute the mass of the solid bounded by the ellipsoid $(x^2/a^2) + (y^2/b^2) + (z^2/c^2) = 1$ when the mass density is $\mu = 1 + \alpha \dfrac{|xy|}{ab}$, α a constant.

We imagine the solid cut into elements of volume by planes drawn parallel to the coordinate planes. For the kth element of volume we can write

$$(\Delta V)_k = (\Delta x)_k(\Delta y)_k(\Delta z)_k,$$

and then, having selected the proper representative point (x_k^*, y_k^*, z_k^*), we obtain

$$(\Delta m)_k = \left[1 + \frac{\alpha|x_k^* \, y_k^*|}{ab}\right](\Delta x)_k(\Delta y)_k(\Delta z)_k.$$

From this element we set up our triple integral for the mass:

$$\text{mass} = \iiint\limits_{\text{solid}} \left(1 + \frac{\alpha|xy|}{ab}\right) dx \, dy \, dz.$$

To compute this triple integral, we turn to iterated single integrals. First observe that the solid can be divided into 8 portions of equal mass, so that we need compute only the mass in the first octant. Then we observe, as in Fig. 12.54, that we can sweep out this solid if (a) a line segment is formed by moving a point in the z direction from $z = 0$ to $z = c\sqrt{1 - (x^2/a^2) - (y^2/b^2)}$, this being the equation of the portion of the ellipsoid in the first octant, (b) a plane section is formed by moving the line segment in the x direction from $x = 0$ to $x = a\sqrt{1 - (y^2/b^2)}$, this being the equation of the ellipse at which the line segment ends its motion, and (c) the plane section is moved in the y direction from $y = 0$ to $y = b$. With this analysis of the solid in mind, we write

$$\text{mass} = \iiint\limits_{\text{solid}} \left(1 + \frac{\alpha|xy|}{ab}\right) dV$$

$$= 8 \int_{y=0}^{b} \left[\int_{x=0}^{a\sqrt{1-(y^2/b^2)}} \left\{ \int_{z=0}^{c\sqrt{1-(x^2/a^2)-(y^2/b^2)}} \left(1 + \frac{\alpha xy}{ab}\right) dz \right\} dx \right] dy,$$

where we integrate (a) with respect to z from $z = 0$ to $z = c\sqrt{1 - (x^2/a^2) - (y^2/b^2)}$, (b) with respect to x from $x = 0$ to $x = a\sqrt{1 - (y^2/b^2)}$ and (c) with respect to y from $y = 0$ to $y = b$.

To shorten the formal antidifferentiation work, we observe that

$$\iiint\limits_{\text{solid}} 1 \, dz \, dx \, dy = \text{volume of solid} = \tfrac{4}{3}\pi abc,$$

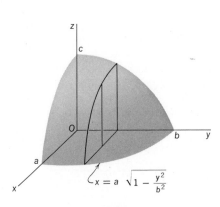

Fig. 12.54

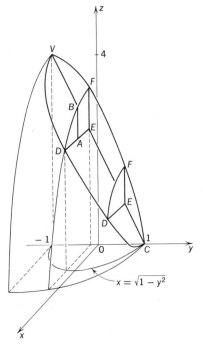

Fig. 12.55

for we deal with the ellipsoid, whose volume formula is well known. Hence

$$\text{mass} = \frac{4}{3}\pi abc + \frac{8\alpha}{ab}\int_{y=0}^{b}\int_{x=0}^{a\sqrt{1-(y^2/b^2)}}\int_{z=0}^{c\sqrt{1-(x^2/a^2)-(y^2/b^2)}} xy\,dz\,dx\,dy$$

$$= \frac{4}{3}\pi abc + \frac{8\alpha c}{ab}\int_{y=0}^{b}\int_{x=0}^{a\sqrt{1-(y^2/b^2)}} xy\sqrt{1-\frac{x^2}{a^2}-\frac{y^2}{b^2}}\,dx\,dy;$$

in this z integration, x and y were held fixed. Then

$$m = \frac{4}{3}\pi abc + \frac{8\alpha c}{ab}\left(-\frac{a^2}{2}\right)\int_{y=0}^{b}\int_{x=0}^{a\sqrt{1-(y^2/b^2)}} y\left[1-\frac{x^2}{a^2}-\frac{y^2}{b^2}\right]^{1/2}\left(-\frac{2}{a^2}x\right)dx\,dy$$

$$= \frac{4}{3}\pi abc - \frac{4\alpha ca}{b}\int_{y=0}^{b} y\frac{2}{3}\left[1-\frac{x^2}{a^2}-\frac{y^2}{b^2}\right]^{3/2}\Big|_{x=0}^{a\sqrt{1-(y^2/b^2)}}\,dy$$

$$= \frac{4}{3}\pi abc + \frac{8}{3}\frac{\alpha ca}{b}\int_{y=0}^{b}\left(1-\frac{y^2}{b^2}\right)^{3/2}y\,dy$$

$$= \frac{4}{3}\pi abc + \frac{8}{3}\frac{\alpha ca}{b}\left(-\frac{b^2}{2}\right)\frac{2}{5}\left(1-\frac{y^2}{b^2}\right)^{5/2}\Big|_{y=0}^{b}$$

$$= \tfrac{4}{3}\pi abc + \tfrac{8}{15}\alpha abc.$$

Example 2. Find the volume of the solid bounded by the paraboloid $x^2 + (y+1)^2 = 4 - z$ and the plane $2y + z = 2$.

The half of this solid that lies in front of the yz plane is shown in Fig. 12.55 where V, D, C, E, A are all points in the plane $2y + z = 2$ and V, D, C, F, B are all points on the paraboloid. Let us divide this solid into elements by drawing planes $x = $ const, $y = $ const, and $z = $ const, and write

$$\Delta V = \Delta x \Delta y \Delta z$$

for a typical element. Then

$$V = \iiint_{\text{solid}} dx\,dy\,dz. \tag{1}$$

To see how to write this triple integral as three iterated single integrals, we observe that the half of the solid sketched in Fig. 12.55 can be swept out (a) if a line segment AB is formed by moving a point in the z direction from the plane $z = 2 - 2y$ to the paraboloid $z = 4 - x^2 - (y+1)^2$, (b) if a plane section DEF is formed by moving the line segment in the x direction from EF (where $x = 0$) to position D on curve CDV, and (c) if the plane section is moved in the y direction from V to C.

Observe that in Step (b) of this analysis the position D on the curve CDV at which we stop moving the line segment AB in the x direction depends on the constant y value at which we are working. The x coordinates for the points of curve CDV appear, for instance, to vary from 0 at V (which is at $y = -1$) to a maximum (perhaps in the plane $y = 0$) to 0 again at C (which is at $y = 1$). Thus, in the x summation we shall soon write, the first x boundary is 0, because we start moving the line AB from the EF position in the plane $x = 0$ and the second x boundary should be a function of y. It remains, then, to find an equation satisfied by the points of curve CDV which can be written in the form $x = f(y)$.

If a point lies on curve CDV, it lies on both the paraboloid and the plane, and its coordinates satisfy the equations of both of these surfaces, as well as any equation derived from them. From the plane equation we have $z = 2 - 2y$; if we substitute for z in the paraboloid equation, we get the new equation

$$x^2 + (y + 1)^2 = 4 - (2 - 2y)$$

or
$$x^2 + y^2 = 1, \qquad x = \pm \sqrt{1 - y^2}. \tag{2}$$

The curve CDV lies on the cylinder with Eq. (2).

Now we return to Eq. (1) and write

$$V = 2 \int_{y=-1}^{1} \int_{x=0}^{\sqrt{1-y^2}} \int_{z=2-2y}^{4-x^2-(y+1)^2} 1 \, dz \, dx \, dy$$

$$= 2 \int_{y=-1}^{1} \int_{x=0}^{\sqrt{1-y^2}} [4 - x^2 - (y + 1)^2 - 2 + 2y] \, dx \, dy$$

$$= 2 \int_{y=-1}^{1} \int_{x=0}^{\sqrt{1-y^2}} [1 - y^2 - x^2] \, dx \, dy$$

$$= 2 \int_{y=-1}^{1} [(1 - y^2)x - \tfrac{1}{3} x^3]_{x=0}^{\sqrt{1-y^2}} \, dy = \tfrac{4}{3} \int_{y=-1}^{1} (1 - y^2)^{3/2} \, dy.$$

Here we can use a table of integrals, or we can use the trigonometric substitution $y = \sin \theta$. In the latter case, we have

$$V = \frac{4}{3} \int_{\theta=-\pi/2}^{\pi/2} \cos^4 \theta \, d\theta = \frac{4}{3} \int_{\theta=-\pi/2}^{\pi/2} \left(\frac{1 + \cos 2\theta}{2}\right)^2 d\theta$$

$$= \frac{1}{3} \int_{\theta=-\pi/2}^{\pi/2} \left[1 + 2 \cos 2\theta + \frac{1 + \cos 4\theta}{2}\right] d\theta$$

$$= \frac{1}{3} \frac{3}{2} \int_{-\pi/2}^{\pi/2} 1 \, d\theta = \frac{1}{2} \pi.$$

Example 3. Let the z axis be vertical. Consider the solid bounded by the elliptic cone $4x^2 + z^2 = y^2$ and the plane $y = 4$, with weight density $\rho = c|z|$, c a constant. Imagine the cone attached to the x axis at the origin, and free to rotate about the x axis under the influence of its own weight. Find M_x.

The solid is symmetric with respect to the yz and xy planes, as is its weight density, and the moment about the x axis for the quarter of the solid in the first octant is one quarter of the moment for the whole solid; this quarter of the solid appears in Fig. 12.56. Let us divide this quarter of the solid into elements by drawing planes $x = $ const, $y = $ const, and $z = $ const, and write

$$(\Delta V)_k = (\Delta x)_k (\Delta y)_k (\Delta z)_k$$

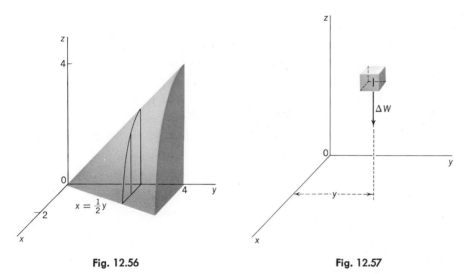

Fig. 12.56   **Fig. 12.57**

for a typical element. Since the weight density is $\rho = cz$, for the weight of this element we can write

$$(\Delta w)_k = c(z_k^*)(\Delta x)_k(\Delta y)_k(\Delta z)_k,$$

where z_k^* is a suitably chosen representative z for this element. The moment about the x axis for this element, due to its weight, is the product of the magnitude of this weight force by the moment arm. As Fig. 12.57 indicates, this moment arm is y, so that

$$(\Delta M)_k = y_k^{**}(\Delta w)_k = cy_k^{**}z_k^*(\Delta x)_k(\Delta y)_k(\Delta z)_k,$$

where y_k^{**} is a suitably chosen representative y for this element. Hence

$$M_x = \iiint\limits_{\text{solid}} cyz \; dx \; dy \; dz.$$

We return to Fig. 12.56 to discuss the setting up of the equivalent iterated single integrals. We can sweep out one quarter of the cone by (a) moving a point in the z direction from $z = 0$ to the cone, $z = \sqrt{y^2 - 4x^2}$, to form a line segment, (b) forming a plane section by moving the line segment in the x direction from $x = 0$ to the xy trace line $x = \frac{1}{2}y$; and (c) moving the plane section from $y = 0$ to $y = 4$. Accordingly, we write

$$M_x = 4 \int_{y=0}^{4} \int_{x=0}^{y/2} \int_{z=0}^{\sqrt{y^2-4x^2}} cyz \; dz \; dx \; dy$$

$$= 4c \int_{y=0}^{4} \int_{x=0}^{y/2} y \left. \frac{z^2}{2} \right|_{z=0}^{\sqrt{y^2-4x^2}} dx \; dy$$

$$= 2c \int_{y=0}^{4} \int_{x=0}^{y/2} (y^3 - 4yx^2) \; dx \; dy$$

$$= \frac{2}{3}c \int_{y=0}^{4} y^4 \; dy = \frac{2c}{15}(4)^5 = \frac{2048}{15}c.$$

● **Remark 1**

In replacing a triple integral by iterated integrals, different orders of integration are often possible, and sometimes the computation is much shorter when one order of integration is used rather than another.

EXERCISES 12.10

1. (a) Use triple integration to find the volume of the tetrahedron bounded by the coordinate planes and $\dfrac{x}{a} + \dfrac{y}{b} + \dfrac{z}{c} = 1$.
   (b) Find the volume a second time, using a different order of integration when evaluating the triple integral.

2. Find the volume of the solid bounded by $(x^2/1) + (z^2/2) = 8 - y$ and the planes $y = 0, x = 1, x = -1, z = 1$, and $z = -1$.

3. Find the volume of the solid bounded above by $x^2 = 4 - z$, below by $x - 2z + 2 = 0$, and to the left and right by $y = 0$ and $y = 6$.

4. Find the volume of the tetrahedron bounded above by $2x + 2y + z = 6$, below by $y + 3z = 3$, to the left by $y = 0$, and in back by $x = 0$.

5. Find the volume of the solid bounded on the right by $y = 4 - x^2$, on the left by $z = 4y$, and above and below by $z = 4$ and $z = 0$.

6. Find the volume of the solid bounded on the right by the paraboloid $x^2 + z^2 = 6 - y$ and on the left by the paraboloid $x^2 + z^2 = 2y$.

7. Find the volume of (a) the pyramid with vertices at $(0, 0, 6)$, $(2, 2, 0)$, $(2, -2, 0)$, $(-2, -2, 0)$, and $(-2, 2, 0)$; and (b) and (c) the volumes of the lower and upper portions formed when the pyramid is cut by the plane $y + z = 2$.

8. The solid bounded by $x = 0$, $x = a$, $y = 0$, $y = b$, $z = 0$, and $z = c$ has mass density $\mu = \alpha(x^2 + y^2 + z^2)$, α a constant. Find its mass.

9. Find the mass of the tetrahedron of Exercise 1 if it has mass density $\mu = 1 - z/c$.

10. That portion of the sphere $x^2 + y^2 + z^2 = 1$ which lies above $z = \frac{1}{2}$ has a mass density $\mu = c|x|$, c a constant. Find the mass.

11. The solid bounded by the paraboloid $(x^2/9) + (y^2/4) = z$ and $z = 4$ has mass density $\mu = 1 - |x|/12$. Find its mass.

12. What is the moment of inertia about the x axis of the solid of Exercise 8?

13. Let the solid of Exercise 2 have constant mass density μ. Find its moment of inertia about the y axis.

14. Find the moment of inertia about the z axis of the prism bounded by $x = 0, y = 0, z = 0, z = 4$, and $x + y = 1$ if the mass density is $\alpha e^{-.1z}$, α constant.

15. Let the solid of Exercise 8 be considered attached to the y axis and free to rotate about the axis under the influence of its own weight. Compute M_y.

16. Let the z axis be vertical and let the hemisphere that lies to the right of the xz plane and is bounded by the xz plane and $x^2 + y^2 + z^2 = a^2$ have weight density $\rho = c|x|/a$, c a constant. Let this solid be considered attached to the x axis and free to rotate about that axis under the influence of its own weight. Compute M_x.

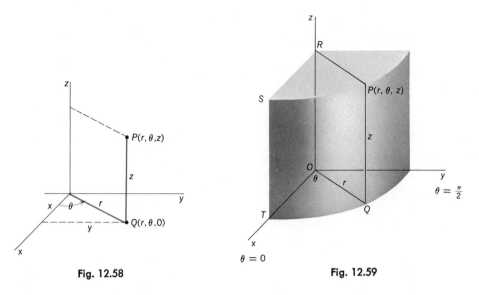

Fig. 12.58   **Fig. 12.59**

12.11 Cylindrical Coordinates

I

Cylindrical coordinates can be looked upon as one extension of plane polar co-ordinates to space. When the cylindrical coordinates (r, θ, z) for a point P are presented, we use the r and θ coordinates as in polar coordinates to locate a preliminary point Q in the xy plane; the z coordinate is used as in Cartesian coordinates to describe how far from the xy plane and in which direction point P lies. See Fig. 12.58. These coordinates are related to the Cartesian coordinates by the equations

$$\left. \begin{aligned} x &= r \cos \theta, \\ y &= r \sin \theta, \\ z &= z \end{aligned} \right\} \tag{1}$$

or

$$\left. \begin{aligned} r^2 &= x^2 + y^2, \\ \tan \theta &= \frac{y}{x}, * \\ z &= z. \end{aligned} \right\} \tag{2}$$

From Eqs. (2) it follows that a coordinate surface $r = $ const is a circular cylinder of radius r with the z axis as axis; hence the name cylindrical coordinates. A coordinate surface $\theta = $ const is a plane through the z axis making angle θ with the xz plane. A surface $z = $ const is, as before, a plane perpendicular to the z axis at a directed distance z from the xy plane. See Fig. 12.59, where S, T, Q, and P lie on

---

* The statement $\tan \theta = y/x$ can be used when $x \neq 0$ if care is taken in choosing the proper value for θ. The two statements $\sin \theta = y/\sqrt{x^2 + y^2}$ and $\cos \theta = x/\sqrt{x^2 + y^2}$ can be used together in place of $\tan \theta = y/x$ except when $x = y = 0$.

the cylinder $r = $ const; O, R, P, and Q lie in the plane $\theta = $ const; and S, R, and P lie in the plane $z = $ const.

We form a cylindrical coordinate element by drawing two nearby surfaces $r = $ const, two more $\theta = $ const, and two more $z = $ const. See Fig. 12.60. The volume of this element will be the product of its base area and height, or

$$\Delta V = (\Delta A)\,\Delta z = \left(r + \frac{\Delta r}{2}\right) \Delta r\, \Delta\theta\, \Delta z,$$

$$\Delta V \approx r\Delta r\, \Delta\theta\, \Delta z.$$

Just as with Cartesian coordinates, if we want to compute a quantity Q for a given solid, we divide the solid into a finite number of cylindrical elements by drawing coordinate surfaces $r = $ const, $\theta = $ const, and $z = $ const. Then if there exists a continuous function f and a point $(r_k^*, \theta_k^*, z_k^*)$ of the kth element such that the value of Q for this element is

$$(\Delta Q)_k = f(r_k^*, \theta_k^*, z_k^*)(\Delta V)_k,$$

we take as the value of Q for the whole solid

$$\lim_{n \to \infty} \sum_{k=1}^{n} (\Delta Q)_k = \iiint\limits_{\text{solid}} f(r, \theta, z)\, dV = \iiint\limits_{\text{solid}} f(r, \theta, z)r\, dr\, d\theta\, dz,$$

it being understood that the largest $(\Delta r)_k$, the largest $(\Delta\theta)_k$, and the largest $(\Delta z)_k$ all approach 0 as n grows beyond all bounds. This triple integral is rewritten as a nest of iterated integrals and then evaluted.

Example 1. Let a solid be bounded by the sphere $r^2 + z^2 = a^2$ (or $x^2 + y^2 + z^2 = a^2$) and have mass density $\mu = ce^{-r^2}|z|$, c a constant. Find its mass.

Because of the sphere's symmetry and the nature of the mass density function, the 8 portions into which the sphere is cut by the coordinate planes all have equal

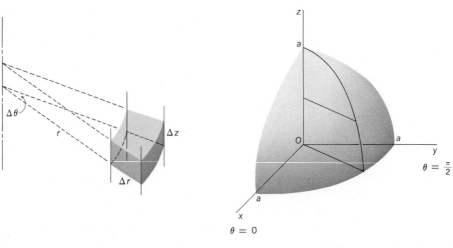

Fig. 12.60   **Fig. 12.61**

mass; the portion in the first octant is drawn in Fig. 12.61. First we divide the solid into cylindrical coordinate elements by drawing coordinate surfaces $r = $ const, $\theta = $ const, and $z = $ const. For the kth element we can write

$$(\Delta V)_k = r_k^*(\Delta r)_k(\Delta\theta)_k(\Delta z)_k,$$

where r_k^* is the average r for this element. The mass density for this element will vary from a minimum value of $ce^{-(r+\Delta r)^2}z$ to a maximum value of $ce^{-r^2}(z + \Delta z)$. We can find a point $(r_k^{**}, \theta_k^{**}, z_k^{**})$ of this element for which the mass of the element is

$$(\Delta m)_k = ce^{-r_k^{**2}}z_k^{**}r_k^*(\Delta r)_k(\Delta\theta)_k(\Delta z)_k.$$

Then for the mass of the whole solid we have

$$\tfrac{1}{8}\,m = \iiint\limits_{\text{octant}} ce^{-r^2}\,zr\,dr\,d\theta\,dz. \tag{3}$$

To replace this triple integral by iterated integrals we observe, as in Fig. 12.61, that the solid can be swept out in three steps by (a) moving a point in the r direction from the z axis $(r = 0)$ to the sphere $r = \sqrt{a^2 - z^2}$ to form a line segment; (b) forming a plane section by moving this line segment in the z direction from the xy plane $(z = 0)$ to the top of the sphere $(z = a)$; (c) sweeping out the solid by rotating this section in the θ direction from $\theta = 0$ to $\theta = \pi/2$. We replace the triple integral in (3) by iterated integrals in which we (a) integrate with respect to r from $r = 0$ to $r = \sqrt{a^2 - z^2}$, (b) integrate with respect to z from $z = 0$ to $z = a$, and (c) integrate with respect to θ from $\theta = 0$ to $\theta = \pi/2$;

$$\tfrac{1}{8}\,m = \int_{\theta=0}^{\pi/2}\int_{z=0}^{a}\int_{r=0}^{\sqrt{a^2-z^2}} ce^{-r^2}rz\,dr\,dz\,d\theta.$$

Now, antidifferentiating step by step, we get

$$m = \frac{8c}{-2}\int_{\theta=0}^{\pi/2}\int_{z=0}^{a} ze^{-r^2}\Big|_{r=0}^{\sqrt{a^2-z^2}} dz\,d\theta$$

$$= -4c\int_{\theta=0}^{\pi/2}\int_{z=0}^{a} z[e^{-(a^2-z^2)} - 1]\,dz\,d\theta$$

$$= -4c\int_{\theta=0}^{\pi/2}\left[\frac{1}{2}e^{-(a^2-z^2)} - \frac{z^2}{2}\right]_{z=0}^{a} d\theta$$

$$= -2c(1 - e^{-a^2} - a^2)\int_{\theta=0}^{\pi/2} 1\,d\theta$$

$$= \pi c[e^{-a^2} + a^2 - 1].$$

Example 2. Find the volume of the solid bounded below by the xy plane, above by the paraboloid $x^2 + y^2 = z$, and on the side by the hyperboloid

$$\frac{x^2}{1} + \frac{y^2}{1} - \frac{z^2}{4} = 1.$$

This solid is divided into four quarters of equal volume by the coordinate planes; the quarter in the first octant is pictured in Fig. 12.62. Because the paraboloid and the hyperboloid are both surfaces of revolution with the z axis as the axis of symmetry, we solve the problem by means of cylindrical coordinates. The paraboloid $r^2 = z$ and hyperboloid $r^2 = 1 + z^2/4$ have as their curve of intersection, AB in Fig. 12.62, the circle $r = \sqrt{2}$ in the plane $z = 2$. This we readily find by solving the surface equations simultaneously, for a point of the curve of intersection lies in both surfaces, and its coordinates satisfy both equations.

For the element of volume we can write

$$\Delta V \approx r \, \Delta r \, \Delta \theta \, \Delta z,$$

and then

$$V = \iiint\limits_{\text{solid}} r \, dr \, d\theta \, dz.$$

One quarter of the solid can be swept out by (a) moving a point in the r direction, holding θ and z fixed, from the paraboloid $r = \sqrt{z}$ to the hyperboloid $r = \sqrt{1 + z^2/4}$, thus forming a line segment; (b) moving this line segment in the z direction from the xy plane, $z = 0$, to the curve of intersection at $z = 2$, thus forming a profile section of the solid; and (c) rotating this profile section about the z axis from $\theta = 0$ to $\theta = \pi/2$. The corresponding iterated integrals read

$$\tfrac{1}{4} V = \int_{\theta=0}^{\pi/2} \int_{z=0}^{2} \int_{r=\sqrt{z}}^{\sqrt{1+z^2/4}} r \, dr \, dz \, d\theta.$$

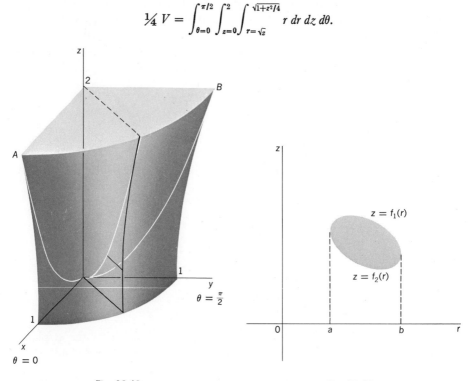

Fig. 12.62   Fig. 12.63

If we antidifferentiate step by step, we get

$$V = 4 \int_{\theta=0}^{\pi/2} \int_{z=0}^{2} \frac{r^2}{2} \Big|_{r=\sqrt{z}}^{\sqrt{1+z^2/4}} dz \, d\theta$$

$$= 2 \int_{\theta=0}^{\pi/2} \int_{z=0}^{2} \left(1 + \frac{z^2}{4} - z\right) dz \, d\theta$$

$$= 2 \int_{\theta=0}^{\pi/2} \tfrac{2}{3} \, d\theta = \tfrac{2}{3} \, \pi.$$

||

We have often found a coordinate of a center of gravity point for a plate by computing moments about an axis twice and then equating results; once we would take a limit of a sum of moments for elements and once we would assume the entire weight as concentrated at the center of gravity point. In this way, if $\rho(x, y)$ is the weight density measured in units of weight per unit of area, and $\bar{x}$ is the x coordinate of the center of gravity point, we find that

$$\bar{x} = \frac{\text{moment of plate about } y \text{ axis}}{\text{weight of plate}} = \frac{\iint\limits_{\text{plate}} \rho(x, y) x \, dx \, dy}{\iint\limits_{\text{plate}} \rho(x, y) \, dx \, dy}.$$

Since the case of a homogeneous plate, for which $\rho(x, y)$ is constant, occurs frequently, it is useful to talk about a centroid point for a plane region.

■ **DEFINITION 1**

The centroid point for a plane region R has coordinates $(\bar{x}, \bar{y})$ where

$$\bar{x} = \frac{\iint\limits_{R} x \, dx \, dy}{\iint\limits_{R} dx \, dy}, \qquad \bar{y} = \frac{\iint\limits_{R} y \, dx \, dy}{\iint\limits_{R} dx \, dy}.$$

■ **THEOREM 1**

*A Theorem of Pappus.**

HYPOTHESIS: (a) Plane region R lies entirely on one side of the line L in its plane or touches L,

(b) R is rotated about L to form a solid of revolution.

CONCLUSION: The volume of the solid of revolution equals the area of R multiplied by the circumference of the circle in which the centroid of R travels during the rotation.

PROOF: Choose the z axis of a plane rz Cartesian coordinate system to be the line L, and let the boundaries of region R be $z = f_1(r)$ and $z = f_2(r)$ for $0 \le a \le r \le b$, with $f_2(r) \le f_1(r)$ for $a \le r \le b$, and perhaps portions of $r = a$ and $r = b$. See Fig. 12.63. If the centroid for region R is the point $(\bar{r}, \bar{z})$, we can say that

---

* Pappus worked in the second half of the third century A.D. He also wrote on the focus-directrix property for the ellipse, parabola, and hyperbola. Theorem 1 is also sometimes called Guldin's theorem, after P. Guldin, 1577–1643, a Swiss mathematician.

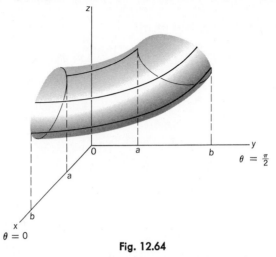

Fig. 12.64

$$\int_{r=a}^{b} \int_{z=f_2(r)}^{f_1(r)} r\, dz\, dr = \bar{r} \int_{r=a}^{b} \int_{z=f_2(r)}^{f_1(r)} dz\, dr = \bar{r}\ (\text{area of } R). \tag{4}$$

If we now rotate region R about the z axis, we form a solid of revolution whose volume can be found by using cylindrical coordinates; see Fig. 12.64, where ¼ of this solid is drawn. For the volume element we write

$$\Delta V \approx r\, \Delta r\, \Delta\theta\, \Delta z,$$

and then
$$V = \int_{\theta=0}^{2\pi} \int_{r=a}^{b} \int_{z=f_2(r)}^{f_1(r)} r\, dz\, dr\, d\theta.* \tag{5}$$

These iterated integral boundaries were determined by observing that the solid can be swept out by (a) moving a point in the z direction from the lower profile curve $z = f_2(r)$ to the upper, $z = f_1(r)$, to form a line segment; (b) moving this line segment in the r direction from $r = a$ to $r = b$ to form the profile section, and (c) rotating the profile section about the z axis. Since no function of θ appears either in the integrand of this nest of iterated integrals or in the boundaries of the first two integrals, we shall find when we have completed the r and z integrations that our problem reads

$$V = \int_{\theta=0}^{2\pi} (\text{const})\, d\theta = 2\pi(\text{const}).$$

Hence we can rewrite Eq. (5) as follows:

$$V = 2\pi \int_{r=a}^{b} \int_{z=f_2(r)}^{f_1(r)} r\, dz\, dr.$$

Now Eq. (4) applies; we get

$$V = 2\pi\bar{r}(\text{area of } R).$$

The conclusion of Theorem 1 puts this statement into words.†

---

* This volume can also be found by single integration, using the summation of concentric shell elements. The integration order θ, z, r in place of the order z, r, θ used in Eq. (5) would correspond to the summation of concentric shell elements.

† See Exercise 12.11-19.

Example 3. Let a torus be formed by rotating a circle of radius b about a line a units from its center, $b \leq a$; see Fig. 12.65, where ⅛ of a torus appears.

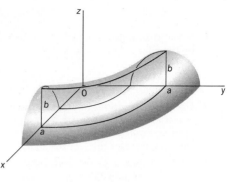

The area of a profile section is πb^2. The centroid of this circular section lies at the center of the circle of radius b, at a distance a from the axis of the torus. Hence the circumference of the circle in which the centroid travels is $2\pi a$ and

Fig. 12.65

$$V = (2\pi a)(\pi b^2) = 2\pi^2 a b^2.*$$

● **Remark 1**

We mention in passing that a centroid point can be defined for a plane curve arc. When the arc rotates about a nonintersecting line in its plane, it sweeps out a surface of revolution, and, corresponding to Theorem 1, there is the fact that the surface area swept out in one revolution is the product of the length of the arc and the circumference of the circle in which the curve's centroid traveled. To illustrate, a cone of base radius r and height h is generated by rotating a straight-line segment of length $\sqrt{r^2 + h^2}$, as is indicated in Fig. 12.66. The centroid for this segment is its midpoint, and this theorem says that for the surface area of the cone we have

$$\text{surface area} = (\sqrt{r^2 + h^2}) \left(2\pi \frac{r}{2}\right) = \pi r \sqrt{r^2 + h^2}.$$

See Exercise 12.11-20.

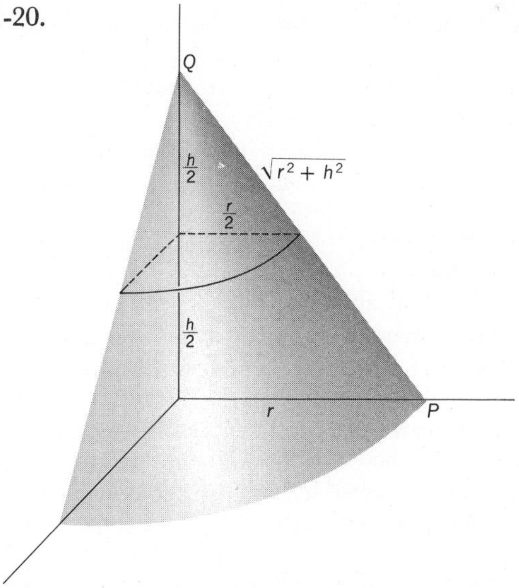

Q

$\frac{h}{2}$ $\sqrt{r^2 + h^2}$

$\frac{r}{2}$

$\frac{h}{2}$

r P

Fig. 12.66

---

* See Example 12.3-2.

EXERCISES 12.11

1. Use a triple integral in cylindrical coordinates to find the volume of the solid enclosed by the ellipsoid of revolution

$$\frac{x^2}{a^2} + \frac{y^2}{a^2} + \frac{z^2}{b^2} = 1.$$

2. Use a triple integral in cylindrical coordinates to find the volume of the hole bored out of a sphere of radius a by a circular cylinder of radius b, $b < a$, the axis of the cylinder coinciding with a diameter of the sphere. *Suggestion:* Let this axis be the z axis and let the center of the sphere be the origin.

3. Find the volume of the solid inside the cylinder $r = a \sin \theta$, below the sphere $r^2 + z^2 = a^2$, and above the upper half of the ellipsoid

$$\frac{r^2}{a^2} + \frac{z^2}{b^2} = 1, \qquad b < a.$$

4. Use triple integration to find the volume of the solid bounded by the paraboloid of revolution $x^2 + y^2 = 4 - z$ and the half of $z^4 = 81(x^2 + y^2)$ for which $z \geq 0$.

5. Find the volume of the solid whose roof is the upper nappe of the cone $z^2 = 4(x^2 + y^2)$, whose base is the xy plane, and whose side walls are the planes $x = 0$, $x = a$, $y = 0, y = a$.

In the next six problems mass densities are measured in units of mass per unit of volume.

6. A circular cylinder of radius r_0 and height h_0 is placed so that its axis is the z axis and its base lies in the xy plane. Its mass density is then given by the formula

$$\mu = \left(a + b \frac{r^2}{r_0^2} \right) e^{-c(z/h_0)},$$

where a, b, and c are constants.
(a) Find its mass.
(b) What would the mass be if we cut out and removed a central core of radius $r_0/4$?

7. A right circular cone of radius r_0 and height h_0 is placed with vertex at the origin and axis along the z axis. Its mass density is then given by the formula

$$\mu = 2 + \frac{|y|}{\sqrt{x^2 + y^2}} \qquad \text{or} \qquad \mu = 2 + |\sin \theta|.$$

Find its mass.

8. Assume that the solid of Exercise 1 has constant mass density μ; find its moment of inertia about the z axis.

9. Find the moment of inertia about the z axis for the solid of Exercise 7.

10. Find the moment of inertia about its axis for the solid of Exercise 6.

11. A sphere of radius a and constant mass density μ is placed so that it is bounded by $x^2 + y^2 + z^2 = a^2$. Find its moment of inertia about the line $x = 0, y = a$.

12. Let a right circular cylinder be formed by rotating a rectangle about one of its sides. Find the volume of the cylinder by the Theorem of Pappus.

13. Let a cylindrical shell be formed by rotating the rectangle with sides $x = r_0$, $x = r_0 + \Delta r$, $y = 0$, $y = h_0$ about the y axis. Find the volume of the cylindrical shell by the Theorem of Pappus.

14. Find the centroid of the right triangle with vertices $(0, 0)$, $(a, 0)$, and $(0, b)$ in the xy plane by considering the volumes of the cones formed when the triangle is rotated about the x and y axes.

15. Find the centroid of a semicircle of radius a from a knowledge of the volume of the sphere formed when the semicircle is rotated about the diameter that bounds it.

16. From a knowledge of the area of the region bounded by one arch of the cycloid $x = a(t - \sin t), y = a(1 - \cos t)$, and the x axis, find the volume of the solid formed by rotating this region about the y axis.*

17. *An extension of the Theorem of Pappus:* Let a region R of a Cartesian r, z plane lie in the half-plane $r \geq 0$. Let W be the solid of revolution formed when R is rotated about the z axis. Let $\mu(r, z)$ be any continuous function defined over R. Define a "moment of order n," $n \geq 0$, for R as

$$M_n = \int\int_R \mu r^n \, dA$$

and a "moment of order n," $n \geq 0$, for W as

$$L_n = \int\int\int_W \mu r^n \, dV.$$

Show that

$$L_n = 2\pi \, M_{n+1}.$$

18. Let $z = f(y)$ be continuous and steadily decreasing for $0 \leq a \leq y \leq b$, with $f(b) = 0$. Let $y = g(z)$ also describe the same arc in the yz plane. Rotate the region of the yz plane bounded by $z = f(y)$, $z = 0$, and $y = a$ about the z axis to form a solid of revolution, one quarter of which is drawn in Fig. 12.67.

If we analyze the solid of revolution by taking sections perpendicular to the z axis, we write

$$V = \pi \int_{z=0}^{f(a)} [g^2(z) - a^2] \, dz. \tag{6}$$

If we analyze the solid by taking concentric cylindrical shells, we write

$$V = 2\pi \int_{y=a}^{b} yf(y) \, dy. \tag{7}$$

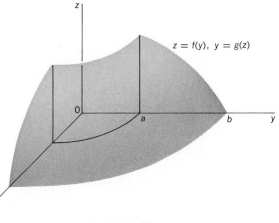

$z = f(y), \ y = g(z)$

Fig. 12.67

---

* You can compare your result with that of Exercise 12.3-9.

If we use prisms parallel to the z axis and polar coordinates in the xy plane, we write

$$V = \int_{\theta=0}^{2\pi} \int_{r=a}^{b} f(r)r \, dr \, d\theta. \tag{8}$$

If we use triple integration in cylindrical coordinates, we can write

$$V = \int_{\theta=0}^{2\pi} \int_{z=0}^{f(a)} \int_{r=a}^{g(z)} r \, dr \, dz \, d\theta \tag{9}$$

or

$$V = \int_{\theta=0}^{2\pi} \int_{r=a}^{b} \int_{z=0}^{f(r)} r \, dz \, dr \, d\theta. \tag{10}$$

Show that all five statements for V are equal in value.

19. The proof of Theorem 1 is valid for a region R which can be described as in the first paragraph of that proof. Such a region is always intersected by a line $r = c$, $a \leq c \leq b$, in one connected interval. If region R' does not have this property but is the sum of two subregions R_1 and R_2 which do have this property, show that the conclusion of Theorem 1 holds for R' also by applying Theorem 1 twice, once to R_1 and once to R_2, and adding results. (If R' had the shape of a kidney bean or crescent, this discussion would be pertinent.)

20. We can also define a centroid point for an arc of a curve.
  Definition 2. Centroid for an arc. Let s be the arc length parameter for an arc C in the x, y plane. Then the centroid point for C has coordinates $(\bar{x}, \bar{y})$ where

$$\bar{x} = \frac{\int_C x \, ds}{\int_C ds}, \qquad \bar{y} = \frac{\int_C y \, ds}{\int_C ds}.$$

Demonstrate the following theorem.
  Theorem 2. A Theorem of Pappus.
  Hypothesis: (a) Arc C of a plane curve lies entirely on one side of line L in its plane or touches line L.
  (b) C is rotated about L to form a surface of revolution.
  Conclusion: The surface area of the surface of revolution is the product of the length of C by the circumference of the circle in which the centroid of C travels during the rotation.

21. Recall that to average n numbers one takes their sum and divides by n. If n is large, it is often efficient to compute the average as follows: Let $x_1, x_2, \cdots, x_p$ be the distinct numbers in the set of n numbers we wish to average, and let these distinct numbers occur with the frequencies $\Delta_1, \Delta_2, \cdots, \Delta_p$, respectively, $\Sigma_{k=1}^{p} \Delta_k = n$. Then the average is

$$\left(\sum_{k=1}^{p} x_k \Delta_k \right) \bigg/ \sum_{k=1}^{p} \Delta_k.$$

Explain in what sense the coordinates of the centroid point of a region R can be considered to be "average" coordinates for R.

12.12   Spherical Coordinates

Spherical coordinates can be looked upon as a different extension of polar coordinates to space. When the spherical coordinates (ρ, θ, ϕ) are presented, we locate the corresponding point P as follows: first, the coordinate ρ, $\rho \geq 0$, tells us the distance from the origin; P lies on a sphere of radius ρ, center at O. Second, the

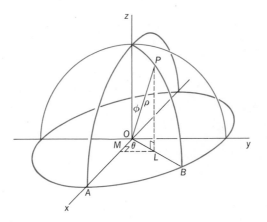

Fig. 12.68

coordinate θ, $0 \leq \theta < 2\pi$ tells us on which great half-circle of this sphere the point P lies; in the xz plane take the half of the circle of radius ρ, center at O, for which $x \geq 0$ and rotate it about the z axis through angle θ, angle AOB of Fig. 12.68. Third, the coordinate ϕ, $0 \leq \phi \leq \pi$, tells us which point on the great half-circle to select; OP makes angle ϕ with the positive z axis. For the origin we have $\rho = 0$, but both θ and ϕ can be chosen arbitrarily. For other points on the z axis we have $\phi = 0$ or π, according as the point lies above the xy plane or below, but θ can be chosen arbitrarily.

Example 1. The points with spherical coordinates $A(1, \pi/3, \pi/6)$, $B(2, \pi/2, 3\pi/4)$ and $C(3/2, 4\pi/3, \pi/2)$ are plotted in Figs. 12.69(a), (b), and (c). In Fig. 12.69 (b) the measure of $\angle ROT$ is $\pi/2$ and the measure of $\angle QOB$ is $3\pi/4$. In Fig. 12.69(c), $\angle VOC$ has measure $4\pi/3$ and $\angle WOC$ has measure $\pi/2$. For the point with Cartesian coordinates $(0, 0, 4)$, we can choose as spherical coordinates $\rho = 4$, $\theta = $ any number, and $\phi = 0$. For the point with Cartesian coordinates $(0, 0, -4)$ we can choose as spherical coordinates $\rho = 4$, $\theta = $ any number, and $\phi = \pi$.

The Cartesian coordinates (x, y, z) and the spherical coordinates (ρ, θ, ϕ) for the same point P are related through the equations

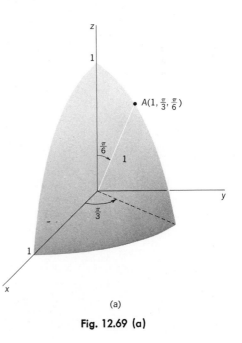

(a)

Fig. 12.69 (a)

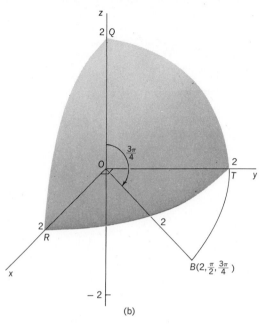

(b)

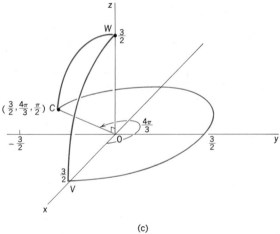

(c)

Fig. 12.69 (b) and (c)

$$\left.\begin{array}{l} x = \rho \sin \phi \cos \theta, \\ y = \rho \sin \phi \sin \theta, \\ z = \rho \cos \phi, \end{array}\right\} \qquad \rho \geq 0, 0 \leq \phi \leq \pi. \tag{1}$$

The third of these equations is derived by drawing a line through P perpendicular to the xy plane, as in Fig. 12.68, and computing

$$z = LP = \rho \cos \phi.$$

In triangle OLP we also compute $OL = \rho \sin \phi$,

and then

$$x = OM = OL \cos \theta = \rho \sin \phi \cos \theta,$$

$$y = ML = OL \sin \theta = \rho \sin \phi \sin \theta.$$

From Eqs. (1) we compute

$$\left. \begin{array}{c} \rho^2 = x^2 + y^2 + z^2, \\[4pt] \tan \theta = \dfrac{y}{x}, \\[8pt] \tan \phi = \dfrac{\sqrt{x^2 + y^2}}{z}. \end{array} \right\} \tag{2}$$

For the first of these equations we square Eqs. (1) and add, simplifying with the help of the identity $\sin^2 \alpha + \cos^2 \alpha = 1$. For the second equation we divide the second of Eqs. (1) by the first. Finally, for the $\tan \phi$ equation we compute $\rho^2 \sin^2 \phi = x^2 + y^2$ from the first two of Eqs. (1), $\rho^2 \cos^2 \phi = z^2$ from the third, and divide.*

From the definitions of ρ, θ, and ϕ or from Eqs. (1) and (2) we see that

(a) a coordinate surface $\rho =$ const is a sphere with center at the origin and radius ρ;

(b) a coordinate surface $\theta =$ const is the half-plane through the z axis obtained by rotating about the z axis through the angle θ that half of the xz plane for which $x \geq 0$;

(c) a coordinate surface $\phi =$ const is a half-cone with vertex at the origin and the z axis as axis of symmetry, all generating lines making the angle ϕ with the positive z half-axis.

In Fig. 12.70 parts of several coordinate surfaces $\theta =$ const and $\phi =$ const are drawn. Spherical coordinates are frequently of value in problems concerned with

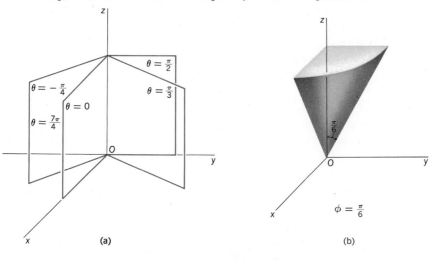

Fig. 12.70 (a) and (b)

* In taking the square root we are careful to observe that ϕ is acute and $\tan \phi$ positive for z positive, while ϕ is obtuse and $\tan \phi$ negative for z negative.

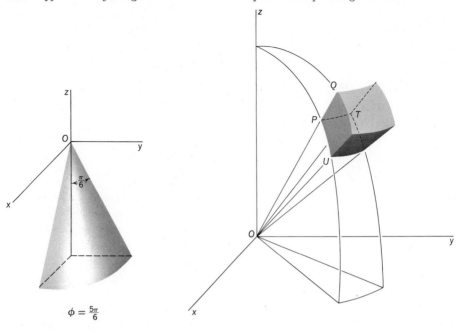

Fig. 12.70 (c)   Fig. 12.71 (a)

such spheres, planes, and cones, because their spherical coordinate equations are relatively simple.

If we draw two nearby coordinate surfaces $\rho = $ const, two more $\theta = $ const, and two more $\phi = $ const, as in Fig. 12.71(a), we form an element of volume. Since we can write $PQ = \Delta\rho$, $\sphericalangle POU = \Delta\phi$ and $PU = \rho\Delta\phi$, $\sphericalangle PVT = \Delta\theta$ and $PT = \rho \sin \phi$ $\Delta\theta$, as Figs. 12.71(b) and (c) indicate, and since adjacent faces of the element of volume are perpendicular, it seems plausible to predict that

$$\Delta V \approx (\Delta\rho)(\rho\Delta\phi)(\rho \sin \phi \, \Delta\theta) = \rho^2 \sin \phi \, \Delta\rho \, \Delta\theta \, \Delta\phi \qquad (3)$$

for the element of volume in spherical coordinates. This is indeed the truth, as we shall show in Exercise 12.12-17.

As before, if we want to compute a quantity Q for a given solid, we divide the solid into a finite number of spherical elements by drawing coordinate surfaces $\rho = $ const, $\theta = $ const, and $\phi = $ const. Then, if there exists a continuous function f and a point $(\rho_k^*, \theta_k^*, \phi_k^*)$ of the kth element such that the value of Q for this element is

$$(\Delta Q)_k = f(\rho_k^*, \theta_k^*, \phi_k^*)(\Delta V)_k,$$

we take as the value of Q for the whole solid

$$\lim_{n \to \infty} \sum_{k=1}^{n} (\Delta Q)_k = \iiint_{\text{solid}} f(\rho,\theta,\phi) \, dV = \iiint_{\text{solid}} f(\rho,\theta,\phi)\rho^2 \sin \phi \, d\rho \, d\theta \, d\phi,$$

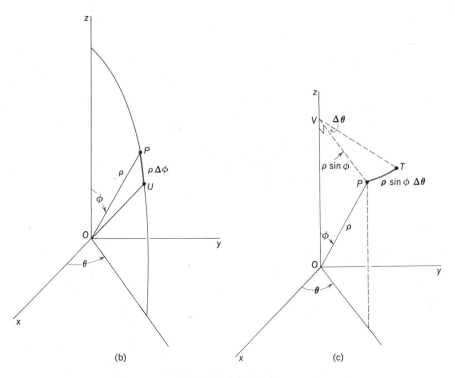

Fig. 12.71 (b) and (c)

it being understood that the largest $(\Delta\rho)_k$, the largest $(\Delta\theta)_k$, and the largest $(\Delta\phi)_k$ all approach 0 as n grows beyond all bounds. This triple integral is rewritten as a nest of iterated single integrals and then evaluated.

Example 2. Let us find the volume of the solid bounded by the spheres $x^2 + y^2 + z^2 = a^2$ and $x^2 + y^2 + z^2 = b^2$, $b > a > 0$, and the upper branch of the cone $x^2 + y^2 = (\tan^2 \alpha)z^2$, $0 < \alpha < \pi/2$.

In spherical coordinates these boundary surfaces have the equations $\rho = a$, $\rho = b$, and $\phi = \alpha$. In the case of the cone, for instance, Eqs. (1) enable us to replace $x^2 + y^2$ and z^2 by $\rho^2 \sin^2 \phi$ and $\rho^2 \cos^2 \phi$; we choose $\phi = \alpha$ rather than $\phi = \pi - \alpha$, because we want the upper branch of the cone. We could also have used Eqs. (2). One quarter of this solid is sketched in Fig. 12.72, where R, Q, W, and S lie on the sphere $\rho = b$, T and U lie on the sphere $\rho = a$, and $\sphericalangle QOR = \sphericalangle QOW = \sphericalangle QOS = \alpha$.

For the element of volume we write

$$\Delta V \approx \rho^2 \sin \phi \, \Delta\rho \, \Delta\theta \, \Delta\phi,$$

and then

$$V = \iiint\limits_{\text{solid}} \rho^2 \sin \phi \, d\rho \, d\theta \, d\phi.$$

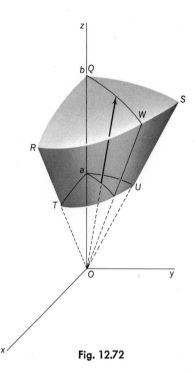

Fig. 12.72

We observe that the solid can be swept out if we (a) form a radial line segment by moving a point in the radial direction from $\rho = a$ to $\rho = b$, (b) form a section by moving this radial line segment in the ϕ direction from $\phi = 0$ to $\phi = \alpha$, and (c) rotate this section in the θ direction from $\theta = 0$ to $\theta = 2\pi$. Thus we replace our triple integral by the nest of iterated integrals

$$V = \int_{\theta=0}^{2\pi} \int_{\phi=0}^{\alpha} \int_{\rho=a}^{b} \rho^2 \sin\phi \, d\rho \, d\phi \, d\theta.$$

The computation is now straightforward. We write

$$V = \int_{\theta=0}^{2\pi} \int_{\phi=0}^{\alpha} \sin\phi \, \frac{b^3 - a^3}{3} \, d\phi \, d\theta$$

$$= \frac{b^3 - a^3}{3} \int_{\theta=0}^{2\pi} -(\cos\alpha - 1) \, d\theta = \frac{2\pi}{3} (b^3 - a^3)(1 - \cos\alpha).$$

Example 3.   We are given a cone of height h and vertex angle α, $0 < \alpha < \pi/2$. Its mass density, measured in units of mass per unit of volume, varies as the nth power of the distance from the vertex, $n \geq 0$. Find the moment of inertia about its axis of symmetry.

We choose the origin of our coordinates to be the vertex of the cone and choose the z axis to be the axis of symmetry of the cone; see Fig. 12.73 where the points Q, R, and S all lie on the cone with equation $\phi = \alpha$ and in the plane with equation $z = h$ or $\rho \cos\phi = h$. For the density we can write $\mu = k\rho^n$, k a constant.

For an element we can write

$$\Delta V \approx \rho^2 \sin \phi \, \Delta\rho \, \Delta\theta \, \Delta\phi,$$

$$\Delta m \approx k\rho^{n+2} \sin \phi \, \Delta\rho \, \Delta\theta \, \Delta\phi,$$

(distance from z axis)$^2 \approx x^2 + y^2 = \rho^2 \sin^2\phi,$

$$\Delta I \approx k\rho^{n+4} \sin^3 \phi \, \Delta\rho \, \Delta\theta \, \Delta\phi,$$

and then for the cone,

$$I_z = k \iiint\limits_{\text{solid}} \rho^{n+4} \sin^3 \phi \, d\rho \, d\theta \, d\phi.$$

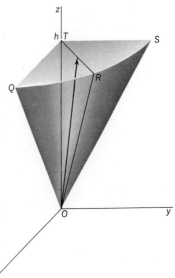

Fig. 12.73

We observe that the solid can be swept out if (a) we form a radial line segment by moving a point in the radial direction from the origin, $\rho = 0$, to the top, $\rho \cos \phi = h$, (b) form a section by moving the radial line segment in the ϕ direction from $\phi = 0$ to $\phi = \alpha$, and (c) rotate this section in the θ direction from $\theta = 0$ to $\theta = 2\pi$. Accordingly, we write

$$I_z = k \int_{\theta=0}^{2\pi} \int_{\phi=0}^{\alpha} \int_{\rho=0}^{h/\cos\phi} \rho^{n+4} \sin^3 \phi \, d\rho \, d\phi \, d\theta.$$

The computation of these iterated single integrals completes the solution. We have, in stages,

$$\int_{\rho=0}^{h/\cos\phi} \rho^{n+4} \sin^3 \phi \, d\rho = \frac{\sin^3 \phi}{n+5} \frac{h^{n+5}}{\cos^{n+5} \phi}$$

$$= \frac{h^{n+5}}{n+5} (\cos \phi)^{-n-5} \sin^2 \phi \sin \phi$$

$$= \frac{h^{n+5}}{n+5} [(\cos \phi)^{-n-5} - (\cos \phi)^{-n-3}] \sin \phi.$$

$$\int_{\phi=0}^{\alpha} \frac{h^{n+5}}{n+5} [(\cos \phi)^{-n-5} - (\cos \phi)^{-n-3}] \sin \phi \, d\phi$$

$$= \frac{h^{n+5}}{n+5}\left[\frac{(\sec \alpha)^{n+4} - 1}{n+4} - \frac{(\sec \alpha)^{n+2} - 1}{n+2} \right]$$

$$I_z = k \int_{\theta=0}^{2\pi} \frac{h^{n+5}}{n+5} \left[\frac{(\sec \alpha)^{n+4} - 1}{n+4} - \frac{(\sec \alpha)^{n+2} - 1}{n+2} \right] d\theta$$

$$= \frac{2\pi k h^{n+5}}{n+5} \left[\frac{(\sec \alpha)^{n+4} - 1}{n+4} - \frac{(\sec \alpha)^{n+2} - 1}{n+2} \right].$$

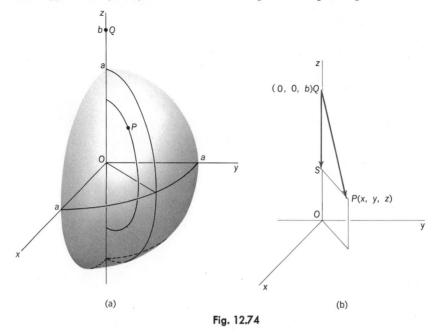

(a)   (b)

Fig. 12.74

Example 4. Consider a sphere of radius a which carries a uniformly distributed charge. Find the force of attraction on a unit charge Q of opposite type located at a distance b from the center of the sphere, $b > a$.

We place the origin of our coordinate system at the center of the sphere and choose the z axis so that it passes through Q; see Fig. 12.74(a), where part of the sphere is drawn. Consider a spherical coordinate element of volume at point P. Coulomb's Law says that $\overrightarrow{\Delta \mathbf{F}}$, the force of attraction on the unit charge Q due to the charge on this element of volume, has the direction of QP and magnitude directly proportional to the product of the charges but inversely proportional to the square of the distance QP. If the charge density, measured in units of charge per unit of volume, is denoted by μ, we can write

$$\text{charge on element} = \mu \, \Delta V,$$

$$\|\overrightarrow{\Delta \mathbf{F}}\| = \frac{c\mu}{x^2 + y^2 + (b - z)^2} \, \Delta V,$$

where c is a constant of proportionality; see Fig. 12.74(b). Because the sphere is symmetric with respect to the xz and yz planes, as is $\|\overrightarrow{\Delta \mathbf{F}}\|$, we need only consider the $-\mathbf{k}$ component of $\overrightarrow{\Delta \mathbf{F}}$, $(\Delta F)_z$; the $\mathbf{i}$ and $\mathbf{j}$ components will cancel out when we sum up over the elements. But

$$(\Delta F)_z = \|\overrightarrow{\Delta \mathbf{F}}\| \cos SQP = \|\overrightarrow{\Delta \mathbf{F}}\| \frac{QS}{QP} = \|\overrightarrow{\Delta \mathbf{F}}\| \frac{b - z}{\sqrt{x^2 + y^2 + (b - z)^2}}$$

$$= \frac{c\mu(b - z)}{[x^2 + y^2 + (b - z)^2]^{3/2}} \, \Delta V = \frac{c\mu(b - \rho \cos \phi)}{[\rho^2 - 2b\rho \cos \phi + b^2]^{3/2}} \, \Delta V.$$

Hence, for the force of attraction of the whole sphere, we write

$$\|\mathbf{F}\| = \int\int\int_{\text{sphere}} \frac{c\mu(b - \rho \cos \phi)}{[\rho^2 - 2b\rho \cos \phi + b^2]^{3/2}} \, dV.$$

As Fig. 12.74(a) indicates, the sphere will be swept out if we (a) form a semicircle by moving a point in the ϕ direction, holding ρ and θ fixed, from the upper half of the z axis ($\phi = 0$) to the lower half ($\phi = \pi$); (b) form a plane section by moving the semicircle from the position $\rho = 0$ to $\rho = a$; and (c), rotate this section in the θ direction from $\theta = 0$ to $\theta = 2\pi$. Accordingly,

$$\|\mathbf{F}\| = \int_{\theta=0}^{2\pi}\int_{\rho=0}^{a}\int_{\phi=0}^{\pi} \frac{c\mu\rho^2(b - \rho \cos \phi) \sin \phi}{[\rho^2 - 2b\rho \cos \phi + b^2]^{3/2}} \, d\phi \, d\rho \, d\theta.$$

The details of the computation we have to make are not as difficult as might at first be feared. For the first integration, with respect to ϕ, we use integration by parts. We choose $u = b - \rho \cos \phi$ and

$$\frac{dv}{d\phi} = \frac{\sin \phi}{[\rho^2 - 2b\rho \cos \phi + b^2]^{3/2}}$$

so that $du/d\phi = \rho \sin \phi$ and

$$v = -\frac{1}{b\rho} \frac{1}{[\rho^2 - 2b\rho \cos \phi + b^2]^{1/2}}.$$

We then find that

$$\int_{\phi=0}^{\pi} \frac{c\mu\rho^2(b - \rho \cos \phi) \sin \phi}{[\rho^2 - 2b\rho \cos \phi + b^2]^{3/2}} \, d\phi = \frac{2c\mu\rho^2}{b^2}.*$$

For the rest of the computation we have

$$\|\mathbf{F}\| = \int_{\theta=0}^{2\pi}\int_{\rho=0}^{a} \frac{2c\mu\rho^2}{b^2} \, d\rho \, d\theta = \int_{\theta=0}^{2\pi} \frac{2c\mu a^3}{3b^2} \, d\theta = \frac{c(4/3 \, \pi a^3)\mu}{b^2}.$$

This result says that the force of attraction is the force that would be expected according to Coulomb's Law if all the charge were considered concentrated at the center of the sphere.

EXERCISES 12.12

1. Find spherical coordinates for the points with Cartesian coordinates:

(a) $(4, 0, 0)$. (d) $(-1, 1, \sqrt{6})$. (g) $(0, 0, 2)$.
(b) $(0, -5, 0)$. (e) $(1, 1, -\sqrt{6})$. (h) $(0, 0, -2)$.
(c) $(1, 1, \sqrt{6})$. (f) $(1, -1, -\sqrt{6})$. (i) $(0, 0, 0)$.

2. Find Cartesian coordinates for the points with spherical coordinates:

(a) $(5, \pi/2, \pi/2)$. (d) $(4, 4\pi/3, \pi/3)$. (g) $(1, \pi/11, 0)$.
(b) $(2, \pi, \pi/2)$. (e) $(4, \pi/3, 2\pi/3)$. (h) $(1, \pi/11, \pi)$.
(c) $(4, \pi/3, \pi/3)$. (f) $(4, -\pi/3, 2\pi/3)$. (i) $(0, \pi/11, \pi/5)$.

*The student is asked to carry out the computation described here in Exercise 12.12-16. Remember that $[\rho^2 - 2b\rho + b^2]^{1/2} = b - \rho$ and *not* $\rho - b$, because $b - \rho > 0$.

3. Describe in spherical coordinates the surfaces with Cartesian descriptions:

(a) $x^2 + y^2 + z^2 = a^2$;

(b) $y = x, x \geq 0$;

(c) $y = -\sqrt{3}\, x, x \leq 0$;

(d) $x^2 + y^2 = z^2, z \geq 0$;

(e) $x^2 + y^2 = z^2, z \leq 0$;

(f) $Ax + By = 0$;

(g) $x^2 + y^2 = a^2 z^2, a > 0$.

4. Describe in Cartesian coordinates the surfaces with spherical coordinate descriptions:

(a) $\rho = b$;

(b) $\theta = \alpha, -\pi/2 < \alpha < \pi/2$;

(c) $\theta = \alpha, \pi/2 < \alpha < 3\pi/2$;

(d) $\theta = 3\pi/2$;

(e) $\phi = \alpha, 0 \leq \alpha < \pi/2$;

(f) $\phi = \alpha, \pi/2 < \alpha \leq \pi$;

(g) $\phi = \pi/2$.

5. Find the volume of the solid bounded by the sphere $x^2 + y^2 + z^2 = a^2$ ($\rho = a$) and the half-cones $x^2 + y^2 = (\tan \alpha)\, z^2, z \geq 0$, and $x^2 + y^2 = (\tan \beta)z^2, z \geq 0, 0 < \alpha < \beta < \pi/2, (\phi = \alpha$ and $\phi = \beta)$.

6. Find the volume of the solid bounded by the spheres $\rho = a$ and $\rho = b, b > a > 0$, and the cones $\phi = \alpha$ and $\phi = \beta, 0 < \alpha < \beta < \pi/2$.

In the next five exercises and in Exercise 14, the mass densities mentioned are measured in units of mass per unit of volume.

7. Let the solid described in Example 2 have mass density $\mu = ka^2/\rho^2$. Find its mass.

8. A solid bounded by the sphere $\rho = a$ has mass density $\mu = 1 - k\rho/a, k$ a constant < 1. Find its mass.

9. The smaller solid bounded by the sphere $x^2 + y^2 + z^2 = a^2$ and the plane $z = b$, $0 < b < a$, has mass density

$$\mu = k \frac{a}{\sqrt{x^2 + y^2 + z^2}}, \qquad k \text{ a constant.}$$

Find its mass.

10. The solid bounded by the cone $\phi = \alpha, 0 < \alpha < \pi/2$, and the plane $z = \rho \cos \phi = h$, $h > 0$, has mass density $\mu = (k/a^n)\, \rho^n, k$ and a positive constants, $n \geq 0$. Find its mass. Check your answer for the case $n = 0$ by common sense.

11. Let the solid of Exercise 5 have mass density $\mu = \kappa\, \dfrac{a^2}{a^2 + \rho^2}, \kappa$ a constant. Find its mass.

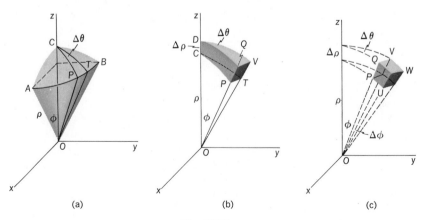

(a)   (b)   (c)

Fig. 12.75

12. Find the volume of the smaller solid bounded by two concentric spheres with radii a and b and a plane that passes a distance c from their center, $0 < c < b < a$. *Suggestion:* Describe the spheres by equations $\rho = a$ and $\rho = b$ and the plane by the equation $z = c$.

13. Find the volume of the smaller solid bounded by the upper branch of the cone $x^2 + y^2 = z^2$, the plane $z = 4$, and the plane $2x = z$.

14. A spherical shell bounded by the spheres $\rho = a$ and $\rho = b$, $b > a > 0$, has mass density $\mu = kb^2/\rho^2$. Find its moment of inertia about a diameter. *Suggestion:* Choose the z axis to be that diameter.

15. Find the moment of inertia about the z axis of the solid of Exercise 9.

16. Carry out the details of the computation of the triple integral of Example 4.

17. Here we guide the reader through a proof of Formula (3),

$$\Delta V \approx \rho^2 \sin \phi \; \Delta\rho \; \Delta\theta \; \Delta\phi.$$

Step (a). Show that the volume bounded by a sphere of radius ρ and a cone of vertex angle ϕ, with vertex at the center of the sphere, is

$$V_1 = \tfrac{2}{3} \pi\rho^3(1 - \cos \phi).$$

(One quarter of this solid is shown in Fig. 12.75(a). To the volume of the conical portion OAB, add the volume of the spherical cap ABC, obtained perhaps by single integration.)

Step (b). Show that the volume $OCPT$ is

$$V_2 = \tfrac{1}{3} \rho^3(1 - \cos \phi) \; \Delta\theta.$$

Step (c). Show that the volume $PTCDQV$ of Fig. 12.75 (b) is

$$V_3 = \tfrac{1}{3} [(\rho + \Delta\rho)^3 - \rho^3](1 - \cos \phi) \; \Delta\theta.$$

Step (d). Show that the volume $PQVWU$ of Fig. 12.75 (c) is

$$\Delta V = \tfrac{1}{3} [(\rho + \Delta\rho)^3 - \rho^3][\cos \phi - \cos (\phi + \Delta\phi)] \; \Delta\theta.$$

Step (e). Use the Theorem of Mean Value to show that there exist ρ^* and ϕ^{**}, $\rho < \rho^* < \rho + \Delta\rho$, $\phi < \phi^{**} < \phi + \Delta\phi$ such that

$$\Delta V = \rho^{*2}\sin \phi^{**} \; \Delta\rho \; \Delta\theta \; \Delta\phi.$$

Infinite Series

13.1   Introduction

I

We meet infinite series in many ways. When we write the fraction ⅓ in decimal form, for instance, ⅓ = .3333 $\cdots$, we are really writing an infinite series

$$\tfrac{1}{3} = .3 + .03 + .003 + .0003 + \cdots.$$

The conclusion of the Binomial Theorem can be written

$$(1 + x)^n = 1 + \frac{n}{1} x^1 + \frac{n(n-1)}{1(2)} x^2 + \frac{n(n-1)(n-2)}{(1)(2)(3)} x^3 + \cdots$$

$$+ \frac{n(n-1)(n-2)\cdots(n-k+1)}{(1)(2)(3)\cdots(k)} x^k + \cdots, \tag{1}$$

as will be shown later in this chapter. Thus we have

$$(1 + x)^4 = 1 + \frac{4}{1} x^1 + \frac{4(3)}{1(2)} x^2 + \frac{4(3)(2)}{1(2)(3)} x^3 + \frac{4(3)(2)(1)}{1(2)(3)(4)} x^4$$

$$+ \frac{(4)(3)(2)(1)(0)}{(1)(2)(3)(4)(5)} x^5 + \cdots$$

$$= 1 + 4x + 6x^2 + 4x^3 + 1x^4;$$

in this case, the coefficients of x^5, x^6, and, in general, x^k for $k \geq 5$ are all 0. Formula (1) is first demonstrated under the hypothesis that n is a positive integer. But let us apply (1) to the case $n = \frac{1}{3}$, just for the sake of curiosity. We write

$$(1 + x)^{1/3} \sim 1 + \frac{\frac{1}{3}}{1} x + \frac{(\frac{1}{3})(-\frac{2}{3})}{1(2)} x^2 + \frac{(\frac{1}{3})(-\frac{2}{3})(-\frac{5}{3})}{1(2)(3)} x^3$$

$$+ \frac{(\frac{1}{3})(-\frac{2}{3})(-\frac{5}{3})(-\frac{8}{3})}{1(2)(3)(4)} x^4 + \cdots *$$

$$(1 + x)^{1/3} \sim 1 + \left(\frac{x}{3}\right) - \frac{2}{2}\left(\frac{x}{3}\right)^2 + \frac{(2)(5)}{(2)(3)}\left(\frac{x}{3}\right)^3 - \frac{(2)(5)(8)}{(2)(3)(4)}\left(\frac{x}{3}\right)^4 + - \cdots.$$

$$(2)$$

We have here an infinite series, for the coefficient of no power of x will vanish.

It would be natural to inquire about the relationship between the series written in Formula (2) and the function $\sqrt[3]{1 + x}$. For instance, can we use the series to compute $\sqrt[3]{1.1}$? We know that $1 + x$ is 1.1 when $x = .1$; can we set $x = .1$ in the series and write

$$\sqrt[3]{1.1} = 1 + \frac{.1}{3} - \frac{2}{2}\frac{(.1)^2}{3^2} + \frac{(2)(5)}{(2)(3)}\frac{(.1)^3}{3^3} - + \cdots$$

$$= 1 + .033333 - .001111 + .000062 - + \cdots?$$

The first three terms suggest the estimate 1.032222 for $\sqrt[3]{1.1}$ and the first four terms suggest the estimate 1.032284; a six-place table gives the value 1.032280. We shall show in Sec. 13.8 below that we can achieve any accuracy desired by taking enough terms of the series.

That Series (2) does not always lead us to the proper values, however, becomes apparent if we take $x = 3$ and compare the series with $\sqrt[3]{1 + 3} = \sqrt[3]{4}$. The series reads, for $x = 3$,

$$1 + \frac{3}{3} - \frac{2}{2}\left(\frac{3}{3}\right)^2 + \frac{2(5)}{2(3)}\left(\frac{3}{3}\right)^3 - \frac{2(5)(8)}{2(3)(4)}\left(\frac{3}{3}\right)^4 + \cdots$$

or $$1 + 1 + \left[-\frac{2}{2} + \frac{2\cdot5}{2\cdot3}\right] + \left[-\frac{2\cdot5\cdot8}{2\cdot3\cdot4} + \frac{2\cdot5\cdot8\cdot11}{2\cdot3\cdot4\cdot5}\right] + \cdots. \qquad (3)$$

The first two terms lead us to the estimate 2, which we know to be too large. Succeeding pairs of terms only increase the estimate, for in each succeeding pair of terms the positive term is obtained from the absolute value of the negative term by multiplying by a number greater than one, thus making the positive term the larger in size. Indeed, it can be shown that the estimates furnished by the series grow beyond all bounds when we consider successive pairs of terms.

Infinite series also arise when we study differential equations. Consider, for instance,

$$\frac{dy}{dx} = y. \qquad (4)$$

This differential equation asks for a function whose derivative is equal to itself, and we know that such a function is e^x. But let us pretend that we do not know a

---

* For the symbol "$\sim$" read "is associated with."

solution and try to guess one. A simple first step might well be "Try a polynomial." Not knowing which degree to choose for the polynomial attempt, we would be a little vague and try to find constants a_0, a_1, a_2, a_3, a_4, $\cdots$ such that

$$y = a_0 + a_1x + a_2x^2 + a_3x^3 + a_4x^4 + \cdots \tag{5}$$

is a solution of Eq. (4). Working formally, we have

$$\frac{dy}{dx} = a_1 + 2a_2x + 3a_3x^2 + 4a_4x^3 + \cdots,$$

and when we substitute in Eq. (4), we get

$$a_1 + 2a_2x + 3a_3x^2 + 4a_4x^3 + 5a_5x^4 + \cdots$$
$$= a_0 + a_1x + a_2x^2 + a_3x^3 + a_4x^4 + \cdots,$$

or

$$(a_1 - a_0) + (2a_2 - a_1)x + (3a_3 - a_2)x^2 + (4a_4 - a_3)x^3 + (5a_5 - a_4)x^4 + \cdots = 0. \tag{6}$$

Equation (6) will be satisfied if we choose the a's in such a way that all the coefficients of that equation vanish. To satisfy $a_1 - a_0 = 0$, $2a_2 - a_1 = 0$, $3a_3 - a_2 = 0$, $4a_4 - a_3 = 0$, $5a_5 - a_4 = 0, \cdots$, we choose

$$
\begin{aligned}
a_1 &= a_0 \\
a_2 &= \frac{1}{2}a_1 = \frac{1}{2}a_0, \\
a_3 &= \frac{1}{3}a_2 = \frac{a_0}{2\cdot3}, \\
a_4 &= \frac{1}{4}a_3 = \frac{a_0}{2\cdot3\cdot4}, \\
a_5 &= \frac{1}{5}a_4 = \frac{a_0}{2\cdot3\cdot4\cdot5},
\end{aligned}
\tag{7}
$$

$$\cdot \quad \cdot \quad \cdot \quad \cdot \quad \cdot \quad \cdot \quad \cdot$$

Let us adopt the following convention.

■ NOTATION CONVENTION 1

When n is a positive integer we shall write $1\cdot2\cdot3\cdot4\cdot5 \cdots n = n!$. For $0!$ we shall take the number 1.*

Then we can summarize Eqs. (7) by writing,

$$a_n = \frac{a_0}{n!}, \quad n = 1, 2, 3, \cdots.$$

---

* The definition $0! = 1$ seems reasonable if we note that $5! = 5(4!)$, $6! = 6(5!)$, and that, in general, $n! = n[(n-1)!]$, $n \geq 2$. If we want to define $0!$ in such a way that this relationship will hold for $n = 1$ also, we must choose $0!$ so that $1! = 1 [0!]$, or $0! = 1$.

Our work suggests that to get a solution of Eq. (4), we can rewrite Eq. (5):

$$y = a_0 + a_0 x + \frac{1}{2!} a_0 x^2 + \frac{1}{3!} a_0 x^3 + \frac{1}{4!} a_0 x^4 + \frac{1}{5!} a_0 x^5 + \cdots$$

$$= a_0 \left(1 + x + \frac{x^2}{2!} + \frac{x^3}{3!} + \frac{x^4}{4!} + \frac{x^5}{5!} + \cdots \right).$$

We knew in advance that $y = (\text{const})e^x$ would be a solution of Eq. (4), and it is natural now to ask whether there is a relationship between e^x and the infinite series

$$1 + x + \frac{x^2}{2!} + \frac{x^3}{3!} + \frac{x^4}{4!} + \frac{x^5}{5!} + \cdots.$$

It turns out that there is a relationship. For all values of x we can compute e^x from the series, and, indeed, this is how the tables for e^x are computed.

In solving other differential equations, we are led to other series, some representing functions we already know, some representing new functions. Thus the differential equation

$$x \frac{d^2 y}{dx^2} + \frac{dy}{dx} + xy = 0$$

comes up in so many problems of mathematical physics that it is given a name; it is the Bessel Equation of order zero. One of its solutions is the infinite series

$$1 - \frac{1}{(1!)^2} \left(\frac{x}{2} \right)^2 + \frac{1}{(2!)^2} \left(\frac{x}{2} \right)^4 - \frac{1}{(3!)^2} \left(\frac{x}{2} \right)^6 + \frac{1}{(4!)^2} \left(\frac{x}{2} \right)^8 - + \cdots.$$

For every value of x this series specifies a computation that can be carried out, and thus defines a function of x for all x. This function of x was not previously known; it is now called the Bessel Function of order 0 and referred to by the symbols $J_0(x)$.

In this chapter we shall address ourselves primarily to three central questions. First, if an infinite series is presented to us, how can we tell whether the computations it calls for can be carried out? Second, given a function $f(x)$ in which we are interested, is there some standard procedure we can use to find an infinite series that will represent the function? Third, when and how can the operations of arithmetic (addition, subtraction, multiplication, division) and the operations of calculus (differentiation, integration) be performed on functions defined by infinite series?

||

In our work with series we must reason frequently with infinite sequences of numbers. We state here definitions for limits of sequences of numbers consistent with the definitions of limit given in Chapter 7, and then we state a theorem which enables us to declare that certain sequences of fairly frequent occurrence have finite limits.

■ DEFINITION 1

The limit of a sequence of numbers. The sequence of numbers u_1, u_2, $u_3, \cdots$ has limit L, written $\lim_{k \to \infty} u_k = L$, if for every positive challenge number ϵ, no matter how small, there exists an integer N such that $|u_k - L| < \epsilon$ for all $k > N$.

In different words, a sequence is said to approach the limit L if for every challenge number, no matter how small, there is a sequence member with the property that all following sequence members differ from L by less than the challenge number. Definition 1 is a precise way of saying that the members of the sequence come as close to the number L as desired and then remain as close to L as desired if one considers sequence members of high enough index.

Example 1.   Let $|r| < 1$. Show that the sequence r, r^2, $r^3, \cdots$, r^k, $\cdots$ approaches 0, or, in different words, that $\lim_{k \to \infty} r^k = 0$.

It is necessary to show that for every positive challenge number ϵ, no matter how small, there is an integer N such that $|r^k - 0| < \epsilon$ for all integers $k > N$. To find such a number N we try to rewrite the inequality $|r|^k < \epsilon$ in such a way that we shall have more direct information about k. If we are to have $|r|^k < \epsilon$ it would suffice to have $\log |r|^k < \log \epsilon$ or

$$k \log |r| < \log \epsilon.$$

Because $|r| < 1$ and $\log |r|$ is negative, we find when we divide by $\log |r|$ and reverse the sense of the inequality that it would suffice to have

$$k > \frac{\log \epsilon}{\log |r|}.$$

If we choose $N = \log \epsilon / \log |r|$, we shall find that $|r^k| < \epsilon$ for $k > N$.

■ DEFINITION 2

The sequence of numbers u_1, u_2, $u_3, \cdots$ is said to grow and remain beyond all bounds, and we write $\lim_{k \to \infty} u_k = \infty$, if whenever a positive number M is specified, no matter how large, there exists an integer N such that $u_k > M$ for all $k > N$.

In words, the sequence is said to grow and remain beyond all bounds if for every bound number M, no matter how large, there is a sequence member with the property that all following sequence members exceed M.

Example 2.   Let $r > 1$. Show that the sequence r, r^2, $r^3, \cdots$, r^k, $\cdots$ grows and remains beyond all bounds, or, in different words, that $\lim_{k \to \infty} r^k = \infty$.

It is necessary to show that for every positive number M, no matter how large, there is an integer N such that $r^k > M$ for all $k > N$. If we are to have $r^k > M$ it will suffice to choose k such that

$$\log r^k > \log M$$

$$k \log r > \log M$$

$$k > \frac{\log M}{\log r};$$

remember that $r > 1$, so that $\log r$ is positive and the sense of the inequality is preserved when we divide by $\log r$. If we choose $N = \log M/\log r$, we shall find $r^k > M$ for $k > N$.

■ DEFINITION 3

Monotonic sequences. The sequence $u_1,\ u_2,\ u_3, \cdots$ is monotonically increasing if $u_k \geq u_{k-1}$ for $k = 2,\ 3,\ 4, \cdots$, and is monotonically decreasing if $u_k \leq u_{k-1}$ for $k = 2,\ 3,\ 4, \cdots$.

In different words, a sequence is monotonically increasing if each member of the sequence is at least as large as the preceding member and monotonically decreasing if each member is never larger than the preceding member.

Example 3. The sequence $r,\ r^2,\ r^3, \cdots,\ r^k, \cdots$ is monotonically decreasing if $0 < r < 1$. Indeed, we have $u_k = r^k = rr^{k-1} < 1 \ r^{k-1} = u_{k-1}$ for $k = 2, 3, 4 \cdots$; each member of the sequence is less than the preceding one. However, the sequence $u_k = (-1)^k$ or $-1,\ 1,\ -1,\ 1,\ \cdots,\ (-1)^k,\ \cdots$ is not monotonic, because each sequence member 1 is greater than the preceding member but each sequence member -1 is less than the preceding member.

■ THEOREM 1

On bounded monotonic sequences.

Hypothesis: (a) $u_{k+1} \geq u_k$ for $k = 1, 2, 3, \cdots$.
(b) There is a number B such that $u_k \leq B$ for $k = 1, 2, 3, \cdots$.

Conclusion: The number $U = \lim_{k \to \infty} u_k$ exists and $U \leq B$.

In words, a monotonically increasing sequence that is bounded from above approaches a limit, and this limit is not greater than the bound. Similarly, a monotonically decreasing sequence that is bounded from below approaches a limit, and this limit is not smaller than the bound.

Plausibility Argument: We must show that there is a number U such that for every positive challenge number ϵ, no matter how small, we shall have u_k within ϵ of U for all suitably large k.

We know that the number B is an upper bound for the numbers u_k by Hypothesis (b). Any number larger than B is again an upper bound, and perhaps there are numbers less than B that are also larger than all the u_k's. Let the number U be the *least* upper bound for the u_k's.

This least upper bound U is the limit approached by the sequence. For, first we have

$$u_k \leq U \qquad \text{for all } k$$

because U is an upper bound. Second, let a positive challenge number ϵ be presented, no matter how small. There will be an integer N such that

$$U - \epsilon < u_N;$$

otherwise $U - \epsilon$, which is less than U, would be an upper bound and U would not be the *least* upper bound. Since the u_k's never decrease, we have

$$U - \epsilon < u_k \leq U \qquad \text{for all } k > N.$$

But this says that the u_k's are within ϵ of U for suitably large k. Our conclusion is achieved.[*]

Example 4. Let $0 < r < 1$. The sequence $r, r^2, r^3, \cdots, r^k, \cdots$ is monotonically decreasing, as we pointed out in Example 2. This sequence is also bounded from below, for we have $r^k > 0$ for every k. Theorem 1 then predicts that this sequence has a limit. We saw in Example 1 that the limit was the number 0.

Example 5. We used Theorem 1 in Exercise 5.3-9 where we showed that the number e, the base we use for natural logarithms, could be defined as the limit of a sequence of numbers. We considered the sequence $u_n = [1 + (1/n)]^n$, or

$$\left(1 + \frac{1}{1}\right)^1, \left(1 + \frac{1}{2}\right)^2, \left(1 + \frac{1}{3}\right)^3, \cdots, \left(1 + \frac{1}{n}\right)^n, \cdots.$$

We showed first that $u_{n+1} > u_n$ for $n = 1, 2, 3, \cdots$, or that the sequence is monotonically increasing, and second that $u_n < 3$ for $n = 1, 2, 3, \cdots$, or that the sequence is bounded from above. Then we quoted the present Theorem 1 to claim that the sequence had a limit number which was not greater than 3.

Example 6. The sequence $u_k = k$, or $1, 2, 3, \cdots, k, \cdots$, is monotonically increasing but not bounded. There is no limit number for this sequence, as we shall prove by contradiction. If there were a limit number L for the sequence, the sequence members would have to come as close to L as desired. Then, since two numbers within ϵ of L are within 2ϵ of each other, we could claim that after a certain member of the sequence has been reached all succeeding members would have to be as close to each other as desired. But successive members of this sequence do not come as close to each other as desired, so that we have a contradiction. This example shows that Hypothesis (a) of Theorem 1, taken alone, is not sufficient to enable one to draw the conclusion of that theorem.

Example 7. The sequence $u_k = (-1)^k$, or $-1, 1, -1, 1, \cdots, (-1)^k, \cdots$ is bounded from above, for $u_k \leq 1$ for all k, but the sequence is not monotonic, as we pointed out in Example 2. There is no limit number for this sequence either, as we can show by an argument very similar to the one used in Example 6. As in that example, successive members of this sequence do not come close to each other. This example shows that Hypothesis (b) of Theorem 1, taken alone, is not sufficient to enable one to draw the conclusion of that theorem.

Example 8. Consider the sequence

$$u_k = \frac{1}{k}(-1)^k, \qquad \text{or} \qquad -1, \frac{1}{2}, -\frac{1}{3}, \frac{1}{4}, -\frac{1}{5}, \cdots, \frac{1}{k}(-1)^k, \cdots.$$

This sequence is not monotonic, because each positive sequence member is greater than the preceding member while each negative sequence member is less than the

---

[*] We have here a plausibility argument and not a proof because we *assumed* that a least upper bound number for the u_k's would exist. It is not obvious that every set of numbers that has an upper bound has a *least* upper bound.

preceding member. But this sequence does have the limit 0 nevertheless. For, if any positive ϵ is specified, no matter how small, we can choose $N > 1/\epsilon$, thus $1/N < \epsilon$, and then say that whenever $k > N$ we have

$$|u_k - 0| = \left|\frac{1}{k}(-1)^k\right| = \frac{1}{k} < \frac{1}{N} < \epsilon.$$

This example shows that the converse of Theorem 1 is not true. The bounded monotonic sequences are not the only sequences that have limits.

13.2 The Definition of Convergence

Consider the series

$$\tfrac{1}{2} + \tfrac{1}{4} + \tfrac{1}{8} + \tfrac{1}{16} + \tfrac{1}{32} + \cdots = \sum_{k=1}^{\infty}(\tfrac{1}{2})^k. \tag{1}$$

The first term is $\tfrac{1}{2}$. Let us give the name S_2 to the sum of the first two terms; $S_2 = \tfrac{1}{2} + \tfrac{1}{4} = \tfrac{3}{4} = 1 - \tfrac{1}{4}$. For the first three terms we have $S_3 = \tfrac{1}{2} + \tfrac{1}{4} + \tfrac{1}{8} = \tfrac{7}{8} = 1 - \tfrac{1}{8}$, and, in general, for the sum of the first n terms we have

$$S_n = \sum_{k=1}^{n}\left(\frac{1}{2}\right)^k = \frac{1}{2} + \frac{1}{4} + \frac{1}{8} + \cdots + \frac{1}{2^n} = 1 - \frac{1}{2^n}.^*$$

Since 2^n grows beyond all bounds as n increases, these partial sums approach 1 as we go farther and farther out in the series, and it seems reasonable to say that the value 1 should be assigned to the Series (1). For the convergence of series in general we have the following definition.

■ **DEFINITION 1**

The convergence of a series. Given an infinite series of numbers,

$$u_1 + u_2 + u_3 + \cdots = \sum_{k=1}^{\infty} u_k. \tag{2}$$

Form the sequence of partial sum numbers $S_1 = u_1$, $S_2 = u_1 + u_2$, and, in general,

$$S_n = \sum_{k=1}^{n} u_k = u_1 + u_2 + u_3 + \cdots + u_n \qquad \text{for } n = 1, 2, 3, \cdots.$$

If $S = \lim_{n \to \infty} S_n$ exists, we say that the series converges to the finite number S. If $\lim_{n \to \infty} S_n$ does not exist, we say that the series diverges.

Example 1. For the arithmetic series

$$\sum_{k=1}^{\infty} u_k = \sum_{k=1}^{\infty} k = 1 + 2 + 3 + \cdots$$

we have

$$S_1 = 1, \qquad S_2 = 1 + 2 = 3, \qquad S_3 = 1 + 2 + 3 = 6, \qquad \cdots,$$

$$S_n = 1 + 2 + 3 + \cdots + n = \frac{n(n+1)}{2};$$

see the footnote to Example 2.4-1B, where this formula for an arithmetic progression is derived. It is clear that $\lim_{n \to \infty} S_n = \infty$, and that this series diverges.

---

* The formula for the sum of n terms in geometric progression will be derived as part of the proof of Theorem 13.2-1.

■ THEOREM 1

The convergence of a geometric series.

HYPOTHESIS: $u_k = ar^{k-1}$.

CONCLUSION: (a) $\sum_{k=1}^{\infty} u_k = a + ar + ar^2 + ar^3 + \cdots$ converges to $a/(1 - r)$ if $|r| < 1$,

(b) $\sum_{k=1}^{\infty} u_k$ diverges if $|r| \geq 1$.

PROOF: *Step(1).*   For this series we can write $S_1 = a$, $S_2 = a(1 + r)$, and, in general,

$$S_n = a(1 + r + r^2 + \cdots + r^{n-1}).$$

If $r \neq 1$, we can multiply by r and subtract to get

$$rS_n = a\,(r + r^2 + r^3 + \cdots + r^n)$$

$$(1 - r)\,S_n = a\,(1 - r^n)$$

$$S_n = a\,\frac{1 - r^n}{1 - r}.$$

Step (2): For $|r| < 1$ we saw in Example 13.1-1 that $\lim_{n \to \infty} r^n = 0$. Hence, in this case,

$$S = \lim_{n \to \infty} S_n = \frac{a}{1 - r},$$

as Conclusion (a) states.

Step (3): If $|r| > 1$, then $\lim_{n \to \infty} |r|^n$ does not exist, as we showed in Example 13.1-2, and neither does $\lim_{n \to \infty} S_n$. In this case the series diverges.

Step (4): If $r = +1$, the series reads

$$a + a + a + a + a + \cdots$$

so that $S_n = na$ and $\lim_{n \to \infty} S_n$ does not exist in this case either.

Step (5): Finally, if $r = -1$, the series reads

$$a - a + a - a + a - a + - \cdots,$$

and the partial sums are $S_1 = a$, $S_2 = a - a = 0$, $S_3 = S_2 + a = a$, $S_4 = S_3 - a = 0$, and so on. These partial sums alternate between a and 0 and do not approach a limit. Since $\lim_{n \to \infty} S_n$ does not exist, the series diverges. This concludes the proof.

■ THEOREM 2

The divergence of the harmonic series.

HYPOTHESIS: $u_k = 1/k$.

CONCLUSION: $\sum_{k=1}^{\infty} u_k = 1 + \frac{1}{2} + \frac{1}{3} + \frac{1}{4} + \cdots$ diverges.

PROOF: For this series we can write

$$S_1 = 1, \qquad S_2 = 1 + \tfrac{1}{2},$$

$$S_4 = 1 + \tfrac{1}{2} + \tfrac{1}{3} + \tfrac{1}{4} > 1 + \tfrac{1}{2} + (\tfrac{1}{4} + \tfrac{1}{4}) = 1 + \tfrac{1}{2} + \tfrac{1}{2},$$

$$S_8 = 1 + \tfrac{1}{2} + \tfrac{1}{3} + \tfrac{1}{4} + \tfrac{1}{5} + \tfrac{1}{6} + \tfrac{1}{7} + \tfrac{1}{8} > 1 + \tfrac{1}{2} + (\tfrac{1}{4} + \tfrac{1}{4})$$

$$+ (\tfrac{1}{8} + \tfrac{1}{8} + \tfrac{1}{8} + \tfrac{1}{8})$$

$$S_8 > 1 + \tfrac{1}{2} + \tfrac{1}{2} + \tfrac{1}{2},$$

and, in general, when writing S_{2^i}, after grouping the last 2^{i-1} terms, each one of value $\geq 1/2^i$,

we have $$S_{2^i} > 1 + i(\tfrac{1}{2}).$$

No matter how large a number M is specified, we can always choose i so large that

$$S_{2^i} > 1 + \frac{i}{2} > M.$$

All succeeding partial sums will be still larger, and thus $\lim_{n \to \infty} S_n = \infty$. The harmonic series diverges.

EXERCISES 13.2

1. For each of the following series compute S_1, S_2, S_3, S_4; describe S_n; and find $S = \lim_{n \to \infty} S_n$ if it exists.

(a) $\displaystyle\sum_{k=1}^{\infty} (\tfrac{1}{3})^k = \tfrac{1}{3} + \tfrac{1}{9} + \tfrac{1}{27} + \tfrac{1}{81} + \cdots.$

(b) $\displaystyle\sum_{k=1}^{\infty} 3(-\tfrac{1}{2})^{k-1} = 3 - \tfrac{3}{2} + \tfrac{3}{4} - \tfrac{3}{8} + - \cdots.$

(c) $\displaystyle\sum_{k=1}^{\infty} .01k = .01 + .02 + .03 + .04 + \cdots.$

(d) $\displaystyle\sum_{k=1}^{\infty} (a + [k-1]d) = a + (a+d) + (a+2d) + (a+3d) + \cdots.$

(e) $\displaystyle\sum_{k=1}^{\infty} \frac{1}{k(k+1)} = \frac{1}{2} + \frac{1}{6} + \frac{1}{12} + \frac{1}{20} + \cdots.$

Suggestion: Observe that

$$\frac{1}{k(k+1)} = \frac{1}{k} - \frac{1}{k+1}.$$

(f) $\displaystyle\sum_{k=1}^{\infty} \frac{1}{\sqrt{k+1}+\sqrt{k}} = \frac{1}{\sqrt{2}+\sqrt{1}} + \frac{1}{\sqrt{3}+\sqrt{2}} + \frac{1}{\sqrt{4}+\sqrt{3}} + \cdots.$

Suggestion: Rewrite $\dfrac{1}{\sqrt{k+1}+\sqrt{k}}$ by rationalizing the denominator.

(g) $\displaystyle\sum_{k=1}^{\infty} (-1)^{k+1}\left[1 + \frac{(-1)^{k+1}}{2^k}\right] = \left(1 + \frac{1}{2}\right) - \left(1 - \frac{1}{4}\right) + \left(1 + \frac{1}{8}\right) - \left(1 - \frac{1}{16}\right)$
$$+ - \cdots.$$

(h) $\displaystyle\sin .1 + \sum_{k=1}^{\infty} 2\cos(.1[2k])(\sin .1)$

$\qquad = \sin .1 + 2(\cos .2)(\sin .1) + 2(\cos .4)(\sin .1) + 2(\cos .6)(\sin .1) + \cdots.$
$\qquad$ *Suggestion:* Use the identity $2 \cos \alpha \sin \beta = \sin(\alpha + \beta) - \sin(\alpha - \beta)$.

2. Which rational number does each of the following repeating decimals represent?

(a) $.33\overset{..}{33}3 = .3 + .03 + .003 + .0003 + .00003 + \cdots.$

(b) $.212121\overset{..}{21} = .21 + .0021 + .000021 + .00000021 + \cdots.$

(c) $.10135\overset{...}{1351}\overset{.}{3}5.$

3. (a) Show that every repeating decimal represents a rational number.

(b) Show that every rational number is represented by a repeating decimal.

$\qquad$ (Analyze the division algorithm. Point out that at any step in the conversion of the proper fraction c/b to decimal form, the remainder must be one of the b numbers $0, 1, 2, \cdots, b - 1$. Therefore in $b + 1$ steps at most a remainder must be repeated.)

13.3 Some General Theorems on Convergence. Convergence by Comparison

We frequently find that a number of terms at the beginning of a series cannot be described by the same formula as the remaining terms of the series, or that they do not have some other property that all the remaining terms have. For instance, it is only from the $k = 4$ term on, in the series

$$\sum_{k=1}^{\infty} \frac{k^2}{2^k} = \frac{1}{2} + \frac{4}{4} + \frac{9}{8} + \frac{16}{16} + \frac{25}{32} + \frac{36}{64} + \cdots,$$

that each term is less than the preceding term.* In such cases we often use a theorem which tells us that a finite number of terms at the beginning of a series may be disregarded if we are interested merely in deciding whether that series converges or diverges. Of course, all the terms of a convergent series must be taken into account when we are looking for the number S to which the series converges.

■ **THEOREM 1**

$\qquad$ HYPOTHESIS: $\displaystyle\sum_{k=i}^{\infty} u_k$ converges (diverges).

$\qquad$ CONCLUSION: $\displaystyle\sum_{k=1}^{\infty} u_k$ converges (diverges).

$\qquad$ PROOF: The series

$$\sum_{k=1}^{\infty} u_k = u_1 + u_2 + u_3 + \cdots$$

---

* Observe that $k^2/2^k < (k-1)^2/2^{k-1}$ only if $k^2 < 2(k-1)^2, k < \sqrt{2}(k-1), \sqrt{2} < (\sqrt{2}-1)k,$ $k > \sqrt{2}/(\sqrt{2}-1) \approx 3.4.$

has for partial sums the numbers $S_1 = u_1$, $S_2 = u_1 + u_2$, and in general,

$$S_n = u_1 + u_2 + \cdots + u_n.$$

The series

$$\sum_{k=i}^{\infty} u_k = u_i + u_{i+1} + u_{i+2} + u_{i+3} + \cdots$$

has for partial sums the numbers $T_1 = u_i$, $T_2 = u_i + u_{i+1}$, and in general,

$$T_n = u_i + u_{i+1} + \cdots + u_{i+n-1}.$$

If we write

$$\alpha = u_1 + u_2 + \cdots + u_{i-1},$$

we have

$$S_i = (u_1 + u_2 + \cdots + u_{i-1}) + u_i = \alpha + T_1,$$
$$S_{i+1} = (u_1 + u_2 + \cdots + u_{i-1}) + (u_i + u_{i+1}) = \alpha + T_2,$$

and in general,

$$S_{i+n-1} = \alpha + T_n, \qquad n = 1, 2, 3, \cdots. \qquad (1)$$

In words, there is a pairing of S's and T's in which each S is α more than the corresponding T.

If the series $\Sigma_{k=i}^{\infty} u_k$ converges, the T_n's approach a limit T; for any positive ϵ specified, no matter how small, the T_n's will, from a certain point on, all be within ϵ of T. But then Eq. (1) says that the S_n's will, from a certain point on, all be within ϵ of $\alpha + T$ and the series $\Sigma_{k=1}^{\infty} u_k$ will converge also. On the other hand, if $\Sigma_{k=i}^{\infty} u_k$ diverges, then the T_n's approach no finite limit. Equation (1) says that the S_n's cannot approach a finite limit either in this case, for, if the S_n's did approach a finite limit, say S, the T_n's would have to approach $S - \alpha$, thus forcing us to a contradiction. When $\Sigma_{k=i}^{\infty} u_k$ diverges, so does $\Sigma_{k=1}^{\infty} u_k$.

Example 1. A rubber ball is dropped vertically from a height of 6 ft. Each time it bounces it rises to a height $\frac{2}{3}$ of the height from which it fell. How far does the ball travel?

When first dropped, the ball travels 6 ft; then it rises 4 ft and falls 4 ft; then it rises and falls $\frac{8}{3}$ ft, and so on. We can write

$$d = 6 + 2(4) + 2(\tfrac{8}{3}) + 2(\tfrac{16}{9}) + 2(\tfrac{32}{27}) + \cdots$$
$$= 6 + 8 + \tfrac{16}{3} + \tfrac{32}{9} + \tfrac{64}{27} + \cdots. \qquad (2)$$

If we neglect the first term, we have a geometric series with ratio $\frac{2}{3}$, which is known to converge. Hence Series (2) converges. Theorem 13.2-1 on geometric series says that

$$d = 6 + \frac{8}{1 - \frac{2}{3}} = 30.$$

■ **THEOREM 2**

HYPOTHESIS: (a) $\Sigma_{k=1}^{\infty} u_k$ $\begin{cases} \text{converges to } S, \\ \text{diverges.} \end{cases}$

(b) $c \neq 0$.

CONCLUSION: $\Sigma_{k=1}^{\infty} cu_k$ $\begin{cases} \text{converges to } cS, \\ \text{diverges.} \end{cases}$

PROOF: If $S_n = u_1 + u_2 + \cdots + u_n$ is a partial sum of $\Sigma_{k=1}^{\infty} u_k$, the corresponding partial sum of $\Sigma_{k=1}^{\infty} cu_k$ is

$$T_n = cu_1 + cu_2 + \cdots + cu_n = c(u_1 + u_2 + \cdots + u_n) = cS_n.$$

If the S_n's approach S, the T_n's approach cS. If the S_n's do not approach a limit, neither do the T_n's.

Example 2.   Each term of the infinite series

$$\frac{1}{2} + \frac{1}{4} + \frac{1}{6} + \frac{1}{8} + \frac{1}{10} + \cdots + \frac{1}{2n} + \cdots \tag{3}$$

is half of the corresponding term of the harmonic series

$$\frac{1}{1} + \frac{1}{2} + \frac{1}{3} + \frac{1}{4} + \cdots + \frac{1}{n} + \cdots,$$

which is known to diverge. Series (3) therefore diverges also.

■ **THEOREM 3**

A test for divergence.

HYPOTHESIS: $\lim_{k \to \infty} u_k$ does not exist or $\lim_{k \to \infty} u_k$ does exist but is not 0.

CONCLUSION: $\Sigma_{k=1}^{\infty} u_k$ diverges.

PROOF: We shall give a proof by contradiction. We know that

$$u_k = (u_1 + u_2 + \cdots + u_{k-1} + u_k) - (u_1 + u_2 + \cdots + u_{k-1}) = S_k - S_{k-1}.$$

If $\Sigma_{k=1}^{\infty} u_k$ converges, its partial sums approach a limit S. But when the partial sums can be made to differ from S by as little as desired for large enough k, they can be made to differ from each other by as little as desired for large enough k. Hence u_k, a difference of successive partial sums, would have to approach 0, contrary to hypothesis. We must conclude that $\Sigma_{k=1}^{\infty} u_k$ does not converge.

Example 3.   We can tell almost at a glance that the series

$$\sum_{k=1}^{\infty} \frac{k}{2k+1} = \frac{1}{3} + \frac{2}{5} + \frac{3}{7} + \frac{4}{9} + \cdots$$

diverges because its terms approach $\frac{1}{2}$; observe that

$$\lim_{k \to \infty} \frac{k}{2k+1} = \lim_{k \to \infty} \frac{1}{2 + 1/k} = \frac{1}{2} \neq 0.$$

● **Remark 1**

Theorem 3 states a conclusion based on the hypothesis that $\lim_{k\to\infty} u_k$ does not exist or that $\lim_{k\to\infty} u_k$ does exist but is not 0. The theorem says nothing if $\lim_{k\to\infty} u_k = 0$; the series may then be convergent or divergent. For a geometric series with $|r| < 1$ we have $\lim_{k\to\infty} u_k = 0$ and a convergent series; for the harmonic series we have $\lim_{k\to\infty} u_k = 0$ and a divergent series.

The key idea on which almost all our practical tests for convergence or divergence rest is the idea of convergence by comparison.

■ **THEOREM 4A**

Convergence by comparison

HYPOTHESIS: (a) $\Sigma_{k=1}^{\infty} v_k$ converges,
(b) For each k, $0 < u_k \le v_k$.

CONCLUSION: $\Sigma_{k=1}^{\infty} u_k$ converges.

In words, if a Series I of positive terms is term by term less than or equal to a Series II that converges, then Series I converges also.

PROOF: Since the terms of the series $\Sigma_{k=1}^{\infty} v_k$ are all positive, and since for the partial sums $T_n = v_1 + v_2 + \cdots + v_n$ we can say that $T_n = T_{n-1} + v_n$, we know that these partial sums are all positive and that each partial sum is greater than the preceding one. Moreover, the partial sums approach a limit T because $\Sigma_{k=1}^{\infty} v_k$ converges, so that we can say that $0 < T_{n-1} < T_n < T$ for all n.

The series $\Sigma_{k=1}^{\infty} u_k$ also consists of positive terms, and for the partial sums $S_n = u_1 + u_2 + \cdots + u_n$ we can also say that each partial sum is positive and greater than the preceding one. Moreover, because of Hypothesis (b), $S_n \le T_n$ for all n. Hence for the sequence of partial sum numbers S_n we have

$$0 < S_{n-1} < S_n \le T_n < T \qquad \text{for all } n;$$

the S_n's are positive, increase steadily, and are bounded above by the number T. By Theorem 13.1-1, the S_n's approach a finite limit, which does not exceed T, and $\Sigma_{k=1}^{\infty} u_k$ converges.

■ **THEOREM 4B**

Divergence by comparison.

HYPOTHESIS: (a) $v_k > 0$ and $\Sigma_{k=1}^{\infty} v_k$ diverges,
(b) $u_k \ge v_k$ for each k.

CONCLUSION: $\Sigma_{k=1}^{\infty} u_k$ diverges.

In words, if a Series I is term by term at least as large as a Series II of positive terms that diverges, then Series I diverges also.

PROOF: Here is a proof by contradiction. Assume that $\Sigma_{k=1}^{\infty} u_k$ converges. Then the series $\Sigma_{k=1}^{\infty} v_k$ is a series of positive terms which is term by term less than, or equal to, the series $\Sigma_{k=1}^{\infty} u_k$. By Theorem 4A, the series $\Sigma_{k=1}^{\infty} v_k$ must then converge. But this is a contradiction of Hypothesis (a), so that we must agree that $\Sigma_{k=1}^{\infty} u_k$ diverges.

Example 4.   The series

$$\sum_{k=1}^{\infty} \frac{1}{\sqrt{k}} = \frac{1}{\sqrt{1}} + \frac{1}{\sqrt{2}} + \frac{1}{\sqrt{3}} + \frac{1}{\sqrt{4}} + \cdots$$

diverges because it is term by term larger than the harmonic series, $\Sigma_{k=1}^{\infty} (1/k)$, already known to diverge. Indeed, for all $k \geq 1$ we have

$$\sqrt{k} \leq k, \qquad \frac{1}{\sqrt{k}} \geq \frac{1}{k}.$$

Example 5

$$\text{Series I} \equiv \sum_{k=1}^{\infty} \frac{1}{2k-1} = \frac{1}{1} + \frac{1}{3} + \frac{1}{5} + \frac{1}{7} + \frac{1}{9} + \cdots$$

contains many of the terms of the harmonic series and hence we suspect that it diverges. When we compare it with the harmonic series, however, we do not find that Series I is term by term greater than the harmonic series. In fact, the opposite is true. We then compare Series I with

$$\text{Series II} \equiv \sum_{k=1}^{\infty} \frac{1}{2} \frac{1}{k}.$$

Series II is known to diverge, because its general term is a constant multiple of the general term of the harmonic series; see Example 2 above. When we compare the general terms of Series I and II we see that

$$2k - 1 < 2k \qquad \text{for all } k \geq 1,$$

$$\frac{1}{2k-1} > \frac{1}{2k} \qquad \text{for all } k \geq 1.$$

Hence Series I diverges.

Example 6.   The series

$$1 + \frac{1}{1!} + \frac{1}{2!} + \frac{1}{3!} + \frac{1}{4!} + \frac{1}{5!} + \cdots \doteq \sum_{k=0}^{\infty} \frac{1}{k!}$$

is important because, as we shall see later, it constitutes one of the possible definitions of the number e. We shall show that this series converges by comparing it with the geometric series of ratio $\frac{1}{2}$,

$$2 + 1 + \frac{1}{2} + \frac{1}{2^2} + \cdots = \sum_{k=0}^{\infty} \left(\frac{1}{2}\right)^{k-1},$$

which is known to converge. The term-by-term comparison is easy to make for the first few terms. For the fourth terms, for instance, we can say that

$$3! = (2)(3) > (2)(2) = 2^2, \qquad \frac{1}{3!} < \frac{1}{2^2}.$$

For the general term,

$$k! = (2)(3)(4)\cdots(k) \geq (2)(2)(2)\cdots(2) = (2)^{k-1} \qquad \text{for } k \geq 2,$$

so that

$$\frac{1}{k!} < \frac{1}{2^{k-1}} \qquad \text{for } k \geq 2,$$

and the term-by-term comparison is completed.

A series that is frequently useful for comparison purposes is the p_2 series.

■ THEOREM 5

The convergence of the p_2 series.

HYPOTHESIS: The p_2 series is the series

$$\sum_{k=1}^{\infty} \frac{1}{k^2} = \frac{1}{1^2} + \frac{1}{2^2} + \frac{1}{3^2} + \cdots.$$

CONCLUSION: The p_2 series converges.

PROOF: Since the terms of this series are positive, each partial sum is greater than the preceding one. Some of the partial sums are

$$S_1 = 1,$$

$$S_3 = 1 + \frac{1}{2^2} + \frac{1}{3^2} < 1 + \frac{1}{2^2} + \frac{1}{2^2} = 1 + 2\left(\frac{1}{2^2}\right) = 1 + \frac{1}{2},$$

$$S_7 = 1 + \frac{1}{2^2} + \frac{1}{3^2} + \frac{1}{4^2} + \frac{1}{5^2} + \frac{1}{6^2} + \frac{1}{7^2} < 1 + \frac{1}{2^2} + \frac{1}{2^2} + \frac{1}{4^2} + \frac{1}{4^2} + \frac{1}{4^2} + \frac{1}{4^2}$$

$$= 1 + 2\left(\frac{1}{2^2}\right) + 4\left(\frac{1}{4^2}\right) = 1 + \frac{1}{2} + \frac{1}{4}.$$

$S_{15} = S_{2^4-1}$ contains 8 terms not in $S_7 = S_{2^3-1}$; each one of these terms is less than, or equal to, $(1/8^2)$ and their sum is less than $8\,(1/8^2) = \frac{1}{8}$. Hence

$$S_{15} < 1 + \frac{1}{2} + \frac{1}{4} + \frac{1}{8}.$$

In general, we can show that

$$S_{2^n-1} < 1 + \frac{1}{2} + \frac{1}{4} + \cdots + \frac{1}{2^{n-1}}.$$

These particular partial sums are less than partial sums of a geometric series known to converge to the value 2 from below. Since any partial sum of the p_2 series will be less than one of the special partial sums S_{2^n-1} for a suitable choice of n, we know that all the partial sums of the p_2 series are less than 2. The partial sums increase steadily and are bounded from above. According to Theorem 13.1-1 they have a limit (which is less than 2).

EXERCISES 13.3

Test each of the following series for convergence or divergence. A suggested procedure is this: (1) Decide quickly, if possible, whether u_n approaches 0 as n grows beyond all bounds. Unless u_n approaches 0, the series diverges. (2) If u_n approaches 0, then venture a guess as to convergence or divergence and attempt a comparison with a known series. Remember that the convergence or divergence of a series is not changed if a finite number of terms at the beginning of the series is deleted, or if all the terms are multiplied by the same constant. A useful list of comparison series would include the geometric series, the harmonic series, and the p_2 series.

1. $\displaystyle\sum_{k=1}^{\infty} \frac{1}{60k} = \frac{1}{60} + \frac{1}{120} + \frac{1}{180} + \cdots.$

2. $\displaystyle\sum_{k=1}^{\infty} \frac{6}{k^2} = 6 + \frac{6}{2^2} + \frac{6}{3^2} + \cdots.$ 3. $\displaystyle\sum_{k=1}^{\infty} \frac{1}{5(k+2)}.$

4. $\displaystyle\sum_{k=1}^{\infty} \frac{1}{(k+3)^2} = \frac{1}{4^2} + \frac{1}{5^2} + \frac{1}{6^2} + \cdots.$

5. $\displaystyle\sum_{k=1}^{\infty} [.1 + (.1)^{k+1}] = .11 + .101 + .1001 + .10001 + \cdots.$

6. $\displaystyle\sum_{k=1}^{\infty} \frac{2 + (-1)^k}{k}.$

7. $\displaystyle\sum_{k=1}^{\infty} \frac{1}{2^k + 1} = \frac{1}{2 + 1} + \frac{1}{4 + 1} + \frac{1}{8 + 1} + \frac{1}{16 + 1} + \cdots.$

8. $\displaystyle\sum_{k=1}^{\infty} \frac{1}{k3^k} = \frac{1}{1(3)} + \frac{1}{2(3)^2} + \frac{1}{3(3)^3} + \cdots.$

9. $\displaystyle\sum_{k=1}^{\infty} \frac{\log k}{k}.$

10. $\displaystyle\sum_{k=1}^{\infty} \frac{1}{k^2 + x^2} = \frac{1}{1 + x^2} + \frac{1}{2^2 + x^2} + \frac{1}{3^2 + x^2} + \cdots.$

11. $\displaystyle\sum_{k=1}^{\infty} \frac{k+1}{10{,}000k} = \frac{2}{10{,}000} + \frac{3}{20{,}000} + \frac{4}{30{,}000} + \frac{5}{40{,}000} + \cdots.$

12. $\displaystyle\sum_{k=1}^{\infty} u_k, \; u_k = \begin{cases} 1 + (-1)^k & \text{for } k \le 235, \\ \left(\dfrac{9}{10}\right)^{k-236} & \text{for } k \ge 236. \end{cases}$

13. $\displaystyle\sum_{k=1}^{\infty} \frac{4}{k^2 + k} = \frac{4}{1^2 + 1} + \frac{4}{2^2 + 2} + \frac{4}{3^2 + 3} + \frac{4}{4^2 + 4} + \cdots.$

14. $\displaystyle\sum_{k=2}^{\infty} \frac{1}{k^2 - 1} = \frac{1}{2^2 - 1} + \frac{1}{3^2 - 1} + \frac{1}{4^2 - 1} + \cdots.$

15. $\displaystyle\sum_{k=1}^{\infty} \frac{1}{\sqrt{k^2 + 4}}.$

16. $\displaystyle\sum_{k=1}^{\infty} \frac{1}{[1 + (k-1)/k]^k} = \frac{1}{1^1} + \frac{1}{(1 + 1/2)^2} + \frac{1}{(1 + 2/3)^3} + \cdots$.

17. $\displaystyle\sum_{k=1}^{\infty} \frac{1}{(1 + 1/k)^k} = \frac{1}{2} + \frac{1}{(1 + 1/2)^2} + \frac{1}{(1 + 1/3)^3} + \frac{1}{(1 + 1/4)^4} + \cdots$.

18. $\displaystyle\sum_{k=1}^{\infty} \frac{(k+2)}{k(k+1)}$.

19. $\displaystyle\sum_{k=1}^{\infty} \frac{2 \cdot 4 \cdot 6 \cdots (2k)}{1 \cdot 3 \cdot 5 \cdots (2k-1)(2k+1)} = \frac{2}{1 \cdot 3} + \frac{2 \cdot 4}{1 \cdot 3 \cdot 5} + \frac{2 \cdot 4 \cdot 6}{1 \cdot 3 \cdot 5 \cdot 7} + \frac{2 \cdot 4 \cdot 6 \cdot 8}{1 \cdot 3 \cdot 5 \cdot 7 \cdot 9} + \cdots$.*

20. $\displaystyle\sum_{k=1}^{\infty} \left(\frac{1}{k^4}\right)^{\sin^2 k\pi/3}$.

21. Prove this theorem.

Theorem 6. A comparison test.

Hypothesis: (a) $u_k > 0$, $v_k > 0$ for $k = 1, 2, 3, \cdots$.

$\qquad$ (b) $\displaystyle\sum_{k=1}^{\infty} u_k \begin{cases} \text{converges} \\ \text{diverges.} \end{cases}$

$\qquad$ (c) $\displaystyle\lim_{k \to \infty} \frac{v_k}{u_k} = r, \qquad r > 0.$

Conclusion: $\displaystyle\sum_{k=1}^{\infty} v_k \begin{cases} \text{converges} \\ \text{diverges.} \end{cases}$

Suggestion for proof: Take the convergent case first.

$\qquad$ Step 1. Explain why $\Sigma_{k=1}^{\infty} (r+1) u_k$ converges.

$\qquad$ Step 2. Explain why $v_k < (r+1) u_k$ for large enough k.

$\qquad$ Step 3. Explain why $\Sigma_{k=1}^{\infty} v_k$ converges.

$\qquad$ Step 4. Give an argument by contradiction to demonstrate the theorem in the divergent case, using the convergent case conclusion already established.

22. Use Theorem 6 to test for convergence or divergence in
(a) Exercise 14.
(b) Exercise 15.

13.4 The Integral Test

Testing an infinite series for convergence or divergence by comparison requires a certain familiarity with a list of series useful for comparison purposes, and, frequently, considerable ingenuity in accomplishing the comparison. We proceed now to establish theorems that will enable us to predict the convergence or divergence of many series without having to derive formulas for the partial sums and without having to devise direct comparisons with other series.

The first of these tests for convergence is the *integral test*. This test compares the various terms of a series with certain contiguous areas under a graph and relates the question of the convergence of the series to the question of the existence of an improper integral.

---

* $2 \cdot 4 \cdot 6 \cdots (2k)$ means the product of 2, 4, 6, and each succeeding even number until you reach $2k$. $1 \cdot 3 \cdot 5 \cdots (2k-1)(2k+1)$ means the product of 1, 3, 5, and each suceeding odd number until you reach $2k + 1$.

■ THEOREM 1

The integral test.

HYPOTHESIS: (a) $u_k > 0$ for $k = 1, 2, 3, \cdots$,
(b) $f(x)$ is such that $f(k) = u_k$ for each k,
(c) $f(x)$ is continuous and monotonically decreasing for $x \geq 1$.

CONCLUSION: (a) $\Sigma_{k=1}^{\infty} u_k$ converges or diverges according as the improper integral $\int_1^{\infty} f(x)dx$ exists or does not exist.
(b) In the convergent case,

$$\int_{x=1}^{\infty} f(x)dx \leq \sum_{k=1}^{\infty} u_k \leq u_1 + \int_{x=1}^{\infty} f(x)\, dx.$$

PROOF: By Hypothesis (b) we know that $f(2) = u_2$, and that the rectangle of Fig. 13.1 with base $1 \leq x \leq 2$ therefore has base 1, height u_2, and area u_2. Similarly, the rectangle with base $2 \leq x \leq 3$ has area u_3 and the rectangle with base $k - 1 \leq x \leq k$ has area u_k. Because f never increases, according to Hypothesis (c), we know that

$$u_2 \leq \int_{x=1}^{2} f(x)\, dx,$$

$$u_2 + u_3 + u_4 + u_5 \leq \int_{x=1}^{5} f(x)\, dx,$$

and, in general, that

$$u_2 + u_3 + u_4 + \cdots + u_n \leq \int_{x=1}^{n} f(x)\, dx,$$

$$S_n = u_1 + (u_2 + u_3 + u_4 + \cdots + u_n) \leq u_1 + \int_{x=1}^{n} f(x)\, dx. \tag{1}$$

On the other hand, it is clear from Fig. 13.2 that

$$\int_{x=1}^{2} f(x)\, dx \leq u_1,$$

$$\int_{x=1}^{5} f(x)\, dx \leq u_1 + u_2 + u_3 + u_4,$$

and, in general, that

$$\int_{x=1}^{n+1} f(x)\, dx \leq u_1 + u_2 + u_3 + \cdots + u_n = S_n. \tag{2}$$

The integral $\int_1^b f(x)\, dx$ increases with b because $f(x) > 0$ for $x \geq 1$. If the improper integral

$$\int_1^{\infty} f(x)\, dx = \lim_{b \to \infty} \int_1^b f(x)\, dx$$

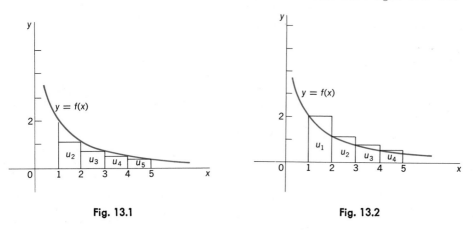

Fig. 13.1   Fig. 13.2

does not exist, it must be that the integrals $\int_1^b f(x)\, dx$ grow beyond all bounds as b grows beyond all bounds, and Inequality (2) would then say that the partial sums S_n grow beyond all bounds. In this case the series $\sum_{k=1}^{\infty} u_k$ must diverge.

On the other hand, if the improper integral $\int_1^{\infty} f(x)\, dx$ does exist and has the value A, then the integrals $\int_1^b f(x)\, dx$ are all less than A and Inequality (1) tells us that the partial sums S_n are all less than $u_1 + A$. With this and the fact that $u_k > 0$ for each k we see that the S_n's are a monotonically increasing sequence of numbers bounded from above. The limit of such a sequence exists, according to Theorem 13.1-1, and therefore the series $\sum_{k=1}^{\infty} u_k$ converges. Conclusion (a) is thus demonstrated.

If we combine Inequalities (1) and (2), we have

$$\int_{x=1}^{n+1} f(x)\, dx \le S_n \le u_1 + \int_{x=1}^{n} f(x)\, dx, \tag{3}$$

and, in the convergent case,

$$\int_1^{\infty} f(x)\, dx \le S = \lim_{n \to \infty} S_n \le u_1 + \int_{x=1}^{\infty} f(x)\, dx.$$

This concludes the proof of Theorem 1.

● **Remark 1**

We should always bear in mind the possibility of neglecting a finite number of terms at the beginning of the series; see Theorem 13.3-1. It may well happen, for instance, that $f(x)$ decreases steadily for $x \ge 3$ instead of for $x \ge 1$, as required in Hypothesis (c). In such a case we would not consider u_1 and u_2 in the comparison arguments of the proof. Conclusion (a) would still be valid, and instead of Conclusion (b) we could write

$$\int_{x=3}^{\infty} f(x)\, dx \le \sum_{k=3}^{\infty} u_k \le u_3 + \int_{x=3}^{\infty} f(x)\, dx.$$

Example 1.   Let us examine the p series,

$$\sum_{k=1}^{\infty} \frac{1}{k^p} = \frac{1}{1^p} + \frac{1}{2^p} + \frac{1}{3^p} + \frac{1}{4^p} + \cdots, \qquad p > 0.$$

The function $f(x) = 1/x^p$ is continuous and decreases steadily for $x \geq 1$, and is such that $f(k) = 1/k^p$, $k = 1, 2, 3, \cdots$. The hypotheses of the integral test are thus satisfied, and the conclusion then suggests that we consider the improper integral $\int_1^{\infty} f(x)\, dx$.

For $p > 1$ we note that

$$\int_1^{\infty} \frac{1}{x^p}\, dx = \lim_{b \to \infty} \int_1^b \frac{1}{x^p}\, dx = \lim_{b \to \infty} \int_1^b x^{-p}\, dx = \lim_{b \to \infty} \frac{x^{-p+1}}{-p+1} \Big|_{x=1}^{b}$$

$$= \frac{1}{1-p} \lim_{b \to \infty} \frac{1}{x^{p-1}} \Big|_1^b = \frac{1}{1-p} \lim_{b \to \infty} \left[\frac{1}{b^{p-1}} - 1 \right] = \frac{1}{p-1}.$$

The integral exists and the series converges.

For $p < 1$ we observe that

$$\int_1^{\infty} \frac{1}{x^p}\, dx = \lim_{b \to \infty} \frac{x^{-p+1}}{-p+1} \Big|_{x=1}^{b} = \frac{1}{1-p} \lim_{b \to \infty} x^{1-p} \Big|_1^b$$

$$= \frac{1}{1-p} \lim_{b \to \infty} [b^{1-p} - 1].$$

Since b^{1-p} grows beyond all bounds when b grows beyond all bounds, the improper integral does not exist, and the series diverges.

For $p = 1$, we consider

$$\int_1^{\infty} \frac{1}{x}\, dx = \lim_{b \to \infty} \int_1^b \frac{1}{x}\, dx = \lim_{b \to \infty} [\log b - \log 1] = \lim_{b \to \infty} \log b.$$

Since $\log b$ grows beyond all bounds when b grows beyond all bounds, the improper integral does not exist and the series diverges.

To summarize, the p series $\sum_{k=1}^{\infty} 1/k^p$, converges for $p > 1$ and diverges for $0 < p \leq 1$.

Example 2.   The integral test can be used not only to decide whether or not a series converges, but also to help estimate the value of a convergent series. We know, for example, that the p_2 series,

$$\sum_{k=1}^{\infty} \frac{1}{k^2} = \frac{1}{1^2} + \frac{1}{2^2} + \frac{1}{3^2} + \frac{1}{4^2} + \cdots,$$

converges. Conclusion (b) of Theorem 1 tells us more. It says that

$$\int_1^{\infty} \frac{1}{x^2}\, dx \leq \sum_{k=1}^{\infty} \frac{1}{k^2} \leq \frac{1}{1^2} + \int_1^{\infty} \frac{1}{x^2}\, dx.$$

Since

$$\int_1^{\infty} \frac{1}{x^2}\, dx = \lim_{b \to \infty} \int_1^b \frac{1}{x^2}\, dx = \lim_{b \to \infty} \left[-\frac{1}{x} \right]_1^b = 1,$$

we see that

$$1 \le \sum_{k=1}^{\infty} \frac{1}{k^2} \le 2.$$

Suppose that in attempting to get a more precise value for $\sum_{k=1}^{\infty} 1/k^2$ we had computed as far as

$$S_9 = \frac{1}{1^2} + \frac{1}{2^2} + \cdots + \frac{1}{9^2}.$$

A natural question would be: "How close to the value of $\sum_{k=1}^{\infty} 1/k^2$ would we be if we stopped here and neglected the terms

$$\sum_{k=10}^{\infty} \frac{1}{k^2} = \frac{1}{10^2} + \frac{1}{11^2} + \cdots ?"$$

Conclusion (b), modified as in Remark 1, says that

$$\int_{10}^{\infty} \frac{1}{x^2} \, dx \le \sum_{k=10}^{\infty} \frac{1}{k^2} \le u_{10} + \int_{10}^{\infty} \frac{1}{x^2} \, dx.$$

But

$$\int_{10}^{\infty} \frac{1}{x^2} \, dx = \lim_{b \to \infty} \int_{10}^{b} \frac{1}{x^2} \, dx = \lim_{b \to \infty} -\frac{1}{x} \Big|_{10}^{b} = \frac{1}{10} = .1$$

and

$$u_{10} = \frac{1}{10^2} = .01,$$

so that

$$.1 \le \sum_{k=10}^{\infty} \frac{1}{k^2} \le .01 + .1 = .11.$$

We have an estimate for the error we would make if we stopped, and can decide whether or not to compute more partial sums, according to the accuracy needed.

Example 3. The integral test shows that the series

$$\sum_{k=2}^{\infty} \frac{1}{k \log k} = \frac{1}{2 \log 2} + \frac{1}{3 \log 3} + \frac{1}{4 \log 4} + \cdots$$

diverges. To see this, consider

$$f(x) = \frac{1}{x \log x}.$$

For $x \ge 2, f$ is continuous and decreases steadily and

$$f(k) = \frac{1}{k \log k}.$$

Hence the hypotheses of the integral test are satisfied and the test may be applied. Since

$$\int_{2}^{\infty} \frac{1}{x \log x} \, dx = \lim_{b \to \infty} \int_{2}^{b} \frac{1}{\log x} \frac{1}{x} \, dx = \lim_{b \to \infty} \log (\log x) \Big|_{2}^{b}$$

$$= \lim_{b \to \infty} [\log (\log b) - \log (\log 2)],$$

and since log (log b) grows beyond all bounds when b grows beyond all bounds, the improper integral does not exist. The series diverges.

Example 4. The series

$$\sum_{k=1}^{\infty} \frac{k}{e^k} = \frac{1}{e} + \frac{2}{e^2} + \frac{3}{e^3} + \cdots$$

may be compared with the improper integral $\int_1^{\infty} (x/e^x)\ dx$ if the hypotheses of Theorem 1 are satisfied. The function $f(x) = x/e^x$ is continuous and $f(k) = k/e^k$, but it is not obvious that $f(x)$ decreases steadily for $x \geq 1$, because both denominator and numerator of $f(x)$ increase as x does. However, we compute

$$f'(x) = \frac{e^x - xe^x}{e^{2x}} = \frac{1 - x}{e^x},$$

and observe that $f'(x) < 0$ for $x > 1$; f decreases steadily for $x \geq 1$.

For the improper integral $\int_1^{\infty} (x/e^x)dx$ we have

$$\int_1^{\infty} \frac{x}{e^x}\ dx = \lim_{b \to \infty} \int_1^b xe^{-x}\ dx = \lim_{b \to \infty} -e^{-x}(x + 1)]_1^b$$

$$= \lim_{b \to \infty} \left[\frac{2}{e} - \frac{b+1}{e^b} \right] = \frac{2}{e}$$

Here we used integration by parts, and, at the very end, the fact that

$$\lim_{b \to \infty} \frac{b}{e^b} = 0.$$

See Theorem 5.6-2.* Hence the improper integral and the series converge together.

EXERCISES 13.4

1. Decide whether each of the following series converges by using the integral test. In many cases a comparison argument will also be instructive and may be shorter.

(a) $\displaystyle\sum_{k=2}^{\infty} \frac{1}{k \log^2 k}$.

(b) $\displaystyle\sum_{k=2}^{\infty} \frac{1}{k\sqrt{\log k}} = \frac{1}{2\sqrt{\log 2}} + \frac{1}{3\sqrt{\log 3}} + \frac{1}{4\sqrt{\log 4}} + \cdots$.

(c) $\displaystyle\sum_{k=1}^{\infty} \frac{1}{k^2 + 1}$.

(d) $\displaystyle\sum_{k=2}^{\infty} \frac{1}{k^2 - k} = \frac{1}{2} + \frac{1}{6} + \frac{1}{12} + \frac{1}{20} + \cdots$.

---

* We showed above that $f(x) = x/e^x$ decreases steadily for $x \geq 1$, but it does not follow from this that $\lim_{b \to \infty} b/e^b = 0$. For any number a that might be named one can easily exhibit a function $g(x)$ which decreases steadily for $x \geq 1$ and is such that $\lim_{x \to \infty} g(x) = a$. In Sec. 13.6 we shall give a second demonstration of the convergence of this series which does not depend on Theorem 5.6-2. Indeed we shall demonstrate Theorem 5.6-2 a second time as a corollary of that demonstration. See Example 13.6-1 and Exercise 13.6-2.

(e) $\displaystyle\sum_{k=1}^{\infty} \frac{1}{(2k+1)(k+1)}.$

(h) $\displaystyle\sum_{k=1}^{\infty} \frac{1}{e^k}.$

(f) $\displaystyle\sum_{k=2}^{\infty} \frac{1}{\sqrt{k^2-1}}.$

(i) $\displaystyle\sum_{k=1}^{\infty} \frac{4}{(e^k+e^{-k})^2} = \sum_{k=1}^{\infty} \frac{1}{\cosh^2 k}.$

(g) $\displaystyle\sum_{k=1}^{\infty} \frac{1}{\sqrt{k^2+1}}.$

(j) $\displaystyle\sum_{k=1}^{\infty} \frac{k^2}{e^k}.$

2. For the series of Exercise 1(c) show that

(a) $\displaystyle\frac{\pi}{4} \le \sum_{k=1}^{\infty} \frac{1}{k^2+1} \le \frac{1}{2} + \frac{\pi}{4};$

(b) $\displaystyle\frac{\pi}{2} - \tan^{-1} 7 \le \sum_{k=7}^{\infty} \frac{1}{k^2+1} \le \frac{1}{50} + \frac{\pi}{2} - \tan^{-1} 7.$

3. For the series of Exercise 1(d) show that

(a) $\displaystyle\log 2 \le \sum_{k=2}^{\infty} \frac{1}{k^2-k} \le \frac{1}{2} + \log 2;$

(b) $\displaystyle\log 11 - \log 10 \le \sum_{k=11}^{\infty} \frac{1}{k^2-k} \le \frac{1}{110} + \log 11 - \log 10.$

4. For the series of Exercise 1(h) show that

$$\frac{1}{e} \le \sum_{k=1}^{\infty} \frac{1}{e^k} \le \frac{2}{e}$$

by using the integral test. This series is also a geometric series. Find its sum as a geometric series and thus check the integral test estimate.

5. *Euler's constant.* We know that the harmonic series $\sum_{k=1}^{\infty} 1/k$ diverges because its partial sums,

$$S_n = 1 + \frac{1}{2} + \cdots + \frac{1}{n},$$

grow beyond all bounds.[*] Formula (3) tells us a little more; the S_n's grow large very much as $\int_1^n (1/x)\, dx = \log n$ does. It therefore seems reasonable to consider the sequence of numbers

$$C_n = 1 + \frac{1}{2} + \cdots \frac{1}{n} - \log n.$$

We have $C_1 = 1 - \log 1 = 1$, $C_2 = 1 + \frac{1}{2} - \log 2 \approx .81$, $C_3 = 1 + \frac{1}{2} + \frac{1}{3} - \log 3 \approx .735$, and so on.

(a) Show that the C_n's are all positive.

(b) Show that $C_{n+1} < C_n$ for all n.

Hint: If you have to estimate the size of $\log (n+1) - \log n$, you can say that

$$\log (n+1) - \log n = \int_n^{n+1} \frac{1}{t}\, dt.$$

This shows that the C_n's are a steadily decreasing sequence bounded from below. Therefore $\lim_{n \to \infty} C_n$ exists. This limit is called Euler's constant; to three decimal places its value is .577.

---

[*] See Example 1 and Theorem 13.2-2.

13.5 Alternating Series. Absolute Convergence

I

There is a theorem that helps us to predict the convergence of certain series whose terms alternate in sign. The following is such a series.

$$\sum_{k=1}^{\infty} (-1)^{k+1} \frac{1}{k} = \frac{1}{1} - \frac{1}{2} + \frac{1}{3} - \frac{1}{4} + \frac{1}{5} - \frac{1}{6} + \cdots. \tag{1}$$

We know that the harmonic series,

$$\sum_{k=1}^{\infty} \frac{1}{k} = \frac{1}{1} + \frac{1}{2} + \frac{1}{3} + \cdots,$$

diverges because its partial sums grow beyond all bounds. But the partial sums for Series (1) will be less than the partial sums for the harmonic series, because of the alternation in sign; for instance, for the third partial sums we have $1 - \frac{1}{2} + \frac{1}{3} = \frac{5}{6}$ and $1 + \frac{1}{2} + \frac{1}{3} = \frac{11}{6}$. It is therefore possible for Series (1) to converge, even though the harmonic series diverges.

■ THEOREM 1

The alternating series test.

HYPOTHESIS: For the series

$$\sum_{k=1}^{\infty} (-1)^{k+1} a_k = a_1 - a_2 + a_3 - a_4 + - \cdots.$$

we have
   (a) $0 < a_{k+1} \le a_k$ for $k = 1, 2, 3, \cdots$,
   (b) $\lim_{k \to \infty} a_k = 0$.

CONCLUSION: The series converges to a number S, and $0 \le S \le a_1$.*

In words, if the terms of an alternating series decrease in absolute value, approaching 0, the series converges. Further, the sum of the series is less than the first term in absolute value.

PROOF: Consider the partial sums

$$S_2 = a_1 - a_2 \qquad \text{and} \qquad S_4 = a_1 - a_2 + a_3 - a_4 = S_2 + (a_3 - a_4).$$

Because $a_2 \le a_1$ by hypothesis, $S_2 \ge 0$. Then because $a_4 \le a_3$, $a_3 - a_4$ is not negative, and $S_4 \ge S_2 \ge 0$. Similarly,

$$S_{2n+2} = S_{2n} + (a_{2n+1} - a_{2n+2}) \qquad \text{and} \qquad S_{2n+2} \ge S_{2n} \ge 0;$$

the even-numbered partial sums are a monotonically increasing sequence of numbers.

---

* One can state conditions under which $0 < S < a_1$. See Exercise 13.5-21, which can be extended directly by writing $S_0 = 0$.

On the other hand, $S_2 = a_1 - a_2 < a_1$, because $a_2 > 0$. Next,

$$S_4 = a_1 - a_2 + a_3 - a_4 = a_1 - [(a_2 - a_3) + a_4].$$

Here $[(a_2 - a_3) + a_4]$ is positive, because $a_2 \geq a_3$ and $a_4 > 0$; hence $S_4 < a_1$. For S_6 we can write

$$S_6 = a_1 - a_2 + a_3 - a_4 + a_5 - a_6 = a_1 - [(a_2 - a_3) + (a_4 - a_5) + a_6],$$

so that $S_6 < a_1$ also. By similar reasoning we can show that

$$S_{2n} < a_1 \qquad \text{for all } n.$$

The even-numbered partial sums are now seen to be a monotonically increasing sequence of numbers bounded above by a_1 and below by 0. They must approach a limit S, and for this limit S we can write $0 \leq S \leq a_1$.

But what of the odd-numbered partial sums $S_1, S_3, S_5, \cdots, S_{2n+1}, \cdots$? They approach the same limit S, because from the statement

$$S_{2n+1} - S_{2n} = (a_1 - a_2 + a_3 - a_4 + - \cdots - a_{2n} + a_{2n+1})$$

$$- (a_1 - a_2 + a_3 - a_4 + - \cdots - a_{2n}) = a_{2n+1}$$

and from Hypothesis (b), which says that the a_k's approach 0, we see that the difference between consecutive odd-numbered and even-numbered partial sums approaches 0. This concludes the proof of Theorem 1.

Example 1. Series (1) converges. For a_k and a_{k+1} we have $1/k$ and $1/(k+1)$, respectively, and it is clear that

$$0 < \frac{1}{k+1} < \frac{1}{k} \qquad \text{for all } k,$$

and that

$$\lim_{k \to \infty} \frac{1}{k} = 0.$$

The hypotheses of the alternating series test are satisfied.

Example 2. Consider the series

$$\sum_{k=1}^{\infty} (-.1)^{k-1} = 1 - .1 + .01 - .001 + .0001 - .00001 + - \cdots.$$

This series is a geometric series with first term 1 and common ratio $-.1$. We know therefore that it converges to the number

$$S = \frac{a}{1 - r} = \frac{1}{1 + .1} = \frac{10}{11},$$

but to illustrate the proof of Theorem 1, let us write out some of its partial sums. We have

$$S_1 = 1, \qquad\qquad S_2 = 1 - .1 = .9,$$
$$S_3 = S_2 + .01 = .91, \qquad S_4 = S_3 - .001 = .909,$$
$$S_5 = S_4 + .0001 = .9091. \qquad S_6 = S_5 - .00001 = .90909.$$

The even-numbered partial sums approach $S = {}^{10}\!/_{11}$ steadily from below; the odd-numbered partial sums approach S steadily from above.

● **Remark 1**

To take into account series for which we wish to leave aside a finite number of terms at the beginning of the series, Theorem 1 can be restated as follows: If from a fixed term onward the terms of a series alternate in sign and decrease steadily in absolute value, approaching 0, the series converges.

Example 3. After the third term, the terms of the series

$$\sum_{k=1}^{\infty} (-1)^k \frac{1}{2k-5} = \frac{1}{3} - 1 - 1 + \frac{1}{3} - \frac{1}{5} + \frac{1}{7} - \frac{1}{9} + \cdots$$

alternate regularly, decrease in absolute value, and approach 0. The series converges.

● **Remark 2**

In summing a convergent series in general, the question of where to stop in the process of taking partial sums usually arises. If we stop with the nth partial sum, we neglect infinitely many terms, starting with the $(n+1)$st. If we have a certain accuracy in mind for the computation, will it do to neglect all those terms?

For an alternating series whose terms decrease steadily in absolute value, approaching 0, we can deal with this question. The neglected terms themselves constitute an alternating series to which the conclusion of Theorem 1 applies. *The absolute value of the sum of the neglected terms will be less than, or equal to, the absolute value of the first of these neglected terms.*

Example 4. The alternating series

$$\sum_{k=1}^{\infty} (-1)^{k+1} \frac{1}{k(10)^k} = \frac{1}{10} - \frac{1}{2(10)^2} + \frac{1}{3(10)^3} - \frac{1}{4(10)^4} + \frac{1}{5(10)^5} - + \cdots$$

converges because the absolute values of its terms decrease, approaching 0. We shall show later* that this series converges to log 1.1. If we want to compute an estimate for log 1.1 from this series, with an error less than .000005, how many terms of this series should we take?

Remark 2 tells us that the error we make by neglecting the jth and all subsequent terms will be at most equal to the absolute value of that jth term. We must find j such that

$$\frac{1}{j(10)^j} < .000005.$$

Numerical experiments soon tell us that $1/[4(10)]^4 = .000025$ but that $1/[5(10)]^5 = .000002$. If we neglect the term $1/[5(10)]^5$ and all subsequent terms, our estimate will be in error by at most .000002. Hence we estimate

$$\log 1.1 \approx \frac{1}{10} - \frac{1}{2(10)^2} + \frac{1}{3(10)^3} - \frac{1}{4(10)^4}$$

$$\approx .1 - .005 + .000333 - .000025 \approx .09531.$$

---

* Exercise 13.8-3.

● **Remark 3**

The Hypotheses (a) and (b) of the alternating series test, Theorem 1, are independent of each other. There are sequences of positive numbers that decrease steadily but approach some finite number other than 0. Such a sequence is $1, .91,$ $.901, .9001, \cdots$; Hypothesis (a) is satisfied, but not Hypothesis (b). On the other hand, there are sequences of positive numbers that approach 0, but not steadily. Such a sequence is $2, \frac{1}{2}, \frac{2}{3}, \frac{1}{4}, \frac{2}{5}, \frac{1}{6}, \cdots$, which is formed according to the instructions $b_k = 2/k$ if k is odd and $b_k = 1/k$ if k is even.

Observe also that these hypotheses are *sufficient* conditions that an alternating series converge, but not *necessary* conditions. If these conditions are not satisfied, the alternating series may diverge or converge. In Exercise 13.5-20 the reader can work with two alternating series whose terms approach 0 in absolute value, but not steadily, and show that one of these series converges while the other diverges.

‖

For some applications, certain alternating series are more useful than others. We distinguish between absolutely and conditionally convergent series.

■ **DEFINITION 1**

Absolute convergence. A series is said to be absolutely convergent if the series of its absolute values converges; that is, $\sum_{k=1}^{\infty} u_k$ converges absolutely if $\sum_{k=1}^{\infty} |u_k|$ converges.

■ **DEFINITION 2**

Conditional convergence. A convergent series is said to be conditionally convergent if the series of its absolute values diverges; that is, $\sum_{k=1}^{\infty} u_k$ converges only conditionally if $\sum_{k=1}^{\infty} u_k$ converges but $\sum_{k=1}^{\infty} |u_k|$ diverges.

Example 5. The series

$$\sum_{k=1}^{\infty} (-.1)^{k-1} = 1 - .1 + .01 - .001 + .0001 - .00001 + - \cdots$$

of Example 2 is not only convergent, but absolutely convergent, for the series of absolute values,

$$\sum_{k=1}^{\infty} (.1)^{k-1} = 1 + .1 + .01 + .001 + .0001 + \cdots,$$

is a geometric series of positive terms with common ratio less than 1, and such a series converges.

Example 6. Series (1), $\sum_{k=1}^{\infty} (-1)^{k+1} (1/k)$, is only conditionally convergent, because, although the series itself converges, the series of absolute values is $\sum_{k=1}^{\infty} 1/k$, the harmonic series, which diverges.

The description "absolutely convergent" carries with it the connotation of convergence. But we cannot agree that a series is convergent just because its description implies that it is. The words "absolutely convergent" would be misleading unless the following theorem were true.

■ **THEOREM 2**

HYPOTHESIS: $\sum_{k=1}^{\infty} |u_k|$ converges.

CONCLUSION: $\sum_{k=1}^{\infty} u_k$ converges.

PROOF: Let us write down a new series, $\sum_{k=1}^{\infty} v_k$, whose terms are the positive terms of $\sum_{k=1}^{\infty} u_k$, and a second new series, $\sum_{k=1}^{\infty} w_k$, whose terms are the absolute values of the negative terms of $\sum_{k=1}^{\infty} u_k$; to be more precise,

$$v_k = \begin{cases} u_k & \text{if } u_k > 0, \\ 0 & \text{if } u_k \leq 0. \end{cases} \qquad w_k = \begin{cases} 0 & \text{if } u_k \geq 0, \\ -u_k & \text{if } u_k < 0. \end{cases}$$

To illustrate, if

$$\sum_{k=1}^{\infty} u_k = \sum_{k=1}^{\infty} (-.1)^{k-1} = 1 - .1 + .01 - .001 + .0001 - .00001 + - \cdots,$$

then

$$\sum_{k=1}^{\infty} v_k = 1 + 0 + .01 + 0 + .0001 + 0 + \cdots$$

and

$$\sum_{k=1}^{\infty} w_k = 0 + .1 + 0 + .001 + \cdots.$$

If we write S_n, T_n, V_n, and W_n for the partial sums of the respective series

$$\sum_{k=1}^{\infty} u_k, \sum_{k=1}^{\infty} |u_k|, \qquad \sum_{k=1}^{\infty} v_k, \qquad \text{and} \qquad \sum_{k=1}^{\infty} w_k,$$

we have

$$S_n = V_n - W_n, \tag{2}$$

$$T_n = V_n + W_n. \tag{3}$$

But the hypothesis says that $\sum |u_k|$ converges. Since $|u_k| \geq 0$ for every k, the partial sums increase steadily as they approach their limit, which limit we shall call T;

$$T_n \leq T \qquad \text{for all } n.$$

The series $\sum v_k$ and $\sum w_k$ also consist of nonnegative terms, and their partial sum sequences are monotonically increasing also. From Eq. (3) we see that

$$V_n \leq T_n \leq T, \qquad W_n \leq T_n \leq T,$$

so that the partial sum sequences $\{V_n\}$ and $\{W_n\}$ are not only monotonically increasing but bounded from above. These sequences must approach limits, which limits we shall call V and W. But then Eq. (2) says that the partial sums S_n approach the limit $V - W$. Our theorem is demonstrated.

● **Remark 4**

The key to our proof of Theorem 2 was the fact that the positive and negative terms of an absolutely convergent series form separate convergent series. But the positive and negative terms of a conditionally convergent series form divergent series when taken separately, as the reader can show in Exercises 13.5-18 and 13.5-19. This difference between absolutely and conditionally convergent series leads to another profound difference in their properties.

It is shown in more advanced courses that the terms of an absolutely convergent series can be rearranged in any order and that the new series will converge again to the very same value. But if the terms of a conditionally convergent series are rearranged, the new series may or may not converge, and, if it does converge, it may converge to a different value.

To illustrate, consider again the conditionally convergent series

$$1 - \tfrac{1}{2} + \tfrac{1}{3} - \tfrac{1}{4} + \tfrac{1}{5} - \tfrac{1}{6} + \tfrac{1}{7} - \tfrac{1}{8} + \tfrac{1}{9} - \tfrac{1}{10} + \tfrac{1}{11} - \tfrac{1}{12} + - \cdots = S.^* \tag{4}$$

If we take $\tfrac{1}{2}$ of each term, we get the new series

$$\tfrac{1}{2} - \tfrac{1}{4} + \tfrac{1}{6} - \tfrac{1}{8} + \tfrac{1}{10} - \tfrac{1}{12} + \tfrac{1}{14} - \cdots = \tfrac{1}{2}S.$$

If we insert some zero terms in this series, we form a new series whose partial sums still approach $\tfrac{1}{2}S$;

$$0 + \tfrac{1}{2} + 0 - \tfrac{1}{4} + 0 + \tfrac{1}{6} + 0 - \tfrac{1}{8} + 0 + \tfrac{1}{10} + 0 - \tfrac{1}{12} + \cdots = \tfrac{1}{2}S. \tag{5}$$

Now let us add the corresponding terms of Series (4) and (5), obtaining the new series

$$1 + 0 + \tfrac{1}{3} - \tfrac{1}{2} + \tfrac{1}{5} + 0 + \tfrac{1}{7} - \tfrac{1}{4} + \tfrac{1}{9} + 0 + \tfrac{1}{11} - \tfrac{1}{6} + \cdots = \tfrac{3}{2}S.$$

If we delete the zero terms, we have

$$1 + \tfrac{1}{3} - \tfrac{1}{2} + \tfrac{1}{5} + \tfrac{1}{7} - \tfrac{1}{4} + \tfrac{1}{9} + \tfrac{1}{11} - \tfrac{1}{6} + + - \cdots = \tfrac{3}{2}S. \tag{6}$$

Series (6) can be formed by taking the first two positive terms of Series (4), then the first negative term, the next two positive terms of (4), the next negative term, and so on. Every term of (4) appears once and only once in (6); every term of (6) appears once and only once in (4). The terms of one series are a rearrangement of the terms of the other, and yet they have different sums!

Because the terms of a conditionally convergent series cannot be rearranged, we find when we study applications that such series cannot be multiplied or divided with assurance. Absolutely convergent series can.

EXERCISES 13.5

1. The series $\sum_{k=1}^{\infty} (-\tfrac{1}{2})^{k-1} = 1 - \tfrac{1}{2} + \tfrac{1}{4} - \tfrac{1}{8} + - \cdots$ is a geometric series.
   (a) Find its sum S.
   (b) Compute its first 8 partial sums and comment on their relationship to S.

---

* We shall see later that $S = \log 2$.

In each of Exercises 2 through 17 explain whether the series diverges, converges conditionally, or converges absolutely. Also answer the additional questions, if any.

2. $\displaystyle\sum_{k=1}^{\infty} (-1)^{k-1} \frac{1}{\sqrt{k}}.$

3. $\displaystyle\sum_{k=1}^{\infty} (-1)^{k+1}[.1 + (.1)^{k+1}].$

4. $\displaystyle\sum_{k=1}^{\infty} (-1)^{k} \frac{1}{3k-10} = \frac{1}{7} - \frac{1}{4} + 1 + \frac{1}{2} - \frac{1}{5} + \frac{1}{8} - + \cdots.$

5. (a) $\displaystyle\sum_{k=2}^{\infty} (-1)^{k} \frac{\log k}{k}.$ (b) Find a bound for the sum of the terms neglected if the term for $k = 10$ and all subsequent terms are neglected. (c) About how many terms of the series must be summed if .001 is to be an upper bound for the sum of the neglected terms?

6. (a) $\displaystyle\sum_{k=1}^{\infty} (-1)^{k+1} \frac{1}{k^4}.$ (b) and (c) Repeat Exercise 5(b) and (c).

7. $\displaystyle\sum_{k=1}^{\infty} (-1)^{k+1} \frac{k+1}{10,000k}.$

8. $\displaystyle\sum_{k=2}^{\infty} (-1)^{k} \frac{k^2}{2(k^2-1)} = \frac{4}{6} - \frac{9}{16} + \frac{16}{30} - + \cdots.$

9. $\displaystyle\sum_{k=1}^{\infty} (-1)^{k+1} \frac{2k}{k^2+9}.$

10. $\displaystyle\sum_{k=1}^{\infty} (-1)^{k+1} \frac{k}{k^2+25}.$

11. $\displaystyle\sum_{k=1}^{\infty} (-1)^{k+1} \left(\frac{1}{k} + \sin^2 \frac{\pi}{2} k \right).$

12. (a) $\displaystyle\sum_{k=1}^{\infty} (-1)^{k+1} \frac{x^k}{k^2}, 0 \leq x \leq 1.$ (b) Let $x = 1$. Find a bound for the sum of the terms neglected if only the first four terms are summed. (c) Do the same for $x = .1$.

13. $\displaystyle\sum_{k=1}^{\infty} (-1)^{k+1} \frac{1}{k+t} = \frac{1}{1+t} - \frac{1}{2+t} + \frac{1}{3+t} - + \cdots, t > -1.$

14. $\displaystyle\sum_{k=1}^{\infty} (-1)^{k+1} \frac{x^{2k-1}}{2k-1} = x - \frac{x^3}{3} + \frac{x^5}{5} - \frac{x^7}{7} + - \cdots, -1 \leq x \leq 1.$

15. (a) $\displaystyle\sum_{k=0}^{\infty} (-1)^{k} \frac{x^{2k}}{(2k)!} = 1 - \frac{x^2}{2!} + \frac{x^4}{4!} - \frac{x^6}{6!} + - \cdots, |x| \leq 1.$ (b) We shall show later that this series represents $\cos x$. What is a bound for the sum of the terms neglected if we take only $1 - (x^2/2!)$ when $x = 1$? (c) when $x = .1$? (d) What is the estimate for $\cos .1$?

16. (a) $\displaystyle\sum_{k=0}^{\infty} (-1)^{k} \frac{x^{2k+1}}{(2k+1)!} = x - \frac{x^3}{3!} + \frac{x^5}{5!} - \frac{x^7}{7!} + - \cdots, |x| \leq 1.$ (b) We shall show later that this series represents $\sin x$. What is a bound for the sum of the terms neglected if we take only $x - (x^3/3!)$ when $x = 1$? (c) when $x = .1$? (d) What is the estimate for $\sin .1$?

17. $\displaystyle\sum_{k=0}^{\infty} (-1)^k \frac{(x-1)^k}{k!} = 1 - (x-1) + \frac{(x-1)^2}{2!} - \frac{(x-1)^3}{3!} + \frac{(x-1)^4}{4!}$

$$- + \cdots, \ 1 \leq x \leq 2.$$

18. Verify the fact that the positive terms of the series $\displaystyle\sum_{k=1}^{\infty} (-1)^{k-1}\frac{1}{k}$, taken separately, diverge. Do the same for the negative terms.

19. Prove this theorem:

Hypothesis: $\Sigma_{k=1}^{\infty} u_k$ converges conditionally.

Conclusion: The positive terms of the series constitute a divergent series; the negative terms of the series constitute a second divergent series.

Suggestion for proof: Try a proof by contradiction. Show that there is a contradiction of the hypothesis if the series of positive terms and the series of negative terms are both assumed to converge, or if one of them is assumed to converge and the other to diverge.

20. (a) Consider $b_k = 2/k$ if k is odd and $b_k = 1/k$ if k is even. Show that the b_k's approach 0, but not steadily, and that

$$\text{Series I} = \sum_{k=1}^{\infty} (-1)^{k+1}b_k$$

diverges.

Suggestion: Pair consecutive terms of Series I. Show that

$$v_m = b_{2m-1} - b_{2m} = \frac{2m+1}{2m(2m-1)} > \frac{1}{2}\frac{1}{m} \qquad \text{for } m = 1, 2, 3, \cdots.$$

Since the partial sums of the harmonic series grow beyond all bounds, so do the partial sums of Series I.

(b) Consider $c_k = 2/k^2$ if k is odd and $c_k = 1/k^2$ if k is even. Show that the c_k's approach 0, but not steadily, and that

$$\text{Series II} = \sum_{k=1}^{\infty} (-1)^{k+1}c_k$$

converges. *Suggestion:* Pair consecutive terms of Series II. Show that

$$w_m = c_{2m-1} - c_{2m} = \frac{4m^2 + 4m - 1}{4m^2(4m^2 - 4m + 1)} < \frac{1}{m^2} \qquad \text{for } m = 2, 3, 4, \cdots.$$

21. Remark 2 can be made more precise. For an alternating series whose terms decrease steadily in absolute value, approaching 0, the difference between the limit approached by the series and the sum of the first n terms is less than the absolute value of the $(n + 1)$st term. Prove Theorem 3.

Theorem 3. On remainders for alternating series.

Hypothesis: For the series $\Sigma_{k=1}^{\infty} (-1)^{k+1}a_k$ we have

(a) $0 < a_{k+1} < |a_k|$ for $k = 1, 2, 3, \cdots$,

(b) $\lim_{k \to \infty} a_k = 0$,

(c) $S_n = \Sigma_{k=1}^{n} (-1)^{k+1}a_k$,

(d) $S = \lim_{n \to \infty} S_n$.

Conclusion: $|S - S_n| < a_{n+1}$ for $n = 1, 2, 3, \cdots$.

Suggestions for proof: Step 1. From the proof for Theorem 1, we have $S_{2n} < S$ for $n = 1, 2, 3, \cdots$.

Step 2: Show that $S_{2n-1} > S_{2n+1} > S$ for $n = 1, 2, 3, \cdots$.

Step 3: From $S_{2n} < S < S_{2n+1}$ we have $|S - S_{2n}| < |S_{2n+1} - S_{2n}| = a_{2n+1}$ and from $S_{2n+2} < S < S_{2n+1}$ we have $|S - S_{2n+1}| = |S_{2n+1} - S| < |S_{2n+1} - S_{2n+2}| = a_{2n+2}$.

13.6 The Ratio Test. The Interval of Convergence

Another theorem designed to predict convergence or divergence is the Ratio Test Theorem. This theorem quotes the result of a comparison with a geometric series.

■ **THEOREM 1**

The Ratio Test Theorem.

$$\text{HYPOTHESIS: } t = \lim_{n \to \infty} \left| \frac{u_{n+1}}{u_n} \right| \begin{cases} < 1, & \text{Case (a),} \\ > 1, & \text{Case (b).} \end{cases}$$

$$\text{CONCLUSION: } \sum_{k=1}^{\infty} u_k \begin{cases} \text{converges absolutely in Case (a),} \\ \text{diverges in Case (b).} \end{cases}$$

We shall illustrate what the theorem says before proving it.

Example 1. For the series

$$\sum_{k=1}^{\infty} \frac{k}{e^k} = \frac{1}{e} + \frac{2}{e^2} + \frac{3}{e^3} + \frac{4}{e^4} + \cdots$$

we write $\qquad u_n = \dfrac{n}{e^n} \qquad \text{and} \qquad u_{n+1} = \dfrac{n+1}{e^{n+1}}.$

Here, we arrived at u_n and u_{n+1} by replacing k by n and $n+1$, respectively, in the instructions for writing out the series. We then form the ratio of two successive terms

$$\frac{u_{n+1}}{u_n} = \frac{n+1}{e^{n+1}} \cdot \frac{e^n}{n} = \frac{n+1}{n} \frac{1}{e},$$

and compute the test number

$$t = \lim_{n \to \infty} \left| \frac{u_{n+1}}{u_n} \right| = \lim_{n \to \infty} \frac{n+1}{n} \frac{1}{e} = \lim_{n \to \infty} \frac{1 + 1/n}{1} \frac{1}{e} = \frac{1 + 0}{1} \frac{1}{e} = \frac{1}{e}.\ast$$

The test number t is less than 1; the Ratio Test Theorem says that the series converges absolutely.

We know that the terms of a convergent series approach 0.† We learn from this example, then, the extra fact that

$$\lim_{k \to \infty} \frac{k}{e^k} = 0.$$

Example 2. For the series

$$\sum_{k=1}^{\infty} \frac{1}{(2k-1)^2} = \frac{1}{1^2} + \frac{1}{3^2} + \frac{1}{5^2} + \frac{1}{7^2} + \cdots$$

we write

$$u_n = \frac{1}{(2n-1)^2} \qquad \text{and} \qquad u_{n+1} = \frac{1}{(2[n+1]-1)^2} = \frac{1}{(2n+1)^2}.$$

---

* It is often convenient to change the form of a fraction by dividing the numerator and denominator by the same number.

† Theorem 13.3-3.

Then we form the ratio of the two successive terms

$$\frac{u_{n+1}}{u_n} = \frac{(2n-1)^2}{(2n+1)^2} = \left(\frac{2n-1}{2n+1}\right)^2,$$

and form the test number

$$t = \lim_{n\to\infty} \left|\frac{u_{n+1}}{u_n}\right| = \lim_{n\to\infty} \left(\frac{2n-1}{2n+1}\right)^2 = \lim_{n\to\infty} \left(\frac{2-1/n}{2+1/n}\right)^2 = 1.$$

But the conclusion of the Ratio Test Theorem cannot be applied when $t = 1$. This series will have to be tested again, in some other way. The integral test or a comparison with the p_2 series would soon establish the convergence of this series.

In Exercise 13.6-10 the student can work with a series for which the conclusion of the Ratio Test Theorem cannot be applied, because the test number t does not exist.

Example 3.   Consider next the series

$$1 + 1 + \sum_{k=2}^{\infty} (-1)^{k+1} \frac{2\cdot5\cdot8\cdots(3k-4)}{k!}$$

$$= 1 + 1 - \frac{2}{2!} + \frac{2\cdot5}{3!} - \frac{2\cdot5\cdot8}{4!} + \frac{2\cdot5\cdot8\cdot11}{5!} - +\cdots,$$

where the expression $2\cdot5\cdot8\cdots(3k-4)$ means the product of 2, 5, 8 and every succeeding third integer until you reach $3k-4$. This is a series one could consider if he attempted to compute $\sqrt[3]{4}$ from the series for $f(x) = (1+x)^{1/3}$; see Formulas 13.1-2 and 13.1-3.

Here we write

$$|u_n| = \frac{2\cdot5\cdot8\cdots(3n-4)}{n!}, \quad |u_{n+1}| = \frac{2\cdot5\cdot8\cdots(3n-4)(3n-1)}{(n+1)!},$$

and

$$\left|\frac{u_{n+1}}{u_n}\right| = \frac{2\cdot5\cdot8\cdots(3n-4)(3n-1)}{1\cdot2\cdot3\cdots n(n+1)} \cdot \frac{1\cdot2\cdot3\cdots n}{2\cdot5\cdot8\cdots(3n-4)} = \frac{3n-1}{n+1}.$$

Then we have for the test number t,

$$t = \lim_{n\to\infty} \left|\frac{u_{n+1}}{u_n}\right| = \lim_{n\to\infty} \frac{3-1/n}{1+1/n} = 3.$$

Since t is greater than 1, the Ratio Test Theorem says that the series diverges.

Now we shall prove the Ratio Test Theorem.

PROOF OF THEOREM 1:   In Case (a) we know that

$$\lim_{n\to\infty} \left|\frac{u_{n+1}}{u_n}\right| = t < 1.$$

Let r be chosen between t and 1, $t < r < 1$. Since $|u_{n+1}/u_n|$ approaches and remains as close to t as desired when n increases beyond all bounds, there is a number N such that $|u_{n+1}/u_n|$ is closer to t than r is for all $n \geq N$;

$$\left|\frac{u_{n+1}}{u_n}\right| < r \quad \text{and} \quad |u_{n+1}| < r|u_n|, \quad \text{for } n \geq N.$$

In greater detail,

$$|u_{N+1}| < r|u_N|, \qquad \text{for } n = N,$$

$$|u_{N+2}| < r|u_{N+1}| < r^2|u_N|, \qquad \text{for } n = N+1,$$

$$|u_{N+3}| < r|u_{N+2}| < r^3|u_N|, \qquad \text{for } n = N+2,$$

and
$$|u_{N+j}| < r^j|u_N|, \qquad j = 1, 2, 3, \cdots. \tag{1}$$

Now let us compare the terms of

$$\sum_{k=N}^{\infty} |u_k| = |u_N| + |u_{N+1}| + |u_{N+2}| + |u_{N+3}| + \cdots \tag{2}$$

with those of

$$\sum_{k=N}^{\infty} |u_N| r^{k-N} = |u_N| + r|u_N| + r^2|u_N| + r^3|u_N| + \cdots. \tag{3}$$

Series (3) is a convergent geometric series of ratio r, $r < 1$. The terms of Series (2) are less than those of Series (3), term by term, according to Formula (1). Consequently Series (2) converges by direct comparison.* But the convergence of Series (2) entails the convergence of $\Sigma_{k=1}^{\infty} |u_k|$, for we obtain Series (2) simply by neglecting the first $N - 1$ terms of $\Sigma_{k=1}^{\infty} |u_k|$.† Hence the series $\Sigma_{k=1}^{\infty} u_k$ converges absolutely.‡

In Case (b) we know that $t > 1$. Let r' be chosen between 1 and t, $1 < r' < t$. Since $|u_{n+1}/u_n|$ approaches and remains as close to t as desired when n increases beyond all bounds, there is a number N such that $|u_{n+1}/u_n|$ is closer to t than r' is whenever $n \geq N$;

$$\left|\frac{u_{n+1}}{u_n}\right| > r' \quad \text{and} \quad |u_{n+1}| > r'|u_n| > 1|u_n|, \quad \text{for } n \geq N.$$

This means that the terms of the series actually increase in size for all $n \geq N$. Such a series diverges.§

Finally, the statement $t = 1$ does not distinguish between convergent and divergent series. In Exercise 3 below the reader can show that $t = 1$ for the convergent p_2 series and that $t = 1$ also for the divergent harmonic series.

---

* Theorem 13.3-4A.
† Theorem 13.3-1.
‡ Definition 13.5-1.
§ Theorem 13.3-3.

Example 4. For the series

$$\sum_{k=0}^{\infty} \frac{x^k}{k!} = 1 + \frac{x^1}{1!} + \frac{x^2}{2!} + \frac{x^3}{3!} + \frac{x^4}{4!} + \cdots$$

we compute

$$u_n = \frac{x^n}{n!}, \quad u_{n+1} = \frac{x^{n+1}}{(n+1)!},$$

and

$$\frac{u_{n+1}}{u_n} = \frac{x^{n+1}}{(n+1)!} \cdot \frac{n!}{x^n} = \frac{x(1 \cdot 2 \cdot 3 \cdots n)}{1 \cdot 2 \cdot 3 \cdots n(n+1)} = \frac{x}{n+1}.$$

Thus, the test number is

$$t = \lim_{n \to \infty} \left| \frac{u_{n+1}}{u_n} \right| = \lim_{n \to \infty} \frac{|x|}{n+1} = 0.$$

No matter what value is chosen for x, large or small in size, we have $t < 1$. This series converges for all x.

Since the terms of a convergent series must approach 0, we can say, in addition, that

$$\lim_{k \to \infty} \frac{x^k}{k!} = 0 \qquad \text{for all } x. \tag{4}$$

The series of powers of x of Example 4 converged for all x, but it is conceivable that another series of powers of x might converge for some x and not for others.

Example 5. Consider the power series

$$\sum_{k=1}^{\infty} \frac{x^{3k-1}}{k^2} = \frac{x^2}{1^2} + \frac{x^5}{2^2} + \frac{x^8}{3^2} + \frac{x^{11}}{4^2} + \cdots.$$

The ratio test suggests that we compute

$$u_n = \frac{x^{3n-1}}{n^2}, \quad u_{n+1} = \frac{x^{3[n+1]-1}}{(n+1)^2} = \frac{x^{3n+2}}{(n+1)^2},$$

and

$$\frac{u_{n+1}}{u_n} = \frac{x^{3n+2}}{(n+1)^2} \cdot \frac{n^2}{x^{3n-1}} = \left(\frac{n}{n+1} \right)^2 x^3.$$

Then the test number t is

$$t = \lim_{n \to \infty} \left| \frac{u_{n+1}}{u_n} \right| = \lim_{n \to \infty} \left(\frac{1}{1+1/n} \right)^2 |x|^3 = |x|^3,$$

and we have absolute convergence if $t = |x|^3 < 1$, divergence if $t = |x|^3 > 1$, and an as yet unresolved situation if $t = |x|^3 = 1$. In a little greater detail, the series converges absolutely if $|x|^3 < 1$, or if $|x| < 1$, or if $-1 < x < 1$, but the ratio test tells us nothing if $x = 1$ or if $x = -1$. We must investigate these cases separately.

For $x = 1$ the series reads

$$\sum_{k=1}^{\infty} \frac{1}{k^2} = \frac{1}{1^2} + \frac{1}{2^2} + \frac{1}{3^2} + \frac{1}{4^2} + \cdots.$$

Here we have the p_2 series, known to be convergent. For $x = -1$, the series reads

$$\sum_{k=1}^{\infty} \frac{(-1)^{3k-1}}{k^2} = \frac{1}{1^2} - \frac{1}{2^2} + \frac{1}{3^2} - \frac{1}{4^2} + \cdots.$$

Since the series of absolute values would be the p_2 series, known to converge, this series is also absolutely convergent. The series originally given to us has for its interval of convergence, then, the interval $-1 \leq x \leq 1$.

Example 6. Find the interval of convergence of the series

$$\sum_{k=0}^{\infty} \frac{(x-1)^k}{2k+1} = 1 + \frac{x-1}{3} + \frac{(x-1)^2}{5} + \frac{(x-1)^3}{7} + \frac{(x-1)^4}{9} + \cdots.$$

We write

$$u_n = \frac{(x-1)^n}{2n+1}, \qquad u_{n+1} = \frac{(x-1)^{n+1}}{2n+3},$$

and

$$\frac{u_{n+1}}{u_n} = \frac{2n+1}{2n+3} \frac{(x-1)^{n+1}}{(x-1)^n} = \frac{2+1/n}{2+3/n}(x-1),$$

and then for the test number t,

$$t = \lim_{n \to \infty} \left| \frac{u_{n+1}}{u_n} \right| = \lim_{n \to \infty} \frac{2+1/n}{2+3/n} |x-1| = |x-1|.$$

The series converges absolutely if $|x-1| < 1$, and thus if $-1 < x-1 < 1$, $0 < x < 2$, but we do not yet know about the convergence if $x = 0$ or if $x = 2$.

When $x = 2$ the series reads

$$\sum_{k=0}^{\infty} \frac{1}{2k+1} = 1 + \frac{1}{3} + \frac{1}{5} + \frac{1}{7} + \frac{1}{9} + \cdots. \tag{5}$$

This series is so much like the harmonic series that comparison with that series is suggested. The series

$$\sum_{k=0}^{\infty} \frac{1}{2k+2} = \frac{1}{2} + \frac{1}{4} + \frac{1}{6} + \frac{1}{8} + \cdots \tag{6}$$

is a multiple of the harmonic series and divergent. The Series (5) is term by term larger than Series (6) and also divergent.

When $x = 0$ the series reads

$$\sum_{k=0}^{\infty} \frac{(-1)^k}{2k+1} = 1 - \frac{1}{3} + \frac{1}{5} - \frac{1}{7} + \frac{1}{9} - + \cdots.$$

This alternating series converges, because the absolute values of its terms are monotonically decreasing and approach 0. The original series has for its interval of convergence, then, the interval $0 \leq x < 2$.

EXERCISES 13.6

Test each of the following series for convergence by the ratio test. If no conclusion can be drawn, test by another method.

1. $\displaystyle\sum_{k=1}^{\infty} \frac{k^2}{e^k} = \frac{1^2}{e^1} + \frac{2^2}{e^2} + \frac{3^2}{e^3} + \cdots.$

2. (a) $\displaystyle\sum_{k=1}^{\infty} \frac{k^p}{e^k}, p > 0.$

(b) Prove that $\displaystyle\lim_{k\to\infty} \frac{k^p}{e^k} = 0$ for any p.

(c) If $a > 1$, prove that $\displaystyle\lim_{k\to\infty} \frac{k^p}{a^k} = 0$ for any p.

3. $\displaystyle\sum_{k=1}^{\infty} \frac{1}{k^p}, p > 0.$

4. $\displaystyle\sum_{k=1}^{\infty} (-1)^{k+1} \frac{(1.1)^k}{k} = \frac{1.1}{1} - \frac{(1.1)^2}{2} + \frac{(1.1)^3}{3} - \frac{(1.1)^4}{4} + - \cdots.$

5. $\displaystyle\sum_{k=0}^{\infty} (-1)^k \frac{1}{2^k(2k)!} = 1 - \frac{1}{2(2!)} + \frac{1}{2^2(4!)} - \frac{1}{2^3(6!)} + - \cdots.$

6. $\displaystyle\sum_{k=0}^{\infty} (-1)^k \frac{2^{2k+1}}{(2k+1)!} = \frac{2}{1!} - \frac{2^3}{3!} + \frac{2^5}{5!} - \frac{2^7}{7!} + \frac{2^9}{9!} - + \cdots.$

7. $\displaystyle\sum_{k=0}^{\infty} (-1)^k \frac{2^{2k+1}}{k!k!}.$ **8.** $\displaystyle\sum_{k=2}^{\infty} \frac{1}{k(k-1)}.$

9. $1 + \dfrac{1}{6} + \displaystyle\sum_{k=2}^{\infty} (-1)^{k+1} \frac{1 \cdot 3 \cdot 5 \cdot 7 \cdots (2k-3)}{6^k(k!)} = 1 + \frac{1}{6} - \frac{1}{6^2(2!)} + \frac{1 \cdot 3}{6^3(3!)}$

$$- \frac{1 \cdot 3 \cdot 5}{6^4(4!)} + \frac{1 \cdot 3 \cdot 5 \cdot 7}{6^5(5!)} - \frac{1 \cdot 3 \cdot 5 \cdot 7 \cdot 9}{6^6(6!)} + - \cdots.$$

10. $\displaystyle\sum_{k=1}^{\infty} u_k$ where $u_k = \begin{cases} \dfrac{1}{2^k} & \text{if } k \text{ is even.} \\[2mm] \dfrac{1}{3^k} & \text{if } k \text{ is odd.} \end{cases}$

11. $\displaystyle\sum_{k=1}^{\infty} \frac{2 \cdot 4 \cdot 6 \cdots (2k)}{1 \cdot 3 \cdot 5 \cdots (2k-1)} \frac{1}{k} = \frac{2}{1} \frac{1}{1} + \frac{2 \cdot 4}{1 \cdot 3} \frac{1}{2} + \frac{2 \cdot 4 \cdot 6}{1 \cdot 3 \cdot 5} \frac{1}{3} + \frac{2 \cdot 4 \cdot 6 \cdot 8}{1 \cdot 3 \cdot 5 \cdot 7} \frac{1}{4} + \cdots.$

12. (a) $\displaystyle\sum_{k=1}^{\infty} \frac{k!}{k^k}.$

(b) Prove that $\displaystyle\lim_{k\to\infty} \frac{k!}{k^k} = 0.$

Find the interval of convergence for each of the following power series. If the interval has end points, decide whether the series converges at the end points.

13. $\displaystyle\sum_{k=1}^{\infty} \frac{x^k}{\sqrt{k}} = \frac{x}{\sqrt{1}} + \frac{x^2}{\sqrt{2}} + \frac{x^3}{\sqrt{3}} + \cdots.$

14. $\displaystyle\sum_{k=1}^{\infty} (-1)^{k+1} \frac{x^k}{k} = x - \frac{x^2}{2} + \frac{x^3}{3} - \frac{x^4}{4} + - \cdots.$

15. $\displaystyle\sum_{k=0}^{\infty} (-1)^k \frac{x^{2k+1}}{2k+1}.$

16. $\displaystyle\sum_{k=1}^{\infty} \frac{x^k}{2^k k^2}.$

17. $\displaystyle\sum_{k=1}^{\infty} \frac{x^{2k-1}}{k(k+1)} = \frac{x}{1\cdot2} + \frac{x^3}{2(3)} + \frac{x^5}{3(4)} + \frac{x^7}{4(5)} +\cdots.$

18. $\displaystyle\sum_{k=0}^{\infty} (-1)^k \frac{x^{2k+1}}{(2k+1)!} = \frac{x}{1!} - \frac{x^3}{3!} + \frac{x^5}{5!} - \frac{x^7}{7!} + -\cdots.$

19. $\displaystyle\sum_{k=0}^{\infty} (-1)^k \frac{x^{2k}}{(2k)!}.$

20. $\displaystyle\sum_{k=0}^{\infty} (-1)^k \frac{1}{k!k!} \left(\frac{x}{2}\right)^{2k}.$

21. $\displaystyle\sum_{k=0}^{\infty} (-1)^k \frac{1}{k!(k+1)!} \left(\frac{x}{2}\right)^{2k+1} = \frac{x}{2} - \frac{1}{1!2!}\left(\frac{x}{2}\right)^3 + \frac{1}{2!3!}\left(\frac{x}{2}\right)^5 - \frac{1}{3!4!}\left(\frac{x}{2}\right)^7 + -\cdots.$

22. $\displaystyle\sum_{k=1}^{\infty} \frac{(x-1)^k}{k} = \frac{x-1}{1} + \frac{(x-1)^2}{2} + \frac{(x-1)^3}{3} + \frac{(x-1)^4}{4} + \cdots.$

23. $\displaystyle\sum_{k=0}^{\infty} \frac{(x+3)^k}{2^k}.$

24. $\displaystyle\sum_{k=1}^{\infty} \frac{(x-4)^{2k}}{3^{k-1}}.$

25. $\displaystyle\sum_{k=1}^{\infty} \frac{(x+2)^k}{k^2} = \frac{x+2}{1^2} + \frac{(x+2)^2}{2^2} + \frac{(x+2)^3}{3^2} + \frac{(x+2)^4}{4^2} + \cdots.$

26. $\displaystyle\sum_{k=0}^{\infty} \frac{(x-5)^k}{(2k-1)^3} = -1 + \frac{x-5}{1^3} + \frac{(x-5)^2}{3^3} + \frac{(x-5)^3}{5^3} + \frac{(x-5)^4}{7^3} + \cdots.$

Show that each of the following series of powers of x converges for $-1 < x < 1$.

27. $\displaystyle x + \sum_{k=2}^{\infty} \frac{1\cdot3\cdot5\cdots(2k-3)}{2\cdot4\cdot6\cdots(2k-2)} \frac{x^{2k-1}}{2k-1} = x + \frac{1}{2}\frac{x^3}{3} + \frac{1\cdot3}{2\cdot4}\frac{x^5}{5} + \frac{1\cdot3\cdot5}{2\cdot4\cdot6}\frac{x^7}{7}$

$$+ \frac{1\cdot3\cdot5\cdot7}{2\cdot4\cdot6\cdot8}\frac{x^9}{9} +\cdots.$$

28. $\displaystyle 1 + \frac{x}{2} + \sum_{k=2}^{\infty} (-1)^{k+1} \frac{1\cdot3\cdot5\cdots(2k-3)}{2\cdot4\cdot6\cdots(2k-2)} \frac{x^k}{2k} = 1 + \frac{x}{2} - \frac{1}{2}\frac{x^2}{4} + \frac{1\cdot3}{2\cdot4}\frac{x^3}{6}$

$$- \frac{1\cdot3\cdot5}{2\cdot4\cdot6}\frac{x^4}{8} + \frac{1\cdot3\cdot5\cdot7}{2\cdot4\cdot6\cdot8}\frac{x^5}{10} - +\cdots.$$

29. $\displaystyle 1 + \frac{x}{3} + \sum_{k=2}^{\infty} (-1)^{k+1} \frac{2\cdot5\cdot8\cdots(3k-4)}{3\cdot6\cdot9\cdots(3k-3)} \frac{x^k}{3k} = 1 + \frac{x}{3} - \frac{2}{3}\frac{x^2}{6} + \frac{2\cdot5}{3\cdot6}\frac{x^3}{9}$

$$- \frac{2\cdot5\cdot8}{3\cdot6\cdot9}\frac{x^4}{12} + \frac{2\cdot5\cdot8\cdot11}{3\cdot6\cdot9\cdot12}\frac{x^5}{15} - +\cdots.$$

30. $\displaystyle 1 + \sum_{k=1}^{\infty} m(m-1)(m-2)\cdots(m-[k-1]) \frac{x^k}{k!} = 1 + m\frac{x^1}{1!} + m(m-1)\frac{x^2}{2!}$

$$+ m(m-1)(m-2)\frac{x^3}{3!} + m(m-1)(m-2)(m-3)\frac{x^4}{4!} +\cdots, \quad m \text{ a positive constant.}$$

Raabe's Theorem is a test that can often be used when the ratio test fails to give information. It amounts to a comparison with a p series, $\sum_{k=1}^{\infty} 1/k^p$, known to converge for $p > 1$. We state it without proof.

Theorem 2. *Raabe's Theorem.*

Hypothesis: $t' = \lim\limits_{n \to \infty} n\left[1 - \left|\dfrac{u_{n+1}}{u_n}\right|\right] \begin{cases} > 1, & \text{Case (a)}, \\ < 1, & \text{Case (b)}. \end{cases}$

Conclusion: $\sum\limits_{k=1}^{\infty} u_k \begin{cases} \text{converges absolutely in Case (a).} \\ \text{does not converge absolutely in Case (b).} \end{cases}$

Note that Raabe's Test gives no information if t' does not exist or if $t' = 1$. Use Raabe's Test for each of the following series.

31. $\sum\limits_{k=1}^{\infty} \dfrac{1}{k^2}.$ **32.** $\sum\limits_{k=1}^{\infty} \dfrac{1}{k}.$

33. The series of Exercise 8. **34.** The series of Exercise 11.

Use Raabe's Test to show that there is convergence for $x = 1$ and for $x = -1$ in the following series.

35. The series of Exercise 27. **37.** The series of Exercise 29.
36. The series of Exercise 28. **38.** The series of Exercise 30.

13.7 Approximation to a Function by Polynomials. Taylor's Theorem

In the last sections we worked with the question of deciding whether a given series presented to us converged or diverged. In this section and the next we try to explain one of the principal sources of these series: many important functions have power series representations, and it is often more convenient to study these functions through their series representations than through the definitions originally given for the functions. In this section we shall attempt to approximate to functions by polynomials. We shall be led to infinite power series in the next section when we seek to improve the approximations by taking polynomials of higher and higher degree.

From our present point of view, the equation of the tangent line should be looked upon as a first-degree polynomial approximation to a function. Our intuition tells us that the tangent line approximates a curve better near the point of tangency than any other straight line could. To get this approximation for $y = f(x)$ near the point $A(a, f(a))$, we (a) select a second point A_1 on $y = f(x)$; (b) take the straight line determined by A and A_1; and (c) let this line approach a limiting position as A_1 approaches A. The tangent line has the equation $y - f(a) = f'(a)(x - a)$, or

$$y = S_1(x) = f(a) + f'(a)(x - a). \tag{1}$$

Observe that

$$S_1(a) = f(a), \quad S_1'(a) = f'(a).$$

If we want a second-degree polynomial approximation to $y = f(x)$ near $A(a, f(a))$, it would seem reasonable (a) to select points A_1 and A_2 on $y = f(x)$; (b) to determine the second-degree polynomial curve, $y = P_{A_1 A_2}(x)$, which passes through A, A_1, and A_2; and (c) to let $y = P_{A_1 A_2}(x)$ approach a limiting parabola, $y = S_2(x)$, as A_1 and A_2 both approach A.

We shall show in Exercise 13.7-1 that $S_2(x)$ must be such that

$$S_2(a) = f(a), \quad S_2'(a) = f'(a), \quad S_2''(a) = f''(a). \tag{2}$$

Let us write

$$S_2(x) = \alpha_0 + \alpha_1(x - a) + \alpha_2(x - a)^2 \tag{3}$$

and seek to determine the constants α_0, α_1, and α_2. Substituting a for x in Eq. (3) and using Eqs. (2), we find that

$$S_2(a) = \alpha_0 + 0 + 0 \quad \text{or} \quad \alpha_0 = S_2(a) = f(a).$$

But from Eq. (3) we get

$$S_2'(x) = \alpha_1 + 2\alpha_2(x - a),$$

$$S_2''(x) = 2\alpha_2.$$

When we substitute a for x and use Eq. (2) again, we learn that

$$\alpha_1 = S_2'(a) = f'(a) \quad \text{and} \quad \alpha_2 = \tfrac{1}{2} S_2''(a) = \tfrac{1}{2} f_2''(a),$$

so that our second-degree polynomial approximation (3) becomes

$$S_2(x) = f(a) + f'(a)(x - a) + f''(a) \frac{(x - a)^2}{2}. \tag{3a}$$

To get $S_3(x)$, a third-degree polynomial approximation to $f(x)$ near $A(a, f(a))$, we would (a) choose points A_1, A_2, and A_3 on $y = f(x)$; (b) take the third-degree polynomial curve $y = P_{A_1A_2A_3}(x)$ determined by the four points A, A_1, A_2, and A_3; and (c) take the cubic curve $y = S_3(x)$ approached by the curves $y = P_{A_1A_2A_3}(x)$ as A_1, A_2, and A_3 all approach A. Instead of the conditions of Eq. (2) we would now have

$$S_3(a) = f(a), \quad S_3'(a) = f'(a), \quad S_3''(a) = f''(a), \quad S_3'''(a) = f'''(a),$$

and when we write

$$S_3(x) = \alpha_0 + \alpha_1(x - a) + \alpha_2(x - a)^2 + \alpha_3(x - a)^3$$

and determine the constants α_0, α_1, α_2, and α_3, we find that

$$S_3(x) = f(a) + f'(a)(x - a) + f''(a) \frac{(x - a)^2}{2!} + f'''(a) \frac{(x - a)^3}{3!}. \tag{4}$$

Finally, continuing with the same intuitively plausible process, we are led to expect that the nth degree polynomial

$$S_n(x) = f(a) + \sum_{k=1}^{n} f^{(k)}(a) \frac{(x - a)^k}{k!}$$

$$= f(a) + f'(a) \frac{(x - a)}{1!} + f''(a) \frac{(x - a)^2}{2!} + \cdots$$

$$+ f^{(n)}(a) \frac{(x - a)^n}{n!} \tag{5}$$

will approximate $f(x)$ well for x near $x = a$.

Example 1. To approximate $y = f(x) = e^x$ for x near $x = 0$ by using the polynomial of degree n suggested by Eq. (5), we compute

$$f(x) = e^x, \qquad f(0) = 1,$$
$$f'(x) = e^x, \qquad f'(0) = 1,$$
$$f''(x) = e^x, \qquad f''(0) = 1,$$

. . . .

$$f^{(n)}(x) = e^x, \qquad f^n(0) = 1$$

and take the polynomial

$$e^x \approx S_n(x) = 1 + \frac{x^1}{1!} + \frac{x^2}{2!} + \frac{x^3}{3!} + \frac{x^4}{4!} + \cdots + \frac{x^n}{n!}.$$

Example 2. To approximate $y = f(x) = \log(1 + x)$ for x near $x = 0$ by using the polynomial of degree n suggested by Eq. (5), we compute

$$f(x) = \log(1 + x), \qquad\qquad f(0) = \log 1 = 0,$$
$$f'(x) = \frac{1}{1 + x} = (1 + x)^{-1}, \qquad f'(0) = (1 + 0)^{-1} = 1,$$
$$f''(x) = -1(1 + x)^{-2}, \qquad\qquad f''(0) = -1,$$
$$f'''(x) = +(2!)(1 + x)^{-3} \qquad\qquad f'''(0) = 2!,$$
$$f^{iv}(x) = -(3!)(1 + x)^{-4}, \qquad\qquad f^{iv}(0) = -(3!),$$

. . . .

$$f^{(n)}(x) = (-1)^{n-1}(n - 1)!(1 + x)^{-n}. \qquad f^{(n)}(0) = (-1)^{n-1}(n - 1)!.$$

Then we take the polynomial

$$\log(1 + x) \approx 0 + 1\frac{x^1}{1!} - 1\frac{x^2}{2!} + 2!\frac{x^3}{3!} - 3!\frac{x^4}{4!} + 4!\frac{x^5}{5!}$$

$$- + \cdots + (-1)^{n-1}(n - 1)!\frac{x^n}{n!}$$

$$\approx x - \frac{x^2}{2} + \frac{x^3}{3} - \frac{x^4}{4} + \frac{x^5}{5} - + \cdots + (-1)^{n-1}\frac{x^n}{n}.$$

In Figs. 13.3(a), (b), and (c) we present $y = \log(1 + x)$ and the approximations

$$y = S_1(x) = x, \qquad y = S_2(x) = x - \frac{x^2}{2},$$

and

$$y = S_4(x) = x - \frac{x^2}{2} + \frac{x^3}{3} - \frac{x^4}{4}$$

for $-1 < x < 1$.

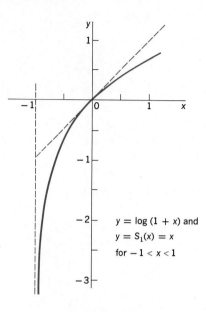

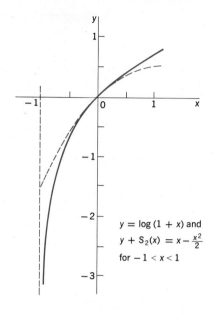

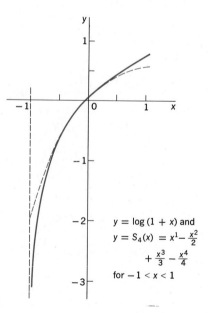

Fig. 13.3 (c)

Example 3. To approximate $y = f(x)$ $= \sin x$ for x near $x = \pi/4$ by using the polynomial of degree 5 suggested by Eq. (5), we compute

$$f(x) \quad = \sin x, \qquad f\!\left(\frac{\pi}{4}\right) \quad = \frac{\sqrt{2}}{2},$$

$$f'(x) \quad = \cos x, \qquad f'\!\left(\frac{\pi}{4}\right) \quad = \frac{\sqrt{2}}{2},$$

$$f''(x) \quad = -\sin x, \qquad f''\!\left(\frac{\pi}{4}\right) = -\frac{\sqrt{2}}{2},$$

$$f'''(x) = -\cos x, \qquad f'''\!\left(\frac{\pi}{4}\right) = -\frac{\sqrt{2}}{2},$$

$$f^{iv}(x) \quad = \sin x, \qquad f^{iv}\!\left(\frac{\pi}{4}\right) = \frac{\sqrt{2}}{2},$$

$$f^{v}(x) \quad = \cos x. \qquad f^{v}\!\left(\frac{\pi}{4}\right) \quad = \frac{\sqrt{2}}{2}.$$

Equation (5) then suggests that we take

$$\sin x \approx S_5(x) = \frac{\sqrt{2}}{2} + \frac{\sqrt{2}}{2}\frac{(x - \pi/4)^1}{1!} - \frac{\sqrt{2}}{2}\frac{(x - \pi/4)^2}{2!} - \frac{\sqrt{2}}{2}\frac{(x - \pi/4)^3}{3!}$$

$$+ \frac{\sqrt{2}}{2} \frac{(x - \pi/4)^4}{4!} + \frac{\sqrt{2}}{2} \frac{(x - \pi/4)^5}{5!}$$

$$\sin x \approx \frac{\sqrt{2}}{2} \left[1 + \frac{(x - \pi/4)}{1!} - \frac{(x - \pi/4)^2}{2!} - \frac{(x - \pi/4)^3}{3!} + \frac{(x - \pi/4)^4}{4!} \right.$$

$$\left. + \frac{(x - \pi/4)^5}{5!} \right]. \qquad (6)$$

But we are too vague if we merely say that $S_n(x)$ approximates $f(x)$ well for values of x near $x = a$. It is desirable to say something precise about $R_n(x)$, the difference between $f(x)$ and $S_n(x)$. We shall conclude this section by deriving a statement for this difference. In the next section we shall consider the question, "Can $R_n(x)$ be made as small as desired by choosing n large enough?"

■ **THEOREM 1**

Taylor's Theorem.

HYPOTHESIS: (a) $f^{(n+1)}(x)$ is continuous for $c \leq x \leq b$,
(b) $c \leq a \leq b$,
(c) $f(x) = S_n(x) + R_n(x)$

$$= f(a) + \sum_{k=1}^{n} f^{(k)}(a) \frac{(x - a)^k}{k!} + R_n(x) \qquad \text{for } c \leq x \leq b.$$

CONCLUSION: There exists a number w, w between a and x, such that

$$R_n(x) = f^{(n+1)}(w) \frac{(x - a)^{n+1}}{(n + 1)!}.$$

● **Remark 1**

We shall call $R_n(x)$ the nth degree remainder.

● **Remark 2**

Other statements can be made for $R_n(x)$. This statement for $R_n(x)$ is called Lagrange's form for the remainder.

PROOF: *Step (a).* Hypothesis (c) can be said to compare $f(x)$ with $f(a)$ or to give us a statement for $f(x) - f(a)$, for it reads $f(x) = f(a) + \cdots$. But there is a definite integral that will give us $f(x) - f(a)$:

$$\int_{t=a}^{x} f'(t)\, dt = f(t) \Big|_{t=a}^{x} = f(x) - f(a).$$

Step (b): We can rewrite this integral by using integration by parts. If we take for our parts $u = f'(t)$ and $dv/dt = 1$, with $du/dt = f''(t)$ and $v = t - x$,* we can write

---

* We consider x fixed and work with respect to t.

$$\int_{t=a}^{x} f'(t)\,dt = [f'(t)(t - x)]_{t=a}^{x} - \int_{t=a}^{x} (t - x)f''(t)\,dt$$

$$= 0 - f'(a)(a - x) + \int_{t=a}^{x} (x - t)f''(t)\,dt,$$

and using the result of Step (a) we have

$$f(x) = f(a) + f'(a)(x - a) + \int_{t=a}^{x} f''(t)(x - t)\,dt.$$

Step (c): If we integrate by parts again, using $u = f''(t)$, $dv/dt = x - t$ as parts, with $du/dt = f'''(t)$ and $v = -(x - t)^2/2$, we get

$$f(x) = f(a) + f'(a)(x - a) + \left[-f''(t)\frac{(x - t)^2}{2} \right]_{t=a}^{x} + \int_{t=a}^{x} \frac{(x - t)^2}{2} f'''(t)\,dt$$

$$= f(a) + f'(a)(x - a) + f''(a)\frac{(x - a)^2}{2!} + \int_{t=a}^{x} f'''(t)\frac{(x - t)^2}{2!}\,dt.$$

Step (d): Continuing to integrate by parts this way we will get

$$f(x) = f(a) + f'(a)(x - a) + f''(a)\frac{(x - a)^2}{2!} + \cdots + f^{(n)}(a)\frac{(x - a)^n}{n!} + R_n(x),$$

where

$$R_n(x) = \int_{t=a}^{x} f^{(n+1)}(t)\frac{(x - t)^n}{n!}\,dt.$$

(a)   (b)

Fig. 13.4

Step (e): Let us assume that $a \leq x \leq b$; the details are not essentially different if $c \leq x \leq a$; consult Fig. 13.4. According to Hypothesis (a), $f^{n+1}(t)$ is continuous for $a \leq t \leq x$ and we know then that $f^{n+1}(t)$ will take on maximum and minimum values, M and m, for this interval. Thus we have

$$m \leq f^{n+1}(t) \leq M \qquad \text{for } a \leq t \leq x$$

$$m\frac{(x - t)^n}{n!} \leq f^{n+1}(t)\frac{(x - t)^n}{n!} \leq M\frac{(x - t)^n}{n!} \qquad \text{for } a \leq t \leq x$$

and

$$\int_{t=a}^{x} m\frac{(x - t)^n}{n!}\,dt \leq R_n(x) = \int_{t=a}^{x} f^{(n+1)}(t)\frac{(x - t)^n}{n!}\,dt \leq \int_{t=a}^{x} M\frac{(x - t)^n}{n!}\,dt.$$

But

$$\int_{t=a}^{x} \frac{(x - t)^n}{n!}\,dt = -\frac{1}{n!}\frac{(x - t)^{n+1}}{n + 1}\bigg|_{t=a}^{x} = \frac{(x - a)^{n+1}}{(n + 1)!},$$

and the last inequalities can be written in the form

$$m \frac{(x-a)^{n+1}}{(n+1)!} \leq R_n(x) \leq M \frac{(x-a)^{n+1}}{(n+1)!}.$$

For some number μ, properly chosen between m and M, we shall have

$$R_n(x) = \mu \frac{(x-a)^{n+1}}{(n+1)!},$$

and because a function continuous on a closed interval takes on all values between its maximum and minimum values, we can say that there is a number w, $a < w < x$, such that $f^{(n+1)}(w) = \mu$, and that therefore

$$R_n(x) = f^{(n+1)}(w) \frac{(x-a)^{n+1}}{(n+1)!}.$$

This completes the proof of Taylor's Theorem.

Example 4. Let us continue the work of Example 1 on $f(x) = e^x$. Since $f^{n+1}(x) = e^x$ is continuous for all x, we can say that for any x there exists a number w, w between 0 and x, such that

$$R_n(x) = e^x - S_n(x) = f^{n+1}(w) \frac{x^{n+1}}{(n+1)!},$$

or

$$R_n(x) = e^w \frac{x^{n+1}}{(n+1)!}.$$

If we chose to use the approximation

$$e^x \approx S_2(x) = 1 + \frac{x^1}{1!} + \frac{x^2}{2!}$$

to compute $e^{.1}$, we could write

$$e^{.1} \approx 1 + \frac{.1}{1} + \frac{.01}{2} = 1.105$$

with

$$R_2 = e^w \frac{(.1)^3}{3!}, \qquad 0 < w < .1.$$

Since e^x increases as x increases, we can be sure that $e^w < e^{.1}$, and since $e < 3$, we can reason that $e^{.5} < \sqrt{3}$, $e^w < e^{.1} < e^{.5} < \sqrt{3}$. Hence, while we do not know R_2 precisely because we do not know w precisely, we can be sure that

$$R_2 < \sqrt{3} \frac{(.1)^3}{6} < .0003.$$

If we take $e^{.1} \approx 1.105$, our error is less than .0003, and since R_2 is positive, the correct value for $e^{.1}$ is slightly larger than 1.105.

Example 5. Let us continue the work of Example 2 on $f(x) = \log(1+x)$ for x close to $x = 0$. We compute

$$f^{(n+1)}(x) = (-1)^n (n!)(1+x)^{-n-1} = (-1)^n \frac{n!}{(1+x)^{n+1}},$$

and observe that $f^{(n+1)}(x)$ is continuous for $x \neq -1$. Then for $x > -1$ we can say that there is a number w, between 0 and x, such that

$$R_n(x) = f^{(n+1)}(w) \frac{x^{n+1}}{(n+1)!} = (-1)^n \frac{n!}{(1+w)^{n+1}} \frac{x^{n+1}}{(n+1)!}$$

$$= (-1)^n \frac{1}{(1+w)^{n+1}} \frac{x^{n+1}}{n+1}.$$

If we wanted to compute log 1.2 from the approximation S_5, we could write

$$\log (1 + x) \approx S_5(x) = x - \frac{x^2}{2} + \frac{x^3}{3} - \frac{x^4}{4} + \frac{x^5}{5},$$

$$\log (1.2) \approx S_5(.2) = .2 - \frac{.04}{2} + \frac{.008}{3} - \frac{.0016}{4} + \frac{.00032}{5} \approx .18233$$

with

$$R_5(.2) = -\frac{1}{(1+w)^6} \frac{(.2)^6}{6}, \qquad 0 < w < .2.$$

We do not know the precise value of w, but we do know that no matter where it falls in the interval $0 < w < .2$ we shall have

$$1 < 1 + w < 1.2, \qquad \frac{1}{1+w} < 1.$$

Hence we can be sure that

$$|R_5(.2)| < \frac{(.2)^6}{6} = \frac{.000064}{6} < .0000107.$$

The error we make in taking $S_5(.2)$ for log 1.2 is less than .0000107, and since R_5 is negative, the correct value for log 1.2 is slightly less than .18233.

Example 6. To continue the work of Example 3 on $f(x) = \sin x$ for x near $x = \pi/4$, we observe that

$$f^{vi}(x) = -\sin x,$$

and that $f^{vi}(x)$ is continuous for all x. Hence for any x there is a number w between $\pi/4$ and x such that

$$R_5(x) = f^{vi}(w) \frac{(x - \pi/4)^6}{6!} = -\sin w \frac{(x - \pi/4)^6}{6!}.$$

Let us try to compute sin 44° from

$$\sin x \approx S_5(x) = \frac{\sqrt{2}}{2} \left[1 + \frac{(x - \pi/4)}{1!} - \frac{(x - \pi/4)^2}{2!} - \frac{(x - \pi/4)^3}{3!} + \frac{(x - \pi/4)^4}{4!} \right.$$

$$\left. + \frac{(x - \pi/4)^5}{5!} \right]. \qquad (6)$$

If we express 44° in radian measure and subtract $\pi/4$, we shall have

$$x - \frac{\pi}{4} \approx -.01745.*$$

—————————
* $1° \approx .0174533$ radians.

and then the computation called for by Eq. (6), while tedious, is straightforward. The error we make is

$$R_5(x) = -\sin w \frac{(-.01745)^6}{6!}, \qquad 44° < w < 45°.$$

We do not know precisely where in the interval $44° < w < 45°$ w will fall, but we do know that $|\sin w| < 1$. Hence

$$|R_5| < \frac{(.01745)^6}{6!} < 9(10)^{-14}.$$

The error is very small, and it is quite likely that for most tabular purposes a polynomial of even lower degree would suffice.†

● **Remark 4**

It is possible to reach the conclusion of Taylor's Theorem by a method that requires only that $f^{(n+1)}(x)$ shall exist for an interval about $x = a$. If this refined result were assumed, then Taylor's Theorem for the case $n = 0$ would be the Theorem of Mean Value. Thus, Taylor's Theorem can be considered to be an extension of the Theorem of Mean Value.

EXERCISES 13.7

1. Let $f''(x)$ be continuous near $x = a$. Choose a_1 and a_2 near $x = a$, and let $P_{A_1 A_2}(x)$ be the second-degree polynomial for which $P_{A_1 A_2}(a) = f(a)$, $P_{A_1 A_2}(a_1) = f(a_1)$, $P_{A_1 A_2}(a_2) = f(a_2)$. Write $\phi_{A_1 A_2}(x) = f(x) - P_{A_1 A_2}(x)$ and observe that $\phi_{A_1 A_2}(a) = \phi_{A_1 A_2}(a_1) = \phi_{A_1 A_2}(a_2) = 0$. If, for the sake of convenience, $a < a_1 < a_2$, explain how Rolle's Theorem provides for numbers u and v such that $a < u < a_1 < v < a_2$ and

$$\phi_{A_1 A_2}{}'(u) = \phi_{A_1 A_2}{}'(v) = 0. \tag{7}$$

Explain how Rolle's Theorem provides for a number w, $u < w < v$, such that

$$\phi_{A_1 A_2}{}''(w) = 0. \tag{8}$$

If a_1 and a_2 approach a, so do the numbers u, v, and w. If the parabolas $y = P_{A_1 A_2}(x)$ approach the parabola $y = S_2(x)$, Statements (7) and (8) become, in the limit,

$$\phi'(a) = 0, \tag{7a}$$

$$\phi''(a) = 0, \tag{8a}$$

where $\phi(x) = f(x) - S_2(x)$. We are thus led to Eqs. (2).

In the next 9 problems, (a) compute an approximating polynomial of the stated degree, and (b) state the remainder in Lagrange's form.

2. $\sin x$, for x near 0, 5th degree.

3. $\cos x$, for x near 0, 8th degree.

4. $(1 + x)^4$, for x near 0, 4th degree.

5. $(1 + x)^{1/2}$, for x near 0, 5th degree.

6. $(1 + x)^{1/3}$, for x near 0, 6th degree.

7. $(1 + x)^m$, for x near 0, nth degree.

† See Exercise 13.7-20.

8. e^x, for x near a, nth degree.

9. $\cos x$, for x near $\pi/3$, 5th degree.

10. $\log x$, for x near 2, nth degree.

In the next 8 problems, compute an approximating polynomial of the degree indicated.

11. $2x^2 - 3x + 5$, 2nd degree, for x near -2.

12. $x^4 - x + 17$, 4th degree, for x near 1. **15.** $\sec x$, 4th degree, for x near 0.

13. $\tan x$, 5th degree, for x near 0. **16.** $\sin^{-1} x$, 3rd degree, for x near 0.

14. $\log \cos x$, 6th degree, for x near 0. **17.** $\tan^{-1} x$, 3rd degree, for x near 0.

18. $\log (x + \sqrt{1 + x^2})$, 3rd degree, for x near 0.

19. If we had used S_5 to compute $e^{\cdot 1}$ in Example 4, what accuracy could we have claimed?

20. If we were to use S_3 to compute $\sin 44°$ in Example 6, what accuracy could we claim?

21. If we were to compute $\log .9$ from S_5 in Example 5 instead of $\log 1.2$, what accuracy could we claim from Lagrange's form for the remainder?

13.8   The Taylor's Series Expansion for a Function

I

In the last section we suggested that the nth-degree polynomial

$$S_n(x) = f(a) + f'(a) \frac{(x - a)^1}{1!} + f''(a) \frac{(x - a)^2}{2!} + \cdots + f^{(n)}(a) \frac{(x - a)^n}{n!}$$

could be expected to approximate $f(x)$ near $x = a$, and we showed that, if $f^{(n+1)}$ was continuous for an interval I that included $x = a$, then for any x of interval I the difference between $f(x)$ and $S_n(x)$ could be written in the form

$$f(x) - S_n(x) = R_n(x) = f^{(n+1)}(w) \frac{(x - a)^{n+1}}{(n + 1)!}, \tag{1}$$

for some number w between a and x. The denominator of Eq. (1) suggests that for a given x we could hope, in general, to find that $R_n(x)$ decreased as n increased. In a case where $\lim_{n \to \infty} R_n(x) = 0$ for x of I, one can say that the polynomials $S_n(x)$ approach $f(x)$ for x of interval I when n grows beyond all bounds. From the very definition of the convergence of an infinite series, Definition 13.2-1, this means that the series

$$f(a) + \sum_{k=1}^{\infty} f^{(k)}(a) \frac{(x - a)^k}{k!}$$

converges to $f(x)$ for x of I. We repeat Definition 13.2-1, applied to this case, for the sake of emphasis.

■ DEFINITION 1

The Taylor series expansion for a function. Let $f(x)$ have derivatives of all orders at $x = a$. Let

$$S_n(x) = f(a) + \sum_{k=1}^{n} f^{(k)}(a) \frac{(x - a)^k}{k!},$$

and let
$$R_n(x) = f(x) - S_n(x).$$

We shall write
$$f(x) = f(a) + f'(a)\frac{(x-a)}{1!} + f''(a)\frac{(x-a)^2}{2!} + \cdots,$$

$$f(x) = f(a) + \sum_{k=1}^{\infty} f^{(k)}(a)\frac{(x-a)^k}{k!}$$

for an interval I which includes $x = a$, and call this infinite series the Taylor series expansion for f for interval I, if $\lim_{n\to\infty} R_n(x) = 0$ for every x of interval I.

There are series representations other than power series expansions. To illustrate, it can be shown that there is a Fourier series expansion for the function $f(x) = x$ valid for x of the interval $-\pi < x < \pi$. The expansion is a series of trigonometric terms:

$$f(x) = x = 2\sin x - \tfrac{2}{2}\sin 2x + \tfrac{2}{3}\sin 3x - + \cdots = \sum_{k=1}^{\infty} (-1)^{k+1}\frac{2}{k}\sin kx.$$

We repeat the convergence definition given above in more general form in order to take representations other than the Taylor series representations into account also.

■ DEFINITION 2

An infinite series expansion for a function. We are given a function $f(x)$ whose domain is an interval I, and an infinite series $\sum_{k=1}^{\infty} u_k(x)$, the domain of each function $u_k(x)$, $k = 1, 2, 3, \cdots$, containing the interval I. Let

$$S_n(x) = \sum_{k=1}^{n} u_k(x)$$

denote the partial sums of the series, and let

$$R_n(x) = f(x) - S_n(x).$$

We shall say that the series converges to $f(x)$ for all x of I if $\lim_{n\to\infty} R_n(x) = 0$ for all x of interval I.

Example 1. For $f(x) = e^x$ we find that $f^{(k)}(x) = e^x$ and $f^{(k)}(0) = 1$ for all k. Since $f^{(n+1)}(x) = e^x$ is continuous for all x we consider

$$S_n(x) = 1 + \frac{x^1}{1!} + \frac{x^2}{2!} + \frac{x^3}{3!} + \cdots + \frac{x^n}{n!}$$

and quote Taylor's Theorem, Theorem 13.7-1, to claim that for any number x there is a number w, w between 0 and x, such that

$$R_n(x) = f(x) - S_n(x) = f^{(n+1)}(w)\frac{x^{n+1}}{(n+1)!} = e^w\frac{x^{n+1}}{(n+1)!}. \tag{2}$$

Now let any number x be presented to us. If x is negative, we have $x < w < 0$ and $e^w < e^0 = 1$. If x is positive, we can choose an integer q that is greater than

x and say that $e^w < e^q$. In both cases, when a specific number x is presented the e^w factor of Eq. (2) is bounded.

But for the $x^{n+1}/(n+1)!$ factor of Eq. (2) we observe that, when we studied the infinite series

$$\sum_{k=0}^{\infty} \frac{x^k}{k!} = 1 + \frac{x^1}{1!} + \frac{x^2}{2!} + \cdots$$

in Example 13.6-4, we found that the series converged for *all* x, and that, consequently, the terms of the series approached 0;

$$\lim_{n\to\infty} \frac{x^{n+1}}{(n+1)!} = 0 \qquad \text{for all } x.$$

Returning to Eq. (2), we conclude that $\lim_{n\to\infty} R_n(x) = 0$ for every x and we write

$$e^x = 1 + \frac{x^1}{1!} + \frac{x^2}{2!} + \frac{x^3}{3!} + \cdots = \sum_{k=0}^{\infty} \frac{x^k}{k!}, \qquad \text{for all } x.$$

Example 2. For the binomial function, $f(x) = (1 + x)^m$, m a constant, we have

$$f(x) = (1 + x)^m, \qquad\qquad f(0) = 1,$$
$$f'(x) = m(1 + x)^{m-1}, \qquad\qquad f'(0) = m,$$
$$f''(x) = m(m - 1)(1 + x)^{m-2}, \qquad\qquad f''(0) = m(m - 1),$$
$$f'''(x) = m(m - 1)(m - 2)(1 + x)^{m-3}, \qquad f'''(0) = m(m - 1)(m - 2),$$

$$\cdots\cdots\cdots\cdots\cdots\cdots\cdots\cdots\cdots\cdots \qquad\qquad \cdots\cdots\cdots\cdots\cdots\cdots\cdots$$

$$f^{(k)}(x) = m(m - 1)(m - 2) \qquad\qquad f^{(k)}(0) = m(m - 1)(m - 2)$$
$$\cdots (m - [k - 1])(1 + x)^{m-k}, \qquad\qquad \cdots (m - [k - 1]),$$

and we write

$$S_n(x) = 1 + \sum_{k=1}^{n} m(m - 1)(m - 2) \cdots (m - [k - 1]) \frac{x^k}{k!}.$$

If m is a positive integer, the factor $(m - [k - 1])$ will be 0 when $k = m + 1$, and we shall find that when $n > m$ the terms of $S_n(x)$ of degree greater than m all vanish. Because $f^{(m+1)}(x) = 0$ for all x in this case, we can quote Taylor's Theorem and say that, for all x,

$$R_m(x) = f(x) - S_m(x) = f^{(m+1)}(w) \frac{x^{m+1}}{(m + 1)!} = 0 \frac{x^{m+1}}{(m + 1)!} = 0.$$

Hence, when m is a positive integer, $f(x) = (1 + x)^m = S_m(x)$; this is the Binomial Theorem of elementary algebra.

But if m is not a positive integer, then $f^{(m+1)}(x)$ is continuous for $x > -1$ and Taylor's Theorem, Theorem 13.7-1, enables us to say that there is a number w, between 0 and x, such that

$$R_n(x) = f^{(n+1)}(w) \frac{x^{n+1}}{(n + 1)!}$$

$$= m(m - 1)(m - 2) \cdots (m - n)(1 + w)^{m-n-1} \frac{x^{n+1}}{(n + 1)!}. \qquad (3)$$

If x is positive, then $0 < w < x$, so that $1 < 1 + w$, $1/(1 + w) < 1$. Then

$$(1 + w)^{m-n-1} = \frac{1}{(1 + w)^{n+1-m}} < (1)^{n+1-m} = 1. \tag{4}$$

Here we have used the fact that when n grows larger the exponent $(m - n - 1)$ becomes negative. Now, from Eq. (3) we have

$$|R_n(x)| \leq \left| m(m - 1)(m - 2)\cdots(m - n) \frac{x^{n+1}}{(n + 1)!} \right|. \tag{5}$$

Since the infinite series with general term

$$m(m - 1)(m - 2)\cdots(m - [k - 1]) \frac{x^k}{k!}$$

converges for $-1 < x < 1$ by the ratio test,* the terms of that series approach 0 when k grows beyond all bounds. Thus, by Eq. (5), $\lim_{n\to\infty} R_n(x) = 0$ for $0 < x < 1$.

For x negative we have $x < w < 0$, and we cannot use Formula (4). But Taylor's Theorem, Theorem 13.7-1, can be stated in other forms. The Cauchy form for the remainder says that, under the same hypotheses, there also exists a number w', between a and x, such that

$$R_n(x) = f^{n+1}(w')(x - w')^n \frac{(x - a)}{n!}.$$

We shall not derive Cauchy's form for the remainder, nor shall we use it here to show that for $-1 < x < 0$ we again have $\lim_{n\to\infty} R_n(x) = 0$. But when this has been demonstrated we can write

$$(1 + x)^m = 1 + \sum_{k=1}^{\infty} m(m - 1)(m - 2)\cdots(m - [k - 1]) \frac{x^k}{k!}, \quad -1 < x < 1. \tag{6}$$

● **Remark 1**

Sometimes, as in the case of $f(x) = e^x$, it is relatively easy to show that the partial sums of the Taylor series expansion approach $f(x)$ for a certain interval; sometimes, as in the case of $f(x) = (1 + x)^m$, it is relatively difficult. But the proof that $\lim_{n\to\infty} R_n(x) = 0$ cannot be dispensed with. There are functions, with derivatives of all orders, for which $\lim_{n\to\infty} R_n(x) \neq 0$. For such an $f(x)$ the series

$$f(a) + \sum_{k=1}^{\infty} f^{(k)}(a) \frac{(x - a)^k}{k!}$$

may converge, but *not* to $f(x)$. Such a function is presented in Exercise 13.8-20.

● **Remark 2**

The Taylor series expansion for the special case $a = 0$ is often called the Maclaurin expansion. But Maclaurin was a student of Taylor and there is no historical justification for this name.

---

* See Exercise 13.6-30. We find that $u_{n+1}/u_n = [(m - n)/(n + 1)]x$ and that $t = \lim_{n\to\infty} |u_{n+1}/u_n| = |x|$.

||

Having defined the Taylor series expansion, we shall now discuss some of its properties. We have already touched on the fact that absolutely convergent series can be multiplied and divided;* it is shown in advanced calculus courses that all series with the property called uniform convergence can be integrated term by term, and that many such series can be differentiated term by term. Series of powers of x, or of powers of $x - a$, are both absolutely and uniformly convergent within their intervals of convergence, and we have the following theorem, which we state without proof.

■ THEOREM 1

Operations on power series.

HYPOTHESIS: (a) $f(x) = \sum_{k=0}^{\infty} a_k x^k, \ -R_1 < x < R_1,$

(b) $g(x) = \sum_{k=0}^{\infty} b_k x^k, \ -R_2 < x < R_2,$

(c) R is the smaller of R_1 and R_2.

CONCLUSION: (a) $f(x) + g(x) = \sum_{k=0}^{\infty} (a_k + b_k) x^k, \ -R < x < R,$

(b) $f'(x) = \sum_{k=1}^{\infty} k a_k x^{k-1}, \ -R_1 < x < R_1,$

(c) $\int_{\alpha}^{\beta} f(x)\, dx = \sum_{k=0}^{\infty} \int_{\alpha}^{\beta} a_k x^k\, dx$

$$= \sum_{k=0}^{\infty} \frac{a_k}{k+1} (\beta^{k+1} - \alpha^{k+1}), \ -R_1 < \alpha < \beta < R_1,$$

(d) $f(x)g(x) = \left(\sum_{k=0}^{\infty} a_k x^k \right)\left(\sum_{j=0}^{\infty} b_j x^j \right), \ -R < x < R,$

(e) $\dfrac{f(x)}{g(x)} = \dfrac{\displaystyle\sum_{k=0}^{\infty} a_k x^k}{\displaystyle\sum_{k=0}^{\infty} b_k x^k}, \ -R' < x < R'$

where R' is either the number R or the absolute value of that solution of $g(x) = 0$ which is closest to 0, whichever is smaller.†

● Remark 3

We have written this theorem for series of powers of x; there is an entirely analogous theorem for series of powers of $x - a$.

---

* Remark 13.5-4.
† Complex solutions of $g(x) = 0$ are to be admitted here.

● Remark 4

We know that polynomials can be added term by term, differentiated and integrated term by term, multiplied, and divided (provided we do not attempt division by 0). This theorem says that power series, within their intervals of convergence, are like polynomials in these respects. There may also be convergence at the boundary numbers of the intervals of convergence, but this will vary from case to case.

Example 3. We know from Example 1 that

$$e^x = 1 + x + \frac{x^2}{2!} + \frac{x^3}{3!} + \frac{x^4}{4!} + \frac{x^5}{5!} + \frac{x^6}{6!} + \cdots, \qquad \text{for all } x. \qquad (7)$$

If we write $x = -y$, we shall have

$$e^{-y} = 1 - y + \frac{y^2}{2!} - \frac{y^3}{3!} + \frac{y^4}{4!} - \frac{y^5}{5!} + \frac{y^6}{6!} - +\cdots, \qquad \text{for all } y$$

or

$$e^{-x} = 1 - x + \frac{x^2}{2!} - \frac{x^3}{3!} + \frac{x^4}{4!} - \frac{x^5}{5!} + \frac{x^6}{6!} - +\cdots, \qquad \text{for all } x. \qquad (8)$$

From Eqs. (7) and (8) we have, by virtue of Conclusion (a) of Theorem 1,

$$\cosh x = \frac{1}{2}(e^x + e^{-x}) = \frac{1}{2}\left(2 + \frac{2x^2}{2!} + \frac{2x^4}{4!} + \frac{2x^6}{6!} + \cdots\right)$$

$$= 1 + \frac{x^2}{2!} + \frac{x^4}{4!} + \frac{x^6}{6!} + \cdots = \sum_{k=0}^{\infty} \frac{x^{2k}}{(2k)!}, \qquad \text{for all } x. \qquad (9)$$

Example 4. Consider Series (7) for $f(x) = e^x$ again. By virtue of Conclusion (b) of Theorem 1 we have

$$f'(x) = 0 + 1 + \frac{2x}{2!} + \frac{3x^2}{3!} + \frac{4x^3}{4!} + \frac{5x^4}{5!} + \frac{6x^5}{6!} + \cdots, \qquad \text{for all } x,$$

$$= 1 + x + \frac{x^2}{2!} + \frac{x^3}{3!} + \frac{x^4}{4!} + \frac{x^5}{5!} + \cdots = e^x, \qquad \text{for all } x.$$

Example 5. Let us take advantage of the fact that

$$\int_0^x \frac{1}{\sqrt{1-x^2}}\, dx = \sin^{-1} x$$

to develop an expansion for $\sin^{-1} x$. A direct attempt at expansion by using the successive derivatives of $\sin^{-1} x$ is quite laborious.*

Equation (6) tells us that

$$(1+y)^m = 1 + my + m(m-1)\frac{y^2}{2!} + m(m-1)(m-2)\frac{y^3}{3!}$$

$$+ m(m-1)(m-2)(m-3)\frac{y^4}{4!} + \cdots, \qquad -1 < y < 1.$$

---

* See Exercise 13.7-16.

If we write $y = -x^2$ and $m = -\frac{1}{2}$, we have

$$(1 - x^2)^{-1/2} = 1 + \frac{1}{2} x^2 - \frac{1}{2} \left(-\frac{3}{2}\right) \frac{x^4}{2!} + \frac{1}{2} \left(-\frac{3}{2}\right) \left(-\frac{5}{2}\right) \frac{x^6}{3!}$$

$$- \frac{1}{2} \left(-\frac{3}{2}\right) \left(-\frac{5}{2}\right) \left(-\frac{7}{2}\right) \frac{x^8}{4!} + \cdots, \qquad -1 < -x^2 < 1,$$

or

$$(1 - x^2)^{-1/2} = 1 + \frac{1}{2} x^2 + \frac{1 \cdot 3}{2 \cdot 4} x^4 + \frac{1 \cdot 3 \cdot 5}{2 \cdot 4 \cdot 6} x^6$$

$$+ \frac{1 \cdot 3 \cdot 5 \cdot 7}{2 \cdot 4 \cdot 6 \cdot 8} x^8 + \cdots, \qquad -1 < x < 1.*$$

Now Conclusion (c) enables us to integrate, term by term, getting

$$\sin^{-1} x = \int_0^x (1 - x^2)^{-1/2} \, dx = x + \frac{1}{2} \frac{x^3}{3} + \frac{1 \cdot 3}{2 \cdot 4} \frac{x^5}{5}$$

$$+ \frac{1 \cdot 3 \cdot 5}{2 \cdot 4 \cdot 6} \frac{x^7}{7} + \frac{1 \cdot 3 \cdot 5 \cdot 7}{2 \cdot 4 \cdot 6 \cdot 8} \frac{x^9}{9} + \cdots, \qquad -1 < x < 1.$$

In more concise form,

$$\sin^{-1} x = x + \sum_{k=1}^{\infty} \frac{1 \cdot 3 \cdot 5 \cdots (2k - 1)}{2 \cdot 4 \cdot 6 \cdots (2k)} \frac{x^{2k+1}}{2k + 1}, \qquad -1 < x < 1.$$

We put aside the question of whether this series might not also give us $\sin^{-1} x$ for $x = \pm 1$.

Example 6.   We already know that

$$e^{-x} = 1 - \frac{x}{1!} + \frac{x^2}{2!} - \frac{x^3}{3!} + \frac{x^4}{4!} - \frac{x^5}{5!} + \frac{x^6}{6!} - + \cdots, \qquad \text{for all } x,$$

and in Exercise 13.8-2 the reader can show that

$$\cos x = 1 - \frac{x^2}{2!} + \frac{x^4}{4!} - \frac{x^6}{6!} + - \cdots, \qquad \text{for all } x.$$

According to Conclusion (d) of Theorem 1, the series for $f(x) = e^{-x} \cos x$ can be obtained by straightforward multiplication. We get, for the first terms,

$$1 - \frac{x}{1} + \frac{x^2}{2} - \frac{x^3}{6} \quad + \frac{x^4}{24} - \frac{x^5}{120} + \frac{x^6}{720} - + \cdots$$

$$- \frac{x^2}{2} + \frac{x^3}{2(1)} - \frac{x^4}{2(2)} + \frac{x^5}{2(6)} - \frac{x^6}{2(24)} + - \cdots$$

$$+ \frac{x^4}{24} - \frac{x^5}{24(1)} + \frac{x^6}{24(2)} - + \cdots$$

$$- \frac{x^6}{720} + - \cdots$$

$$\cdots \cdots$$

$$e^{-x} \cos x = 1 - x + 0x^2 + \frac{x^3}{3} - \frac{x^4}{6} + \frac{x^5}{30} + 0x^6 \cdots.$$

---

* Observe, for instance, that $2^3(3!) = 2^3(1)(2)(3) = 2(4)(6)$; also note that if $-1 < -x^2 < 1$, then, upon multiplying by -1, we get $1 > x^2 > -1$, and this reduces to $-1 < x < 1$.

If we worked out instructions for writing all the terms of this series, as the reader can in Exercise 13.8-21, we would have a representation for $e^{-x} \cos x$ valid for all x.

Example 7. Let us find a series representation for $\tan x$ from the fact that $\tan x = \sin x / \cos x$. The direct computation of the successive derivatives of $\tan x$ is tedious.*

The reader can show in Exercises 13.8-1 and 13.8-2 that

$$\sin x = x - \frac{x^3}{3!} + \frac{x^5}{5!} - \frac{x^7}{7!} + - \cdots, \qquad \text{for all } x$$

and

$$\cos x = 1 - \frac{x^2}{2!} + \frac{x^4}{4!} - \frac{x^6}{6!} + - \cdots, \qquad \text{for all } x.$$

We know, also, that $\cos (\pi/2) = 0$. Conclusion (e) of Theorem 1 then tells us that we will get an expansion for $\tan x$ by straightforward long division, and that this representation will be valid for $-\pi/2 < x < \pi/2$. We write

$$x + \frac{x^3}{3} + \frac{2}{15} x^5 + \frac{17}{315} x^7 + \cdots$$

$$1 - \frac{x^2}{2} + \frac{x^4}{24} - \frac{x^6}{720} + - \cdots \overline{\smash{\big)}\ x - \frac{x^3}{6} + \frac{x^5}{120} - \frac{x^7}{5040} + - \cdots}$$

$$x - \frac{x^3}{2} + \frac{x^5}{24} - \frac{x^7}{720} + - \cdots$$

$$+ \frac{x^3}{3} - \frac{x^5}{30} + \frac{x^7}{840} \cdots$$

$$\frac{x^3}{3} - \frac{x^5}{6} + \frac{x^7}{72} \cdots$$

$$\frac{2}{15} x^5 - \frac{4x^7}{315} \cdots$$

$$\frac{2}{15} x^5 - \frac{1}{15} x^7 \cdots$$

$$+ \frac{17x^7}{315} \cdots .$$

$$\tan x = x + \frac{x^3}{3} + \frac{2}{15} x^5 + \frac{17}{315} x^7 \cdots .$$

Since $\tan (\pi/2)$ is not defined, there is no question of the validity of the representation for $x = \pm\pi/2$.

III

A natural question that now arises is this: Suppose we have two power series expansions for the same function, one obtained perhaps by using Taylor's Theorem,

---

* Exercise 13.7-13.

and one perhaps by long division. Must the two expansions be identical? The answer is "yes!" A given function can have only one power series expansion for a given interval.

■ THEOREM 2

The uniqueness theorem for power series expansions.

HYPOTHESIS: (a) $f(x) = \sum_{k=0}^{\infty} a_k x^k, \ -R < x < R,$

(b) $f(x) = \sum_{k=0}^{\infty} b_k x^k, \ -R < x < R.$

CONCLUSION: $a_k = b_k, \ k = 1, 2, 3 \cdots.$

PROOF: *Step (1).* Substituting $x = 0$ in Hypothesis (a), we get $f(0) = a_0.$ Hypothesis (b) tells us that $f(0) = b_0.$ Thus $a_0 = b_0.$

Step (2):   Theorem 1 tells us that we can differentiate a power series representation term by term to get the derivative of the function represented by the power series. Hence

$$f'(x) = \sum_{k=1}^{\infty} k a_k x^{k-1} = \sum_{k=1}^{\infty} k b_k x^{k-1}, \qquad -R < x < R.$$

If we substitute $x = 0$ again, we find that $f'(0) = 1a_1 = 1b_1.$

Step (3): When we apply Theorem 1 to the two power series for $f'(x)$ and differentiate, we get

$$f''(x) = \sum_{k=2}^{\infty} k(k-1) a_k x^{k-2} = \sum_{k=2}^{\infty} k(k-1) b_k x^{k-2}, \qquad -R < x < R.$$

If we now substitute $x = 0$ again, we find that $f''(0) = 2(1)a_2 = 2(1)b_2,$ or $a_2 = b_2.$

Step (4):   If we continue in this way, we can demonstrate each statement of the conclusion.

EXERCISES 13.8

1. Show that $\sin x = \sum_{k=0}^{\infty} \dfrac{(-1)^k x^{2k+1}}{(2k+1)!} = \dfrac{x}{1!} - \dfrac{x^3}{3!} + \dfrac{x^5}{5!} - + \cdots$ for all $x.$

2. Show that $\cos x = \sum_{k=0}^{\infty} (-1)^k \dfrac{x^{2k}}{(2k)!} = 1 - \dfrac{x^2}{2!} + \dfrac{x^4}{4!} - \dfrac{x^6}{6!} + - \cdots$ for all $x.$

3. Use Taylor's Theorem to show that

(a) $\log (1 + x) = \sum_{k=1}^{\infty} (-1)^{k+1} \dfrac{x^k}{k} = x - \dfrac{x^2}{2} + \dfrac{x^3}{3} - \dfrac{x^4}{4} + - \cdots$ for $0 \le x \le 1.$

(b) The same as Part (a) for $-\frac{1}{2} \le x \le 0.$*

---

*It is true that $\log (1 + x) = \sum_{k=1}^{\infty} (-1)^{k+1} x^k/k$ for $-1 < x < -\frac{1}{2}$ also, but this cannot be demonstrated directly by using Taylor's Theorem with the remainder in Lagrange's form. See Exercise 13.8-14, however.

4. (a) Use long division to demonstrate the algebraic identity

$$\frac{1}{1+x} = 1 - x + x^2 - x^3 + \cdots(-1)^n x^n + \frac{(-1)^{n+1}x^{n+1}}{1+x}$$

$$= \sum_{k=0}^{n} (-1)^k x^k + R_n(x),$$

where
$$R_n(x) = (-1)^{n+1}\frac{x^{n+1}}{1+x}.$$

(b) Show that $\dfrac{1}{1+x} = \displaystyle\sum_{k=0}^{\infty} (-1)^k x^k$ for $-1 < x < 1$ by showing that $\displaystyle\lim_{n\to\infty} R_n(x)$
$= 0$ for $-1 < x < 1$.

5. Derive the expansion $\sinh x = \displaystyle\sum_{k=0}^{\infty} \frac{x^{2k+1}}{(2k+1)!} = \frac{x^1}{1!} + \frac{x^3}{3!} + \frac{x^5}{5!} + \cdots$ for all x from

those for e^x and e^{-x}.

6. (a) Derive the power series expansion for $\cos 2x$ from that for $\cos x$.

(b) Use the identity $\sin^2 x = \dfrac{1 - \cos 2x}{2}$ to derive the power series expansion for

$\sin^2 x$.

7. Assume that the power series expansion of Exercise 3 for $\log (1 + x)$ is valid for
$-1 < x < 1$.* (a) Find power series expansions for $\log (1 - x)$ and $\log \dfrac{1 + x}{1 - x}$.

For which x are these expansions valid?
(b) Show that the series for $\log [(1 + x)/(1 - x)]$ can be used to compute $\log q$ for
any number $q > 0$ by showing that for any such q there is an x of $-1 < x < 1$ such
that $q = (1 + x)/(1 - x)$.

8. Imagine $\sin x$ and $\cos x$ defined by the power series expansions given in Exercises
1 and 2. Show that

$$\frac{d \sin x}{dx} = \cos x \qquad \text{and} \qquad \frac{d \cos x}{dx} = - \sin x.$$

9. Imagine $\sinh x$ and $\cosh x$ defined by the power series expansions given in Exercise 5
and Eq. (9). Show that

$$\frac{d \sinh x}{dx} = \cosh x \qquad \text{and} \qquad \frac{d \cosh x}{dx} = \sinh x.$$

10. The equation

$$J_0(x) = \sum_{k=0}^{\infty} (-1)^k \frac{1}{k!k!} \left(\frac{x}{2}\right)^{2k}$$

$$= 1 - \left(\frac{x}{2}\right)^2 + \frac{1}{2!2!}\left(\frac{x}{2}\right)^4 - \frac{1}{3!3!}\left(\frac{x}{2}\right)^6 + \cdots$$

defines the Bessel function of order zero for all x.† Find the power series expansions

---

* See Exercise 13.8-14.
† We showed that this series converges for all x in Exercise 13.6-20.

for (a) $\dfrac{dJ_0(x)}{dx}$ and (b) $\dfrac{d^2J_0(x)}{dx^2}$, and (c) show that $y = J_0(x)$ is a solution of

$$x\frac{d^2y}{dx^2} + \frac{dy}{dx} + xy = 0.$$

11. The equation

$$J_1(x) = \sum_{k=0}^{\infty} \frac{(-1)^k}{k!(k+1)!}\left(\frac{x}{2}\right)^{2k+1}$$

$$= \frac{x}{2} - \frac{1}{1!2!}\left(\frac{x}{2}\right)^3 + \frac{1}{2!3!}\left(\frac{x}{2}\right)^5 - + \cdots$$

defines the Bessel function of order one for all x.* Find the power series expansions

for (a) $\dfrac{dJ_1(x)}{dx}$ and (b) $\dfrac{d^2J_1(x)}{dx^2}$, and (c) show that $y = J_1(x)$ is a solution of

$$x^2\frac{d^2y}{dx^2} + x\frac{dy}{dx} + (x^2 - 1)y = 0.$$

12. Let $J_0(x)$ and $J_1(x)$ be defined as in Exercises 10 and 11. Show that

(a) $\dfrac{d}{dx}(xJ_1(x)) = xJ_0(x).$

(b) $\dfrac{d}{dx}(J_0(x)) = -J_1(x).$

13. (a) Use either Eq. (6) or Exercise 4(b) to write a series expansion for $1/(1+y)$, $-1 < y < 1$.

(b) From this expansion write one for $\dfrac{1}{1+x^2}$.

(c) Use the fact that $\tan^{-1} x = \displaystyle\int_0^x \frac{1}{1+x^2}\,dx$ to show that

$$\tan^{-1} x = \sum_{k=0}^{\infty} (-1)^k \frac{x^{2k+1}}{2k+1}$$

$$= x - \frac{x^3}{3} + \frac{x^5}{5} - \frac{x^7}{7} + \frac{x^9}{9} - + \cdots, \qquad -1 < x < 1.$$

14. (a) Use either Eq. (6) or Exercise 4(b) to write a series expansion for $\dfrac{1}{1+x}$, $-1 < x < 1$.

(b) Use the fact that $\log(1+x) = \displaystyle\int_0^x \frac{1}{1+x}\,dx$ to show that

$$\log(1+x) = \sum_{k=1}^{\infty} (-1)^{k+1}\frac{x^k}{k}$$

$$= x - \frac{x^2}{2} + \frac{x^3}{3} - \frac{x^4}{4} + \frac{x^5}{5} - + \cdots, \qquad -1 < x < 1.$$

* We showed that this series converges for all x in Exercise 13.6-21.

15. From the series expansions for e^{-x} and $\sin x$ work out the expansion for $e^{-x} \sin x$ through the term of sixth degree.

16. Check on the first three terms of the computation of Exercise 6(b) by multiplying the expansion for $\sin x$ by itself.

17. Use the $\cos x$ expansion and long division to show that

$$\sec x = 1 + \frac{x^2}{2} + \frac{5x^4}{24} + \frac{61x^6}{720} + \cdots, \qquad \text{for } -\frac{\pi}{2} < x < +\frac{\pi}{2}.$$

18. The expansions for $\sinh x$ and $\cosh x$ are given in Exercise 5 and Eq. (9). From these expansions show that

$$\tanh x = x - \frac{x^3}{3} + \frac{2x^5}{15} - \frac{17x^7}{315} \cdots, \qquad \text{for all } x.$$

19. The expansions for $\log (1 + x)$ and $\dfrac{1}{1 + x}$ are given in Exercises 14 and 4. Show that

$$\frac{\log (1 + x)}{1 + x} = 1x - (1 + \tfrac{1}{2}) x^2 + (1 + \tfrac{1}{2} + \tfrac{1}{3}) x^3 - (1 + \tfrac{1}{2} + \tfrac{1}{3} + \tfrac{1}{4}) x^4 \cdots$$

for $-1 < x < 1$.

20. Let f be defined by

$$f(x) = \begin{cases} e^{-1/x^2}, & x \neq 0 \\ 0, & x = 0. \end{cases}$$

Step (a). For $x \neq 0$, we have $f'(x) = \dfrac{2}{x^3} e^{-1/x^2}$, but to get $f'(0)$ we must work directly from the definition of the derivative;

$$f'(0) = \lim_{h \to 0} \frac{f(h) - f(0)}{h} = \lim_{h \to 0} \frac{e^{-1/h^2}}{h} = \lim_{q \to \infty} \frac{\pm \sqrt{q}}{e^q} = 0, \qquad \text{if } q = \frac{1}{h^2}.*$$

Step (b). By similar arguments we show that $f''(0) = 0, f'''(0) = 0, f^{\text{iv}}(0) = 0$, and so on.

Step (c). But then Taylor's Theorem says that

$$f(x) = 0 + 0 \frac{x^1}{1!} + 0 \frac{x^2}{2!} + 0 \frac{x^3}{3!} + \cdots + 0 \frac{x^n}{n!} + R_n(x);$$

in other words, $R_n(x) = e^{-1/x^2}$ for $x \neq 0$, and $\lim\limits_{n \to \infty} R_n(x) \neq 0$ for $x \neq 0$.

21. Return to Example 6. We shall use the sum notation more systematically in writing out the expansion for $e^{-x} \cos x$. Justify the following computations.

Step 1. $e^{-x} = \sum\limits_{k=0}^{\infty} (-1)^k \dfrac{x^k}{k!}, \qquad \cos x = \sum\limits_{j=0}^{\infty} (-1)^j \dfrac{x^{2j}}{(2j)!},$

$$e^{-x} \cos x = \left(\sum_{k=0}^{\infty} (-1)^k \frac{x^k}{k!} \right) \left(\sum_{j=0}^{\infty} (-1)^j \frac{x^{2j}}{(2j)!} \right) = \sum_{k=0}^{\infty} \sum_{j=0}^{\infty} (-1)^{k+j} \frac{x^{k+2j}}{(k!)(2j)!}.$$

Step 2. At the end of Example 6 we grouped like terms through the terms of the sixth degree. We can accomplish the same thing here if we write $k + 2j = m$, to get

$$e^{-x} \cos x = \sum_{k=0}^{\infty} \sum_{j=0}^{\infty} (-1)^{m-j} \frac{x^m}{(m - 2j)! \, (2j)!},$$

---

* See Exercise 13.6-2.

and ask which j indices can lead to x^m terms. Clearly, since $m = k + 2j$ and k can only be nonnegative, we can only use integers j of the interval $0 \le j \le m^*$, where m^* is the greatest integer less than, or equal to, $m/2$. We have

$$e^{-x} \cos x = \sum_{m=0}^{\infty} (-1)^m \left\{ \sum_{j=0}^{m^*} \frac{(-1)^j}{(m-2j)! \, (2j)!} \right\} x^m.$$

Step 3. In detail, when $m = 0$ we have $m^* = 0$ and the x^0 term of the expansion has the coefficient $(-1)^0 \dfrac{(-1)^0}{0!0!} = 1$. When $m = 1$ we have $m^* = 0$ again and the x term of the expansion has the coefficient $(-1)^1 \dfrac{(-1)^0}{1! \, 0!} = -1$. When $m = 2$ we have $m^* = 1$ and the x^2 term has the coefficient $(-1)^2 \left(\dfrac{(-1)^0}{2! \, 0!} + \dfrac{(-1)^1}{0! \, 2!} \right) = 0$.

22. Return to Exercise 19. Use the sum notation to prove that

$$\frac{\log (1+x)}{1+x} = \sum_{k=1}^{\infty} (-1)^{k-1} \left\{ \sum_{j=1}^{k} \frac{1}{j} \right\} x^k, \qquad -1 < x < 1.$$

23. Theorem 1 says that the derivative of a function defined by a series of powers of x is the new series obtained by differentiating the given series term by term. Here is an exercise that shows that, when a function is defined by some other kind of infinite series, we cannot always be sure of getting a derivative by differentiating the given series term by term. (a) Show that the series $\sum_{k=1}^{\infty} \dfrac{\sin kx}{k^2}$ converges absolutely for all x by pointing out that $|\sin kx| \le 1$ for all x and all k and by comparing with the p_2 series. Write $\phi(x) = \sum_{k=1}^{\infty} \dfrac{\sin kx}{k^2}$. (b) Show that the series one gets by differentiating the series for $\phi(x)$ term by term, namely $\sum_{k=1}^{\infty} \dfrac{\cos kx}{k}$, does not converge for $x = 0$.

13.9   Applications 1

Infinite series are of wide application; we can only touch on several applications in this first course.

First, many functions are defined by infinite series expansions and these series are used to compute tables of values for the functions; the Bessel functions are such functions. Many functions are defined in other ways, but their infinite series expansions furnish the most practical means of computing tables of values for them also. The function values for the trigonometric, exponential, and logarithmic functions are computed this way. In computing function values, a partial sum of the series, S_n, is used and infinitely many terms, R_n, are neglected. An upper bound must be established for the terms neglected so that we can know with how much confidence to use the approximation furnished by S_n. If the terms neglected are an alternating series of terms that decrease steadily in absolute value, approaching 0, then we can say that the remainder neglected is less than the first neglected term in absolute value. If we deal with a series of powers of $x - a$, perhaps derived by a Taylor's Theorem argument, we can try to estimate R_n by using the statement that

$$R_n(x) = f^{n+1}(w) \frac{(x-a)^{n+1}}{(n+1)!}, \qquad w \text{ between } x \text{ and } a.$$

Sometimes the infinitely many terms neglected can be compared with an improper integral; sometimes they can be compared with other series of terms for which bounds can be set up.

Example 1.   The Bessel function of order zero is defined by the series

$$J_0(x) = \sum_{k=0}^{\infty} (-1)^k \frac{1}{k!k!} \left(\frac{x}{2}\right)^{2k}$$

$$= 1 - \left(\frac{x}{2}\right)^2 + \frac{1}{2!2!}\left(\frac{x}{2}\right)^4 - \frac{1}{3!3!}\left(\frac{x}{2}\right)^6 + -\cdots, \qquad \text{for all } x.$$

Compute $J_0(1)$ with error less than 0.00005.

The series we are to deal with is an alternating series whose terms decrease steadily in absolute value when $x = 1$, approaching 0. Let the $k = j$ term be the first neglected term; we must determine j so that

$$\frac{1}{j!j!2^{2j}} < 0.00005, \tag{1}$$

for in such an alternating series the absolute value of the remainder is less than the absolute value of the first neglected term. A little numerical experimenting tells us that $j = 3$ will not satisfy the requirement of (1) but that $j = 4$ will. Hence we are safe if we write

$$J_0(1) \approx 1 - \left(\frac{1}{2}\right)^2 + \frac{1}{2!2!}\left(\frac{1}{2}\right)^4 - \frac{1}{3!3!}\left(\frac{1}{2}\right)^6 = 1 - \frac{1}{4} + \frac{1}{64} - \frac{1}{36(64)} \approx 0.7652.$$

Examples 4, 5, and 6 of Sec. 13.7 illustrate the use of Taylor's Theorem in computing function values for the exponential, logarithmic, and trigonometric functions. We illustrate Taylor's Theorem again in a case of more difficult detail.

Example 2.   To illustrate a computation of $\sqrt[3]{100}$ by using the series for $(1 + x)^{1/3}$, we start by writing

$$\sqrt[3]{100} = \sqrt[3]{125}\,\sqrt[3]{\frac{100}{125}} = 5\sqrt[3]{.8} = 5[1 - .2]^{1/3}.$$

If we refer to Eq. (6) of Sec. 13.8 we have

$$(1 + x)^{1/3} = 1 + \frac{1}{3}x + \left(\frac{1}{3}\right)\left(-\frac{2}{3}\right)\frac{x^2}{2!} + \left(\frac{1}{3}\right)\left(-\frac{2}{3}\right)\left(-\frac{5}{3}\right)\frac{x^3}{3!}$$

$$+ \left(\frac{1}{3}\right)\left(-\frac{2}{3}\right)\left(-\frac{5}{3}\right)\left(-\frac{8}{3}\right)\frac{x^4}{4!} + \cdots$$

$$(1 - .2)^{1/3} = 1 - \frac{.2}{3} - \frac{2}{3^2}\frac{(.2)^2}{2!} - \frac{2 \cdot 5}{3^3}\frac{(.2)^3}{3!} - \frac{2 \cdot 5 \cdot 8}{3^4}\frac{(.2)^4}{4!} - \cdots.$$

We refer to the remainder statement of Taylor's Theorem, Eq. (3) of Sec. 13.8:

$$R_4 = \frac{1}{3}\left(-\frac{2}{3}\right)\left(-\frac{5}{3}\right)\left(-\frac{8}{3}\right)\left(-\frac{11}{3}\right)(1 + w)^{1/3-5}\frac{(-.2)^5}{5!}, \qquad -.2 < w < 0,$$

notice that R_4 is negative, and then write

$$|R_4| = \frac{2 \cdot 5 \cdot 8 \cdot 11}{3 \cdot 6 \cdot 9 \cdot 12 \cdot 15} \frac{(1+w)^{1/3}}{(1+w)^5} (.2)^5.$$

Since w is a number of the interval $-.2 < w < 0$, $1 + w$ is a number of the interval $.8 < 1 + w < 1$, so that

$$(1+w)^{1/3} < 1^{1/3} = 1 \qquad \text{and} \qquad \frac{1}{(1+w)^5} < \frac{1}{(.8)^5}.$$

Also, $\frac{2}{3}, \frac{5}{6}, \frac{8}{9}$, and $\frac{11}{12}$ are all less than 1, so that we now have

$$|R_4| < 1 \cdot 1 \cdot 1 \cdot 1 \cdot \frac{1}{15} \frac{1}{(.8)^5} (.2)^5 = \frac{1}{15} \left(\frac{1}{4}\right)^5 < .000066.$$

Thus

$$(1 - .2)^{1/3} \approx 1 - \frac{.2}{3} - \frac{2}{3^2} \frac{(.2)^2}{2!} - \frac{2 \cdot 5}{3^3} \frac{(.2)^3}{3!} - \frac{2 \cdot 5 \cdot 8}{3^4} \frac{(.2)^4}{4!} \approx .9283$$

and

$$\sqrt[3]{100} = 5 \sqrt[3]{.8} \approx 5(.9283) = 4.6415.$$

Because R_4 was negative, our answer is too large, but the error is not more than $5(.000066) = .000330$. If we had wanted a more accurate result, we could have used more terms of the series.

The computation of function values is part of a more general application, that of furnishing polynomial approximations to functions.

Example 3. The length L of a metal rod varies with the temperature T. A rod that is twice as long as another will increase in length by twice as much for the same increase in T: $dL/dT = \alpha L$, where α is a physical constant of proportionality, quite small for most metals. Hence we have

$$\frac{1}{L} \frac{dL}{dT} = \alpha, \qquad \log L = \alpha T + C, \qquad \text{and} \qquad L = e^{\alpha T + C} = e^{\alpha T} e^C.$$

If at $T = 0$, we have $L = L_0$, then

$$L_0 = e^0 e^C, \qquad e^C = L_0, \qquad \text{and} \qquad L = L_0 e^{\alpha T}.$$

We can write

$$L = L_0 \left[1 + \alpha T + \frac{(\alpha T)^2}{2!} + \frac{(\alpha T)^3}{3!} + \frac{(\alpha T)^4}{4!} + \cdots\right].$$

For most applications α is so small that the linear approximation will suffice, and the formula

$$L \approx L_0[1 + \alpha T]$$

is often used.

If questioned on the accuracy of this formula, we could state, much as we did in Example 13.7-4, that

$$R_1 = L_0 e^w \frac{(\alpha T)^2}{2!}, \qquad 0 < w < \alpha T,$$

and that

$$R_1 < L_0 \tfrac{3}{2}(\alpha T)^2,$$

for we could say that $\alpha T < 1$, $e^w < e^1 < 3$.

Many a definite integral that cannot be evaluated directly by the antidifferentiation technique offers less resistance when its integrand is described by an infinite series.

Example 4. The definite integral $\int_0^z e^{-x^2}\,dx$ represents an area under the "normal probability graph," $y = e^{-x^2}$, and is of great importance in many statistical problems.

Since we can write

$$e^t = 1 + \frac{t^1}{1!} + \frac{t^2}{2!} + \frac{t^3}{3!} + \frac{t^4}{4!} + \frac{t^5}{5!} + \cdots = \sum_{k=0}^{\infty} \frac{t^k}{k!}, \qquad \text{for all } t,$$

we have

$$e^{-x^2} = 1 - \frac{x^2}{1!} + \frac{x^4}{2!} - \frac{x^6}{3!} + \frac{x^8}{4!} - \frac{x^{10}}{5!} + - \cdots = \sum_{k=0}^{\infty} (-1)^k \frac{x^{2k}}{k!}, \qquad \text{for all } x.$$

Theorem 13.8-1 tells us that we can now integrate term by term. Therefore

$$\int_0^x e^{-x^2}\,dx = x - \frac{x^3}{3(1!)} + \frac{x^5}{5(2!)} - \frac{x^7}{7(3!)} + \frac{x^9}{9(4!)} - + \cdots$$

$$= \sum_{k=0}^{\infty} (-1)^k \frac{x^{2k+1}}{(2k+1)(k!)}, \qquad \text{for all } x.$$

This is an alternating series whose terms decrease steadily in absolute value, approaching 0,* and whose remainders are therefore relatively easy to estimate.

Example 5. The parametric equations $x = a \sin t$, $y = b \cos t$, $0 \le t \le 2\pi$, describe an ellipse of semimajor and semiminor axes a and b if $a > b$. The reader can show in Exercise 13.9-23 that the circumference of this ellipse is given by the definite integral

$$L = 4a \int_{t=0}^{\pi/2} \sqrt{1 - e^2 \sin^2 t}\,dt,$$

where e is the eccentricity of the ellipse.

Again the antidifferentiation technique does not help us, and we try to rewrite the integrand in series form. We know that

$$(1 + x)^{1/2} = 1 + \frac{1}{2}\frac{x}{1!} + \frac{1}{2}\left(-\frac{1}{2}\right)\frac{x^2}{2!} + \frac{1}{2}\left(-\frac{1}{2}\right)\left(-\frac{3}{2}\right)\frac{x^3}{3!}$$

$$+ \frac{1}{2}\left(-\frac{1}{2}\right)\left(-\frac{3}{2}\right)\left(-\frac{5}{2}\right)\frac{x^4}{4!} + \cdots, \qquad -1 < x < 1.$$

Since the eccentricity of an ellipse is less than 1 and $|\sin t| \le 1$ also, we can write $x = -e^2 \sin^2 t$,

$$(1 - e^2 \sin^2 t)^{1/2} = 1 - \frac{e^2}{2} \sin^2 t - \frac{1}{2 \cdot 4} e^4 \sin^4 t$$

$$- \frac{1 \cdot 3}{2 \cdot 4 \cdot 6} e^6 \sin^6 t - \frac{1 \cdot 3 \cdot 5}{2 \cdot 4 \cdot 6 \cdot 8} e^8 \sin^8 t - \cdots.$$

---

* From a certain term on, if $x > 1$.

We have shown that

$$\int_0^{\pi/2} \sin^{2n} t \, dt = \frac{1 \cdot 3 \cdot 5 \cdots (2n-1)}{2 \cdot 4 \cdot 6 \cdots 2n} \frac{\pi}{2}, \qquad n \geq 1,*$$

and hence we have

$$L = 4a \int_{t=0}^{\pi/2} \left[1 - \frac{e^2}{2} \sin^2 t - \frac{1}{2 \cdot 4} \frac{e^4}{\sin^4} t - \frac{1 \cdot 3}{2 \cdot 4 \cdot 6} \frac{e^6}{\sin^6} t - \cdots \right] dt$$

$$L = 4a \frac{\pi}{2} \left[1 - \frac{1}{2} \frac{e^2}{2} - \frac{1 \cdot 3}{2 \cdot 4} \frac{e^4}{2 \cdot 4} - \frac{1 \cdot 3 \cdot 5}{2 \cdot 4 \cdot 6} \frac{1 \cdot 3}{2 \cdot 4 \cdot 6} e^6 - \frac{1 \cdot 3 \cdot 5 \cdot 7}{2 \cdot 4 \cdot 6 \cdot 8} \frac{1 \cdot 3 \cdot 5}{2 \cdot 4 \cdot 6 \cdot 8} e^8 - \cdots \right]$$

$$L = 2\pi a \left[1 - \left(\frac{1}{2}\right)^2 \frac{e^2}{1} - \left(\frac{1 \cdot 3}{2 \cdot 4}\right)^2 \frac{e^4}{3} - \left(\frac{1 \cdot 3 \cdot 5}{2 \cdot 4 \cdot 6}\right)^2 \frac{e^6}{5} - \left(\frac{1 \cdot 3 \cdot 5 \cdot 7}{2 \cdot 4 \cdot 6 \cdot 8}\right)^2 \frac{e^8}{7} - \cdots \right]. \quad (2)$$

One way of estimating the remainders here would be to compare them with those of the geometric series $e^2 + e^4 + e^6 + e^8 + \cdots$.† Observe, as a check, that for $e = 0$ the ellipse is a circle and Eq. (2) reads $L = 2\pi a$. In this example we have evaluated an *elliptic integral*.

EXERCISES 13.9

1. (a) What approximate value do you get for log (1.05) by using 3 terms of the series for log $(1 + x)$? (b) Estimate your error.

2. Repeat the directions of Exercise 1 for $\sqrt[3]{10} = \sqrt[3]{8}\sqrt[3]{10/8} = \sqrt[3]{8}\sqrt[3]{1.25}$ and 2 terms of the series for $(1 + x)^{1/3}$.

3. Repeat the directions of Exercise 1 for $\sqrt[5]{36}$ and 3 terms of the series for $(1 + x)^{1/5}$.

4. (a) How many terms of the series for sin x do you need to compute sin .2 with error less than 0.000005? (b) Compute it.

5. The same for the series for cos x and cos .2.

6. The series for the Bessel function of order 1 is

$$J_1(x) = \sum_{k=0}^{\infty} \frac{(-1)^k}{k!(k+1)!} \left(\frac{x}{2}\right)^{2k+1}.$$

(a) How many terms of the series do you need to compute $J_1(.2)$ with error less than 0.000005? (b) Compute it.

7. Repeat the directions of Exercise 1 for log (.95) and 3 terms of the series for log $(1 + x)$.

8. (a) How many terms of the series for $(1 + x)^{1/2}$ do you need to compute $\sqrt{99}$ with error less than 0.0005? (b) Compute it.

9. (a) Why can't we compute log 3 directly from the series for log $(1 + x)$? (b) Consider

$$\log \frac{1+x}{1-x} = 2\left[x + \frac{x^3}{3} + \frac{x^5}{5} + \frac{x^7}{7} + \cdots \right], \qquad -1 < x < 1.‡$$

Observe that for $x = \frac{1}{2}$ we get log 3. Indicate the infinite series of terms neglected if

---

* See Example 6.7-5 and Exercise 6.7-41.
† See Exercise 24.
‡ See Exercise 13.8-7.

log 3 is computed from the first 5 terms. Estimate this remainder by comparing it with the geometric series $2 \, \tfrac{1}{11}(\tfrac{1}{2})^{11}[1 + \tfrac{1}{4} + \tfrac{1}{16} + \tfrac{1}{64} + \cdots]$.

10. If we start with the fact that $e < 3$, which terms of the series for e^x will we need to compute e with an error less than .000005?

11. We derived a series for $\sin^{-1} x$ in Example 13.8-5. If we substitute $x = \tfrac{1}{2}$, the series will give us $\pi/6$ and thus a way of computing π. Write down the terms neglected if we take the terms of the series for $\sin^{-1} \tfrac{1}{2}$ through the $(\tfrac{1}{2})^7$ term. By comparing the neglected terms with the series

$$\frac{1\cdot3\cdot5\cdot7}{2\cdot4\cdot6\cdot8}\left(\frac{1}{2}\right)^9 \frac{1}{9}\left[1 + \frac{1}{4} + \frac{1}{16} + \frac{1}{64} + \cdots\right],$$

estimate the error made in computing $\pi/6$ this way.

12. The series

$$\tan^{-1} x = x - \frac{x^3}{3} + \frac{x^5}{5} - \frac{x^7}{7} + \frac{x^9}{9} - + \cdots, \qquad -1 < x < 1,$$

was derived in Exercise 13.8-13. Even if we justified the expansion for $x = 1$ also, we would have difficulty in computing $\pi/4$, because the series converges so slowly for $x = 1$. But

$$\frac{\pi}{4} = 4 \tan^{-1} \tfrac{1}{5} - \tan^{-1} \tfrac{1}{239}.*$$

(a) How many terms of the series for $\tan^{-1} x$ are needed to compute $4 \tan^{-1} \tfrac{1}{5}$ with an error less than $(10)^{-6}$? (b) The same for $\tan^{-1} \tfrac{1}{239}$.

13. We are given that a is much smaller than s, so that a/s is small. Find a second-degree polynomial in a/s that approximates $s/(s - a)$. What can you say about the error made in using this formula?

14. Repeat the directions of Exercise 13 for a fourth-degree polynomial to approximate

$$\sqrt{s^2 + a^2} = s\sqrt{1 + \left(\frac{a}{s}\right)^2}.$$

15. Repeat the directions of Exercise 13 for a polynomial of two terms to approximate

$$\frac{1}{\sqrt[3]{s^3 + a^3}}.$$

Find values with the indicated accuracy for the following definite integrals:

16. $\displaystyle\int_0^{.1} e^{-x^2}\, dx$, error < 0.000005.

20. $\displaystyle\int_0^{1} \sin\sqrt{t}\, dt$, error < 0.0005.

17. $\displaystyle\int_0^{1} e^{-x^2}\, dx$, error < 0.0005.

21. $\displaystyle\int_0^{1} \sin(t^2)\, dt$, error < 0.0005.

18. $\displaystyle\int_0^{.1} x^2 e^{-x^2}\, dx$, error < 0.000005.

22. $\displaystyle\int_0^{\pi/2} \sqrt{4 + \sin^2 x}\, dx$, error < 0.01.

19. $\displaystyle\int_0^{1/2} \sqrt{1 + x^3}\, dx$, error < 0.0005.

---

* To demonstrate this trigonometric fact, use the identity $\tan 2A = 2 \tan A/(1 - \tan^2 A)$ twice to show that $\tan(4 \tan^{-1} 1/5) = 120/119$ and then use the identity for $\tan(A - B)$.

23. Show that the definite integral presented in Example 5 represents the circumference of the ellipse described there.

24. Find the circumference of the ellipse with semimajor and semiminor axes $\sqrt{10}$ and 3, making the error less than 0.005. *Suggestion:* Compare the terms of the series of Eq. (2) after the third with those of the geometric series

$$2\pi \sqrt{10} \left(\frac{1 \cdot 3 \cdot 5}{2 \cdot 4 \cdot 6} \right)^2 \frac{1}{(10)^3} \frac{1}{5} \left(1 + \frac{1}{10} + \frac{1}{100} + \frac{1}{1000} + \cdots \right).$$

13.10 Applications 2

The new form with which we describe a function when we write down a series expansion (or a polynomial approximation plus remainder if we use Taylor's Theorem) is often useful to us in theoretical discussions.

Let us return to our discussion of the concavity of curves in Sec. 3.19 and apply Taylor's Theorem to Theorem 3.19-1.

■ THEOREM 1A

On concavity.

HYPOTHESIS: $f''(x) \begin{cases} >0 \\ <0 \end{cases}$ and is continuous throughout an interval.

CONCLUSION: The curve $y = f(x)$ faces $\begin{cases} \text{up} \\ \text{down} \end{cases}$ in this interval.

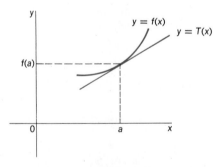

Fig. 13.5

PROOF: Take the case $f''(x) > 0$. Let $x = a$ be a point of the interval. For the tangent line to $y = f(x)$ at $x = a$, we have the equation

$$y - f(a) = f'(a)(x - a),$$

or $y = T(x) = f(a) + f'(a)(x - a).$

We must show that we have $f(x) > T(x)$ for all x of the interval other than $x = a$; see Fig. 13.5.

But Taylor's Theorem says that

$$f(x) = f(a) + f'(a)(x - a) + f''(w)\frac{(x - a)^2}{2!},$$

where w is a number that lies between x and a. Hence

$$f(x) = T(x) + f''(w)\frac{(x - a)^2}{2!}. \tag{1}$$

Here $f''(w)$ is positive by hypothesis and $(x - a)^2$ is positive for x other than a because it is a square. Thus $f(x) > T(x)$, the curve lies above the tangent line, and the theorem is demonstrated for the case $f''(x) > 0$. The proof for the case $f''(x) < 0$ is left to the reader as Exercise 13.10-1.

■ THEOREM 1B

HYPOTHESIS: (a) The curve $y = f(x)$ faces $\begin{cases} \text{up} \\ \text{down} \end{cases}$ throughout an interval.

(b) f'' exists and is continuous throughout the interval.

CONCLUSION: $f'' \begin{cases} \geq 0 \\ \leq 0 \end{cases}$ throughout the interval.

PROOF: Let us take the case where the curve faces down throughout the interval and give a proof by contradiction. Suppose that for $x = a$ in the interval we have $f''(a) > 0$. Since f'' is continuous at $x = a$ by Hypothesis (b), and cannot change abruptly there, a subinterval, centered at $x = a$, will exist for every point of which $f''(x) > 0$. But now Eq. (1) tells us that $f(x) > T(x)$ for the x of this subinterval because $f''(w)$ and $(x - a)^2$ are both positive. The curve faces up for this subinterval, thus contradicting the original assumption that the curve faces down throughout the interval. It must be that there is no point a for which $f''(a) > 0$; we have $f'' \leq 0$ throughout the interval. A similar argument can be given when the curve faces up throughout the interval.

In Theorem 3.19-3 we discussed the role of the second derivative in testing for the maximum and minimum properties of a function at a point where the first derivative vanished, but could not give a complete statement in the ambiguous case where the second derivative also vanished. Taylor's Theorem helps us demonstrate a more detailed statement.

■ THEOREM 2

On testing for maxima and minima.

HYPOTHESIS: (a) $f'(c) = f''(c) = \cdots = f^{n-1}(c) = 0$, $f^{(n)}(c) \neq 0$, $n \geq 2$.
(b) There is an interval centered at $x = c$ for which $f^{(n)}(x)$ is continuous (and has the same sign as $f^{(n)}(c)$), with

Case (1): n even and $f^{(n)}(c) > 0$,

Case (2): n even and $f^{(n)}(c) < 0$,

Case (3): n odd.

CONCLUSION:

Case (1): f has a relative minimum at $x = c$,

Case (2): f has a relative maximum at $x = c$.

Case (3): f has a point of inflection at $x = c$.

PROOF: Taylor's Theorem and Hypotheses (a) and (b) enable us to say that there exists a number w between x and c such that

$$f(x) = f(c) + 0(x - c) + 0\frac{(x - c)^2}{2!} + \cdots + 0\frac{(x - c)^{n-1}}{(n - 1)!} + f^{(n)}(w)\frac{(x - c)^n}{n!},$$

$$= f(c) + f^{(n)}(w)\frac{(x - c)^n}{n!}.$$

Now, if n is even, $(x - c)^n$ is positive except for $x = c$, and if, further $f^{(n)}(x) > 0$ throughout the interval, we can be sure that $f^{(n)}(w) > 0$, so that for all x of the interval except $x = c$, $f(x) > f(c)$. But this means that f has a relative minimum at $x = c$. The conclusion follows in Case (2) in a similar way. The reader can demonstrate the conclusion in Case (3) in Exercise 2 below by showing that $g(x) = f''(x)$ has opposite signs for the two sides of $x = c$ when n is odd.

||

We can often use series to advantage in working with limits.

Example 1.   Consider $\lim_{x \to 0} \dfrac{e^x - 1}{\log\ (1 + x)}.$ Both $e^x - 1$ and $\log\ (1 + x)$ approach 0 as x does and hence we can make no prediction for the limit of their quotient by referring to the quotient of their limits. But

$$e^x - 1 = \left(1 + x + \frac{x^2}{2!} + \frac{x^3}{3!} + \cdots\right) - 1 = x + \frac{x^2}{2!} + \frac{x^3}{3!} + \cdots$$

is a series representation for $e^x - 1$ valid for all x, and

$$\log\ (1 + x) = x - \frac{x^2}{2} + \frac{x^3}{3} - \frac{x^4}{4} + - \cdots$$

represents $\log\ (1 + x)$ for $-1 < x < 1$.* Hence we can write

$$\frac{e^x - 1}{\log\ (1 + x)} = \frac{x + x^2/2! + x^3/3! + \cdots}{x - x^2/2 + x^3/3 - + \cdots} = \frac{1 + x/2! + x^2/3! + \cdots}{1 - x/2 + x^2/3 - + \cdots}, \qquad (2)$$

for x of $-1 < x < 1$ other than $x = 0$, and then

$$\lim_{x \to 0} \frac{e^x - 1}{\log\ (1 + x)} = \frac{1}{1} = 1. \qquad (3)$$

Observe that we divided numerator and denominator in Eq. (2) by x, which is permissible because we do not inquire about $x = 0$ when we ask for $\lim_{x \to 0}$ but only about x near 0.†

---

* See Example 13.8-1 and either Exercise 13.8-3 or 13.8-14.

† In Eq. (3) we tacitly assumed that

$$\lim_{x \to 0} \left[1 + \frac{x}{2!} + \frac{x^2}{3!} + \cdots\right] = 1.$$

In advanced calculus it is shown that a power series defines a *continuous* function within its interval of convergence, and, since the particular power series whose limit is taken here converges for all x, it defines a function continuous for all x, which function we can denote by $\phi(x)$. Observe that $\phi(0) = 1$ and that $\lim_{x \to 0} \phi(x)$ must be $\phi(0)$, because $\phi(x)$ is continuous at $x = 0$. Similarly, $\lim_{x \to 0} [1 - x/2 + x^2/3 - + \cdots] = 1$, because that power series converges for $-1 < x < 1$, thus defining a continuous function for these x, call it $\tau(x)$, and $\tau(0) = 1$.

Example 2. Consider

$$\lim_{x \to 0} \frac{1}{x}\left[\frac{1}{x} - \frac{1}{\tan x}\right].$$

We know that the factor $1/x$ grows beyond all bounds as $x \to 0$, but we cannot predict a limit for $1/x - 1/\tan x$ easily, because the difference between two large numbers is sometimes large and sometimes small.

But write

$$\frac{1}{x}\left[\frac{1}{x} - \frac{1}{\tan x}\right] = \frac{1}{x}\frac{\tan x - x}{x \tan x} = \frac{\sin x - x \cos x}{x^2 \sin x},$$

and then use the representations

$$\sin x = \frac{x^1}{1!} - \frac{x^3}{3!} + \frac{x^5}{5!} - + \cdots,$$

$$\cos x = 1 - \frac{x^2}{2!} + \frac{x^4}{4!} - + \cdots,$$

$$x \cos x = x - \frac{x^3}{2!} + \frac{x^5}{4!} - + \cdots,$$

$$\sin x - x \cos x = \left(\frac{1}{2!} - \frac{1}{3!}\right)x^3 - \left(\frac{1}{4!} - \frac{1}{5!}\right)x^5 \cdots = \frac{1}{3}x^3 - \frac{1}{30}x^5 \cdots,$$

$$x^2 \sin x = \frac{x^3}{1!} - \frac{x^5}{3!} + \frac{x^7}{5!} - + \cdots,$$

which are valid for all x,* to write

$$\frac{1}{x}\left[\frac{1}{x} - \frac{1}{\tan x}\right] = \frac{\frac{1}{3} x^3 - \frac{1}{30} x^5 + \cdots}{x^3 - \frac{1}{6} x^5 + \cdots} = \frac{\frac{1}{3} - \frac{1}{30} x^2 + \cdots}{1 - \frac{1}{6} x^2 + \cdots}, \qquad x \neq 0,$$

$$\lim_{x \to 0} \frac{1}{x}\left[\frac{1}{x} - \frac{1}{\tan x}\right] = \frac{\frac{1}{3}}{1} = \frac{1}{3}.$$

III

Examples 1 and 2 deal with problems that can also be handled by the following rule.

■ **THEOREM 3**

L'Hospital's Rule.

HYPOTHESIS: (a) $\lim_{x \to a} f(x) = 0$ and $\lim_{x \to a} g(x) = 0$.
(b) f' and g' exist for each x of an interval about $x = a$ except possibly for $x = a$ itself.
(c) $g' \neq 0$ for $x \neq a$ in this interval.
(d) $\lim_{x \to a} [f'(x)/g'(x)] = A$.

CONCLUSION: $\lim_{x \to a} [f(x)/g(x)] = A$.

---

* See Exercises 13.8-1, 2 and Theorem 13.8-1.

● **Remark 1**

Hypothesis (a) can be replaced by the alternate hypothesis, $\lim_{x\to a} f(x) = \infty$ and $\lim_{x\to a} g(x) = \infty$.

Crudely, L'Hospital's Rule might be restated this way. When $\lim_{x\to a} f(x) = \lim_{x\to a} g(x) = 0$ (or $\lim_{x\to a} f(x) = \lim_{x\to a} g(x) = \infty$) so that $\lim_{x\to a} [f(x)/g(x)]$ cannot be determined directly as a quotient of limits, consider instead $\lim_{x\to a} [f'(x)/g'(x)]$ which may be easier to evaluate. If $\lim_{x\to a} f'(x)/g'(x)$ exists, then, for suitable f and g, $\lim_{x\to a} [f(x)/g(x)]$ will be the same number.

PROOF OF A SPECIAL CASE OF L'HOSPITAL'S THEOREM: A complete proof of L'Hospital's Rule would take more effort than we care to devote to it, but we can demonstrate a special case fairly easily by referring to the Theorem of Mean Value, of which Taylor's Theorem is an extension.

Let us replace Hypotheses (a) and (b) by the stronger assumptions that $f(a) = g(a) = 0$ and f' and g' are continuous for an interval about $x = a$, with $g'(a) \neq 0$. By the Theorem of Mean Value, there exist numbers v and w between a and x such that

$$f(x) - f(a) = f'(v)(x - a),$$

$$g(x) - g(a) = g'(w)(x - a).$$

Then, dividing, and using $f(a) = g(a) = 0$ as well as Hypothesis (c), we obtain

$$\frac{f(x)}{g(x)} = \frac{f'(v)}{g'(w)}.$$

But v and w approach a when x does, and, since we are assuming at the moment that f' and g' are continuous for an interval about $x = a$, we have

$$\lim_{x\to a} \frac{f(x)}{g(x)} = \lim_{x\to a} \frac{f'(v)}{g'(w)} = \frac{\lim_{x\to a} f'(v)}{\lim_{x\to a} g'(w)} = \frac{f'(a)}{g'(a)}.$$

Example 1A. Consider

$$\lim_{x\to 0} \frac{e^x - 1}{\log (1 + x)}$$

again. For $f(x) = e^x - 1$ and $g(x) = \log (1 + x)$, we have $f'(x) = e^x$ and $g'(x) = 1/(1 + x)$. We compute

$$\lim_{x\to 0} \frac{f'(x)}{g'(x)} = \lim_{x\to 0} \frac{e^x}{1/(1 + x)} = 1,$$

and then observe that, since the hypotheses of L'Hospital's Rule are satisfied, we also have

$$\lim_{x\to 0} \frac{f(x)}{g(x)} = \lim_{x\to 0} \frac{e^x - 1}{\log (1 + x)} = 1.$$

Example 2A. Consider

$$\lim_{x \to 0} \frac{1}{x}\left(\frac{1}{x} - \frac{1}{\tan x}\right) = \lim_{x \to 0} \frac{\sin x - x \cos x}{x^2 \sin x}$$

again. For

$$f(x) = \sin x - x \cos x \quad \text{and} \quad g(x) = x^2 \sin x$$

we have

$$f'(x) = \cos x - (\cos x - x \sin x) = x \sin x$$

and

$$g'(x) = x^2 \cos x + 2x \sin x.$$

But

$$\lim_{x \to 0} \frac{f'(x)}{g'(x)} = \lim_{x \to 0} \frac{x \sin x}{x^2 \cos x + 2x \sin x} = \lim_{x \to 0} \frac{\sin x}{x \cos x + 2 \sin x}$$

is still not determined, and we try L'Hospital's Rule again. For

$$\phi(x) = \sin x \quad \text{and} \quad \tau(x) = x \cos x + 2 \sin x$$

we have

$$\phi'(x) = \cos x$$

and

$$\tau'(x) = \cos x - x \sin x + 2 \cos x = 3 \cos x - x \sin x.$$

Now

$$\lim_{x \to 0} \frac{\phi'(x)}{\tau'(x)} = \lim_{x \to 0} \frac{\cos x}{3 \cos x - x \sin x} = \frac{1}{3},$$

and the functions f, g, ϕ, τ are such that the hypotheses of L'Hospital's Rule are satisfied each time we use the rule. Hence we can say that

$$\lim_{x \to 0} \frac{f'(x)}{g'(x)} = \lim_{x \to 0} \frac{\phi(x)}{\tau(x)} = \frac{1}{3}$$

because

$$\lim_{x \to 0} \frac{\phi'(x)}{\tau'(x)} = \frac{1}{3},$$

and then

$$\lim_{x \to 0} \frac{f(x)}{g(x)} = \frac{1}{3}$$

because

$$\lim_{x \to 0} \frac{f'(x)}{g'(x)} = \frac{1}{3}.$$

IV

The three series representations,

$$e^x = 1 + \frac{x^1}{1!} + \frac{x^2}{2!} + \frac{x^3}{3!} + \frac{x^4}{4!} + \frac{x^5}{5!} + \frac{x^6}{6!} + \frac{x^7}{7!} + \cdots,$$

$$\cos x = 1 - \frac{x^2}{2!} + \frac{x^4}{4!} - \frac{x^6}{6!} + - \cdots,$$

and

$$\sin x = x - \frac{x^3}{3!} + \frac{x^5}{5!} - \frac{x^7}{7!} + - \cdots,$$

are enough alike to suggest that there is a relationship between the exponential and trigonometric functions. If we write

$$\cos x + \sin x = 1 + x - \frac{x^2}{2!} - \frac{x^3}{3!} + \frac{x^4}{4!} + \frac{x^5}{5!} - \frac{x^6}{6!} - \frac{x^7}{7!} + + - - \cdots,$$

we get a series that represents neither e^x nor e^{-x}. But the sequence of signs suggests the complex number i, for we know that the sequence $i^0 = +1$, $i^1 = +i$, $i^2 = -1$, $i^3 = -i$, $i^4 = +1$, $i^5 = +i$, $i^6 = -1, \cdots$ has the same sequence of signs. Experimenting, then, on a purely formal basis, we write

$$e^{ix} = 1 + \frac{(ix)^1}{1!} + \frac{(ix)^2}{2!} + \frac{(ix)^3}{3!} + \frac{(ix)^4}{4!} + \frac{(ix)^5}{5!} + \frac{(ix)^6}{6!} + \frac{(ix)^7}{7!} + \cdots$$

$$= 1 + ix - \frac{x^2}{2!} - \frac{ix^3}{3!} + \frac{x^4}{4!} + \frac{ix^5}{5!} - \frac{x^6}{6!} - \frac{ix^7}{7!} + + - - \cdots.$$

Collecting real and imaginary parts, we have

$$e^{ix} = \left(1 - \frac{x^2}{2!} + \frac{x^4}{4!} - \frac{x^6}{6!} + - \cdots\right) + i\left(x - \frac{x^3}{3!} + \frac{x^5}{5!} - \frac{x^7}{7!} + - \cdots\right)$$

or
$$e^{ix} = \cos x + i \sin x. \tag{4}$$

This formula is called Euler's Formula. The series representations we have used are valid for all real x, and we suspect that Euler's Formula is valid for all x. Euler's Formula is indeed valid for all x, but we have developed only a theory for series of real numbers and can only accept Euler's Formula as plausible.

Example 3. Assuming Euler's Formula and working in a purely formal manner, we can write

$$e^{ix}e^{iy} = (\cos x + i \sin x)(\cos y + i \sin y),$$

$$e^{ix+iy} = \cos x \cos y + i \sin x \cos y + i \cos x \sin y - \sin x \sin y,$$

$$e^{i(x+y)} = (\cos x \cos y - \sin x \sin y) + i(\sin x \cos y + \cos x \sin y).$$

But, if we write $w = x + y$, $e^{iw} = \cos w + i \sin w$ becomes

$$e^{i(x+y)} = \cos (x + y) + i \sin(x + y).$$

Hence,

$$\cos (x + y) + i \sin (x + y) = (\cos x \cos y - \sin x \sin y) + i(\sin x \cos y + \cos x \sin y),$$

and if we equate real and imaginary parts, we get the well-known trigonometric identities

$$\cos (x + y) = \cos x \cos y - \sin x \sin y,$$

$$\sin (x + y) = \sin x \cos y + \cos x \sin y.*$$

---

* We have not "demonstrated" these identities, even if all our formal work is justifiable, because they were first used in deriving the derivatives of the sine and cosine functions; these derivatives were then used in deriving the series expansions.

EXERCISES 13.10

1. Prove Theorem 1A for the case $f''(x) < 0$.

2. Demonstrate the conclusion of Case (3) of Theorem 2.

3. $\lim\limits_{x \to 0} \dfrac{e^x - 1}{x} = ?$

4. $\lim\limits_{x \to 0} \dfrac{1 - e^{-x^2}}{x} = ?$

5. $\lim\limits_{x \to 0} \dfrac{\log (1 + x)}{x} = ?$

6. $\lim\limits_{x \to 0} \dfrac{\sqrt{1 + x} - 1}{x} = ?$

7. $\lim\limits_{x \to 0} \dfrac{\sqrt[3]{1 + x^2} - 1}{x} = ?$

8. $\lim\limits_{x \to 0} \left[\dfrac{1}{\sin x} - \dfrac{1}{x} \right] = ?$

9. $\lim\limits_{\phi \to 0} \left| \dfrac{1 - \cos \phi}{\phi - \sin \phi} \right| = ?$

10. $\lim\limits_{x \to 0} \dfrac{\sin 2x}{\sin x + \sin 3x} = ?$

11. $\lim\limits_{x \to 0} \dfrac{\tan^2 bx}{1 - \cos ax} = ?$

12. $\lim\limits_{x \to 0} \dfrac{\log \cos x}{x} = ?$

13. Assume that Euler's Formula, Eq. (4), is valid. Cube both sides of the equation and arrive at formulas for $\cos 3x$ and $\sin 3x$.

14. Write $-5 = 5(\cos \pi + i \sin \pi)$. Assume that Euler's Formula is valid. Find an expression for $\log (-5)$.

15. Repeat the directions of Exercise 14 for (a) $i = 1 \left(\cos \dfrac{\pi}{2} + i \sin \dfrac{\pi}{2} \right)$ and $\log i$;

(b) $1 + i = \sqrt{2} \left(\cos \dfrac{\pi}{4} + i \sin \dfrac{\pi}{4} \right)$ and $\log (1 + i)$.

16. Show that $\lim\limits_{\theta \to \pi/4} (1 - \tan \theta) \sec 2\theta = 1$.

Suggestion: Write $\sec 2\theta = 1/\cos 2\theta$ and use L'Hospital's Rule.

17. (a) Show that $\lim\limits_{x \to 0^+} x \log x = 0$. *Suggestion:* Write $x = 1/(1/x)$ and use L'Hospital's Rule. (b) Show that $\lim\limits_{x \to 0^+} x^x = 1$.

Suggestion: Write $y = x^x$ and consider $\log y$.

18. Show that $\lim\limits_{x \to 0^+} \sqrt{x} \log \sin x = 0$.

19. Show that $\lim\limits_{x \to 0} (1 + bx)^{c/x} = e^{bc}$.

Suggestion 1: Write $y = (1 + bx)^{c/x}$ and consider $\log y$. *Suggestion* 2: Write $bx = w$.

20. Show that $\lim\limits_{x \to 1} x^{1/(1-x)} = 1/e$.

Suggestion 1: Write $y = x^{1/(1-x)}$ and consider $\log y$. *Suggestion* 2: Write $1 - x = -w$.

21. Show that $\lim\limits_{x \to 0^+} (\sin x)^{\tan x} = 1$.

22. Show that $\lim\limits_{y \to 1} \left[\dfrac{y}{y - 1} - \dfrac{1}{\log y} \right] = \dfrac{1}{2}$.

Differential Equations

14.1 Introduction

I

An ordinary differential equation is an equation that is to be satisfied by a function of one variable and one or more of its derivatives. The order of the differential equation* is the order of the derivative of highest order appearing in the equation. Thus

$$\frac{dy}{dx} = -y \tag{1}$$

and

$$y^2\left(\frac{dy}{dx}\right)^2 + y^2 = 1 \tag{2}$$

are both differential equations of the first order, because only first derivatives appear in these equations;

$$\frac{d^2x}{dt^2} = -32, \tag{3}$$

$$\frac{d^2y}{dt^2} + y = 0, \tag{4}$$

and

$$\frac{d^2y/dx^2}{[1 + (dy/dx)^2]^{3/2}} = 1 \tag{5}$$

are differential equations of the second order; and

$$\frac{d^3x}{dt^3} + 5\frac{d^2x}{dt^2} + 7\frac{dx}{dt} - 13x = \sin t$$

is a differential equation of the third order.

---

* We often write "differential equation" for "ordinary differential equation."

An equation that is to be satisfied by a function of several variables and one or more of its partial derivatives is called a partial differential equation. Again, the order of the partial derivative of highest order appearing in the equation is the order of the partial differential equation. Thus

$$\frac{\partial^2 \varphi}{\partial x^2} + \frac{\partial^2 \varphi}{\partial y^2} + \frac{\partial^2 \varphi}{\partial z^2} = 0$$

is written in terms of second partial derivatives and is a frequently studied partial differential equation of the second order. In this chapter we shall only attempt to study some of the easier parts of the theory of ordinary differential equations. Differential equations appear so frequently, because so many relationships one studies deal directly or indirectly with rates of change. Equation (3) above, for instance, describes the acceleration (or rate of change of velocity) of a body falling freely under the influence of gravity near the earth's surface and Eq. (5) describes plane curves of constant curvature 1.

By a solution of a differential equation we shall mean a function which, together with its derivatives, satisfies that differential equation. Thus it is easily verified that

$$y = e^{-x}$$

is one of the solutions of Eq. (1) and that

$$y = \sin t \qquad \text{and} \qquad y = \cos t$$

are two of the solutions of Eq. (4).

Since these equations seem to have many solutions, we can attempt to distinguish between the solutions by asking for solutions that meet specific requirements. One can easily verify that

$$y = 2e^{-x}$$

is a solution of Eq. (1) for which $y = 2$ when $x = 0$, and that $y = \sin t + 2 \cos t$ is a solution of Eq. (4) for which $y = 2$ and $dy/dt = 1$ when $t = 0$. The question of how far one can go in specifying additional requirements for solutions is a basic question. A little judicious guessing may convince the reader that he can meet almost any two requirements for a solution of Eq. (4). Thus one can find a real solution for which $y = y_1$ when $t = t_1$ and for which $y = y_2$ when $t = t_2$, y_1 and y_2 any real numbers, and t_1 and t_2 any two distinct real numbers that do not differ by a multiple of π.* But it turns out that usually one cannot ask for a solution of Eq. (1) that meets two requirements; there is no solution of Eq. (1) for which $y = 2$ and $dy/dx = 1$ when $x = 0$.† In the case of Eq. (2) it turns out that one cannot even find a real solution to meet the one requirement that y shall be 2 when x is 0.‡

Not only are we interested in the question of whether solutions with specific properties exist, but we are also interested in questions of uniqueness. If we find a

---

* See Exercises 14.1-13 and 14.1-14.
† See Exercise 14.1-15.
‡ See Example 14.1-5 and Exercise 14.1-22.

solution that meets a specific requirement, can we be sure that there is no other solution that meets the same requirement? We shall consider questions of existence and uniqueness for first order equations in the remainder of this section, dealing first with specific equations and ultimately stating a precise theorem on existence and uniqueness.

We discussed differential equations of the form

$$\frac{dy}{dx} = f(x) \tag{6}$$

as far back as Chapter 2 without using the name "differential equation." If $f(x)$ is continuous, we know that we can always find solutions and that these different solutions can be described with the help of one arbitrary constant. Sometimes these solutions can be written in terms of functions already known, as in the case of

$$\frac{dy}{dx} = x + 5,$$

where we know that we can write

$$y = \tfrac{1}{2} x^2 + 5x + C, \tag{7}$$

C any constant; sometimes these solutions are described by using the definite integral notation, as in the case of

$$\frac{dy}{dx} = e^{-x^2}$$

where we can write

$$y = \int_{t=0}^{x} e^{-t^2} dt + C.* \tag{8}$$

Moreover, in these cases we know that *all* solutions of the differential equations can be written as in Eqs. (7) and (8) by choosing the arbitrary constants appropriately, because Theorems 2.1-1 and 7.5-3 tell us that two functions with the same derivative can only differ by a constant. Because $y = \tfrac{1}{2} x^2 + 5x$ is one solution of $dy/dx = x + 5$ and every other solution automatically has the same derivative, we are sure that every other solution can differ from $y = \tfrac{1}{2} x^2 + 5x$ only by a constant and can be written in the form of Eq. (7).

The fact that one arbitrary constant is available when the solutions are written usually enables us to meet one requirement or condition. For instance, if we know that the solutions can be written

$$y = \varphi(x) + C,$$

we can meet the requirement that y shall be y_0 when x is x_0 by writing

$$y_0 = \varphi(x_0) + C$$

and choosing the constant C to be $y_0 - \varphi(x_0)$, provided $\varphi(x_0)$ exists.

---

* See Theorem 2.6-6 and Theorem 7.7-2.

A differential equation of the first order of the form

$$g(y)\frac{dy}{dx} = f(x), \tag{9}$$

where $f(x)$ and $g(y)$ are both continuous, will also have a set of solutions with the freedom of choice afforded by one arbitrary constant. For, if $\varphi(y)$ and $\psi(x)$ are such that $d\varphi/dy = g(y)$ and $d\psi/dx = f(x)$, the function y described implicitly by

$$\varphi(y) = \psi(x) + C$$

is a solution of Eq. (9); to see this, we need only differentiate implicitly with respect to x and use the Chain Rule to write

$$\frac{d\varphi}{dy}\frac{dy}{dx} = \frac{d\psi}{dx}$$

or

$$g(y)\frac{dy}{dx} = f(x)$$

Equation (9) is often written in the differential notation. If we remember that $dy = (dy/dx)\ dx$ by definition, we can rewrite Eq. (9) as

$$g(y)dy = f(x)\ dx. \tag{9a}$$

One often says that he has separated the variables when he has written a differential equation in one of the forms, Eqs. (9) or (9a).

Example 1. Find the solution of $dr/d\theta = r^2 \sin \theta$ for which $r = 1$ when $\theta = \pi/2$.

We can write the equation in the separated form

$$\frac{1}{r^2}\ dr = \sin \theta\ d\theta$$

if we divide by r^2, and say that

$$-\frac{1}{r} = -\cos \theta + C$$

are solutions. If we want $r = 1$ when $\theta = \pi/2$ we must write

$$-1 = -0 + C$$

and choose C to be -1. The solution we want can then be written in the forms

$$-\frac{1}{r} = -\cos \theta - 1$$

and

$$r = \frac{1}{1 + \cos \theta}. \tag{10}$$

Observe that the division by r^2 at the very beginning tacitly assumed that we would not consider $r = 0$ in the remainder of that discussion. For no value of θ will the proposed solution, Eq. (10), assign the value $r = 0$. Direct substitution in the original differential equation $dr/d\theta = r^2 \sin \theta$ shows, however, that $r = 0$ is a formal solution of that equation, but, of course, not a solution for which $r = 1$ when $\theta = \pi/2$. If r and θ are interpreted to be polar coordinates, then Eq. (10) represents a parabola; see Sec. 9.4.

Example 2. Find the solution of

$$\frac{y}{x}\frac{dy}{dx} = \frac{1+y^2}{1+x^2}$$

for which $y = 2$ when $x = 1$.

Let us separate the variables by writing

$$\frac{y}{1+y^2}\,dy = \frac{x}{1+x^2}\,dx,$$

or, for integration purposes,

$$\frac{2y}{1+y^2}\,dy = \frac{2x}{1+x^2}\,dx,$$

and observe that we get solutions of this equation if we take

$$\log\,(1+y^2) = \log(1+x^2) + C. \tag{11}$$

We rewrite by observing that $\log e^C = C$ and by using the laws of logarithms;

$$\log\,(1+y^2) = \log(1+x^2) + \log e^C,$$

$$\log\,(1+y^2) = \log e^C(1+x^2),$$

$$1+y^2 = e^C(1+x^2). \tag{12}$$

If we want to have $y = 2$ when $x = 1$, we must choose C so that

$$5 = e^C(2), \qquad e^C = \tfrac{5}{2}.$$

Hence our solution can be written

$$1+y^2 = \tfrac{5}{2}(1+x^2),$$

or

$$y^2 = \tfrac{5}{2}x^2 + \tfrac{3}{2}.$$

A little maneuvering with constants in this work would have been avoided if we had observed, when Eq. (11) was written, that for any choice of the constant C there is a corresponding choice for the constant K such that $C = \log K$. Equation (11) would then have been written

$$\log\,(1+y^2) = \log\,(1+x^2) + \log K \tag{11a}$$

and Eq. (12) would have appeared in the form

$$1+y^2 = K(1+x^2).$$

‖

But not every first order differential equation is given to us in separable form or in a form that can easily be converted to separable form. Will there be the freedom of choice afforded by one arbitrary constant when writing the solutions of the first order differential equation of more general form

$$\frac{dy}{dx} = f(x, y)?$$

And, further, if a set of solutions with one arbitrary constant can be found, will *all* the solutions be given by appropriate choices for that one arbitrary constant?

To start to develop some feeling for the answers to these questions, we shall look at a simple differential equation in unseparated form from two different points of view.

The first point of view interprets the variables x and y in the differential equation

$$\frac{dy}{dx} = f(x, y)$$

to be Cartesian coordinates, the solutions to be curves in the xy plane, and the equation itself to be a statement for the slope of the solution curve through the point (x, y). If at each point (x, y) at which $f(x, y)$ is defined, we draw a short straight line segment of slope $f(x, y)$, then we know that these straight line segments are tangent to the solution curves. Can we learn something by trying to piece solution curves together on a chart of tangent segments?

Example 3. The differential equation

$$\frac{dy}{dx} = y + x - 1$$

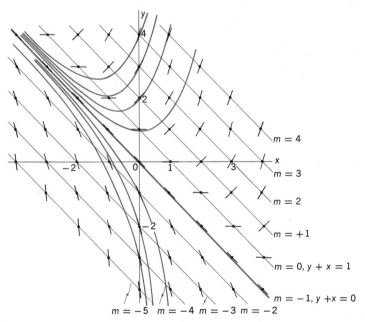

Fig. 14.1

gives us a slope statement for each point in the xy plane. At the point $(0, 0)$ the slope is -1; the slope is 2 at the point $(1, 2)$. We can start by drawing short straight line segments at many points fairly efficiently, as in Fig. 14.1, if we observe that the slope drawn should be 0 at every point selected on the straight line $y + x = 1$ (we determine this by setting $dy/dx = 0$ in the differential equation), that the slope should be 1 at every point selected on the line $y + x = 2$ (determined by setting $dy/dx = 1$), and so forth.

In Fig. 14.1 we then sketched several curves that seem to have the correct slope at each point and therefore to have equations that satisfy the original differential equation $dy/dx = y + x - 1$. It would appear that one can start at any point on the y axis, for example, sketch to the right and to the left by crossing each line of constant slope carefully with the correct slope, and thus draw a solution curve. This would mean that in finding solutions one can meet the requirement that y shall be any real number C when x is 0, and suggests that in writing the solutions of $dy/dx = y + x - 1$ there is the freedom of choice afforded by one arbitrary constant. Actually, these guesses are all correct, as we shall see in Examples 4 and 14.5-2.

III

Another idea one can apply to the study of a differential equation of the form

$$\frac{dy}{dx} = f(x, y) \tag{13}$$

is this. Assume that f has partial derivatives of all orders in a neighborhood of the point $P_0(x_0, y_0)$. The differential equation itself tells us the value of dy/dx at P_0;

$$\left(\frac{dy}{dx}\right)_{P_0} = f(x_0, y_0).$$

If we differentiate both members of Eq. (13) with respect to x, we shall get a statement for d^2y/dx^2 in terms of x, y, and dy/dx; in detail

$$\frac{d^2y}{dx^2} = \frac{\partial f}{\partial x} + \frac{\partial f}{\partial y}\frac{dy}{dx}. *$$

Now we can evaluate (d^2y/dx^2) at P_0. If we continue to differentiate and evaluate, it is possible, in theory at least, to evaluate the derivatives of y of all orders at P_0. But if we know the derivatives of all orders of a function y at a particular point, we can study the Taylor expansion for y, and, if the convergence of that expansion to y is established, we have determined a solution y.

In this process we are free to start at many different points (x_0, y_0); for instance, we might choose $x_0 = 0$ and $y_0 = C$, C being constant. It is at least plausible to think that there might be a solution each time, and this would mean again that in finding solutions we can meet the requirement that y shall be any real number C when x is 0. Again, this would suggest that in writing the solutions of $dy/dx = f(x, y)$, with

---

* Compare Example 11.5-1, replacing t there by x.

$f(x, y)$ differentiable infinitely often, there is the freedom of choice afforded by one arbitrary constant.

Example 4. Consider again the differential equation

$$\frac{dy}{dx} = y + x - 1 \tag{14}$$

considered in Example 3. A solution which is such that

$$y = C \qquad \text{when } x = 0 \tag{15a}$$

would have to have

$$\frac{dy}{dx} = C - 1 \qquad \text{when } x = 0. \tag{15b}$$

If we differentiate Eq. (14), we get

$$\frac{d^2y}{dx^2} = \frac{dy}{dx} + 1, \tag{14a}$$

$$\frac{d^2y}{dx^2} = (C - 1) + 1 = C \qquad \text{when } x = 0. \tag{15c}$$

If we differentiate Eq. (14a) we get

$$\frac{d^3y}{dx^3} = \frac{d^2y}{dx^2},$$

$$\frac{d^4y}{dx^4} = \frac{d^3y}{dx^3} = \frac{d^2y}{dx^2},$$

and, indeed,

$$\frac{d^ky}{dx^k} = \frac{d^2y}{dx^2} \qquad \text{for } k \geq 3$$

so that

$$\frac{d^ky}{dx^k} = C \qquad \text{when } x = 0 \text{ for } k \geq 2. \tag{15d}$$

Thus we see that, if there is to be a solution that has derivatives of all orders and that satisfies Condition (15a), it will also have to satisfy Conditions (15b), (15c), and (15d). Our work with Taylor's expansion in Chapter 13 immediately suggests that we consider

$$y = (y)_{x=0} + \left(\frac{dy}{dx}\right)_{x=0} x + \left(\frac{d^2y}{dx^2}\right)_{x=0} \frac{x^2}{2!} + \left(\frac{d^3y}{dx^3}\right)_{x=0} \frac{x^3}{3!} + \cdots$$

$$y = C + (C - 1)x + C\frac{x^2}{2!} + C\frac{x^3}{3!} + \cdots + C\frac{x^k}{k!} + \cdots .$$

Here we may well recognize the series for the function e^x. We can write

$$y = -x + C\left[1 + x + \frac{x^2}{2!} + \frac{x^3}{3!} + \cdots + \frac{x^k}{k!} + \cdots\right]$$

$$y = -x + Ce^x. \tag{16}$$

When we try this suggested solution in the original equation, we find that the equation is indeed satisfied;

$$\frac{dy}{dx} = y + x - 1,$$

because

$$-1 + Ce^x = (-x + Ce^x) + x - 1.$$

Equation (16) constitutes a set of solutions with arbitrary constant C.*

IV

Examples 1, 2, 3, and 4 suggest that many of the solutions of the first order differential equation

$$\frac{dy}{dx} = f(x, y)$$

will be described by an equation which contains one arbitrary constant. The following example points out that not in every case will *all* the solutions be described by that equation with one arbitrary constant which seems to describe most of the solutions.

Example 5.   We show first by direct computation that any circle of the one-parameter family

$$(x - C)^2 + y^2 = 1 \tag{17}$$

will be a solution of the differential equation

$$y^2\left(\frac{dy}{dx}\right)^2 + y^2 = 1.† \tag{2}$$

For any circle of the family described by Eq. (17) we compute

$$2(x - C) + 2y\frac{dy}{dx} = 0,$$

$$\frac{dy}{dx} = -\frac{x - C}{y},$$

and then, for the differential equation,

$$y^2\left(\frac{dy}{dx}\right)^2 + y^2 = y^2\frac{(x - C)^2}{y^2} + y^2$$

$$= (x - C)^2 + y^2$$

$$= 1.$$

Here we used Eq. (17) at the very end.

---

* The fact that we recognized the series in this particular example is not essential. A convergent power series defines a differentiable function whether we happen to recognize that particular function from earlier experience or not.

† The reader can derive these solutions ab initio in Exercise 6 at the end of this section.

But not every solution of the Eq. (2) is described by Eq. (17) with an appropriate choice for the constant C. Indeed, the straight lines $y = +1$ and $y = -1$ are also solutions of Eq. (2), as direct computation will quickly show, but these lines are not members of the family of circles described in Eq. (17). The geometric explanation for these so-called "singular" solutions is not hard to follow in Fig. 14.2. The

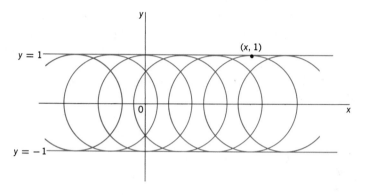

Fig. 14.2

straight lines $y = +1$ and $y = -1$ constitute an "envelope" for the family of circles. Each point $(x, 1)$ of the line $y = 1$ is also a point on one of the circles of the family, and the circle and line are tangent at that point, thus having the same slope. Since the slope for the circle and the coordinates for the point satisfy Eq. (2), the slope for the envelope line and the coordinates for the point must also satisfy Eq. (2).

In this case, if one asks for a solution of $y^2(dy/dx)^2 + y^2 = 1$ for which $y = 1$ when $x = 0$, there are two solutions, namely, $x^2 + y^2 = 1$ and $y = 1$. The reader can point out in Exercise 14.1-22 that there is no real solution of this differential equation for which $y = 2$ when $x = 0$.

▽

We shall state a theorem that tells us when we can be sure to find one and only one solution of a first order differential equation meeting one specified requirement of a standard type. The complete, detailed proof of this theorem will be left for a more intensive course in differential equations, but we shall present a sketch of the proof in Sec. 14.6 when we discuss the Picard technique for approximating to a solution of a first order equation.

■ THEOREM 1

An existence and uniqueness theorem for first order equations.

HYPOTHESIS: (a) $f(x, y)$ is continuous in and on a rectangle R with center at (x_0, y_0).

(b) There is a constant k such that for any two points (x, y_1) and (x, y_2) of the rectangle we have

$$|f(x, y_2) - f(x, y_1)| \le k|y_2 - y_1|.$$

CONCLUSION: (a) There is a function $y = \varphi(x)$, defined on an interval I: $x_0 - h < x < x_0 + h$, which satisfies the differential equation $dy/dx = f(x, y)$ for x of interval I, and which is such that $y = y_0$ when $x = x_0$.

(b) Any other function that satisfies $dy/dx = f(x, y)$ on I and has the value y_0 when $x = x_0$ must coincide with $y = \varphi(x)$ on the interval I.

● **Remark 1**

The half-width of the interval on which the solution $y = \varphi(x)$ is sure to exist can be specified in greater detail. If the rectangle R on which $f(x, y)$ is assumed to be continuous is the rectangle $x_0 - r \leq x \leq x_0 + r$, $y_0 - s \leq y \leq y_0 + s$, and if M is an upper bound for f on R, then h is at least as large as the smaller of r and s/M.

● **Remark 2**

Hypothesis (b) is not a very difficult hypothesis for a function $f(x, y)$ to meet. For instance, if $\partial f/\partial y$ exists and $|\partial f/\partial y| \leq k$ on the rectangle R, then by the Theorem of Mean Value we have

$$|f(x, y_2) - f(x, y_1)| \leq k|y_2 - y_1|.$$

This Hypothesis (b) is often called the "Lipschitz Condition."

● **Remark 3**

The Hypotheses (a) and (b) are sufficient to enable us to draw the conclusion of the theorem, but not necessary. These hypotheses can be replaced by weaker ones, but these weaker hypotheses cannot, however, be stated quite as simply.

In Exercises 14.1-20 to 14.1-23, the reader is invited to illustrate the statement of Theorem 1 in several specific cases.

EXERCISES 14.1

Find a one-parameter family of solutions in each of Exercises 1 to 6.

1. $\dfrac{dy}{dt} = 2 \cos 2\pi t.$

2. $\dfrac{dy}{dx} = \dfrac{2x + 1}{y}.$

3. $\dfrac{dy}{dx} = 3y^{2/3}.$

4. $\dfrac{dx}{dt} = tx + 5x.$

5. $\dfrac{ds}{dw} = \cos w \cos s.$

6. $y^2 \left(\dfrac{dy}{dx}\right)^2 + y^2 = 1.$

Find a solution that meets the specified condition in each of Exercises 7 to 10.

7. (a) $\dfrac{dy}{dx} = -xy$, and $y = 2$ when $x = 3$.

   (b) $\dfrac{dy}{dx} = -xy$, and $y = -2$ when $x = 3$.

8. $\dfrac{dv}{dt} = \sqrt{1 - v^2}$; and $v = \frac{1}{2}$ when $t = 0$.

9. $\dfrac{dy}{dx} = \dfrac{1 + y^2}{1 + x^2}$, and $y = 1$ when $x = 0$.

10. (a) $\dfrac{dy}{dx} = (1 - y)(2 - y)$, and $y = 3$ when $x = 0$.

   (b) $\dfrac{dy}{dx} = (1 - y)(2 - y)$, and $y = \frac{3}{2}$ when $x = 0$.

11. Find a curve $y = f(x)$ that passes through $(0, 1)$, never crosses the x axis, and has the property that the area bounded by the curve, the x axis, and every two ordinate lines is precisely the arc length cut off by these ordinate lines.
Suggestion: Write integrals for the area and arc length determined by the ordinate lines at a and x, equate the integrals, and differentiate the functions defined by these integrals to get the differential equation

$$\sqrt{1 + \left(\frac{dy}{dx}\right)^2} = y.$$

Show that $y = \cosh x$ and $y = 1$ must be the solutions.

12. In Sec. 2.2 we considered the motion of an object falling in a straight line in such a way that the force of gravity was assumed to be constant and also to be the only force acting on the object. Suppose now that an object falls under the influence of gravity, again assumed to be constant, but that there is a frictional force proportional to the velocity. Let y be the height at time t and y_0 the height at time $t = 0$, the y axis being so chosen that $y = 0$ is at the ground and points above ground have positive y's. Let the velocity at time $t = 0$ be v_0. Then, at any time, the forces acting on the object are its weight, $-mg$, and the frictional force, which we can describe by $-mkv$. Here mk is a constant of proportionality, and we have observed that the frictional force is opposed to the velocity. The basic physical statement $F = ma$ becomes $a = -(kv + g)$. Derive the statements

$$v = \frac{1}{k}(kv_0 + g)e^{-kt} - \frac{g}{k}$$

$$y = \frac{1}{k^2}(kv_0 + g)(1 - e^{-kt}) - \frac{g}{k}t + y_0$$

for the velocity and height at any time t.

13. Show that

$$y = (y_0 \sin t_0 + y_0' \cos t_0) \sin t + (y_0 \cos t_0 - y_0' \sin t_0) \cos t$$

is a solution of $\dfrac{d^2y}{dt^2} + y = 0$ for which $y = y_0$ and $\dfrac{dy}{dt} = y_0'$ when $t = t_0$.

14. Show that $y = \left[\dfrac{y_1 \cos t_2 - y_2 \cos t_1}{\sin(t_1 - t_2)}\right] \sin t + \left[\dfrac{y_2 \sin t_1 - y_1 \sin t_2}{\sin(t_1 - t_2)}\right] \cos t$

is a solution of $d^2y/dt^2 + y = 0$ for which $y = y_1$ when $t = t_1$ and $y = y_2$ when $t = t_2$, provided that t_1 and t_2 are distinct and do not differ by a multiple of π.

15. Show that there is no solution of $dy/dx = -y$ for which $y = 2$ and $dy/dx = 1$ when $x = 0$.

16. Consider $dy/dx = x^2 + y^2$. Observe that dy/dx is 0 at $(0, 0)$ and that dy/dx is C^2 on the circle $x^2 + y^2 = C^2$. Sketch the circles $x^2 + y^2 = 1$, $x^2 + y^2 = 4$, $x^2 + y^2 = 9$, construct tangent line segments at selected points on these circles and at the origin, and attempt to sketch the five solution curves for which $y = C$ when $x = 0$, $C = 0$, ± 1, ± 2.

17. In Example 4 we worked with many derivatives of a function y which satisfied a given differential equation, and we eventually found the function y. But often, just the computation of a second derivative will help to discover some of a function's properties. Show that every solution of $dy/dx = y^2 + x^2$ must face up in the first quadrant but down in the third quadrant.

18. Follow the method illustrated in Example 4 to find a solution (in series form) of $dy/dx = xy + 1$ for which $y = 0$ when $x = 0$.

19. Show that for each choice of the constant C the straight line $y = Cx + C^2$ is a solution of the differential equation $y = \left(\dfrac{dy}{dx}\right)x + \left(\dfrac{dy}{dx}\right)^2$. Show that the parabola $x^2 + 4y = 0$ is also a solution. Sketch the straight lines $y = Cx + C^2$ for $C = 0$, ± 1, ± 2 and the parabola $x^2 + 4y = 0$, all on one diagram.

20. In Example 1 we looked for a solution of $dr/d\theta = r^2 \sin\theta$ for which $r = 1$ when $\theta = \pi/2$. Show that the hypotheses of Theorem 1 are satisfied in this case and hence that there must be one and only one solution of the type sought.

21. In Examples 3 and 4 we considered $dy/dx = y + x - 1$. Show that there must be one and only one solution for which $y = 2$ when $x = 0$ by showing that the hypotheses of Theorem 1 are satisfied in this case.

22. (a) In Example 5 we pointed out that there were two solutions of $y^2\left(\dfrac{dy}{dx}\right)^2 + y^2 = 1$

   for which $y = 1$ when $x = 0$. Show that the hypotheses of Theorem 1 are not satisfied in this case.

   (b) Show that there can be no real solution of $y^2\left(\dfrac{dy}{dx}\right)^2 + y^2 = 1$ for which $y = 2$

   when $x = 0$.

23. (a) $y = x^3$ and $y = 0$ are both solutions of $dy/dx = 3y^{2/3}$ for which $y = 0$ when $x = 0$. Show that the Lipschitz Condition, Hypothesis (b) of Theorem 1, cannot be satisfied in this case.

   (b) Show that there exists one, but not more than one, solution of $dy/dx = 3y^{2/3}$ for which $y = 1$ when $x = 0$.

14.2   Families of Curves

The fundamental existence theorem, stated at the end of the last section, explains that, under rather general conditions, a first order differential equation will have a one-parameter family of solutions; there is the freedom of choice afforded by one arbitrary constant in selecting a specific solution. Now we turn to a converse question: if we are given a one-parameter family of curves, can we expect to find a first order differential equation that will be satisfied by all the members of the family of curves?

Example 1A.   Consider the one-parameter family F of curves

$$y = C \tan x, \qquad -\frac{\pi}{2} < x < \frac{\pi}{2}. \tag{1}$$

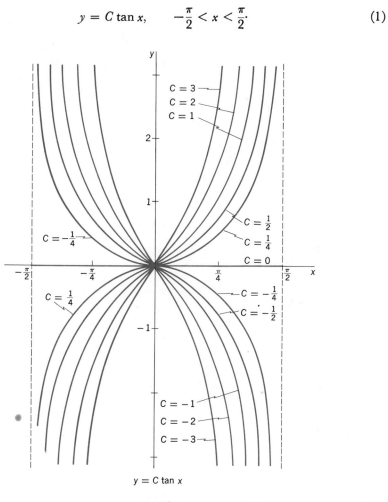

$$y = C \tan x$$

Fig. 14.3

For each choice of the parameter C we get one curve of the family; see Fig. 14.3. If we differentiate with respect to x we get the one-parameter system of differential equations

$$\frac{dy}{dx} = C \sec^2 x. \tag{2}$$

So far we can say that the one curve $y = 2 \tan x$, determined by selecting $C = 2$ in Eq. (1), satisfies the one differential equation $dy/dx = 2 \sec^2 x$ determined by selecting $C = 2$ in Eq. (2) and that, similarly, the curve obtained by selecting $C = 3$ in Eq. (1) satisfies the *different* differential equation obtained by setting $C = 3$ in

Eq. (2). We do not yet have *one* differential equation satisfied by *all* the curves of the family F.

But when the curve determined by a specific choice for C in Eq. (1) satisfies Eq. (2) for the same value of C, it satisfies every equation one can obtain from these two special equations (1) and (2). In particular, the curve would satisfy the equation one gets by eliminating C between Eqs. (1) and (2). Thus

$$y = 2 \tan x \tag{1a}$$

satisfies
$$\frac{dy}{dx} = 2 \sec^2 x \tag{2a}$$

and must also satisfy

$$\frac{dy}{dx} = \frac{y}{\tan x} \sec^2 x = y \frac{1}{\sin x \cos x} \tag{3}$$

obtained by solving for 2 in Eq. (1a) and substituting in Eq. (2a). Similarly,

$$y = 3 \tan x$$

satisfies
$$\frac{dy}{dx} = 3 \sec^2 x$$

and also satisfies
$$\frac{dy}{dx} = \frac{y}{\tan x} \sec^2 x = y \frac{1}{\sin x \cos x}. \tag{3}$$

With any choice for C we have

$$y = C \tan x,$$

$$\frac{dy}{dx} = C \sec^2 x,$$

$$\frac{dy}{dx} = \frac{y}{\tan x} \sec^2 x,$$

$$\frac{dy}{dx} = y \frac{1}{\sin x \cos x}. \tag{3}$$

Equation (3), obtained by eliminating the parameter C between Eqs. (1) and (2), is *one* first order differential equation satisfied by *all* the members of the family F.

In greater generality, we start with the one-parameter family F of curves described by

$$f(x, y, C) = 0. \tag{4}$$

Differentiation with respect to x will, in general, give us one differential equation for each curve described in Eq. (4). In Sec. 11.5 we explained that we would have

$$\frac{\partial f}{\partial x} + \frac{\partial f}{\partial y} \frac{dy}{dx} = 0,$$

or, in differential language,

$$\frac{\partial f}{\partial x} dx + \frac{\partial f}{\partial y} dy = 0 \tag{5}$$

if $\partial f/\partial x$ and $\partial f/\partial y$ were both continuous and, of course, not both 0. In general, since f itself was a function of C, one would have to expect $\partial f/\partial x$ and $\partial f/\partial y$ to be functions of C. Hence Eq. (5) represents, in general, a one-parameter family of differential equations. We do not yet have *one* differential equation satisfied by all curves of the family F.

But if $\partial f/\partial C$ does not vanish, then an Implicit Function Theorem slightly more general than Theorem 11.7-1 will enable us to solve for C in terms of x and y in Eq. (4). If we then substitute this expression for C in Eq. (5) we shall have

$$\left(\frac{\partial f}{\partial x}\right)_{C \text{ replaced}} dx + \left(\frac{\partial f}{\partial y}\right)_{C \text{ replaced}} dy = 0. \tag{6}$$

Since it is the parameter C that distinguishes between the members of family F and since Eq. (6) is independent of C, Eq. (6) is *one* differential equation of the first order satisfied by *all* members of family F. This discussion parallels that of Example 1A directly; the $f(x, y, C)$ here is simply $y - C \tan x$ there, Eq. (5) here is Eq. (2) there, and Eq. (6) here is Eq. (3) there.

Example 2A.   Laplace's equation,

$$\frac{\partial^2 u}{\partial x^2} + \frac{\partial^2 u}{\partial y^2} = 0,$$

has a fundamental role to play in studying temperature distributions, electrostatic potential distributions, and many topics of mathematical physics. The reader can verify easily that

$$u = \sin x \, \sinh y$$

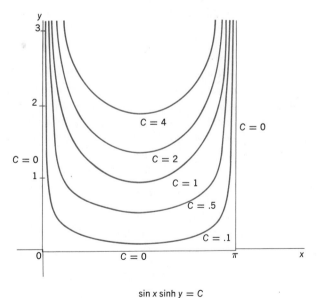

$$\sin x \, \sinh y = C$$

Fig. 14.4

satisfies Laplace's equation by computing $\partial^2 u/\partial x^2 + \partial^2 u/\partial y^2$ for this u. It happens that this u vanishes along the path $x = 0, y = 0, x = \pi$ pictured in Fig. 14.4. It is not so easy to plot the curve $\sin x \sinh y = .1$, along which $u = .1$, but this can be done by patient table work. In general, the curves

$$\sin x \sinh y = C \tag{7}$$

are the curves along which u is constant.

If we differentiate in Eq. (7) with respect to x, we get

$$\cos x \sinh y + \sin x \cosh y \frac{dy}{dx} = 0. \tag{8}$$

Here, because the parameter C entered in a special way in Eq. (7), we already have a differential equation with C eliminated, and we already have the first order differential equation satisfied by the one-parameter family of curves $u = \sin x \sinh y = C$.

● **Remark 1**

The fact that the parameter C was eliminated automatically upon differentiation in Example 2A suggests that, as a matter of technique, one ought to consider before differentiating whether the equation which describes a one-parameter family of curves can be rewritten in such a way as to isolate that parameter. Thus, in Example 1A, if we had rewritten

$$y = C \tan x$$

as

$$y \cot x = C$$

or as

$$\log y = \log C + \log \tan x,$$

and then differentiated, we would have arrived at Eq. (3) without having to eliminate C between two equations.

We saw in Sec. 11.3 that the direction of no change for a function of two variables is perpendicular to (or orthogonal to) the gradient direction, the direction of the greatest rate of change. Hence, if we know a family of curves that have at each point the direction of no change for a variable u, the curves that intersect these at right angles have at each point the direction of greatest rate of change for u. This second family of curves, intersecting the first family at right angles, is called the family of *orthogonal trajectories*.

Example 2B.   The curves of the one-parameter family

$$\sin x \sinh y = C \tag{7}$$

are the curves along which the variable $u = \sin x \sinh y$ is constant. We saw in Example 2A that the curves of this family are all described by the first order differential equation

$$\cos x \sinh y + \sin x \cosh y \frac{dy}{dx} = 0 \tag{8}$$

or

$$\frac{dy}{dx} = -\frac{\cos x \sinh y}{\sin x \cosh y}.$$

Since curves that intersect at right angles have negative reciprocal slopes, the family of orthogonal trajectories must be described by the differential equation

$$\frac{dy}{dx} = +\frac{\sin x \cosh y}{\cos x \sinh y}. \tag{9}$$

Fortunately, this differential equation is separable and we can solve it;

$$\frac{\sinh y}{\cosh y}\,dy = \frac{\sin x}{\cos x}\,dx,$$

$$\log \cosh y = \begin{cases} -\log\cos x + \log K, & \text{for } 0 \le x < \dfrac{\pi}{2} \\[2ex] -\log\left(-\cos x\right) + \log K & \text{for } \dfrac{\pi}{2} < x \le \pi, \end{cases}$$

$$\log \cosh y + \log\left(\pm\cos x\right) = \log K,$$

$$\begin{cases} \cosh y \cos x = K & \text{for } 0 \le x < \dfrac{\pi}{2} \\[2ex] \cosh y \cos x = -K & \text{for } \dfrac{\pi}{2} < x \le \pi. \end{cases} \tag{10}$$

The curves described in Eq. (10) are orthogonal trajectories of the curves $\sin x \sinh y = C$. In Eq. (9) we tacitly assumed that $\cos x$ did not vanish, and thus the subsequent work does not consider the straight line $\cos x = 0$ or $x = \pi/2$. If Eq. (9) is rewritten in the differential form

$$\sin x \cosh y\,dx - \cos x \sinh y\,dy = 0,$$

we see directly that the straight line $x = \pi/2$ should also be considered a solution,[*] and therefore also an orthogonal trajectory. The orthogonal trajectories are sketched in Fig. 14.5.

Example 1B.   In Example 1A we saw that the one-parameter family of curves

$$y = C \tan x \tag{1}$$

is described by the first order differential equation

$$\frac{dy}{dx} = y\,\frac{1}{\sin x \cos x} = \frac{2y}{\sin 2x}. \tag{3}$$

The orthogonal trajectories would be described by the differential equation

$$\frac{dy}{dx} = -\frac{\sin 2x}{2y},$$

which is separable;

$$2y\,dy = -\sin 2x\,dx.$$

---

[*] Strictly speaking, we should say that the straight line is described by the parametric equations $x = \pi/2, y = t$ for values of the parameter t greater than 0.

The orthogonal trajectories are

$$y^2 = \tfrac{1}{2} \cos 2x + K,$$
$$K \geq -\tfrac{1}{2}.$$

These curves are sketched in Fig. 14.6.

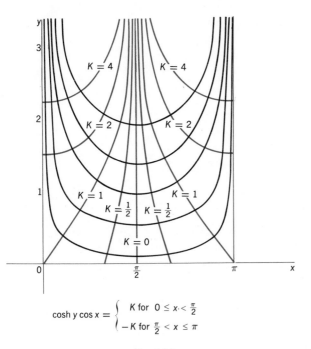

$$\cosh y \cos x = \begin{cases} K \text{ for } 0 \leq x < \frac{\pi}{2} \\ -K \text{ for } \frac{\pi}{2} < x \leq \pi \end{cases}$$

Fig. 14.5

Example 3. We saw in Example 3.20-4 that the one-parameter family of curves F

$$\frac{x^2}{k^2} + \frac{y^2}{k^2 - 4} = 1$$

(11a)

consisted of ellipses with foci at $(\pm 2, 0)$ for parameter choices $k > 2$ and of hyperbolas with the same foci for parameter choices $0 < k < 2$, and it was pointed out that the ellipses and hyperbolas intersected at right angles. Thus one could say that the family F was self-orthogonal. Let us find the first order differential equation satisfied by all the members of the family.

If we differentiate with respect to x and divide by 2 we find that

$$\frac{1}{k^2} x + \frac{1}{k^2 - 4} y \frac{dy}{dx} = 0.$$

(11b)

To eliminate the parameter k between Eqs. (11a) and (11b), we shall solve for k in Eq. (11b) and substitute into Eq. (11a). We can write

$$(k^2 - 4)x + k^2 yy' = 0$$
$$(x + yy')k^2 = 4x$$
$$k^2 = \frac{4x}{x + yy'}, \qquad k^2 - 4 = \frac{4x}{x + yy'} - 4 = -\frac{4yy'}{x + yy'},$$

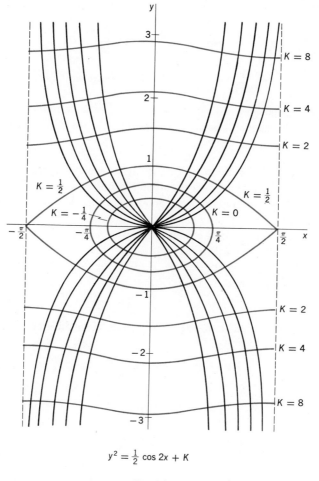

$$y^2 = \tfrac{1}{2} \cos 2x + K$$

Fig. 14.6

and then, from Eq. (11a),

$$\frac{x + yy'}{4x} x^2 - \frac{x + yy'}{4yy'} y^2 = 1$$

$$(x + yy')xy' - (x + yy')y = 4y'$$

$$xy \left(\frac{dy}{dx}\right)^2 + (x^2 - y^2 - 4) \frac{dy}{dx} - xy = 0. \tag{12}$$

Equation (12) is a first order differential equation satisfied by all the members of family *F*.

Since the orthogonal trajectories have negative reciprocal slopes, they satisfy the differential equation

$$xy \left(-\frac{1}{dy/dx}\right)^2 + (x^2 - y^2 - 4) \left(-\frac{1}{dy/dx}\right) - xy = 0,$$

obtained by replacing dy/dx by $-1/(dy/dx)$, and this equation, upon multiplication by $(dy/dx)^2$, reduces to

$$xy - (x^2 - y^2 - 4)\frac{dy}{dx} - xy\left(\frac{dy}{dx}\right)^2 = 0$$

or

$$xy\left(\frac{dy}{dx}\right)^2 + (x^2 - y^2 - 4)\frac{dy}{dx} - xy = 0. \tag{12}$$

The orthogonal trajectories satisfy the same differential equation that family F does. This was to be expected, because we knew before we began that the family F was self-orthogonal.

We shall not consider them as frequently as we considered one-parameter families of curves, but there are two-parameter families of curves, three-parameter families of curves, and, in general, n-parameter families. We usually find that the members of an n-parameter family all satisfy a differential equation of order n, and that conversely, for a differential equation of order n there is a family of solutions described with the help of n arbitrary constants.

Example 4.   Consider the family F of all circles of radius 1. This two-parameter family is described by the equation

$$(x - h)^2 + (y - k)^2 = 1 \tag{13}$$

where the parameters h and k can take on all values. If we differentiate with respect to x twice, we get

$$2(x - h) + 2(y - k)\frac{dy}{dx} = 0,$$

$$(x - h) + (y - k)\frac{dy}{dx} = 0 \tag{14}$$

and then

$$1 + (y - k)\frac{d^2y}{dx^2} + \left(\frac{dy}{dx}\right)^2 = 0. \tag{15}$$

We can eliminate the parameters h and k by solving for them in terms of x, y, y', and y'' in Eqs. (14) and (15) and then substituting in Eq. (13). From Eq. (15) we find that

$$y - k = -\frac{1 + (y')^2}{y''};$$

then from Eq. (14)

$$x - h = -(y - k)y' = \frac{1 + (y')^2}{y''}y';$$

finally, in Eq. (13),

$$\left[\frac{1 + (y')^2}{y''}\right]^2 (y')^2 + \left[\frac{1 + (y')^2}{y''}\right]^2 = 1$$

$$\frac{[1 + (y')^2]^3}{(y'')^2} = 1$$

$$\frac{y''}{[1 + (y')^2]^{3/2}} = \pm 1. \tag{16}$$

Equation (16) is a *second* order differential equation satisfied by all the members of the *two*-parameter family F. Of course, Eq. (16) says that the curvature shall be 1, and this was to be expected for a family of circles of radius 1.

In general, if we deal with an n-parameter family of curves we can differentiate n times and thus get $n + 1$ equations in all for the family. The last of these equations would contain a derivative of the nth order. If we can solve any n of the $n + 1$ equations for the n parameters and substitute into the remaining equation, we shall have an nth order differential equation independent of the parameters and satisfied by all the members of the n-parameter family with which we started.

EXERCISES 14.2

1. Find a first order differential equation satisfied by all the circles of radius 1 with centers on the x axis.
2. Find a first order differential equation satisfied by all the straight lines that are tangent to $y = x^2$. Is there any other curve that satisfies the same differential equation?
3. Find a first order differential equation satisfied by all the straight lines that have positive x and y intercepts and which, together with the coordinate axes, form triangles of area 1.

In each of Exercises 4, 5, 6, 7, and 8: (a) find a first order differential equation satisfied by the one-parameter family of curves given, (b) find the orthogonal trajectories, and (c) sketch both families of curves on the same diagram.

4. The straight lines through the origin: $(\cos \theta)y = (\sin \theta)x, 0 \leq \theta < \pi$.
5. $y = Ce^x$, C real.
6. The line $y = 0$ and the parabolas with vertex at the origin and x axis as axis of symmetry: $y^2 = 2Cx$, C real.
7. $y = \log (x + C)$, C real.
8. $y = Ce^{-x^2}$, C real.

In each of Exercises 9, 10, 11, 12, and 13: (a) find a first order differential equation satisfied by the one-parameter family of curves given, and (b) find the orthogonal trajectories.

9. $y = C \cosh x$, C real.
10. $\sin x \cos y = C, -1 \leq C \leq 1$.
11. The ellipses and hyperbolas with vertices at $(\pm 1, 0)$ and the lines $x = \pm 1$: $x^2 + Cy^2 = 1$, C real.
12. $y = x^n$ for $0 < x \leq 1$, n real.
13. $y = \sin (x + C)$ for $0 \leq x \leq \dfrac{\pi}{2}, -\dfrac{\pi}{2} \leq C \leq 0$.

14. The parabolas $y^2 = -2p\left(x - \dfrac{p}{2}\right)$ all have focus at the origin. In Exercises 3.20-3c and 3.20-5 it was pointed out that the parabolas for $p > 0$ intersect those for $p < 0$ orthogonally. Find a first order differential equation satisfied by all the parabolas of the family and show again that the family is self-orthogonal.

15. The curves of constant height on the upper half of the ellipsoid $\dfrac{x^2}{a^2} + \dfrac{y^2}{b^2} + \dfrac{z^2}{c^2} = 1$ are the ellipses that lie in the planes $z = K, 0 \leq K \leq c$. The projections of those

ellipses in the xy plane are the curves $\dfrac{x^2}{a^2} + \dfrac{y^2}{b^2} = 1 - \dfrac{K^2}{c^2}$ with parameter K. If a drop of water were to fall on the upper half of the ellipsoid, it would move on a path along which the height changed most rapidly. Describe the curves along which the height changes most rapidly.

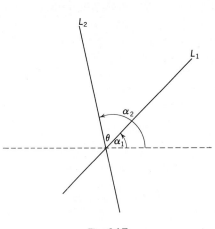

Fig. 14.7

16. Find a second order differential equation satisfied by all the members of the two-parameter family of curves $y = e^{-x} (C_1 \cos x + C_2 \sin x)$.

17. Find a second order differential equation satisfied by all parabolas with vertices on the y axis and axes of symmetry parallel to the x axis.

18. Find a third order differential equation satisfied by all ellipses with eccentricity $\tfrac{1}{2}$ and major axis in the x direction.

19. Find a third order differential equation satisfied by all the members of the three-parameter family of curves $y = C_1 e^x + C_2 e^{2x} + C_3 x e^x$.

20. If we are given a line L_1 with slope m_1 and inclination angle α_1 and asked for a second line L_2 whose inclination angle α_2 is greater than that of L_1 by a given amount θ, $0 \le \theta < \dfrac{\pi}{2}$, as in Fig. 14.7, we can compute the slope of L_2 with the help of a trigonometric identity;

$$m_2 = \tan \alpha_2 = \tan (\alpha_1 + \theta) = \frac{\tan \alpha_1 + \tan \theta}{1 - \tan \alpha_1 \tan \theta} = \frac{m_1 + \tan \theta}{1 - m_1 \tan \theta}.$$

Hence if a curve C_2 with slope $(dy/dx)_2$ is to intersect curve C_1 with slope $(dy/dx)_1$ at a given angle θ, $0 \le \theta < \pi/2$, we must have

$$\left(\frac{dy}{dx}\right)_2 = \frac{(dy/dx)_1 \pm \tan \theta}{1 \mp (dy/dx)_1 \tan \theta},$$

the signs to be chosen according as the inclination of C_2 is to be greater, or less, than that of C_1. (a) Find either of the two families of curves that intersect the parabolas $y = x^2 + C$ at a 60° angle. (b) Find either of the two families of curves that intersect the curves

$$y = \tan (x + C) \qquad \text{for } 0 \le x < \frac{\pi}{2}, -\frac{\pi}{2} < C \le 0, \text{ at a 45° angle.}$$

21. Show that spheres and right circular cylinders are the only surfaces of revolution for which the surface area between every pair of planes perpendicular to the axis of revolution is proportional to the distance between the two planes.
Suggestion: Let the curve $y = f(x)$, $y > 0$, be rotated about the x axis to form a surface of revolution. Let the planes perpendicular to the axis of revolution be those formed by rotating vertical lines with abscissas a and x. Write an integral equation which says that the surface area and distance between the planes are proportional. Differentiate with respect to x to get a differential equation, and solve.

22. Which surfaces of revolution, other than special right circular cylinders, have the property that the volume bounded by the surface and every pair of planes perpendicular to the axis of revolution is proportional to the surface area included between the two planes?

Suggestions: Let the curve $y = f(x)$, $y > 0$, be rotated about the x axis; let the planes be those formed by rotating vertical lines with abscissas a and x; let the constant of proportionality be b. Write an integral equation which says that the volume enclosed is b times the surface area. Differentiate this equation with respect to x to get the differential equation $1 + \left(\dfrac{dy}{dx}\right)^2 = \left(\dfrac{y}{2b}\right)^2$. Show that $y = 2b \cosh\left(\dfrac{x}{2b} + C\right)$ and $y = 2b$ are the solutions.

14.3 Homogeneous First Order Equations

Thus far we have worked primarily with separable first order differential equations. In general, however, a first order equation is not directly separable and it is necessary either to reduce the equation to a separable equation or to use a different idea. In this section we shall consider an easily recognized case that can always be reduced to the separable case and then studied as before.

A polynomial in two variables is homogeneous if all of its terms are of the same degree. Thus $x^2 + 3xy + y^2$ is homogeneous and of degree 2 while $x^3 + xy$ is not homogeneous, because its first term is of degree 3 while its second term is of degree 2. In Exercise 10.3-6 a definition of homogeneity was given that applied to polynomials and to other functions as well. That more general definition is repeated here for the sake of easy reference.

■ **DEFINITION 1**

Homogeneous functions. Let region R contain the points (tx, ty), $t > 0$, whenever it contains the point (x, y). We shall say that $f(x, y)$ is homogeneous of degree k in R if $f(tx, ty) = t^k f(x, y)$ for all (x, y) of R and all $t > 0$.

Example 1A. According to this definition, $f(x, y) = x^2 + 3xy + y^2$ is homogeneous of degree 2 in the entire xy plane, because we have

$$f(tx, ty) = (tx)^2 + 3(tx)(ty) + (ty)^2$$
$$= t^2 x^2 + 3t^2 xy + t^2 y^2$$
$$= t^2 f(x, y)$$

for all points (x, y) and all $t > 0$.

Example 2. According to Definition 1, $f(x, y) = x^3 + xy$ is not homogeneous in any region R which contains at least one point not on either coordinate axis and which contains the points (tx, ty), $t > 0$, whenever it contains the point (x, y). For we compute

$$f(tx, ty) = (tx)^3 + (tx)(ty) = t^2 (tx^3 + xy) = t^3 \left(x^3 + \frac{1}{t} xy\right).$$

We cannot write $f(tx, ty) = t^2 f(x, y)$ for all $t > 0$ and all points (x, y) of region R; neither is it possible to write $f(tx, ty) = t^3 f(x, y)$ for all $t > 0$ and all points (x, y) of region R.

Example 3A. $f(x, y) = \sqrt{x + y}$ is of degree $\frac{1}{2}$ in the region R which is the half-plane $x + y \geq 0$. For, in the first place, for any point (x, y) such that $x + y \geq 0$ we see that (tx, ty) is such that $tx + ty = t(x + y) \geq 0$ when $t > 0$, so that (tx, ty) belongs to R for $t > 0$ whenever (x, y) does. Then we can compute

$$f(tx, ty) = \sqrt{tx + ty} = \sqrt{t}\sqrt{x + y}$$
$$f(tx, ty) = t^{1/2}\sqrt{x + y}$$

for all points (x, y) of region R and all $t > 0$.

Example 4

$$f(x, y) = \frac{1}{x + y} e^{y/x}$$

is of degree -1 in the region R defined by $x > 0, y > 0$. For any point (x, y) of R we can xay that $tx > 0, ty > 0$ for $t > 0$, so that (tx, ty) belongs to R when (x, y) does for all $t > 0$. Further,

$$f(tx, ty) = \frac{1}{tx + ty} e^{ty/tx} = \frac{1}{t}\frac{1}{x + y} e^{y/x}$$
$$f(tx, ty) = t^{-1} f(x, y)$$

for all (x, y) of R and all $t > 0$.

■ DEFINITION 2

Homogeneous first order differential equation. We shall say that the first order differential equation $P(x, y) dx + Q(x, y)dy = 0$ is homogeneous if there is a region R in which $P(x, y)$ and $Q(x, y)$ are both homogeneous of the same degree.

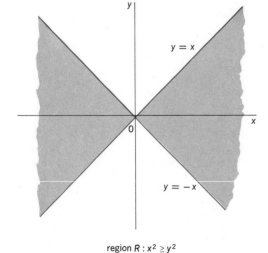

region $R : x^2 \geq y^2$

Fig. 14.8

Example 5A.   The equation

$$(4x^2 + 6xy + y^2) dx - x^2 dy = 0$$

is homogeneous, because the functions $4x^2 + 6xy + y^2$ and $-x^2$ are both homogeneous of degree 2 in the entire xy plane.

Example 6A.   The equation

$$y dx - (x + \sqrt{x^2 - y^2}) dy = 0$$

is homogeneous, because the functions y and $-x - \sqrt{x^2 - y^2}$ are both homogeneous of degree 1 in the region R defined by $x^2 \geq y^2$. This region is pictured in Fig. 14.8.

Example 7.   The equation

$$(x^3 + y^3) dx + (x^2 + y^2) dy = 0$$

is not homogeneous, because $x^3 + y^3$ and $x^2 + y^2$, while both homogeneous, are not of the same degree.

Example 5B. Let us find the solution of the homogeneous differential equation

$$(4x^2 + 6xy + y^2)\, dx - x^2\, dy = 0 \tag{1}$$

for which $y = -2$ when $x = 1$. If we rewrite this equation in the form

$$\frac{dy}{dx} = 4 + 6\left(\frac{y}{x}\right) + \left(\frac{y}{x}\right)^2, \tag{2}$$

we see immediately that the expression y/x has a very prominent role to play in the problem, and this suggests the substitution of a new letter for y/x. Let us try then the substitution

$$\frac{y}{x} = v \qquad \text{or} \qquad y = vx.$$

If we agree to rewrite y in this way, we must also write

$$\frac{dy}{dx} = v + x\frac{dv}{dx},$$

and then Eq. (2) becomes

$$v + x\frac{dv}{dx} = 4 + 6v + v^2$$

or

$$x\frac{dv}{dx} = 4 + 5v + v^2$$

$$\frac{dv}{v^2 + 5v + 4} = \frac{dx}{x}.$$

The last equation is already separated and we can solve as before. By using the partial fraction device we can write

$$-\frac{1}{3}\frac{dv}{v + 4} + \frac{1}{3}\frac{dv}{v + 1} = \frac{dx}{x},$$

and then, since we shall be concerned with the special value $v = -2$ (because y shall be -2 when $x = 1$ and $v = y/x$),

$$-\tfrac{1}{3}\log (v + 4) + \tfrac{1}{3}\log (-v - 1) = \log x + \log C.$$

Here, since $v = -2$ when $x = 1$,

$$-\tfrac{1}{3}\log 2 + 0 = 0 + \log C,$$

and we continue with

$$- \tfrac{1}{3} \log (v + 4) + \tfrac{1}{3} \log (-v - 1) = \log x - \tfrac{1}{3} \log 2$$

$$- \log (v + 4) + \log (-v - 1) = 3 \log x - \log 2$$

$$\log \frac{-v - 1}{v + 4} = \log \frac{x^3}{2}$$

$$\frac{-v - 1}{v + 4} = \frac{x^3}{2}$$

$$\frac{-y/x - 1}{y/x + 4} = \frac{x^3}{2}$$

$$\frac{-y - x}{y + 4x} = \frac{x^3}{2}$$

$$x^3(y + 4x) + 2(y + x) = 0$$

$$(x^3 + 2)y = -(4x^4 + 2x)$$

$$y = -2 \frac{x(2x^3 + 1)}{x^3 + 2}.$$

Observe that when we divided by x^2 in going from Eq. (1) to Eq. (2) we tacitly assumed that x did not vanish. This was permissible in this special example, because we wanted a solution for which x was 1 and not 0, but, in general, one must check to be sure that solutions are not being thus ignored; the straight line $x = 0$ is a solution of Eq. (1).*

Example 6B.   The homogeneous differential equation

$$y \, dx - (x + \sqrt{x^2 - y^2}) \, dy = 0$$

can be rewritten in the form

$$\frac{y}{x} \, dx - \left(1 + \sqrt{1 - \left(\frac{y}{x}\right)^2}\right) dy = 0$$

for $x > 0$, and again we see that the coefficients of both differentials can be written as functions of y/x alone. If again we make the substitution

$$\frac{y}{x} = v \quad \text{or} \quad y = vx$$

and write

$$dy = v \, dx + x \, dv,$$

our equation becomes

$$v \, dx - (1 + \sqrt{1 - v^2}) \, (v \, dx + x \, dv) = 0$$

or

$$-v\sqrt{1 - v^2} \, dx - x(1 + \sqrt{1 - v^2}) \, dv = 0$$

$$\frac{dx}{x} + \frac{1 + \sqrt{1 - v^2}}{v\sqrt{1 - v^2}} \, dv = 0.$$

---

* This solution is perhaps easier to check directly in Eq. (1) if one describes the line in the parametric form $x = 0$, $y = t$

Again the substitution $v = y/x$ enables us to rewrite a homogeneous differential equation as a separable one. The reader can work further on the solution of this equation in Exercise 14.3-9.

Examples 5 and 6 suggest that many, perhaps all, homogeneous equations can be rewritten in a form where the coefficients of both differentials are functions of y/x alone, and that the substitution $v = y/x$ will then enable us to rewrite the differential equation in separable form. We investigate this possibility in Theorems 1 and 2.

■ THEOREM 1

A property of homogeneous functions.

HYPOTHESIS: $f(x,y)$ is homogeneous of degree k in region R.

CONCLUSION: $f(x, y) = \begin{cases} x^k f\left(1, \dfrac{y}{x}\right) & \text{for } (x, y) \text{ in } R \text{ and } x > 0 \\ \\ (-x)^k f\left(-1, -\dfrac{y}{x}\right) & \text{for } (x, y) \text{ in } R \text{ and } x < 0. \end{cases}$

PROOF: The very definition of a homogeneous function tells us that for any point (x, y) in R and for every $t > 0$ we can write

$$f(tx, ty) = t^k f(x, y). \tag{3}$$

If we are interested in a point (x, y) of R for which $x > 0$, then we can take $t = 1/x$ and write

$$f\left(1, \frac{y}{x}\right) = \left(\frac{1}{x}\right)^k f(x, y),$$

or, multiplying by x^k, we can write

$$f(x, y) = x^k f\left(1, \frac{y}{x}\right),$$

which is the first part of our conclusion. If, on the other hand, we are interested in a point (x, y) of R for which $x < 0$, then we can take $t = -(1/x)$ in Eq. (3) and write

$$f\left(-1, -\frac{y}{x}\right) = \left(-\frac{1}{x}\right)^k f(x, y).$$

This leads to the other part of the conclusion of the theorem.

Example 1B. We saw in Example 1A that

$$f(x, y) = x^2 + 3xy + y^2$$

was homogeneous of degree 2 in the entire x, y plane. We can write

$$f(x, y) = x^2\left[1 + 3\frac{y}{x} + \left(\frac{y}{x}\right)^2\right] = x^2 f\left(1, \frac{y}{x}\right) \qquad \text{for } x > 0$$

and

$$f(x, y) = x^2 \left[1 + 3\frac{y}{x} + \left(\frac{y}{x}\right)^2 \right] = (-x)^2 \left[(-1)^2 + 3(-1)\left(\frac{-y}{x}\right) + \left(\frac{-y}{x}\right)^2 \right]$$

$$= (-x)^2 f\left(-1, \frac{-y}{x}\right) \qquad \text{for } x < 0.$$

In this case we happen to get the same replacement for $x^2 + 3xy + y^2$, namely,

$$x^2 \left[1 + 3\frac{y}{x} + \left(\frac{y}{x}\right)^2 \right],$$

for both negative and positive x.

Example 3B.   We saw in Example 3A that

$$f(x, y) = \sqrt{x + y}$$

was homogeneous of degree $\frac{1}{2}$ in the region $R\colon x + y \geq 0$. We can write

$$f(x, y) = \sqrt{x} \sqrt{1 + \frac{y}{x}} = x^{1/2} f\left(1, \frac{y}{x}\right) \qquad \text{for } x > 0$$

and

$$f(x, y) = \sqrt{-x} \sqrt{-1 - \frac{y}{x}} = (-x)^{1/2} f\left(-1, \frac{-y}{x}\right) \qquad \text{for } x < 0.$$

In this case we do not get replacements for $f(x, y)$ of the same form when x is positive and when x is negative.

■ THEOREM 2

Homogeneous equations rendered separable.

Hypothesis: $P(x, y)$ and $Q(x, y)$ are both homogeneous of degree k in region R.

Conclusion: $P(x, y)\, dx + Q(x, y)\, dy = 0$ can be rewritten in separable form for (x, y) in R and $x \neq 0$ by using the substitution $v = y/x$.

Proof: Consider first the case where $x > 0$. Theorem 1 enables us to write in this case

$$P(x, y)\, dx + Q(x, y)\, dy = 0$$

$$(x)^k P\left(1, \frac{y}{x}\right) dx + (x)^k Q\left(1, \frac{y}{x}\right) dy = 0$$

$$P\left(1, \frac{y}{x}\right) dx + Q\left(1, \frac{y}{x}\right) dy = 0. \tag{4}$$

Now we recognize that variables appear in the coefficients only in the combination y/x and if we substitute $v = y/x$ we get

$$P(1, v)\, dx + Q(1, v)(v\, dx + x\, dv) = 0$$

$$[P(1, v) + vQ(1, v)]\, dx + xQ(1, v)\, dv = 0$$

$$\frac{dx}{x} + \frac{Q(1, v)}{P(1, v) + vQ(1, v)}\, dv = 0.$$

The differential equation is now in separated form.

On the other hand, if we consider the case where $x < 0$, we write

$$P(x,y)\, dx + Q(x,y)\, dy = 0$$

$$(-x)^k P\left(-1, -\frac{y}{x}\right) dx + (-x)^k Q\left(-1, -\frac{y}{x}\right) dy = 0$$

$$P\left(-1, -\frac{y}{x}\right) dx + Q\left(-1, -\frac{y}{x}\right) dy = 0, \tag{5}$$

and, with the same substitution $v = y/x$, we get

$$P(-1, -v)\, dx + Q(-1, -v)(x\, dv + v\, dx) = 0$$

$$\frac{dx}{x} + \frac{Q(-1, -v)}{P(-1, -v) + vQ(-1, -v)}\, dv = 0;$$

again the differential equation is written in separated form and the proof of the theorem is now complete.

There is another way of separating the variables in a homogeneous equation.

■ THEOREM 3

Homogeneous equations rendered separable.

HYPOTHESIS: $P(x, y)\, dx + Q(x, y)\, dy = 0$ is a homogeneous differential equation.

CONCLUSION: The differential equation can be rewritten in separable form by changing to polar coordinates:

$$x = r \cos \theta, \qquad y = r \sin \theta.$$

PROOF: The reader may prove this theorem in Exercise 14.3-23.

We conclude this section with an example that illustrates how a translation of coordinates can sometimes convert a nonhomogeneous equation to a homogeneous equation.

Example 8. The equation

$$(x + 2y + 5)\, dx - (2x + y + 4)\, dy = 0 \tag{6}$$

is not homogeneous, because $x + 2y + 5$ and $-(2x + y + 4)$ are not homogeneous. But in analytic geometry problems we often removed constant terms by translating coordinates; we can do the same thing here. Let us try to choose h and k in such a way that the substitutions

$$x = x' + h, \qquad y = y' + k$$

will lead to homogeneous replacements for $x + 2y + 5$ and $-2x - y - 4$. We have

$$\left.\begin{array}{l} x + 2y + 5 = (x' + h) + 2(y' + k) + 5 = x' + 2y' + (h + 2k + 5) \\ -2x - y - 4 = -2(x' + h) - (y' + k) - 4 = -2x' - y' - (2h + k + 4) \end{array}\right\}. \tag{7}$$

We want to choose h and k such that

$$h + 2k + 5 = 0$$
$$2h + k + 4 = 0, \tag{8}$$

for then Eqs. (7) will give us homogeneous replacements for the coefficients of Eq. (6). Equations (8) are easily solved; one ought to choose $h = -1$ and $k = -2$. Hence the substitution we try is

$$x = x' - 1, \qquad y = y' - 2.$$

Since we can write $dx = dx'$ and $dy = dy'$, Eq. (6) becomes

$$(x' + 2y') \, dx' - (2x' + y') \, dy' = 0.$$

This is a homogeneous equation in x' and y' which can be made separable by the substitution $y'/x' = v$. The ultimate solution is left to the reader in Exercise 14.3-14.

EXERCISES 14.3

Find a one-parameter family of solutions in each of Exercises 1–8.

1. $(3x + 4y) \, dx + y \, dy = 0$.

2. $2(x + y) \, dx - (3x + y) \, dy = 0$.

3. $\dfrac{dy}{dx} = \dfrac{2y^2}{(x + y)^2}$.

4. $\dfrac{dy}{dx} = \dfrac{2xy + 3y^2}{4x^2 + y^2}$.

5. $(2x^2 + 2xy + y^2) \, dx - (x^2 + 2xy) \, dy = 0$.

6. $(y^3 - xy^2 - x^2y + 2x^3) \, dx - x^2y \, dy = 0$.

7. $\dfrac{dy}{dx} = e^{y/x} + \dfrac{y}{x}$.

8. $\dfrac{dy}{dx} = \dfrac{y}{x} + \sqrt{1 + \dfrac{y}{x}}$.

9. (a) Complete the work presented in Example 6B and show that $x - \sqrt{x^2 - y^2} = C$, $y = x$, and $y = -x$ are all solutions for $x > 0$.
   (b) Show that $x - \sqrt{x^2 - y^2} = C$, $y = x$, and $y = -x$ are all solutions for $x < 0$ also. Remember that $\sqrt{x^2} = -x$ for $x < 0$.

10. (a) Find a solution of $(2y + \sqrt{x^2 + y^2}) \, dx - 2x \, dy = 0$ for which $y = 3$ when $x = 4$.
   (b) Find a solution for which $y = 3$ when $x = -4$.
   (c) Find a solution for which $y = 3$ when $x = 0$.

11. Find a one-parameter family of solutions of $xy \, dx - (x^2 + y\sqrt{y^2 - x^2}) \, dy = 0$, assuming that $y \geq x > 0$.

12. Find a one-parameter family of solutions of $(xy - y^2 + x\sqrt{x^2 - y^2}) \, dx - (x^2 - xy) \, dy = 0$, assuming that $x < 0$ and that $|y| \leq |x|$.

13. Find a solution of $\dfrac{dy}{dx} = \sqrt{\dfrac{y}{x}} + 2$ for which $y = -1$ when $x = -1$.

14. Finish Example 8.

Find a one-parameter family of solutions in each of Exercises 15, 16, and 17.

15. $(4x + 5y + 6) \, dx - (x - y - 3) \, dy = 0$.

16. $(2x - y + 2) \, dx + (6x + 2y + 1) \, dy = 0$.

17. $(x + y + 3)^2 \, dx - 4(x + 2)^2 \, dy = 0$.

18. Consider $(y - 2x + 5) \, dx - (y - 2x + 3) \, dy = 0$. Substitutions of the form $x = x'$ $+ h, y = y' + k$ cannot render both $y - 2x + 5$ and $-(y - 2x + 3)$ homogeneous simultaneously, but the fact that $y - 2x$ appears twice suggests that the substitution $v = y - 2x$ may be helpful. Make this substitution and find a solution for which $y = 3$ when $x = 0$.

19. Find a solution of $(y - x + 2)^2 \, dx - (y - x + 1)^2 \, dy = 0$ for which $y = 0$ when $x = 3$.

20. The circles $(x - C)^2 + y^2 = C^2$ are tangent to the y axis at the origin. Find their orthogonal trajectories.

21. Use the ideas of Exercise 14.2-20 to find a family of curves that intersects the family of concentric circles $x^2 + y^2 = C^2$ at an angle of $45°$.

22. Find a family of curves orthogonal to the family $x(3x + 5y)^4 = C$.

23. Carry out a proof for Theorem 3 by pointing out that Eq. (4) holds for $r > 0$ and $-\pi/2 < \theta < \pi/2$ because $x = r \cos \theta$ is then >0 while Eq. (5) holds for $r > 0$ and $\pi/2 < \theta < 3\pi/2$, and by replacing Cartesian coordinates by polar coordinates in these equations.

Two population problems follow.

24. Assume that a radioactive element disintegrates in such a way that the number N of atoms present at time t decreases at a rate proportional to N itself.

(a) If this constant of proportionality is α and N_0 is the number of atoms present at $t = 0$, show that

$$N = N_0 e^{-\alpha t}.$$

(b) Show that the "half-life" time, the time required for half the atoms present at $t = 0$ to disintegrate, is $t = (1/\alpha) \log 2$.

(c) Let us assume that living organic material contains the C^{12} and C^{14} isotopes in a fixed proportion, that the C^{12} atoms do not disintegrate radioactively, but that C^{14} atoms do disintegrate with a half-life time of 5568 years and that these C^{14} atoms are not replaced once the organic material dies. A sample of wood in an American Indian cliff dwelling is measured to have 88.7 percent of the C^{14} isotope expected for living wood. What is the estimated age of the piece of wood?

25. In each of the following cases find a formula for the number N of a certain population present at time t, writing N_0 for the number present at $t = 0$.

(a) The birth and death rates are fixed at b percent and d percent of N.

(b) The death rate is fixed at d percent, but the birth rate decreases steadily with time and can be written $(b - ct)$ percent for $t < b/c$.

(c) The food supply available will only support a "saturation" population S and the rate of change of N is proportional to $N(S - N)$, with constant of proportionality k.

14.4 Exact First Order Equations. Integrating Factors

I

It is sometimes possible to recognize derivatives in a first order differential equation and to write the solution almost immediately. Thus in the differential equation

$$\sec 3\theta \, \frac{dr}{d\theta} + 3r \sec 3\theta \tan 3\theta = 0 \tag{1}$$

we observe that the left member consists of two terms. Since the derivative of a product usually leads to two terms, and since the term sec $3\theta \, dr/d\theta$ of Eq. (1) suggests that we held the factor sec 3θ of the product r sec 3θ fixed and differentiated the factor r with respect to θ, we ask ourselves whether the left member of Eq. (1) is the derivative of r sec 3θ. We quickly find that it is, and that Eq. (1) can be written

$$\frac{d}{d\theta} (r \sec 3\theta) = 0.$$

Then we see that the solutions of Eq. (1) are given by

$$r \sec 3\theta = C.$$

We shall treat such equations a little more systematically in this section. It is customary to write the basic definitions and theorems in the language of differentials rather than derivatives.

■ DEFINITION 1A

Exact differential. We shall say that $P \, dx + Q \, dy$ is exact if there exists a function $u(x, y)$ with continuous first partial derivatives for which we can write

$$du = P(x, y) \, dx + Q(x, y) \, dy. \tag{2}$$

● Remark 1

When $P \, dx + Q \, dy$ is exact, the equation

$$P(x, y) \, dx + Q(x, y) \, dy = 0$$

can be written $$du = 0$$

for some function $u(x, y)$, and we can say immediately that the equations

$$u(x, y) = C$$

constitute a one-parameter family of solutions.

According to the definition of the total differential, Definition 11.2-3, we can write

$$du = \frac{\partial u}{\partial x} \, dx + \frac{\partial u}{\partial y} \, dy.$$

Hence, by comparison with Eq. (2), Definition 1A can be rewritten in an alternate form.

■ DEFINITION 1B

Exact differential. We shall say that $P \, dx + Q \, dy$ is exact if there exists a function $u(x, y)$ with continuous first partial derivatives for which we can write

$$\frac{\partial u}{\partial x} = P(x, y) \tag{3a}$$

and $$\frac{\partial u}{\partial y} = Q(x, y). \tag{3b}$$

There is a simple test for exactness suggested by Eqs. (3a) and (3b). These equations say that

$$\frac{\partial P}{\partial y} = \frac{\partial^2 u}{\partial y\,\partial x} \quad \text{and} \quad \frac{\partial Q}{\partial x} = \frac{\partial^2 u}{\partial x\,\partial y}.$$

But we know from Theorem 11.6-1 that these mixed partial derivatives of u are equal under fairly general conditions, and hence we can say that, under these conditions, $\partial P/\partial y$ and $\partial Q/\partial x$ must be equal. We have demonstrated the following theorem.

■ THEOREM 1A

A criterion for exactness.

    HYPOTHESIS: (a) $P(x, y)\, dx + Q(x, y)\, dy$ is exact.
(b) P and Q have continuous first partial derivatives.

    CONCLUSION: $\dfrac{\partial P}{\partial y} = \dfrac{\partial Q}{\partial x}.$

The converse theorem is also true.

■ THEOREM 1B

A criterion for exactness.

    HYPOTHESIS: (a) $P(x, y)$ and $Q(x, y)$ have continuous first partial derivatives.

(b) $\dfrac{\partial P}{\partial y} = \dfrac{\partial Q}{\partial x}.$

    CONCLUSION: $P(x, y)\, dx + Q(x, y)\, dy$ is exact.

The proof of the converse theorem is instructive, because it teaches us how to construct the function $u(x, y)$ whose differential is precisely $P\, dx + Q\, dy$, when we know that $P\, dx + Q\, dy$ is exact but cannot guess $u(x, y)$ by observation. We illustrate with a specific example before proving this theorem.

    Example 1.   Consider the equation

$$\frac{1}{y}\, dx + \left(\frac{1}{y} - \frac{x}{y^2}\right) dy = 0.$$

If we write

$$P(x, y) = \frac{1}{y}, \qquad Q(x, y) = \frac{1}{y} - \frac{x}{y^2}$$

and compute

$$\frac{\partial P}{\partial y} = -\frac{1}{y^2}, \qquad \frac{\partial Q}{\partial x} = -\frac{1}{y^2},$$

then we see from Theorem 1B that our differential equation is exact. We know that there exists a function $u(x, y)$ such that

$$\frac{\partial u}{\partial x} = \frac{1}{y} \tag{4a}$$

and

$$\frac{\partial u}{\partial y} = \frac{1}{y} - \frac{x}{y^2}. \tag{4b}$$

To find such a function $u(x, y)$ we try first to meet the condition imposed by Eq. (4a). We integrate with respect to x, holding y fixed, and write

$$u(x, y) = \frac{x}{y} + \varphi(y),$$

the function $\varphi(y)$ as yet undetermined. If this $u(x, y)$ is also to meet the condition imposed by Eq. (4b), we must now choose $\varphi(y)$ so that

$$\frac{\partial u}{\partial y} = \frac{1}{y} - \frac{x}{y^2},$$

$$-\frac{x}{y^2} + \varphi'(y) = \frac{1}{y} - \frac{x}{y^2},$$

$$\varphi'(y) = \frac{1}{y}.$$

A suitable choice for $\varphi(y)$ is

$$\varphi(y) = \log y,$$

and we can then take

$$u(x, y) = \frac{x}{y} + \log y.$$

The differential equation can be rewritten

$$d\left(\frac{x}{y} + \log y\right) = 0,$$

with solution

$$\frac{x}{y} + \log y = C.$$

Of course this was a relatively simple example, and we could have pieced the function $u(x, y)$ together by observation as soon as we knew that the equation was exact. We could have written the equation in the forms

$$\frac{1}{y} dx - \frac{x}{y^2} dy + \frac{1}{y} dy = 0$$

$$\frac{y \, dx - x \, dy}{y^2} + \frac{1}{y} dy = 0$$

$$d\left(\frac{x}{y}\right) + d(\log y) = 0$$

$$\frac{x}{y} + \log y = C.$$

Now we turn to the proof of Theorem 1B.

PROOF: 1. According to Definition 1B the conclusion will be established if we can construct a function $u(x, y)$ with the properties

$$\frac{\partial u}{\partial x} = P(x, y) \tag{3a}$$

$$\frac{\partial u}{\partial y} = Q(x, y). \tag{3b}$$

2.   There are many functions that satisfy the condition imposed by Eq. (3a) alone. One of them is the function

$$v(x, y) = \int_{s=a}^{x} P(s, y) \, ds$$

[y fixed]

defined by means of a definite integral, the choice of the boundary constant a being arbitrary and the integration being carried out with respect to s alone, y being held fixed. Because $P(s, y)$ is a continuous function of s by hypothesis, this integral exists and

$$\frac{\partial v}{\partial x} = P(x, y);$$

see Theorem 7.7-2. If we write

$$u(x, y) = v(x, y) + \varphi(y), \tag{5}$$

$\varphi(y)$ thus far arbitrary, we can be sure that all the possible functions $u(x, y)$ thus described meet the conditon imposed by Eq. (3a), because

$$\frac{\partial u}{\partial x} = \frac{\partial v}{\partial x} + 0 = P(x, y).$$

3.   But can we choose $\varphi(y)$ in Eq. (5) so that the $u(x, y)$ thus selected also meets the condition imposed by Eq. (3b)? We would have to choose a $\varphi(y)$ that satisfied

$$\frac{\partial v}{\partial y} + \varphi'(y) = Q(x, y)$$

or
$$\varphi'(y) = Q(x, y) - \frac{\partial v}{\partial y}. \tag{6}$$

It will be possible to find a $\varphi(y)$ that meets the requirement imposed by Eq. (6) if the right member of that equation is a continuous function of y alone. In that case we can find a suitable $\varphi(y)$ by integration with respect to y.

4.   Let us give the name $R(x, y)$ to the right member of Eq. (6);

$$R(x, y) = Q(x, y) - \frac{\partial v}{\partial y}.$$

We can show that $R(x, y)$ is a function of y alone by showing that $\partial R/\partial x = 0$. We have

$$\frac{\partial R}{\partial x} = \frac{\partial Q}{\partial x} - \frac{\partial^2 v}{\partial x \, \partial y}$$

$$= \frac{\partial Q}{\partial x} - \frac{\partial^2 v}{\partial y \, \partial x} = \frac{\partial Q}{\partial x} - \frac{\partial}{\partial y}\left(\frac{\partial v}{\partial x}\right)$$

$$= \frac{\partial Q}{\partial x} - \frac{\partial P}{\partial y}$$

$$= 0$$

because $\partial P/\partial y$ and $\partial Q/\partial x$ are equal by hypothesis. In this work it is necessary to show that $v(x, y)$ is such that

$$\frac{\partial v}{\partial y}, \frac{\partial^2 v}{\partial x\, \partial y}, \frac{\partial^2 v}{\partial y\, \partial x}$$

all exist in the first place, and that

$$\frac{\partial^2 v}{\partial x\, \partial y} = \frac{\partial^2 v}{\partial y\, \partial x}.$$

Advanced calculus texts study functions defined by integrals and prove theorems that justify all these assertions. We shall accept these assertions without proof.

5.   We shall also accept without proof the assertion that $\partial v/\partial y$ is a continuous function of y. $Q(x, y)$ is continuous in y, by hypothesis, and thus $R = Q - \partial v/\partial y$ is a continuous function of y alone. This means that we can integrate to find a $\varphi(y)$ that satisfies Eq. (6) and that we can use this $\varphi(y)$ in Eq. (5) to complete the construction of the function $u(x, y)$ that meets the conditions imposed by Eqs. (3a) and (3b). This completes the proof of Theorem 1B.

■ DEFINITION 2

Exact first order differential equation. We shall say that the equation $P\, dx + Q\, dy = 0$ is exact if $P\, dx + Q\, dy$ is exact.

Example 2.   The equation

$$\frac{x + 2y}{(x + y)^2}\, dx + \frac{y}{(x + y)^2}\, dy = 0$$

is homogeneous, but it is also exact, as we shall soon see. We write

$$P(x, y) = \frac{x + 2y}{(x + y)^2}, \qquad Q(x, y) = \frac{y}{(x + y)^2},$$

and compute

$$\frac{\partial P}{\partial y} = \frac{(x + y)^2 2 - (x + 2y)2(x + y)}{(x + y)^4} = 2\frac{(x + y) - (x + 2y)}{(x + y)^3}$$

$$= \frac{-2y}{(x + y)^3}$$

$$\frac{\partial Q}{\partial x} = -\frac{2y}{(x + y)^3} = \frac{\partial P}{\partial y}.$$

Now we know that there is a function $u(x, y)$ that meets the conditions

$$\frac{\partial u}{\partial x} = \frac{x + 2y}{(x + y)^2} \qquad (7a)$$

and

$$\frac{\partial u}{\partial y} = \frac{y}{(x + y)^2}. \qquad (7b)$$

It seems to be easier to meet the requirement of Eq. (7b) first. Let us write

$$v(x, y) = \int \frac{y}{(x + y)^2}\, dy$$

[x fixed]

and then, with the substitution $w = x + y$,

$$v(x, y) = \int \frac{w - x}{w^2} \, dw = \int \left(\frac{1}{w} - \frac{x}{w^2} \right) dw$$

[x fixed]   [x fixed]

$$v(x, y) = \log w + \frac{x}{w} = \log (x + y) + \frac{x}{(x + y)}.$$

Now take

$$u(x, y) = \log (x + y) + \frac{x}{(x + y)} + \varphi(x)$$

and try to choose $\varphi(x)$ so that the requirement of Eq. (7a) is met. We must have

$$\frac{\partial u}{\partial x} = \frac{x + 2y}{(x + y)^2},$$

$$\frac{1}{x + y} + \frac{(x + y)1 - x(1)}{(x + y)^2} + \varphi'(x) = \frac{x + 2y}{(x + y)^2},$$

$$\varphi'(x) = 0,$$

and it suffices to choose

$$\varphi(x) = 0$$

$$u(x, y) = \log (x + y) + \frac{x}{x + y}.$$

The equation with which we started can therefore be written

$$d\left[\log (x + y) + \frac{x}{x + y} \right] = 0;$$

its solution is

$$\log (x + y) + \frac{x}{x + y} = C.$$

Here was a case where it would have been a little harder to piece the function $u(x, y)$ together by observation. The reader can solve this equation as a homogeneous equation in Exercise 14.4-11.

II

Equations that are not exact can often be made exact by suitable rewriting. Thus the equation

$$y \, dx - x \, dy = 0$$

is not exact as written, but if we multiply by $1/y^2$ and write

$$\frac{y \, dx - x \, dy}{y^2} = 0$$

$$d\left(\frac{x}{y} \right) = 0$$

we see that the equation can be rewritten so as to become exact. The quantity $1/y^2$ by which we multiplied to make the equation exact is called an integrating factor.

■ DEFINITION 3

Integrating factor. We say that $I(x, y)$ is an integrating factor for $P(x, y) \, dx + Q(x, y) \, dy$ if $I(x, y)[P(x, y) \, dx + Q(x, y) \, dy]$ is exact.

We can show that every first order equation that has a family of solutions can be made exact.

■ THEOREM 2

The existence of integrating factors for first order equations.

HYPOTHESIS: $u(x, y) = C$ is a one-parameter family of solutions for $P(x, y) \, dx + Q(x, y) \, dy = 0$.

CONCLUSION: $I(x, y) = \dfrac{\partial u}{\partial x} \div P(x, y)$ is an integrating factor for $P(x, y) \, dx + Q(x, y) dy = 0$.

PROOF: By hypothesis $u(x, y) = C$ are solution curves of $P(x, y) \, dx + Q(x, y) \, dy = 0$

or of

$$\frac{dy}{dx} = -\frac{P(x, y)}{Q(x, y)}. \tag{8}$$

But $u(x, y) = C$ are also solution curves of

$$du = 0,$$

$$\frac{\partial u}{\partial x} \, dx + \frac{\partial u}{\partial y} \, dy = 0,$$

or of

$$\frac{dy}{dx} = -\frac{\partial u/\partial x}{\partial u/\partial y}. \tag{9}$$

Since a solution curve can have only one slope at a given point, Eqs. (8) and (9) tell us that

$$\frac{P(x, y)}{Q(x, y)} = \frac{\partial u/\partial x}{\partial u/\partial y}$$

or

$$\frac{\partial u/\partial x}{P(x, y)} = \frac{\partial u/\partial y}{Q(x, y)}. \tag{10}$$

Let us give the name $I(x, y)$ to the ratios declared equal in Eq. (10). Then

$$\frac{\partial u/\partial x}{P(x, y)} = \frac{\partial u/\partial y}{Q(x, y)} = I(x, y),$$

or $\partial u/\partial x = I(x, y) \, P(x, y), \qquad \partial u/\partial y = I(x, y) \, Q(x, y).$

But then

$$I(x, y)[P(x, y) \, dx + Q(x, y) \, dy] = 0$$

becomes

$$\frac{\partial u}{\partial x} \, dx + \frac{\partial u}{\partial y} \, dy = 0$$

or

$$du = 0.$$

We see that $I(x, y)$ is an integrating factor for $P \, dx + Q \, dy$, as we claimed.

Theorem 2 tells us that an integrating factor exists for each equation that has a solution family, but it only tells us how to find the integrating factor if we already know the solution, and hence Theorem 2 will not be of direct practical assistance in solving differential equations. Some of the exercises of this section state other theorems on integrating factors; other exercises show how to find integrating factors for certain specific types of differential equations. In the next section we shall deal in some detail with linear first order equations; these equations have especially simple integrating factors.

EXERCISES 14.4

In Exercises 1 through 10 show that the differential equation is exact and find its solution.

1. $(y^2 + 2x) \, dx + (2xy + 1) \, dy = 0$.

2. $(e^y + ye^x) + (xe^y + e^x + 1) \dfrac{dy}{dx} = 0$.

3. $(1 + \cos \theta) \, dr - r \sin \theta \, d\theta = 0$.

4. $3x(x \, dx + dy) + y(3dx - 2 \, dy) = 0$.

5. $(2xy^3 - 3y) + \left(3x^2 y^2 - 3x + \dfrac{1}{y}\right) \dfrac{dy}{dx} = 0$.

6. $\cos x \cosh y \, (dy + dx) + \sin x \sinh y \, (dy - dx) = 0$.

7. $\dfrac{x + y + 1}{x + y} \, dx + \dfrac{2x + 2y + 1}{x + y} \, dy = 0$.

8. $e^{-(x^2+y^2)} [(1 - 2x^2) \, dx - 2xy \, dy] = 0$.

9. $\dfrac{(x + y) \, dy + (4x - y) \, dx}{4 \, x^2 + y^2} = 0$.

10. $\dfrac{x^2 - y}{x\sqrt{x^2 - y^2}} \, dx + \dfrac{1 - y}{\sqrt{x^2 - y^2}} \, dy = 0$.

11. Solve the differential equation of Example 2 by considering it to be a homogeneous equation.

12. In Theorem 2 we showed that every first order differential equation $P \, dx + Q \, dy = 0$ that had a solution family $u(x, y) = C$ had an integrating factor $I(x, y)$. Actually, such an equation has infinitely many integrating factors. Show that $F(u(x, y))I(x, y)$ is an integrating factor whenever $F(u)$ is a continuous function of u.

13. Furnish the details for this outline of a proof.
Theorem 3. On integrating factors for a first order equation.
Hypothesis: $I(x, y)$ and $J(x, y)$ are distinct integrating factors for the equation $P(x, y) \, dx + Q(x, y) \, dy = 0$.

Conclusion: $\dfrac{\mathcal{J}(x,\,y)}{I(x,\,y)} = C$ is a one-parameter family of solutions of $P(x, y)\, dx + Q(x,y)$
$dy = 0$.

Proof: (1) I and $\mathcal{J}$ satisfy

$$\mathcal{J}\frac{\partial P}{\partial y} + P\frac{\partial \mathcal{J}}{\partial y} = \mathcal{J}\frac{\partial Q}{\partial x} + Q\frac{\partial \mathcal{J}}{\partial x}$$

$$I\frac{\partial P}{\partial y} + P\frac{\partial I}{\partial y} = I\frac{\partial Q}{\partial x} + Q\frac{\partial I}{\partial x}.$$

(2) Multiply these equations by I and $\mathcal{J}$, respectively, subtract, and
divide by I^2 to get

$$P\frac{\partial}{\partial y}\left(\frac{\mathcal{J}}{I}\right) = Q\frac{\partial}{\partial x}\left(\frac{\mathcal{J}}{I}\right) \qquad \text{or} \qquad \frac{P}{Q} = \frac{\dfrac{\partial}{\partial x}\left(\dfrac{\mathcal{J}}{I}\right)}{\dfrac{\partial}{\partial y}\left(\dfrac{\mathcal{J}}{I}\right)}.$$

(3) $\dfrac{\mathcal{J}}{I} = C$ satisfies $d\left(\dfrac{\mathcal{J}}{I}\right) = 0,$ or $\dfrac{dy}{dx} = -\dfrac{\dfrac{\partial}{\partial x}\left(\dfrac{\mathcal{J}}{I}\right)}{\dfrac{\partial}{\partial y}\left(\dfrac{\mathcal{J}}{I}\right)}.$

Hence $\dfrac{\mathcal{J}}{I} = C$ also satisfies $\dfrac{dy}{dx} = -\dfrac{P}{Q}$ or $P\, dx + Q\, dy = 0$.

14. Show that $W(x, y) = F(u(x,y)) = C$ is a solution family of $P\, dx + Q\, dy = 0$ whenever
$u(x, y) = C$ is, provided $F'(u)$ exists. Now Exercise 12 suggests that a new integrating
factor is obtained every time a given one is multiplied by $V(x, y)$, where $V(x, y) = C$
is a solution family for the original equation. Prove this. Observe that Exercise 13
states a converse. If we write $V = \mathcal{J}/I$ or $\mathcal{J} = VI$, Exercise 13 states that any integrating factor $\mathcal{J}$ can be obtained from a given one I by multiplying by some function
$V(x, y)$ which is such that $V(x, y) = C$ is a solution family for the equation.

15. (a) For which α and β will $x^\alpha y^\beta$ be an integrating factor for $(y^2 + yx^2)\, dx + (2xy$
$- 3x^3)\, dy = 0$?
(b) Solve the differential equation.

16. Show that α and β can be chosen so that $x^\alpha y^\beta$ will be an integrating factor for

$$x^a y^b(jy\, dx + kx\, dy) + x^c y^d(my\, dx + nx\, dy) = 0$$

if we do not have $j/k = m/n$.

17. Complete this outline of a proof of Euler's Theorem for homogeneous functions.
Hypothesis: (a) $f(x, y)$ is homogeneous of degree k for a suitable region R.

(b) $\dfrac{\partial f}{\partial x}, \dfrac{\partial f}{\partial y}$ exist for (x, y) of R.

Conclusion: $x\dfrac{\partial f}{\partial x} + y\dfrac{\partial f}{\partial y} = kf$ in R.

(1) By Hypothesis (a) we can write $f(tx, ty) = t^k f(x, y)$ for (x, y) in R, $t > 0$.
(2) Now differentiate with respect to t and then set $t = 1$.

18. Show that $\dfrac{1}{Px + Qy}$ is an integrating factor for the homogeneous equation
$P\, dx + Q\, dy = 0$ by using Theorem 1 and Exercise 17.

19. We shall find the equations of the lines of force induced by two positive charges of equal magnitude. Fill in the details of the following argument. Let the charges be placed at $A_1(-a, 0)$ and $A_2(a, 0)$ as in Fig. 14.9. By Coulomb's Law the force $\vec{F}_1$ exerted on a unit positive charge at $P(x, y)$ by the charge at $(-a, 0)$ has magnitude inversely proportional to $(\overline{A_1P})^2$ and we can write

$$\vec{F}_1 = \frac{c}{(x + a)^2 + y^2} \; \frac{(x + a)\vec{i} + y\vec{j}}{\sqrt{(x + a)^2 + y^2}},$$

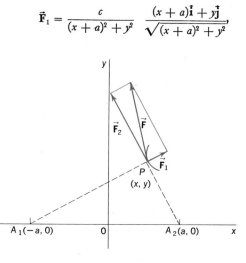

Fig. 14.9

where c is a constant. Similarly,

$$\vec{F}_2 = c\frac{(x - a)\vec{i} + y\vec{j}}{[(x - a)^2 + y^2]^{3/2}}$$

and the resultant of the forces is

$$\vec{F} = \vec{F}_1 + \vec{F}_2.$$

When we consider the tangent of the inclination angle of $\vec{F}$ we can write

$$\frac{dy}{dx} = \frac{\dfrac{y}{[(x - a)^2 + y^2]^{3/2}} + \dfrac{y}{[(x + a)^2 + y^2]^{3/2}}}{\dfrac{x - a}{[(x - a)^2 + y^2]^{3/2}} + \dfrac{x + a}{[(x + a)^2 + y^2]^{3/2}}}$$

for the slope of the line of force through $P(x, y)$. This leads to the differential equation

$$\frac{y \, dx - (x - a) \, dy}{[(x - a)^2 + y^2]^{3/2}} + \frac{y \, dx - (x + a) \, dy}{[(x + a)^2 + y^2]^{3/2}} = 0.$$

Show that, if the integrating factor y is used, the equation becomes exact with solution

$$\frac{x - a}{[(x - a)^2 + y^2]^{1/2}} + \frac{x + a}{[(x + a)^2 + y^2]^{1/2}} = C.$$

14.5 First Order Linear Equations

■ DEFINITION 1

Linear differential equation. In a linear differential equation every term is either of the first degree in the dependent variable and its derivatives or does not contain the dependent variable and its derivatives at all.

Thus

$$\frac{dy}{dx} + ay = e^{bx}$$

is a first order linear equation, and

$$\frac{d^2y}{dx^2} + R(x)\frac{dy}{dx} + S(x)y = T(x)$$

is a second order linear equation, but

$$\frac{dy}{dx} + xy = y^2$$

is not a linear equation, and neither is

$$y\frac{dy}{dx} + \frac{d^2y}{dx^2} = 1.$$

We shall see that certain simple theorems on the solutions of linear differential equations lead to significant physical applications. In this section linear equations of the first order are discussed. These differential equations furnish a good illustration of the usefulness of integrating factors.

Every linear equation of the first order can be written in the form

$$\frac{dy}{dx} + R(x)y = S(x) \tag{1a}$$

or in the form

$$(Ry - S)\, dx + 1\, dy = 0. \tag{1b}$$

This equation is not exact in general, because we find that if we write $P = Ry - S$ and $Q = 1$ we get

$$\frac{\partial P}{\partial y} = R, \qquad \frac{\partial Q}{\partial x} = 0.$$

In searching for an integrating factor it is natural to look for as simple an integrating factor as possible. Let us multiply Eq. (1b) by a factor $I(x)$, rather than by a function of x and y, and see if it is possible to choose $I(x)$ in such a way that we get an exact equation. We rewrite the equation in the form

$$(IRy - IS)\, dx + I\, dy = 0,$$

and if we now write $P = IRy - IS$, $Q = I$ we find this time that the criterion for exactness, namely, $\partial P/\partial y = \partial Q/\partial x$, is

$$IR = \frac{dI}{dx}.$$

We can find an $I(x)$ that meets this criterion if we continue with

$$\frac{1}{I}\frac{dI}{dx} = R$$

$$\log I = \int R\,dx$$

$$I(x) = e^{\int R(x)\,dx}.$$

We have demonstrated

■ THEOREM 1

Integrating factors for first order linear equations.

HYPOTHESIS: A first order linear equation is written in the form

$$\frac{dy}{dx} + R(x)y = S(x). \tag{2}$$

CONCLUSION: $I(x) = e^{\int R(x)\,dx}$ will be an integrating factor.

Example 1. The equation

$$\frac{dy}{dx} + ay = e^{bx}, \qquad a \text{ and } b \text{ constants}, \tag{3}$$

is a linear first order equation. Theorem 1 says that $e^{\int a\,dx} = e^{ax}$ will be an integrating factor, and we multiply by that factor to get

$$e^{ax}\frac{dy}{dx} + ae^{ax}y = e^{bx}e^{ax}.$$

This is supposed to be an exact equation, and it may be possible to piece together by observation the functions that were differentiated to form the equation. Indeed, we can guess from the fact that the left member consists of two terms that a product was differentiated, and from the first term of the left member that the product was $e^{ax}y$. The equation becomes

$$\frac{d}{dx}(e^{ax}y) = e^{(b+a)x},$$

and if $b \neq -a$, the solution is

$$e^{ax}y = \frac{1}{b+a}e^{(b+a)x} + C$$

or

$$y = \frac{1}{b+a}e^{bx} + Ce^{-ax}, \qquad b \neq -a.$$

In the special case where $b = -a$ Eq. (3) can be written

$$\frac{dy}{dx} + ay = e^{-ax}$$

and the solution proceeds as follows:

$$e^{ax} \frac{dy}{dx} + ae^{ax}y = 1$$

$$\frac{d}{dx}(e^{ax}y) = 1$$

$$e^{ax}y = x + C$$

$$y = xe^{-ax} + Ce^{-ax}.$$

Example 2.   The equation

$$\cos x \frac{dy}{dx} + 2(\sin x)y = \cos x + \cos^2 x$$

is a linear equation and can be written in the form of Eq. (2) of the hypothesis of Theorem 1 if we divide by cos x. We write

$$\frac{dy}{dx} + 2 \frac{\sin x}{\cos x}y = 1 + \cos x.$$

Now Theorem 1 tells us that $1/\cos^2 x$ will be an integrating factor, because

$$e^{\int (2 \sin x/\cos x)\, dx} = e^{-2 \log \cos x} = \left(e^{\log \cos x}\right)^{-2}$$

$$= (\cos x)^{-2} = \frac{1}{\cos^2 x}.$$

If we multiply by that factor our equation becomes

$$\frac{1}{\cos^2 x}\frac{dy}{dx} + \frac{2 \sin x}{\cos^3 x}y = \frac{1}{\cos^2 x} + \frac{1}{\cos x}.$$

Again the left member is a sum of two terms and we can try to form a product of which it would be the derivative. The first term suggests that the equation can be rewritten in the form

$$\frac{d}{dx}\left(\frac{1}{\cos^2 x}y\right) = \sec^2 x + \sec x,$$

and it is not hard to verify that this is indeed the case. The solution can then be written

$$\frac{1}{\cos^2 x}y = \tan x + \log(\sec x + \tan x) + C$$

or $$y = \sin x \cos x + \cos^2 x \log(\sec x + \tan x) + C \cos^2 x.$$

An equation of the form

$$\frac{dy}{dx} + T(x)y = U(x)y^n, \qquad n \neq 1,$$

often called a Bernoulli equation, can be written as a linear equation after a change of variable. Divide both members by y^n,

$$y^{-n}\frac{dy}{dx} + T(x)y^{-n+1} = U(x),$$

and write $y^{-n+1} = w$, $(-n+1)y^{-n}dy/dx = dw/dx$, to get

$$\frac{1}{1-n}\frac{dw}{dx} + T(x)w = U(x).$$

We now have a linear equation in w.

Example 3. The equation

$$\frac{dy}{dx} + \frac{x}{x^2-1}y = \frac{1}{x}y^2$$

is of the Bernoulli type. We divide both members by y^2 to get

$$y^{-2}\frac{dy}{dx} + \frac{x}{x^2-1}y^{-1} = \frac{1}{x},$$

and write

$$w = y^{-1}, \frac{dw}{dx} = -y^{-2}\frac{dy}{dx}$$

so that the equation becomes

$$-\frac{dw}{dx} + \frac{x}{x^2-1}w = \frac{1}{x}$$

or

$$\frac{dw}{dx} - \frac{x}{x^2-1}w = -\frac{1}{x}.$$

Now we have a linear equation in w written in such a form that the conclusion of Theorem 1 applies. We compute

$$\int -\frac{x}{x^2-1}\,dx = -\frac{1}{2}\int \frac{2x}{x^2-1}\,dx = -\frac{1}{2}\log(x^2-1)$$

and then assert that $1/\sqrt{x^2-1}$ is an integrating factor, because

$$e^{(-1/2)\log(x^2-1)} = [e^{\log(x^2-1)}]^{-1/2}$$

$$= (x^2-1)^{-1/2} = \frac{1}{\sqrt{x^2-1}}.$$

When we multipy $1/\sqrt{x^2-1}$, we can write

$$\frac{1}{\sqrt{x^2-1}}\frac{dw}{dx} - \frac{x}{(x^2-1)^{3/2}}w = -\frac{1}{x\sqrt{x^2-1}}$$

$$\frac{d}{dx}\left(\frac{1}{\sqrt{x^2-1}}w\right) = -\frac{1}{x\sqrt{x^2-1}}$$

$$\frac{1}{\sqrt{x^2-1}}w = -\int \frac{1}{x\sqrt{x^2-1}}\,dx + C$$

$$\frac{1}{\sqrt{x^2-1}}w = -\sec^{-1}x + C$$

$$\frac{1}{\sqrt{x^2-1}}\frac{1}{y} = -\sec^{-1}x + C.$$

The formal integration called for in this computation can be accomplished by using a trigonometric substitution.

EXERCISES 14.5

1. In Exercise 14.1-12 we considered a body falling under the influence of gravity but subject to a frictional force proportional to the velocity. We were led there to the differential equation $dv/dt = -(kv + g)$, subject to the initial condition that $v = v_0$ when $t = 0$. Solve this equation as a linear equation and derive again the result

$$v = \frac{1}{k}(kv_0 + g)e^{-kt} - \frac{g}{k}.$$

2. In Examples 14.1-3 and 14.1-4 we considered the equation $dy/dx = y + x - 1$. Solve as a linear equation and show again that $y = -x + Ce^x$.

3. Find the solution of $dy/dx + a_1xy = a_2x^3 + a_3x$ for which $y = 0$ when $x = 0$.

4. (a) Derive the solution $ye^{ax^{n+1}/(n+1)} = \int S(x)e^{ax^{n+1}/(n+1)}\ dx + C$ for $dy/dx + ax^ny = S(x)$ when $n \neq -1$.

   (b) Derive the solution $yx^a = \int S(x)x^a\ dx + C$ for $dy/dx + (a/x)y = S(x)$.

5. Solve $x(x - 2)\ dy + (4y - x^2 + 2x)\ dx = 0$.

6. Solve $(2xy - y - x^3 + 3x^2 - 2x)\ dx + (x^2 - 3x + 2)\ dy = 0$.

7. Solve $(y^2 + b)\ dx + y(x - y^2 - b)\ dy = 0$.

8. Solve $\cos x \dfrac{dy}{dx} + 2y - \cos^2 x = 0$.

9. Solve $x^{ax}\left(\dfrac{dy}{dx} + ay\ \log x\right) = 1$.

10. Solve $(2y^3 + e^{-x})\ dx + 3xy^2\ dy = 0$.

11. Solve $dy + (2y - 4y^{1/2}\ \sin x)\ dx = 0$.

12. Solve $\sin x \dfrac{dy}{dx} + y\ \cos x - \dfrac{1}{y^3} = 0$.

13. Solve $2\ \cos x \dfrac{dy}{dx} - y - \dfrac{1}{y}\ \cos x = 0$.

14. As in Exercise 5.4-11 on Newton's Law of Cooling, the temperature T of a body decreases at a rate proportional to $T - T^*$, where T^* is the temperature of the surrounding medium. Let T and T^* be T_0 and T_0^*, respectively, at time $t = 0$, let the constant of proportionality be k, and assume that T^* is increasing slowly according to the formula $T^* = T_0^* + \alpha t$, α a constant. Show that the formula for T at any time is given by $T = T^* - \alpha/k + (T_0 - T_0^* + \alpha/k)e^{-kt}$.

15. Find the orthogonal trajectories of the family of curves $x - y - 1 = Ce^{2y}$.

16. Find the orthogonal trajectories of the family of curves $y = 2x + Ce^x$.

17. We have a gal of pure water in a tank to start with, admit b gal of brine per min in one place, allow b gal of the solution to leave per min in another place, and keep the solution uniform by stirring. If each gal of brine admitted contains c lb of salt per gal, find a formula for the number of lb of salt in the tank as a function of time.

18. Suppose, in Exercise 17, that the concentration of salt in the brine pumped into the tank is not constant but decreases gradually so that at time t the brine contains $c - \alpha t$ lb of salt per gal, $0 \le t \le c/\alpha$. Again find a formula for the number of lb of salt in the tank as a function of time.

In the exercises of earlier sections of this chapter, and in the exercises above, the reader could often tell which method to use in solving a first order equation because he knew which method the exercises were intended to illustrate in the section at hand. Exercises 19 through 33 constitute a mixed list of exercises. In each case (a) state which method you would use to solve the equation, and (b) solve the equation.

19. $\sin y \cos x(dx - 2\ dy) - \cos y \sin x(2\ dx - dy) = 0.$

20. $y(x^2 - y^2)\ dx + x(x^2 + y^2)\ dy = 0.$

21. $(x^4 + b^2x^2 + 2xy)\ dx - (x^2 + b^2)\ dy = 0.$

22. $\sinh y \cosh x\ dx + \cosh y \sinh x\ dy = 0.$

23. $\dfrac{y + x^2}{x\sqrt{x^2 - y^2}}\ dx - \dfrac{1 + y}{\sqrt{x^2 - y^2}}\ dy = 0.$

24. $\dfrac{y + x}{x\sqrt{x^2 - y^2}}\ dx - \dfrac{1}{\sqrt{x^2 - y^2}}\ dy = 0.$

25. $y[1 - (x + 1)\ (x^2 - 1)y^2]\ dx - (x^2 - 1)\ dy = 0.$

26. $\cos x\ dy - (3y \sin x + \sin 2x \cos x)\ dx = 0.$

27. $\cos x\ dy - (3y \sin x + \sin x)\ dx = 0.$

28. $\dfrac{2y}{x(x - 2y)}\ dx + \dfrac{x - 2y - 2}{x - 2y}\ dy = 0.$

29. $(y + xy)\ dx + (x - 2xy)\ dy = 0.$

30. $(x + 2y - 3)\ dx + (y + 2x - 4)\ dy = 0.$

31. $(x + 2y - 3)\ dx + (y - 2x - 4)\ dy = 0.$

32. $\dfrac{2x - y}{x^2 + y^2}\ dx + \dfrac{2y + x}{x^2 + y^2}\ dy = 0.$

33. $y^3\ dx + (axy + b)\ dy = 0.$

34. Theorem 1 shows that an integrating factor which is a function of x alone can be found for a linear first order equation. Is it true that, conversely, if an integrating factor which is a function of x alone can be found for a first order equation, that equation must be linear?

14.6 A Method of Successive Approximations

I

There are many first order differential equations that cannot be solved by using the methods we have thus far discussed for separable, homogeneous, exact, and linear equations. In this section we shall discuss a method of successive approximations, often called the Picard method, which is not only of a certain practical significance but of great theoretical significance.

Suppose that we are asked to find a solution of the first order equation

$$\frac{dy}{dx} = f(x, y) \tag{1}$$

for which

$$y = y_0 \quad \text{when} \quad x = x_0. \tag{2}$$

The Picard method suggests that as a first approximation to the solution we take the simple constant function

$$y = Y_1 = y_0.$$

While $y = Y_1$ usually will not satisfy Eq. (1), it will at least satisfy the additional condition of Statement (2). We then let Eq. (1) itself suggest the procedure for getting our second approximation to the solution. We substitute $Y_1 = y_0$ for y in the right member of Eq. (1), thus getting the new differential equation

$$\frac{dy}{dx} = f(x, y_0),$$

and take for Y_2 that solution of this separable equation which has the value y_0 when x is x_0. To get the third approximation we substitute $Y_2(x)$ for y in the right member of Eq. (1), getting the separable differential equation

$$\frac{dy}{dx} = f(x, Y_2(x)),$$

and take for Y_3 that solution of this equation which has the value y_0 when x is x_0.

Continuing in similar fashion, this process gives us a sequence of functions, the $Y_n(x)$'s, and under certain rather general conditions already stated in Theorem 14.1-1 and to be repeated later in this section, it can be shown that these successive approximation functions approach a limit function which is the desired solution. By taking more and more steps in this approximation method we approximate more and more closely to the solution we seek.

Example 1. Let us use this method of successive approximations to approximate to that solution of

$$\frac{dy}{dx} = y + x - 1 \tag{3}$$

for which $\qquad y = 1 \qquad$ when $\qquad x = 0.$ $\tag{4}$

We take as our first approximation the constant function

$$y = Y_1 = 1.$$

If we substitue Y_1 for y in the right member of Eq. (3) we get the new equation

$$\frac{dy}{dx} = Y_1 + x - 1 = x,$$

which we solve in the form

$$y = \tfrac{1}{2} x^2 + C.$$

We must take $C = 1$ if we are to satisfy Condition (4), and our choice for the second approximating function then is

$$y = Y_2 = \tfrac{1}{2} x^2 + 1.$$

Now we substitute Y_2 for y in the right member of Eq. (3) to get the new equation

$$\frac{dy}{dx} = Y_2 + x - 1 = \tfrac{1}{2} x^2 + x,$$

and go on to choose

$$y = Y_3 = \frac{x^3}{3!} + \frac{x^2}{2!} + 1.$$

Another step of this method brings us to the differential equation

$$\frac{dy}{dx} = Y_3 + x - 1 = \frac{x^3}{3!} + \frac{x^2}{2!} + x$$

and

$$y = Y_4 = \frac{x^4}{4!} + \frac{x^3}{3!} + \frac{x^2}{2!} + 1.$$

Equation (1) was solved in Example 14.1-4 and again in Exercise 14.5-2, and we know that the solution we seek actually is

$$y = -x + e^x,$$

or, in series form,

$$y = -x + \left(1 + x + \frac{x^2}{2!} + \frac{x^3}{3!} + \frac{x^4}{4!} + \frac{x^5}{5!} + \cdots\right)$$

$$y = 1 + \frac{x^2}{2!} + \frac{x^3}{3!} + \frac{x^4}{4!} + \frac{x^5}{5!} + \cdots.$$

If we compare Y_1, Y_2, Y_3, Y_4 with the series form of the solution, we see how the Picard method approximates the solution step by step in this case.

Example 2.   Let us try to approximate to that solution of

$$\frac{dy}{dx} = y^2 + 1 \tag{5}$$

for which

$$y = 0 \quad \text{when} \quad x = 0. \tag{6}$$

First we choose

$$y = Y_1 = 0$$

and write the new equation

$$\frac{dy}{dx} = Y_1^2 + 1 = 1.$$

Then we select

$$y = Y_2 = x,$$

making sure that Condition (6) was satisfied when we determined the arbitrary constant that arose in the integration. Next we write the equation

$$\frac{dy}{dx} = Y_2^2 + 1 = x^2 + 1$$

and choose

$$y = Y_3 = \tfrac{1}{3} x^3 + x.$$

After that we have

$$\frac{dy}{dx} = Y_3^2 + 1 = \tfrac{1}{9} x^6 + \tfrac{2}{3} x^4 + x^2 + 1,$$

$$y = Y_4 = \tfrac{1}{63} x^7 + \tfrac{2}{15} x^5 + \tfrac{1}{3} x^3 + x;$$

we could go on if we wished to, although the details would become more and more onerous.

It happens that Eq. (5) is separable and that its solution is

$$y = \tan x.$$

In Example 13.8-7 we worked out part of the infinite series for $\tan x$:

$$y = \tan x = x + \frac{1}{3}x^3 + \frac{2}{15}x^5 + \frac{17}{315}x^7 + \cdots.$$

The statements $y = Y_1, y = Y_2, y = Y_3, y = Y_4$ seem to be approximating the solution more and more closely.

II

The fact that Picard's method seemed to be of value in two cases, which we could have solved by other methods, does not give us much assurance that Picard's method will be of wide application. Actually, even in these two cases, we did not show that the approximating functions Y_n could be found for all n, and that for every choice of a positive number ϵ, no matter how small, we could choose N so large that Y_N and all successive Y_n's were within ϵ of the solution for all x of a certain interval. This is what we mean, strictly speaking, when we say that the approximating functions approach the solution. One of the reasons Picard's method is important is that it enables us to prove the basic existence and uniqueness theorem for first order differential equations. Any differential equation to which that theorem applies can be solved, in theory at least, by the Picard method. We restate Theorem 14.1-1 here for the sake of emphasis.

■ THEOREM 1

An existence and uniqueness theorem for first order equations.

HYPOTHESIS: (a) $f(x, y)$ is continuous in and on a rectangle R with center at (x_0, y_0).

(b) There is a constant k such that for any two points (x, y_1) and (x, y_2) of the rectangle we have

$$|f(x, y_2) - f(x, y_1)| \le k|y_2 - y_1|.$$

CONCLUSION: (a) There is a function $y = \varphi(x)$, defined on an interval $I: x_0 - h < x < x_0 + h$, which satisfies the differential equation

$$\frac{dy}{dx} = f(x, y)$$

for x of interval I and which is such that $y = y_0$ when $x = x_0$.

(b) Any other function that satisfies $dy/dx = f(x, y)$ on I and has the value y_0 when $x = x_0$ must coincide with $y = \varphi(x)$ on the interval I.

As we stated in Remark 14.1-2, there are many functions $f(x, y)$ which meet the hypotheses of this theorem; hence the theorem applies to a wide class of first order differential equations.

III

SKETCH OF THE PROOF OF THEOREM 1: The proof consists of three parts. First one must show that the functions $Y_1, Y_2, Y_3, \cdots, Y_n, \cdots$ approach a limiting function $\varphi(x)$ for x of some interval I: $x_0 - h < x < x_0 + h$. Then one must show that $y = \varphi(x)$ satisfies the differential equation $dy/dx = f(x, y)$ for x of I and is such that $\varphi(x_0) = y_0$. Finally one must show that if there exists a function $\psi(x)$ such that $y = \psi(x)$ also satisfies $dy/dx = f(x, y)$ for x of I and $\psi(x_0) = y_0$, then $\varphi(x) = \psi(x)$ for x of I.

The proof starts by pointing out that, if x is properly chosen, the point (x, y_0) lies in the rectangle R in which $f(x, y)$ is said to be continuous in Hypothesis (a). The integral $\int_{x_0}^x f(x, y_0)\, dx$ would then exist and define a function of x because its integrand is continuous, and if one appeals to theorems on functions defined by integrals one can go further and say that the function so defined is itself continuous and even differentiable, with derivative $f(x, y_0)$. Consequently the statements

$$\frac{dY_2}{dx} = f(x, Y_1) = f(x, y_0) \text{ with } Y_2(x_0) = y_0$$

can be written in the alternate integral form

$$Y_2(x) = y_0 + \int_{x_0}^x f(x, y_0)\, dx.$$

If, as in more detailed expositions, we show how to choose the number h so that $(x, Y_j(x))$ will lie in rectangle R for I: $x_0 - h < x < x_0 + h$ when $(x, Y_{j-1}(x))$ does, we can continue with

$$\frac{dY_3}{dx} = f(x, Y_2), \qquad Y_3(x) = y_0 + \int_{x_0}^x f(x, Y_2)\, dx$$

$$\frac{dY_4}{dx} = f(x, Y_3), \qquad Y_4(x) = y_0 + \int_{x_0}^x f(x, Y_3)\, dx$$

$$\frac{dY_j}{dx} = f(x, Y_{j-1}), \qquad Y_j(x) = y_0 + \int_{x_0}^x f(x, Y_{j-1})\, dx,$$

each function $Y_n(x)$ differentiable for x of interval I. When we subtract the integrals for Y_{j+1} and Y_j, we get

$$Y_{j+1}(x) - Y_j(x) = y_0 + \int_{x_0}^x f(x, Y_j)\, dx - y_0 - \int_{x_0}^x f(x, Y_{j-1})\, dx$$

$$= \int_{x_0}^x [f(x, Y_j) - f(x, Y_{j-1})]\, dx.$$

Now Hypothesis (b), often called the Lipschitz Condition, plays its role. If we take absolute values and remember that the absolute value of a sum is less than or equal to the sum of the absolute values, and that an integral is a limit of a sum, we write

$$|\Upsilon_{j+1}(x) - \Upsilon_j(x)| = \left| \int_{x_0}^{x} [f(x, \Upsilon_j) - f(x, \Upsilon_{j-1})] \, dx \right|$$

$$|\Upsilon_{j+1}(x) - \Upsilon_j(x)| \leq \int_{x_0}^{x} |f(x, \Upsilon_j) - f(x, \Upsilon_{j-1})| \, dx$$

$$|\Upsilon_{j+1}(x) - \Upsilon_j(x)| \leq k \int_{x_0}^{x} |\Upsilon_j(x) - \Upsilon_{j-1}(x)| \, dx. \tag{7}$$

We use this inequality over and over again to study our differences. In detail, to start,

$$|\Upsilon_2(x) - \Upsilon_1(x)| = \left| y_0 + \int_{x_0}^{x} f(x, y_0) \, dx - y_0 \right| = \left| \int_{x_0}^{x} f(x, y_0) \, dx \right|$$

$$\leq \int_{x_0}^{x} |f(x, y_0)| \, dx. \tag{8}$$

But $f(x, y)$ is bounded on rectangle R, because it is continuous there, as in Theorem 7.4-1; hence there exists a number M such that

$$|f(x, y)| < M$$

for (x, y) of R, and we can continue Inequality (8) with

$$|\Upsilon_2(x) - \Upsilon_1(x)| \leq \int_{x_0}^{x} M \, dx = M(x - x_0).$$

Then using Inequality (7),

$$|\Upsilon_3(x) - \Upsilon_2(x)| \leq k \int_{x_0}^{x} |\Upsilon_2(x) - \Upsilon_1(x)| \, dx \leq k \int_{x_0}^{x} M(x - x_0) \, dx = Mk \frac{(x - x_0)^2}{2!}$$

$$|\Upsilon_4(x) - \Upsilon_3(x)| \leq k \int_{x_0}^{x} |\Upsilon_3(x) - \Upsilon_2(x)| \, dx \leq k \int_{x_0}^{x} Mk \frac{(x - x_0)^2}{2!} \, dx = Mk^2 \frac{(x - x_0)^3}{3!}$$

$$|\Upsilon_{j+1}(x) - \Upsilon_j(x)| \leq Mk^{j-1} \frac{(x - x_0)^j}{j!}.$$

Here we have taken $x \geq x_0$, so that $|x - x_0| = x - x_0$; the details are not essentially different if $x < x_0$.

We can use the "telescope" device to write

$$\Upsilon_n = \Upsilon_1 + (\Upsilon_2 - \Upsilon_1) + (\Upsilon_3 - \Upsilon_2) + \cdots + (\Upsilon_n - \Upsilon_{n-1}). \tag{9}$$

Each term of this sum is not greater in absolute value than the corresponding term of the sum

$$y_0 + M(x - x_0) + Mk \frac{(x - x_0)^2}{2!} + Mk^2 \frac{(x - x_0)^3}{3!} + \cdots$$

$$+ Mk^{n-2} \frac{(x - x_0)^{n-1}}{(n - 1)!}. \tag{10}$$

The terms of the sum in Eq. (10) after the first are terms of the Taylor series for the function $(M/k)e^{k(x-x_0)}$, a series known to converge. Hence if we let n grow beyond all bounds, Eq. (9) tells us by a comparison argument on infinite series that $\lim_{n\to\infty} Y_n(x)$ exists, and we can call this limit $\varphi(x)$;

$$\varphi(x) = \lim_{n\to\infty} Y_n(x) \qquad \text{for } x \text{ of } I: x_0 - h < x < x_0 + h.$$

This completes our sketch of the first part of the proof.

In the second part of the proof we sketch quickly an argument to show that $y = \varphi(x)$ will satisfy the differential equation and that $y_0 = \varphi(x_0)$. Remember that the functions $Y_n(x)$, one after the other, are continuous and even differentiable. By quoting theorems which explain when functions defined as limits of sequences of continuous functions are themselves continuous, we can assert that $\varphi(x)$ is continuous. This, together with the fact that the point $(x, \varphi(x))$ lies in or on R if x is in the interval I enables one to say that the integral $\int_{x_0}^{x} f(x, \varphi(x))\, dx$ exists, and then one could say that $y = \varphi(x)$ will satisfy

$$\frac{dy}{dx} = f(x, y) \qquad \text{with } y = y_0 \text{ when } x = x_0$$

if it could be shown that

$$\varphi(x) = y_0 + \int_{x_0}^{x} f(x, \varphi(x))\, dx.$$

But we can show this, because we can compute

$$\varphi(x) - y_0 - \int_{x_0}^{x} f(x, \varphi)\, dx = \varphi(x) - y_0 - \int_{x_0}^{x} f(x, \varphi)\, dx + Y_n(x) - Y_n(x)$$

$$= \varphi(x) - Y_n(x) - y_0 - \int_{x_0}^{x} f(x, \varphi)\, dx + y_0 + \int_{x_0}^{x} f(x, Y_{n-1})\, dx$$

$$= [\varphi(x) - Y_n(x)] + \int_{x_0}^{x} [f(x, Y_{n-1}) - f(x, \varphi)]\, dx$$

and

$$\left| \varphi(x) - y_0 - \int_{x_0}^{x} f(x, \varphi)\, dx \right| \leq |\varphi(x) - Y_n(x)| + \left| \int_{x_0}^{x} f(x, Y_{n-1}) - f(x, \varphi)\, dx \right|$$

$$\leq |\varphi(x) - Y_n(x)| + \int_{x_0}^{x} |f(x, Y_{n-1}) - f(x, \varphi)|\, dx$$

$$\leq |\varphi(x) - Y_n(x)| + k \int_{x_0}^{x} |Y_{n-1}(x) - \varphi(x)|\, dx,$$

using the Lipschitz Condition at the last step. Because the Y_n's can be shown to approach $\varphi(x)$ uniformly for x of interval I, however, the absolute values appearing in the right member of the last inequality can be made less than any positive number ϵ that might be specified, for all x of I, by choosing n large enough. This would ultimately mean that

$$\left| \varphi(x) - y_0 - \int_{x_0}^{x} f(x, \varphi)\, dx \right| \leq \epsilon + k(x - x_0)\epsilon$$

for any positive ϵ, no matter how small, or that

$$\varphi(x) - y_0 - \int_{x_0}^{x} f(x, \varphi) \, dx = 0$$

$$\varphi(x) = y_0 + \int_{x_0}^{x} f(x, \varphi) \, dx$$

so that
$$\frac{d\varphi}{dx} = f(x, \varphi) \quad \text{and} \quad \varphi(x_0) = y_0.$$

Finally, the third part of the proof shows that there cannot be a function $\psi(x)$ different from $\varphi(x)$ such that $y = \psi(x)$ also satisfies $dy/dx = f(x, y)$ with $\psi(x_0) = y_0$, or such that

$$\psi(x) = y_0 + \int_{x_0}^{x} f(x, \psi) \, dx \qquad \text{for } x \text{ of } x_0 - h < x < x_0 + h.$$

For, if there were such a $\psi(x)$ we could write

$$|\varphi(x) - \psi(x)| = \left| \int_{x_0}^{x} [f(x, \varphi) - f(x, \psi)] \, dx \right|$$

$$\leq \int_{x_0}^{x} |f(x, \varphi) - f(x, \psi)| \, dx$$

$$\leq k \int_{x_0}^{x} |\varphi - \psi| \, dx, \tag{11}$$

assuming as before that $x \geq x_0$. If $x < x_0$ the details are not essentially different. Let the maximum of the difference between φ and ψ for x of interval I be m. Then we can continue in Inequality (11) with

$$|\varphi(x) - \psi(x)| \leq k \int_{x_0}^{x} m \, dx = km(x - x_0). \tag{12}$$

If we apply Inequality (12) to Inequality (11) we get

$$|\varphi(x) - \psi(x)| \leq k \int_{x_0}^{x} km(x - x_0) \, dx = k^2 m \frac{(x - x_0)^2}{2!},$$

and returning again and again to Inequality (11) we get

$$|\varphi(x) - \psi(x)| \leq k \int_{x_0}^{x} k^2 m \frac{(x - x_0)^2}{2!} \, dx = k^3 m \frac{(x - x_0)^3}{3!}$$

$$|\varphi(x) - \psi(x)| \leq k^j m \frac{(x - x_0)^j}{j!} \qquad \text{for any integer } j. \tag{13}$$

But the series with general term $k^j(x - x_0)^j/j!$ converges to $e^{k(x-x_0)}$ for all x, and the terms of a convergent series must approach 0 as one goes further out into the series. As a consequence, for every positive number ϵ specified, no matter how small, we can choose j so large that

$$\left| k^j m \frac{(x - x_0)^j}{j!} \right| < \epsilon,$$

and, then by Inequality (13), for every $\epsilon > 0$ we have

$$|\varphi(x) - \psi(x)| < \epsilon.$$

This says that $\varphi(x) - \psi(x) = 0$ or $\psi(x) = \varphi(x)$, and our sketch of the proof of Theorem 1 is concluded.

EXERCISES 14.6

1. (a) Find the first four approximations to that solution of $dy/dx = 2y + 2x - 2x^2$ for which $y = 0$ when $x = 0$. (b) Verify the fact that the solution is $y = x^2$. How much smaller than the solution are Y_2, Y_3, and Y_4 when $x = .1$?

2. (a) Find the first four approximations to that solution of $dy/dx = y - (x^2 - 3x + 2)$ for which $y = 1$ when $x = 0$.
   (b) Verify the fact that the solution is $y = 1 - x + x^2$. By how much do Y_2, Y_3, and Y_4 exceed the solution when $x = 1$?

3. (a) Find the first four approximations to that solution of $dy/dx + ay = 0$ for which $y = 1$ when $x = 0$. (b) Verify the fact that the solution is $y = e^{-ax}$. Compare your approximations to the series form of the solution.

4. (a) Find the first four approximations to that solution of $dy/dx + ay = x$ for which $y = 0$ when $x = 0$. (b) Verify the fact that the solution is $y = \dfrac{x}{a} - \dfrac{1}{a^2} + \dfrac{1}{a^2} e^{-ax}$.
   Compare your approximations to the series form of the solution.

5. Find the first four approximations to that solution of $dy/dx + ay = e^{-ax}$ for which $y = C$ when $x = 0$. Compare with Example 14.5-1.

6. (a) Find the first four approximations to that solution of $dy/dx = y/x$ for which $y = 1$ when $x = 1$. (b) Compare these approximations with the solution, $y = x$.

7. (a) Find the first five approximations to that solution of $dy/dx = y/x + 1$ for which $y = 0$ when $x = 1$. (b) Verify the fact that $y = x \log x$ is the solution. Compare your approximations with the series form of the solution obtained by writing $x = e^{\log x}$ and using the exponential series.

8. (a) Find the first four approximations to that solution of $dy/dx = y^2$ for which $y = 1$ when $x = 1$. (b) Verify the fact that $y = 1/(2 - x)$ is the solution. By how much do Y_2, Y_3, and Y_4 exceed the solution when $x = 0$?

9. Find the first four approximations to that solution of $dy/dx = y^2 + x$ for which $y = 0$ when $x = 0$.

10. (a) Find four successive approximations to that solution of $d^2y/dx^2 + y = 0$ for which $y = 1$ and $dy/dx = 0$ when $x = 0$.
    Suggestion: Take $Y_1 = 1$, because then $Y_1 = 1$ and $dY_1/dx = 0$. Then work with $d^2Y_2/dx^2 = -Y_1$.
    (b) Verify the fact that the solution is $y = \cos x$ and compare your approximations with the solution.

11. (a) Find three successive approximations to that solution of $(d^2y/dx^2) - (dy/dx) = 1$ for which $y = 1$ and $dy/dx = -1$ when $x = 0$.
    Suggestion: Take $Y_1 = 1 - x$, because $Y_1 = 1$ and $dY_1/dx = -1$ when $x = 0$. Then work with

$$\frac{d^2Y_2}{dx^2} = \frac{dY_1}{dx} + 1.$$

    (b) What solution do your approximations suggest? Check this proposed solution.

12. (a) Find four successive approximations to that solution of $\dfrac{d^2y}{dx^2} = -2\dfrac{dy}{dx} - 2y$ for which $y = 1$ and $\dfrac{dy}{dx} = -1$ when $x = 0$.

Suggestion: Take $Y_1 = 1 - x$ and work with

$$\frac{d^2Y_2}{dx^2} = -2\frac{dY_1}{dx} - 2Y_1.$$

(b) Verify the fact that $y = e^{-x}\cos x$ is the solution. Compare your approximations with the terms of the series form of the solution worked out in Example 13.8-6.

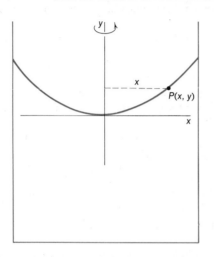

Fig. 14.10

13. *The rotating pail.* Water in a pail rotates about the pail's axis of symmetry with constant angular velocity ω. Fill in the details of this argument to show that the surface is a paraboloid of revolution.

Assume that equilibrium has been reached and let the profile curve for the surface have the equation $y = f(x)$ when the axes have been chosen as in Fig. 14.10. The forces acting on a particle at $P(x, y)$ of the surface are $-mg\vec{\jmath}$, the force of gravity, and $c[-(dy/dx)\vec{\imath} + \vec{\jmath}]$, the reaction of the rest of the water. (This reaction must be normal to the surface, because we would not have equilibrium if there were a non-zero component along the surface.)

But we know that the particle will travel with constant speed $x\omega$ on a circular path of radius x, center on the y axis. Hence its acceleration in normal and tangential components is

$$\frac{dv}{dt}\vec{t} + v^2 K\vec{n} = -(x\omega)^2\frac{1}{x}\vec{\imath}.$$

Now work with the $\vec{\imath}, \vec{\jmath}$ components of the $F = ma$ equation to show that $y = (\omega^2/2g)x^2$. As a check, observe that this answer predicts that the greater ω the steeper the parabola; this agrees with observation.

14.7 Some Second Order Equations That Can Be Reduced to First Order

If a second order differential equation for y does not contain y explicitly, then the simple substitution of the letter p for dy/dx will enable us to rewrite the equation as a first order equation for p.

■ THEOREM 1

Reducing the order of an equation that does not contain the dependent variable explicitly.

HYPOTHESIS: A second order differential equation can be written in the form

$$f\left(x, \frac{dy}{dx}, \frac{d^2y}{dx^2}\right) = 0. \tag{1a}$$

CONCLUSION: This second order equation can be written in the form

$$f\left(x, p, \frac{dp}{dx}\right) = 0. \tag{1b}$$

PROOF: We need merely observe that, if we replace dy/dx by p wherever it occurs, we can also replace d^2y/dx by dp/dx. We will then have in Eq. (1b) a first order equation for p, when we started with a second order equation for y in Eq. (1a).

Example 1. We know that all circles of radius 1 have constant curvature 1, but one can ask whether all curves of constant curvature 1 must be circles of radius 1. One way to answer this question is to look for the solutions of the second order differential equation

$$K = \frac{|d^2y/dx^2|}{[1 + (dy/dx)^2]^{3/2}} = 1$$

or

$$\frac{d^2y}{dx^2} = \pm\left[1 + \left(\frac{dy}{dx}\right)^2\right]^{3/2}. \tag{2}$$

This equation does not contain the dependent variable y explicitly. If we write

$$\frac{dy}{dx} = p, \qquad \frac{d^2y}{dx^2} = \frac{dp}{dx},$$

we can rewrite Eq. (2) in the form

$$\frac{dp}{dx} = \pm(1 + p^2)^{3/2},$$

or in the separated form

$$\pm\frac{1}{(1 + p^2)^{3/2}} \, dp = dx. \tag{2a}$$

If we make the trigonometric substitution $p = \tan\theta$ and use the fact that $dp/d\theta = \sec^2\theta$ we can continue with

$$\pm\frac{1}{\sec^3\theta}\sec^2\theta \, d\theta = dx$$

$$\pm\cos\theta \, d\theta = dx$$

$$\pm\sin\theta = x + C_1 \tag{3a}$$

$$\pm\frac{p}{\sqrt{1 + p^2}} = x + C_1. \tag{3b}$$

Then, squaring and solving for p, we find that

$$p = \pm\frac{x + C_1}{\sqrt{1 - (x + C_1)^2}} \tag{3c}$$

$$\frac{dy}{dx} = \pm\frac{x + C_1}{\sqrt{1 - (x + C_1)^2}} = \mp\frac{1}{2}[1 - (x + C_1)^2]^{-1/2}[-2(x + C_1)].$$

We can integrate again to get

$$y = \mp[1 - (x + C_1)^2]^{1/2} + C_2$$

$$y - C_2 = \mp[1 - (x + C_1)^2]^{1/2}$$

$$(x + C_1)^2 + (y - C_2)^2 = 1.$$

The curves of constant curvature 1 are indeed circles of unit radius.

We were fortunate in Example 1 above to be able to solve for p as a function of x in Eq. (3b) and then to continue by replacing p by dy/dx and solving for y through a second integration. If it is not feasible to solve for p as a function of x, but it is feasible to solve for x as a function of p instead, then one may be able to find solutions in parametric form with p as parameter. Thus, if one can solve for x explicitly and write

$$x = \varphi(p) \tag{4a}$$

(instead of $p = \psi(x)$, as we did in Eq. (3c) of Example 1), we can differentiate with respect to y and get

$$\frac{dx}{dy} = \frac{d\varphi}{dp}\frac{dp}{dy}$$

$$\frac{1}{p} = \varphi'(p)\frac{dp}{dy}$$

$$dy = p\varphi'(p)\,dp.$$

Now one may be able to solve for y and write

$$y = \tau(p). \tag{4b}$$

Equations (4a) and (4b) together would constitute a solution in parametric form with p as parameter.

Example 2. Consider the equation

$$x\frac{dy}{dx}\frac{d^2y}{dx^2} = \frac{dy}{dx} - 1,$$

where again the dependent variable y does not appear explicitly. If we replace dy/dx by p and d^2y/dx^2 by dp/dx we get

$$xp\frac{dp}{dx} = p - 1,$$

which is a first order equation for p, as predicted by Theorem 1. We can solve by separating variables to get

$$\frac{p}{p-1}\,dp = \frac{dx}{x}$$

$$\left[1 + \frac{1}{p-1}\right]dp = \frac{dx}{x}$$

$$p + \log(p - 1) + \log C_1 = \log x$$

$$C_1(p - 1)e^p = x. \tag{5a}$$

In this work we assumed that both x and $p - 1$ were positive. If either one or both were negative we would still be led to Eq. (5a), although it might be necessary to rewrite the constant $-C_1$ as C_2 to reach a precise equivalent of Eq. (5a). If $p - 1 = 0$ or $x = 0$, however, then we cannot write Eq. (5a). Inspection of the original differential equation shows that $x = 0$ is not a solution of that equation but that the possibility $p - 1 = 0$ or

$$p = \frac{dy}{dx} = 1$$

$$y = x + C_2 \tag{6}$$

does lead to solutions.

Equation (5a) is very difficult to solve for p, but is already solved for x. If we differentiate both members of Eq. (5a) with respect to y we get

$$\frac{dx}{dy} = C_1 [(p - 1) e^p + e^p] \frac{dp}{dy}$$

$$\frac{1}{p} = C_1 pe^p \frac{dp}{dy}$$

$$dy = C_1 p^2 e^p \, dp.$$

Now if we integrate by parts twice we get

$$y = C_1 e^p (p^2 - 2p + 2) + C_3. \tag{5b}$$

We already had
$$x = C_1 e^p (p - 1). \tag{5a}$$

Equations (5a) and (5b) together give us solutions in parametric form, parameter p. There are two arbitrary constants, C_1 and C_3, which is to be expected in studying a second order equation. One must not forget the additional solutions furnished by Eq. (6).

The ideas we have used for equations that do not contain the dependent variable y explicitly can be varied slightly to take into account equations that do not contain the independent variable x explicitly. Again we substitute p for dy/dx but this time we write

$$\frac{d^2y}{dx^2} = \frac{dp}{dx} = \frac{dp}{dy} \frac{dy}{dx} = p \frac{dp}{dy}.$$

■ THEOREM 2

Reducing the order of an equation that does not contain the independent variable explicitly.

HYPOTHESIS: A second order differential equation can be written in the form

$$f\left(y, \frac{dy}{dx}, \frac{d^2y}{dx^2}\right) = 0. \tag{7a}$$

CONCLUSION: This second order differential equation can be written in the form

$$f\left(y, p, p\frac{dp}{dy}\right) = 0 \tag{7b}$$

by using the substitution $dy/dx = p$.

PROOF: We need merely observe that after the substitution

$$\frac{dy}{dx} = p, \quad \frac{d^2y}{dx^2} = p\frac{dp}{dy}$$

we have in Eq. (7b) a first order equation for p when we started with a second order equation for y in Eq. (7a).

Example 3.   Let us return to the curves of constant curvature 1 of Example 1; these curves satisfied the differential equation

$$\frac{d^2y}{dx^2} = \pm\left[1 + \left(\frac{dy}{dx}\right)^2\right]^{3/2}. \tag{2}$$

Equation (2) did not contain the dependent variable y explicitly, but neither does it contain the independent variable x explicitly. We can substitute

$$\frac{dy}{dx} = p, \quad \frac{d^2y}{dx^2} = \frac{dp}{dx} = \frac{dp}{dy}\frac{dy}{dx} = p\frac{dp}{dy}$$

and rewrite Eq. (2) in the form

$$p\frac{dp}{dy} = \pm(1 + p^2)^{3/2}$$

or in the separated form

$$dy = \pm\frac{p}{(1 + p^2)^{3/2}}\, dp = \pm\tfrac{1}{2}(1 + p^2)^{-3/2}\,(2p)\, dp.$$

It happens that this equation can be integrated with a little less labor than the corresponding Eq. (2a) in Example 1. We get

$$y = \mp\frac{1}{\sqrt{1 + p^2}} + C_1.$$

Here we can solve for p,

$$p = \pm\frac{\sqrt{1 - (y - C_1)^2}}{y - C_1}, \tag{8}$$

and then integrate again by separating variables;

$$\frac{dy}{dx} = \pm\frac{\sqrt{1 - (y - C_1)^2}}{y - C_1}$$

$$\frac{y - C_1}{\sqrt{1 - (y - C_1)^2}}\, dy = \pm dx$$

$$-\tfrac{1}{2}[1 - (y - C_1)^2]^{-1/2}\,[-2(y - C_1)]\, dy = \pm dx$$

$$\mp[1 - (y - C_1)^2]^{1/2} = x + C_2$$

$$(x + C_2)^2 + (y - C_1)^2 = 1.$$

Again we found that the curves of constant curvature 1 were circles of radius 1.

If one cannot solve easily for p as a function of y, as was done in Eq. (8) of Example 3, but can solve for y as a function of p, it may be possible to get solutions in parametric form with p as parameter. Thus, if we can write

$$y = \varphi(p) \tag{9a}$$

we can differentiate with respect to x to get

$$\frac{dy}{dx} = \frac{d\varphi}{dp}\frac{dp}{dx}$$

$$p = \varphi'(p)\frac{dp}{dx},$$

or, in separated form,

$$dx = \frac{1}{p}\varphi'(p)\,dp.$$

If now we can carry out the indicated integration we would have

$$x = \tau(p), \tag{9b}$$

and Eqs. (9a) and (9b) together would constitute a solution in parametric form with p as parameter.

Example 4. Consider the second order differential equation

$$\left[\left(\frac{dy}{dx}\right)^2 + y\right]\frac{d^2y}{dx^2} = \left(\frac{dy}{dx}\right)^2 \tag{10a}$$

in which the independent variable x does not appear explicitly. Let us write

$$\frac{dy}{dx} = p, \quad \frac{d^2y}{dx^2} = \frac{dp}{dx} = \frac{dp}{dy}\frac{dy}{dx} = p\frac{dp}{dy},$$

so that the original equation becomes

$$(p^2 + y)p\frac{dp}{dy} = p^2. \tag{10b}$$

Here we have a first order equation for p, as predicted by Theorem 2.

Clearly, $p = 0$ is a solution of Eq. (10b). But $p = 0$ means $dy/dx = 0$ or

$$y = C_1, \tag{11}$$

and it is easy to verify directly that these are solutions of Eq. (10a). If, having considered the possibility $p = 0$, we next consider the possibility $p \neq 0$ and divide by p in Eq. (10b), we have

$$(p^2 + y)\frac{dp}{dy} = p.$$

This equation is not separable or homogeneous, and is not linear in p, but it is linear in y. We can write

$$\frac{dp}{dy} = \frac{p}{p^2 + y}$$

$$\frac{dy}{dp} = \frac{p^2 + y}{p}$$

$$\frac{dy}{dp} - \frac{1}{p}y = p.$$

It soon appears that $e^{-\int 1/p \, dp} = e^{-\log p} = (e^{\log p})^{-1} = p^{-1}$ is an integrating factor and that

$$\frac{1}{p}\frac{dy}{dp} - \frac{1}{p^2}y = 1$$

$$\frac{1}{p}y = p + C_2.$$

At this point we could solve a quadratic equation for p, but it is easier to solve for y:

$$y = p^2 + C_2 p. \tag{11a}$$

If we differentiate with respect to x, we have

$$\frac{dy}{dx} = (2p + C_2)\frac{dp}{dx}$$

$$p = (2p + C_2)\frac{dp}{dx}$$

$$dx = \left(2 + \frac{C_2}{p}\right) dp$$

$$x = 2p + \tfrac{1}{2} C_2 \log p^2 + C_3. \tag{11b}$$

We already had

$$y = p^2 + C_2 p. \tag{11a}$$

Equations (11a) and (11b) together furnish solutions of the original differential equation in parametric form, with p as parameter. There are two arbitrary constants, C_2 and C_3, and this is to be expected because we started with a second order equation. Do not overlook the solutions furnished by Eqs. (11).

We conclude this section with a timely example on rectilinear motion.

Example 5.   *The initial velocity necessary for "escape."*

In Sec. 2.2 we studied the rectilinear motion of an object moving under the influence of gravity alone near the earth's surface, and we generalized our work by taking a special force of friction into account in Exercise 14.1-12. Now let us consider an object moving under the influence of gravity alone, but not necessarily always near the earth's surface.

Assume, with Newton, that the force of attraction between the earth and an object is given by

$$F = -k\frac{1}{r^2}, \tag{12}$$

where r is the distance from the object to the center of the earth. Let the object have mass m and weight w, as measured on the earth, and let the object be fired straight up from the earth's surface at time $t = 0$ with initial velocity v_0. We shall try to see how large v_0 must be if the object is to "escape" from the earth.

In order to have a more precise statement for the constant of proportionality in Newton's Law of Gravitation, Eq. (12), we consider the object when it is near the earth's surface. At that time the force of attraction F is the weight of the object as measured on the earth's surface, and we can write

$$-w = -k\frac{1}{(4000)^2},$$

assuming that the earth is a sphere of radius 4000 miles, so that

$$k = (4000)^2 w$$

and the basic Eq. (12) can be written

$$F = -(4000)^2 w\frac{1}{r^2}. \tag{12a}$$

But one of Newton's Laws of Motion tells us that

$$F = ma. \tag{12b}$$

The object we are studying is going to be fired straight up from the earth's surface and the distance it moves is described by r, its speed by dr/dt, and its linear acceleration by d^2r/dt^2. If we also remember that an object's mass and its weight at the earth's surface are related by $w = mg$, where $g = 32$ ft/sec², we can rewrite Eq.(12b) in the form

$$F = \frac{w}{g}\frac{d^2r}{dt^2}. \tag{12c}$$

Equations (12a) and (12c) together say that

$$\frac{w}{g}\frac{d^2r}{dt^2} = -(4000)^2 w\frac{1}{r^2}$$

or that

$$\frac{1}{g}\frac{d^2r}{dt^2} = -(4000)^2\frac{1}{r^2}. \tag{13}$$

Here is a second order equation in which the independent variable t does not appear explicitly. We substitute for dr/dt and proceed as suggested by Theorem 2. Write

$$\frac{dr}{dt} = v, \quad \frac{d^2r}{dt^2} = \frac{dv}{dt} = \frac{dv}{dr}\frac{dr}{dt} = v\frac{dv}{dr}$$

in Eq. (13) to get

$$\frac{1}{g}v\frac{dv}{dr} = -(4000)^2\frac{1}{r^2}$$

$$v\,dv = -(4000)^2 g\frac{1}{r^2}\,dr$$

$$\frac{v^2}{2} = (4000)^2 g\frac{1}{r} + C_1. \tag{14}$$

But we know that $v = v_0$ when $t = 0$ and that the object is at the earth's surface, $r = 4000$, when $t = 0$. Hence

$$\frac{v_0^2}{2} = (4000)^2 g \frac{1}{4000} + C_1,$$

$$C_1 = \tfrac{1}{2} v_0^2 - 4000g,$$

and Eq. (14) becomes

$$\tfrac{1}{2} v^2 = (4000)^2 g \frac{1}{r} + (\tfrac{1}{2} v_0^2 - 4000g). \tag{15}$$

We want to choose v_0 so that the object fired at the earth's surface does not return to the earth. This will be the case if the object's velocity v, initially v_0, remains positive, and that velocity v will remain positive if it never becomes 0. If we examine Eq. (15) we see that the first term of the right member is always positive, but that it decreases in size as r increases. If v_0 is chosen so that the second term of the right member is also positive, then v^2 can never be 0, and neither can v. Hence if we choose v_0 so that

$$\tfrac{1}{2} v_0^2 - 4000g \geq 0$$

$$v_0^2 \geq 8000g$$

$$v_0 \geq \sqrt{\frac{8000 \, (32)}{5280}} \, \frac{\text{miles}}{\text{sec}}$$

$$v_0 \geq 6.97 \, \frac{\text{miles}}{\text{sec}},$$

we can be sure that v will remain positive and that the object will "escape" from the earth's field of attraction. In our computation we took into account the fact that g had been measured in ft/sec^2 while the radius of the earth had been described in miles.

EXERCISES 14.7

1. Solve $x^2 \dfrac{d^2y}{dx^2} = \left(\dfrac{dy}{dx}\right)^2$.

2. Solve $\dfrac{d^2y}{dx^2} = \left(\dfrac{dy}{dx}\right)^2 + 1$.

3. Find the solutions of $(x + 1) \dfrac{d^2y}{dx^2} + \dfrac{dy}{dx} + 2x + 1 = 0$ for which $y = 0$ and $dy/dx = 1$ when $x = 0$.

4. Find the solution of $\dfrac{d^2y}{dx^2} = x \left(\dfrac{dy}{dx} - 1\right)^2$: (a) for which $y = 1$ and $dy/dx = 3$ when $x = 0$; (b) for which $y = 1$ and $dy/dx = 1$ when $x = 0$.

5. Solve $\dfrac{d^3y}{dx^3} = \dfrac{d^2y}{dx^2} + 1$.

6. Solve $\dfrac{d^4y}{dx^4} = \dfrac{3}{x - 1} \dfrac{d^3y}{dx^3} + \dfrac{1}{(x - 1)^4}$.

7. Solve $\left[\left(\dfrac{dy}{dx}\right)^2 + 1\right] \dfrac{d^2y}{dx^2} = \dfrac{dy}{dx}$.

8. Solve $\left(\dfrac{dy}{dx}\right)^2 - \dfrac{dy}{dx} + x\left(2\dfrac{dy}{dx} - 1\right)\dfrac{d^2y}{dx^2} = 0.$

9. Solve $y\dfrac{d^2y}{dx^2} = \left(\dfrac{dy}{dx}\right)^3.$

10. Solve $y^2\dfrac{d^2y}{dx^2} = a\dfrac{dy}{dx}.$

11. Solve $y\dfrac{d^2y}{dx^2} - 2\left(\dfrac{dy}{dx}\right)^2 = y^3\dfrac{dy}{dx}.$

12. Solve $\left(y\dfrac{dy}{dx} - 2\right)\dfrac{d^2y}{dx^2} = \left(\dfrac{dy}{dx}\right)^3.$

13. Solve $\dfrac{d^2y}{dx^2} = e^y\dfrac{dy}{dx}.$

14. Solve $\dfrac{d^2y}{dx^2} = 2y\dfrac{dy}{dx}.$

15. In Examples 1 and 3 we have already shown that the curves of constant curvature 1 are the circles of radius 1. Find the solutions of

$$\frac{d^2y}{dx^2} = \pm\left[1 + \left(\frac{dy}{dx}\right)^2\right]^{3/2} \tag{2}$$

in parametric form this time. If you wish to, you can work with Eq. (3a) of Example 1, but remember that $\tan\theta = p$ in that equation.

16. Find the equation of the curve that passes through $(1, 0)$ with slope 0, faces up everywhere, and has curvature always equal to $1/x^2$.

17. Find the equations of the curves that pass through $(3, 8)$ with slope 1, face up everywhere, and have radius of curvature always equal to $y^{3/2}$.

18. *Clairaut's Equation.* Derive the solutions

$$\begin{cases} x = -f'(p) \\ y = -pf'(p) + f(p) \end{cases} \quad \text{and} \quad y = C_1 x + f(C_1)$$

for the equation $y = x\dfrac{dy}{dx} + f\left(\dfrac{dy}{dx}\right).$

19. *The simple pendulum.* Assume that a pendulum is of length L and that all of its mass is concentrated at the bob. The forces acting on the bob are its weight w and a certain pull in the direction of the string BP; see Fig. 14.11. We know that the bob will move in a circular path, perpendicular to BP at B. The component of the weight $-w\mathbf{j}$ in the direction of the path has magnitude $-w\sin\theta$, while the pull in the string has no component in the direction of the path. Since the acceleration in the path is

$$\frac{d^2s}{dt^2} = L\frac{d^2\theta}{dt^2},$$

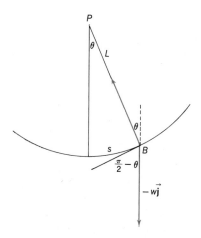

Fig. 14.11

the basic statement $F = ma$ becomes

$$-w \sin \theta = mL \frac{d^2\theta}{dt^2},$$

or, because $w = mg$,

$$\frac{d^2\theta}{dt^2} + \frac{g}{L} \sin \theta = 0. \tag{16}$$

Show that this equation can be integrated once and brought to the form

$$\frac{d\theta}{dt} = \pm\sqrt{C_1 + \frac{2g}{L} \cos \theta}. \tag{17}$$

20. It is usually very difficult to integrate again in Eq. (17) and thus to solve for θ in terms of familiar functions. If the motion of the pendulum is such that θ is always small, then θ is a reasonable approximation for $\sin \theta$ and Eq. (16) can be replaced by

$$\frac{d^2\theta}{dt^2} + \frac{g}{L} \theta = 0. \tag{18}$$

Show that the difference between $\sin \theta$ and θ is less than $\tfrac{1}{6} \theta^3$. Replace $d\theta/dt$ by ω and $d^2\theta/dt^2$ by $d\omega/dt = \omega \, d\omega/d\theta$ in Eq. (18) and derive the solutions

$$\theta = C_1 \sin (kt + C_2), \qquad \text{where } k^2 = \frac{g}{L}$$

or
$$\theta = C_3 \sin kt + C_4 \cos kt.$$

These solutions are periodic with period $2\pi\sqrt{L/g}$. We shall discuss easier methods of solving second order linear equations like Eq. (18) in Sec. 14.8.

21. The equation

$$\frac{d^2y}{dx^2} + \sin y = 0$$

is very much like Eq. (16). Derive the solution $\log (\sec y/2 + \tan y/2) = x + \tfrac{1}{2} \log 3$ in the special case where $x = 0$ and $dy/dx = \sqrt{3}$ when $y = \pi/3$.

14.8   Second Order Linear Equations. I

We repeat Definition 14.5-1.

■ DEFINITION 1

Linear differential equation. In a linear differential equation every term is either of the first degree in the dependent variable and its derivatives or does not contain the dependent variable and its derivatives at all.

It follows from this definition that a second order linear differential equation can be written in the form

$$\frac{d^2y}{dx^2} + R(x) \frac{dy}{dx} + S(x) y = T(x).$$

We shall discuss a special case first.

■ DEFINITION 2

Reduced linear equation. A linear differential equation in which every term contains the dependent variable or one of its derivatives is called a reduced or homogeneous linear equation.

A reduced second order linear equation can be written in the form

$$\frac{d^2y}{dx^2} + R(x)\frac{dy}{dx} + S(x)\,y = 0.$$

For these reduced equations we have a theorem which tells us how to obtain new solutions from known solutions in a simple fashion.

■ THEOREM 1

Linear combinations of solutions of reduced second order linear equations.

HYPOTHESIS: (a) $y = u(x)$ and $y = v(x)$ are solutions of a reduced second order linear equation for x of an interval I.
(b) $w(x) = C_1u(x) + C_2v(x)$ for x of I, C_1 and C_2 constant.

CONCLUSION: $y = w(x)$ is a solution of the reduced equation for x of I.

PROOF: Let us write the reduced equation in the form

$$y'' + R(x)y' + S(x)y = 0.$$

Then, by Hypothesis (a) we know that

$$u'' + R(x)u' + S(x)u = 0, \qquad v'' + R(x)v' + S(x)v = 0. \tag{1}$$

The equation $y = w(x)$ will be a solution if and only if

$$w'' + R(x)w' + S(x)w = 0.$$

But we can compute

$$w'' + R(x)w' + S(x)w = [C_1u'' + C_2v'']$$
$$+ R(x)[C_1u' + C_2v'] + S(x)[C_1u + C_2v]$$
$$= C_1[u'' + R(x)u' + S(x)u] + C_2[v'' + R(x)v' + S(x)v],$$

and then, because of Eqs. (1),

$$w'' + R(x)w' + S(x)w = C_1(0) + C_2(0) = 0.$$

This completes the proof. The reader is invited to show in Exercises 14.8-1 and 14.8-2 that the conclusion of Theorem 1 is not valid for nonlinear equations or for linear equations that are not reduced. He can show in Exercise 14.8-3 that a theorem corresponding to Theorem 1 is also true for first order reduced linear equations.

The even more special case of a reduced linear equation with constant coeffi-cients occurs frequently in applications, and some of these applications are discussed later in Sec. 14.10. A reduced linear equation of the second order with constant coefficients can be written in the form

$$y'' + ry' + sy = 0, \qquad r \text{ and } s \text{ constant.} \tag{2}$$

This equation says that the sum of y'' and multiples of y' and y shall be 0 for all x of a certain interval. This could happen in simplest fashion if y, y', and y'' are all multiples of the same function f, and if the sum of the multiples of f that appear when $y'' + ry' + sy$ is written is 0. There is an elementary function whose derivatives are all multiples of the function itself, namely, the exponential function, and hence it makes sense to try $y = e^{mx}$ as a solution of Eq. (2).

When we write

$$y = e^{mx}, \qquad y' = me^{mx}, \qquad y'' = m^2 e^{mx}$$

we find that Eq. (2) will be satisfied if we choose m so that

$$m^2 e^{mx} + rm e^{mx} + s e^{mx} = 0,$$

and then, since e^{mx} never vanishes, if we choose m so that

$$m^2 + rm + s = 0. \tag{3}$$

Equation (3) can be called the auxiliary algebraic equation. There are now three possibilities, according as the roots of the quadratic equation (3) are real and distinct, real and equal, or not real.

Case (a): $r^2 - 4s > 0$. In this case we can write

$$m = m_1 = \frac{-r + \sqrt{r^2 - 4s}}{2}, \qquad m = m_2 = \frac{-r - \sqrt{r^2 - 4s}}{2}$$

for the two real solutions of Eq. (3) and say that $y = e^{m_1 x}$ and $y = e^{m_2 x}$ are solutions of Eq. (2). Theorem 1 would then enable us to go further and to say that

$$y = C_1 e^{m_1 x} + C_2 e^{m_2 x}$$

is a solution of Eq. (2) for each choice of the constants C_1 and C_2.

Case (b): $r^2 - 4s < 0$. In this case we can say that $4s - r^2 > 0$ and that the two complex conjugate roots of Eq. (3) are

$$m = m_1 = -\tfrac{1}{2}r + \tfrac{1}{2}\sqrt{4s - r^2}\, i = \alpha + \beta i$$

$$m = m_2 = -\tfrac{1}{2}r - \tfrac{1}{2}\sqrt{4s - r^2}\, i = \alpha - \beta i,$$

where we have written

$$\alpha = -\tfrac{1}{2}r, \qquad \beta = \tfrac{1}{2}\sqrt{4s - r^2}. \tag{4}$$

We cannot claim as in Case (a) that

$$y = e^{m_1 x} = e^{(\alpha + \beta i)x}$$

is a solution of Eq. (2), because we have not defined what we mean by the exponential function when the exponent is not real. But let us continue on a formal basis and then check any suggested solutions by direct substitution in Eq. (2). If suitable meaning can be attached to exponentials with nonreal exponents, we suspect that

$$y = e^{m_1 x} = e^{(\alpha+\beta i)x}, \qquad y = e^{m_2 x} = e^{(\alpha-\beta i)x}$$

are solutions of Eq. (2). If Theorem 1 applied to such solutions,

$$y = C_1 e^{(\alpha+\beta i)x} + C_2 e^{(\alpha-\beta i)x}$$

would also be a solution for each choice of C_1 and C_2, and, if the same laws of exponents that apply to real exponents could be presumed to apply also to complex exponents,

$$y = e^{\alpha x}(C_1 e^{\beta ix} + C_2 e^{-\beta ix}) \tag{5}$$

would be a solution for each choice of C_1 and C_2. Formal experiment with infinite series for the exponential and trigonometric functions in Sec. 13.10 suggested Euler's Formula:

$$e^{ix} = \cos x + i \sin x,$$

for all x. In our case we could try

$$e^{\beta ix} = e^{i\beta x} = \cos \beta x + i \sin \beta x$$

$$e^{-\beta ix} = e^{i(-\beta x)} = \cos(-\beta x) + i \sin (-\beta x) = \cos \beta x - i \sin \beta x.$$

Hence we rewrite the formal trial solution that we wrote in Eq. (5) in the form

$$y = e^{\alpha x}[C_1 (\cos \beta x + i \sin \beta x) + C_2(\cos \beta x - i \sin \beta x)]$$

or in the form

$$y = e^{\alpha x}(C_3 \cos \beta x + C_4 \sin \beta x), \tag{6}$$

where we have replaced the constants $C_1 + C_2$ and $i(C_1 - C_2)$ by C_3 and C_4. To summarize, we have been led to the suggestion that

$$y = e^{\alpha x}\cos \beta x \qquad \text{and} \qquad y = e^{\alpha x} \sin \beta x,$$

with $\qquad \alpha = -\tfrac{1}{2}r \qquad \text{and} \qquad \beta = \tfrac{1}{2}\sqrt{4s - r^2}, \tag{4}$

are solutions of the differential equation

$$y'' + ry' + sy = 0. \tag{2}$$

We shall check the first of these suggestions right here and invite the reader to check the second in Exercise 14.8-4. If

$$y = e^{\alpha x} \cos \beta x,$$

then straightforward computation will show that

$$y' = e^{\alpha x}(-\beta \sin \beta x + \alpha \cos \beta x)$$

$$y'' = e^{\alpha x}[-2\alpha\beta \sin \beta x + (\alpha^2 - \beta^2) \cos \beta x],$$

and that

$$y'' + ry' + sy = e^{\alpha x} \sin \beta x(-2\alpha\beta - r\beta) + e^{\alpha x} \cos \beta x(\alpha^2 - \beta^2 + r\alpha + s).$$

When we take Eqs. (4) into account, we find that

$$-2\alpha\beta - r\beta = r\beta - r\beta = 0$$

$$\alpha^2 - \beta^2 + r\alpha + s = \tfrac{1}{4}r^2 - \tfrac{1}{4}(4s - r^2) - \tfrac{1}{2}r^2 + s = 0,$$

so that

$$y'' + ry' + sy = e^{\alpha x}\sin\beta x(0) + e^{\alpha x}\cos\beta x(0) = 0.$$

To repeat, when the auxiliary algebraic equation (3) has the complex conjugate roots $\alpha \pm i\beta$, then

$$y = e^{\alpha x}(C_3 \cos\beta x + C_4 \sin\beta x) \tag{6}$$

is a solution for each choice of constants C_3 and C_4.

Case (c): $r^2 - 4s = 0$. In this case we can say that $s = \tfrac{1}{4}r^2$ and that the original differential equation (2) reads

$$y'' + ry' + \tfrac{1}{4}r^2 y = 0. \tag{7}$$

But now the auxiliary algebraic equation (3) reads

$$m^2 + rm + \tfrac{1}{4}r^2 = (m + \tfrac{1}{2}r)^2 = 0.$$

There is only one real root, $m_1 = -r/2$, and we have determined only one solution of Eq. (7), namely, $y = e^{-(r/2)x}$. We suspect that there is a second, independent solution, and we ask if there is a way of modifying or varying the one solution we already have to get a second. A more precise way of asking the question is this: Can we find $w(x)$ such that $y = w(x)\, e^{-(r/2)x}$ is also a solution of Eq. (7)? This idea of determining useful multipliers for parts of solutions of equations is a fruitful one, exploited efficiently by the mathematician Lagrange, and we shall use it frequently.

We try then to determine $w(x)$ so that $y = we^{-(r/2)x}$ will be a solution of Eq. (7). We compute

$$y = we^{-(r/2)x}, \qquad y' = \left(w' - \frac{r}{2}w\right)e^{-(r/2)x},$$

$$y'' = \left(w'' - rw' + \frac{r^2}{4}w\right)e^{-(r/2)x}$$

and

$$y'' + ry' + \tfrac{1}{4}r^2 y = \left[\left(w'' - rw' + \frac{r^2}{4}w\right) + \left(rw' - \frac{r^2}{2}w\right) + \left(\frac{r^2}{4}w\right)\right]e^{-(r/2)x}$$

$$= w''e^{-(r/2)x}.$$

Thus, $y = we^{-(r/2)x}$ is a solution of Eq. (7) if and only if

$$w'' = 0,$$

$$w = C_1 x + C_2,$$

$$y = (C_1 x + C_2)e^{-(r/2)x} = C_1 x e^{-(r/2)x} + C_2 e^{-(r/2)x}.$$

This computation shows that when the auxiliary algebraic equation (3) has only one real root, $m = -r/2$, then $y = C_1 x e^{-(r/2)x} + C_2 e^{-(r/2)x}$ is a solution of Eq. (2) for each choice of the constants C_1 and C_2. Two particular solutions, corresponding to the choices $C_1 = 0$, $C_2 = 1$ and $C_1 = 1$, $C_2 = 0$ are $y = e^{-(r/2)x}$ and $y = x e^{-(r/2)x}$.

To summarize the results of our long discussion of the reduced second order linear equation with constant coefficients, we state Theorem 2.

■ **THEOREM 2**

Solutions of reduced second order linear equations with constant coefficients.

HYPOTHESIS: The constant coefficients of $y'' + ry' + sy = 0$ are such that the auxiliary algebraic equation $m^2 + rm + s = 0$ has

Case (a): distinct real roots, m_1 and m_2.
Case (b): complex conjugate roots, $\alpha + i\beta$ and $\alpha - i\beta$.
Case (c): one real root, $-(r/2)$.

CONCLUSION: For each choice of constants C_1 and C_2

Case (a): $y = C_1 e^{m_1 x} + C_2 e^{m_2 x}$,
Case (b): $y = e^{\alpha x}(C_1 \cos \beta x + C_2 \sin \beta x)$,
Case (c): $y = C_1 x e^{-(r/2)x} + C_2 e^{-(r/2)x}$

is a solution of $y'' + ry' + sy = 0$.

Example 1.   Find a solution of $4y'' + 4y' - 3y = 0$ for which $y = 2$ and $y' = -1$ when $x = 0$.

If we try $y = e^{mx}$, and, with it, $y' = m e^{mx}$ and $y'' = m^2 e^{mx}$, we are led to

$$4m^2 e^{mx} + 4m e^{mx} - 3e^{mx} = 0,$$

and to the auxiliary algebraic equation

$$4m^2 + 4m - 3 = 0,$$

or

$$(2m + 3)(2m - 1) = 0$$

with solutions

$$m = -\tfrac{3}{2}, \qquad m = \tfrac{1}{2}.$$

Hence, by Theorem 2,

$$y = C_1 e^{-(3/2)x} + C_2 e^{(1/2)x}$$

would be a solution for any choice of C_1 and C_2. For such a y we would also have

$$y' = -\tfrac{3}{2}C_1 e^{-(3/2)x} + \tfrac{1}{2}C_2 e^{(1/2)x}.$$

Hence, if we are to have $y = 2$ and $y' = -1$ when $x = 0$, we ought to choose C_1 and C_2 so that

$$2 = C_1 + C_2, \qquad -1 = -\tfrac{3}{2} C_1 + \tfrac{1}{2} C_2.$$

The choices $C_1 = 1$ and $C_2 = 1$ are now the only ones possible; the solution we seek is

$$y = e^{-(3/2)x} + e^{(1/2)x}.$$

Example 2. Find a two-parameter family of solutions of $y'' - 3y' + 3y = 0$. If we try $y = e^{mx}$, and, with it, $y' = me^{mx}$ and $y'' = m^2 e^{mx}$, we are led to

$$m^2 e^{mx} - 3me^{mx} + 3e^{mx} = 0,$$

and the auxiliary algebraic equation

$$m^2 - 3m + 3 = 0,$$

whose roots are

$$m = \frac{3 \pm \sqrt{9 - 12}}{2} = \frac{3 \pm \sqrt{3}i}{2}.$$

Here, working on a purely formal basis, we suggest that

$$y = C_1 e^{[(3/2)+(\sqrt{3}/2)i]x} + C_2 e^{[(3/2)-(\sqrt{3}/2)i]x}$$

$$y = e^{(3/2)x} [C_1 e^{(\sqrt{3}/2)ix} + C_2 e^{-(\sqrt{3}/2)ix}]$$

$$y = e^{(3/2)x} \left[C_1 \left(\cos \frac{\sqrt{3}}{2}x + i \sin \frac{\sqrt{3}}{2}x \right) + C_2 \left(\cos \frac{\sqrt{3}}{2}x - i \sin \frac{\sqrt{3}}{2}x \right) \right]$$

$$y = e^{(3/2)x} \left(C_3 \cos \frac{\sqrt{3}}{2}x + C_4 \sin \frac{\sqrt{3}}{2}x \right) \tag{8}$$

are solutions. The check computations performed at the end of our work in Case (b) above and in Exercise 14.8-4 assure the validity of these suggestions.

Example 3. Find a solution of $4y'' + 4y' + y = 0$ for which $y = y_0$ and $y' = y_0'$ when $x = 0$.

If we try $y = e^{mx}$, we are led to the auxiliary algebraic equation

$$4m^2 + 4m + 1 = 0,$$

$$(2m + 1)^2 = 0,$$

which has the one real root $m = -\frac{1}{2}$. At this point, then, we have determined one solution, $y = e^{-(1/2)x}$. But we proved in Case (c) that, if we looked for a second solution of the form $y = w(x)e^{-(1/2)x}$, we would find that $y = xe^{-(1/2)x}$ is a second solution. Hence, by Theorem 1, for each choice of C_1 and C_2,

$$y = C_1 xe^{-(1/2)x} + C_2 e^{-(1/2)x}$$

is a solution of the original differential equation. For such a solution

$$y' = C_1 e^{-(1/2)x} - \frac{1}{2} C_1 xe^{-(1/2)x} - \frac{1}{2} C_2 e^{-(1/2)x},$$

and, if we are to have $y = y_0$ and $y' = y_0'$ when $x = 0$, we must choose C_1 and C_2 so that

$$y_0 = 0 + C_2, \qquad y_0' = C_1 - \frac{1}{2} C_2,$$

or

$$C_2 = y_0, \qquad C_1 = y_0' + \frac{1}{2} y_0.$$

The solution we seek is

$$y = (y_0' + \tfrac{1}{2}y_0)xe^{-(1/2)x} + y_0e^{-(1/2)x}.$$

||

We have shown that every reduced second order linear equation with constant coefficients has solutions, and, indeed, Theorem 2 explains in detail that in this special case we can adjust two arbitrary constants in attempting to meet two conditions on the solutions. Suppose, however, that one is given a more general second order linear equation, not necessarily reduced and not necessarily with constant coefficients. Will there still be a solution that meets two conditions? And are the solutions unique?

■ **THEOREM 3**

Existence and uniqueness of solutions for second order linear equations.

HYPOTHESIS: (a) $R(x)$, $S(x)$, $T(x)$ are continuous for x of interval I.
(b) x_0 is a point of interval I.
(c) y_0 and y_0' are constants.

CONCLUSION: There is one and only one solution of $y'' + R(x)y' + S(x)y = T(x)$ on interval I for which $y(x_0) = y_0$ and $y'(x_0) = y_0'$.

The second order equation in the one dependent variable y,

$$y'' + R(x)y' + S(x)y = T(x),$$

can be replaced by a system of *two* first order equations in the *two* dependent variables y and p:

$$\begin{cases} y' = p \\ p' + R(x)p + S(x)y = T(x). \end{cases}$$

In Sec. 14.6 we described the Picard successive approximation argument which can be used in working out the existence and uniqueness theorem for *one* first order equation in *one* dependent variable, Theorem 14.6-1. A modification of this argument can be applied to work out an existence and uniqueness theorem for a system of n first order equations in n dependent variables. This is done in more advanced and more detailed differential equations courses, and Theorem 3 just given is then demonstrated.

III

Theorem 1 says that if $y = u(x)$ and $y = v(x)$ are solutions of the reduced second order linear equation

$$y'' + R(x)y' + S(x)y = 0 \tag{9}$$

for x of an interval I, then $y = C_1u(x) + C_2v(x)$ is also a solution for x of I. It is natural to ask the converse question. Can *all* solutions for the interval I be written as linear combinations of $u(x)$ and $v(x)$? If $y = w(x)$ is a solution, do there exist constants C_1 and C_2 such that $w(x) = C_1 u(x) + C_2 v(x)$ for x of I?

In the first place, it is clear that we ought not to use solutions $y = u(x)$ and $y = v(x)$ with either u or v a multiple of the other. For, if there is a constant a such that $v(x) = au(x)$ then the family of solutions

$$y = C_1 u(x) + C_2 v(x) \qquad (10)$$

can be written

$$y = (C_1 + C_2 a)u(x) = C_3 u(x),$$

using only one arbitrary constant, and we cannot hope to meet two conditions as required by Theorem 3.

Equation (9) has $y = 0$ as one of its solutions, as direct substitution will immediately verify. It is also clear that we ought not to take $y = u(x)$ or $y = v(x)$ to be the solution that is identically 0, for, again, the family of solutions (10) would reduce to a family described by one arbitrary constant. We can describe both of these possibilities in one definition.

■ DEFINITION 3

Linear dependence of two functions. The functions $u(x)$ and $v(x)$ are said to be linearly dependent on an interval I if there exist constants a and b, not both 0, such that $au(x) + bv(x) = 0$ for each x of I. If no such constants a and b exist, we say that $u(x)$ and $v(x)$ are linearly independent on I.

Example 4. The functions $u(x) = x^2 + 7$ and $v(x) = 5(x^2 + 7)$ are linearly dependent on any interval, for we can say that

$$5u(x) - 1v(x) = 0 \qquad \text{for all } x.$$

The constants a and b of Definition 3 are $a = 5$ and $b = -1$ in this case.

Example 5. The functions $u(x) = x^2 + 7$ and $v(x) = 0$ are linearly dependent on any interval, for we can say that

$$0u(x) + 1v(x) = 0 \qquad \text{for all } x.$$

The constants a and b of Definition 3 are $a = 0$ and $b = 1$.

Example 6. The functions $u(x) = x$ and $v(x) = x^2$ are linearly independent on the interval $0 \leq x \leq 1$. For, if we write

$$ax + bx^2 = 0 \qquad \text{for all } x \text{ of} \qquad 0 \leq x \leq 1,$$

we find that a and b must satisfy

$$\tfrac{1}{2} a + \tfrac{1}{4} b = 0 \qquad \text{and} \qquad a + b = 0$$

when $x = \tfrac{1}{2}$ and $x = 1$ are chosen. The only possible choices are $a = b = 0$, and Definition 3 requires that not both a and b be 0 if we are to have linear dependence.

Now we can state a converse to Theorem 1.

■ **THEOREM 4**

Linear combinations of solutions of reduced linear equations.

HYPOTHESIS: (a) $R(x)$ and $S(x)$ are continuous for x of interval I.
  (b) $y = u(x)$ and $y = v(x)$ are linearly independent solutions of $y'' + R(x)y' + S(x)y = 0$ on interval I.
  (c) $y = w(x)$ is a solution on interval I.

CONCLUSION: There exist constants C_1 and C_2 such that

$$w(x) = C_1 u(x) + C_2 v(x) \qquad \text{for } x \text{ of } I.$$

PROOF: *Step (1).* Because $u(x)$ and $v(x)$ are linearly independent on I, $u(x)$ is not identically 0 on I and there is a point x_0 of I where u does not vanish; $u(x_0) \neq 0$. Compute the six numbers $u_0 = u(x_0)$, $u_0' = u'(x_0)$, $v_0 = v(x_0)$, $v_0' = v'(x_0)$, $w_0 = w(x_0)$, $w_0' = w'(x_0)$.

Step (2): The equations

$$\begin{cases} w_0 = C_1 u_0 + C_2 v_0 \\ w_0' = C_1 u_0' + C_2 v_0', \end{cases} \tag{11}$$

considered as two equations in the two unknowns C_1 and C_2, will have solutions

$$C_1 = \frac{w_0 v_0' - w_0' v_0}{u_0 v_0' - u_0' v_0} \qquad \text{and} \qquad C_2 = \frac{u_0 w_0' - u_0' w_0}{u_0 v_0' - u_0' v_0} \tag{12}$$

provided that

$$u_0 v_0' - u_0' v_0 \neq 0.$$

We shall show in Step (4) that $u_0 v_0' - u_0' v_0$ cannot be 0, and, assuming this here, we take C_1 and C_2 as described in Eqs. (12).

Step (3): Now write $z(x) = C_1 u(x) + C_2 v(x)$. Equations (11) say that $w(x_0) = z(x_0)$, $w'(x_0) = z'(x_0)$. But $y = z(x)$ is a solution, by Theorem 1, and the uniqueness part of Theorem 3 says that, if two solutions and their first derivatives agree at a single point, these solutions must be identical; hence

$$w(x) = z(x) = C_1 u(x) + C_2 v(x).$$

This would establish our conclusion and complete the proof.

Step (4): It remains to show, however, in Step (2) that we cannot have $u_0 v_0' - u_0' v_0 = 0$. The function

$$W(x) = u(x)v'(x) - u'(x)v(x) = \begin{vmatrix} u(x) & v(x) \\ u'(x) & v'(x) \end{vmatrix}$$

is of considerable importance in this work and is usually called the "Wronskian for u and v." We want to show that the Wronskian cannot vanish at x_0, for $u_0 v_0' - u_0' v_0$ is precisely $W(x_0)$.

Because $u(x)$ and $v(x)$ are solutions, we can write

$$u'' + Ru' + Su = 0, \qquad v'' + Rv' + Sv = 0.$$

If we multiply the first of these equations by v and the second by u and subtract, we get

$$u''v - uv'' + R(u'v - uv') = 0$$

$$\frac{d}{dx}(u'v - uv') + R(u'v - uv') = 0$$

$$\frac{dW}{dx} + RW = 0.$$

If we use the integrating factor $e^{\int R\,dx}$ here, we write

$$e^{\int R\,dx}\frac{dW}{dx} + Re^{\int R\,dx}\,W = 0$$

$$e^{\int R\,dx}\,W = k \qquad \text{for some constant } k,$$

$$W = ke^{-\int R\,dx}.$$

By hypothesis, $R(x)$ was continuous and therefore $\int R\,dx$ exists. The exponential function is always positive, and hence the last equation says that the Wronskian can vanish at x_0 only if the constant k vanishes. But in this case the Wronskian would vanish for all x of interval I.

If the Wronskian vanished for all x of interval I we would have

$$u(x)v'(x) - u'(x)\,v(x) = 0$$

$$\frac{u(x)v'(x) - u'(x)\,v(x)}{u^2(x)} = 0$$

for all x of I, or, if u can vanish on I, for all x of some subinterval $\mathcal{J}$ on which $u(x)$ did not vanish. This subinterval would include the point x_0. Then

$$\frac{d}{dx}\left(\frac{v(x)}{u(x)}\right) = 0$$

$$\frac{v(x)}{u(x)} = \bar{k} \qquad \text{for some constant } \bar{k}$$

$$v(x) = \bar{k}\,u(x).$$

If the last equation is valid for all x of I, then v is a multiple of u for interval I and we have a contradiction of Hypothesis (b). If the last equation is valid only for some subinterval $\mathcal{J}$, then we can write

$$h(x) = v(x) - \bar{k}u(x),$$

and observe that $y = h(x)$ is a solution by Theorem 1, that $h(x_0) = 0$ and $h'(x_0) = 0$, because x_0 is an interior point of $\mathcal{J}$. By the uniqueness part of Theorem 3 again, the solutions $y = h(x)$ and $y = 0$ must coincide for I, and then

$$v(x) = \bar{k}u(x) \qquad \text{for } x \text{ of } I$$

so that we arrive at the same contradiction of Hypothesis (b) as before.

EXERCISES 14.8

1. The equation $y'' + R(x)y' + S(x)y^2 = 0$ is not linear. Let $y = u(x)$ and $y = v(x)$ be solutions and let C_1 and C_2 be constants. Is it true that $y = w(x) = C_1 u(x)$ is a solution? Is $y = z(x) = C_1 u(x) + C_2 v(x)$ a solution?

2. The equation $y'' + R(x)y' + S(x)y = T(x)$, $T(x) \neq 0$, is linear, but not a reduced equation. Let $y = u(x)$ and $y = v(x)$ be solutions and let C_1 and C_2 be constants. Is $y = w(x) = C_1 u(x)$ a solution? Is $y = z(x) = C_1 u(x) + C_2 v(x)$ a solution?

3. Prove this theorem.
   Theorem 5. Multiples of solutions of reduced first order linear equations.
   Hypothesis: (a) $y = u(x)$ is a solution of a reduced first order linear equation for x of interval I.
   (b) $w(x) = Cu(x)$ for x of I, with C a constant.
   Conclusion: $y = w(x)$ is also a solution of the reduced first order linear equation for x of interval I.

4. Return to Case (b) of the proof of Theorem 2. Show that $y = e^{\alpha x} \sin \beta x$, with $\alpha = -\frac{1}{2}r$ and $\beta = \frac{1}{2}\sqrt{4s - r^2}$, $4s - r^2 > 0$, is a solution of $y'' + ry' + sy = 0$.

5. Solve $y'' - a^2 y = 0$.

6. Find the solution of $y'' - .4y' = 0$ for which $y = 1$ and $y' = -1$ when $x = 0$.

7. Find the solution of $y'' - 2y' - 3y = 0$ for which $y = 1$, $y' = 0$ when $x = 1$.

8. Find the solution of $y'' + 3y' + 2y = 0$ for which $y = 1$ when $x = 0$ and $y = \frac{1}{2}$ when $x = 1$.

9. Find the solution of $y'' - 6y' + 9y = 0$ for which $y = 2$ and $y' = -1$ when $x = 2$.

10. Find the solution of $y'' + 2y' + y = 0$ for which $y = 1$ when $x = 0$ and $y = 1$ when $x = 1$.

11. Find the solution of $y'' + k^2 y = 0$ for which $y = y_0$ and $y' = y_0'$ when $x = 0$.

12. Find the solution of $y'' + k^2 y = 0$ for which $y = 0$ and $y' = 1$ when $x = \alpha$.

13. Find the solution of $y'' + k^2 y = 0$ for which $y = a$ when $x = 0$ and $y = b$ when $x = \alpha$, $k\alpha$ not an integer multiple of π.

14. Solve $2y'' - 6y' + 7y = 0$.

15. Solve $y'' + .1y' + .02y = 0$.

16. Find the solution of $y'' + 2y' + 2y = 0$ for which $y = 1$, $y' = 0$ when $x = 0$.

17. Find the solution of $y'' + .2y' + (.01 + 4\pi^2) y = 0$ for which $y = 0$, $y' = 1$ when $x = 0$.

18. Find a reduced linear equation with constant coefficients satisfied by (a) $y = 1$, (b) $y = x$, (c) $y = x^n$, n a positive integer.

19. Find a reduced linear equation with constant coefficients satisfied by (a) $y = e^{\alpha x}$, α a real constant, (b) $y = xe^{\alpha x}$.

20. (a) Find the reduced second order linear equation with constant coefficients satisfied by $y = 3e^{-.2x} \cos \pi x$.
    (b) Find the solution of this equation for which $y = 0$, $y' = 1$ when $x = 0$.

21. Find the reduced second order linear equation with constant coefficients satisfied by $y = .1e^{-x} \cos 2(x - \pi/3)$.

22. (a) Show that the functions $u(x) = x$ and $v(x) = |x|$ are linearly dependent on the interval $-3 \leq x \leq -1$.
    (b) Show that these functions are linearly independent on the interval $-1 \leq x \leq 1$.

23. (a) Show that $u(x) = e^{\alpha x}$ and $v(x) = e^{\beta x}$, $\alpha \neq \beta$, are linearly independent on the interval $0 \leq x \leq 1$.
    (b) The same for $u(x) = e^{\alpha x}$ and $v(x) = xe^{\alpha x}$.
    (c) The same for $u(x) = e^{\alpha x} \sin \beta x$ and $v(x) = e^{\alpha x} \cos \beta x$, $\beta \neq 0$.

14.9   Second Order Linear Equations. II

I

In the last section most of our detailed work was concerned with reduced linear equations. We start this section by explaining a strategy for solving second order linear equations that are not reduced.

■ THEOREM 1A

Solutions for general linear equations related to solutions for reduced equations.

HYPOTHESIS: (a) $y = w(x)$ is a solution of $y'' + Ry' + Sy = T$. (b) $y = q(x)$ is a solution of $y'' + Ry' + Sy = 0$.

CONCLUSION: $y = w(x) + q(x)$ is a solution of $y'' + Ry' + Sy = T$.

PROOF: The conclusion follows by direct substitution and application of the hypotheses:

$$(w + q)'' + R(w + q)' + S(w + q)$$
$$= (w'' + Rw' + Sw) + (q'' + Rq' + Sq)$$
$$= T + 0 = T.$$

To repeat, this theorem tells us that if we know one solution of a linear equation

$$y'' + Ry' + Sy = T, \tag{1}$$

call it $y = w(x)$, and also a solution of the corresponding reduced equation

$$y'' + Ry' + Sy = 0, \tag{2}$$

call it $y = q(x)$, then we know a new solution of the original Equation (1), namely, $y = w(x) + q(x)$. But can *all* solutions of Eq. (1) be obtained from one particular known solution by adding solutions of the corresponding reduced equation? To answer this question we prove a theorem converse to Theorem 1A.

■ THEOREM 1B

Solutions for general linear equations related to solutions for reduced equations.

HYPOTHESIS: $y = w(x)$ and $y = z(x)$ are solutions of $y'' + Ry' + Sy = T$.

CONCLUSION: $y = z(x) - w(x)$ is a solution of $y'' + Ry' + Sy = 0$.

PROOF: The proof follows by direct substitution and application of the hypothesis. Write $q(x) = z(x) - w(x)$ and compute

$$q'' + Rq' + Sq = (z - w)'' + R(z - w)' + S(z - w)$$
$$= (z'' + Rz' + Sz) - (w'' + Rw' + Sw)$$
$$= T - T = 0.$$

● **Remark 1**

   This theorem tells us that if we know one solution of Eq. (1), say $y = w(x)$, then for any other solution, say $y = z(x)$, we can write

$$z(x) = w(x) + q(x),$$

where $y = q(x)$ is some solution of the corresponding reduced equation (2), for we need only write

$$z(x) = w(x) + [z(x) - w(x)],$$

and the conclusion of Theorem 2 says that $y = z(x) - w(x)$ is a solution of Eq. (2). But Theorem 14.8-4 said that if $R(x)$ and $S(x)$ were continuous, and that if we knew two linearly independent solutions of Eq. (2), say $y = u(x)$ and $y = v(x)$, then *every* solution of Eq. (2) could be written in the form $y = C_1 u(x) + C_2 v(x)$ for suitably chosen constants C_1 and C_2. Hence the two theorems together say that, if we are asked to write *all* the solutions of a linear equation (1) with continuous coefficients $R(x)$ and $S(x)$, we should first find any two linearly independent solutions of the corresponding reduced equation (2), say $y = u(x)$ and $y = v(x)$, then any one particular solution of the original equation (1), say $y = w(x)$, and write

$$y = w(x) + C_1 u(x) + C_2 v(x).$$

Example 1.   We shall find all the solutions of

$$y'' + y' - 2y = 5 \sin x. \tag{3}$$

   First we consider the corresponding reduced equation

$$y'' + y' - 2y = 0. \tag{4}$$

This equation has constant coefficients. When we substitute $y = e^{mx}$, we find that the auxiliary algebraic equation is

$$m^2 + m - 2 = 0,$$

with solutions $m = 1$ and $m = -2$, so that every solution of Eq. (4) can be written in the form

$$y = C_1 e^x + C_2 e^{-2x}$$

with suitably chosen constants C_1 and C_2.

   Remark 1 tells us how to write all the solutions of Eq. (2), once one particular solution is known. We shall try next, then, to guess one particular solution. The right member of Eq. (3) suggests first that we try to choose the constant A in $y = A \sin x$ in such a way that $y = A \sin x$ will be one particular solution of Eq. (3). If we compute

$$y = A \sin x, \quad y' = A \cos x, \quad y'' = -A \sin x$$

and substitute in Eq. (3) we find that we must choose A so that

$$(-A \sin x) + (A \cos x) - 2(A \sin x) = 5 \sin x$$

or, by collecting like terms,

$$(-3A - 5) \sin x + A \cos x = 0.$$

We cannot choose A in such a way that the coefficients of both terms will vanish, $-3A - 5 = 0$ and $A = 0$, and we failed in this first attempt to guess one particular solution. We failed because we did not take into account the fact that a $\cos x$ term would appear as soon as we differentiated $A \sin x$ in order to substitute; we would like to have coefficients of *two* terms vanish and this will require the determining of *two* constants in general.

Hence on our second attempt we try to choose constants A and B in such a way that $y = A \sin x + B \cos x$ will be one particular solution of Eq. (3). If we compute

$$y = A \sin x + B \cos x, \quad y' = A \cos x - B \sin x,$$

$$y'' = -A \sin x - B \cos x$$

and substitute in Eq (4) we find that we must choose A and B so that

$$(-A \sin x - B \cos x) + (A \cos x - B \sin x)$$

$$-2(A \sin x + B \cos x) = 5 \sin x,$$

or, by collecting like terms, so that

$$(-3A - B - 5) \sin x + (A - 3B) \cos x = 0.$$

But we can choose A and B such that

$$-3A - B - 5 = 0, \qquad A - 3B = 0;$$

indeed, we need only choose $A = -\tfrac{3}{2}$, $B = -\tfrac{1}{2}$. Thus we see that

$$y = -\tfrac{3}{2} \sin x - \tfrac{1}{2} \cos x$$

is one solution of Eq. (3), and then Remark 1 tells us that all the solutions of Eq. (3) can be written in the form

$$y = -\tfrac{3}{2} \sin x - \tfrac{1}{2} \cos x + C_1 e^x + C_2 e^{-2x}.$$

Example 2.   We shall find the solution of

$$y'' + y' - 2y = 2x^2 - 2x \tag{5}$$

for which $y = 0$ and $y' = 0$ when $x = 0$.

First we consider the corresponding reduced equation

$$y'' + y' - 2y = 0 \tag{4}$$

and find its solutions

$$y = C_1 e^x + C_2 e^{-2x},$$

as in Example 1. Then, to guess one particular solution of Eq. (5) we study the right member of that equation. The derivatives of x^2 and x will appear if we substitute $y = Ax^2 + Bx$ in Eq. (5), and these derivatives will include constant terms. Hence we try to determine constant coefficients A, B, and C such that $y = Ax^2 + Bx + C$ is a solution of Eq. (5). We compute

$$y = Ax^2 + Bx + C, \quad y' = 2Ax + B, \quad y'' = 2A,$$

and when we substitute we get

$$(2A) + (2Ax + B) - 2(Ax^2 + Bx + C) = 2x^2 - 2x,$$

or, by collecting like terms,

$$(-2A - 2)x^2 + (2A - 2B + 2)x + (2A + B - 2C) = 0.$$

But we can choose A, B, C such that

$$-2A - 2 = 0, \quad 2A - 2B + 2 = 0, \quad 2A + B - 2C = 0;$$

indeed, we can take $A = -1$, $B = 0$, $C = -1$. Thus we see that

$$y = -x^2 - 1$$

is one solution of Eq. (5). Then Remark 1 tells us that any solution can be written in the form

$$y = -x^2 - 1 + C_1 e^x + C_2 e^{-2x} \tag{6}$$

with the proper choice of C_1 and C_2. Since we want $y = 0$ and $y' = 0$ when $x = 0$, we differentiate in Eq. (6) to get

$$y' = -2x + C_1 e^x - 2C_2 e^{-2x}, \tag{7}$$

and then, in Eqs. (6) and (7) we must choose C_1 and C_2 so that

$$0 = 0 - 1 + C_1 + C_2$$

$$0 = 0 + C_1 - 2C_2.$$

Solving, we find that $C_1 = \frac{2}{3}$, $C_2 = \frac{1}{3}$. The solution of Eq. (5) that we seek is

$$y = -x^2 - 1 + \frac{2}{3} e^x + \frac{1}{3} e^{-2x}.$$

Example 3. Let us find the solutions of

$$y'' + k^2 y = \sin kx. \tag{8}$$

First we consider the corresponding reduced equation

$$y'' + k^2 y = 0. \tag{8a}$$

If we substitute $y = e^{mx}$, we are led to the auxiliary algebraic equation

$$m^2 + k^2 = 0$$

with complex conjugate solutions $m = \pm ki$. As we saw in the last section, the solutions of Eq. (8a) are then

$$y = C_1 \cos kx + C_2 \sin kx.$$

Because the right member of Eq. (8) is $\sin kx$ and the first two derivatives of $\sin kx$ are multiples of $\cos kx$ and $\sin kx$ itself, it might seem feasible at first to try to determine coefficients A and B in $y = A \sin kx + B \cos kx$ in such a way as to obtain a solution of Eq. (8). We compute

$$y = A \sin kx + B \cos kx, \quad y' = kA \cos kx - kB \sin kx,$$

$$y'' = -k^2 A \sin kx - k^2 B \cos kx$$

and substitute, finding that A and B must be such that

$$(-k^2 A \sin kx - k^2 B \cos kx) + k^2(A \sin kx + B \cos kx) = \sin kx$$

or, by collecting like terms, such that

$$0 = \sin kx.$$

It is not possible to determine coefficients A and B in such a way that $y = A \sin kx + B \cos kx$ will be a solution of Eq. (8).

The difficulty encountered in this first attempt to find one particular solution of Eq. (8) arose from the fact that our trial solution was a solution of the corresponding reduced equation (8a). When we computed the left member of Eq. (8) for that trial solution, we should have expected that the left member would be 0 and we should have realized that it would then be impossible to satisfy an equation like Eq. (8) whose right member is not 0. The term $x \sin kx$, however, is not a solution of Eq. (8a), and is about as simple a term whose derivative includes the term $\sin kx$ as one could guess. The derivatives of $x \sin kx$ will also include multiples of $x \cos kx$ and $\cos kx$, and for a second attempt we can try to determine coefficients A and B in such a way that $y = Ax \sin kx + Bx \cos kx$ will be a solution of Eq. (8). We no longer attempt to use multiples of $\sin kx$ and $\cos kx$, because multiples of solutions of the reduced equation (8a) will contribute 0 in the computation of the left member of the original equation (8).

We compute

$$y = Ax \sin kx + Bx \cos kx$$

$$y' = kAx \cos kx + A \sin kx - kBx \sin kx + B \cos kx$$

$$y'' = -k^2 Ax \sin kx + 2kA \cos kx - k^2 Bx \cos kx - 2kB \sin kx,$$

and then upon substitution in Eq. (8) we find that A and B must be chosen so that

$$(-k^2 Ax \sin kx + 2kA \cos kx - k^2 Bx \cos kx - 2kB \sin kx)$$

$$+ k^2(Ax \sin kx + Bx \cos kx) = \sin kx$$

or, by collecting like terms, so that

$$(-2kB - 1) \sin kx + 2kA \cos kx = 0.$$

We can choose A and B so that

$$-2kB - 1 = 0, \qquad 2kA = 0;$$

we choose $A = 0$ and $B = -1/2k$. Thus we find that

$$y = -\frac{1}{2k} x \cos kx$$

is one particular solution of Eq. (8) and that all solutions of Eq. (8) are included in the set

$$y = -\frac{1}{2k} x \cos kx + C_1 \cos kx + C_2 \sin kx.$$

‖

● **Remark 2**

In Example 3 we were led to consider $x \sin kx$ for a term of the trial particular solution of Eq. (8), because $x \sin kx$ is about as simple a function as one could guess whose derivatives would include terms that were multiples of $\sin kx$. In greater generality, in the very special case where $y = u(x)$ is a solution of

$$y'' + ry' + sy = 0, \qquad r \text{ and } s \text{ constants}, \tag{9}$$

and we have to try to find one particular solution of

$$y'' + ry' + sy = x^n u(x), \tag{10}$$

it is futile to include a multiple of $u(x)$ as a term of the trial solution. But if we consider $y = x^k u(x)$, we compute

$$y = x^k\, u(x), \quad y' = kx^{k-1}\, u(x) + x^k u'(x),$$

$$y'' = k(k-1)x^{k-2}\, u(x) + 2kx^{k-1}\, u'(x) + x^k u''(x)$$

and

$$y'' + ry' + sy = [k(k-1)x^{k-2}u + 2kx^{k-1}\, u' + x^k u''] + r[kx^{k-1}u + x^k u'] + s[x^k u]$$

$$y'' + ry' + sy = x^k(u'' + ru' + su) + kx^{k-1}(2u' + ru) + k(k-1)x^{k-2}u$$

$$y'' + ry' + sy = kx^{k-1}(2u' + ru) + k(k-1)x^{k-2}u, \tag{11}$$

taking into account at the last step the fact that $u'' + ru' + su = 0$.

We saw in Theorem 14.8-2 that a reduced equation with constant coefficients, like Eq. (9), has solutions of three types according as $r^2 - 4s > 0, < 0, = 0$. The reader can show by direct computation in Exercise 14.9-8 that in the cases $r^2 - 4s > 0$ and $r^2 - 4s < 0$ we can take $k = n + 1$ in Eq. (11); $y'' + ry' + sy$ with $y = x^{n+1}u(x)$, $n \neq -1$, will contain a term that is a multiple of $x^n u(x)$. In Exercise 14.9-12, the reader can show that, in the case $r^2 - 4s = 0$, one must take $k = n + 2$ in Eq. (11) and use $y = x^{n+2}u(x)$, $n \neq -1, -2$, if $y'' + ry' + sy$ is to contain a term that is a multiple of $x^n u(x)$. Of course, when composing a trial particular solution for Eq. (10) one must also take the derivatives of the trial terms into account, but not $u(x)$ itself.

Example 4. We shall find the solutions of

$$y'' + y' - 2y = xe^x. \tag{12}$$

First we consider the corresponding reduced equation

$$y'' + y' - 2y = 0$$

whose solutions were determined in Example 1 to be

$$y = C_1 e^x + C_2 e^{-2x}.$$

Because $y = e^x$ is a solution of the reduced equation and the right member of Eq. (12) is of the form $x^n e^x$, the computation of Eq. (11) and the comment that follows suggest that we try to determine coefficients A and B of $y = Ax^2e^x + Bxe^x$ in working out a trial solution of Eq. (12). We compute

$$y = Ax^2e^x + Bxe^x, \qquad y' = Ax^2e^x + (2A + B)xe^x + Be^x,$$

$$y'' = Ax^2e^x + (4A + B)xe^x + (2A + 2B)e^x$$

and then substitute into Eq. (12) to get

$$[Ax^2e^x + (4A + B)xe^x + (2A + 2B)e^x]$$
$$+ [Ax^2e^x + (2A + B)xe^x + Be^x] - 2[Ax^2e^x + Bxe^x] = xe^x,$$

or, by collecting like terms, we find that

$$0x^2e^x + (6A - 1)xe^x + (2A + 3B)e^x = 0.$$

We can determine A and B so that

$$6A - 1 = 0, \qquad 2A + 3B = 0;$$

we choose $A = \frac{1}{6}$ and $B = -\frac{1}{9}$. Hence one particular solution of Eq. (12) is

$$y = \frac{1}{6}x^2\,e^x - \frac{1}{9}xe^x$$

and all the solutions of Eq. (12) are included in the set

$$y = \frac{1}{6}x^2\,e^x - \frac{1}{9}xe^x + C_1e^x + C_2e^{-2x}.$$

III

In Examples 1, 2, 3, and 4 thus far considered we limited ourselves to linear equations with constant coefficients and, even further, to equations whose right members were of an especially simple type. The method of "undetermined coefficients" we used in these examples could not be applied, for instance, to the equation

$$(\sin^2 x)y'' - (3 \sin x \cos x)y' + (1 + 2 \cos^2 x)y = \cos x,$$

which does not have constant coefficients. It could not be applied either, to the equation

$$y'' + k^2 y = \tan kx,$$

which has constant coefficients but a right member that, upon substitution in the equation, would lead us to multiples of infinitely many terms. For, if we try $y = A \tan kx$, we shall be led to multiples of $y'' = 2Ak^2 \sec^2 kx \tan kx$ also; if we try $y = A \tan kx + B \sec^2 kx \tan kx$, we will be led to still more complicated terms, and so on.

An idea we have already used fruitfully in the exposition of Theorem 14.8-2, and which we shall use here in a little more general context, is the idea of "varying" one solution of the reduced equation already known to find all the solutions of the original equation. Theorem 2, which follows, explains how this can be done, in theory at least.

▪ THEOREM 2

Reducing the solution of a second order equation to the solution of a first order equation.

HYPOTHESIS: $y = u(x)$ is a solution of $y'' + R(x)y' + S(x)y = 0$.

CONCLUSION: The determination of $w(x)$ such that $y = w(x)u(x)$ is a solution of $y'' + R(x)y' + S(x)y = T(x)$ can be reduced to the solution of a first order linear equation.

PROOF: We compute, straightforwardly, that

$$y = wu, \quad y' = w'u + wu', \quad y'' = w''u + 2w'u' + wu''$$

and, upon substitution, that $w(x)$ must be such that

$$(w''u + 2w'u' + wu'') + R(w'u + wu') + Swu = T,$$

$$uw'' + (2u' + Ru)w' + (u'' + Ru' + Su)w = T,$$

$$uw'' + (2u' + Ru)w' = T, \tag{13}$$

using the hypothesis of the theorem at the last step. Now if we write $w' = p$, as we did in Theorem 14.7-1, Eq. (13) becomes

$$up' + (2u' + Ru)p = T.$$

Here we have a first order linear equation for p which we can solve according to the ideas of Sec. 14.5, although the actual details of formal integration may be formidable. Once p was determined, we could work our way back to w by another integration because $w' = p$, again provided that we can carry out the details of formal integration.

Example 5. We shall find the solutions of

$$(\sin^2 x)y'' - (3 \sin x \cos x)y' + (1 + 2 \cos^2 x)y = \cos x. \tag{14}$$

First we consider the corresponding reduced equation

$$(\sin^2 x)y'' - (3 \sin x \cos x)y' + (1 + 2 \cos^2 x)y = 0.$$

We have no set method for solving this equation, because the coefficients are not constants; we are reduced to guessing. The coefficients suggest that $y = \sin x$ and $y = \cos x$ might be reasonable first guesses, and, fortunately, $y = \sin x$ is a solution, as the reader can easily verify; $y = \cos x$ is not a solution.

Theorem 2 suggests that we try to "vary" the solution $y = \sin x$ by looking for a function $w(x)$ such that $y = w(x) \sin x$ will be a solution of Eq. (14). We compute

$$y = w \sin x, \quad y' = w' \sin x + w \cos x$$

$$y'' = w'' \sin x + 2w' \cos x - w \sin x.$$

If we substitute in Eq. (14) we see that $w(x)$ must be chosen so that

$$\sin^2 x(w'' \sin x + 2w' \cos x - w \sin x) - 3 \sin x \cos x(w' \sin x + w \cos x)$$
$$+ (1 + 2 \cos^2 x)w \sin x = \cos x,$$

$$\sin^3 x \, w'' - \sin^2 x \cos x \, w' + (- \sin^3 x - \sin x \cos^2 x + \sin x)w = \cos x,$$

$$\sin^3 x \, w'' - \sin^2 x \cos x \, w' = \cos x.$$

If we write $w' = p$, we find that p must be chosen so that

$$\sin^3 x \, p' - \sin^2 x \cos x \, p = \cos x;$$

we must solve a first order linear equation, as predicted by Theorem 2. We divide by $\sin^3 x$

$$p' - \frac{\cos x}{\sin x} p = \frac{\cos x}{\sin^3 x}$$

and then choose $I(x) = e^{-\log \sin x} = 1/\sin x$ as the integrating factor;

$$\frac{1}{\sin x} p' - \frac{\cos x}{\sin^2 x} p = \frac{\cos x}{\sin^4 x}$$

$$\frac{1}{\sin x} p = - \frac{1}{3} \frac{1}{\sin^3 x} + C_1$$

$$w' = p = - \tfrac{1}{3} \csc^2 x + C_1 \sin x$$

$$w = \tfrac{1}{3} \cot x - C_1 \cos x + C_2.$$

The solution of Eq. (14) can be written

$$y = w \sin x = \tfrac{1}{3} \cos x - C_1 \sin x \cos x + C_2 \sin x,$$

or, replacing C_1 by $-C_3$, we obtain

$$y = \tfrac{1}{3} \cos x + C_3 \sin x \cos x + C_2 \sin x.$$

IV

Theorem 2 explained how we could take advantage of knowledge of one solution of the reduced equation. If we know two linearly independent solutions of the reduced equation we can "vary" a linear combination of the two solutions and reduce the solution of the original linear equation to two formal integrations. The method is often called Lagrange's method.

■ THEOREM 3

Lagrange's method.

HYPOTHESIS: $y = u(x)$ and $y = v(x)$ are linearly independent solutions of $y'' + R(x)y' + S(x)y = 0$.

CONCLUSION: The determination of $w_1(x)$ and $w_2(x)$ such that $y = w_1(x)u(x) + w_2(x)v(x)$ is a solution of $y'' + R(x)y' + S(x)y = T(x)$ can be reduced to two formal integrations.

PROOF: If we substitute $y = w_1u + w_2v$ into the equation whose solution we seek we shall have one requirement to be met by w_1 and w_2. Since the two functions w_1 and w_2 can be expected in general to meet two requirements, we are free to impose a second requirement on w_1 and w_2 as we work along.

We compute, to start with,

$$y = w_1u + w_2v$$

$$y' = w_1u' + w_2v' + (w_1{}'u + w_2{}'v).$$

It turns out to be convenient to choose

$$w_1'u + w_2'v = 0 \tag{15}$$

as our second requirement on w_1 and w_2. This simplifies our statement for y' to

$$y' = w_1u' + w_2v',$$

and enables us to go on to

$$y'' = w_1u'' + w_2v'' + w_1'u' + w_2'v'.$$

Substitution in the equation to be solved yields

$$y'' + Ry' + Sy = T$$

$$(w_1u'' + w_2v'' + w_1'u' + w_2'v') + R(w_1u' + w_2v')$$

$$S(w_1u + w_2v) = T,$$

$$w_1'u' + w_2'v' + w_1(u'' + Ru' + Su) + w_2(v'' + Rv' + Sv) = T,$$

and, finally, using the fact that $y = u(x)$ and $y = v(x)$ are solutions of the corresponding reduced equation by hypothesis,

$$w_1'u' + w_2'v' = T. \tag{16}$$

Equations (15) and (16) can be regarded as two algebraic equations for the two unknowns w_1' and w_2'. They are easily solved, by determinants perhaps, or by solving for one of w_1', w_2' in Eq. (15) and substituting in Eq. (16). The solutions are

$$w_1' = -\frac{Tv}{uv' - u'v}, \qquad w_2' = \frac{Tu}{uv' - u'v}. \tag{17}$$

Observe that Step (4) of the proof of Theorem 14.8-4 explains that the Wronskian, $uv' - u'v$, cannot vanish, and thus that the solutions written in Eqs. (17) are valid. From Eqs. (17) we arrive at w_1 and w_2 by two formal integrations, often not easy to carry out, however, and then we can write the solution $y = w_1u + w_2v$ we seek.

Example 6. We shall find the solutions of

$$y'' + k^2y = \tan kx. \tag{18}$$

First we write down the corresponding reduced equation

$$y'' + k^2y = 0; \tag{8a}$$

two linearly independent solutions are $y = \cos x$ and $y = \sin x$, as we saw in Example 3. Lagrange's method suggests next that we look for functions $w_1(x)$ and $w_2(x)$ such that

$$y = w_1 \cos kx + w_2 \sin kx$$

shall be a solution of Eq. (18). We compute

$$y' = -kw_1 \sin kx + kw_2 \cos kx + (w_1' \cos kx + w_2' \sin kx)$$

or, if we set

$$w_1' \cos kx + w_2' \sin kx = 0, \tag{19}$$

$$y' = -kw_1 \sin kx + kw_2 \cos kx.$$

Then

$$y'' = -k^2w_1 \cos kx - k^2w_2 \sin kx - kw_1' \sin kx + kw_2' \cos kx,$$

and Eq. (18) becomes

$$(-k^2w_1 \cos kx - k^2w_2 \sin kx - kw_1' \sin kx + kw_2' \cos kx)$$

$$+ k^2(w_1 \cos kx + w_2 \sin kx) = \tan kx$$

or

$$-kw_1' \sin kx + kw_2' \cos kx = \tan kx. \tag{20}$$

Equations (19) and (20) can be solved algebraically for w_1' and w_2'. Indeed, we can solve for w_1' in Eq. (19) and substitute in Eq. (20) to get

$$w_1' = -\frac{\sin kx}{\cos kx} w_2'$$

$$k \frac{\sin^2 kx}{\cos kx} w_2' + k \cos kx \, w_2' = \tan kx,$$

$$w_2' = \frac{1}{k} \sin kx, \qquad w_1' = -\frac{1}{k} \frac{\sin^2 kx}{\cos kx}.$$

But now we can find suitable w_1 and w_2;

$$w_2 = \frac{1}{k} \int \sin kx \, dx = -\frac{1}{k^2} \cos kx$$

$$w_1 = -\frac{1}{k} \int \frac{\sin^2 kx}{\cos kx} \, dx = -\frac{1}{k} \int \frac{1 - \cos^2 kx}{\cos kx} \, dx$$

$$= -\frac{1}{k} \int (\sec kx - \cos kx) \, dx$$

$$= -\frac{1}{k^2} \log (\sec kx + \tan kx) + \frac{1}{k^2} \sin kx.$$

One particular solution of Eq. (18) is

$$y = w_1 \cos kx + w_2 \sin kx$$

$$y = -\frac{1}{k^2} \cos kx \log (\sec kx + \tan kx) + \frac{1}{k^2} \sin kx \cos kx - \frac{1}{k^2} \cos kx \sin kx,$$

$$y = -\frac{1}{k^2} \cos kx \log (\sec kx + \tan kx).$$

All the solutions of Eq. (18) can be written in the form

$$y = -\frac{1}{k^2} \cos kx \log (\sec kx + \tan kx) + C_1 \cos kx + C_2 \sin kx.$$

EXERCISES 14.9

1. Find the solution of $y'' + k^2 y = 2$ for which $y = y_0$ and $y' = y_0'$ when $x = 0$.
2. Solve $y'' + k^2 y = x^2 + 2$.
3. Solve $y'' + y' - 2y = 4e^{-x}$.
4. Solve $2y'' + 6y' + 5y = 10$.
5. Solve $2y'' + 6y' + 5y = 13 \cos \frac{1}{2} x$.
6. Solve $y'' + 2ay' + a^2 y = 3x$.
7. Find the solution of $y'' + 2ay' + a^2 y = e^{bx}$, $b \neq -a$, for which $y = 0$ and $y' = 0$ when $x = 0$.
8. Let $u(x)$ be such that $u'' + ru' + su = 0$. We stated in Eq. (11) that, if $y = x^k u$, then $y'' + ry' + sy = kx^{k-1} (2u' + ru) + k(k - 1)x^{k-2}u$.
   (a) We know that, if $r^2 - 4s > 0$, then we can take $u = e^{mx}$, with $m = \frac{1}{2}(-r \pm \sqrt{r^2 - 4s})$. Compute $kx^{k-1} (2u' + ru)$ for $u = e^{mx}$ and show that $y'' + ry' + sy$ will contain a multiple of $x^n u$, $n \neq -1$, if we choose $y = x^k u$ with $k = n + 1$.
   (b) We know that, if $r^2 - 4s < 0$, then we can take $u = e^{\alpha x} \cos \beta x$ or $u = e^{\alpha x} \sin \beta x$ with $\alpha = -(r/2)$, $\beta = \frac{1}{2}\sqrt{4s - r^2}$. Compute $kx^{k-1} (2u' + ru)$ for $u = e^{\alpha x} \cos \beta x$ and $u = e^{\alpha x} \sin \beta x$; show that $y'' + ry' + sy$ will contain multiples of $x^n e^{\alpha x} \cos \beta x$ and $x^n e^{\alpha x} \sin \beta x$, $n \neq -1$, if we choose $y = Ax^k e^{\alpha x} \cos \beta x + Bx^k e^{\alpha x} \sin \beta x$ with $k = n + 1$.
9. Find the solution of $y'' + y' - 2y = 3e^{-2x}$ for which $y = 1$ and $y' = 0$ when $x = 0$.
10. Solve $y'' + y' - 2y = x^2 e^x$.
11. Solve $y'' + k^2 y = 4x \sin kx$.
12. Return again to Eq. (11) where we showed that, if $y = x^k u$ where $u'' + ru' + su = 0$, then $y'' + ry' + sy = kx^{k-1} (2u' + ru) + k(k - 1)x^{k-2}u$. This time take the case where $r^2 - 4s = 0$ or $s = \frac{1}{4} r^2$ so that the two solutions of $y'' + ry' + \frac{1}{4}r^2 y = 0$ are $y = e^{-(r/2)x}$ and $y = xe^{-(r/2)x}$. Compute $kx^{k-1} (2u' + ru) + k(k - 1)x^{k-2}u$ for $u = e^{-(r/2)x}$ and show that $y'' + ry' + sy$ will contain a multiple of $x^n u$, $n \neq -2$ and $n \neq -1$, if we choose $y = x^k u$ with $k = n + 2$.
13. Solve $y'' + 2ay' + a^2 y = 3xe^{-ax}$.
14. Consider again an equation $y'' + ry' + sy = T(x)$ with constant coefficients whose right member is a solution of the reduced equation or such a solution multiplied by a power of x. Remark 2, amplified by Exercises 8 and 12, explains that one must use slightly different trial forms in trying to guess one particular solution, according as the roots of the algebraic equation $m^2 + rm + s = 0$ are distinct or not distinct. This makes it harder to remember the "undetermined coefficients" procedure. One can treat the case of nondistinct roots, however, rather easily by "varying" the one exponential solution that arises in this case.

(a) Determine $w(x)$ such that $y = w(x)e^{-ax}$ is a solution of $y'' + 2ay' + a^2y = 3xe^{-ax}$ and thus solve Exercise 13 again.

(b) Solve $y'' + 2ay' + a^2y = bx^ne^{-ax}$ by determining $w(x)$ such that $y = w(x)e^{-ax}$ shall be a solution.

15. Solve the equation of Exercise 10 by determining $w(x)$ such that $y = we^x$ shall be a solution.

16. Solve $x^2y'' + xy' - y = x^4$. *Suggestion* 1: Determine two solutions of the reduced equation by substituting $y = x^m$ in the reduced equation; then "vary" one of these solutions. *Suggestion* 2: Use Lagrange's method.

17. Show that $y = \cos x$ is a solution of $\cos^2 x\,y'' + \sin x \cos x\,y' + y = 0$. Then find all the solutions.

18. Consider $\sin^2 x\,y'' - \sin x \cos x\,y' + y = \sin^3x$. Show that $y = \sin x$ is a solution of the reduced equation. Find all the solutions of the original equation.

19. Consider $4x^2 (x + 1)\,y'' + 4x^2y' + (1 - x)\,y = 0$. Find one solution of the form $y = x^m$. Find all the solutions.

20. Consider $4x^2y'' + 8x^3y' + (4x^2 - 3)y = 4x^{7/2}$. Find one solution of the reduced equation in the form $y = x^m$. Then find all the solutions of the original equation.

21. Solve $y'' + k^2y = \sec kx$.

22. Solve $x^2y'' - 2xy' + 2y = \log x$.
    Suggestion: First find two solutions of the reduced equation of the form $y = x^m$.

23. Solve $y'' - (\tan x)y' - (\sec^2 x)y = \sec x$.
    Suggestion: First show that $y = \tan x$ and $y = \sec x$ are solutions of the reduced equation.

24. Solve $(x - 1)y'' - xy' + y = (x - 1)^2$.
    Suggestion: Find one solution of the reduced equation in the form $y = x^m$ and one in the form $y = e^{mx}$.

25. Solve $(x^2 + 2x)y'' - 2(x + 1)y' + 2y = (x + 2)^2$.
    Suggestion: Find one solution of the reduced equation in the form $y = x^m$ and one in the form $y = x + m$.

26. Prove this theorem.
    Theorem 4.
    Hypothesis: (a) $y = z_1(x)$ is a solution of $y'' + Ry' + Sy = T_1$.
               (b) $y = z_2(x)$ is a solution of $y'' + Ry' + Sy = T_2$.
    Conclusion: $y = z_1(x) + z_2(x)$ is a solution of $y'' + Ry' + Sy = T_1 + T_2$.
        This theorem enables one to assemble one particular solution for a more complex equation from particular solutions for simpler equations.

27. Solve $y'' + k^2y = x + \tan kx$.

28. Let $y = u(x)$ be a solution of $y'' + Ry' + Sy = 0$. Determine $w(x)$ such that $y = wu$ will be a second solution and thus show that $y = u\left[\displaystyle\int \frac{e^{-\int R\,dx}}{u^2}\,dx\right]$ is a second solution.

14.10   Linear Equations with Constant Coefficients. Some Applications

I

    Consider an object of mass m in equilibrium position at the end of a helical spring, as in Fig. 14.12(a). If this object is displaced a distance x from equilibrium, as in Fig. 14.12(b), and if we accept Hooke's Law for such displacements, then we know that there is a restoring force proportional to the displacement and oppositely directed. We can write

$$F_1 = -kx \qquad (1)$$

for this restoring force, where k is a constant of proportionality which will depend on the physical properties of the spring. On the other hand, we can also write

$$F_1 = ma = m\frac{d^2x}{dt^2} \qquad (2)$$

for the motion of the object of mass m. From Eqs. (1) and (2) we are led to the differential equation

$$m\frac{d^2x}{dt^2} + kx = 0 \qquad (3)$$

to describe the motion when only a restoring force is taken into account.

The solutions of Eq. (3) can all be written in the form

$$x = C_1 \cos\sqrt{\frac{k}{m}}t + C_2 \sin\sqrt{\frac{k}{m}}t, \qquad (4)$$

as we saw in Sec. 14.8. From this equation we conclude that the object at the end of the spring will move in simple harmonic motion with period $2\pi\sqrt{m/k}$; see Example 4.2-5. The stiffer the spring, the greater the k, and then the shorter the period and the greater the frequency.

If we take friction into account also and assume that the frictional force is proportional to the velocity and oppositely directed, then we have

$$F_2 = -nv = -n\frac{dx}{dt} \qquad (5)$$

for this frictional force, where n is a physical constant that depends on the shape of the moving object, the nature of its surface, and the properties of the medium through which it moves. Now we have

$$F_1 + F_2 = ma = m\frac{d^2x}{dt^2}, \qquad (6)$$

and from Eqs. (1), (5), and (6) we are led to the differential equation

$$m\frac{d^2x}{dt^2} + n\frac{dx}{dt} + kx = 0 \qquad (7)$$

to describe the motion.

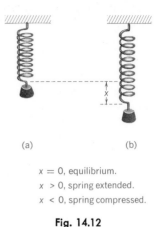

(a)   (b)

$x = 0$, equilibrium.

$x > 0$, spring extended.

$x < 0$, spring compressed.

Fig. 14.12

To find the solutions of Eq. (7) we write $x = e^{rt}$ and consider the auxiliary algebraic equation

$$mr^2 + nr + k = 0. \tag{7a}$$

Here we know that three cases must be considered.

Take first the case where the discriminant of the quadratic equation is negative, or $n^2 - 4mk < 0$, $n^2 < 4mk$. The solutions of Eq. (7a) are

$$r = \frac{-n \pm \sqrt{n^2 - 4mk}}{2m} = -\frac{n}{2m} \pm i\sqrt{\frac{k}{m} - \frac{n^2}{4m^2}},$$

and the solutions for Eq. (7) are

$$x = e^{-(n/2m)t}\left(C_1 \cos\sqrt{\frac{k}{m} - \frac{n^2}{4m^2}}\,t + C_2 \sin\sqrt{\frac{k}{m} - \frac{n^2}{4m^2}}\,t\right). \tag{8}$$

As we pointed out in Example 5.4-4, Eq. (8) represents a damped harmonic motion. If $n^2 < 4mk$, or, in words, if the frictional constant n is small enough, Eq. (8) applies and says that the object will move alternately from one side of the equilibrium position to the other, completing one cycle in the time $2\pi/\sqrt{(k/m) - (n^2/4m^2)}$, but that the motion will gradually damp out (because of energy losses to friction), the damping being governed by the exponential factor $e^{-(n/2m)t}$. If n is negligible and taken to be 0, Eq. (8) reduces to Eq. (4); we have the simple harmonic motion case. As n increases, approaching $\sqrt{4mk}$, the time required for one cycle increases and the damping takes place more quickly.

The second and third cases to consider in studying Eq. (7a) are the cases in which the discriminant is 0 and positive, the cases in which $n^2 = 4mk$ and $n^2 > 4mk$. The reader can show in Exercises 14.10-2 and 14.10-3 that, if $n \geq \sqrt{4mk}$, and if the motion starts by displacing the object to one side of the equilibrium position, the object will move steadily back to the equilibrium position but not go past it.

If we take into account not only the restoring force of the spring and the frictional force already considered but also an external force, $F_3(t)$, then the differential equation for the motion is

$$F_1 + F_2 + F_3 = ma,$$

or

$$m\frac{d^2x}{dt^2} + n\frac{dx}{dt} + kx = F_3(t). \tag{9}$$

A very important case is the one in which the external force is periodic. To take as simple a periodic case as possible, consider the case where $F_3(t) = a \sin bt$, so that Eq. (9) becomes

$$m\frac{d^2x}{dt^2} + n\frac{dx}{dt} + kx = a \sin bt. \tag{9a}$$

We know that the solutions of the corresponding reduced equation are those written in Eq. (8) in the case in which $n^2 < 4mk$. To get one particular solution of Eq. (9a) we take the term $\sin bt$ of the right member into account, together with the term cos bt which will arise from it upon differentiation, and try to determine coefficients A and B in such a way that $x = A \sin bt + B \cos bt$ will be a solution. If we substitute in Eq. (9a), we find that A and B must be chosen so that

$$m(-Ab^2 \sin bt - Bb^2 \cos bt) + n(bA \cos bt - Bb \sin bt)$$

$$+ k(A \sin bt + B \cos bt) = a \sin bt,$$

or, upon collecting sin bt and cos bt terms and setting coefficients to 0, A and B must be chosen so that

$$\begin{cases} -mAb^2 - nBb + kA = a \\ -mBb^2 + nAb + kB = 0 \end{cases}$$

$$\begin{cases} (k - mb^2)A - nbB = a \\ nbA + (k - mb^2)B = 0. \end{cases}$$

Solving for the unknowns A and B, we find that we must choose

$$A = \frac{a(k - mb^2)}{(k - mb^2)^2 + n^2b^2}, \qquad B = -\frac{anb}{(k - mb^2)^2 + n^2b^2};$$

one particular solution of Eq. (9a) is

$$x = \frac{a}{(k - mb^2)^2 + n^2b^2} [(k - mb^2) \sin bt - nb \cos bt].$$

With the help of a trigonometric identity we can rewrite this solution in the forms

$$x = \frac{a}{\sqrt{(k - mb^2)^2 + n^2b^2}} \left[\frac{k - mb^2}{\sqrt{(k - mb^2)^2 + n^2b^2}} \sin bt \right.$$

$$\left. - \frac{nb}{\sqrt{(k - mb^2)^2 + n^2b^2}} \cos bt \right]$$

$$x = \frac{a}{\sqrt{(k - mb^2)^2 + n^2b^2}} [\sin bt \cos \alpha - \cos bt \sin \alpha]$$

$$x = \frac{a}{\sqrt{(k - mb^2)^2 + n^2b^2}} \sin (bt - \alpha),$$

where

$$\cos \alpha = \frac{k - mb^2}{\sqrt{(k - mb^2)^2 + n^2b^2}}, \quad \sin \alpha = \frac{nb}{\sqrt{(k - mb^2)^2 + n^2b^2}}.$$

Finally, all the solutions of Eq. (9a) are included in the set

$$x = \frac{a}{\sqrt{(k - mb^2)^2 + n^2b^2}} \sin (bt - \alpha)$$

$$+ e^{-(n/2m)t} \left[C_1 \cos \sqrt{\frac{k}{m} - \frac{n^2}{4m^2}} t + C_2 \sin \sqrt{\frac{k}{m} - \frac{n^2}{4m^2}} t \right] \tag{10}$$

in the case where $n^2 < 4mk$.

The second term of the right member of Eq. (10) will damp out because of the factor $e^{-(n/2m)t}$, and the damping will take place more or less quickly according as $n/2m$ is relatively large or small. Because it dies away, this part of the solution is called the "transient" part. The first term of the right member of Eq. (10) represents a simple harmonic motion of exactly the same period as the external force $F_3 = a \sin bt$ and with amplitude given by the formula

$$\text{amplitude} = \frac{a}{\sqrt{(k - mb^2)^2 + n^2 b^2}}. \tag{11}$$

This part of the solution is called the "steady state" part because it does not damp out as t increases, but remains. It is clear from Eq. (11) that the larger the amplitude a of the external force F_3, the larger the amplitude of the steady state response. It is also clear that the amplitude of the response is a function of b, and thus takes on different values for external forces of different periods and frequencies. In Exercises 14.10-5, 14.10-6 and 14.10-7 the reader can determine which frequency for the external force leads to maximum amplitude for the steady state response. This is the beginning of the study of the phenomenon known as resonance.

II

The theory of electrical circuits offers a rather striking analogue to the theory of springs just discussed. The fact that two different physical phenomena have the same mathematical description makes it possible to use information gained in the study of one phenomenon in the study of the other.

Every electrical circuit has some resistance. Ohm's Law says that the electromotive force E_1, the current i, and the resistance R are related through

$$E_1 = iR. \tag{12}$$

If the current varies, the magnetic field induced by the current will vary; then, in turn, there will be a second current induced in the original circuit, because of the varying magnetic field. The electromotive force E_2, caused by this self-inductance effect, is proportional to the rate of change of the current;

$$E_2 = L\frac{di}{dt}, \tag{13}$$

where L is a constant of proportionality. Finally, if a condenser with a capacitance C has charges $+q$ and $-q$ on its plates, the associated electromotive force, E_3, is given by the "law of the condenser";

$$E_3 = \frac{1}{C}q. \tag{14}$$

Kirchhoff's Law for the circuit says that the sum of the electromotive forces must vanish, or

$$E_1 + E_2 + E_3 = 0,$$

$$Ri + L\frac{di}{dt} + \frac{1}{C}q = 0. \tag{15}$$

If we take into account the fact that the current is the rate at which the charges flow, then we can say that $i = dq/dt$ and we get

$$L\frac{d^2i}{dt^2} + R\frac{di}{dt} + \frac{1}{C}i = 0 \tag{16}$$

when we differentiate Eq. (15). This differential equation describes the electric circuit with resistance R, inductance L, and capacitance C.

In determining the solutions of Eq. (16) we write $i = e^{mt}$ as usual and proceed to the auxiliary algebraic equation

$$Lm^2 + Rm + \frac{1}{C} = 0. \tag{16a}$$

Again we have three cases to discuss, according as the discriminant is negative, 0, or positive. If $R^2 - (4L/C) < 0$ or $R^2 < 4L/C$, then the solutions will be

$$i = e^{-(R/2L)t}\left[C_1 \cos\sqrt{\frac{1}{LC} - \frac{R^2}{4L^2}}t + C_2 \sin\sqrt{\frac{1}{LC} - \frac{R^2}{4L^2}}t\right] \tag{17}$$

as the reader can verify in Exercise 14.10-8. The current i will be alternately positive and negative, completing each cycle in the time $2\pi/\sqrt{(1/LC) - (R^2/4L^2)}$, and damping out because of the factor $e^{-(R/2L)t}$. The larger the ratio R/L, the faster the alternating current will damp out.

The cases where $R^2 = 4L/C$ and $R^2 > 4L/C$ are cases where we do not have alternating current, as the reader can prove in Exercise 14.10-9.

Just as we considered the case of a spring with an external force, so we can consider the case of a circuit with an external electromotive force $E(t)$. Kirchhoff's Law leads to the statement

$$L\frac{di}{dt} + Ri + \frac{1}{C}q = E(t)$$

or, upon differentiation, to

$$L\frac{d^2i}{dt^2} + R\frac{di}{dt} + \frac{1}{C}i = F(t), \tag{18}$$

where we have written $F(t) = E'(t)$. If the external electromotive force is sinusoidal, Eq. (18) becomes

$$L\frac{d^2i}{dt^2} + R\frac{di}{dt} + \frac{1}{C}i = a \sin bt. \tag{18a}$$

Equations (9a) and (18a) are identical if we identify m, n, and k in the spring equation with L, R, $1/C$ in the circuit equation. This identification of constants enables us to read the solution of Eq. (18a) from the solution of Eq. (9a). From Eq. (10) we have, for the case where $R^2 < 4L/C$,

$$i = \frac{a}{\sqrt{((1/C) - Lb^2)^2 + R^2b^2}} \sin(bt - \alpha)$$

$$+ e^{-(R/2L)t}\left[C_1 \cos\sqrt{\frac{1}{LC} - \frac{R^2}{4L^2}}t + C_2 \sin\sqrt{\frac{1}{LC} - \frac{R^2}{4L^2}}t \right], \tag{19}$$

with

$$\cos\alpha = \frac{(1/C) - Lb^2}{\sqrt{((1/C) - Lb^2)^2 + R^2b^2}}, \qquad \sin\alpha = \frac{Rb}{\sqrt{((1/C) - Lb^2)^2 + R^2b^2}}.$$

Again we have a "transient" part of the solution and a "steady state" part; the amplitude of the steady state part is

$$\text{amplitude} = \frac{a}{\sqrt{((1/C) - Lb^2)^2 + R^2b^2}}. \tag{20}$$

Again, the amplitude of the steady state part of the response varies with the frequency of the external electromotive force. The reader can study this response further in Exercise 14.10-11.

EXERCISES 14.10

1. (a) Suppose that a given spring is stretched 3 in. (= $\frac{1}{4}$ ft) when an object of weight 5 lb is suspended from it, and that Hooke's Law describes the behavior of this spring. What is the constant in the statement of Hooke's Law?

   (b) Suppose that this object is pulled down 2 in. from the equilibrium position, held for a moment, and released. Assuming that frictional forces are negligible, derive the equation of the ensuing simple harmonic motion. What is the period of the motion? the frequency? the amplitude? Remember that the mass and weight of the object are related: $W = mg$. Take g to be 32.2 ft/sec^2.

   (c) Suppose that the object is set into motion from the equilibrium position by giving it a push which makes the initial velocity 10 in. per sec. Again write the equation of the ensuing simple harmonic motion and determine its period, frequency, and amplitude.

2. Consider Eq. (7) for the case in which $n^2 = 4mk$.

   (a) Show that the solutions are $x = C_1 e^{-(n/2m)t} + C_2 t e^{-(n/2m)t}$.

   (b) Show that $x = x_0\left(1 + \frac{n}{2m}t\right)e^{-(n/2m)t}$ is the solution for which $x = x_0$ and $v = 0$ when $t = 0$.

   (c) Assume that $x_0 > 0$; show that $x > 0$ and $v < 0$ for all t. This means that, if the motion starts by displacing the object to one side of the equilibrium position, the object will move steadily back toward the equilibrium position but will not go past it.

3. Consider Eq. (7) for the case in which $n^2 > 4mk$.

   (a) Show that the solutions are $x = C_1 e^{-s_1 t} + C_2 e^{-s_2 t}$ where $s_1 = \frac{1}{2m}(n - \sqrt{n^2 - 4mk})$

   and $s_2 = \frac{1}{2m}(n + \sqrt{n^2 - 4mk})$. Observe that $0 < s_1 < s_2$.

(b) Show that

$$x = \frac{x_0}{s_2 - s_1} [s_2 e^{-s_1 t} - s_1 e^{-s_2 t}] = \frac{x_0 s_1 s_2}{s_2 - s_1} \left[\frac{1}{s_1 e^{s_1 t}} - \frac{1}{s_2 e^{s_2 t}} \right]$$

is the solution for which $x = x_0$ and $v = 0$ when $t = 0$.

(c) Assuming that $x_0 > 0$, show that $x > 0$ and $v < 0$ for all t.

4. Consider again the spring and object of Exercise 1, but assume this time that there is a frictional force, opposed to the velocity, whose magnitude is $\frac{1}{10}$ that of the velocity.

(a) Derive the differential equation that describes the motion.

(b) Suppose that the object is set into motion by pulling it down 2 in. from the equilibrium position, holding it for a moment, and releasing it. Find the equation of the ensuing motion.

5. Consider again the spring and object of Exercise 1, friction assumed to be negligible. Suppose the sinusoidal external force $a \sin bt$ is applied. Show that the response is

$$x = \frac{g\,a}{5(4g - b^2)} \sin bt + C_1 \sin 2\sqrt{g}\,t + C_2 \cos 2\sqrt{g}\,t \qquad \text{if } b \neq 2\sqrt{g}$$

and

$$x = -\frac{a\sqrt{g}}{20} t \cos 2\sqrt{g}\,t + C_1 \sin 2\sqrt{g}\,t + C_2 \cos 2\sqrt{g}\,t \qquad \text{if } b = 2\sqrt{g}.$$

Remember that the response for the spring without external force was periodic with period $\pi/\sqrt{g}$. These equations say that the closer the period of the external force is to $\pi/\sqrt{g}$, the larger is the amplitude of the response term with the same frequency as the external force, and that if the period of the external force is precisely $\pi/\sqrt{g}$, then the response has a term, $t \cos 2\sqrt{g}\,t$, which will oscillate beyond all bounds as time goes on.

6. In a case in which there is friction proportional to the velocity, Eq. (11) gives the amplitude of the steady state part of the response to an external sinusoidal force $F_3 = a \sin bt$ as a function of b. Show that

$$(k - mb^2)^2 + n^2 b^2 = m^2 \left(b^2 - \frac{2km - n^2}{2m^2} \right)^2 + k^2 - \frac{(2km - n^2)^2}{4m^2}.$$

For which choice of b is the amplitude a maximum? What is that maximum?

7. Consider again the spring and object of Exercise 4, with the frictional force described there. Suppose the sinusoidal force $a \sin bt$ is applied. For which choice of b is the amplitude of the steady state response a maximum? What is that maximum?

8. Derive Eq. (17) either directly from Eq. (16) or by comparing coefficients in Eqs. (7) and (16) and rewriting Eq. (8).

9. Equation (17) is the solution of Eq. (16) for a circuit with inductance, resistance, and capacitance in the case $R^2 < 4L/C$. Derive

(a) the solution

$$i = C_1 e^{-(R/2L)t} + C_2 t e^{-(R/2L)t}$$

for the case $R^2 = 4L/C$.

(b) the solution

$$i = C_1 e^{-s_1 t} + C_2 e^{-s_2 t},$$

where $s_1 = \dfrac{R}{2L} - \sqrt{\dfrac{R^2}{4L^2} - \dfrac{1}{LC}}$, $s_2 = \dfrac{R}{2L} + \sqrt{\dfrac{R^2}{4L^2} - \dfrac{1}{LC}}$, for the case $R^2 > 4L/C$.

Reference to Exercises 2 and 3 above shows that the current is not alternating in these cases.

10. Solve Eq. (18) in the case in which the external electromotive force is exponentially decreasing. Let $F(t) = ae^{-bt}$ with a and b positive. Assume $R^2 < 4L/C$.

11. In the case in which the external electromotive force is sinusoidal and $F(t)$ of Eq. (18) can be written $a \sin bt$, Eq. (20) gives the amplitude of the steady state part of the response as a function of b.

(a) As in Exercise 6 above, show that

$$\left(\frac{1}{C} - Lb^2 \right)^2 + R^2 b^2 = L^2 \left[b^2 - \left(\frac{1}{LC} - \frac{R^2}{2L^2} \right) \right]^2 + \frac{R^2}{4L^2} \left(\frac{4L}{C} - R^2 \right).$$

Assume that $R^2 < 2L/C$. Show that the amplitude will be a maximum for

$$b = \frac{1}{\sqrt{2L}} \sqrt{\frac{2L}{C} - R^2}.$$

(b) Show that if we choose $L = d$, $1/C = \sqrt{2}d$, $R = \sqrt{2} \sqrt{\sqrt{2} - 1}d$, d any positive constant, we have

$$\text{amplitude} = \frac{a}{d} \frac{1}{\sqrt{(b^2 - 1)^2 + 1}} \qquad \text{and} \qquad R^2 < \frac{2L}{C},$$

while if we choose $L = 10d$, $1/C = \sqrt{101}d$, $R = \sqrt{20} \sqrt{\sqrt{101} - 10}d$ we have

$$\text{amplitude} = \frac{a}{d} \frac{1}{\sqrt{100(b^2 - 1)^2 + 1}} \qquad \text{and} \qquad R^2 < \frac{2L}{C}.$$

In both cases we would have maximum amplitude for $b = 1$.

(c) Sketch $y = \dfrac{1}{\sqrt{(x^2 - 1)^2 + 1}}$ and $y = \dfrac{1}{\sqrt{100(x^2 - 1)^2 + 1}}$ for $0 \le x \le 2$. A comparison of these graphs suggests that if R, L, and C are chosen carefully, the steady state response can be made relatively large for a narrow band of external electromotive force frequencies and relatively small for other frequencies. Then, if nearby radio "transmitters" are assigned spaced frequencies, and if the operator of a radio "receiver" circuit wished to "tune" his circuit to a transmitter with a particular frequency $b/2\pi$ (or period $2\pi/b$), he could adjust his L, C, and R so that $\dfrac{1}{\sqrt{2L}} \sqrt{\dfrac{2L}{C} - R^2} = b$. The steady state current of frequency $b/2\pi$ flowing in his circuit would have relatively large amplitude; the amplitudes of currents responding to other frequencies would be relatively small.

12. We have already discussed the simple pendulum in Exercises 14.7-19 and 14.7-20. Suppose that we are willing to replace $\sin \theta$ by θ for a motion with very small θ, as in Exercise 14.7-20, and that we assume a frictional force opposed to the velocity and proportional to it, with constant of proportionality n.

(a) Show that the differential equation for the motion then becomes

$$mL \frac{d^2\theta}{dt^2} = -nL \frac{d\theta}{dt} - w \sin \theta,$$

$$\frac{d^2\theta}{dt^2} + \frac{gn}{w} \frac{d\theta}{dt} + \frac{g}{L} \theta = 0.$$

(b) Suppose a pendulum of length $L = 2$ ft has a bob that weighs 8 lb and that the constant n is taken to be .2 in units consistent with ft, sec, lb. Let the pendulum be displaced an angle of .1 radians from the equilibrium position and then released. Find its displacement at any later time.

13. Let a cylinder of cross-section area A sq ft float in a liquid of weight b lb per cu ft. Archimedes' Law for floating bodies says that, if the cylinder is pushed down a distance x feet from its equilibrium position, as in Fig. 14.13, the buoyant force

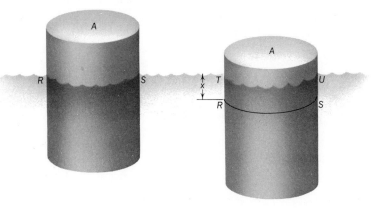

equilibrium position

displacement $x > 0$
volume of $RSTU$ is Ax

Fig. 14.13

tending to restore the cylinder to the equilibrium position is equal to the weight of the liquid displaced when the cylinder was pushed down the x feet. Show that the buoyant force is $F_1 = -Axb$. If the cylinder weighs w lb, and if there is a frictional force of magnitude $F_2 = -n \, (dx/dt)$, show that the motion of the cylinder will be governed by the differential equation

$$\frac{w}{g}\frac{d^2x}{dt^2} + n\frac{dx}{dt} + Abx = 0,$$

and that if $n^2 < \dfrac{4wAb}{g}$, the solutions will all be of the form

$$x = e^{-(ng/2w)t}\left[C_1 \cos \frac{g}{2w}\sqrt{\frac{4wAb}{g} - n^2}\,t + C_2 \sin \frac{g}{2w}\sqrt{\frac{4wAb}{g} - n^2}\,t \right].$$

14. Consider a metal rod of length L with circular cross-section of radius r; see Fig. 14.14. Let the ends at $x = 0$ and $x = L$ be maintained at the fixed temperatures T_0 and T_L, and suppose that the medium in which the rod is immersed has a fixed temperature a. We shall take the case where $T_0 > T_L > a$. Heat will flow along the rod from $x = 0$ to $x = L$ and also from the rod into the surrounding medium. In due

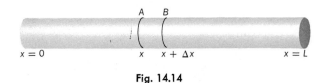

$x = 0$ A   B x $x + \Delta x$ $x = L$

Fig. 14.14

time equilibrium will be reached, and we seek $T(x)$, the temperature distribution along the rod at that time.

Consider the portion of the rod between cross-sections A and B at x and at $x + \Delta x$. Since the rate at which heat flows in the rod is proportional to the rate of change of the temperature, and since the cross-section area is πr^2, the rate at which heat flows into this portion of the rod through cross-section A is $-k_1 \pi r^2 T'(x)$, where k_1 is a physical constant that depends on the metal of which the bar is made and where the negative sign is used because $T'(x)$ is negative. Similarly, the rate at which heat flows out of this portion of the rod through cross-section B is $-k_1 \pi r^2 T'(x + \Delta x)$. The rate at which heat flows from this portion of the rod into the surrounding medium is proportional to the surface area of this portion of the rod and the difference between the temperature of this portion of the rod and the temperature of the surrounding medium; this rate is $k_2 (2\pi r \, \Delta x) [T(x^*) - a]$, where x^* is a suitably chosen number between x and $x + \Delta x$, and k_2 is another physical constant.

The rates at which heat flows into and out of the portion of the rod studied must be equal when equilibrium is reached. Hence

$$-k_1 \pi r^2 \, T'(x) = -k_1 \pi r^2 \, T'(x + \Delta x) + k_2(2\pi r \, \Delta x) [T(x^*) - a],$$

$$k_1 \pi r^2 \frac{T'(x + \Delta x) - T'(x)}{\Delta x} = k_2 2\pi r \, [T(x^*) - a].$$

In the limit, as $\Delta x \to 0$,

$$\pi r^2 k_1 T''(x) - 2\pi r k_2 T(x) = -2\pi r k_2 a,$$

or
$$T'' - b^2 T = -b^2 a, \qquad \text{where } b^2 = \frac{2k_2}{rk_1}.$$

Show that the temperature distribution is

$$T = a + \frac{(T_L - a) - (T_0 - a)e^{-bL}}{e^{bL} - e^{-bL}} e^{bx} + \frac{(T_0 - a)e^{bL} - (T_L - a)}{e^{bL} - e^{-bL}} e^{-bx}.$$

14.11   Higher Order Linear Equations

I

In this section we shall sketch parts of the theory of higher order linear equations analogous to the theory we have developed for second order equations.

As a generalization of Theorem 14.8-1 we write this theorem.

■ THEOREM 1A

Linear combinations of solutions of reduced linear equations.

HYPOTHESIS: (a) $y = u_k(x)$, $k = 1, \cdots, n$, are all solutions of a reduced linear equation for x of interval I.

(b) $w(x) = C_1 u_1(x) + C_2 u_2(x) + \cdots + C_n u_n(x) = \sum_{k=1}^{n} C_k u_k(x)$, with C_k, $k = 1, \cdots, n$, all constants.

CONCLUSION: $y = w(x)$ is also a solution of the reduced equation for x of I.

PROOF: The reader can write out a proof in Exercise 1 below, using the proof of Theorem 14.8-1 as a model if necessary.

Corresponding to the existence and uniqueness theorem for second order linear equations, Theorem 14.8-3, there is a more general existence and uniqueness theorem.

■ THEOREM 2

Existence and uniqueness of solutions for linear equations.

HYPOTHESIS: (a) $R_1(x), R_2(x), \cdots, R_{n+1}(x)$ are all continuous for x of interval I.
(b) x_0 is a point of interval I.
(c) $y_0, y_0', y_0'', \cdots, y_0{}^{(n-1)}$ are constants.

CONCLUSION: There is one and only one solution of

$$\frac{d^n y}{dx^n} + R_1(x)\frac{d^{n-1}y}{dx^{n-1}} + R_2(x)\frac{d^{n-2}y}{dx^{n-2}} + \cdots + R_n(x)y = R_{n+1}(x) \tag{1}$$

on interval I for which $y(x_0) = y_0, y'(x_0) = y_0', y''(x_0) = y_0'', \cdots, y^{(n-1)}(x_0) = y_0{}^{(n-1)}$.

As in our discussion of the proof of Theorem 14.8-3, we can replace Eq. (1), which is an nth order equation for the one dependent variable y, by a system of n first order equations for the n dependent variables $y, p_1, p_2, \cdots, p_{n-1}$ by writing

$$
\begin{cases}
\dfrac{dy}{dx} = p_1 \\[2mm]
\dfrac{dp_1}{dx} = p_2 \left(= \dfrac{d^2 y}{dx^2} \right) \\[2mm]
\dfrac{dp_2}{dx} = p_3 \left(= \dfrac{d^3 y}{dx^3} \right) \\[2mm]
\quad \cdots\cdots\cdots\cdots \\[2mm]
\dfrac{dp_{n-2}}{dx} = p_{n-1} \left(= \dfrac{d^{n-1} y}{dx^{n-1}} \right) \\[2mm]
\dfrac{dp_{n-1}}{dx} + R_1(x)p_{n-1} + R_2(x)p_{n-2} + \cdots + R_n(x)y = R_{n+1}(x).
\end{cases}
$$

A modification of the Picard successive approximation method used in proving the existence and uniqueness theorem for one first order equation in one dependent variable, Theorem 14.6-1, can be applied to prove an existence and uniqueness theorem in the present, more general situation. When this is done in more advanced and more detailed courses in differential equations, Theorem 2 is demonstrated.

A converse to Theorem 1 above can be stated in concise form if we first explain what we mean by linearly independent functions.

■ DEFINITION 1

Linear dependence of n functions. The n functions $u_k(x)$, $k = 1, \cdots, n$ are said to be linearly dependent on an interval I if there exist constants c_k, $k = 1, \cdots, n$, not all 0, such that

$$\sum_{k=1}^{n} c_k u_k(x) = c_1 u_1(x) + c_2 u_2(x) + \cdots + c_n u_n(x) = 0$$

for all x of I. If no such constants c_k, $k = 1, \cdots, n$ exist, we say that the $u_k(x)$, $k = 1, \cdots, n$ are linearly independent on I.

Example 1. We can show that $u_1(x) = \sin x$, $u_2(x) = \cos x$, and $u_3(x) = \sin (x - \alpha)$ are linearly dependent for any interval. For, we can write

$$u_3(x) = \sin (x - \alpha) = \sin x \cos \alpha - \cos x \sin \alpha,$$

$$u_3(x) = \cos \alpha \, u_1(x) - \sin \alpha \, u_2(x),$$

$$\cos \alpha \, u_1(x) - \sin \alpha \, u_2(x) - 1 \, u_3(x) = 0$$

for all x. We have

$$c_1 u_1(x) + c_2 u_2(x) + c_3 u_3(x) = 0$$

for all x with the constants $c_1 = \cos \alpha$, $c_2 = -\sin \alpha$, $c_3 = -1$ not all 0.

■ THEOREM 1B

Linear combinations of solutions of reduced linear equations.

HYPOTHESIS: (a) $R_1(x)$, $R_2(x)$, $\cdots$, $R_n(x)$ are continuous for x of interval I.
(b) $y = u_1(x)$, $y = u_2(x)$, $\cdots$, $y = u_n(x)$ are linearly independent solutions of

$$y^{(n)} + R_1(x)y^{(n-1)} + \cdots + R_{n-1}(x)y' + R_n(x)y = 0$$

on interval I.
(c) $y = w(x)$ is a solution on interval I.

CONCLUSION: There exist constants c_1, c_2, $\cdots$, c_n such that $w(x) = c_1 u_1(x) + c_2 u_2(x) + \cdots + c_n u_n(x)$ for x of I.

PROOF: The proof of this theorem follows the ideas of the proof of Theorem 14.8-4 but is much more detailed. We leave the proof to more exhaustive treatises. To summarize, Theorem 1A says that linear combinations of solutions of reduced linear equations are themselves solutions and Theorem 1B says that, if n linearly independent solutions are selected, then *all* solutions are linear combinations of these.

Rather detailed methods for solving second order reduced linear equations with constant coefficients are summarized in Theorem 14.8-2. Essentially the same methods can be used for a higher order reduced linear equation with constant coefficients. We again try to determine a constant m such that $y = e^{mx}$ is a solution, and we are again led to an auxiliary algebraic equation, this time of higher degree. If $m = m_1$ is a real solution of the auxiliary algebraic equation, then $y = e^{m_1 x}$ is a solution of the differential equation, as before. If $m_1 = \alpha + i\beta$ and $m_2 = \alpha - i\beta$ are complex conjugate solutions of the auxiliary algebraic equation, then $y = e^{\alpha x}(C_1 \cos \beta x + C_2 \sin \beta x)$ is a solution of the differential equation, as before. If $m = m_1$ is a real solution of the auxiliary algebraic equation of multiplicity j, then $y = e^{m_1 x}(C_1 + C_2 x + c_3 x^2 + \cdots + C_j x^{j-1})$ is a solution of the differential equation, generalizing a result for the second order case. Finally, if $m_1 = \alpha + i\beta$

and $m_2 = \alpha - i\beta$ are complex conjugate solutions of the auxiliary algebraic equation of multiplicity j, then

$$y = e^{\alpha x}(C_1 \cos \beta x + C_2 \sin \beta x + C_3 x \cos \beta x + C_4 x \sin \beta x$$

$$+ \cdots + C_{2j-1}x^{j-1} \cos \beta x + C_{2j}x^{j-1} \sin \beta x)$$

is a solution of the differential equation. These facts are demonstrated later in Theorem 6.

Example 2. Consider the fourth order equation with constant coefficients

$$y'''' - 7y'' + 4y' + 20y = 0. \tag{2}$$

If we try to find m such that $y = e^{mx}$ is a solution, we substitute $y' = me^{mx}$, $y'' = m^2 e^{mx}$, $y'''' = m^4 e^{mx}$ and we are led to the auxiliary algebraic equation

$$m^4 - 7m^2 + 4m + 20 = 0. \tag{3}$$

In general, $m = p/q$ can be a solution of $am^n + bm^{n-1} + \cdots + gm + h = 0$ only if p is a divisor of h and q is a divisor of a. Accordingly, when we try to guess a rational solution of Eq. (3) we need only try $m = \pm 1, \pm 2, \pm 4, \pm 5, \pm 10, \pm 20$. Direct arithmetic trial will show that $m = -2$ is a solution and the Factor Theorem of algebra then states that $m + 2$ is a factor of the left member of Eq. (3). After division we write Eq. (3) in the form

$$(m + 2)(m^3 - 2m^2 - 3m + 10) = 0$$

and consider the cubic factor. Further guesses at a rational solution are restricted to $m = \pm 1, \pm 2, \pm 5$, and ± 10. Again $m = -2$ is found to be a solution by direct arithmetic trial, and after a second division the algebraic problem is reduced to a quadratic problem:

$$(m + 2)(m + 2)(m^2 - 4m + 5) = 0.$$

The solutions of Eq. (3) are $m = -2, -2, 2 + i, 2 - i$, and

$$y = C_1 e^{-2x} + C_2 x e^{-2x} + e^{2x}(C_3 \cos x + C_4 \sin x) \tag{4}$$

is a solution of Eq. (2) for any choice of the constants C_1, C_2, C_3, and C_4.

Theorems 14.9-1A and 14.9-1B generalize to linear equations of higher order than the second almost without change of wording. In Exercises 14.11-14 and 14.11-15 the reader can write out proofs for the following theorems:

■ THEOREM 3A

Solutions for general linear equations related to solutions for reduced equations.

Hypothesis: (a) $y = w(x)$ is a solution of $y^{(n)} + R_1 y^{(n-1)} + \cdots + R_n y = R_{n+1}$.

(b) $y = q(x)$ is a solution of $y^{(n)} + R_1 y^{(n-1)} + \cdots + R_n y = 0$.

Conclusion: $y = w(x) + q(x)$ is a solution of $y^{(n)} + R_1 y^{(n-1)} + \cdots + R_n y = R_{n+1}$.

■ THEOREM 3B

HYPOTHESIS: $y = w(x)$ and $y = z(x)$ are solutions of $y^{(n)} + R_1 y^{(n-1)} + \cdots + R_n y = R_{n+1}$.

CONCLUSION: $y = z(x) - w(x)$ is a solution of $y^{(n)} + R_1 y^{(n-1)} + \cdots + R_n y = 0$.

In words, Theorem 3A says that, if we add a solution of the reduced equation to a solution of the nonreduced equation, we get a new solution of the nonreduced equation. Conversely, Theorem 3B says that, if we take one particular solution of the nonreduced equation, say $y = w(x)$, then any other solution of the nonreduced equation, say $y = z(x)$, differs from the first one by a solution of the reduced equation. This is the same thing as saying that all solutions of the nonreduced equation can be obtained by adding solutions of the reduced equation to one particular solution of the nonreduced equation. Hence, these theorems suggest that we work with nonreduced equations of order higher than the second, just as we did with second order equations. When given a nonreduced equation, we first write down the corresponding reduced equation and try to find the solutions of that equation. Then we try to find one particular solution of the given nonreduced equation, either by a method of undetermined coefficients or by a method of varying a known solution of the reduced equation. By adding the solutions of the reduced equation to the one particular solution of the nonreduced equation, we get the solutions of the nonreduced equation.

Example 3.   Consider the fourth order equation

$$y'''' - 7y'' + 4y' + 20y = x^2. \tag{5}$$

The corresponding reduced equation is precisely Eq. (2) of Example 2 above, with solutions given in Eq. (4). To find one particular solution of Eq. (5), we can try to determine coefficients A, B, and C of $y = Ax^2 + Bx + C$ properly. We compute

$$y = Ax^2 + Bx + C, \; y' = 2Ax + B, \; y'' = 2A, \; y''' = y'''' = 0,$$

and upon substitution in Eq. (5) find that that we must choose A, B, and C so that

$$0 - 7(2A) + 4(2Ax + B) + 20(Ax^2 + Bx + C) = x^2.$$

Equating coefficients of the x^2, x, and constant terms, we arrive at

$$20A = 1, \; 8A + 20B = 0, \; -14A + 4B + 20C = 0$$

and we choose

$$A = \tfrac{1}{20}, \qquad B = -\tfrac{1}{50}, \qquad C = \tfrac{39}{1000}.$$

The solutions of Eq. (5) are

$$y = \tfrac{1}{20} x^2 - \tfrac{1}{50} x + \tfrac{39}{1000} + C_1 e^{-2x} + C_2 x e^{-2x}$$
$$+ e^{2x}(C_3 \cos x + C_4 \sin x).$$

Example 4. Consider the linear equation of the third order

$$xy''' - y'' - xy' + y = x^2. \tag{6}$$

This equation does not have constant coefficients.

The reduced equation is

$$xy''' - y'' - xy' + y = 0. \tag{7}$$

If we try to guess a solution of the form $y = x^m$, we find that we must choose m so that

$$xm(m - 1)(m - 2)x^{m-3} - m(m - 1)x^{m-2} - xmx^{m-1} + x^m = 0$$

or so that

$$m(m - 1)(m - 3)x^{m-2} - (m - 1)x^m = 0.$$

This can only be done if we choose $m = 1$; $y = x$ is a solution of Eq. (7).

If we try to guess a solution of Eq. (7) of the form $y = e^{mx}$, we find that we must choose m so that

$$xm^3e^{mx} - m^2e^{mx} - xme^{mx} + e^{mx} = 0$$

or so that

$$m(m^2 - 1)xe^{mx} - (m^2 - 1)e^{mx} = 0.$$

This can only be done if we choose $m = 1$ or -1;

$$y = C_1x + C_2e^x + C_3e^{-x}$$

is a solution of Eq. (7) for any choice of the constants C_1, C_2, and C_3.

To get a solution of Eq. (6) we can try to "vary" the solutions we found for Eq. (7). Let us try to find functions $w_1(x)$, $w_2(x)$, and $w_3(x)$ subject to the condition that

$$y = w_1x + w_2e^x + w_3e^{-x} \tag{8}$$

shall be a solution of Eq. (6). In general, the three unknowns w_1, w_2, and w_3 can meet three conditions, and we are free to add two more conditions as we work. We compute

$$y' = w_1 + w_2e^x - w_3e^{-x} + (w_1'x + w_2'e^x + w_3'e^{-x})$$

and take as one of our conditions

$$w_1'x + w_2'e^x + w_3'e^{-x} = 0, \tag{9}$$

so that y' is then simpler:

$$y' = w_1 + w_2e^x - w_3e^{-x}.$$

Then we compute

$$y'' = w_2e^x + w_3e^{-x} + (w_1' + w_2'e^x - w_3'e^{-x})$$

and take

$$w_1' + w_2'e^x - w_3'e^{-x} = 0 \tag{10}$$

as the last of our conditions, so that

$$y'' = w_2 e^x + w_3 e^{-x}$$

$$y''' = w_2 e^x - w_3 e^{-x} + w_2' e^x + w_3' e^{-x}.$$

Hence, when we substitute the y of Eq. (8) into Eq. (6) we see that we ought to choose w_1, w_2, and w_3 so that

$$x(w_2 e^x - w_3 e^{-x} + w_2' e^x + w_3' e^{-x}) - (w_2 e^x + w_3 e^{-x}) - x(w_1 + w_2 e^x - w_3 e^{-x})$$

$$+ (w_1 x + w_2 e^x + w_3 e^{-x}) = x^2$$

or so that

$$w_2' e^x + w_3' e^{-x} = x. \tag{11}$$

Equations (9), (10), and (11) can be considered to be a system of three simultaneous equations in the three unknowns w_1', w_2', and w_3'. If we compare Eqs. (9) and (11), we find immediately that we must select

$$w_1' = -1$$

and it will soon follow from Eqs. (10) and (11) that we must select

$$w_2' = \frac{1}{2} \frac{x+1}{e^x}, \qquad w_3' = \frac{1}{2} \frac{x-1}{e^{-x}}.$$

Fortunately, integration by parts will enable us to choose w_1, w_2, and w_3; we have

$$w_1 = -x + C_1$$

$$w_2 = \frac{1}{2} \int (x+1) e^{-x} \, dx = -\frac{1}{2}(x+2)e^{-x} + C_2$$

$$w_3 = \frac{1}{2} \int (x-1) e^x \, dx = \frac{1}{2}(x-2)e^x + C_3.$$

The solutions of Eq. (6) are

$$y = w_1 x + w_2 e^x + w_3 e^{-x}$$

$$y = -x^2 - \frac{1}{2}(x+2) + \frac{1}{2}(x-2) + C_1 x + C_2 e^x + C_3 e^{-x}$$

$$y = -x^2 - 2 + C_1 x + C_2 e^x + C_3 e^{-x}.$$

||

It was asserted above that essentially the same methods are used to solve reduced linear equations with constant coefficients in the higher order cases as in the second order equations treated in Theorem 14.8-2. The justification for this assertion can be presented more concisely if we introduce some operator notation.

■ NOTATION CONVENTION 1

For any suitably differentiable function y and any positive integer k, $D^k y$ shall represent $d^k y / dx^k$. The term $D^0 y$ shall represent y.

■ NOTATION CONVENTION 2

For any suitably differentiable function y, any constants a and b and any nonnegative integers k and j, $D^k D^j y$ shall represent $D^k(D^j y)$ and $(aD^k + bD^j)y$ shall represent $aD^k y + bD^j y$.

■ THEOREM 4

Some properties of the operator D.

HYPOTHESIS: y and z are suitably differentiable functions; a, b, and c constants; and h, j, and k nonnegative integers.

CONCLUSION: (a) $(aD^k + bD^j)y = (bD^j + aD^k)y$.
(b) $[(aD^k + bD^j) + cD^h]y = [aD^k + (bD^j + cD^h)]y$.
(c) $D^k D^j y = D^j D^k y = D^{k+j} y$.
(d) $[D^k(D^j D^h)]y = [(D^k D^j)D^h]y = D^{k+j+h} y$.
(e) $D^k(y + z) = D^k y + D^k z$.
(f) $[D^h(aD^k + bD^j)]y = [(aD^k + bD^j)D^h]y = [aD^{h+k} + bD^{h+j}]y$.

PROOF: These conclusions are justified quickly by referring to the basic properties of the derivative.

The following notation convention is consistent with Conclusion (b) of Theorem 4.

■ NOTATION CONVENTION 3

For any suitably differentiable function y, any constants a_n, and any nonnegative integers k_n, $n = 1, 2, \cdots$, $p, (a_1 D^{k_1} + a_2 D^{k_2} + \cdots + a_p D^{k_p})y$ shall represent $a_1 D^{k_1} y + a_2 D^{k_2} y + \cdots + a_p D^{k_p} y$.

■ THEOREM 5

Factoring polynomial operators.

HYPOTHESIS: $P(m)$, $Q(m)$, $R(m)$ are polynomials and $P(m) = [Q(m)] [R(m)]$.

CONCLUSION: $P(D)y = Q(D) [R(D)y] = R(D) [Q(D)y]$.

PROOF: The meaning of $P(D)y, R(D)y, Q(D)y$ is stated in Notation Convention 3. The meaning of an expression like $Q(D)[R(D)y]$ will follow from a second application of Notation Convention 3, replacing y by $R(D)y$. If $P(D)y, Q(D)[R(D)y]$ and $R(D)[Q(D)y]$ are then written out and compared, using Theorem 4 and the hypothesis of this theorem, the validity of the conclusion of this theorem follows immediately.

With this much operator notation we can present fairly concisely our discussion of solutions of higher order reduced linear equations with constant coefficients.

■ THEOREM 6

Solutions of reduced linear equations with constant coefficients.

HYPOTHESIS: $P(m)$ is a polynomial, and for $P(m) = 0$ we have
Case (a) $m = m_1$ as a real solution.
Case (b) $m = \alpha + i\beta$, $m = \alpha - i\beta$ as complex conjugate solutions.
Case (c) $m = m_1$ as a real solution of multiplicity j.
Case (d) $m = \alpha + i\beta$, $m = \alpha - i\beta$ as complex conjugate solutions of multiplicity j.

CONCLUSION: For the linear differential equation $P(D)y = 0$ we have
Case (a) $y = e^{m_1 x}$ as a solution.
Case (b) $y = e^{\alpha x}(C_1 \cos \beta x + C_2 \sin \beta x)$ as a solution for each choice of constants C_1 and C_2.
Case (c) $y = (C_1 + C_2 x + \cdots + C_j x^{j-1})e^{m_1 x}$ as a solution for each choice of constants $C_1, C_2, \cdots, C_j$.
Case (d) $y = e^{\alpha x}(C_1 \cos \beta x + C_2 \sin \beta x + C_3 x \cos \beta x + C_4 x \sin \beta x + \cdots + C_{2j-1} x^{j-1} \cos \beta x + C_{2j} x^{j-1} \sin \beta x)$ as a solution for each choice of constants. $C_1, C_2, \cdots, C_{2j}$.

PROOF OF CASE (a): Since $m = m_1$ is a solution of $P(m) = 0$, there is a polynomial $Q(m)$ such that

$$P(m) = Q(m) \cdot (m - m_1),$$

and Theorem 5 tells us that the differential equation we wish to solve can be written in the form

$$P(D)y = Q(D)([D - m_1]y) = 0.$$

But we easily compute that

$$[D - m_1]e^{m_1 x} = De^{m_1 x} - m_1 e^{m_1 x}$$
$$= m_1 e^{m_1 x} - m_1 e^{m_1 x} = 0.$$

Hence

$$P(D)e^{m_1 x} = Q(D)([D - m_1]e^{m_1 x}) = Q(D)(0) = 0$$

and $y = e^{m_1 x}$ is a solution of $P(D)y = 0$.

PROOF OF CASE (b): Since $m = \alpha + i\beta$ and $m = \alpha - i\beta$ are solutions of $P(m) = 0$, there is a polynomial $Q(m)$ such that

$$P(m) = Q(m) \cdot (m - \alpha - i\beta) \cdot (m - \alpha + i\beta)$$
$$= Q(m) \cdot (m^2 - 2\alpha m + \alpha^2 + \beta^2).$$

Then Theorem 5 tells us that we can write

$$P(D)y = Q(D)[(D^2 - 2\alpha D + \alpha^2 + \beta^2)y] = 0$$

for the differential equation we wish to solve. But we saw in Theorem 14.8-2 that $y = y_1 = e^{\alpha x}(C_1 \cos \beta x + C_2 \sin \beta x)$ is a solution of $[D^2 - 2\alpha D + \alpha^2 + \beta^2]y = 0$. Hence $y = y_1$ is a solution of the higher degree equation also, for we can write

$$P(D)y_1 = Q(D)([D^2 - 2\alpha D + \alpha^2 + \beta^2]y_1) = Q(D)(0) = 0.$$

PROOF OF CASE (c): It suffices to find the solution of the differential equation

$$(D - m_1)^j y = 0. \tag{12}$$

The conclusion we wish to draw would then follow, as in the earlier cases, when we wrote

$$P(D)y = Q(D)([D - m_1]^j y) = Q(D)(0) = 0.$$

The conclusion for Case (a) tells us that $y = e^{m_1 x}$ is one solution of Eq. (12). Let us try to find $w(x)$ such that $y = w(x)e^{m_1 x}$ is also a solution. We can write

$$(D - m_1)(we^{m_1 x}) = D(we^{m_1 x}) - m_1 we^{m_1 x} = w'e^{m_1 x},$$

and, using this result, perhaps with w replaced by $w', w'', w''', \cdots$ on occasion,

$$(D - m_1)^2(we^{m_1 x}) = (D - m_1)(D - m_1)(we^{m_1 x})$$

$$= (D - m_1)(w'e^{m_1 x}) = w''e^{m_1 x},$$

. . . .

$$(D - m_1)^j(we^{m_1 x}) = w^{(j)}e^{m_1 x}.$$

Hence $y = we^{m_1 x}$ will be a solution of Eq. (12) if

$$w^{(j)}e^{m_1 x} = 0,$$

$$w^{(j)} = \frac{d^j w}{dx^j} = 0,$$

$$w = C_1 + C_2 x + C_3 x^2 + \cdots + C_j x^{j-1}.$$

PROOF OF CASE (d): For this case it will suffice to find the solutions of the differential equation

$$(D^2 - 2\alpha D + \alpha^2 + \beta^2)^j y = 0. \tag{13}$$

The conclusion for Case (b) tells us that $y = e^{\alpha x} \cos \beta x$ and $y = e^{\alpha x} \sin \beta x$ are solutions of Eq. (13). Let us try to find $w(x)$ such that $y = we^{\alpha x} \cos \beta x$ and $y = we^{\alpha x} \sin \beta x$ are also solutions. We can compute

$$\left. \begin{array}{l} (D^2 - 2\alpha D + \alpha^2 + \beta^2)(we^{\alpha x} \cos \beta x) = w''e^{\alpha x} \cos \beta x - 2\beta w'e^{\alpha x} \sin \beta x \\ (D^2 - 2\alpha D + \alpha^2 + \beta^2)(we^{\alpha x} \sin \beta x) = w''e^{\alpha x} \sin \beta x + 2\beta w'e^{\alpha x} \cos \beta x \end{array} \right\}. \tag{14}$$

If we use these results, with w replaced by w', w'', w''', and so forth, we find that $(D^2 - 2\alpha D + \alpha^2 + \beta^2)^j(we^{\alpha x} \cos \beta x)$ and $(D^2 - 2\alpha D + \alpha^2 + \beta^2)^j(we^{\alpha x} \sin \beta x)$ are linear combinations of terms containing $w^j, w^{j+1}, \cdots, w^{(2j)}$. These terms will vanish if

$$\frac{d^j w}{dx^j} = w^{(j)} = 0,$$

$$w = C_1 + C_2 x + C_3 x^2 + \cdots + C_j x^{j-1}.$$

This establishes the conclusion for Case (d). The reader can verify some of these computations in Exercise 14.11-29.

EXERCISES 14.11

1. Prove Theorem 1A.
2. Show that $u_1(x) = x + 2$, $u_2(x) = 2x - 1$, $u_3(x) = 3x + 4$ are linearly dependent for any interval.
3. Show that $u_1(x) = 1$, $u_2(x) = x$, $u_3(x) = x^2$ are linearly independent for $0 \le x \le 1$.
4. Show that $u_1(x) = e^{\alpha x}$, $u_2(x) = e^{\beta x}$, $u_3(x) = e^{\gamma x}$ are linearly independent for $0 \le x \le 1$ if no two of α, β, γ are equal.
5. Are $u_1(x) = \sin x$, $u_2(x) = \cos x$, $u_3(x) = \sin 2x$ linearly independent for $0 \le x \le \pi/2$? Explain.

Find the solutions for the equations of Exercises 6-13.

6. $y''' + y'' - 2y' = 0$.
7. $y''' - y'' + y' - y = 0$.
8. $y''' + y'' - 4y' - 4y = 0$.
9. $y''' - y = 0$.
10. $y'''' - 5y'' + 4y = 0$.
11. $y'''' - 3y''' + 3y'' - 3y' + 2y = 0$.
12. $y''' + 3y'' + 3y' + y = 0$.
13. $y'''' + y = 0$.
14. Prove Theorem 3A.
15. Prove Theorem 3B.

Find the solutions for the equations of Exercises 16-25.

16. $y''' - y'' - y' + y = 0$.
17. $y''' - y'' - y' + y = 2x$.
18. $y''' - y'' - y' + y = \sin x$.
19. $y''' - y'' - y' + y = e^{-x}$.
20. $y''' - y'' - y' + y = x^2 e^x$.
    Suggestion: Find $w(x)$ such that $y = w(x)e^x$ is a solution.
21. $y'''' - y = 0$.
22. $y'''' - y = xe^x$.
23. $y'''' + 2y'' + y = 0$.
24. $y'''' + 2y'' + y = \sin x$.
25. $(x^2 + 2x + 2)y''' + x^2 y'' - 2xy' + 2y = \dfrac{(x^2 + 2x + 2)^2}{x^2}$.

    Suggestion: Try first to find solutions of the reduced equation of the form $y = x^m$ and $y = e^{mx}$.
26. Illustrate Theorem 5 by computing $(D^2 - D)y$, $D[(D - 1)y]$, $(D - 1)(Dy)$.
27. Read the proof of the conclusion for Case (c) of Theorem 6. Then solve $(D - m_1)^j y = Ax^k e^{m_1 x}$, $k \ne -1, -2, \ldots, -j$.
28. Solve $(D - a)^3 y = \dfrac{1}{x^3} e^{ax}$.
29. Use Eqs. (14) to show that $(D^2 - 2\alpha D + \alpha^2 + \beta^2)^2 (we^{\alpha x} \cos \beta x) = w'''' e^{\alpha x} \cos \beta x - 4\beta w''' e^{\alpha x} \sin \beta x - 4\beta^2 w'' e^{\alpha x} \cos \beta x$ and thus illustrate part of the proof of the conclusion for Case (d) of Theorem 6.

14.12   Series Solutions for Linear Equations. Ordinary Points

I

The solution of every reduced linear equation with constant coefficients can be written in terms of polynomials and exponential and trigonometric functions, as we saw in Theorems 14.8-2 and 14.11-6. However, our work so far with linear equations whose coefficients were not constant was rather sketchy and depended upon fortunate guesses for the most part. The reason for this is the fact that the solutions of linear equations with nonconstant coefficients are usually functions that cannot be expressed as combinations of the more familiar ones in a finite number of steps. One can attempt to describe these new functions from at least three points of view; one can attempt to use power series, continued fractions, or definite integrals. We shall use power series in this section and the next but make no attempt to use the other tools in this elementary text.

II

■ DEFINITION 1

Ordinary point. We shall say that the point $x = a$ is an ordinary point for the differential equation $y'' + R(x)y' + S(x)y = 0$ if and only if the functions $R(x)$ and $S(x)$ have expansions in series of positive integer powers of $(x - a)$. A point that is not an ordinary point will be called a *singular point*.

Example 1A.   The point $x = 0$ is an ordinary point for the equation

$$(1 - x^2)y'' - 2xy' + 2y = 0. \tag{1}$$

For, we can write the equation in the form

$$y'' - \frac{2x}{1 - x^2}y' + \frac{2}{1 - x^2}y = 0,$$

and the functions $R(x) = -2x/(1 - x^2) = -2x(1 + x^2 + x^4 + \cdots)$, $S(x) = 2/(1 - x^2) = 2(1 + x^2 + x^4 + \cdots)$ both have Taylor series expansions about the point $x = 0$ with interval of convergence $-1 < x < 1$. The points $x = 1$ and $x = -1$, however, are singular points for the equation.

Example 2A.   The point $x = 0$ is also an ordinary point for the equation

$$(1 + x^2)y'' - 2y = 0 \tag{2}$$

as we see when we write

$$y'' - \frac{2}{1 + x^2}y = 0$$

and consider $R(x) = 0$, $S(x) = -\dfrac{2}{1 + x^2}$. The complex conjugate points $x = i$ and $x = -i$ are singular points, however.

■ THEOREM 1

Series solutions at ordinary points.

HYPOTHESIS: (a) $x = a$ is an ordinary point for the differential equation

$$y'' + R(x)y' + S(x)y = 0. \tag{3}$$

(b) The singular point in the complex plane that is nearest to $x = a$ is at a distance d, as distances are measured in the complex plane.

CONCLUSION: There will be two linearly independent solutions of Eq. (3) which can be described by series of positive integer powers of $(x - a)$. The interval of convergence for each of these series will be at least as large as $a - d < x < a + d$.

● **Remark 1**

The proof of this theorem is too difficult to present here. It depends on existence and uniqueness theorems for linear equations which we have only stated, not proved, and uses the theory of functions of a complex variable, which we have not studied. But the existence of solutions in series of positive integer powers of $(x - a)$ can be made to appear plausible.

The fact that $x = a$ is an ordinary point for the equation means that $R(x)$ and $S(x)$ have expansions in series of positive integer powers of $(x - a)$, and thus derivatives of all orders at $x = a$, for the coefficients in these expansions are the values of the derivatives, divided by appropriate factorial constants. To get an expansion in series of positive integer powers of $(x - a)$ for a solution y of Eq. (3) means essentially to determine the values of the derivatives of y of all orders at $x = a$. If $y(a)$ and $y'(a)$ are chosen arbitrarily, $y''(a)$ can be determined as $-R(a)y'(a) - S(a)y(a)$ when Eq. (3) is written in the form

$$y'' = -R(x)y' - S(x)y.$$

If we differentiate this equation we have

$$y''' = -Ry'' - R'y' - Sy' - S'y,$$

from which we can determine $y'''(a)$. Differentiating again and again, we would expect to determine the derivatives of y of all orders at $x = a$ and thus an expansion for y.

Example 1B. Return to Eq. (1) of Example 1A. We saw there that $x = 0$ was an ordinary point, while $x = 1$ and $x = -1$ were singular points. In Fig. 14.15 we plot these points in the complex plane according to the convention that the complex number $a + bi$ shall correspond to the

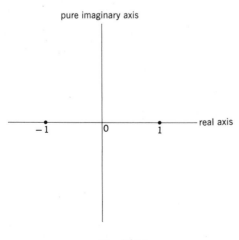

pure imaginary axis

real axis

Fig. 14.15

Cartesian point (a, b). We see that the distance from $x = 0$ to the nearest singularity is 1, and Theorem 1 says, accordingly, that Eq. (1) will have two linearly independent solutions which can be described as series of positive integer powers of x and that each one of these series will converge for the interval $-1 < x < 1$ at least. The solutions of Eq. (1) are determined later in Example 5.

Example 2B. Return to Eq. (2) of Example 2A. Again the point $x = 0$ was an ordinary point, but this time $x = i$ and $x = -i$ were singular points. When these points are plotted in the complex plane, again using the convention that the complex number $a + bi$ shall correspond to the Cartesian point (a, b), we see that the distance from $x = 0$ to the nearest singularity is 1; see Fig. 14.16. Accordingly, Theorem 1 claims that Eq. (2) will have two linearly independent solutions which can be written as series of positive integer powers of x, and that each of these series will converge in an interval at least as large as $-1 < x < 1$. The determination of these solutions is called for in Exercise 14.12-12.

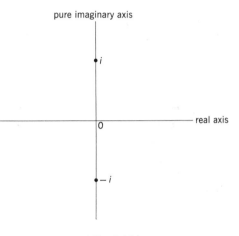

Fig. 14.16

Example 3. Consider

$$y'' - xy' + y = 0. \qquad (4)$$

Because the coefficient functions $-x$ and 1 have no singularities, Theorem 1 says that Eq. (4) will have two linearly independent solutions that can be described by series of positive integer powers of x and that each of these power series will converge for all x.

To find these power series let us write

$$y = a_0 + a_1x + a_2x^2 + a_3x^3 + \cdots = \sum_{k=0}^{\infty} a_k x^k \qquad (5)$$

and determine the coefficients a_k. As we stated in Theorem 13.8-1, the derivative of a function defined by means of a power series can be obtained by differentiating the individual terms of the power series and summing. Hence

$$y' = \frac{dy}{dx} = 0 + a_1 + 2a_2x + 3a_3x^2 + \cdots = \sum_{k=1}^{\infty} ka_k x^{k-1} \qquad (6)$$

and $\qquad y'' = \frac{dy'}{dx} = 0 + 0 + 2a_2 + 2(3)a_3x + \cdots = \sum_{k=2}^{\infty} k(k-1)a_k x^{k-2}. \qquad (7)$

Observe that the series written for y in Eq. (5) includes a term for $k = 0$ but that the series written for y' in Eq. (6) does not. We could have written the latter series as $\sum_{k=0}^{\infty} ka_k x^{k-1}$, but the term contributed for $k = 0$ has value 0 and we choose not to write it. Similarly, the series for y'' written in Eq. (7) could have been written as a summation for k which started with $k = 0$ instead of with $k = 2$, but the terms contributed for $k = 0$ and $k = 1$ both have value 0 and we choose not to write them.

If we substitute from Eqs. (5), (6), and (7) into Eq. (4) we get

$$\sum_{k=2}^{\infty} k(k-1)a_k x^{k-2} - x \sum_{k=1}^{\infty} ka_k x^{k-1} + \sum_{k=0}^{\infty} a_k x^k \doteq 0, \tag{8a}$$

and, multiplying each term of the series of the second term by x, we get

$$\sum_{k=2}^{\infty} k(k-1)a_k x^{k-2} - \sum_{k=1}^{\infty} ka_k x^k + \sum_{k=0}^{\infty} a_k x^k = 0. \tag{8b}$$

Here the first series has the general term x^{k-2} while the others have the general term x^k, and the series are hard to combine. We can rewrite that first series by substituting for the index of summation; let $k = j + 2$. Then for this first series we have

$$\sum_{k=2}^{\infty} k(k-1)a_k x^{k-2} = \sum_{j=0}^{\infty} (j+2)(j+1)a_{j+2} x^j. \tag{9a}$$

The summation proceeded in the left member from the $k = 2$ term on. But we have $j = 0$ when $k = 2$; hence the summation in the new form proceeds from $j = 0$. The reader can check the fact that the sums in Eq. (9a) are equivalent by writing both sums out; in both cases we get

$$2(1)a_2 + 3(2)a_3 x + 4(3)a_4 x^2 + \cdots.$$

Finally, since we would not want the different series of Eq. (8b) to use different indices of summation, we shall substitute k for j in the second member of Eq. (9a);

$$\sum_{k=2}^{\infty} k(k-1)a_k x^{k-2} = \sum_{j=0}^{\infty} (j+2)(j+1)a_{j+2} x^j = \sum_{k=0}^{\infty} (k+2)(k+1)a_{k+2} x^k. \tag{9b}$$

When the first series in Eq. (8b) is replaced according to Eq. (9b), we have

$$\sum_{k=0}^{\infty} (k+2)(k+1)a_{k+2} x^k - \sum_{k=1}^{\infty} ka_k x^k + \sum_{k=0}^{\infty} a_k x^k = 0. \tag{8c}$$

Now all three series are written in terms of x^k, but we still cannot combine the series because they do not all start with $k = 0$ terms. If we separate out the $k = 0$ terms for the first and third series, then we would have three series starting with $k = 1$ terms. Equation (8c) can be rewritten in the forms:

$$2(1)a_2 + \sum_{k=1}^{\infty} (k+2)(k+1)a_{k+2} x^k - \sum_{k=1}^{\infty} ka_k x^k + a_0 + \sum_{k=1}^{\infty} a_k x^k = 0$$

$$(2a_2 + a_0) + \sum_{k=1}^{\infty} [(k+2)(k+1)a_{k+2} - (k-1)a_k]x^k = 0. \tag{8d}$$

We can, if we so choose, read this equation from right to left and interpret the equation to say that the function 0 has a certain power series expansion; the constant term is $2a_2 + a_0$ and for each $k \geq 1$ the coefficient of x^k is $(k+2)(k+1)a_{k+2} - (k-1)a_k$. But the function 0 has another very simple power series expansion, namely, one with coefficients all 0, and the uniqueness theorem for such power series expansions, Theorem 13.8-2, says that the expansions must be identical. Hence, equating coefficients, we learn from Eq. (8d) that

$$2a_2 + a_0 = 0, \qquad a_2 = -\tfrac{1}{2} a_0$$

$$(k + 2)(k + 1)a_{k+2} - (k - 1)a_k = 0,$$

$$a_{k+2} = \frac{k - 1}{(k + 2)(k + 1)} a_k \qquad \text{for } k \geq 1. \tag{10}$$

Equation (10) will enable us to determine later a_k's from earlier ones; it is called a *recurrence relation*. We write

$$k = 1, \; a_3 = 0$$

$$k = 2, \; a_4 = \frac{1}{4(3)} a_2 = -\frac{1}{4(3)(2)} a_0 = -\frac{1}{4!} a_0$$

$$k = 3, \; a_5 = \frac{2}{5(4)} a_3 = 0$$

$$k = 4, \; a_6 = \frac{3}{6(5)} a_4 = -\frac{3 \cdot 1}{6(5)4!} a_0 = -\frac{1 \cdot 3}{6!} a_0$$

$$k = 5, \; a_7 = \frac{4}{7(6)} a_5 = 0$$

$$k = 6, \; a_8 = \frac{5}{8(7)} a_6 = -\frac{1 \cdot 3 \cdot 5}{8!} a_0$$

and, in general,

$$a_{2k+1} = 0 \text{ for } k \geq 1$$

$$a_{2k} = -\frac{1 \cdot 3 \cdot 5 \cdots (2k - 3)}{(2k)!} a_0 \qquad \text{for } k \geq 2.$$

The information we have just compiled for the a_k's from the recurrence relation, Eq. (10), enables us to go back to Eq. (5) and write out our solution. We have

$$y = a_0 + a_1 x + a_2 x^2 + a_3 x^3 + \cdots = \sum_{k=0}^{\infty} a_k x^k$$

$$y = a_0 + a_1 x + \left(-\frac{1}{2} a_0\right) x^2 + (0)x^3 + \left(-\frac{1}{4!} a_0\right) x^4$$

$$+ (0)x^5 + \left(-\frac{1 \cdot 3}{6!} a_0\right) x^6 + \cdots$$

$$y = a_0 \left[1 - \frac{1}{2} x^2 - \frac{1}{4!} x^4 - \frac{1 \cdot 3}{6!} x^6 - \frac{1 \cdot 3 \cdot 5}{8!} x^8 - \cdots \right] + a_1[x]$$

$$y = a_0 \left[1 - \frac{1}{2} x^2 - \sum_{k=2}^{\infty} \frac{1 \cdot 3 \cdot 5 \cdots (2k - 3)}{(2k)!} x^{2k} \right] + a_1[x]. \tag{11}$$

Equation (11) says that two solutions of the original Eq. (4) are

$$y = y_1 = 1 - \frac{1}{2} x^2 - \sum_{k=2}^{\infty} \frac{1 \cdot 3 \cdot 5 \cdots (2k - 3)}{(2k)!} x^{2k} \qquad \text{and} \qquad y = y_2 = x,$$

and that we can get all the solutions by taking linear combinations of these, for a_0 and a_1 in Eq. (11) are arbitrary. Observe that y_1 and y_2 are linearly independent. The ratio test will show that the series used in describing y_1 converges for all x.

Example 4. Consider

$$y'' - xy' + y = x^2, \qquad (12a)$$

for which the corresponding reduced equation is precisely Eq. (4). We know, from our work in Sec. 14.9, that if we can find any one particular solution of Eq. (12a) we can find all others by adding on solutions of the reduced equation, and we have these solutions of the reduced equation in Eq. (11).

Let us return to our series work of Example 3. Equation (8d) says that $y'' - xy' + y$ can be written

$$(2a_2 + a_0) + \sum_{k=1}^{\infty} [(k+2)(k+1)a_{k+2} - (k-1)a_k]x^k$$

under the assumption $y = \sum_{k=0}^{\infty} a_k x^k$. Under the same assumption Eq. (12a) can be written

$$(2a_2 + a_0) + \sum_{k=1}^{\infty} [(k+2)(k+1)a_{k+2} - (k-1)a_k]x^k = x^2$$

or $\qquad (2a_2 + a_0) + 3(2)a_3 x + [4(3)a_4 - a_2]x^2$

$$+ \sum_{k=3}^{\infty} [(k+2)(k+1)a_{k+2} - (k-1)a_k]x^k = x^2. \qquad (12b)$$

If again we say that we have two power series descriptions for the same function, this time for the function x^2, and that the series must be identical, then we must equate coefficients in Eq. (12b) and choose the constants a_k so that we shall have

$$2a_2 + a_0 = 0 \qquad (13a)$$

$$6a_3 = 0 \qquad (13b)$$

$$12a_4 - a_2 = 1 \qquad (13c)$$

$$(k+2)(k+1)a_{k+2} - (k-1)a_k = 0$$

or $\qquad a_{k+2} = \dfrac{k-1}{(k+2)(k+1)}a_k \qquad$ for $k \geq 3$. $\qquad (13d)$

Any one choice for the a_k's will do, because we need only one particular solution. We already have $a_3 = 0$ by Eq. (13b). If we choose $a_4 = 0$, then repeated applications of Eq. (13d) will require that a_5 vanish because a_3 does, that a_6 vanish because a_4 does, and that, indeed, $a_k = 0$ for $k \geq 3$. Our choice $a_4 = 0$ will force us to choose $a_2 = -1$ in order to satisfy Eq. (13c). Then we must choose $a_0 = 2$ in order to satisfy Eq. (13a). Equations (13a) to (13d) impose no condition on a_1. Since we want as simple a particular solution as we can devise, let us choose $a_1 = 0$ also. The particular solution we have found is

$$y = a_0 + a_1 x + a_2 x^2 + \cdots = \sum_{k=0}^{\infty} a_k x^k$$

$$y = 2 + 0x - 1x^2 + 0x^3 + 0x^4 + \cdots$$

$$y = 2 - x^2.$$

Example 5. *Legendre's Equation.* Consider

$$(1 - x^2)y'' - 2xy' + n(n + 1)y = 0 \qquad (14a)$$

or $$y'' - \frac{2x}{1 - x^2}y' + \frac{n(n + 1)}{1 - x^2}y = 0.$$

Here we have a family of differential equations, the parameter n serving to distinguish between the members. The coefficient functions $R(x) = -2x/(1 - x^2)$ and $S(x) = [n(n + 1)]/(1 - x^2)$ have finite singularities only at $x = 1$ and $x = -1$; $x = 0$ is an ordinary point. As we saw in Examples 1A and 1B, where the special case $n = 1$ is considered, Theorem 1 predicts in this case that there will be two linearly independent solutions which can be described by series of positive integer powers of x and that both power series will converge for the interval $-1 < x < 1$ at least.

To find these series let us write

$$y = \sum_{k=0}^{\infty} a_k x^k = a_0 + a_1 x + a_2 x^2 + a_3 x^3 + \cdots$$

as in Example 3 and determine the coefficients a_k. We have

$$y' = \sum_{k=1}^{\infty} k a_k x^{k-1} = a_1 + 2a_2 x + 3a_3 x^2 + \cdots$$

$$y'' = \sum_{k=2}^{\infty} k(k - 1)a_k x^{k-2} = 2a_2 + 3(2)a_3 x + \cdots$$

and Eq. (14a) can be written

$$y'' - x^2 y'' - 2xy' + n(n + 1)y = 0$$

$$\sum_{k=2}^{\infty} k(k - 1)a_k x^{k-2} - \sum_{k=2}^{\infty} k(k - 1)a_k x^k - \sum_{k=1}^{\infty} 2k a_k x^k + \sum_{k=0}^{\infty} n(n + 1)a_k x^k = 0. \quad (14b)$$

Here the first series has general term x^{k-2}, while the others have general term x^k. If we change the summation index for that first series by writing $k = j + 2$, we can write

$$\sum_{k=2}^{\infty} k(k - 1)a_k x^{k-2} = \sum_{j=0}^{\infty} (j + 2)(j + 1)a_{j+2} x^j,$$

and, if we then write $j = k$, Eq. (14b) becomes

$$\sum_{k=0}^{\infty} (k + 2)(k + 1)a_{k+2} x^k - \sum_{k=2}^{\infty} k(k - 1)a_k x^k - \sum_{k=1}^{\infty} 2k a_k x^k + \sum_{k=0}^{\infty} n(n + 1)a_k x^k = 0.$$

Since the second series starts with the x^2 term while the others start with constant or x terms, we separate out the terms of degree less than 2 and write

$$2(1)a_2 + 3(2)a_3x + \sum_{k=2}^{\infty} (k+2)(k+1)a_{k+2}x^k$$

$$-\sum_{k=2}^{\infty} k(k-1)a_kx^k - 2a_1x - \sum_{k=2}^{\infty} 2ka_kx^k + n(n+1)a_0$$

$$+ n(n+1)a_1x + \sum_{k=2}^{\infty} n(n+1)a_kx^k = 0$$

$$[2a_2 + n(n+1)a_0] + [3(2)a_3 + (n^2+n-2)a_1]x$$

$$+ \sum_{k=2}^{\infty} [(k+2)(k+1)a_{k+2} + (n^2+n-k^2-k)a_k]x^k = 0. \qquad (14c)$$

If we now take the coefficients of the various powers of x and set them to 0, because the function 0 which appears as the right member of Eq. (14c) can only have the Taylor series expansion with all coefficients 0, we get

$$a_2 = -\frac{n(n+1)}{2}a_0$$

$$a_3 = -\frac{(n-1)(n+2)}{2(3)}a_1$$

$$a_{k+2} = -\frac{(n-k)(n+k+1)}{(k+2)(k+1)}a_k \qquad \text{for } k \geq 2.$$

From this recurrence relation we read, seriatim,

$$k = 2, a_4 = -\frac{(n-2)(n+3)}{4(3)}a_2 = \frac{n(n-2)(n+1)(n+3)}{4!}a_0$$

$$k = 4, a_6 = -\frac{(n-4)(n+5)}{6(5)}a_4 = -\frac{n(n-2)(n-4)(n+1)(n+3)(n+5)}{6!}a_0$$

$$a_{2k} = (-1)^k$$

$$\frac{[n(n-2)(n-4)\cdots(n-2k+2)][(n+1)(n+3)(n+5)\cdots(n+2k-1)]}{(2k)!}a_0$$

$$k = 3, a_5 = -\frac{(n-3)(n+4)}{5(4)}a_3 = \frac{(n-1)(n-3)(n+2)(n+4)}{5!}a_1$$

$$k = 5, a_7 = -\frac{(n-5)(n+6)}{7(6)}a_5$$

$$= -\frac{(n-1)(n-3)(n-5)(n+2)(n+4)(n+6)}{7!}a_1$$

$$a_{2k+1} = (-1)^k$$

$$\frac{[(n-1)(n-3)(n-5)\cdots(n-2k+1)][(n+2)(n+4)(n+6)\cdots(n+2k)]}{(2k+1)!}a_1.$$

Hence our solution reads

$$y = a_0 + a_1 x + a_2 x^2 + a_3 x^3 + \cdots$$

$$y = a_0 + a_1 x - \frac{n(n+1)}{2!} a_0 x^2 - \frac{(n-1)(n+2)}{3!} a_1 x^3$$

$$+ \frac{n(n-2)(n+1)(n+3)}{4!} a_0 x^4 + \cdots$$

$$y = a_0 \left[1 - \frac{n(n+1)}{2!} x^2 + \frac{n(n-2)(n+1)(n+3)}{4!} x^4 \right.$$

$$\left. - \frac{n(n-2)(n-4)(n+1)(n+3)(n+5)}{6!} x^6 + \cdots \right]$$

$$+ a_1 \left[x - \frac{(n-1)(n+2)}{3!} x^3 + \frac{(n-1)(n-3)(n+2)(n+4)}{5!} x^5 \right.$$

$$\left. - \frac{(n-1)(n-3)(n-5)(n+2)(n+4)(n+6)}{7!} x^7 + \cdots \right]$$

$$y = a_0 \left[1 + \sum_{k=1}^{\infty} (-1)^k \right.$$

$$\left. \frac{\{n(n-2)(n-4)\cdots(n-2k+2)\}\{(n+1)(n+3)(n+5)\cdots(n+2k-1)\}}{(2k)!} x^{2k} \right]$$

$$+ a_1 \left[x + \sum_{k=1}^{\infty} (-1)^k \right.$$

$$\left. \frac{\{(n-1)(n-3)(n-5)\cdots(n-2k+1)\}\{(n+2)(n+4)(n+6)\cdots(n+2k)\}}{(2k+1)!} \right.$$

$$\left. x^{2k+1} \right].$$

We see from this equation that two linearly independent solutions are

$$y = y_1 = 1 + \sum_{k=1}^{\infty} (-1)^k$$

$$\frac{\{n(n-2)(n-4)\cdots(n-2k+2)\}\{(n+1)(n+3)(n+5)\cdots(n+2k-1)\}}{(2k)!} x^{2k} \tag{15a}$$

and

$$y = y_2 = x + \sum_{k=1}^{\infty} (-1)^k$$

$$\frac{\{(n-1)(n-3)(n-5)\cdots(n-2k+1)\}\{(n+2)(n+4)(n+6)\cdots(n+2k)\}}{(2k+1)!} x^{2k+1} \tag{15b}$$

and that other solutions can be written as linear combinations of these. If n is an even integer, the solution $y = y_1$ given by Eq. (15a) will reduce to a polynomial;

if n is an odd integer, the solution $y = y_2$ given by Eq. (15b) will reduce to a polynomial. Thus we have for linearly independent solutions in some of these special cases

$$n = 0: y = y_1 = 1, y = y_2 = x + \frac{x^3}{3} + \frac{x^5}{5} + \frac{x^7}{7} + \cdots = \sum_{k=0}^{\infty} \frac{x^{2k+1}}{2k+1}$$

$$n = 1: y = y_1 = 1 - x^2 - \frac{x^4}{3} - \frac{x^6}{5} - \cdots = -\sum_{k=0}^{\infty} \frac{x^{2k}}{2k-1}, y = y_2 = x$$

$$n = 2: y = y_1 = 1 - 3x^2, y = y_2 = x - \tfrac{2}{3} x^3 - \tfrac{1}{5} x^5 - \tfrac{4}{35} x^7 - \cdots$$

$$= -\sum_{k=0}^{\infty} \frac{k+1}{(2k-1)(2k+1)} x^{2k+1}$$

$$n = 3: y = y_1 = 1 - 6x^2 + 3x^4 + \frac{4}{5} x^6 + \cdots = \sum_{k=0}^{\infty} \frac{3(k+1)}{(2k-3)(2k-1)} x^{2k},$$

$$y = y_2 = x - \tfrac{5}{3} x^3.$$

The reader can check some of these computations from Eqs. (15a) and (15b) and can compute other Legendre Functions in Exercise 14.12-2. He can also show in Exercise 14.12-3 that the series given in Eqs. (15a) and (15b) converge for $-1 < x < 1$, as predicted by Theorem 1.

III

In Examples 3, 4, and 5 we worked out solutions in series of positive integer powers of x. Such series converge relatively rapidly for x of small absolute value. If we were especially interested in series solutions that converged relatively rapidly for an interval of the form $a - \delta < x < a + \delta$ we could develop solutions in series of powers of $(x - a)$ by using the very same technique we have already used; we would determine constants a_k such that

$$y = a_0 + a_1(x - a) + a_2(x - a)^2 + \cdots = \sum_{k=0}^{\infty} a_k(x - a)^k$$

was a solution of the differential equation. Alternatively, we could substitute t for $x - a$, rewrite the differential equation as an equation for y as a function of t, and solve for y in series of powers of $t = x - a$.

If we want solutions for x of large absolute value, we can substitute $1/w$ for x, rewrite the differential equation as an equation for y as a function of w, and solve for y in series of powers of w. Values of x of large absolute value would correspond to values of w of small absolute value.

Example 6.   Find the solutions of

$$x^2(x^2 + 1) \frac{d^2y}{dx^2} + x(2x^2 + 1) \frac{dy}{dx} - 4y = 0 \tag{16a}$$

in series that will converge relatively rapidly for x of large absolute value.

If we write

$$x = \frac{1}{w}, \quad w = \frac{1}{x}$$

$$\frac{dy}{dx} = \frac{dy}{dw}\frac{dw}{dx} = \frac{dy}{dw}\left(-\frac{1}{x^2}\right)$$

$$\frac{d^2y}{dx^2} = \frac{d}{dx}\left(\frac{dy}{dx}\right) = \frac{dy}{dw}\left(\frac{2}{x^3}\right) + \left(-\frac{1}{x^2}\right)\frac{d}{dx}\left(\frac{dy}{dw}\right)$$

$$= \frac{2}{x^3}\frac{dy}{dw} - \frac{1}{x^2}\left[\frac{d}{dw}\left(\frac{dy}{dw}\right)\right]\frac{dw}{dx}$$

$$= \frac{2}{x^3}\frac{dy}{dw} + \frac{1}{x^4}\frac{d^2y}{dw^2},$$

Eq. (16a) becomes

$$x^2(x^2+1)\left[\frac{2}{x^3}\frac{dy}{dw} + \frac{1}{x^4}\frac{d^2y}{dw^2}\right] + x(2x^2+1)\left(-\frac{1}{x^2}\right)\frac{dy}{dw} - 4y = 0$$

$$\left(1 + \frac{1}{x^2}\right)\frac{d^2y}{dw^2} + \frac{1}{x}\frac{dy}{dw} - 4y = 0$$

$$(1+w^2)\frac{d^2y}{dw^2} + w\frac{dy}{dw} - 4y = 0. \tag{16b}$$

Equation (16b) will have solutions in powers of w that will converge for $-1 < w < 1$, according to Theorem 1, and we proceed to find these solutions. Write

$$y = \sum_{k=0}^{\infty} a_k w^k, \quad y' = \sum_{k=1}^{\infty} k a_k w^{k-1}, \quad y'' = \sum_{k=2}^{\infty} k(k-1) a_k w^{k-2},$$

and substitute in Eq. (16b) to get

$$y'' + w^2 y'' + wy' - 4y = 0$$

$$\sum_{k=2}^{\infty} k(k-1)a_k w^{k-2} + \sum_{k=2}^{\infty} k(k-1)a_k w^k + \sum_{k=1}^{\infty} k a_k w^k - \sum_{k=0}^{\infty} 4a_k w^k = 0. \tag{16c}$$

Here, in the first series, substitute $k = j + 2$ and then $j = k$ to get

$$\sum_{k=2}^{\infty} k(k-1)a_k w^{k-2} = \sum_{j=0}^{\infty} (j+2)(j+1)a_{j+2} w^j$$

$$= \sum_{k=0}^{\infty} (k+2)(k+1)a_{k+2} w^k,$$

so that Eq. (16c) becomes

$$\sum_{k=0}^{\infty} (k+2)(k+1)a_{k+2}w^k + \sum_{k=2}^{\infty} k(k-1)a_k w^k + \sum_{k=1}^{\infty} k a_k w^k - \sum_{k=0}^{\infty} 4a_k w^k = 0$$

$$[2(1)a_2 - 4a_0] + [3(2)a_3 - 3a_1]w$$

$$+ \sum_{k=2}^{\infty} [(k+2)(k+1)a_{k+2} + (k^2-4)a_k]w^k = 0. \tag{16d}$$

Now, if we set the coefficients of powers of w to 0, we have the recurrence relations

$$a_2 = 2a_0, \quad a_3 = \tfrac{1}{2} a_1,$$

$$a_{k+2} = -\frac{k^2 - 4}{(k + 2)(k + 1)} a_k = -\frac{k - 2}{k + 1} a_k \quad \text{for } k \geq 2,$$

from which it follows that

$$k = 2, a_4 = 0$$

$$k = 4, a_6 = -\tfrac{2}{5} a_4 = 0$$

$$a_{2k} = 0 \text{ for } k \geq 2$$

$$k = 3, a_5 = -\frac{1}{4} a_3 = -\frac{1}{2 \cdot 4} a_1 = -\frac{1}{2^2 \, 2!} a_1$$

$$k = 5, a_7 = -\frac{3}{6} a_5 = \frac{1 \cdot 3}{2 \cdot 4 \cdot 6} a_1 = \frac{1 \cdot 3}{2^3 \, 3!} a_1$$

$$k = 7, a_9 = -\frac{5}{8} a_7 = -\frac{1 \cdot 3 \cdot 5}{2 \cdot 4 \cdot 6 \cdot 8} a_1 = -\frac{1 \cdot 3 \cdot 5}{2^4 \, 4!} a_1$$

$$a_{2k+1} = (-1)^{k+1} \frac{1 \cdot 3 \cdot 5 \cdots (2k - 3)}{2^k \, k!} a_1.$$

Hence the solutions for Eq. (16d) are

$$y = a_0 + a_1 w + a_2 w^2 + a_3 w^3 + \cdots$$

$$y = a_0[1 + 2w^2] + a_1\left[w + \frac{1}{2} w^3 - \frac{1}{2^2 \, 2!} w^5 + \frac{1 \cdot 3}{2^3 \, 3!} w^7 + \cdots \right]$$

$$y = a_0[1 + 2w^2] + a_1\left[w + \tfrac{1}{2} w^3 + \sum_{k=2}^{\infty} (-1)^{k+1} \frac{1 \cdot 3 \cdot 5 \cdots (2k - 3)}{2^k \, k!} w^{2k+1} \right], \tag{17a}$$

and the solutions for Eq. (16a) are

$$y = a_0\left[1 + \frac{2}{x^2} \right] + a_1\left[\frac{1}{x} + \frac{1}{2}\frac{1}{x^3} + \sum_{k=2}^{\infty} (-1)^{k+1} \frac{1 \cdot 3 \cdot 5 \cdots (2k - 3)}{2^k \, k!} \frac{1}{x^{2k+1}} \right]. \tag{17b}$$

These solutions converge for $|x| > 1$, because the solutions given in Eq. (17a) converged for $|w| < 1$ or $-1 < w < 1$. The larger the absolute value of x, the more rapidly the series written in Eq. (17b) converges.

EXERCISES 14.12

1. Show that $x = 0$ is an ordinary point. Find the singular points. Theorem 1 assures convergence on a certain interval for solutions written as series of positive integer powers of x. Which interval?
   (a) $(x^2 + 4)(x^2 - 1)y'' + (x^2 + 4)y' + (x^2 - 1)y = 0$.
   (b) $(x^2 + x + 2)y'' + xy' - 5y = 0$.
2. In Example 5 solutions of the Legendre Equation were computed from Eqs. (15a) and (15b) for the special cases $n = 0, 1, 2, 3$.
   (a) Check the solutions computed for the case $n = 2$.
   (b) Compute a polynomial solution for the case $n = 4$.

3. Consider the series solution for Legendre's Equation given by Eq. (15b) for the case $n = 2$. Show that this series converges for $-1 < x < 1$, as predicted by Theorem 1.

4. Consider $(1 - x)y' - y = 0$. (a) Find a solution in series of positive integer powers of x. (b) Solve as a separable equation.

5. Consider $y'' + y = 0$ and its solutions in series of positive integer powers of x.
   (a) For which x does Theorem 1 predict convergence?
   (b) Find the series solutions.
   (c) Check by solving as in Sec. 14.8.

6. Repeat Exercise 5 for $y'' - y' = 0$.

7. Refer to Example 3.
   (a) Find one particular solution of $y'' - xy' + y = x$.
   (b) Find the terms through x^6 for any one particular solution of $y'' - xy' + y = e^x$.

   Remember that $e^x = \displaystyle\sum_{k=0}^{\infty} \frac{1}{k!} x^k$.

8. Consider $y'' - xy' = 0$ and its solutions in series of positive integer powers of x.
   (a) For which x does Theorem 1 predict convergence?
   (b) Find the series solutions.
   (c) Also solve by using the ideas of Sec. 14.7.

9. Find one particular solution of $y'' - xy' = 1$.

10. Find the terms through x^7 of the solution of $y'' - xy' = \sin x$ for which $y = y' = 0$ when $x = 0$.

11. (a) Find the solutions of $y'' + xy = 0$ in series of positive integer powers of x.
   (b) Show that one of these solutions converges for all x.
   (c) Find the solutions of $y'' + xy = x$.
   Suggestion: Find one particular solution by observation.
   (d) Find the solutions of $y'' + xy = 1$.

12. Consider $(1 + x^2)y'' - 2y = 0$ and its solutions in series of positive integer powers of x.
   (a) For which x does Theorem 1 predict convergence?
   (b) Find the series solutions.
   (c) Find the interval of convergence for your series solutions.

13. Repeat Exercise 12 for $(1 + x^3)y'' + 6x^2y' + 6xy = 0$.

14. Repeat Exercise 12 for $(1 - x^3)y'' + 12xy = 0$.

15. Consider $y'' + xy' + x^2y = 0$ and its solutions in series of positive integer powers of x. Find the terms through x^5 of that solution for which $y = 1$ and $y' = 0$ when $x = 0$.

16. Consider $(x - 1)y'' + xy' + y = 0$ and its solutions in series of positive integer powers of x. Find the terms through x^5 of that solution for which $y = 1$ and $y' = 0$ when $x = 0$.

17. Consider $(1 - x)^2y'' - 2y = 0$ and its solution in series of positive integer powers of x for which $y = 0$ and $y' = 1$ when $x = 0$. Show that all terms after the x^2 term have the coefficient $\frac{1}{3}$. From this show that the solution is $y = \dfrac{1}{3}\dfrac{1}{1 - x} - \dfrac{1}{3}(1 - x)^2$.

18. Find the solutions of $x^5 \dfrac{d^2y}{dx^2} + (2x^4 - x)\dfrac{dy}{dx} + 3y = 0$ in series that will converge relatively rapidly for x of large absolute value. For which x will these series solutions converge?

14.13 Series Solutions for Linear Equations. Regular Singular Points

In the last section we discussed solutions in series of positive integer powers for the equation

$$y'' + R(x)y' + S(x)y = 0 \tag{1}$$

at an ordinary point. As we said in the discussion of Theorem 14.12-1, there is reason to try for such a series solution at such a point, because $R(x)$ and $S(x)$ have Taylor series expansions at an ordinary point and hence derivatives of all orders there. The equation itself would prescribe the value of y'' at the point in question from given values for y and y', and from differentiated forms of Eq. (1) there would be prescribed the values of y''', y'''',$\cdots$. In particular, the equation for y''' is

$$y''' = -Ry'' - R'y' - Sy' - S'y. \tag{2}$$

The values of y, y', y'', y''',$\cdots$ at the ordinary point, divided by the appropriate factorial numbers, are the coefficients in the Taylor expansion for y, and thus one would hope that the differential equation itself could prescribe the solution in series form. Indeed, Theorem 14.12-1 explains when this is the case.

But if the point under discussion is a singular point, one of R and S does not have a Taylor series expansion there, not all the derivatives of R and S exist at the point, and it may not be possible to compute the derivatives of y and the Taylor expansion for y. To illustrate, if R' does not exist, then one may not be able to compute the value of y''' at the singular point from Eq. (2). At a singular point, then, one would not expect always to describe a solution y by means of a Taylor series.

Without real loss of generality, let us assume that the singular point we wish to discuss is $x = 0$; the substitution $t = x - a$ would associate the point $t = 0$ with $x = a$ if we had a different point $x = a$ to discuss. Among the simplest functions that do not have Taylor expansions at $x = 0$ are $x^{5/2}$, x^{-1}, and $\log x$. For $f(x) = x^{5/2}$, for instance, we can compute $f(0)$, $f'(0)$, and $f''(0)$, but $f'''(0)$ does not exist. It would seem to make sense therefore to see if one could find a solution of the form

$$y = x^c[a_0 + a_1 x + a_2 x^2 + a_3 x^3 + \cdots] = x^c \sum_{k=0}^{\infty} a_k x^k$$

when $x = 0$ is a singular point. By proper choice of the constant c, perhaps as a negative number or as a positive number that is not an integer, one might be able to arrive at a description of a solution of Eq. (1) that is not a Taylor series expansion. Another experiment that might make sense would be an attempt to find a solution in the form

$$y = \log x[a_0 + a_1 x + a_2 x^2 + a_3 x^3 + \cdots] = \log x[\sum_{k=0}^{\infty} a_k x^k].$$

Example 1. Consider the equation

$$y'' + \left(1 + \frac{1}{2x}\right)y' + \frac{2}{x}y = 0 \tag{3a}$$

or $\qquad\qquad\qquad xy'' + (x + \tfrac{1}{2})y' + 2y = 0. \tag{3b}$

The coefficients $R(x) = 1 + 1/2x$ and $S(x) = 2/x$ do not have expansions in positive integer powers of x, and $x = 0$ is a singular point for the equation. We shall not attempt, then, to find a solution in the form $y = \sum_{k=0}^{\infty} a_k x^k$, as we did for ordinary points in the last section, but we shall try instead to choose constants c and $a_0, a_1, a_2, \cdots$ in such a way that

$$y = x^c(a_0 + a_1 x + a_2 x^2 + \cdots) = x^c \sum_{k=0}^{\infty} a_k x^k = \sum_{k=0}^{\infty} a_k x^{c+k} \qquad (4)$$

is a solution.

Let us assume, as is discussed in an advanced calculus course, that the new series one gets by summing the derivatives of the terms of the series in Eq. (4) represents y'. Then we shall have

$$y' = \sum_{k=0}^{\infty} (c + k) a_k x^{c+k-1}, \qquad y'' = \sum_{k=0}^{\infty} (c + k)(c + k - 1) a_k x^{c+k-2}$$

and Eq. (3b) becomes

$$\sum_{k=0}^{\infty} (c + k)(c + k - 1) a_k x^{c+k-1} + \sum_{k=0}^{\infty} (c + k) a_k x^{c+k}$$

$$+ \sum_{k=0}^{\infty} \tfrac{1}{2} (c + k) a_k x^{c+k-1} + \sum_{k=0}^{\infty} 2 a_k x^{c+k} = 0.$$

If we now replace k by $j + 1$ in the first and third series, and then replace j by k, our differential equation becomes

$$\sum_{k=-1}^{\infty} (c + k + 1)(c + k) a_{k+1} x^{c+k} + \sum_{k=0}^{\infty} (c + k) a_k x^{c+k}$$

$$+ \sum_{k=-1}^{\infty} \tfrac{1}{2}(c + k + 1) a_{k+1} x^{c+k} + \sum_{k=0}^{\infty} 2 a_k x^{c+k} = 0.$$

Let us combine the first and third series, and also the second and fourth, and let the sums start in each case with the $k = 0$ term. The differential equation becomes

$$[c(c - 1) + \tfrac{1}{2} c] a_0 x^{c-1}$$

$$+ \sum_{k=0}^{\infty} \{[(c + k + 1)(c + k) + \tfrac{1}{2} (c + k + 1)] a_{k+1} + [(c + k) + 2] a_k\} x^{c+k} = 0$$

or

$$c(c - \tfrac{1}{2}) a_0 x^{c-1} + \sum_{k=0}^{\infty} [(c + k + 1)(c + k + \tfrac{1}{2}) a_{k+1} + (c + k + 2) a_k] x^{c+k}$$
$$= 0. \qquad (5)$$

When we equate the coefficient of the x^{c-1} term to 0, we see that a_0 will vanish unless we choose $c = 0$ or $c = \tfrac{1}{2}$. Let us consider the choice $c = 0$ first. If we set the coefficients of all the other powers of x equal to 0, we find the recurrence relation

$$(c + k + 1)(c + k + \tfrac{1}{2})a_{k+1} + (c + k + 2)a_k = 0,$$

$$a_{k+1} = -\frac{k + 2}{(k + 1)(k + 1/2)} a_k = -\frac{2(k + 2)}{(k + 1)(2k + 1)} a_k \qquad \text{for } k \geq 0.$$

From this equation we find upon substituting $k = 0, 1, 2, \cdots$ that

$$a_1 = -\frac{2(2)}{1(1)} a_0 = -2\frac{2}{1} a_0$$

$$a_2 = -\frac{2(3)}{2(3)} a_1 = (2)^2 \frac{3}{1 \cdot 3} a_0$$

$$a_3 = -\frac{2(4)}{3(5)} a_2 = -(2)^3 \frac{4}{1 \cdot 3 \cdot 5} a_0$$

$$a_4 = -\frac{2(5)}{4(7)} a_3 = (2)^4 \frac{5}{1 \cdot 3 \cdot 5 \cdot 7} a_0$$

$$a_k = (-1)^k 2^k \frac{k + 1}{1 \cdot 3 \cdot 5 \cdots (2k - 1)} a_0.$$

Hence the solution our computation suggests is

$$y = x^c(a_0 + a_1 x + a_2 x^2 + a_3 x^3 + \cdots)$$

$$y = 1a_0\left[1 - 2\frac{2}{1}x + 2^2 \frac{3}{1 \cdot 3}x^2 - 2^3 \frac{4}{1 \cdot 3 \cdot 5}x^3 + 2^4 \frac{5}{1 \cdot 3 \cdot 5 \cdot 7}x^4 - \cdots \right]$$

$$y = a_0\left[1 + \sum_{k=1}^{\infty} (-1)^k 2^k \frac{k + 1}{1 \cdot 3 \cdot 5 \cdots (2k - 1)}x^k \right], \tag{6}$$

where a_0 is an arbitrary constant.

Let us consider next the possibility $c = \tfrac{1}{2}$. When we return to Eq. (5) and set coefficients to 0 again, we get the recurrence relations

$$a_{k+1} = -\frac{k + 5/2}{(k + 3/2)(k + 1)} a_k = -\frac{2k + 5}{(2k + 3)(k + 1)} a_k \qquad \text{for } k \geq 0.$$

Now we must choose

$$a_1 = -\frac{5}{3(1)} a_0$$

$$a_2 = -\frac{7}{5(2)} a_1 = \frac{7}{3(2!)} a_0$$

$$a_3 = -\frac{9}{7(3)} a_2 = -\frac{9}{3(3!)} a_0$$

$$a_4 = -\frac{11}{9(4)} a_3 = \frac{11}{3(4!)} a_0$$

$$a_k = (-1)^k \frac{2k + 3}{3(k!)} a_0$$

and the solution suggested is

$$y = x^c(a_0 + a_1x + a_2x^2 + a_3x^3 + \cdots)$$

$$y = x^{1/2}a_0\left[1 - \frac{5}{3(1!)}x + \frac{7}{3(2!)}x^2 - \frac{9}{3(3!)}x^3 + \cdots\right]$$

$$y = \tfrac{1}{3}\,a_0x^{1/2}\sum_{k=0}^{\infty}(-1)^k\frac{2k+3}{k!}x^k, \tag{7}$$

where $\tfrac{1}{3}a_0$ is an arbitrary constant.

The series stated in Eqs. (6) and (7) converge for all x, as the reader can show in Exercise 14.13-1. Perhaps one would have guessed this to be the case, for Eq. (3a) has no other singular point at a finite distance from $x = 0$. By taking linear combinations of the solutions offered by Eqs. (6) and (7) we can get all other solutions of Eq. (3a).

Example 2. The reduced equation for

$$xy'' + (x + \tfrac{1}{2})y' + 2y = x \tag{8}$$

is precisely Eq. (3b). Hence if we can find any one particular solution of Eq. (8) we can find all others by adding already known solutions of Eq. (3b).

If we write $y = x^c\sum_{k=0}^{\infty}a_kx^k$ again, then we learn from Eq. (5) that Eq. (8) can be rewritten as

$$c(c - \tfrac{1}{2})a_0x^{c-1} + \sum_{k=0}^{\infty}[(c + k + 1)(c + k + \tfrac{1}{2})a_{k+1} + (c + k + 2)a_k]x^{c+k}$$

$$= x. \tag{9}$$

If we choose $c = 0$, we shall have integral powers of x for the left member and it may be possible to equate coefficients for the left and right members of Eq. (9). In greater detail, Eq. (9) becomes

$$(\tfrac{1}{2}a_1 + 2a_0) + (3a_2 + 3a_1)x$$

$$+ \sum_{k=2}^{\infty}[(k + 1)(k + \tfrac{1}{2})a_{k+1} + (k + 2)a_k]x^k = x,$$

and if we equate coefficients we find that we must choose the a_k's so that

$$\tfrac{1}{2}a_1 + 2a_0 = 0 \tag{10a}$$

$$3a_2 + 3a_1 = 1 \tag{10b}$$

$$a_{k+1} = -\frac{k+2}{(k+1)(k+1/2)}a_k \qquad \text{for } k \geq 2. \tag{10c}$$

Perhaps the simplest alternative is to choose $a_2 = 0$. Then Eqs. (10c) will be satisfied if $a_3 = a_4 = \cdots = 0$, Eq. (10b) will be satisfied if $a_1 = \tfrac{1}{3}$, and Eq. (10a) will be satisfied if $a_0 = -\tfrac{1}{12}$. The particular solution we found for Eq. (8) is

$$y = x^c(a_0 + a_1x + a_2x^2 + a_3x^3 + \cdots)$$

$$y = -\tfrac{1}{12} + \tfrac{1}{3}x.$$

Can we state a theorem which will tell us when the modified power series approach that we used successfully in Example 1 can be expected to lead us to solutions? Suppose then that $x = 0$ is a singular point for the differential equation

$$y'' + R(x)y' + S(x)y = 0 \qquad (1)$$

and that we try to find a solution in the form

$$y = x^c \sum_{k=0}^{\infty} a_k x^k = \sum_{k=0}^{\infty} a_k x^{k+c}.$$

When we write

$$y' = \sum_{k=0}^{\infty} (k + c)a_k x^{k+c-1}, \qquad y'' = \sum_{k=0}^{\infty} (k + c)(k + c - 1)a_k x^{k+c-2}$$

the differential equation becomes

$$\sum_{k=0}^{\infty} (k + c)(k + c - 1)a_k x^{k+c-2} + R(x) \left[\sum_{k=0}^{\infty} (k + c)a_k x^{k+c-1} \right]$$

$$+ S(x) \left[\sum_{k=0}^{\infty} a_k x^{k+c} \right] = 0,$$

or, if we multiply by x^2,

$$\sum_{k=0}^{\infty} (k + c)(k + c - 1)a_k x^{k+c} + xR(x) \left[\sum_{k=0}^{\infty} (k + c)a_k x^{k+c} \right]$$

$$+ x^2 S(x) \left[\sum_{k=0}^{\infty} a_k x^{k+c} \right] = 0. \qquad (11)$$

This equation suggests that it might be possible to combine series, set coefficients to 0, and ultimately find a solution if the functions $xR(x)$ and $x^2 S(x)$ can be described by series of positive integer powers of x. In particular, suppose that

$$xR(x) = r_0 + r_1 x + r_2 x^2 + \cdots$$

$$x^2 S(x) = s_0 + s_1 x + s_2 x^2 + \cdots.$$

Then, if we try to arrange the terms of Eq. (11) in ascending order, we get

$$[c(c - 1) + r_0 c + s_0]a_0 x^c + \{[(c + 1)c + r_0(c + 1) + s_0]a_1 + [r_1 c + s_1]a_0\}x^{c+1}$$

$$+ \cdots + \{[(k + c)(k + c - 1) + r_0 (k + c) + s_0] a_k + \cdots + [r_k c + s_k]a_0\}$$

$$x^{c+k} + \cdots = 0. \qquad (12a)$$

For the sake of abbreviation we can write

$$\tau(b) = b(b - 1) + r_0 b + s_0,$$

and rewrite Eq. (12a) in the form

$$\tau(c)a_0 x^c + \{\tau(1 + c)a_1 + [r_1 c + s_1]a_0\}x^{c+1} + \cdots$$

$$+ \{\tau(k + c)a_k + \cdots + [r_k c + s_k]a_0\}x^{c+k} + \cdots = 0. \qquad (12b)$$

The process of setting coefficients to 0 starts with the quadratic equation

$$\tau(c) = c(c - 1) + r_0 c + s_0 = 0,$$

called the *indicial equation*. In general this indicial equation will have two roots, say c_1 and c_2, and except in the case where these roots are equal or differ by an integer, one could expect to determine two solutions. For, by choosing $c = c_1$, so that $\tau(c_1) = 0$, the coefficient of x^{c_1} in Eq. (12b) is made to vanish without forcing a_0 to be 0. By setting the x^{c_1+1} coefficient to 0 we determine a_1 in terms of a_0; by setting the x^{c_1+2} coefficient to 0 we determine a_2 in terms of a_0 and a_1, and so on. By choosing $c = c_2$ we could hope to determine a second solution by a similar process.

This procedure cannot be counted on, however, if the two roots of the indicial equation differ by an integer. Suppose, for instance, that $c_2 = c_1 + m$, m an integer. Then $\tau(c_2) = 0$ or $\tau(c_1 + m) = \tau(m + c_1) = 0$ and the x^{c_1+m} coefficient of Eq. (12b), which in general is

$$\tau(m + c_1)a_m + \cdots + [r_m c_1 + s_m]a_0,$$

would not contain a_m, thus making it impossible to determine a_m from the earlier $a_0, a_1, \cdots, a_{m-1}$ by this particular process.

We can summarize this discussion by stating a definition and theorem.

■ DEFINITION 1

Regular singular point. The point $x = a$ is a regular singular point for the differential equation

$$y'' + R(x)y' + S(x)y = 0 \tag{1}$$

if one or both of $R(x)$ and $S(x)$ do not have expansions in positive integer powers of $(x - a)$ but if both $(x - a)R(x)$ and $(x - a)^2 S(x)$ do.

■ THEOREM 1

On solutions at regular singular points.

HYPOTHESIS: (a) $x = 0$ is a regular singular point for $y'' + R(x)y' + S(x)y = 0$ and $xR(x)$ has the series description $r_0 + r_1 x + r_2 x^2 + \cdots$ while $x^2 S(x)$ has the series description $s_0 + s_1 x + s_2 x^2 + \cdots$.

(b) The roots c_1 and c_2 of the indicial equation $c(c - 1) + r_0 c + s_0 = 0$ are distinct and do not differ by an integer.

(c) The singular point nearest to $x = 0$ is at a distance d, as measured in the complex plane.

CONCLUSION: (a) There are two linearly independent solutions for $y'' + R(x)y' + S(x)y = 0$, one in the form

$$y = x^{c_1} \sum_{k=0}^{\infty} a_k x^k$$

and the other in the form

$$y = x^{c_2} \sum_{k=0}^{\infty} b_k x^k.$$

(b) The series that arise in these solutions will converge at least for the interval $-d < x < d$.

● **Remark 1**

We have tried to make this theorem plausible, but the proof, like the proof of Theorem 14.12-1, is beyond the scope of this book. Among other things, the proof requires more background in complex variable theory than this book could present.

Example 3.   *The Bessel Equation.* Consider the equation

$$x^2 y'' + xy' + (x^2 - n^2)y = 0 \tag{13a}$$

or

$$y'' + \frac{1}{x}y' + \left(1 - \frac{n^2}{x^2}\right)y = 0. \tag{13b}$$

Here n is a parameter; for different choices of n we get different equations. The point $x = 0$ is a regular singular point, because $xR(x) = 1$ and $x^2 S(x) = x^2 - n^2$ have obvious expansions in positive integral powers of x. Theorem 1 predicts then that we can find two linearly independent solutions of the form $x^c \sum_{k=0}^{\infty} a_k x^k$ in the cases in which the indicial equation has distinct roots which do not differ by an integer.

Let us write

$$y = \sum_{k=0}^{\infty} a_k^{c+k}, \qquad y' = \sum_{k=0}^{\infty} (c + k)a_k x^{c+k-1},$$

$$y'' = \sum_{k=0}^{\infty} (c + k)(c + k - 1)a_k x^{c+k-2}.$$

Equation (13a) becomes, upon substitution,

$$\sum_{k=0}^{\infty} (c + k)(c + k - 1)a_k x^{c+k} + \sum_{k=0}^{\infty} (c + k)a_k x^{c+k}$$

$$\sum_{k=0}^{\infty} a_k x^{c+k+2} - \sum_{k=0}^{\infty} n^2 a_k x^{c+k} = 0.$$

If we replace k by $j - 2$ and then j by k in the third sum, and combine the first, second, and fourth sums, we have

$$\sum_{k=0}^{\infty} [(c + k)^2 - n^2]a_k x^{c+k} + \sum_{k=2}^{\infty} a_{k-2} x^{c+k} = 0,$$

which can be written

$$(c^2 - n^2)a_0 x^c + [(c + 1)^2 - n^2]a_1 x^{c+1}$$

$$+ \sum_{k=2}^{\infty} \{[(c + k)^2 - n^2]a_k + a_{k-2}\} x^{c+k} = 0. \tag{13c}$$

When we equate the coefficient of the x^c term to 0, we get the indicial equation

$$c^2 - n^2 = 0,$$

whose roots are $c = n$ and $c = -n$.

For the choice $c = n$ we find as we continue to equate coefficients in Eq. (13c) to 0 that, unless $n = -\frac{1}{2}$, we must have

$$a_1 = 0$$

$$a_k = -\frac{1}{(n+k)^2 - n^2}a_{k-2} = -\frac{1}{k(k+2n)}a_{k-2} \quad \text{for } k \geq 2.$$

Hence

$$a_2 = -\frac{1}{2(2+2n)}a_0 = -\frac{1}{2^2(1!)(1+n)}a_0$$

$$a_4 = -\frac{1}{4(4+2n)}a_2 = \frac{1}{2^4(2!)(1+n)(2+n)}a_0$$

$$a_6 = -\frac{1}{6(6+2n)}a_4 = -\frac{1}{2^6(3!)(1+n)(2+n)(3+n)}a_0$$

$$a_{2k} = (-1)^k \frac{1}{2^{2k}(k!)(1+n)(2+n)(3+n)\cdots(k+n)}a_0 \quad \text{for } k \geq 1,$$

while

$$a_3 = -\frac{1}{3(3+2n)}a_1 = 0$$

$$a_{2k+1} = 0 \quad \text{for } k \geq 0.$$

The solution suggested by our work is

$$y = x^c(a_0 + a_1x + a_2x^2 + \cdots)$$

$$y = x^n a_0\left[1 - \frac{1}{2^2(1!)(1+n)}x^2 + \frac{1}{2^4(2!)(1+n)(2+n)}x^4 - \cdots\right]$$

$$y = a_0 x^n\left[1 + \sum_{k=1}^{\infty} (-1)^k \frac{1}{2^{2k}(k!)(1+n)(2+n)(3+n)\cdots(k+n)}x^{2k}\right],$$

$$\tag{14a}$$

where a_0 is an arbitrary constant.

If we return to the indicial equation and take the choice $c = -n$, we find that, unless $n = \frac{1}{2}$, Eq. (13c) forces us to choose

$$a_1 = 0$$

$$a_k = -\frac{1}{k(k-2n)}a_{k-2} \quad \text{for } k \geq 2,$$

and then ultimately to choose

$$a_{2k} = (-1)^k \frac{1}{2^{2k}(k!)(1-n)(2-n)(3-n)\cdots(k-n)}a_0 \quad \text{for } k \geq 1$$

$$a_{2k+1} = 0 \quad \text{for } k \geq 0.$$

This time the suggested solution is

$$y = a_0 x^{-n} \left[1 - \frac{1}{2^2(1!)(1-n)}x^2 + \frac{1}{2^4(2!)(1-n)(2-n)}x^4 - \cdots \right]$$

$$y = a_0 x^{-n} \left[1 + \sum_{k=1}^{\infty} (-1)^k \frac{1}{2^{2k}(k!)(1-n)(2-n)(3-n)\cdots(k-n)}x^{2k} \right],$$
(14b)

where a_0 is an arbitrary constant.

If $n = 0$ we have a Bessel equation whose indicial equation has only the one root $c = 0$. The solutions written in Eqs. (14a) and (14b) are identical in this case, and we get only one solution of the Bessel equation by this process. If n is a positive integer, then, the roots of the indicial equation differ by $(n) - (-n) = 2n$, which is an integer, and we find that the solution suggested by Eq. (14b) makes no sense because the coefficients of the terms are not finite from a certain term on. Again, we get only one solution by this process.

The reader can show, however, in Exercises 14.13-9 and 14.13-10 that there are two solutions when $n = \frac{1}{2}$ and again when $n = \frac{3}{2}$, even though the roots of the indicial equation differ by an integer in each of these cases also. This points out that Theorem 1 predicts what will happen when the roots of the indicial equation are distinct and do not differ by an integer. Theorem 1 says nothing about the case in which the roots of the indicial equation are equal or do differ by an integer. If the hypotheses of Theorem 1 are not satisfied, the conclusion of Theorem 1 may or may not hold.

Finally, $x = 0$ is the only singular point in finite position for the Bessel equation and Theorem 1 predicts that the solutions we get will converge for all x. The reader can show in Exercise 14.13-8 that the solution suggested by Eq. (14a) converges for all x, except of course in the case where n is a negative integer, in which case this solution does not exist.

To conclude this discussion of series solutions for linear equations at regular singular points, we make two suggestions for trying to get a second solution in cases where the trial $y = x^c \sum_{k=0}^{\infty} a_k x^k$ could only lead to one solution. The first suggestion is to find the second solution by varying the first, as was done in Secs. 14.8 and 14.9. Thus, if $y = y_1(x)$ is known to be a solution, it is sometimes useful to try to determine $w(x)$ such that $y = w(x)y_1(x)$ shall be a solution. Exercises 14.13-14 and 14.13-15 consider this idea.

The second suggestion is to try to find a solution in the form $y = (\log x)$ $(\sum_{k=0}^{\infty} a_k x^{k+c})$. In this connection we state the following extension of Theorem 1 without proof.

■ THEOREM 2

On solutions at regular singular points.

HYPOTHESIS: (a) $x = 0$ is a regular singular point for $y'' + R(x)y' + S(x)y = 0$ and $xR(x)$ has the series description $r_0 + r_1 x + r_2 x^2 + \cdots$ while $x^2 S(x)$ has the series description $s_0 + s_1 x + s_2 x^2 + \cdots$.

(b) The roots c_1 and c_2 of the indicial equation $c(c-1) + r_0c + s_0 = 0$ are equal or differ by an integer, $c_1 \geq c_2$.

(c) The singular point nearest to $x = 0$ is at a distance d, as measured in the complex plane.

CONCLUSION: (a) There are two linearly independent solutions for y'' $+ R(x)y' + S(x)y = 0$, one in the form

$$y = x^{c_1} \sum_{k=0}^{\infty} a_k x^k$$

and the other in the form

$$y = x^{c_2} \sum_{k=0}^{\infty} b_k x^k + b \, x^{c_1} \log x \sum_{k=0}^{\infty} a_k \, x^k \,, \, b \text{ a constant.}$$

(b) The series that arise in these solutions will converge at least for the interval $-d < x < d$.

Exercises 14.13-11 and 14.13-14 illustrate the statement of this theorem.

EXERCISES 14.13

1. In Example 1 solutions given by Eqs. (6) and (7) were computed. Show that there is convergence for all x for the solution of (a) Eq. (6) and (b) Eq. (7).

2. Find two linearly independent solutions for $x^2y'' + (\frac{3}{16} + \frac{1}{16}x) \, y = 0$ using series of powers of x. For which x does Theorem 1 predict convergence?

3. Repeat Exercise 2 for $x^2y'' + xy' + (x-2)y = 0$.

4. Repeat Exercise 2 for $x(x^2+3)y'' + (5x^2+1)y' + 4xy = 0$.

5. Repeat Exercise 2 for $x^2(x^2-2)y'' + xy' + 2y = 0$.

6. (a) Repeat Exercise 2 for $x^2y'' + x(x - \frac{1}{2})y' + \frac{1}{2}y = 0$.
   (b) Find a particular solution of $x^2y'' + x(x - \frac{1}{2})y' + \frac{1}{2}\,y = 1$ by observation.
   (c) Find a particular solution of $x^2y'' + x(x - \frac{1}{2})y' + \frac{1}{2}\,y = x^2$.

7. (a) Repeat Exercise 2 for $x^2(x+1)y'' + xy' - (\frac{10}{9}x + \frac{1}{9})y = 0$.
   (b) Find a particular solution of $x^2(x+1)y'' + xy' - (\frac{10}{9}x + \frac{1}{9})y = x$.

8. Show that the solution of the Bessel equation furnished by Eq. (14a) converges for all x, as the conclusion of Theorem 1 requires.

9. Consider the Bessel equation (13a) for the case $n = \frac{1}{2}$. Use the indicial equa-
   tion root $c = -\frac{1}{2}$ in Eq. (13c). Derive the solution $y = x^{-1/2}\left[a_0 \sum_{k=0}^{\infty} (-1)^k \frac{x^{2k}}{(2k)!} \right.$
   $\left. + a_1 \sum_{k=0}^{\infty} (-1)^k \frac{x^{2k+1}}{(2k+1)!} \right] = x^{-1/2} [a_0 \cos x + a_1 \sin x].$

10. Consider the Bessel equation (13a) for the case $n = \frac{3}{2}$. Write out the solutions furnished by Eqs. (14a) and (14b) and observe that they are linearly independent.

11. Consider the Bessel equation (13a) for the case $n = 0$. In this case Eqs. (14a) and (14b) furnish the same solution, namely,

$$y = \sum_{k=0}^{\infty} (-1)^k \frac{1}{(k!)^2} \left(\frac{x}{2}\right)^{2k}.$$

The second solution, in Neuman's form, is

$$y = \log x \left[\sum_{k=0}^{\infty} (-1)^k \frac{1}{(k!)^2} \left(\frac{x}{2} \right)^{2k} \right]$$

$$+ \sum_{k=1}^{\infty} (-1)^{k+1} \frac{1}{(k!)^2} \left(1 + \frac{1}{2} + \frac{1}{3} + \cdots + \frac{1}{k} \right) \left(\frac{x}{2} \right)^{2k}.$$

(a) Checking this second solution by substitution in the differential equation is tedious, but substitute the approximation you get by taking the terms in the series through the x^4 term and see what happens.

(b) Explain in detail how Neuman's solution serves as an illustration of Theorem 2.

12. (a) Find two linearly independent solutions for $xy'' + 2y' + x^2y = 0$ using series of powers of x. Note that one gets two linearly independent solutions even though the roots of the indicial equation differ by an integer.

(b) Find a particular solution of $xy'' + 2y' + x^2y = 1$.

13. (a) Find two linearly independent solutions for $xy'' + (x^3 - 1)y' + x^2y = 0$, using series of powers of x. Note that one gets two linearly independent solutions even though the roots of the indicial equation differ by an integer.

(b) Find a particular solution of $xy'' + (x^3 - 1)y' + x^2y = \dfrac{1}{x^2}$.

14. (a) Consider $x(1 - x)y'' + xy' - y = 0$. Show that the roots of the indicial equation differ by an integer. Derive the solution $y = x$.

(b) Derive a second solution by determining $w(x)$ such that $y = wx$ is a solution. Explain in detail how your second solution is an illustration of Theorem 2.

(c) Find one particular solution of $x(1 - x)y'' + xy' - y = x^{1/2}$.

15. (a) Consider $xy'' + xy' + y = 0$. Show that the roots of the indicial equation differ

by an integer. Derive the solution $y = \sum_{k=1}^{\infty} (-1)^{k-1} \dfrac{1}{(k-1)!} x^k = xe^{-x}$.

(b) Derive a second solution by determining $w(x)$ such that $y = wxe^{-x}$ is a solution.

(c) Find one particular solution of $xy'' + xy' + y = x^2$.

16. *The hypergeometric equation.* **Consider**

$$x(1 - x)\, y'' + [\gamma - (\alpha + \beta + 1)x]\, y' - \alpha\beta y = 0,$$

where α, β, γ are constants.

(a) Show that 0 and $1 - \gamma$ are the roots of the indicial equation and that the solution corresponding to the root 0 is

$$y = 1$$

$$+ \sum_{k=1}^{\infty} \frac{[\alpha(\alpha + 1)(\alpha + 2)\cdots(\alpha + k - 1)][\beta(\beta + 1)(\beta + 2)\cdots(\beta + k - 1)]}{k![\gamma(\gamma + 1)(\gamma + 2)\cdots(\gamma + k - 1)]} x^k.$$

Let us refer to this solution as $y = F(\alpha, \beta; \gamma; x)$.

(b) Show that the solution corresponding to the indicial equation root $1 - \gamma$ is
$$y = x^{1-\gamma} F(1 + \alpha - \gamma, 1 + \beta - \gamma; 2 - \gamma; x).$$
Suggestion: Observe that the recursion formula used for this solution reduces to that used for the first solution if $1 + \alpha - \gamma$, $1 + \beta - \gamma$, and $2 - \gamma$ are identified with α, β, and γ.

(c) Show by direct differentiation that $\dfrac{d}{dx} F(\alpha, \beta; \gamma; x) = \dfrac{\alpha\beta}{\gamma} F(\alpha + 1, \beta + 1; \gamma + 1; x)$.

Appendix

A1   Inequalities

We shall assume that when given two real numbers the reader can tell which one is larger. One way of describing the ordering of the real numbers is to set up a one-to-one correspondence between the real numbers and the points on a horizontal line, as indicated in Fig. A1.1, and to say that number a is greater than

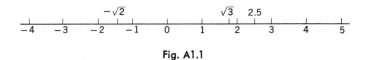

Fig. A1.1

number b if and only if the point corresponding to a lies to the right of the point corresponding to b.

Example 1.   5 is greater than 3, or 3 is less than 5.
Example 2.   2.5 is greater than $\sqrt{3}$, or $\sqrt{3}$ is less than 2.5.
Example 3. -1 is less than 0.
Example 4. -1 is greater than -3.
Example 5. $-\sqrt{2}$ is less than -1 and greater than -2.

■ NOTATION CONVENTION 1

$a > b$ means a is greater than b.
$c < d$ means c is less than d.

■ NOTATION CONVENTION 2

$a \geq b$ means a is greater than, or equal to, b.
$c \leq d$ means c is less than, or equal to, d.

■ NOTATION CONVENTION 3

$a < b < c$ means $a < b$ and $b < c$.
$a \leq b \leq c$ means $a \leq b$ and $b \leq c$.
$a \leq b < c$ means $a \leq b$ and $b < c$.
$a < b \leq c$ means $a < b$ and $b \leq c$.

Examples 1 to 5 may be rewritten in the inequality notation as follows.

Example 1A. $5 > 3$, or $3 < 5$.
Example 2A. $2.5 > \sqrt{3}$, or $\sqrt{3} < 2.5$.
Example 3A. $-1 < 0$.
Example 4A. $-1 > -3$.
Example 5A. $-2 < -\sqrt{2} < -1$.
Example 6. $\sqrt{x}$ is a real number if and only if $x \geq 0$.
Example 7.   The quadratic formula tells us that the roots of $ax^2 + bx + c = 0$ are

$$x = \frac{-b \pm \sqrt{b^2 - 4ac}}{2a}.$$

These roots are real if $b^2 - 4ac \geq 0$ and not real if $b^2 - 4ac < 0$.

Example 8.   In trigonometry we learn that $-1 \leq \sin \theta \leq 1$ for any real number θ. Similarly, $-1 \leq \cos \theta \leq 1$.

We can rewrite inequalities by using the following theorems.

■ THEOREM 1

HYPOTHESIS: $a > b$.

CONCLUSION: $a + c > b + c$.

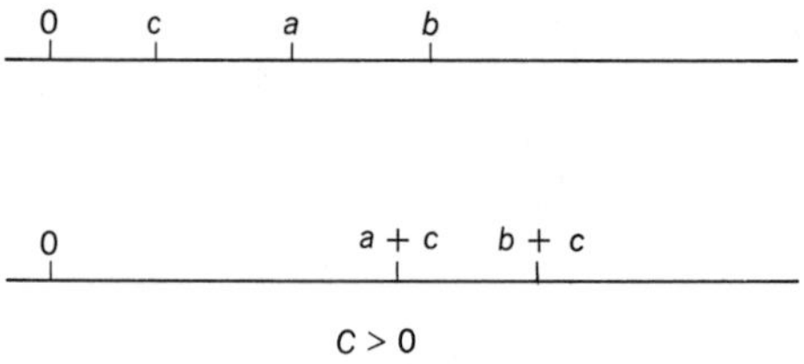

c > 0

Fig. A1.2

In words, if we add the same number to both members of an inequality, the sense of the inequality is preserved.

PROOF: If c is a positive number, the numbers $a + c$ and $b + c$ are represented by points that lie c units to the right of the points that represent a and b. The numerical operation of adding c amounts to shifting a point on the number scale of Fig. A1.2 to the right a distance c. If c had been negative, the points on the number scale would have been shifted to the left. In both cases the relative right-left order of two points is preserved.

Example 9.   We know that $3 < 4$. If we add 5 to both members, we get $8 < 9$; the left member is again smaller than the right member. If we add -5 to both members, we get $-2 < -1$. The sense of the inequality is preserved again.

■ THEOREM 2

HYPOTHESIS: (a) $a > b$,
(b) $c > 0$.

CONCLUSION: $ca > cb$.

In words, if we multiply both members of an inequality by a *positive* number, the sense of the inequality is preserved.

PROOF: Hypothesis (b) says that c is positive, and from Hypothesis (a) we find by adding $-b$ to both members that $a - b > b - b = 0$, so that $a - b$ is positive also. Hence $ca - cb = c(a - b)$ is the product of two positive numbers and positive; $ca - cb > 0$. If we now add cb to both members, we arrive at our conclusion.

Example 10.   We know that $3 < 4$. If we multiply both members by 2, we get $6 < 8$. The left member is again smaller than the right member.

Example 11.   We know that $-3 > -4$. If we multiply both members by $\frac{1}{2}$ we get $-\frac{3}{2} > -2$. The sense of the inequality is preserved.

■ THEOREM 3

HYPOTHESIS: (a) $a > b$,
(b) $d < 0$.

CONCLUSION: $da < db$.

In words, if we multiply both members of an inequality by a *negative* number, the sense of the inequality is reversed.

PROOF: The proof can be modeled after that of Theorem 2, and is left to the reader as an exercise.

Example 12.   We know that $1 < 2$. If we multiply both members by -3, we get $-3 > -6$. Where the left member of the first inequality was the smaller number, the left member of the second inequality is the larger. The sense of the inequality was reversed.

Example 13.   If we multiply both members of $-2 < 1$ by $-\frac{1}{2}$, we get $1 > -\frac{1}{2}$.

■ THEOREM 4

HYPOTHESIS: (a) $a > b$,
(b) $c > d$.

CONCLUSION: $a + c > b + d$.

PROOF: We know that $a - b > 0$, for we can add $-b$ to both members of the statement of Hypothesis (a). Similarly, $c - d > 0$, by Hypothesis (b). But $(a + c) - (b + d) = (a - b) + (c - d)$ and must be positive, because it is the sum of two positive numbers; $(a + c) - (b + d) > 0$. If we now add $b + d$ to both members, we obtain the statement in the conclusion.

■ THEOREM 5

HYPOTHESIS: (a) $a > b$ and $a > 0$,
              (b) $c > d > 0$.

CONCLUSION: $ac > bd$.

PROOF: Because d is positive, we have

$$ad > bd \tag{1}$$

by Theorem 2. Because a and $c - d$ are positive, their product is positive:

$$a(c - d) > 0. \tag{2}$$

Theorem 4 enables us to add Inequalities (1) and (2):

$$ad + a(c - d) > bd + 0 \quad \text{or} \quad ac > bd.$$

Example 14.   Write a statement for $2x - 1$ if $-1 < x < 1$.

If we multiply all members of the inequality by 2, we have $-2 < 2x < 2$. If now we add -1 to all members, we have $-3 < 2x - 1 < 1$.

Example 15A.   Write a statement for x^2 if $0 < x < 2$.

Theorem 5 enables us to conclude that $4 > x^2$ from $2 > x > 0$ and $2 > x > 0$. Since the product of two positive numbers is positive, $x^2 = x(x) > 0$. Then the complete statement is $0 < x^2 < 4$.

Example 15B.   Write a statement for x^2 if $-2 < x < 0$.

Theorem 5 does not apply at once, but, if we multiply all members of the inequality by -1, we get $2 > -x > 0$ or $0 < -x < 2$. Now we can apply the reasoning of Example 15A. We find that $0^2 < (-x)^2 < 4$, or $0 < x^2 < 4$.

Example 16.   For which x is it true that $3x + 5 < x - 4$?

We add $-x$ to both members and then -5, getting $2x + 5 < -4$ and then $2x < -9$. Next we multiply both members by $\frac{1}{2}$, getting $x < -\frac{9}{2}$.

Example 17.   For which x is it true that $x^2 \geq 10$?

We shall have $x^2 \geq 10$ if we have (a) x positive and $x \geq \sqrt{10}$, or (b) x negative and $x \leq -\sqrt{10}$. We can justify Part (a) of the answer by applying the conclusion of Theorem 5 to the inequalities $x \geq \sqrt{10}$ and $x \geq \sqrt{10}$. Part (b) of the answer is equivalent to $-x \geq \sqrt{10}$. If we remember that $-x$ is positive, we can justify this part of the answer by applying the conclusion of Theorem 5 to $-x \geq \sqrt{10}$ and $-x \geq \sqrt{10}$.

Example 18.   For which x is it true that $2x^2 - 7x + 3 < 0$?

We can write $2x^2 - 7x + 3 = (2x - 1)(x - 3)$. This product will be negative if its factors are of opposite sign; thus if (a) $2x - 1 > 0$ and $x - 3 < 0$ or if (b) $2x - 1 < 0$ and $x - 3 > 0$. In Case (a) we have $2x > 1$ or $x > \frac{1}{2}$ and $x < 3$, thus $\frac{1}{2} < x < 3$. In Case (b) we have $2x < 1$ or $x < \frac{1}{2}$ and $x > 3$. But a number x cannot be less than $\frac{1}{2}$ and more than 3 at the same time. Case (b) is untenable and we conclude that $2x^2 - 7x + 3 < 0$ if $\frac{1}{2} < x < 3$.

EXERCISES A1

1. Insert the proper inequality sign in the following pairs.
(a) 2   5.
(b) 7 $\sqrt{50}$.
(c) $\sqrt{.7}$ 0.
(d) -1 3.
(e) -3 1.
(f) -2 $-\frac{5}{2}$.
(g) -3 $-\sqrt{10}$.

2. Use inequalities to describe
(a) the numbers y that are greater than 3 and less than 4;
(b) the numbers z that are greater than 3 and less than, or equal to, 4.
(c) the numbers x that are less than, or equal to, -1.

3. If $1 < x < 3$, what can be said for (a) $2x + 3$, (b) $5 - x$, (c) x^2, (d) $4 - 2x^2$?

4. If $-2 \le x < 2$, what can be said for (a) $\frac{1}{2}x + 3$, (b) $3 - 2x$, (c) x^2, (d) x^3?

5. If $2 < x < 4$, what can be said for (a) $x - 1$, (b) $\dfrac{1}{x+2}$, (c) $\dfrac{x-1}{x+2}$?

6. If $0 < x < 4$ and $1 < y < 2$, what can be said for (a) $x + y$, (b) $x - y$, (c) xy, (d) x/y?

7. Find the numbers x for which
(a) $3x - 1 < 0$.
(b) $2x + 3 \ge \frac{1}{2}x - 4$.
(c) $2 < \dfrac{2x+3}{5} < 3$.
(d) $x^2 < 16$.
(e) $x^2 \ge 9$.
(f) $x^2 - 3x + 2 < 0$.
(g) $6x^2 - 11x + 3 \ge 0$.
(h) $x^2 - 2x - 2 \le 0$.
(i) $\dfrac{x-3}{x-2} > 0$.
(j) $\dfrac{x-3}{x-2} > 1$.
(k) $\dfrac{2x+5}{x-4} < 4$.

8. Prove Theorem 3.

9. Prove this theorem:
Hypothesis: $0 < a < b$.
Conclusion: $1/a > 1/b$.

10. Prove that $a^2 + b^2 \ge 2ab$ for any real numbers a and b.

A2   Absolute Value Notation

■ DEFINITION 1

Let the real numbers be set into one-to-one correspondence with the points on a horizontal line. By the absolute value of a number we mean the undirected distance from the point which represents that number to the origin.

Example 1A.   The absolute value of 3 is 3; the absolute value of -2 is 2. See Fig. A2.1.

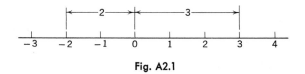

Fig. A2.1

We can write the definition of absolute value in algebraic form.

■ NOTATION CONVENTION 1

$|a|$ is the absolute value of a.

■ DEFINITION 2

$$|a| = \begin{cases} a, & \text{if } a \geq 0, \\ -a, & \text{if } a < 0. \end{cases}$$

Example 1B. $|3| = 3$, using the first line of Definition 2. $|-2| = -(-2) = 2$, using the second line of Definition 2.

● Remark 1

$|0| = 0$. For any real number other than 0 the absolute value is positive.

Example 2. The statement

$$|t| \leq a \tag{1}$$

is equivalent to the statement

$$-a \leq t \leq a, \tag{2}$$

for Eq. (1) says that the point which represents t has a distance from the origin not greater than a. As Fig. A2.2 points out, t must be a or $-a$, or else lie between these numbers.

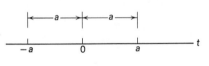

Fig. A2.2

Example 3. If $|t| \geq b$, then either t is positive and $t \geq b$ or t is negative and $t \leq -b$.

Example 4A. If $|x - 3| < .1$, then, with t of Example 2 replaced by $x - 3$, we get $-.1 < x - 3 < .1$. Finally, adding 3 to all members, we have $2.9 < x < 3.1$.

Example 4B. If $|x - a| < \delta$, we can write $-\delta < x - a < \delta$ and then $a - \delta < x < a + \delta$.

● Remark 2

$|a - b|$ can be interpreted as the undirected distance between the points that represent a and b on a number scale. In Example 4A we asked for the points whose distance from the 3 mark was less than .1, and were led to the interval $2.9 < x < 3.1$. In Example 4B we asked for the points whose distance from the a mark was less than δ and were led to the interval $a - \delta < x < a + \delta$; we traveled a distance δ from the a mark in both directions.

Two frequently used statements about absolute values are given by the following theorems.

■ THEOREM 1

HYPOTHESIS: a and b are real numbers.

CONCLUSION: $|ab| = |a||b|$.

■ **THEOREM 2**

HYPOTHESIS: *a* and *b* are real numbers.

CONCLUSION: $|a + b| \leq |a| + |b|$.

In words, the absolute value of a product is the product of the absolute values of the factors, but the absolute value of a sum is less than, or equal to, the sum of the absolute values of the terms.

PROOF OF THEOREM 1:   There are three cases to consider.

(a) If $a \geq 0$ and $b \geq 0$, then $ab \geq 0$ and $|a| = a$, $|b| = b$, $|ab| = ab$. The conclusion to be demonstrated is simply $ab = a \cdot b$.

(b) If one of *a* and *b* is negative, the other not, we can take $a < 0$ and $b \geq 0$. Then $ab \leq 0$, $|a| = -a$, $|b| = b$, $|ab| = -ab$, and the conclusion to be demonstrated is simply $-ab = (-a) \cdot b$.

(c) If $a < 0$ and $b < 0$, then *ab* is positive, because it is a product of two negatives, and $|a| = -a$, $|b| = -b$, $|ab| = ab$. The conclusion to be demonstrated is $ab = (-a) \cdot (-b)$.

PROOF OF THEOREM 2:   Again there are separate cases to consider. The details of the separate cases are left to the reader as an exercise.

Example 5.   The fact that $|2| \, |-3| = |-6|$ is easily verified. Since $|-3| = 3$ and $|-6| = 6$, we have $(2)(3) = 6$.

Example 6.   The fact that $|2 + (-3)| \leq |2| + |-3|$ is easily verified. Indeed, we have $|2 + (-3)| = |-1| = 1$, and $|2| + |-3| = 2 + 3 = 5$.

Example 7.   The fact that $|(-2) + (-3)| \leq |-2| + |-3|$ is easily verified. We have $|(-2 + (-3)| = |-5| = 5$, and $|-2| + |-3| = 2 + 3 = 5$.

EXERCISES A2

1. Find the absolute values of the following numbers

(a) $\frac{7}{5}$;   (b) $-\frac{3}{4}$;   (c) $-\frac{\pi}{4}$;   (d) $\sin\frac{\pi}{4}$;   (e) $\sin\left(-\frac{\pi}{4}\right)$.

2. Show that $\sqrt{a^2} = |a|$ for all *a*.

3. Write equivalent statements that do not use absolute value symbols:

(a) $|x| < 25$.

(b) $|y| \leq 50$.

(c) $|x| > 4$.

(d) $|t| \geq \frac{9}{4}$.

(e) $1 < |s| < 2$.

(f) $0 < |x| < 1$.

(g) $|x - 3| < .04$.

(h) $|y + 1| < .2$.

(i) $|y - b| < \epsilon$.

4. Rewrite in the form $|x - a| < \delta$ with suitable *a* and δ:

(a) $-.1 < x - 2 < .1$.

(b) $-.01 < x < .01$.

(c) $2.8 < x < 3.2$.

(d) $4 < x < 6$.

(e) $-2.1 < x < -1.9$.

(f) $1 < x < 2$.

5. Prove Theorem 2.

TABLE I NATURAL TRIGONOMETRIC FUNCTIONS

Degrees	Radians	Sine	Tangent	Cotangent	Cosine		
0	0	0	0	———	1.0000	1.5708	90
1	.0175	.0175	.0175	57.290	.9998	1.5533	89
2	.0349	.0349	.0349	28.636	.9994	1.5359	88
3	.0524	.0523	.0524	19.081	.9986	1.5184	87
4	.0698	.0698	.0699	14.301	.9976	1.5010	86
5	.0873	.0872	.0875	11.430	.9962	1.4835	85
6	.1047	.1045	.1051	9.5144	.9945	1.4661	84
7	.1222	.1219	.1228	8.1443	.9925	1.4486	83
8	.1396	.1392	.1405	7.1154	.9903	1.4312	82
9	.1571	.1564	.1584	6.3138	.9877	1.4137	81
10	.1745	.1736	.1763	5.6713	.9848	1.3963	80
11	.1920	.1908	.1944	5.1446	.9816	1.3788	79
12	.2094	.2079	.2126	4.7046	.9781	1.3614	78
13	.2269	.2250	.2309	4.3315	.9744	1.3439	77
14	.2443	.2419	.2493	4.0108	.9703	1.3265	76
15	.2618	.2588	.2679	3.7321	.9659	1.3090	75
16	.2793	.2756	.2867	3.4874	.9613	1.2915	74
17	.2967	.2924	.3057	3.2709	.9563	1.2741	73
18	.3142	.3090	.3249	3.0777	.9511	1.2566	72
19	.3316	.3256	.3443	2.9042	.9455	1.2392	71
20	.3491	.3420	.3640	2.7475	.9397	1.2217	70
21	.3665	.3584	.3839	2.6051	.9336	1.2043	69
22	.3840	.3746	.4040	2.4751	.9272	1.1868	68
23	.4014	.3907	.4245	2.3559	.9205	1.1694	67
24	.4189	.4067	.4452	2.2460	.9135	1.1519	66
25	.4363	.4226	.4663	2.1445	.9063	1.1345	65
26	.4538	.4384	.4877	2.0503	.8988	1.1170	64
27	.4712	.4540	.5095	1.9626	.8910	1.0996	63
28	.4887	.4695	.5317	1.8807	.8829	1.0821	62
29	.5061	.4848	.5543	1.8040	.8746	1.0647	61
30	.5236	.5000	.5774	1.7321	.8660	1.0472	60
31	.5411	.5150	.6009	1.6643	.8572	1.0297	59
32	.5585	.5299	.6249	1.6003	.8480	1.0123	58
33	.5760	.5446	.6494	1.5399	.8387	.9948	57
34	.5934	.5592	.6745	1.4826	.8290	.9774	56
35	.6109	.5736	.7002	1.4281	.8192	.9599	55
36	.6283	.5878	.7265	1.3764	.8090	.9425	54
37	.6458	.6018	.7536	1.3270	.7986	.9250	53
38	.6632	.6157	.7813	1.2799	.7880	.9076	52
39	.6807	.6293	.8098	1.2349	.7771	.8901	51
40	.6981	.6428	.8391	1.1918	.7660	.8727	50
41	.7156	.6561	.8693	1.1504	.7547	.8552	49
42	.7330	.6691	.9004	1.1106	.7431	.8378	48
43	.7505	.6820	.9325	1.0724	.7314	.8203	47
44	.7679	.6947	.9657	1.0355	.7193	.8029	46
45	.7854	.7071	1.0000	1.0000	.7071	.7854	45
	Cosine	Cotangent	Tangent	Sine		Radians	Degrees

Rad.	Sin	Tan	Ctn	Cos	Rad.	Sin	Tan	Ctn	Cos
0.00	.00000	.00000	—	1.00000	0.50	.47943	.54630	1.8305	.87758
.01	.01000	.01000	99.997	0.99995	.51	.48818	.55936	1.7878	.87274
.02	.02000	.02000	49.993	.99980	.52	.49688	.57256	1.7465	.86782
.03	.03000	.03001	33.323	.99955	.53	.50553	.58592	1.7067	.86281
.04	.03999	.04002	24.987	.99920	.54	.51414	.59943	1.6683	.85771
.05	.04998	.05004	19.983	.99875	.55	.52269	.61311	1.6310	.85252
.06	.05996	.06007	16.647	.99820	.56	.53119	.62695	1.5950	.84726
.07	.06994	.07011	14.262	.99755	.57	.53963	.64097	1.5601	.84190
.08	.07991	.08017	12.473	.99680	.58	.54802	.65517	1.5263	.83646
.09	.08988	.09024	11.081	.99595	.59	.55636	.66956	1.4935	.83094
0.10	.09983	.10033	9.9666	.99500	0.60	.56464	.68414	1.4617	.82534
.11	.10978	.11045	9.0542	.99396	.61	.57287	.69892	1.4308	.81965
.12	.11971	.12058	8.2933	.99281	.62	.58104	.71391	1.4007	.81388
.13	.12963	.13074	7.6489	.99156	.63	.58914	.72911	1.3715	.80803
.14	.13954	.14092	7.0961	.99022	.64	.59720	.74454	1.3431	.80210
.15	.14944	.15114	6.6166	.98877	.65	.60519	.76020	1.3154	.79608
.16	.15932	.16138	6.1966	.98723	.66	.61312	.77610	1.2885	.78999
.17	.16918	.17166	5.8256	.98558	.67	.62099	.79225	1.2622	.78382
.18	.17903	.18197	5.4954	.98384	.68	.62879	.80866	1.2366	.77757
.19	.18886	.19232	5.1997	.98200	.69	.63654	.82534	1.2116	.77125
0.20	.19867	.20271	4.9332	.98007	0.70	.64422	.84229	1.1872	.76484
.21	.20846	.21314	4.6917	.97803	.71	.65183	.85953	1.1634	.75836
.22	.21823	.22362	4.4719	.97590	.72	.65938	.87707	1.1402	.75181
.23	.22798	.23414	4.2709	.97367	.73	.66687	.89492	1.1174	.74517
.24	.23770	.24472	4.0864	.97134	.74	.67429	.91309	1.0952	.73847
.25	.24740	.25534	3.9163	.96891	.75	.68164	.93160	1.0734	.73169
.26	.25708	.26602	3.7591	.96639	.76	.68892	.95045	1.0521	.72484
.27	.26673	.27676	3.6133	.96377	.77	.69614	.96967	1.0313	.71791
.28	.27636	.28755	3.4776	.96106	.78	.70328	.98926	1.0109	.71091
.29	.28595	.29841	3.3511	.95824	.79	.71035	1.0092	.99084	.70385
0.30	.29552	.30934	3.2327	.95534	0.80	.71736	1.0296	.97121	.69671
.31	.30506	.32033	3.1218	.95233	.81	.72429	1.0505	.95197	.68950
.32	.31457	.33139	3.0176	.94924	.82	.73115	1.0717	.93309	.68222
.33	.32404	.34252	2.9195	.94604	.83	.73793	1.0934	.91455	.67488
.34	.33349	.35374	2.8270	.94275	.84	.74464	1.1156	.89635	.66746
.35	.34290	.36503	2.7395	.93937	.85	.75128	1.1383	.87848	.65998
.36	.35227	.37640	2.6567	.93590	.86	.75784	1.1616	.86091	.65244
.37	.36162	.38786	2.5782	.93233	.87	.76433	1.1853	.84365	.64483
.38	.37092	.39941	2.5037	.92866	.88	.77074	1.2097	.82668	.63715
.39	.38019	.41105	2.4328	.92491	.89	.77707	1.2346	.80998	.62941
0.40	.38942	.42279	2.3652	.92106	0.90	.78333	1.2602	.79355	.62161
.41	.39861	.43463	2.3008	.91712	.91	.78950	1.2864	.77738	.61375
.42	.40776	.44657	2.2393	.91309	.92	.79560	1.3133	.76146	.60582
.43	.41687	.45862	2.1804	.90897	.93	.80162	1.3409	.74578	.59783
.44	.42594	.47078	2.1241	.90475	.94	.80756	1.3692	.73034	.58979
.45	.43497	.48306	2.0702	.90045	.95	.81342	1.3984	.71511	.58168
.46	.44395	.49545	2.0184	.89605	.96	.81919	1.4284	.70010	.57352
.47	.45289	.50797	1.9686	.89157	.97	.82489	1.4592	.68531	.56530
.48	.46178	.52061	1.9208	.88699	.98	.83050	1.4910	.67071	.55702
.49	.47063	.53339	1.8748	.88233	.99	.83603	1.5237	.65631	.54869
0.50	.47943	.54630	1.8305	.87758	1.00	.84147	1.5574	.64209	.54030
Rad.	Sin	Tan	Ctn	Cos	Rad.	Sin	Tan	Ctn	Cos

Rad.	Sin	Tan	Ctn	Cos	Rad.	Sin	Tan	Ctn	Cos
1.00	.84147	1.5574	.64209	.54030	**1.30**	.96356	3.6021	.27762	.26750
1.01	.84683	1.5922	.62806	.53186	1.31	.96618	3.7471	.26687	.25785
1.02	.85211	1.6281	.61420	.52337	1.32	.96872	3.9033	.25619	.24818
1.03	.85730	1.6652	.60051	.51482	1.33	.97115	4.0723	.24556	.23848
1.04	.86240	1.7036	.58699	.50622	**1.34**	.97348	4.2556	.23498	.22875
1.05	.86742	1.7433	.57362	.49757	1.35	.97572	4.4552	.22446	.21901
1.06	.87236	1.7844	.56040	.48887	1.36	.97786	4.6734	.21398	.20924
1.07	.87720	1.8270	.54734	.48012	1.37	.97991	4.9131	.20354	.19945
1.08	.88196	1.8712	.53441	.47133	1.38	.98185	5.1774	.19315	.18964
1.09	.88663	1.9171	.52162	.46249	1.39	.98370	5.4707	.18279	.17981
1.10	.89121	1.9648	.50897	.45360	**1.40**	.98545	5.7979	.17248	.16997
1.11	.89570	2.0143	.49644	.44466	1.41	.98710	6.1654	.16220	.16010
1.12	.90010	2.0660	.48404	.43568	1.42	.98865	6.5811	.15195	.15023
1.13	.90441	2.1198	.47175	.42666	1.43	.99010	7.0555	.14173	.14033
1.14	.90863	2.1759	.45959	.41759	1.44	.99146	7.6018	.13155	.13042
1.15	.91276	2.2345	.44753	.40849	1.45	.99271	8.2381	.12139	.12050
1.16	.91680	2.2958	.43558	.39934	1.46	.99387	8.9886	.11125	.11057
1.17	.92075	2.3600	.42373	.39015	1.47	.99492	9.8874	.10114	.10063
1.18	.92461	2.4273	.41199	.38092	1.48	.99588	10.983	.09105	.09067
1.19	.92837	2.4979	.40034	.37166	1.49	.99674	12.350	.08097	.08071
1.20	.93204	2.5722	.38878	.36236	**1.50**	.99749	14.101	.07091	.07074
1.21	.93562	2.6503	.37731	.35302	1.51	.99815	16.428	.06087	.06076
1.22	.93910	2.7328	.36593	.34365	1.52	.99871	19.670	.05084	.05077
1.23	.94249	2.8198	.35463	.33424	1.53	.99917	24.498	.04082	.04079
1.24	.94578	2.9119	.34341	.32480	1.54	.99953	32.461	.03081	.03079
1.25	.94898	3.0096	.33227	.31532	1.55	.99978	48.078	.02080	.02079
1.26	.95209	3.1133	.32121	.30582	1.56	.99994	92.621	.01080	.01080
1.27	.95510	3.2236	.31021	.29628	1.57	1.00000	1255.8	.00080	.00080
1.28	.95802	3.3413	.29928	.28672	1.58	.99996	−108.65	−.00920	−.00920
1.29	.96084	3.4672	.28842	.27712	1.59	.99982	−52.067	−.01921	−.01920
1.30	.96356	3.6021	.27762	.26750	**1.60**	.99957	−34.233	−.02921	−.02920
Rad.	**Sin**	**Tan**	**Ctn**	**Cos**	**Rad.**	**Sin**	**Tan**	**Ctn**	**Cos**

TABLE III RADIANS TO DEGREES, MINUTES, AND SECONDS

	Radians	Tenths	Hundredths	Thousandths	Ten-thousandths
1	57° 17′ 44.″8	5° 43′ 46.″5	0° 34′ 22.″6	0° 3′ 26.″3	0° 0′ 20.″6
2	114° 35′ 29.″6	11° 27′ 33.″0	1° 8′ 45.″3	0° 6′ 52.″5	0° 0′ 41.″3
3	171° 53′ 14.″4	17° 11′ 19.″4	1° 43′ 07.″9	0° 10′ 18.″8	0° 1′ 01.″9
4	229° 10′ 59.″2	22° 55′ 05.″9	2° 17′ 30.″6	0° 13′ 45.″1	0° 1′ 22.″5
5	286° 28′ 44.″0	28° 38′ 52.″4	2° 51′ 53.″2	0° 17′ 11.″3	0° 1′ 43.″1
6	343° 46′ 28.″8	34° 22′ 38.″9	3° 26′ 15.″9	0° 20′ 37.″6	0° 2′ 03.″8
7	401° 4′ 13.″6	40° 6′ 25.″4	4° 0′ 38.″5	0° 24′ 03.″9	0° 2′ 24.″4
8	458° 21′ 58.″4	45° 50′ 11.″8	4° 35′ 01.″2	0° 27′ 30.″1	0° 2′ 45.″0
9	515° 39′ 43.″3	51° 33′ 58.″3	5° 9′ 23.″8	0° 30′ 56.″4	0° 3′ 05.″6
	Radians	**Tenths**	**Hundredths**	**Thousandths**	**Ten-thousandths**

TABLE IV NATURAL LOGARITHMS OF NUMBERS

This table contains logarithms of numbers from 1 to 10 to the base e. To obtain the natural logarithms of other numbers, use the formulas:

$$\log_e (10^r \, N) = \log_e N + \log_e 10^r$$

$$\log_e \left(\frac{N}{10^r}\right) = \log_e N - \log_e 10^r$$

$\log_e 10 = 2.302585$	$\log_e 10^4 = 9.210340$
$\log_e 10^2 = 4.605170$	$\log_e 10^5 = 11.512925$
$\log_e 10^3 = 6.907755$	$\log_e 10^6 = 13.815511$

N	0	1	2	3	4	5	6	7	8	9
1.0	0.0 0000	0995	1980	2956	3922	4879	5827	6766	7696	8618
1.1	0.0 9531	*0436	*1333	*2222	*3103	*3976	*4842	*5700	*6551	*7395
1.2	0.1 8232	9062	9885	*0701	*1511	*2314	*3111	*3902	*4686	*5464
1.3	0.2 6236	7003	7763	8518	9267	*0010	*0748	*1481	*2208	*2930
1.4	0.3 3647	4359	5066	5767	6464	7156	7844	8526	9204	9878
1.5	0.4 0547	1211	1871	2527	3178	3825	4469	5108	5742	6373
1.6	0.4 7000	7623	8243	8858	9470	*0078	*0682	*1282	*1879	*2473
1.7	0.5 3063	3649	4232	4812	5389	5962	6531	7098	7661	8222
1.8	0.5 8779	9333	9884	*0432	*0977	*1519	*2078	*2594	*3127	*3658
1.9	0.6 4185	4710	5233	5752	6269	6783	7294	7803	8310	8813
2.0	0.6 9315	9813	*0310	*0804	*1295	*1784	*2271	*2755	*3237	*3716
2.1	0.7 4194	4669	5142	5612	6081	6547	7011	7473	7932	8390
2.2	0.7 8846	9299	9751	*0200	*0648	*1093	*1536	*1978	*2418	*2855
2.3	0.8 3291	3725	4157	4587	5015	5442	5866	6289	6710	7129
2.4	0.8 7547	7963	8377	8789	9200	9609	*0016	*0422	*0826	*1228
2.5	0.9 1629	2028	2426	2822	3216	3609	4001	4391	4779	5166
2.6	0.9 5551	5935	6317	6698	7078	7456	7833	8208	8582	8954
2.7	0.9 9325	9695	*0063	*0430	*0796	*1160	*1523	*1885	*2245	*2604
2.8	1.0 2962	3318	3674	4028	4380	4732	5082	5431	5779	6126
2.9	1.0 6471	6815	7158	7500	7841	8181	8519	8856	9192	9527
3.0	1.0 9861	*0194	*0526	*0856	*1186	*1514	*1841	*2168	*2493	*2817
3.1	1.1 3140	3462	3783	4103	4422	4740	5057	5373	5688	6002
3.2	1.1 6315	6627	6938	7248	7557	7865	8173	8479	8784	9089
3.3	1.1 9392	9695	9996	*0297	*0597	*0896	*1194	*1491	*1788	*2083
3.4	1.2 2378	2671	2964	3256	3547	3837	4127	4415	4703	4990
3.5	1.2 5276	5562	5846	6130	6413	6695	6976	7257	7536	7815
3.6	1.2 8093	8371	8647	8923	9198	9473	9746	*0019	*0291	*0563
3.7	1.3 0833	1103	1372	1641	1909	2176	2442	2708	2972	3237
3.8	1.3 3500	3763	4025	4286	4547	4807	5067	5325	5584	5841
3.9	1.3 6098	6354	6609	6864	7118	7372	7624	7877	8128	8379
4.0	1.3 8629	8879	9128	9377	9624	9872	*0118	*0364	*0610	*0854
4.1	1.4 1099	1342	1585	1828	2070	2311	2552	2792	3031	3270
4.2	1.4 3508	3746	3984	4220	4456	4692	4927	5161	5395	5629
4.3	1.4 5862	6094	6326	6557	6787	7018	7247	7476	7705	7933
4.4	1.4 8160	8387	8614	8840	9065	9290	9515	9739	9962	*0185
4.5	1.5 0408	0630	0851	1072	1293	1513	1732	1951	2170	2388
4.6	1.5 2606	2823	3039	3256	3471	3687	3902	4116	4330	4543
4.7	1.5 4756	4969	5181	5393	5604	5814	6025	6235	6444	6653
4.8	1.5 6862	7070	7277	7485	7691	7898	8104	8309	8515	8719
4.9	1.5 8924	9127	9331	9534	9737	9939	*0141	*0342	*0543	*0744
5.0	1.6 0944	1144	1343	1542	1741	1939	2137	2334	2531	2728
N	0	1	2	3	4	5	6	7	8	9

TABLE IV NATURAL LOGARITHMS OF NUMBERS (CONT.)

N	0	1	2	3	4	5	6	7	8	9
5.0	1.6 0944	1144	1343	1542	1741	1939	2137	2334	2531	2728
5.1	1.6 2924	3120	3315	3511	3705	3900	4094	4287	4481	4673
5.2	1.6 4866	5058	5250	5441	5632	5823	6013	6203	6393	6582
5.3	1.6 6771	6959	7147	7335	7523	7710	7896	8083	8269	8455
5.4	1.6 8640	8825	9010	9194	9378	9562	9745	9928	*0111	*0293
5.5	1.7 0475	0656	0838	1019	1199	1380	1560	1740	1919	2098
5.6	1.7 2277	2455	2633	2811	2988	3166	3342	3519	3695	3871
5.7	1.7 4047	4222	4397	4572	4746	4920	5094	5267	5440	5613
5.8	1.7 5786	5958	6130	6302	6473	6644	6815	6985	7156	7326
5.9	1.7 7495	7665	7843	8002	8171	8339	8507	8675	8842	9009
6.0	1.7 9176	9342	9509	9675	9840	*0006	*0171	*0336	*0500	*0665
6.1	1.8 0829	0993	1156	1319	1482	1645	1808	1970	2132	2294
6.2	1.8 2455	2616	2777	2938	3098	3258	3418	3578	3737	38,6
6.3	1.8 4055	4214	4372	4530	4688	4845	5003	5160	5317	5473
6.4	1.8 5630	5786	5942	6097	6253	6408	6563	6718	6872	7026
6.5	1.8 7180	7334	7487	7641	7794	7947	8099	8251	8403	8555
6.6	1.8 8707	8858	9010	9160	9311	9462	9612	9762	9912	*0061
6.7	1.9 0211	0360	0509	0658	0806	0954	1102	1250	1398	1545
6.8	1.9 1692	1839	1986	2132	2279	2425	2571	2716	2862	3007
6.9	1.9 3152	3297	3442	3586	3730	3874	4018	4162	4305	4448
7.0	1.9 4591	4734	4876	5019	5161	5303	5445	5586	5727	5869
7.1	1.9 6009	6150	6291	6431	6571	6711	6851	6991	7130	7269
7.2	1.9 7408	7547	7685	7824	7962	8100	8238	8376	8513	8650
7.3	1.9 8787	8924	9061	9198	9334	9470	9606	9742	9877	*0013
7.4	2.0 0148	0283	0418	0553	0687	0821	0956	1089	1223	1357
7.5	2.0 1490	1624	1757	1890	2022	2155	2287	2419	2551	2683
7.6	2.0 2815	2946	3078	3209	3340	3471	3601	3732	3862	3992
7.7	2.0 4122	4252	4381	4511	4640	4769	4898	5027	5156	5284
7.8	2.0 5412	5540	5668	5796	5924	6051	6179	6306	6433	6560
7.9	2.0 6686	6813	6939	7065	7191	7317	7443	7568	7694	7819
8.0	2.0 7944	8069	8194	8318	8443	8567	8691	8815	8939	9063
8.1	2.0 9186	9310	9433	9556	9679	9802	9924	*0047	*0169	*0291
8.2	2.1 0413	0535	0657	0779	0900	1021	1142	1263	1384	1505
8.3	2.1 1626	1746	1866	1986	2106	2226	2346	2465	2585	2704
8.4	2.1 2823	2942	3061	3180	3298	3417	3535	3653	3771	3889
8.5	2.1 4007	4124	4242	4359	4476	4593	4710	4827	4943	5060
8.6	2.1 5176	5292	5409	5524	5640	5756	5871	5987	6102	6217
8.7	2.1 6332	6447	6562	6677	6791	6905	7020	7134	7248	7361
8.8	2.1 7475	7589	7702	7816	7929	8042	8155	8267	8380	8493
8.9	2.1 8605	8717	8830	8942	9054	9165	9277	9389	9500	9611
9.0	2.1 9722	9834	9944	*0055	*0166	*0276	*0387	*0497	*0607	*0717
9.1	2.2 0827	0937	1047	1157	1266	1375	1485	1594	1703	1812
9.2	2.2 1920	2029	2138	2246	2354	2462	2570	2678	2786	2894
9.3	2.2 3001	3109	3216	3324	3431	3538	3645	3751	3858	3965
9.4	2.2 4071	4177	4284	4390	4496	4601	4707	4813	4918	5024
9.5	2.2 5129	5234	5339	5444	5549	5654	5759	5863	5968	6072
9.6	2.2 6176	6280	6384	6488	6592	6696	6799	6903	7006	7109
9.7	2.2 7213	7316	7419	7521	7624	7727	7829	7932	8034	8136
9.8	2.2 8238	8340	8442	8544	8646	8747	8849	8950	9051	9152
9.9	2.2 9253	9354	9455	9556	9657	9757	9858	9958	*0058	*0158
10.0	2.3 0259	0358	0458	0558	0658	0757	0857	0956	1055	1154
N	0	1	2	3	4	5	6	7	8	9

TABLE V EXPONENTIAL AND HYPERBOLIC FUNCTIONS

When x is beyond the limits of the table (that is, when $x > 6.5$) sinh x and cosh x may be obtained to five significant figures by the formula sinh x = cosh x = $\frac{1}{2}e^x$; furthermore, for such values of x, tanh x = 1.0000.

x	e^x	e^{-x}	sinh x	cosh x	tanh x	x
0.0	1.0000	1.0000	.00000	1.0000	.00000	**0.0**
0.1	1.1052	.90484	.10017	1.0050	.09967	0.1
0.2	1.2214	.81873	.20134	1.0201	.19738	0.2
0.3	1.3499	.74082	.30452	1.0453	.29131	0.3
0.4	1.4918	.67032	.41075	1.0811	.37995	0.4
0.5	1.6487	.60653	.52110	1.1276	.46212	0.5
0.6	1.8221	.54881	.63665	1.1855	.53705	0.6
0.7	2.0138	.49659	.75858	1.2552	.60437	0.7
0.8	2.2255	.44933	.88811	1.3374	.66404	0.8
0.9	2.4596	.40657	1.0265	1.4331	.71630	0.9
1.0	2.7183	.36788	1.1752	1.5431	.76159	**1.0**
1.1	3.0042	.33287	1.3356	1.6685	.80050	1.1
1.2	3.3201	.30119	1.5095	1.8107	.83365	1.2
1.3	3.6693	.27253	1.6984	1.9709	.86172	1.3
1.4	4.0552	.24660	1.9043	2.1509	.88535	1.4
1.5	4.4817	.22313	2.1293	2.3524	.90515	1.5
1.6	4.9530	.20190	2.3756	2.5775	.92167	1.6
1.7	5.4739	.18268	2.6456	2.8283	.93541	1.7
1.8	6.0496	.16530	2.9422	3.1075	.94681	1.8
1.9	6.6859	.14957	3.2682	3.4177	.95624	1.9
2.0	7.3891	.13534	3.6269	3.7622	.96403	**2.0**
2.1	8.1662	.12246	4.0219	4.1443	.97045	2.1
2.2	9.0250	.11080	4.4571	4.5679	.97574	2.2
2.3	9.9742	.10026	4.9370	5.0372	.98010	2.3
2.4	11.023	.09072	5.4662	5.5569	.98367	2.4
2.5	12.182	.08208	6.0502	6.1323	.98661	2.5
2.6	13.464	.07427	6.6947	6.7690	.98903	2.6
2.7	14.880	.06721	7.4063	7.4735	.99101	2.7
2.8	16.445	.06081	8.1919	8.2527	.99263	2.8
2.9	18.174	.05502	9.0596	9.1146	.99396	2.9

TABLE V EXPONENTIAL AND HYPERBOLIC FUNCTIONS (CONT.)

x	e^x	e^{-x}	sinh x	cosh x	tanh x	x
3.0	20.086	.04979	10.018	10.068	.99505	**3.0**
3.1	22.198	.04505	11.076	11.122	.99595	3.1
3.2	24.533	.04076	12.246	12.287	.99668	3.2
3.3	27.113	.03688	13.538	13.575	.99728	3.3
3.4	29.964	.03337	14.965	14.999	.99777	3.4
3.5	33.115	.03020	16.543	16.573	.99818	3.5
3.6	36.598	.02732	18.285	18.313	.99851	3.6
3.7	40.447	.02472	20.211	20.236	.99878	3.7
3.8	44.701	.02237	22.339	22.362	.99900	3.8
3.9	49.402	.02024	24.691	24.711	.99918	3.9
4.0	54.598	.01832	27.290	27.308	.99933	**4.0**
4.1	60.340	.01657	30.162	30.178	.99945	4.1
4.2	66.686	.01500	33.336	33.351	.99955	4.2
4.3	73.700	.01357	36.843	36.857	.99963	4.3
4.4	81.451	.01228	40.719	40.732	.99970	4.4
4.5	90.017	.01111	45.003	45.014	.99975	4.5
4.6	99.484	.01005	49.737	49.747	.99980	4.6
4.7	109.95	.00910	54.969	54.978	.99983	4.7
4.8	121.51	.00823	60.751	60.759	.99986	4.8
4.9	134.29	.00745	67.141	67.149	.99989	4.9
5.0	148.41	.00674	74.203	74.210	.99991	**5.0**
5.1	164.02	.00610	82.008	82.014	.99993	5.1
5.2	181.27	.00552	90.633	90.639	.99994	5.2
5.3	200.34	.00499	100.17	100.17	.99995	5.3
5.4	221.41	.00452	110.70	110.71	.99996	5.4
5.5	244.69	.00409	122.34	122.35	.99997	5.5
5.6	270.43	.00370	135.21	135.22	.99997	5.6
5.7	298.87	.00335	149.43	149.44	.99998	5.7
5.8	330.30	.00303	165.15	165.15	.99998	5.8
5.9	365.04	.00274	182.52	182.52	.99998	5.9
6.0	403.43	.00248	201.71	201.72	.99999	**6.0**
6.1	445.86	.00224	222.93	222.93	.99999	6.1
6.2	492.75	.00203	246.37	246.38	.99999	6.2
6.3	544.57	.00184	272.29	272.29	.99999	6.3
6.4	601.85	.00166	300.92	300.92	.99999	6.4
6.5	665.14	.00150	332.57	332.57	1.0000	6.5

TABLE VI DEGREES, MINUTES, AND SECONDS TO RADIANS

°	Radians	°	Radians	°	Radians	′	Radians	″	Radians
0	0.000 000	60	1.047 198	120	2.094 395	0	0.000 000	0	0.000 000
1	0.017 453	61	1.064 651	121	2.111 848	1	0.000 291	1	0.000 005
2	0.034 907	62	1.082 104	122	2.129 302	2	0.000 582	2	0.000 010
3	0.052 360	63	1.099 557	123	2.146 755	3	0.000 873	3	0.000 014
4	0.069 813	64	1.117 011	124	2.164 208	4	0.001 164	4	0.000 019
5	0.087 266	65	1.134 464	125	2.181 662	5	0.001 454	5	0.000 024
6	0.104 720	66	1.151 917	126	2.199 115	6	0.001 745	6	0.000 029
7	0.122 173	67	1.169 371	127	2.216 568	7	0.002 036	7	0.000 034
8	0.139 626	68	1.186 824	128	2.234 021	8	0.002 327	8	0.000 039
9	0.157 080	69	1.204 277	129	2.251 475̄	9	0.002 618	9	0.000 044
10	0.174 533	70	1.221 730	130	2.268 928	10	0.002 909	10	0.000 048
11	0.191 986	71	1.239 184	131	2.286 381	11	0.003 200	11	0.000 053
12	0.209 439	72	1.256 637	132	2.303 835̄	12	0.003 491	12	0.000 058
13	0.226 893	73	1.274 090	133	2.321 288	13	0.003 781	13	0.000 063
14	0.244 346	74	1.291 544	134	2.338 741	14	0.004 072	14	0.000 068
15	0.261 799	75	1.308 997	135	2.356 194	15	0.004 363	15	0.000 073
16	0.279 253	76	1.326 450	136	2.373 648	16	0.004 654	16	0.000 074
17	0.296 706	77	1.343 903	137	2.391 101	17	0.004 945	17	0.000 082
18	0.314 159	78	1.361 357	138	2.408 554	18	0.005 236	18	0.000 087
19	0.331 613	79	1.378 810	139	2.426 008	19	0.005 527	19	0.000 092
20	0.349 066	80	1.396 263	140	2.443 461	20	0.005 818	20	0.000 097
21	0.366 519	81	1.413 717	141	2.460 914	21	0.006 109	21	0.000 102
22	0.383 972	82	1.431 170	142	2.478 367	22	0.006 399	22	0.000 107
23	0.401 426	83	1.448 623	143	2.495 821	23	0.006 690	23	0.000 111
24	0.418 879	84	1.466 077	144	2.513 274	24	0.006 981	24	0.000 116
25	0.436 332	85	1.483 530	145	2.530 727	25	0.007 272	25	0.000 121
26	0.453 786	86	1.500 983	146	2.548 188	26	0.007 563	26	0.000 126
27	0.471 239	87	1.518 436	147	2.565 634	27	0.007 854	27	0.000 131
28	0.488 692	88	1.535 890	148	2.583 087	28	0.008 145	28	0.000 136
29	0.506 145	89	1.553 343	149	2.600 547	29	0.008 436	29	0.000 141
30	0.523 599	90	1.570 796	150	2.617 994	30	0.008 727	30	0.000 145
31	0.541 052	91	1.588 250	151	2.635 447	31	0.009 017	31	0.000 150
32	0.558 505	92	1.605 703	152	2.652 900	32	0.009 308	32	0.000 155
33	0.575 959	93	1.623 156	153	2.670 354	33	0.009 599	33	0.000 160
34	0.593 412	94	1.640 609	154	2.687 807	34	0.009 890	34	0.000 165̄
35	0.610 865	95	1.658 063	155	2.705 260	35	0.010 181	35	0.000 170
36	0.628 318	96	1.675 516	156	2.722 714	36	0.010 472	36	0.000 174
37	0.645 772	97	1.692 969	157	2.740 167	37	0.010 763	37	0.000 179
38	0.663 225	98	1.710 423	158	2.757 620	38	0.011 054	38	0.000 184
39	0.680 678	99	1.727 876	159	2.775 073	39	0.011 345̄	39	0.000 189
40	0.698 132	100	1.745 329	160	2.792 527	40	0.011 635	40	0.000 194
41	0.715 585	101	1.762 782	161	2.809 980	41	0.011 926	41	0.000 199
42	0.733 038	102	1.780 236	162	2.827 433	42	0.012 217	42	0.000 204
43	0.750 492	103	1.797 689	163	2.844 887	43	0.012 508	43	0.000 208
44	0.767 945̄	104	1.815 142	164	2.862 340	44	0.012 799	44	0.000 213
45	0.785 398	105	1.832 596	165	2.879 793	45	0.013 090	45	0.000 218
46	0.802 851	106	1.850 049	166	2.897 247	46	0.013 381	46	0.000 223
47	0.820 305̄	107	1.867 502	167	2.914 700	47	0.013 672	47	0.000 228
48	0.837 758	108	1.884 956	168	2.932 153	48	0.013 963	48	0.000 233
49	0.855 211	109	1.902 409	169	2.949 606	49	0.014 253	49	0.000 238
50	0.872 665̄	110	1.919 862	170	2.967 060	50	0.014 544	50	0.000 242
51	0.890 118	111	1.937 315	171	2.984 513	51	0.014 835	51	0.000 247
52	0.907 571	112	1.954 769	172	3.001 966	52	0.015 126	52	0.000 252
53	0.925 024	113	1.972 222	173	3.019 420	53	0.015 417	53	0.000 257
54	0.942 478	114	1.989 675	174	3.036 873	54	0.015 708	54	0.000 262
55	0.959 931	115	2.007 129	175	3.054 326	55	0.015 999	55	0.000 267
56	0.977 384	116	2.024 582	176	3.071 779	56	0.016 290	56	0.000 271
57	0.994 838	117	2.042 035	177	3.089 233	57	0.016 581	57	0.000 276
58	1.012 291	118	2.059 488	178	3.106 686	58	0.016 871	58	0.000 281
59	1.029 744	119	2.076 942	179	3.124 139	59	0.017 162	59	0.000 286
60	1.047 198	120	2.094 395	180	3.141 593	60	0.017 453	60	0.000 291

Answers to Alternate Exercises

Exercises 1.1

6. (a) All real x, all real y; (c) $x \neq -2, y \neq 0$; (e) $x \neq -2, y \neq 0$; (g) $x > 0$, all real y; (i) all real $x, y > 0$.

7. $y = \frac{1}{2}x + 10$, $? \leq x \leq ?$

Exercises 1.2

1. $F(0) = 0$, $F(\frac{1}{2}) = \pi/6$, $F(3) = 36\pi$, $F(a) = \frac{4}{3}\pi a^3$, $F(r+h) = \frac{4}{3}\pi(r+h)^3$, $F(2r) = \frac{32}{3}\pi r^3$ **3.** $f(-2) = 2, f(\frac{1}{6}) = \frac{1}{6}, \sqrt{f(\frac{1}{4})} = \frac{1}{2}, 3f(2) = 6$.

5. $x = f(t) = \begin{cases} 3t, & 0 \leq t \leq 7, \\ 35 - 2t, & 7 \leq t \leq 17.5 \\ 0, & t \geq 17.5 \end{cases}$ $f(3) = 9, f(7) = 21$, $f(10) = 15, f(20) = 0$.

7. $\phi(2) = 9$, $\Phi(9) = -2$; $\Phi(30) = -5$, $\phi(-5) = 30$; $\Phi(\phi(x)) = x$ for $x \leq 0$.

9. $f(1) = 1, f(\frac{1}{9}) = \frac{1}{3}, f(a^2) = \begin{cases} a \text{ if } a \geq 0 \\ -a \text{ if } a < 0 \end{cases}$,
$f(a^2 + b^2) = \sqrt{a^2 + b^2}, f(a+b) \neq f(a) + f(b)$.

11. $\psi(1) = 0, \psi(10) = 1, \psi(100) = 2, \psi(\frac{1}{10}) = -1, \psi(\sqrt{10}) = \frac{1}{2}$.

15. $F(0,0) = 1$, $F(\pi/2, \pi/4) = \sqrt{2}/2$, $F(\pi/4, \pi/2) = \sqrt{2}/2$.

Exercises 1.3

1. $0, 5, -1$; SU does not have finite slope.   **5.** Slope of tangent at P_1 is 2.

7. $1 - 2x, 1, -2$; tangent horizontal at $(\frac{1}{2}, \frac{1}{4})$.   **9.** $-(1/x^2), -1, -4$; tangent horizontal at no point.

Exercises 1.4

1. 112 ft per sec is the velocity at $t = 1$.   **3.** $v = 144 - 32t$; (a) $t = 9$; (b) -144 ft per sec; (d) $t = \frac{9}{2}$; (e) 324 ft.   **5.** $v = -48 - 32t$; -112 ft per sec.

7. $v = 24t, t = 1.5$; $v = 4\sqrt{3x}$.   **9.** $v = 50 - 10t, a = -10, t = 5, x = 125$, force constant.   **11.** (a) $v = 3t^2, a = 6t$; (b) 3.01.

Exercises 1.5

1. (a) $4x^3$; (c) $-(3/x^4)$; (e) $\frac{1}{3}\,1/x^{2/3}$, $x \neq 0$.   **2.** (a) $2ax + b$; (c) $2/x^2$;

(e) $-a/(x+b)^2$; (g) $\dfrac{-1}{2\sqrt{1-x}}$, $x \neq 1$.   **3.** $-2x$; (a) 3.9; (b) 4.   **5.** $4kT^3$,

$1.08k(10)^8$.   **7.** (a) $x^3 + c$; (c) $2^y + c$; (e) $\sqrt[3]{x} + c$.

Exercises 1.6

1. (a) $15x^2 + 14x - 6$; (c) $2ax + b$; (e) $8\pi r$; (g) $-2/t^2 - 6/t^3$; (i) $2 - 4/r^2$;
(k) $\frac{5}{2}\,x^{3/2} - \frac{15}{2}\,x^{1/2} + x^{-(1/2)} + 5x^{-(3/2)}$; (m) $6t + 1/(2\sqrt{t})$, $24 + \frac{1}{4}$;
(o) $3x^{1/2} - \frac{10}{3}\,x^{-1/3}$; (q) $-1.4kv^{-2.4}$.   **3.** $120 - 32t$, -32; 88, -88.
5. 1.7, 4.10.

Exercises 1.7

2. (a) $-24(4 - t)^3$; (c) $20(x^2 + x + 7)^3(2x + 1)$; (e) $80s(1 - 2s^2)^4$; (g) $-12x(1 - x^2)^9$;
(i) $-\frac{8}{3}t\sqrt[3]{4 - t^2}$; (k) $64(2 - 5x)^{-5}$; (m) $-\frac{1}{2}\,y(y^2 - 1)^{-4/3}$.
3. (a) 2; (b) $(\frac{5}{2}, 4)$.   **5.** $6/\sqrt{61}$.

Exercises 1.8

1. $10x(x - 1)(2x - 5)^2$.   **3.** $(r + 2)^2(2r - 3)^6(20r + 19)$.   **5.** $\dfrac{s(10 - 3s^2)}{\sqrt{5 - s^2}}$.

7. $\dfrac{15 - 4x}{3(5 - x)^{2/3}}$.   **9.** $\dfrac{1}{(3x - 4)^2}$.   **11.** $a - (b/u^2)$.   **13.** $\dfrac{-2(8x + 11)}{(4x - 5)^4}$.

15. $\dfrac{(x + 5)^2(x^2 + 20x + 4)}{(4 - 3x^2)^3}$.   **17.** $\dfrac{-5}{s^2(5 - s^2)^{1/2}}$.   **19.** $\dfrac{(t^2 + 7)^{1/2}(t^2 - 14)}{t^3}$.

21. $\dfrac{3x^2 + 16x - 10}{6(4 + x)^{3/2}}$.   **23.** $\dfrac{5}{3}\,\dfrac{3 - x}{(1 - x)^{5/3}}$.   **25.** $\dfrac{-16t(t^2 + 10)}{(t^2 - 5)^{5/2}}$.   **27.** -1.

Exercises 1.9

1. $\dfrac{2}{3}\,\dfrac{(1 - x)}{y^2}$.   **3.** $-\dfrac{3x^2 + 2xy^2}{2x^2y + 6y^2}$.   **5.** $-\dfrac{y^{1/3}}{x^{1/3}}$.   **7.** $\dfrac{(x + y)^{1/2} + (x - y)^{1/2}}{(x + y)^{1/2} - (x - y)^{1/2}} = \dfrac{18}{y}$.

9. $\frac{3}{4}$.   **11.** $-\dfrac{\gamma P}{V}$.   **13.** $-\dfrac{2r^2 + h^2}{rh}$.

Exercises 1.10

1. 0.   **3.** $n(n - 1)(n - 2)\cdots(3)(2)(1)$.   **5.** $6t^{-4}$.   **7.** $192(1 + 2x)$.

9. $-\dfrac{21}{4}\,(x + 1)^{-(9/2)}$.   **11.** $6t(2 - 3t)^2(63t^2 - 36t + 4)$.   **13.** $2bu^{-3}$.

15. $-\dfrac{36}{7y^3}$, $\dfrac{648}{49}\,\dfrac{x}{y^5}$.   **17.** $\dfrac{1}{8}\,\dfrac{1}{x^{3/2}}$.   **19.** $\dfrac{12}{5y^4(y + x)^3}$.   **21.** $\dfrac{9(3 + 10x^2)}{x^6y^7}$.

23. 99.2, 80.8, 30.8, $-.6$.

Exercises 2.1

1. $y = x^3 + \frac{5}{2} x^2 + 6x + 3.$ **3.** $\phi(z) = \frac{1}{3} a_2 z^3 + \frac{1}{2} a_1 z^2 + a_0 z + C.$
5. $f(x) = \frac{2}{3} x^{3/2} - \frac{4}{3}.$ **7.** $g(x) = \frac{3}{2} \sqrt[3]{3} x^{4/3} + 4$ or equivalent forms.
9. $v = -\dfrac{2}{3t^2} + \dfrac{1}{t^3} - \dfrac{3}{t^4} + C.$ **11.** $y = \frac{2}{11}(3 + x)^{11} + C.$

13. $f(x) = -\dfrac{1}{x^3 + 7} + \dfrac{1}{7}.$ **15.** $g(x) = -\frac{7}{16}(9 - 2x^2)^4 + \frac{23}{16}.$
17. $y = (x + 1)^{2/3} + 1.$ **19.** Problem does not satisfy hypotheses of Theorem 5.
v cannot be found yet.   **23.** No.

Exercises 2.2

1. $-32t + 54, -16t^2 + 54t$; $45\frac{9}{16}$ ft; $3\frac{3}{8}$ sec.   **3.** $-32t + 40, -16t^2 + 40t + 200$;
$\frac{5}{2}$ sec.   **5.** $48 \sqrt{2}$ ft per sec.   **7.** $v = 14t$, $x = 7t^2$; $v = 2\sqrt{7x}.$
9. $\alpha = \sin^{-1}(.05) \approx 3°.$ **11.** 9.375 ft per sec^2.   **13.** 120 sec, 14,400 ft.
15. 7 min.

Exercises 2.3

1. 31.5   **3.** 6.   **5.** $38\frac{2}{3}$.   **7.** $\frac{44}{75}$.   **9.** $2\sqrt{6} \approx 4.90$.   **11.** 36.
13. $243\frac{3}{8}$.   **15.** $512\frac{2}{15} \approx 34.13$.   **17.** $-32\frac{2}{61}$.

Exercises 2.4

3. 4.   **5.** $\frac{2}{3}$.   **7.** $.19484 < \int_{.10}^{.30} \cos x \, dx < .19644.$

Exercises 2.5

1. 12.   **3.** (a) $.19824 \leq$ distance traveled $\leq .19904$;
(b) $.19846 \leq$ distance traveled $\leq .19886.$

Exercises 2.6

1. $\frac{2}{3}$.   **3.** $38\frac{2}{3}$.   **5.** 1.   **7.** $\frac{1}{3}(13^{3/2} - 8^{3/2}).$ **9.** $\frac{2}{15}$.   **11.** $-\frac{3}{2}$.
13. Yes.   **15.** (a) $21\frac{1}{2}$; (c) $\frac{1}{2}$.

Exercises 2.7

1. 36.   **3.** 8.   **5.** 25.6.   **7.** 121.5.   **9.** $\frac{2}{3}$.   **11.** 6.
13. $21\frac{1}{16}$.   **15.** $61\frac{1}{15}$, $61\frac{1}{15}$.   **17.** $63\frac{3}{32}$, $\frac{2}{3}$.

Exercises 2.8

1. 1.2.   **3.** 2.   **5.** 64 lb; 80,000 mile-lb.   **7.** 1406.25π ft-lb.
9. 3700π ft-lb.   **11.** (b) 46.875 ft-lb.

Exercises 3.3

1. (a) Isosceles; (c) isosceles; (e) neither; (g) isosceles, right.
2. (a) Rectangle; (c) trapezoid; (e) rhombus; (g) not one of the figures mentioned; (i) square.   **4.** (a) Yes; (c) yes.

Exercises 3.4

3. $-\vec{a} + \vec{b}$, $4(\vec{a} - \vec{b})$; $TS : SU = 1 : 3$.   **13.** $AF : FE = 1 : 2$.

Exercises 3.5

1. (a) $3\vec{i} + 5\vec{j}$; (c) $-6\vec{i} - 3\vec{j}$.   **4.** (a) $\sqrt{85}, 5, \sqrt{40}$.   **5.** $(3, 2)$.
7. $(\%, -\%)$.   **9.** (a) $(6, ^{10}\!\!/\!_3)$.

Exercises 3.6

1. (a) No; (c) yes.   **2.** (a) $\frac{1}{5}(4\vec{i} + 3\vec{j})$; (c) $\dfrac{1}{\sqrt{37}}(\vec{i} + 6\vec{j})$.

3. (a) $\pm\frac{1}{5}(3\vec{i} - 4\vec{j})$; (c) $\pm(1/\sqrt{37})(6\vec{i} - \vec{j})$;   **4.** (a) $\cos O = \dfrac{7}{\sqrt{170}}$, $\cos R$

$= \dfrac{13}{\sqrt{290}}$, $\cos S = \dfrac{3}{\sqrt{493}}$; (c) $\cos W = \dfrac{63}{\sqrt{5650}}$, $\cos M = \dfrac{-13}{\sqrt{1850}}$, $\cos R$

$= \dfrac{50}{\sqrt{4181}}$.   **5.** (a1) $9/\sqrt{10}$, (a3) $-12/\sqrt{13}$, (b1) $^9\!/\!_{10}(3\vec{i} + \vec{j})$,
(b3) $^{12}\!/\!_{13}(3\vec{i} + 2\vec{j})$.   **7.** -11.   **8.** (a) $3\vec{i} + \vec{j}$; (c) $4\vec{i} - \vec{j}$.

Exercises 3.7

1. $(3, 2)$.   **3.** No intersection, no real solution.   **5.** $\left(\dfrac{3 + \sqrt{39}}{5}, \dfrac{-1 + 3\sqrt{39}}{5}\right)$,

$\left(\dfrac{3 - \sqrt{39}}{5}, \dfrac{-1 - 3\sqrt{39}}{5}\right)$.

Exercises 3.8

1. (a) $4x - 3y = 0$, $x + 2y - 11 = 0$, $2x - 7y = 0$; (c) $x = 4$, $4x - 5y + 14 = 0$,
$6x + 5y - 4 = 0$.   **3.** $3x - 5y - 1 = 0$, $x = 2$, $5x + 3y - 13 = 0$, $(6, \%)$,
$5y - 3 = 0$.   **4.** (a) $y = 2x$, (c) $y = 2$.   **5.** (a) $6x + 8y - 25 = 0$,
(c) $10x + 8y - 47 = 0$.   **6.** (a) $y = 2$, (c) $16x + 5y - 44 = 0$.
7. $\cos \theta = ^2\!/\!_{25}\sqrt{5}$.   **9.** $\cos \theta = -(33/\sqrt{1450})$.   **11.** (a) $11/\sqrt{5}$, 11;
(c) 5, 25.   **12.** (a) $24/\sqrt{13}$; (c) $^{21}\!/\!_{13}$; (e) 4.   **13.** $4/\sqrt{10}$.
16. (a) $1\frac{1}{2}$; (c) 7.   **17.** $\%$.   **18.** (a) $^{22}\!/\!_{29}$; (c) 50.

Exercises 3.9

1. (a) $C(4, 3)$, $r = 4$; (c) $C(\frac{3}{4}, -\frac{5}{4})$, $r = \frac{3}{4}\sqrt{2}$; (e) no real locus.
2. (a) $(x + 3)^2 + (y - 4)^2 = 53$.   **3.** $(x + \frac{1}{2})^2 + (y - 3)^2 = \frac{89}{4}$.
4. (a) $(x - 1)^2 + (y - 3)^2 = 29$.   **5.** $(x - \frac{3}{2})^2 + (y + 2)^2 = \frac{97}{4}$.
7. $(x - 4)^2 + y^2 = 20$.   **8.** (a) $(x - 2)^2 + y^2 = 25$.
9. $(x - 1)^2 + (y + 3)^2 = 50$.   **11.** $(x + 2)^2 + (y - \frac{9}{2})^2 = \frac{9}{4}$.
13. $(x - 6)^2 + (y + 2)^2 = 10$ and $x^2 + (y + 4)^2 = 10$.   **18.** (a) $\sqrt{26} - 4$.
19. $\sqrt{41} - 3$.   **21.** $y + 1 = -3(x - 4)$ and $y + 1 = \frac{1}{3}(x - 4)$.

Exercises 3.10

1. (a) $(10, 0)$, $x = -10$; (c) $(-\frac{5}{2}, 0)$, $x = \frac{5}{2}$.   **2.** (a) $x^2 = 16y$; (c) $y^2 = 12x$.
5. $x^2 + y^2 - 8x - 8y - 2xy = 0$.   **7.** $\dfrac{(4.5)^2}{18.8} \approx 1.08$ units from vertex.

Exercises 3.11

1. (a) $(\pm 4, 0)$, $(0, \pm 2)$, $(\pm\sqrt{12}, 0)$, $\dfrac{\sqrt{3}}{2}$; (c) $(0, \pm\frac{2}{3})$, $(\pm\frac{1}{3}, 0)$, $\left(0, \pm\dfrac{\sqrt{3}}{3}\right)$, $\dfrac{\sqrt{3}}{2}$.
2. (a) $x^2/36 + y^2/64 = 1$; (c) $x^2/13 + y^2/49 = 1$; (e) $x^2/100 + y^2/84 = 1$;
     (g) $5x^2 + y^2 = 21$; (i) $3x^2 + 4y^2 = 64$.
7. $5x^2 + 8y^2 - 4xy - 36 = 0$.   **9.** Area of ellipse is πab.

Exercises 3.12

1. (a) $(\pm 4, 0)$, $(\pm 4\sqrt{2}, 0)$, $y = \pm x$, $\sqrt{2}$; (c) $(0, \pm 4)$, $(0, \pm 5)$, $y = \pm\frac{4}{3} x$, $\frac{5}{4}$;
     (e) $(\pm\frac{3}{2}, 0)$, $(\pm\sqrt{10}/2, 0)$, $y = \pm\frac{1}{3} x$, $\sqrt{10}/3$.   **2.** (a) $9x^2 - 16y^2 = 144$;
     (c) $4y^2 - 7x^2 = 36$; (e) $3x^2 - y^2 = 47$; (g) $4x^2 - 9y^2 = 135$.
3. $x^2 + 4x - 8y^2 + 16y + 4 = 0$.   **9.** $b^2x_1x - a^2y_1y = a^2b^2$.

Exercises 3.13

1. (a) $(4, 0)$, $(7, 0)$, $x = 1$; (c) $(-\frac{7}{2}, -1)$, $(-\frac{7}{2}, -3)$, $y = +1$.   **2.** (a) $(3, 4)$;
     $(3, 6)$, $(3, 2)$; $(4, 4)$, $(2, 4)$; $(3, 4 + \sqrt{3})$, $(3, 4 - \sqrt{3})$; (c) $(5, -3)$; $(10, -3)$, $(0, -3)$;
     $(5, -3 + \sqrt{20})$, $(5, -3 - \sqrt{20})$; $(5 + \sqrt{5}, -3)$, $(5 - \sqrt{5}, -3)$; $\sqrt{5}/5$.
3. (a) $(0, 2)$; $(4, 2)$, $(-4, 2)$; $(\sqrt{32}, 2)$, $(-\sqrt{32}, 2)$; $y - 2 = \pm x$; $\sqrt{2}$;
     (c) $(1, \frac{2}{3})$; $(7, \frac{2}{3})$, $(-5, \frac{2}{3})$; $(1 + \sqrt{52}, \frac{2}{3})$, $(1 - \sqrt{52}, \frac{2}{3})$; $y - \frac{2}{3} =$
     $\pm\frac{2}{3}(x - 1)$; $\sqrt{13}/3$.   **4.** (a) $(x - 1)^2 = -12(y - 4)$; (c) $(y - 1)^2 =$
     $-8(x - 3)$; (e) $\dfrac{(x + 2)^2}{9} + \dfrac{(y + 1)^2}{5} = 1$; (g) $\dfrac{(x - 7)^2}{1} - \dfrac{(y - 1)^2}{3} = 1$;
     (i) $\dfrac{(x - 3)^2}{20} - \dfrac{(y - 2)^2}{5} = 1$.

Exercises 3.14

1. (a) $\theta = 45°$; $x'^2 = 4\sqrt{2}y'$; $F(-1, 1)$; directrix: $x - y - 2 = 0$;
     (c) $\theta = 60°$; $4x'^2 + y'^2 = 16$; $C(0, 0)$; $A_1(-2\sqrt{3}, 2)$, $A_2(2\sqrt{3}, -2)$; $B_1(1, \sqrt{3})$,

$B_2(-1, -\sqrt{3})$; $F_1(-3, \sqrt{3})$, $F_2(3, -\sqrt{3})$; (e) $\theta = 45°$; $x'^2 - y'^2 = 2a^2$;
$C(0, 0)$; $A_1(a, a)$, $A_2(-a, -a)$; $F_1(\sqrt{2}a, \sqrt{2}a)$, $F_2(-\sqrt{2}a, -\sqrt{2}a)$; $x = 0, y = 0$.
3. $29x^2 + 4xy + 26y^2 = 150$.

Exercises 3.15

1. (a) $x = \pm(4/\sqrt{3})$; (c) $x = 7$, $x = -1$; (e) $x = \pm 1$; (g) $y = {}^{26}\!\!/_5$, $y = -{}^{6}\!\!/_5$.
2. (a) $5x^2 + 9y^2 = 180$; (c) $7x^2 + 9y^2 - 34x + 18y + 40 = 0$.
3. (a) $x^2 - 3y^2 + 12 = 0$; (c) $x^2 - 9y^2 + 36x + 36y - 72 = 0$.
7. (a) $(92.9)(.983) \approx 91.32$ million miles; $(92.9)(1.017) \approx 94.48$ million miles.

Exercises 3.17

1. (a) y axis symmetry; intercepts $(0, 0)$, $(\pm 2, 0)$; max at $(0, 0)$, min at $(\pm\sqrt{2}, -4)$;
(c) x axis symmetry; intercepts $(-2, 0)$, $(1, 0)$, $(6, 0)$, $(0, \pm 2)$; max at $(-{}^{2}\!\!/_3, {}^{20}\!\!/_9)$,
min at $(-{}^{2}\!\!/_3, -{}^{20}\!\!/_9)$; (e) x axis symmetry; intercepts $(-6, 0)$, $(0, 0)$; $(-6, 0)$ is an
isolated point; (g) intercept $(2, 0)$; asymptotes $x = 0$, $y = 1$; min $(2, 0)$; (i) x axis symmetry; intercept $(3, 0)$; asymptote $y = 0$; max $(6, 1)$, min $(6, -1)$; (k) origin
symmetry; asymptotes $x = 0$ and $y = x/2$; min $(\sqrt{3}, \sqrt{3})$, max $(-\sqrt{3}, -\sqrt{3})$;
(m) origin symmetry; intercepts $(0, 0)$, $(0, \pm\sqrt{6})$.   **2.** (a) compare with
$2y^2 = x^3 - 8$; symmetric with respect to $y = -2$; crosses axis of symmetry at $(3, -2)$.
3. One answer is (a) $y = {}^{3}\!\!/_4(x^2 - 1)(x^2 - 4)$; (c) one answer is $y^2 = x(x - 3)$;
(e) one answer is $y = \dfrac{2(x + 1)(x - 2)}{x - 4}$; (g) one answer is $y^2 = \dfrac{x^4 + 32}{(x - 2)(x - 4)}$;
(i) one answer is $y^2 = \dfrac{(1 - x)(x + 3)^2}{x^4}$; (k) one answer is $y = \dfrac{(x + 2)^2}{x + 1}$.

Exercises 3.18

1. (a) $(0, 0)$ is one intercept; $(-1, 7)$ is a maximum point; $(2, -20)$ is a minimum point;
(c) $(0, 0)$ is one intercept; $(-2, -24)$ is a minimum point; $f'(1) = 0$ but $(1, 3)$ is
neither max nor min; (e) $(0, 0)$ is the intercept; $f'(-3) = f'(0) = 0$ but $(-3, -3)$
and $(0, 0)$ are neither max nor min; (g) $(0, 0)$ is intercept; origin symmetry; vertical
tangent at $(0, 0)$; absolute max at $(1, 1)$, absolute min at $(-1, -1)$; (i) $(0, 0)$, $(1, 0)$
are the intercepts; min at $(0, 0)$, $(1, 0)$; absolute max at $(2, 64)$; relative max at $(-1,$
$16\sqrt[3]{4})$, $({}^{3}\!\!/_4, 9/\sqrt[3]{16})$; (k) $(\pm 1, 0)$ are the intercepts; y axis symmetry; $x = 0$ and
$y = 0$ are asymptotes; $(\pm\sqrt{2}, 1)$ are maxima.
2. (a) max at $(0, 0)$; min at $(3, {}^{3}\!\!/_2)$; curve has greater slope $(= {}^{9}\!\!/_{80})$;
(c) max at $(2, \sqrt{2})$; min at $(2, -\sqrt{2})$; vertical tangent at $(0, 0)$, no cusp there; slope
of tangent to upper branch $\to\sqrt{6}/4$ as $x \to 6^+$, $\to -\sqrt{6}/4$ as $x \to 6^-$; (e) x coordinate is a maximum at $({}^{1}\!\!/_4, 4)$.

Exercises 3.19

2. (a) Intercepts at $(0, 0)$, $(3, 0)$; min at $(3, 0)$, max at $(1, 4)$; point of inflection at $(2, 2)$;
(c) intercepts at $(0, 0)$, $(4, 0)$; min at $(3, -27\!/_5)$, horizontal tangent at $(0, 0)$; points
of inflection at $(0, 0)$, $(2, -16\!/_5)$; (e) intercepts at $(0, 0)$, $(5, 0)$; max at $(0, 0)$, min at
$(4, -2.56)$; point of inflection at $(3, -1.62)$ only; (g) intercepts at $(0, 0)$, $(4, 0)$; max at

$(3, 1)$; vertical tangent and point of inflection at $(4, 0)$; point of inflection at $(6, -2\sqrt[3]{2})$; (i) intercept at $(3, 0)$; $x = 1$ and $y = 1$ are asymptotes; min at $(3, 0)$; point of inflection at $(4, \frac{1}{9})$.

Exercises 3.20

1. (a) $y - 1 = 1(x - 3)$; $x = 3$ not a member; $\cos \theta(y - 1) = \sin \theta(x - 3)$;
(e) $y = 2, y = -2$; (g) $x = 2, x = -2, y = 0$; (k) $y = 1$. **2.** (a) One answer is
$(\cot \alpha)y = x - 3$, where α is inclination angle; (c) one answer is $(x - h)^2 + (y - 1)^2$
$= 1$; (e) one answer is $y^2 = 2ax$; (g) one answer is $\dfrac{x^2}{a^2} + \dfrac{y^2}{\frac{3}{4} a^2} = 1, a > 0$;

(i) one answer is $\dfrac{x^2}{k^2} + \dfrac{\pi^2 k^2 y^2}{25} = 1, k > 0$; (k) one answer is $\dfrac{y^2}{a^2} - \dfrac{x^2}{16 - a^2} = 1, 0 < a < 4$.

3. (a) F_1: circles through origin, centers on x axis; F_2: circles through origin, centers on y axis; (c) F_1: parabolas, x axis symmetry, common focus at origin, vertices to right of origin; F_2: parabolas, x axis symmetry, common focus at origin, vertices to left of origin. **7.** (a) One answer is $(3x + 2y - 6) + k(5x - 4y + 20) = 0$;
(c) $22x - 33y + 151 = 0$. **8.** (a) $2x^2 + 2y^2 - 9x + 7y - 18 = 0$.
9. Parabolas with x axis symmetry, passing through $(1, \pm\sqrt{2})$; the line $x = 1(k = -1)$; the pair of lines $y = \pm\sqrt{2}(k = 1)$.

Exercises 4.1

1. (a) $\pi/2$; (c) $3\pi/4$; (e) $3\pi/2$; (g) .06980; (i) .24928. **2.** (a) $30°$; (c) $330°$;
(e) $225°$; (g) $10° \, 10'$; (i) $24° \, 32'$. **5.** (a) $\cos t = \sqrt{5}/3$, $\tan t = 2/\sqrt{5}$ or
$\cos t = -\sqrt{5}/3$, $\tan t = -(2/\sqrt{5})$; (c) $\sin t = 2/\sqrt{5}$, $\cos t = 1/\sqrt{5}$ or $\sin t = -(2/\sqrt{5})$, $\cos t = -(1/\sqrt{5})$; (e) $\sin t = \sqrt{15}/4$, $\tan t = -\sqrt{15}$ or
$\sin t = -(\sqrt{15}/4)$, $\tan t = \sqrt{15}$. **7.** (a) $3, \pi/2$; (c) $1, 2$; (e) $\frac{1}{3}, \frac{1}{2}$;
(g) $2, 2\pi$. **9.** (a) $f(x) = 3 \sin \frac{1}{2} x$; (c) $f(x) = .02 \sin 1024\pi x$.

Exercises 4.2

1. (a) $dy/dx = 6 \cos 2x - 8 \sin 2x$; (c) $dy/dx = 8\pi \sin^3 \pi x \cos \pi x$;
(e) $dy/dx = x \cos x + \sin x$; (g) $dx/dt = 1/(\cos t - 1)$; (i) $dy/dx = \cos x/\sin y$.
2. (a) $(1/a) \sin ax + C$; (c) $\frac{2}{3}(\sin x)^{3/2} + C$; (e) $-\dfrac{1}{a} \dfrac{1}{\sin ax} + C$; (g) $\dfrac{2}{(\cos x)^{1/2}} + C$.

4. (a) period 2π, amplitude 1; x intercepts at $\left(\dfrac{\pi}{2}, 0\right), \left(\dfrac{3\pi}{2}, 0\right)$; max at $(0, 1)$, min at

$(\pi, -1)$; points of inflection at $\left(\dfrac{\pi}{2}, 0\right), \left(\dfrac{3\pi}{2}, 0\right)$; (c) period 2π; intercepts at $(0, 0)$,

$(\pi, 0)$; max at $\left(\dfrac{\pi}{2}, 1\right)$; min at $\left(\dfrac{3\pi}{2}, -1\right)$; points of inflection at $(0, 0)$, $(\pi, 0)$,

$(\tan^{-1}\sqrt{2}, \sqrt{8/27})$, $(\pi - \tan^{-1}\sqrt{2}, \sqrt{8/27})$, $(\pi + \tan^{-1}\sqrt{2}, -\sqrt{8/27})$,
$(2\pi - \tan^{-1}\sqrt{2}, -\sqrt{8/27})$; (e) no max or min points; horizontal tangents at

$\left(\dfrac{\pi}{2} + 2n\pi, \dfrac{\pi}{2} + 2n\pi\right), n = 0, \pm 1, \pm 2, \cdots$; points of inflection at $\left(\dfrac{\pi}{2} + n\pi, \dfrac{\pi}{2} + n\pi\right)$,

$n = 0, \pm 1, \pm 2, \pm 3, \cdots$. **6.** (a) K.E. $= 2\pi^2 k^2 b^2 m$. **7.** (a) 2; (c) $\dfrac{4 - \pi}{4\pi}$;

(e) $\pi/2$. **9.** $v = -(a/mb) \cos bt + (a/mb)$, $x = -(a/mb^2) \sin bt + (a/mb)t + d$.

Exercises 4.3

3. (a) $dl/dt = 12 \sec^2 3t$; (c) $dy/dx = 3 \sec^3 x \tan x$; (e) $dx/dt = 6 \sec 3t (\sec 3t + \tan 3t)^2$;

(g) $dy/dx = \sec^2 x \tan^2 x (3 \sec^2 x + 2 \tan^2 x)$; (i) $\dfrac{dy}{dx} = \dfrac{-a \csc ax \cot ax}{(\csc ax + 1)^2}$;

(k) $\dfrac{dv}{du} = -\dfrac{\sec^2 u \tan u}{(1 + \sec^2 u)^{3/2}}$. **4.** (a) $\dfrac{dy}{dx} = \dfrac{\tan y - y \sec^2 x}{\tan x - x \sec^2 y}$; (c) $\dfrac{dy}{dx} = \dfrac{\sec^2 x \tan x}{\csc^2 y \cot y}$.

5. (a) $2 \tan \frac{1}{2} x + C$; (c) $-\frac{1}{3} \csc 3t + C$; (e) $2 (\tan x + 2)^{1/2} + C$; (g) $\frac{1}{5} \sec^5 x + C$;

(i) $\dfrac{1}{an} \sec^n ax + C$; (k) $-\frac{2}{5} (\cot x)^{5/2} + C$; (m) $-(1/4a) \csc^4 ax + C$. **6.** (a) $\frac{1}{2}$;

(c) $\frac{7}{3}$. **9.** $\left(\dfrac{\pi}{4}, 2\right)$. **11.** $\pi/2 - 1$.

Exercises 4.4

1. $f^{-1}(v) = 2(v - 6), \; 6 \le v \le 9$. **3.** (a) $\pi/3$; (c) $\pi/3$; (e) .9; (g) $-.3$; (i) .7;

(k) $\pi/6$. **4.** (a) $\dfrac{4}{\sqrt{1 - 16x^2}}$; (c) $\dfrac{6}{4 + x^2}$; (e) $\dfrac{x}{\sqrt{1 + x^2}} + \sin^{-1} x$;

(g) $\dfrac{x - (1 + x^2) \tan^{-1} x}{x^2 (1 + x^2)}$. **5.** (a) $\pi/3$; (c) 1; (e) $\pi/8$; (g) $\pi/6a$.

7. (a) $\cos^{-1} x$ is a number $y, \; 0 \le y \le \pi$, which is such that $\cos y = x$;

(d) $\dfrac{d \cos^{-1} x}{dx} = -\dfrac{1}{\sqrt{1 - x^2}}$. **9.** $\cos \theta = \dfrac{4 + 3\sqrt{3}}{\sqrt{91}}$.

Exercises 5.2

2. (a) 2; (c) $\frac{7}{2}$. **3.** (a) e^3; (c) $e^{4/3}$. **4.** (a) 4.49981; (c) $.89463 - 1$;

(e) 1.09861. **5.** (a) 70; (c) .08. **6.** (a) 1.22964; (c) -5.67812;

(e) 3.80444. **7.** (a) 5.02; (c) 0.502; (e) 740,000. **8.** (a) 1.754; (c) 1.734.

Exercises 5.3

1. (a) $1 + \log x$; (c) $\dfrac{1}{x + 1} - \dfrac{2x}{x^2 + 1}$; (e) $\dfrac{2}{x} + \dfrac{1}{2x - 3}$; (g) $\dfrac{1}{x \log x}$; (i) $\cot x$; (k) $\csc x$;

(m) $\dfrac{1 - 2 \log x}{x^3}$; (o) $(\log 4)4^x$; (q) $y \left[\dfrac{1}{x + 5} + \dfrac{1}{2x - 1} - \dfrac{2x}{3(x^2 + 4)} \right]$;

(s) $-y(\tan x + 2 \tan 2x + 3 \tan 3x + 4 \tan 4x)$; (u) $-\dfrac{y(x + 1)}{x(y + 1)}$.

2. (a) $\log (x + 2) + C$ or $\log [-(x + 2)] + C$; (c) $-\frac{1}{2} \log (1 - 2t) + C$ or $-\frac{1}{2} \log$ $(2t - 1) + C$; (e) $-(1 - x^2)^{1/2} + C$; (g) $\tan^{-1} t + C$; (i) $\log \sin x + C$ or $\log$ $(-\sin x) + C$; (k) $2\sqrt{\tan x} + C$; (m) $\log (1 - \cos x) + C$. **3.** (a) Intercept $(0, 0)$; y axis symmetry; min $(0, 0)$; points of inflection at $(1, \log 2), (-1, \log 2)$.

5. $\log 2 \approx .693$. **7.** (a) $\log 3 \approx 1.099$; (c) $\log 4 \approx 1.386$.

Exercises 5.4

1. (a) $-.2e^{-.2x}$; (c) $ax^{n-1}e^{bx}(bx + n)$; (e) $\dfrac{2e^{2x}(x - 1)}{x^3}$; (g) $-\dfrac{e^{ay} + aye^{ax}}{e^{ax} + axe^{ay}}$; (i) $e^x e^x = e^{(x+e^x)}$.

2. (a) $-\frac{1}{4}e^{-4x} + C$; (c) same as (a); (e) $2e^{\sqrt{x}} + C$. **3.** $y \geq 0$; as $x \to +\infty$, $y \to x$ axis asymptotically; graph descends always; graph faces up everywhere; $y = e^x$ and $y = e^{-x}$ are symmetric with respect to the y axis. **7.** $a^2(e^{h/a} - e^{-h/a})$.
9. $L = L_0 e^{kt}$; $k = \frac{1}{100}\log 1.0012$. **11.** $T = 74 + 36e^{-.02t}$.

13. $m = \dfrac{-b \pm \sqrt{b^2 - 4ac}}{2a}$.

Exercises 5.5

4. (a) $6\cosh 3x + 9\sinh 3x$; (c) $t\cosh t + \sinh t$; (e) $a\dfrac{\sinh ax - \cosh ax - 1}{(\sinh ax + 1)^2}$;

(g) $-\dfrac{\cosh y + y\cosh x}{x\sinh y + \sinh x}$. **5.** (a) $4\sinh x + 3\cosh x + C$; (c) $\frac{1}{4}\sinh^4 x + C$;

(e) $-\dfrac{1}{2}\dfrac{1}{\cosh 2x + 1} + C$. **7.** $\frac{1}{4}$. **9.** If $\beta + \alpha \begin{cases} > 0 \\ = 0, \text{ limit } y = \\ < 0, \end{cases} \begin{cases} +\infty \\ 0 \\ -\infty \end{cases}$.

11. $(\pm \tanh^{-1}\sqrt{\frac{1}{2}}, \sqrt{\frac{1}{2}})$ or $(\pm.88, .71)$.

Exercises 6.1

1. $(4/3)x^3 + 6\log x + 3/x + C$. **3.** $\frac{1}{8}\log(1 + 4x^2) + C$. **5.** $\frac{1}{4}\sec^4 x + C$.
7. $6\sqrt{x} - 2\sqrt{x^5} + C$. **9.** $(1/a)\tan ax + C$. **11.** $\sinh 3x - \frac{1}{3}\cosh 3x + C$.
13. $2\sec\frac{1}{2}z + C$. **15.** $\log(\sin x + 2) + C$.
17. Not of one of the types (1)–(13). **19.** $\frac{1}{4}\cosh^4 x + C$.
21. $-\dfrac{1}{a}\csc ax + C$. **23.** $\frac{1}{2}\tan^{-1}2x + C$.

Exercises 6.2

1. $\frac{1}{4}\sin^4 x + C$. **3.** $\frac{1}{4}\sin^4 x - \frac{1}{6}\sin^6 x + C$. **5.** $\frac{1}{2}\tan 2x - x + C$.
7. $\frac{1}{2}x + (1/4a)\sin 2ax + C$. **9.** $\frac{3}{8}x + (1/4a)\sin 2ax + (1/32a)\sin 4ax + C$.
11. $\frac{1}{8}x - \frac{1}{32}\sin 4x + C$. **13.** $\frac{1}{16}x - \frac{1}{48}\sin^3 2x - \frac{1}{64}\sin 4x + C$.
15. $\frac{3}{2}x + 2\sin x + \frac{1}{4}\sin 2x + C$. **17.** $\frac{1}{6}\sec^6 x - \frac{1}{4}\sec^4 x + C$.
19. $\frac{1}{7}\tan^7 x + \frac{1}{5}\tan^5 x + C$.
21. $-(1/a)\log\cos ax + C$ or $-(1/a)\log(-\cos ax) + C$.
23. $(1/2a)\tan^2 ax + (1/a)\log\cos ax + C$ or $(1/2a)\tan^2 ax + (1/a)\log(-\cos ax) + C$.
25. $(1/a)\tan ax$. **27.** $-(1/3a)\cot^3 ax + (1/a)\cot ax + x + C$.
29. $-\dfrac{1}{m+3}\cot^{m+3}x - \dfrac{1}{m+1}\cot^{m+1}x + C$ if $m \neq -1, -3$;
$-\frac{1}{2}\cot^2 x - \frac{1}{2}\log\cot^2 x + C$ if $m = -1$; $-\frac{1}{2}\log\cot^2 x + \frac{1}{2}\tan^2 x + C$ if $m = -3$.

Exercises 6.3

1. $\frac{1}{2}(a^2\sin^{-1}x/a - x\sqrt{a^2 - x^2}) + C$. **3.** $-\frac{1}{3}(1 - x^2)^{3/2} + C$.
5. $\frac{1}{4}\dfrac{x}{\sqrt{x^2 + 4}} + C$. **7.** $\sqrt{x^2 - 5} + C$. **9.** $-\frac{1}{15}(3x^2 + 16)(8 - x^2)^{3/2} + C$.

11. $\frac{1}{2} \log |x^2 - a^2| - \dfrac{a^2}{2(x^2 - a^2)} + C.$ **13.** $\log (2 + \sqrt{3}) \approx 1.32.$ **15.** 0.

19. (a) $\sinh^{-1} \sqrt{3} = \log (2 + \sqrt{3})$; (b) same answer as Exercise 9.

Exercises 6.4

In each case that a logarithm appears, it is assumed that the argument is positive. If it is negative, one takes the logarithm of its absolute value.

1. $\dfrac{1}{2a} \log \dfrac{x - a}{x + a} + C.$ **3.** $\log [x(x - 3)(x - 1)^2] + C.$

5. $-\dfrac{3}{x} - 2 \log x - \dfrac{1}{x + 2} + 2 \log (x + 2) + C.$

7. $\log x - \frac{1}{2} \log (x^2 + 4) + \frac{1}{2} \tan^{-1} (x/2) + C.$

9. $\frac{1}{2} \log (x^2 + 1) + \frac{2}{3} \tan^{-1} (x/3) + C.$ **11.** $\log 108 \approx 4.68.$

13. $1 - 7 \log 2 \approx -3.85.$

Exercises 6.5

1. $2\sqrt{x} - 2 \tan^{-1} \sqrt{x} + C.$ **3.** $(2x - 1)^{1/2} + C.$

5. $-x - 2\sqrt{x} - 2 \log |1 - \sqrt{x}| + C.$

7. $\frac{2}{3}\sqrt{x + 4} (x + 16) + 8 \log \left| \dfrac{\sqrt{x + 4} - 2}{\sqrt{x + 4} + 2} \right| + C.$ **9.** $-\frac{1}{3}(a^2 - x^2)^{3/2} + C.$

11. $\sqrt{x^2 - 1} - \tan^{-1} \sqrt{x^2 - 1} + C.$

13. $\dfrac{1}{3}(x^2 + 4a^2) \sqrt{a^2 + x^2} + \dfrac{a^3}{2} \log \dfrac{\sqrt{x^2 + a^2} - a}{\sqrt{x^2 + a^2} + a} + C.$

15. $2 \log |\tan x - 2| - 2 \log |\sec x| + x + C.$ **17.** $\frac{2}{9}\sqrt{x^3 + 8} (x^3 - 16) + C.$

19. $a \sin^{-1} \sqrt{x/a} - 2\sqrt{a}\sqrt{a - x} - \sqrt{a - x}\sqrt{x} + C.$ **21.** $\frac{1}{3} \log 2.5 \approx .31.$

23. $\frac{14}{5}\sqrt{3a^5}.$ **25.** $562\frac{2}{35}.$

Exercises 6.6

1. $-x \cos x + \sin x + C.$ **3.** $y \tan y + \log \cos y + C.$

5. $\frac{1}{4} x^2 - (1/4a)x \sin 2ax - (1/8a^2) \cos 2ax + C.$

7. $t^3 \sin t + 3t^2 \cos t - 6t \sin t - 6 \cos t + C.$ **9.** $\dfrac{x^{n+1}}{n + 1}\left(\log x - \dfrac{1}{n + 1}\right) + C.$

11. $x \tan^{-1} x - \frac{1}{2} \log (1 + x^2) + C.$ **13.** $\frac{1}{3} x^3 \tan^{-1} x - \frac{1}{6} x^2 + \frac{1}{6} \log (x^2 + 1) + C.$

15. $-\dfrac{\log y}{y - 1} - \log y + \log (y - 1) + C.$ **17.** $x(\log x)^2 - 2x \log x + 2x + C.$

19. $-\frac{1}{2} \csc t \cot t - \frac{1}{2} \log (\csc t + \cot t) + C.$

21. $\frac{1}{2} x\sqrt{1 + x^2} - \frac{1}{2} \log (\sqrt{1 + x^2} + x) + C.$

23. (a) $\frac{1}{2} x\sqrt{x^2 - a^2} - \frac{1}{2} a^2 \log (x + \sqrt{x^2 - a^2}) + C.$

Exercises 6.7

1. (a) $\dfrac{1}{3} \tan^{-1} \dfrac{x + 2}{3} + C$; (c) $\sin^{-1} \dfrac{x - 1}{2} + C$; (e) $+ \dfrac{1}{2\sqrt{24}} \log \left| \dfrac{x + 6 - \sqrt{24}}{x + 6 + \sqrt{24}} \right|$;

(g) $\frac{1}{2}(x+3)\sqrt{x^2+6x+25} + 8 \log (\sqrt{x^2+6x+25} + x + 3) + C.$

5. (b) $\frac{1}{7} \sin x \left[\cos^6 x + \frac{6}{5} \cos^4 x + \frac{6(4)}{5(3)} \cos^2 x + \frac{6(4)(2)}{5(3)} \right] + C;$ (c) $\frac{7 \cdot 5 \cdot 3 \cdot 1}{8 \cdot 6 \cdot 4 \cdot 2}\pi.$

7. (b) $\frac{2}{7}(x+1)^{3/2}[x^2 - \frac{4}{5}x + \frac{8}{15}] + C;$ (c) $\frac{2}{3}, \frac{26}{15}, \frac{478}{105}.$

9. $\frac{9}{2} \sin^{-1} \frac{x}{3} - \frac{1}{2}x\sqrt{9-x^2} + C.$ **11.** $-\frac{1}{4}e^{-2x}(2x+1) + C.$

13. $-\frac{1}{8} \cos^4 2t + C.$ **15.** $t - 6\sqrt{t} + 18 \log (\sqrt{t}+3) + C.$

17. $\sqrt{5-x^2} - \sqrt{5} \log \left| \frac{\sqrt{5}+\sqrt{5-x^2}}{x} \right| + C.$

19. $\frac{1}{4}(\sin 2t \sinh 2t - \cos 2t \cosh 2t).$ **21.** $\frac{3}{2}x - \frac{1}{4a} \sin 2ax - \frac{2}{a} \cos ax + C.$

23. $\frac{2}{21}(\tan t)^{3/2}[3 \tan^2 t + 7] + C.$ **25.** $2\sqrt{x+2}(x-4) + C.$

27. $\frac{9}{2}x + \frac{1}{8} \sin 4x + 2 \tan 2x + C.$

29. $\log |x| - \frac{1}{2} \log (x^2+4) + \frac{1}{2} \tan^{-1} (x/2) + C.$

31. $\sqrt{y^2+4} - \tan^{-1} \sqrt{y^2+4} + C.$ **33.** $3(t^{1/3} - \tan^{-1} t^{1/3}) + C.$

35. $\frac{1}{2} \log^2 z + C.$ **37.** $x \log (x + \sqrt{x^2+1}) - \sqrt{x^2+1} + C.$

39. $\frac{1}{3} \log |x-1| - \frac{1}{\sqrt{3}} \tan^{-1} \frac{2x+1}{\sqrt{3}} - \frac{1}{6} \log (x^2+x+1) + C.$

Exercises 6.8

1. (a) .4055; (c) 2.337; (e) .00065. **3.** (a) .4056; (c) 2.342; (e) .00073.

Exercises 7.1

3. $2 - (\epsilon/2) < x < 2 + (\epsilon/2).$ **6.** (a) True; (c) False. **7.** (a) true; (c) true; (e) false.

Exercises 7.2

6. (a) $-5;$ (c) 0; (e) $-2/t^3;$ (g) $\infty;$ (i) 0; (k) 0.

Exercises 7.3

1. A suitable neighborhood is $2 - \epsilon/3 < x < 2 + \epsilon/3.$ **3.** A suitable neighborhood is the smaller of $2 - \epsilon < x < 2 + \epsilon$ and $1 < x < 3.$ The algebraic identity $\sqrt{a} - \sqrt{b}$ $= \frac{\sqrt{a}-\sqrt{b}}{1} \frac{\sqrt{a}+\sqrt{b}}{\sqrt{a}+\sqrt{b}}$ may be useful in the inequality reasoning.
4. (a) Continuous; (c) not defined; (e) continuous. **5.** (a) $f(2) = \frac{1}{2};$ (c) definition cannot be completed; (e) definition cannot be completed; (g) definition cannot be completed.

Exercises 7.4

5. $\delta = \frac{1}{2} \epsilon$ would be a uniformly suitable neighborhood half-width. See Example 5.
7. $\delta = \frac{1}{7} \epsilon$ would be a uniformly suitable neighborhood half-width.

Exercises 7.5

1. (a) $w = 0$; (c) theorem does not apply; (e) $w = (1/\log 2) \approx 1.44$; (g) $w = \sqrt{\dfrac{4 - \pi}{\pi}}$

$\approx .52$; (i) $w = \dfrac{1}{3\sqrt{3}}$. **2.** (a) $3.0025 < \sqrt{9.02} < 3.0033$;

(c) $2.002 < \sqrt[3]{8.06} < 2.005$; (e) $(\pi/4) + .0098 < \tan^{-1} 1.02 < (\pi/4) + .01$.

Exercises 7.6

1. (b) $\sin b$.

Exercises 8.1

1. Square of side 6. **3.** $x = 15\sqrt{3}$, $y = \frac{50}{3}\sqrt{3}$. **5.** $\dfrac{10 - \sqrt{28}}{3} \approx 1.57$.

7. Radius 3, central angle 2 radians. **9.** Front dimensions 10 and 6, side 12.5 and 6.

11. $r = \dfrac{20}{\pi} \approx 6.37, h = 20$. **13.** $a^2/2$. **15.** $r = h = \sqrt[3]{\dfrac{30}{\pi}} \approx 2.12$.

17. $r^4 + r^3 - \dfrac{V}{2\pi} r - \dfrac{V}{2\pi^2} = 0$. **19.** (a) $h = \dfrac{1}{\sqrt{3}} a, r = \sqrt{\frac{2}{3}}\, a$; (b) $\theta = 2\pi(1 - \sqrt{\frac{2}{3}})$

$\approx .18(2\pi)$. **21.** (a) $[a^{2/3} + b^{2/3}]^{3/2}$; (b) $a^{1/3}[a^{2/3} + b^{2/3}]$. **23.** $\theta = \tan^{-1} \mu$.
25. $15\frac{2}{3}$. **29.** 1.25. **31.** $(5, 0), (-5, 0)$. **33.** 90 cents. **35.** $2.00.
37. (a) $(0, -3)$; (b) $(\frac{1}{2}, -\frac{19}{16})$.

Exercises 8.2

1. $2\pi ab$ ft^2 per sec. **3.** $dr/dt = k$. **5.** 3 percent per day. **7.** $\frac{1}{160}$ ft per

min $= .00625$ ft per min. **9.** 3840 K.E. units per sec. **11.** $-3\gamma \dfrac{P_1}{V_1}$.

13. $\frac{29}{2}\pi$ miles per min ≈ 45.55 miles per min. **15.** $(\frac{1000}{9})\pi$ ft per sec ≈ 349 ft per sec.

17. $64 \dfrac{\sin 45°}{\sin 40°}$ ft per sec ≈ 70.4 ft per sec. **19.** (a) $dx/dt = 2\sqrt{5}, dy/dt = -\sqrt{5}$;

(b) $-\frac{4}{5}\sqrt{5} \approx -1.79$. **21.** $\frac{1}{100} \dfrac{1}{\sqrt{76}} (76 - 8\sqrt{3}\pi)$ cm per hour $\approx .037$ cm

per hr.

Exercises 8.3

1. $dA = .4, \Delta A = .4004$. **3.** $.004/\pi \approx .0013$. **5.** $.050\pi$ g $\approx .157$ g.

7. (a) 10.01; (b) too large. **9.** (a) $\dfrac{\pi}{6} + \dfrac{.02}{\sqrt{3}} \approx .535$; (b) too small.

11. (a) .48821; (b) .87279. **13.** $-.2$ percent. **15.** .0011.

Exercises 8.4

1. (a) $x + 2y = 3$; (c) $x^2 = 4y$; (e) $(x - 2)^2 + (y + 1)^2 = 9$; (g) $\dfrac{(x + 1)^2}{9} + y^2 = 1$;

(i) that portion of $\dfrac{x^2}{4} - y^2 = 1$ for which $x > 0$; (k) $(1 - y)^3 = x^2$;

(m) that portion of $y = 1 - 2x^2$ for which $-1 \le x \le 1$. **7.** $\frac{3}{8}\,\pi a^2$.

Exercises 8.5

1. (a) $-\frac{1}{2}, 0$; (c) $v, \frac{1}{2}$; (e) $-\cot\theta, -\frac{1}{3}\csc^3\theta$; (g) $-\frac{1}{3}\cot\theta, -\frac{1}{9}\csc^3\theta$; (i) $\frac{1}{2}\coth u$, $-\frac{1}{4}\operatorname{csch}^3 u$; (k) $-2/3t, 2/9t^4$; (m) $-4\sin\phi, -4$. **3.** (a) $\tan\theta, (1/a\theta)\sec^3\theta$;

(c) $\dfrac{t(2 - t^3)}{1 - 2t^3}, \frac{2}{3}\,\dfrac{(1 + t^3)^4}{(1 - 2t^3)^3}$.

Exercises 8.6

1. (a) $\frac{3}{2} + \frac{1}{4}\log 2 \approx 1.673$; (c) $\log\,(2 + \sqrt{3}) \approx 1.32$;

(e) $\sqrt{1 + e^4} + 2 - \sqrt{2} - \log\,(\sqrt{1 + e^4} + 1) + \log\,(\sqrt{2} + 1)$;

(g) $\frac{13}{24}$; (i) $6a$; (k) $\frac{5}{32}\,\pi^2 a$; (m) $a(\log\cosh 2 + \log\cosh 1)$. **3.** $2(t\mathbf{i} + \mathbf{j})$; $2\mathbf{j}$.

Exercises 8.7

3. (a) $K = \dfrac{\sin x}{(1 + \cos^2 x)^{3/2}}$; 1. **7.** (a) $K = \dfrac{ab}{(a^2\sinh^2 u + b^2\cosh^2 u)^{3/2}}$. **11.** $\frac{32}{25}$.

13. $1/\sqrt{2}$. **15.** $.02/\sqrt{2} \approx .014$ radians.

Exercises 8.9

1. 125 lb. **3.** 300π lb. **5.** 120,000 lb = 60 tons. **7.** $\sqrt{592} - 20 \approx 4.33$ ft

below top of gate. **9.** $\dfrac{\pi a^2 b}{c}\,(1 - e^{-ch})$.

Exercises 8.10

1. (a) $\frac{32}{3}$; (b) $\frac{32}{3}$. **3.** (a) 100; (b) $\frac{308}{5} = 61.6$. **5.** $c\left[\dfrac{1}{2 + \cos t_2} - \dfrac{1}{2 + \cos t_1}\right]$.

7. (a) $-\log 3 \approx -1.10$. **9.** $\dfrac{\alpha(2ac)}{b\sqrt{a^2 + b^2}}$.

Exercises 8.11

1. (a) 13.6; (b) 12.8; (c) .4; (d) $\left(3, \dfrac{13.6}{13.2}\right) \approx (3, 1.03)$. **3.** (a) $\dfrac{2}{3}\rho ba^2$; (b) $\left(\dfrac{4}{3\pi}a, 0\right)$.

5. (a) $\dfrac{2}{3}\,a^3 + \dfrac{\pi a^4 \alpha}{8}$; (b) $\alpha = \dfrac{2}{a}$. **7.** (a) $\frac{2}{3}\,\rho a^3 \sin\alpha$; (b) $\left(\frac{2}{3}\,a\,\dfrac{\sin\alpha}{\alpha}, 0\right)$.

Exercises 8.12

1. $\mu a^3/12 = (\text{mass})(a^2/12)$.   **3.** $\alpha/\beta = 7$.   **5.** $\mu b a^3/12 = (\text{mass})(a^2/6)$.
7. $\frac{5}{4}\pi\mu a^4$.   **9.** $\frac{1}{4}\pi\mu a b^3 = \frac{1}{4}(\text{mass})b^2$.   **11.** $\mu(\pi^2/2 - 4) \approx .935\mu \approx .467(\text{mass})$.

Exercises 8.13

1. (a) improper, 2; (c) improper, divergent; (e) improper, divergent; (g) improper, π;
(i) improper, divergent; (k) improper, divergent; (m) improper, divergent;
(o) improper, $\frac{1}{2}$; (q) improper, divergent.
3. (a) 1/384; (d) an upper bound is 1/384.

Exercises 9.1

1. (a) $(4, 2\pi)$, $(-4, \pi)$; (c) $(3, -3\pi/4)$, $(-3, \pi/4)$; (e) $(1, 7\pi/4)$, $(-1, 3\pi/4)$.
3. All.   **4.** (a) $(4, 0)$; (c) $(-3/\sqrt{2}, -3/\sqrt{2})$; (e) $(1/\sqrt{2}, -1/\sqrt{2})$.
5. (a) $(2, 0)$; (c) $(3, 3\pi/2)$; (e) $(2, 4\pi/3)$; (g) $(\sqrt{2}, -\pi/4)$.

Exercises 9.2

2. (a) $x^2 + y^2 = -4x$; (c) $x^2 + y^2 = -2y$; (e) $y = -2$; (g) $4x^2 + 3y^2 = 12y + 36$;
(i) $(x^2 + y^2)^2 = 2a^2xy$; (k) $(x^2 + y^2)^2 = ax(x^2 - 3y^2)$;
(m) $(x^2 + y^2 - ax)^2 = a^2(x^2 + y^2)$; (o) $(x^2 + y^2 - 2ax)^2 = a^2(x^2 + y^2)$;
(q) $(x^2 + y^2)^3 = (x + y)^4$; (s) $(x^2 + y^2)^3 = y^2$;
(u) $(x^2 + y^2)(x - 1)^2 = 4x^2$ or $y^2 = -\dfrac{x^2(x - 3)(x + 1)}{(x - 1)^2}$;

(w) $y = \sqrt{x^2 + y^2}\,\sin\dfrac{a}{\sqrt{x^2 + y^2}}$.

3. (a) $r = a \sin 2\theta$ ($r = -a \sin 2\theta$ is same graph); (c) $r = 2a \tan \theta \sin \theta$ (cissoid).
5. (a) and (b).   **8.** (a) $r = a \sin \theta$; (c) $r = (a/2)(\cos \theta + \sqrt{3}\sin \theta)$.

Exercises 9.3

1. $\left(a, \dfrac{\pi}{6}\right)$, $\left(a, \dfrac{5\pi}{6}\right)$.   **3.** None.   **5.** $\left(1, \dfrac{\pi}{2}\right)$, $\left(1, \dfrac{3\pi}{2}\right)$.

Exercises 9.4

1. (a) Parabola, $r \cos \theta = 4, 8$; (c) $e = 3$, $r \cos \theta = -\frac{4}{3}, 8$; (e) parabola, $r \sin \theta = \frac{5}{2}, 5$.

2. (a) $r = \dfrac{4}{1 + \sin \theta}$; (c) $r = \dfrac{6}{2 - \cos \theta}$ or $r = \dfrac{2}{2 + \cos \theta}$; (e) $r = \dfrac{8}{1 - \cos \theta}$.

5. $r = a \cos \theta$.   **7.** $r = a \sec \theta + b$ ($r = a \sec \theta - b$ is same curve!).

9. $r = a\left(2 \cos \theta - \dfrac{1}{2 \cos \theta}\right) = \dfrac{a}{2} \sec \theta (4 \cos^2 \theta - 1)$.   **11.** $r = a \csc 2\theta$.

13. $r = a + b \cos \theta$.

Exercises 9.5

1. (a) $\pi/2$; (c) $\tan^{-1}\dfrac{\sqrt{3}}{2} \approx 41°$; (e) $2\pi/3$; (g) $5\pi/6$; (i) $\tan^{-1} 5\pi/2 \approx 83°$.

2. (a) 0; (c) $\dfrac{\pi}{6} + \tan^{-1}\dfrac{\sqrt{3}}{2} \approx 71°$; (e) $\pi/2$; (g) $\pi/4$; (i) $\pi/2 + \tan^{-1} 5\pi/2 \approx 173°$.

5. (a) $\pi/3$; (c) 0 and $\pi/2$; (e) $\pi/4$.

Exercises 9.6

1. $\pi a^2/4$.   **3.** $9\pi a^2/2$.   **5.** $\pi a^2/8$.   **7.** $2b^2/3$.

9. $a^2\left(\dfrac{\pi}{3} + \dfrac{\sqrt{3}}{2}\right) \approx 1.91a^2$.   **11.** $\dfrac{21\sqrt{3}}{16} \approx 2.27$.   **13.** $\dfrac{\pi+1}{2} - \dfrac{9\sqrt{3}}{8} \approx .12$.

17. $2\pi \displaystyle\int_0^a rg(r)\, dr$.

Exercises 9.7

1. (e) $(a/2)[2\pi\sqrt{4\pi^2+1} + \log(\sqrt{4\pi^2+1} + 2\pi)] \approx 21.3a$; (g) $\dfrac{a}{2}\left(\beta - \dfrac{3}{2}\sin\dfrac{2\beta}{3}\right)$.

3. (a) $K = 1/a$; (c) $K = 0$; (e) $K = \dfrac{1}{e^{a\theta}\sqrt{a^2+1}}$; (g) $K = \dfrac{3}{a}(\cos 2\theta)^{1/2} = \dfrac{3r}{a^2}$.

Exercises 10.1

1. (a) $OR = 3\sqrt{2}$; (c) $VK = WK = \sqrt{45}$.

2. (a) Sides: $x = -5, y = 0, z = 4$; edges: $x = -5, y = 0$; $x = -5, z = 4$; $y = 0, z = 4$.

3. $V = 40$.   **4.** (a) $(0, 0, 0)$, $(3, 0, 0)$, $(3, 7, 0)$, $(0, 7, 0)$, $(0, 0, 4)$, $(3, 0, 4)$, $(3, 7, 4)$, $(0, 7, 4)$.   **7.** (a) center $(0, 0, 0)$, vertices $(\pm 3, 0, 0)$ and $(0, 0, \pm 1)$; (c) center $(0, 0, 0)$, vertices $(0, \pm 1, 0)$; (e) center $(0, 0, 4)$, vertices $(0, \pm 4, 4)$ and $(\pm 2, 0, 4)$; (g) center $(0, 0, 5)$, vertices $(0, \pm 4, 5)$.

9. (a) $(a, b, 0)$, $(a, 0, c)$, $(0, b, c)$.

Exercises 10.3

1. $x^2/a^2 + y^2/b^2 = 1$.   **9.** $36x^2 + 9y^2 - 4z^2 = 0$.   **12.** (a) A useful section is

$x = 1, y^2 + z^2 = \frac{1}{16}$.   **13.** (b) $x^2 + z^2 = 9$.

19. Case (1): $\sqrt{x^2 + z^2} + y = 0$; case (2): $-\sqrt{x^2 + z^2} + y = 0$.

Exercises 10.4

1. $(0, 12/5, 8)$.   **3.** $(5, -11/2, -5)$.   **5.** (a) Rectangle; (c) square.

7. (a) $\cos U = \sqrt{10}/6$.   **11.** (a) $8/\sqrt{14}$; (b) $\frac{4}{7}(\mathbf{i} - 2\mathbf{j} + 3\mathbf{k})$;

(c) $\frac{1}{7}(10\mathbf{i} - 13\mathbf{j} - 12\mathbf{k})$; (d) $\sqrt{413}/7$.   **15.** $(x + 1)^2 + (y - 2)^2 + (z - 6)^2 = 14$.

17. $x^2 + z^2 = 2py$.

Exercises 10.5

1. (a) $9\vec{i} - 6\vec{k}$; (c) $5(-6\vec{i} + 4\vec{j} - 9\vec{k})$; (e) $2(16\vec{i} - 14\vec{j} - 33\vec{k})$;

2. (a) $\dfrac{\pm 1}{\sqrt{42}}(4\vec{i} + 5\vec{j} - \vec{k})$; (c) $\dfrac{\pm 1}{\sqrt{6}}(-\vec{i} + \vec{j} - 2\vec{k})$.   **3.** (a) $\sqrt{42}$.

4. (a) 6; (c) $\dfrac{1}{2}\sqrt{\begin{vmatrix} 1 & 1 & 1 \\ y_1 & y_2 & y_3 \\ z_1 & z_2 & z_3 \end{vmatrix}^2 + \begin{vmatrix} x_1 & x_2 & x_3 \\ 1 & 1 & 1 \\ z_1 & z_2 & z_3 \end{vmatrix}^2 + \begin{vmatrix} x_1 & x_2 & x_3 \\ y_1 & y_2 & y_3 \\ 1 & 1 & 1 \end{vmatrix}^2}$.

5. (a) $\dfrac{1}{\sqrt{2}}$; (b) $\dfrac{1}{2}(-\vec{i} + \vec{j})$; (c) $\dfrac{5}{2}(\vec{i} + \vec{j})$; (d) $\dfrac{5}{\sqrt{2}}$.   **15.** $\dfrac{25}{\sqrt{34}}$.

Exercises 10.6

1. (a) $5x + 21y + 2z = 31$; (c) $5x + 7y - 6z = -14$.   **2.** (a) $\dfrac{8}{\sqrt{75}}$;

(c) $\dfrac{1}{\sqrt{6}}$.   **3.** $p_a \parallel p_c$, $p_a \perp p_d$, $p_c \perp p_d$.   **4.** (a) $2x + 3y - z = -1$.

5. (a) $2x + 3y - z = 0$.   **6.** (a) $\dfrac{13}{\sqrt{6}}$; (c) 2.

8. (a) $\dfrac{x-1}{1} = \dfrac{y}{-1} = \dfrac{z-5}{-2}$ or $\dfrac{x-2}{1} = \dfrac{y+1}{-1} = \dfrac{z-3}{-2}$.   **9.** (a) $\cos^{-1}\dfrac{3}{\sqrt{14}}$.

11. $L_b \parallel L_c$, $L_a \perp L_b$, $L_a \perp L_c$, $L_a \perp L_d$.   **12.** (a) $2x + y - 5z = 19$.

13. (a) $\dfrac{x}{1} = \dfrac{y-2}{2} = \dfrac{z}{-3}$ (points other than $(0, 2, 0)$ can be used).

14. (a) $\dfrac{\pi}{2} - \cos^{-1}\dfrac{1}{\sqrt{21}}$.   **15.** (a) $x + 5y - 4z = 7$.   **16.** (a) $x - 2y = 5$.

17. (a) No; (b) yes; (c) no.   **18.** (a) $(7, \frac{7}{2}, 2\frac{1}{2})$; (c) $(1, 0, -1)$.

19. (a) $\sqrt{89/17}$.   **23.** $12x - y - 17z = 12$.

Exercises 10.7

1. (b) $(3/\sqrt{10})(-\sin u\,\vec{i} + \cos u\,\vec{j} + \frac{1}{3}\vec{k})$; (c) $\frac{9}{10}$; (d) $-(\cos u\,\vec{i} + \sin u\,\vec{j})$; (e) $\dfrac{2\pi\sqrt{10}}{3}$.

3. (a) $\dfrac{1}{(5+u)^{1/2}}(\vec{i} + 2\vec{j} + u^{1/2}\vec{k})$; (b) $\dfrac{\sqrt{5}}{2\sqrt{u}(5+u)^{3/2}}$; (c) $\dfrac{-u^{1/2}\vec{i} - 2u^{1/2}\vec{j} + 5\vec{k}}{\sqrt{5u+25}}$;

(d) $\frac{2}{3}(27 - 5^{3/2})$; (e) $y = 2x$.   **5.** (a) $\cos^2 u\,\vec{i} - \cos u \sin u\,\vec{j} - \sin u\,\vec{k}$;

(b) $(1/a)\cos u\sqrt{1 + \cos^2 u}$; (c) $-\dfrac{1}{\sqrt{1 + \cos^2 u}}(\sin 2u\,\vec{i} + \cos 2u\,\vec{j} + \cos u\,\vec{k})$;

(d) $a \log (2 + \sqrt{3})$.

Exercises 11.1

1. $3(x + 2y)^2$, $6(x + 2y)^2$, 3, $6(a + 2b)^2$.   **3.** $\dfrac{xe^{2z}}{\sqrt{x^2 + y^2}}$, $\dfrac{ye^{2z}}{\sqrt{x^2 + y^2}}$, $2e^{2z}\sqrt{x^2 + y^2}$.

5. $\dfrac{2x}{x^2 + y^2 + z^2}, \dfrac{2y}{x^2 + y^2 + z^2}, \dfrac{2z}{x^2 + y^2 + z^2}, -\frac{1}{3}$

7. $(2\pi/a) \cos (2\pi/a) \, x \sin (2\pi/b) \, y \, e^{-.1t} \cos \pi t$, $(2\pi/b) \sin (2\pi/a) \, x \cos (2\pi/b) \, y \, e^{-.1t} \cos \pi t$,
$-\sin (2\pi/a) \, x \sin (2\pi/b) \, y \, e^{-.1t}[\pi \sin \pi t + .1 \cos \pi t]$, boundaries and lines $x = a/2$,
$y = b/2$. **9.** $-\sin (x + ct) - \sin (x - ct)$, $-c \sin (x + ct) + c \sin (x - ct)$.

11. (a) $\dfrac{\partial z}{\partial x} = \dfrac{4x(x^2 - y - 2z) + y^2 z^2}{4(x^2 - y - 2z) - 2xy^2 z} = 1$ at $(1, 0, 2)$,

$\dfrac{\partial z}{\partial y} = \dfrac{-x^2 + y + 2z + xyz^2}{2(x^2 - y - 2z) - xy^2 z} = -\dfrac{1}{2}$ at $(1, 0, 2)$. **15.** 2. **17.** $-\frac{5}{4}$.

19. (a) 1.3; (b) .4. **21.** $(1, 1, 2)$.

Exercises 11.2

1. (a) $du = \dfrac{1}{2\sqrt{x + 2y}} \, dx + \dfrac{1}{\sqrt{x + 2y}} \, dy$; (c) $dv = \dfrac{2y^3}{(x^2 + y^2)^{3/2}} \, dx + \dfrac{2x^3}{(x^2 + y^2)^{3/2}} \, dy$;
   (e) $du = (2x + y^2 z^3) \, dx + (2y + 2xyz^3) \, dy + (2z + 3xy^2 z^2) \, dz$.
3. .03. **5.** 1.5 percent. **7.** $-.5$ percent, $+.5$ percent. **9.** $W = 24$,
   ± 1.11 approx. **11.** Computed E too large by approx $.00016k$.

Exercises 11.3

1. (a) $3(x + 2y)^2[\mathbf{i} + 2\mathbf{j}]$;

(c) $\dfrac{-1}{4x + 2y + 2v + xy}[(8x + 4y + 4v + yv)\mathbf{i} + (4x + 2y + 2v + xv)\mathbf{j}]$;

3. $\frac{1}{3}$. **5.** $\pm \dfrac{43}{9\sqrt{5}}$. **7.** (a) direction of $-b\mathbf{i} + a\mathbf{j}$, $\dfrac{1}{\sqrt{a^2 + b^2}}$, $a\mathbf{i} + b\mathbf{j}$.

9. 273, -1, $\dfrac{3}{\sqrt{5}}$, direction of $\mathbf{i} - \mathbf{j}$, $\sqrt{2}$, direction of $\mathbf{i} + \mathbf{j}$.

11. max at $\left(\dfrac{a}{3}, 0\right)$, $\left(\dfrac{a}{3}, b\right)$; min at $\left(\dfrac{a}{3}, \dfrac{b}{2}\right)$.

Exercises 11.4

1. (a) $z = 4$, $4x + z = 8$; (b) no; normal never perpendicular to z axis.
3. (a) $3x + 2y + \sqrt{6}z = -2$; (b) $(4\sqrt{2/5}, -\sqrt{2/5}, -2\sqrt{2/5})$, $(-4\sqrt{2/5}, \sqrt{2/5}, 2\sqrt{2/5})$.
5. (a) $3x + 4y = 5a$. **7.** (a) $\sqrt{2} \, h(x + z) - 2ay = 0$.
9. (c) $3 \cosh 1\mathbf{i} + 2\sqrt{3} \cosh 1\mathbf{j} - 2 \sinh 1\mathbf{k}$. **11.** (c) $a \sin \theta_1 \mathbf{i} - a \cos \theta_1 \mathbf{j} + r_1 \mathbf{k}$;
   $\sqrt{2}\mathbf{i} - \sqrt{2}\mathbf{j} + \mathbf{k}$. **13.** $\pi/3$.

Exercises 11.5

1. $(y + z) + (x + z)2t + (y + x)3t^2 = 3t^2 + 4t^3 + 5t^4$. **3.** 0, $\cos 2\theta$.
5. $\dfrac{\partial u}{\partial x}, \dfrac{\partial u}{\partial y}$. **7.** $v \dfrac{\partial u}{\partial x} + w \dfrac{\partial u}{\partial y}, -w \dfrac{\partial u}{\partial x} + v \dfrac{\partial u}{\partial y}$. **9.** (a) $(1/r)(x\mathbf{i} + y\mathbf{j} + z\mathbf{k})$;
   (b) $nr^{n-2}(x\mathbf{i} + y\mathbf{j} + z\mathbf{k})$; (c) $n = -1$.
11. (b) $-2 \cos u_0 \sin u_0 \mathbf{i} + (\cos^2 u_0 - \sin^2 u_0)\mathbf{j} + \cos u_0 \mathbf{k}$; (c) $\cos^2 u_0 \mathbf{i} + \cos u_0 \sin u_0 \mathbf{j} + \sin u_0 \mathbf{k}$.
13. $\dfrac{\partial u}{\partial r} = \dfrac{\partial u}{\partial x} \cos \theta + \dfrac{\partial u}{\partial y} \sin \theta$, $\dfrac{\partial u}{\partial \theta} = -r \sin \theta \dfrac{\partial u}{\partial x} + r \cos \theta \dfrac{\partial u}{\partial y}$, $\dfrac{\partial u}{\partial z} = \dfrac{\partial u}{\partial z}$.

Exercises 11.6

1. (a) $6(x + 2y)$, $12(x + 2y)$, $12(x + 2y)$, 6; (c) $4L$, $-L$, $-2 \cosh 2r \sin \theta$, $-2 \cosh 2r$
$\sin \theta$; (e) $2x(2u^2 - 1)$, $4uvx$, $4uvx$, $2x(2v^2 - 1)$; (g) $-u$, $-c^2u$.

6. (a) $\dfrac{9}{16}\dfrac{4z^2 - 9x^2}{z^3}$, $-\dfrac{81}{4}\dfrac{xy}{z^3}$; (c) $\dfrac{2}{(1 + 2y + 2z)^3}$, $\dfrac{2}{(1 + 2y + 2z)^3}$.

7. $\dfrac{\partial^2 u}{\partial x'^2} = \dfrac{\partial^2 u}{\partial x^2}$, $\dfrac{\partial^2 u}{\partial x' \, \partial y'} = \dfrac{\partial^2 u}{\partial x \, \partial y}$, $\dfrac{\partial^2 u}{\partial y'^2} = \dfrac{\partial^2 u}{\partial y^2}$.

9. $\dfrac{\partial^2 u}{\partial r^2} = \cos^2 \theta \, \dfrac{\partial^2 u}{\partial x^2} + 2 \sin \theta \cos \theta \, \dfrac{\partial^2 u}{\partial x \, \partial y} + \sin^2 \theta \, \dfrac{\partial^2 u}{\partial y^2}$,

$\dfrac{\partial^2 u}{\partial \theta^2} = r^2 \sin^2 \theta \, \dfrac{\partial^2 u}{\partial x^2} + r^2 \cos^2 \theta \, \dfrac{\partial^2 u}{\partial y^2} - 2r^2 \sin \theta \cos \theta \, \dfrac{\partial^2 u}{\partial x \, \partial y} - r \cos \theta \, \dfrac{\partial u}{\partial x} - r \sin \theta \, \dfrac{\partial u}{\partial y}$.

11. $\dfrac{\partial^2 u}{\partial v^2} = \sinh^2 v \cos^2 w \, \dfrac{\partial^2 u}{\partial x^2} + 2 \sinh v \cosh v \sin w \cos w \, \dfrac{\partial^2 u}{\partial x \, \partial y} + \cosh^2 v \sin^2 w \, \dfrac{\partial^2 u}{\partial y^2}$

$+ \cosh v \cos w \, \dfrac{\partial u}{\partial x} + \sinh v \sin w \, \dfrac{\partial u}{\partial y}$,

$\dfrac{\partial^2 u}{\partial w^2} = \cosh^2 v \sin^2 w \, \dfrac{\partial^2 u}{\partial x^2} - 2 \sinh v \cosh v \sin w \cos w \, \dfrac{\partial^2 u}{\partial x \, \partial y} + \sinh^2 v \cos^2 w \, \dfrac{\partial^2 u}{\partial y^2}$

$- \cosh v \cos w \, \dfrac{\partial u}{\partial x} - \sinh v \sin w \, \dfrac{\partial u}{\partial y}$.

19. Depth 30, height 30, front length 20.

Exercises 11.7

1. $y = f(x) = x^{1/3}$.

Exercises 12.2

1. (a) $64\pi/15$; (b) 4π.   **3.** (a) $\tfrac{4}{3} \pi a^3$; (b) $(\pi/3)(2a^3 - 3a^2h + h^3) = (\pi/3)d^2(3a - d)$,

where $d = a - h$; (c) $\tfrac{3}{8} a$ units from center.   **5.** 32π.   **7.** $\dfrac{16\sqrt{3}}{3} \pi$.

9. $\dfrac{16\pi a^3}{105}$.   **11.** $\dfrac{\pi}{3} a^3 \tanh^3 2$.   **13.** (a) $\pi\left(1 - \dfrac{2}{e}\right)$; (b) $\dfrac{\mu\pi}{2} \displaystyle\int_{e^{-1}}^{1} (1 + \log y)^4 \, dy$.

15. $(256 - .00256)\pi$.   **19.** 12π.   **21.** $\dfrac{\rho\pi}{400} \displaystyle\int_{y=0}^{4} (26 + 4y - y^2)^2(4 - y) \, dy$.

Exercises 12.3

1. $\tfrac{1}{3} \pi r^2 h$.   **3.** $\pi/60$.   **5.** (a) 2π; (b) $\pi^2/4$; (c) $\pi(\pi - 2)$; (d) $(\pi/4)(8 - \pi)$.

7. $\pi/8$.   **9.** $2\pi a^3 \displaystyle\int_{0}^{2\pi} (\theta - \sin \theta)(1 - \cos \theta)^2 \, d\theta = 6\pi^3 a^3$.   **11.** $\dfrac{\mu\pi^2 ab^2}{2} (4a^2 + 3b^2)$.

13. (a) $\pi(1 - e^{-L^2})$; (b) π.

Exercises 12.4

1. (a) $\tfrac{515}{64} \pi$; (b) $(\pi/2)(15 + \log 2)$.   **3.** (a) $\dfrac{2\sqrt{2}}{5} \pi[2e^\pi + 1]$;

(b) $\dfrac{2\sqrt{2}}{5}\,\pi[2e^{\pi}+5e^{\pi/2}-4]$.   **5.** (a) $2\pi a^2(1-\text{sech } 2)$;

(b) $2\pi a^2(2-\text{sech } 1-\text{sech } 2)$.   **7.** (a) $(\pi/27)[(10)^{3/2}-1]$;

(b) $(\pi/6)[3\sqrt{10}+\log(3+\sqrt{10})]$.   **9.** 3π.

11. (a) $\pi[2\sqrt{5}+\log(2+\sqrt{5})-\sqrt{2}-\log(1+\sqrt{2})]$;

(b) $\pi\left[\sqrt{2}-3\log(1+\sqrt{2})+\log(2+\sqrt{5})+2\log\dfrac{1+\sqrt{5}}{2}\right]$.

13. $2\pi a^2+\dfrac{2\pi b^2 a}{\sqrt{a^2-b^2}}\,\log\dfrac{\sqrt{a^2-b^2}+a}{b}$.

Exercises 12.5

1. (a) 5; (b) 22.5; (c) 12.5.   **3.** (a) 7; (b) 34.   **5.** (a) 8.5; (b) 23.

Exercises 12.6

1. $25\!\!/\!\!2$.   **3.** $232\!\!/\!\!15\approx15.47$.   **5.** $88\!\!/\!\!3$.   **7.** $16(\pi-2\!\!/\!\!3)\approx39.60$.

9. $8\!\!/\!\!9[3\!\!/\!\!2+\log 4]$. Use prism elements parallel to the y axis.   **11.** $\dfrac{4\pi}{35}\,a^3$.

13. (b) $\displaystyle\int_{x=1}^{4}\int_{y=x}^{4}x^2\,dy\,dx$.   **15.** (b) $\displaystyle\int_{y=0}^{1}\int_{z=y}^{1}\sqrt{9-y^2-z^2}\,dz\,dy$.

Exercises 12.7

1. (a) $\dfrac{ka^2b^2}{4}$; (b) $\dfrac{ka^2b^4}{8}$; (c) $\dfrac{kb^4a^2}{48}$; (d) $\left(\dfrac{2}{3}\,a,\,\dfrac{2}{3}\,b\right)$.   **3.** (a) $k\,\dfrac{a^2b}{3}$; (b) $\dfrac{kb^3a^2}{15}$; (c) $\dfrac{kba^4}{30}$;

(d) $\left(\dfrac{3}{4}\,a,\,\dfrac{3}{8}\,b\right)$; (e) $\dfrac{kga^3b}{12}$.   **5.** $13\!\!/\!\!15\,k$.   **7.** $4\sqrt{3}-2\log(2+\sqrt{3})-4\!\!/\!\!3\approx2.96$.

9. $(8\!\!/\!\!5,\,0)$.   **11.** (a) $\displaystyle\int_{x=0}^{2}\int_{y=0}^{\cosh x}(1-.1y)\,dy\,dx$;

(b) $\sinh 2-.0125\sinh 4-.05\approx3.24$; (c) $\displaystyle\int_{x=0}^{2}\int_{y=0}^{\cosh x}x(1-.1y)\,dy\,dx$; (d) 3.92.

Exercises 12.8

1. $3\!\!/\!\!4\sqrt{61}$.   **3.** $8ab$.   **7.** $(1\!\!/\!\!12)[5^{3/2}-1]$.   **9.** $4a^2(\pi-2)$.

11. $(a/12)[3\sqrt{10}+\log(3+\sqrt{10})]$.   **13.** $(7\!\!/\!\!5)[2+\sqrt{2}\log(1+\sqrt{2})]$.

17. $(3\pi/2)a^3$.

Exercises 12.9

1. $\pi a^2/4$.   **3.** $a^2\left(\sqrt{3}-\dfrac{\pi}{3}\right)$.   **5.** $3\pi/16+2\!\!/\!\!3$.

7. $\frac{2}{3}(\beta - \alpha)a^3\left(= \frac{\beta - \alpha}{2\pi}\frac{4}{3}\pi a^3\right)$ or $\frac{2}{3}[(\alpha + \pi) - \beta]a^3$.   **9.** $\frac{2}{9}(3\pi - 4)a^3$.

11. (a) $\frac{3}{2}\pi\mu a^4$; (b) $\frac{1}{4}\pi\mu a^4$; (c) $\frac{5}{4}\pi\mu a^4$.   **13.** (a) $\frac{1}{8}\pi\mu a^4$; (b) $\frac{1}{48}\mu a^4(3\pi - 8)$;

(c) $\frac{1}{48}\mu a^4(3\pi + 8)$.   **15.** $(\frac{5}{6}a, 0)$.   **17.** $2\pi a(a - h)$.   **19.** $\frac{5}{9} - \frac{\pi}{12}$.

Exercises 12.10

1. $\frac{1}{6}abc$.   **3.** $343\frac{3}{8}$.   **5.** $(^{32}/_{15})(32 - 9\sqrt{3})$.   **7.** (a) 32; (b) 20; (c) 12.
9. $abc/8$.   **11.** $(^{16}/_{5})(15\pi - 8)$.   **13.** $(^{292}/_{15})\mu$.
15. $g\alpha(a^2bc/12)(3a^2 + 2b^2 + 2c^2)$.

Exercises 12.11

1. $\frac{4}{3}\pi a^2 b$.   **3.** $\frac{1}{9}(a - b)a^2(3\pi - 4)$.   **5.** $\frac{2}{3}a^3[\sqrt{2} + \log(\sqrt{2} + 1)]$.
7. $\frac{2}{3}r_0^2 h_0[\pi + 1]$.   **9.** $(\frac{1}{5})(\pi + 1)h_0 r_0^4$.   **11.** $^{28}/_{15}\pi\mu a^5$.
13. $2\pi\left(r_0 + \frac{\Delta r}{2}\right)h_0\,\Delta r$.   **15.** Point on axis of symmetry of semicircle at a distance of
$(4/3\pi)\,a$ from the center.

Exercises 12.12

1. (a) $\left(4, 0, \frac{\pi}{2}\right)$; (c) $\left(\sqrt{8}, \frac{\pi}{4}, \frac{\pi}{6}\right)$; (e) $\left(\sqrt{8}, \frac{\pi}{4}, \frac{5\pi}{6}\right)$; (g) $\rho = 2$, θ arbitrary, $\phi = 0$;
(i) $\rho = 0$, θ and ϕ arbitrary.   **2.** (a) $(0, 5, 0)$; (c) $(\sqrt{3}, 3, 2)$;
(e) $(\sqrt{3}, 3, -2)$; (g) $(0, 0, 1)$; (i) $(0, 0, 0)$.   **3.** (a) $\rho = a$; (c) $\theta = 2\pi/3$;
(e) $\phi = 3\pi/4$; (g) $\phi = \tan^{-1}a$ and $\phi = \pi - \tan^{-1}a$.   **4.** (a) $x^2 + y^2 + z^2 = b^2$;
(c) $y = (\tan\alpha)x$, $x \le 0$; (e) $x^2 + y^2 = (\tan^2\alpha)z^2$, $z \ge 0$; (g) $z = 0$.
5. $\frac{2}{3}\pi a^3(\cos\alpha - \cos\beta)$.   **7.** $2\pi k(1 - \cos\alpha)(b - a)a^2$.   **9.** $\pi k a(a - b)^2$.
11. $\frac{1}{2}\pi k a^3(\cos\alpha - \cos\beta)(4 - \pi)$.   **13.** $(^{16}/_9)(4\pi - 3\sqrt{3})$.
15. $(\pi k a/3)(a^2 - b^2)(a - b)^2$.

Exercises 13.2

1. (a) $S_n = \frac{1}{2}[1 - (\frac{1}{3})^n]$; $S = \frac{1}{2}$; (c) $S_n = .005n(n + 1)$; $\lim_{n \to \infty} S_n = \infty$;
(e) $S_n = n/(n + 1)$; $S = 1$;
(g) $S_{2n-1} = 2 - \dfrac{1}{2^{2n-1}}$ but $S_{2n} = 1 - \dfrac{1}{2^{2n}}$; $\lim_{n \to \infty} S_n$ does not exist.
2. (a) $\frac{1}{3}$; (c) $^{15}/_{148}$.

Exercises 13.3

1. Divergent.   **3.** Divergent.   **5.** Divergent.   **7.** Convergent.
9. Divergent.   **11.** Divergent.   **13.** Convergent.   **15.** Divergent.
17. Divergent.   **19.** Divergent.

Exercises 13.4

1. (a) Converges; (c) converges; (e) converges; (g) diverges; (i) converges.

Exercises 13.5

1. (a) $\frac{2}{3}$. **3.** Diverges. **5.** (a) Converges conditionally; (b) $\log 10/10 \approx .230$;
(c) about 9200. **7.** Diverges. **9.** Converges conditionally.
11. Diverges. **13.** Conditionally convergent for all t of the interval $t > -1$.
15. (a) Absolutely convergent for $|x| \leq 1$; (b) remainder $< \frac{1}{24} < .0417$;

(c) remainder $< \dfrac{.0001}{24} < .00000417$; (d) .995. **17.** Absolutely convergent for

$1 \leq x \leq 2$.

Exercises 13.6

1. Convergent. **3.** Ratio test fails; convergent for $p > 1$, divergent for $0 < p \leq 1$.
5. Convergent. **7.** Convergent. **9.** Convergent. **11.** Ratio test fails;
divergent. **13.** $-1 \leq x < 1$. **15.** $-1 \leq x \leq 1$. **17.** $-1 \leq x \leq 1$.
19. All x. **21.** All x. **23.** $-5 < x < -1$. **25.** $-3 \leq x \leq -1$.
31. Convergent. **33.** Convergent.

Exercises 13.7

3. (a) $S_8 = 1 - \dfrac{x^2}{2!} + \dfrac{x^4}{4!} - \dfrac{x^6}{6!} + \dfrac{x^8}{8!}$; (b) $R_8 = -\sin w \, \dfrac{x^9}{9!}$, w between 0 and x.

5. (a) $S_5 = 1 + \dfrac{1}{2}\dfrac{x^1}{1!} - \dfrac{1}{2^2}\dfrac{x^2}{2!} + \dfrac{1\cdot 3}{2^3}\dfrac{x^3}{3!} - \dfrac{1\cdot 3\cdot 5}{2^4}\dfrac{x^4}{4!} + \dfrac{1\cdot 3\cdot 5\cdot 7}{2^5}\dfrac{x^5}{5!}$;

(b) $R_5 = -\dfrac{1\cdot 3\cdot 5\cdot 7\cdot 9}{2^6(1+w)^{11/2}}\dfrac{x^6}{6!}$, w between 0 and x.

7. (a) $S_n = 1 + \sum_{k=1}^{n} m(m-1)(m-2)\cdots(m-k+1)\dfrac{x^k}{k!}$;

(b) $R_n = m(m-1)(m-2)\cdots(m-n)(1+w)^{m-n-1}\dfrac{x^{n+1}}{(n+1)!}$, w between 0 and x.

9. (a) $S_5 = \dfrac{1}{2} - \dfrac{\sqrt{3}}{2}[x-(\pi/3)] - \dfrac{1}{2}\dfrac{[x-(\pi/3)]^2}{2!} + \dfrac{\sqrt{3}}{2}\dfrac{[x-(\pi/3)]^3}{3!} + \dfrac{1}{2}\dfrac{[x-(\pi/3)]^4}{4!}$

$-\dfrac{\sqrt{3}}{2}\dfrac{[x-(\pi/3)]^5}{5!}$; (b) $R_5 = -\cos w \, \dfrac{[x-(\pi/3)]^6}{6!}$, w between $\pi/3$ and x.

11. $S_2 = 19 - 11(x+2) + 4\dfrac{(x+2)^2}{2!}$. **13.** $S_5 = x + \dfrac{x^3}{3} + \dfrac{2x^5}{15}$.

15. $S_4 = 1 + \dfrac{x^2}{2} + \dfrac{5x^4}{24}$. **17.** $S_3 = x - (x^3/3)$.

19. $|R_5| < \sqrt{3}\,\dfrac{.000001}{720} < 2.5(10)^{-9}$. **21.** $|R_5| < \dfrac{1}{(.9)^6}\dfrac{(.1)^6}{6} = \dfrac{1}{6}\dfrac{1}{9^6} < 3.2(10)^{-7}$.

Exercises 13.8

7. (b) $\log \dfrac{1+x}{1-x} = 2 \displaystyle\sum_{k=1}^{\infty} \dfrac{x^{2k-1}}{2k-1}$ for $-1 < x < 1$.

11. (a) $\mathcal{J}_1' = \displaystyle\sum_{k=0}^{\infty} \dfrac{(-1)^k (2k+1)}{k!(k+1)!2} \left(\dfrac{x}{2}\right)^{2k}$ for all x;

(b) $\mathcal{J}_1'' = \displaystyle\sum_{k=1}^{\infty} \dfrac{(-1)^k (2k+1)}{(k-1)!(k+1)!2} \left(\dfrac{x}{2}\right)^{2k-1}$.

15. $e^{-x} \sin x = x - x^2 + \dfrac{x^3}{3} - \dfrac{x^5}{30} + \dfrac{x^6}{90} \cdots$, for all x.

Exercises 13.9

1. (a) $.04879166$; (b) $<.0000016$.   **3.** (a) 2.04750; (b) $<.0002$.
5. (a) Three; (b) $.98007$.   **7.** (a) $-.05129$;

(b) $< \dfrac{1}{(.95)^4} \dfrac{(.05)^4}{4} = \dfrac{1}{4(19)^4} < .000002$.

9. (b) remainder $< \dfrac{2}{11} \left(\dfrac{1}{2}\right)^{11} \dfrac{4}{3} < .00012$.

11. remainder $< \dfrac{1 \cdot 3 \cdot 5 \cdot 7}{2 \cdot 4 \cdot 6 \cdot 8} \left(\dfrac{1}{2}\right)^9 \dfrac{1}{9} \dfrac{4}{3} < .00008$.   **13.** $\dfrac{s}{s-a} \approx 1 + \dfrac{a}{s} + \left(\dfrac{a}{s}\right)^2$;

remainder $= \dfrac{a^3}{s^2(s-a)}$.   **15.** $\dfrac{1}{\sqrt[3]{s^3+a^3}} \approx \dfrac{1}{s}\left[1 - \dfrac{1}{3}\left(\dfrac{a}{s}\right)^3\right]$;

$|\text{remainder}| < \dfrac{1}{s}\dfrac{2}{9}\left(\dfrac{a}{s}\right)^6$.   **17.** $.747$.   **19.** $.508$.   **21.** 0.310.

Exercises 13.10

3. 1.   **5.** 1.   **7.** 0.   **9.** ∞.   **11.** $2b^2/a^2$.
13. $\cos 3x = \cos^3 x - 3 \cos x \sin^2 x$, $\sin 3x = 3 \cos^2 x \sin x - \sin^3 x$.
15. (a) $\log i = (\pi/2)i$; (b) $\log (1+i) = \frac{1}{2} \log 2 + (\pi/4)i$.

17. $y = a_1 \left[x + \dfrac{x^2}{2!1!} + \dfrac{x^3}{3!2!} + \dfrac{x^4}{4!3!} + \cdots \right] = a_1 \displaystyle\sum_{k=1}^{\infty} \dfrac{x^k}{(k!)(k-1)!}$; valid for all x.

Exercises 14.1

1. $y = (1/\pi) \sin 2\pi t + C$.   **3.** $y^{1/3} = x + C$.   **5.** $\log (\sec s + \tan s) = \sin w + C$
or $\sec s + \tan s = C' e^{\sin w}$.   **7.** (a) $y = 2e^{1/2(9-x^2)}$; (b) $y = -2e^{1/2(9-x^2)}$.

9. $\tan^{-1} y = \tan^{-1} x + \dfrac{\pi}{4}$ or $y = \dfrac{1+x}{1-x}$.

Exercises 14.2

1. $y^2(dy/dx)^2 + y^2 = 1$.   **3.** $x^2(dy/dx)^2 + 2(1 - xy)\, dy/dx + y^2 = 0$.
5. (a) $dy/dx = y$; (b) $y^2 = -2(x - K)$.   **7.** (a) $dy/dx = e^{-y}$;
(b) $y = -\log (x + K)$.   **9.** (a) $dy/dx = y(\sinh x / \cosh x)$;

(b) $y^2 = -\log \sinh^2 x + K$ and $x = 0$.   **11.** (a) $(x^2 - 1)\,dy/dx = xy$;

(b) $x^2 + y^2 = \log x^2 + K$ and $x = 0$.   **13.** (a) $dy/dx = \sqrt{1 - y^2}$;

(b) $\sin^{-1} y + y\sqrt{1 - y^2} + 2x = K$.   **15.** Curves on upper half of ellipsoid whose

xy plane projections have the equation $y = K'x^{a^2/b^2}$, parameter K', and $x = 0$.

17. $2x\dfrac{d^2y}{dx^2} + \dfrac{dy}{dx} = 0.$ **19.** $\dfrac{d^3y}{dx^3} - 4\dfrac{d^2y}{dx^2} + 5\dfrac{dy}{dx} - 2y = 0.$

Exercises 14.3

1. $(y + 3x)^3 = C(y + x)$ (and $y = -x$).   **3.** $ye^{2\tan^{-1}(y/x)} = C.$

5. $(y - 2x)^5(y + x) = Cx^3$ (and $x = 0$).   **7.** $\log x^2 + 2e^{-(y/x)} = C.$

11. $\sqrt{y^2 - x^2} + y\log y = y\log C$ (and $y = x$).

13. $(2 - \sqrt{y/x})^4(\sqrt{y/x} + 1)^2 x^3 = -4.$

15. $y + 2x = Ce^{-[3\,x-1)/(y+2x)]}$ (and $y + 2x = 0$).

17. $x + 2 = Ce^{-[4(x+2)/(y-x-1)]}$ (and $y = x + 1$).

19. $\log \tfrac{1}{3}(2x - 2y - 3) + 2(y - x)^2 + 2y - 10x + 12 = 0.$

21. $(x^2 + y^2)e^{2\tan^{-1}(y/x)} = K$ or $(x^2 + y^2)e^{-2\tan^{-1}(y/x)} = K.$

25. (a) $N = N_0 e^{((b-d)/100)t}$; (b) $N = N_0 e^{(b-d]/100)\,t - (c/50)\,t^2}$; (c) $N = \dfrac{SN_0 e^{kSt}}{S - N_0 + N_0 e^{kSt}}$

Exercises 14.4

1. $x^2 + y + y^2 x = C.$ **3.** $r(1 + \cos\theta) = C.$ **5.** $x^2 y^3 - 3xy + \tfrac{1}{2}\log y^2 = C.$

7. $x + 2y + \tfrac{1}{2}\log(x + y)^2 = C.$ **9.** $\tan^{-1}(y/2x) + \log(4x^2 + y^2) = C.$

15. (a) $\alpha = -2,\ \beta = -4$; (b) $y^{-3} x - x^{-1} y^{-2} = C.$

Exercises 14.5

3. $y = \left(\dfrac{a_3}{a_1} - \dfrac{2a_2}{a_1^2}\right) + \dfrac{a_2}{a_1}x^2 + \left(\dfrac{2a_2}{a_1^2} - \dfrac{a_3}{a_1}\right)e^{-(a_1 x^2/2)}.$

5. $(x - 2)^2 y = x^3 - 4x^2 \log x - 4x + Cx^2.$ **7.** $x = \tfrac{1}{3}(y^2 + b) + C(y^2 + b)^{-1/2}.$

9. $y = -\dfrac{1}{a}\dfrac{1}{x^{ax}} + C\left(\dfrac{e}{x}\right)^{ax}.$ **11.** $y^{1/2} = \sin x - \cos x + Ce^{-x}.$

13. $y^2 = (\sec x + \tan x)[\log(1 + \sin x) + C].$ **15.** $y = x + Ce^{2x}.$

17. $x = ca[1 - e^{-(b/a)t}].$ **19.** (a) Exact; (b) $\sin x \sin y + 2\cos x \cos y = C.$

21. (a) Linear; (b) $y = (x^2 + b^2)(x - b\tan^{-1}(x/b) + C).$ **23.** (a) Exact;

(b) $\sqrt{x^2 - y^2} - \sin^{-1} y/x = C$ if $x > 0$, $\sqrt{x^2 - y^2} + \sin^{-1} y/x = C$ if $x < 0.$

25. (a) Bernoulli type; (b) $\dfrac{1}{y^2} = x^2 - 1 + C\dfrac{x+1}{x-1}.$ **27.** (a) Separable, linear;

(b) $(3y + 1)\cos^3 x = C.$ **29.** (a) Separable; (b) $\log x^2 y^2 + 2(x - 2y) = C.$

31. (a) Can be made homogeneous by a translation of coordinates;

(b) $\log[(y - 2)^2 + (x + 1)^2] - 4\tan^{-1}\dfrac{y-2}{x+1} = C.$ **33.** (a) Linear;

(b) $x = -(b/a^2)[a/y + 1] + Ce^{a/y}.$

Exercises 14.6

1. (a) $Y_4 = x^2 - \tfrac{2}{15}x^5$; (b) $.000\dot{6},\ .0000\dot{3},\ .000000\dot{1}\dot{3}.$

3. (a) $Y_4 = 1 - ax + \frac{1}{2!}a^2x^2 - \frac{1}{3!}a^3x^3.$

5. $Y_4 = C\left(1 - ax + \frac{1}{2!}a^2x^2 - \frac{1}{3!}a^3x^3\right) - \frac{3}{a}e^{-ax} + \frac{1}{a}\left(3 - 2ax + \frac{1}{2}a^2x^2\right).$

7. (a) $Y_5 = 4x - \frac{1}{3!}(\log x)^3 - (\log x)^2 - 3\log x - 4.$

9. $Y_4 = \frac{1}{4400}x^{11} + \frac{1}{160}x^8 + \frac{1}{20}x^5 + \frac{1}{2}x^2.$ **11.** (a) $Y_3 = 1 - x.$

Exercises 14.7

1. $y = \frac{1}{C_1}x - \frac{1}{2C_1^2}\log(1 + C_1x)^2 + C_2$ and $y = \frac{1}{2}x^2 + C_3$ and $y = C_4.$

3. $y = \log(x + 1) - \frac{1}{2}x^2.$ **5.** $y = C_1e^x - \frac{1}{2}x^2 + C_2x + C_3.$

7. $\begin{cases} x = \frac{1}{2}p^2 + \frac{1}{2}\log p^2 + C_1 \\ y = \frac{1}{3}p^3 + p + C_2 \end{cases}$ and $y = C_3.$

9. $x = -\frac{1}{2}y\log y^2 + C_1y + C_2$ and $y = C_3.$

11. $x = -\frac{1}{C_1}\frac{1}{y} - \frac{1}{2C_1^2}\log y^2 + \frac{1}{2C_1^2}\log(y + C_1)^2 + C_2$ and $x = -\frac{1}{2}\frac{1}{y^2} + C_3$ and $y = C_4.$

13. $x = \frac{1}{C_1}y - \frac{1}{2C_1}\log(e^y + C_1)^2 + C_2$ and $x = -e^{-y} + C_3$ and $y = C_4.$

15. $\begin{cases} x = \pm\sin\theta - C_1. \\ y = \mp\cos\theta + C_2. \end{cases}$ **17.** $x + 5 = 4\sqrt{y - 4}.$

Exercises 14.8

5. $y = C_1e^{ax} + C_2e^{-ax}$ or $y = k_1\cosh ax + k_2\sinh ax.$ **7.** $y = \frac{1}{4}e^{3(x-1)} + \frac{3}{4}e^{1-x}.$

9. $y = 16e^{3(x-2)} - 7xe^{3(x-2)}.$ **11.** $y = y_0\cos kx + (1/k)y_0'\sin kx.$

13. $y = a\cos kx + \frac{b - a\cos ka}{\sin ka}\sin kx.$

15. $y = e^{-.05x}(C_1\cos(\sqrt{7}/20)x + C_2\sin(\sqrt{7}/20)x).$ **17.** $y = \frac{1}{2\pi}e^{-.1x}\sin 2\pi x.$

19. (a) $y' - \alpha y = 0;$ (b) $y'' - 2\alpha y' + \alpha^2 y = 0.$ **21.** $y'' + 2y' + 5y = 0.$

Exercises 14.9

1. $y = \frac{y_0'}{k}\sin kx + \left(y_0 - \frac{2}{k^2}\right)\cos kx + \frac{2}{k^2}.$ **3.** $y = -2e^{-x} + C_1e^x + C_2e^{-2x}.$

5. $y = \frac{4}{3}\sin\frac{1}{2}x + 2\cos\frac{1}{2}x + e^{-(3/2)x}(C_1\cos\frac{1}{2}x + C_2\sin\frac{1}{2}x)$

7. $y = -\frac{1}{(b + a)^2}e^{-ax} - \frac{1}{b + a}xe^{-ax} + \frac{1}{(b + a)^2}e^{bx}.$ **9.** $y = e^x - xe^{-2x}.$

11. $y = -(1/k)x^2\cos kx + (1/k^2)x\sin kx + C_1\sin kx + C_2\cos kx.$

13. $y = \frac{1}{2}x^3e^{-ax} + C_1e^{-ax} + C_2xe^{-ax}.$

15. $y = \frac{1}{9}x^3e^x - \frac{1}{9}x^2e^x + \frac{2}{27}xe^x + C_1e^x + C_2e^{-2x}.$

17. $y = C_1\cos x\log(\sec x + \tan x) + C_2\cos x.$ **19.** $y = C_1x^{1/2} + C_2x^{1/2}\log[x^2/(x + 1)^2].$

21. $y = (1/k)x\sin kx + (1/k^2)\cos kx\log\cos kx + C_1\sin kx + C_2\cos kx.$

23. $y = \tan x\log(\sec x + \tan x) + \sec x\log\cos x + C_1\tan x + C_2\sec x.$

25. $y = \frac{1}{2}x^2\log x^2 - x^2 - 2x + C_1x^2 + C_2(x + 1).$

27. $y = \frac{1}{k^2}x - \frac{1}{k^2}\cos kx\log(\sec kx + \tan kx) + C_1\cos kx + C_2\sin kx.$

Exercises 14.10

1. (a) 20; (b) $x = \frac{1}{6} \cos 2\sqrt{g}\, t \approx \frac{1}{6} \cos 11.35\, t$, period $= \pi/\sqrt{g}$ sec $\approx .554$ sec, frequency $= \sqrt{g}/\pi \approx 1.81$, amplitude $= \frac{1}{6}$ ft; (c) $x = (1/2.4\sqrt{g}) \sin 2\sqrt{g}\, t \approx .0734$ $\sin 11.35\, t$, period $= \pi/\sqrt{g}$ sec, frequency $= \sqrt{g}/\pi$, amplitude $= (1/2.4\sqrt{g})$ ft $\approx .0734$ ft.

7. $b = \sqrt{4g - .0002g^2} \approx 11.34$; maximum amplitude is $\dfrac{1000\, a}{\sqrt{40000g - g^2}} \approx .88a$.

Exercises 14.11

5. Yes.   **7.** $y = C_1 e^x + C_2 \cos x + C_3 \sin x$.

9. $y = C_1 e^x + e^{-(1/2)x} \left(C_2 \cos \dfrac{\sqrt{3}}{2} x + C_3 \sin \dfrac{\sqrt{3}}{2} x \right)$.

11. $y = C_1 e^x + C_2 e^{2x} + C_3 \cos x + C_4 \sin x$.

13. $y = e^{(\sqrt{2}/2)x} \left(C_1 \cos \dfrac{\sqrt{2}}{2} x + C_2 \sin \dfrac{\sqrt{2}}{2} x \right) + e^{-(\sqrt{2}/2)x} \left(C_3 \cos \dfrac{\sqrt{2}}{2} x + C_4 \sin \dfrac{\sqrt{2}}{2} x \right)$.

17. $y = 2x + 2 + C_1 e^{-x} + C_2 e^x + C_3 x e^x$.

19. $y = \frac{1}{4} x e^{-x} + C_1 e^{-x} + C_2 e^x + C_3 x e^x$.

21. $y = C_1 e^x + C_2 e^{-x} + C_3 \cos x + C_4 \sin x$.

23. $y = C_1 \cos x + C_2 \sin x + C_3 x \cos x + C_4 x \sin x$.

25. $y = x^2 \log x - 2x \log x - x^2 - x + 1 + C_1 x + C_2 x^2 + C_3 e^{-x}$.

27. $y = e^{m_1 x} \left[\dfrac{Ax^{k+i}}{(k+1)(k+2)\cdots(k+j)} + C_1 + C_2 x + C_3 x^2 + \cdots + C_j x^{i-1} \right]$.

Exercises 14.12

1. (a) $x = 1, -1, 2i, -2i$; $-1 < x < 1$; (b) $x = -\frac{1}{2} \pm (\sqrt{7}/2)i$; $-\sqrt{2} < x < \sqrt{2}$.

5. (a) All x; (b) $y = a_0 \displaystyle\sum_{k=0}^{\infty} (-1)^k \frac{x^{2k}}{(2k)!} + a_1 \sum_{k=0}^{\infty} (-1)^k \frac{x^{2k+1}}{(2k+1)!}$.

7. (a) $y = \displaystyle\sum_{k=1}^{\infty} \frac{2^{k-1}(k-1)!}{(2k+1)!} x^{2k+1}$ is one particular solution;

(b) $y = \dfrac{1}{2!} x^2 + \dfrac{1}{3!} x^3 + \dfrac{2}{4!} x^4 + \dfrac{3}{5!} x^5 + \dfrac{7}{6!} x^6 + \cdots$ is the way one particular solution begins.

9. $y = \displaystyle\sum_{k=1}^{\infty} \frac{2^{k-1}(k-1)!}{(2k)!} x^{2k}$ is one particular solution.

11. (a) $y = a_0 \left[1 + \displaystyle\sum_{k=1}^{\infty} (-1)^k \frac{1 \cdot 4 \cdot 7 \cdots (3k-2)}{(3k)!} x^{3k} \right]$

$\qquad + a_1 \left[x + \displaystyle\sum_{k=1}^{\infty} (-1)^k \frac{2 \cdot 5 \cdot 8 \cdots (3k-1)}{(3k+1)!} x^{3k+1} \right]$.

(c) $y = 1$ is one particular solution; (d) $y = \displaystyle\sum_{k=0}^{\infty} (-1)^k \frac{3^k k!}{(3k+2)!} x^{3k+2}$ is one particular

solution.   **13.** (a) $-1 < x < 1$; (b) $y = a_0 \displaystyle\sum_{k=0}^{\infty} (-1)^k x^{3k} + a_1 \sum_{k=0}^{\infty} (-1)^k x^{3k+1}$

$= a_0 \dfrac{1}{1 + x^3} + a_1 \dfrac{x}{1 + x^3}$; (c) $-1 < x < 1$.   **15.** $y = 1 - \frac{1}{12} x^4 + \frac{1}{90} x^6 + \cdots$.

Exercises 14.13

3. $y = x^{\sqrt{2}}\left[1 + \sum_{k=1}^{\infty}(-1)^k \frac{1}{k!\,(1+2\sqrt{2})(2+2\sqrt{2})\cdots(k+2\sqrt{2})}x^k\right];$

$y = x^{-\sqrt{2}}\left[1 + \sum_{k=1}^{\infty}(-1)^k \frac{1}{k!\,(1-2\sqrt{2})(2-2\sqrt{2})\cdots(k-2\sqrt{2})}x^k\right];$

convergence predicted for all x.

5. $y = x^{-1/2}\left[1 - \frac{3}{8}x^2 - \sum_{k=2}^{\infty}\frac{3}{8^k}\frac{1\cdot5\cdot9\cdots(4k-7)}{k!}x^{2k}\right];$

$y = x^2\left[1 + \sum_{k=1}^{\infty}\frac{1\cdot3\cdot5\cdots(2k-1)}{9\cdot13\cdot17\cdots(4k+5)}x^{2k}\right];$ convergence predicted for $-\sqrt{2} < x < \sqrt{2}$.

7. (a) $y = x^{1/3}\sum_{k=0}^{\infty}(-1)^k\frac{1}{(3k-4)(3k-1)(3k+2)}x^k; y = x^{-1/3}(1+2x+x^2);$ convergence

predicted for $-1 < x < 1$; (b) $y = 9\sum_{k=0}^{\infty}(-1)^{k+1}\frac{1}{(3k-2)(3k+1)(3k+4)}x^{k+1}$ is one

particular solution. **13.** (a) $y = \sum_{k=0}^{\infty}(-1)^k\frac{1}{k!}\left(\frac{x^3}{3}\right)^k = e^{-(1/3)x^3};$

$y = \sum_{k=0}^{\infty}(-1)^k\frac{1}{2\cdot5\cdot8\cdots(3k+2)}x^{3k+2};$ convergence predicted for all x; (b) $y = 1/3x$ is

one particular solution. **15.** (b) $y = x(\log x)e^{-x} + e^{-x}\left[-1 + \sum_{k=2}^{\infty}\frac{1}{k!(k-1)}x^k\right];$

(c) $y = -\frac{1}{3}x + \frac{1}{3}x^2$ is one particular solution.

Exercises, A1

1. (a) $<$; (c) $>$; (e) $<$; (g) $>$. **2.** (a) $3 < y < 4$; (c) $x \leq -1$.
3. (a) $5 < 2x + 3 < 9$; (c) $1 < x^2 < 9$. **4.** (a) $2 \leq \frac{1}{2}x + 3 < 4$; (c) $0 \leq x^2 \leq 4$.
5. (a) $1 < x - 1 < 3$; (c) $\frac{1}{6} < \frac{x-1}{x+2} < \frac{3}{4}.$

$\left(\text{It is possible to show that } \frac{1}{4} < \frac{x-1}{x+2} < \frac{1}{2}.\right)$ **6.** (a) $1 < x + y < 6$;

(c) $0 < xy < 8$. **7.** (a) $x < \frac{1}{3}$; (c) $\frac{7}{2} < x < 6$; (e) $x \geq 3$ or $x \leq -3$;
(g) $x \leq \frac{1}{3}$ or $x \geq \frac{3}{2}$; (i) $x < 2$ or $x > 3$; (k) $x < 4$ and $x > 2\frac{1}{2}$.

Exercises, A2

1. (a) $\frac{7}{5}$; (c) $\pi/4$; (e) $\sqrt{2}/2$. **3.** (a) $-25 < x < 25$; (c) $x > 4$ and $x < -4$;
(e) $1 < s < 2$ and $-2 < s < -1$; (g) $2.96 < x < 3.04$; (i) $b - \epsilon < y < b + \epsilon$.
4. (a) $|x - 2| < .1$; (c) $|x - 3| < .2$; (e) $|x + 2| < .1$.

INDEX